CARNEGIE LEARNING

High School Math Solution

MATHbook

GEOMETRY • VOL. 1 TEACHER IMPLEMENTATION GUIDE

4th Edition

AUTHORING TEAM

Sandy Bartle Finocchi | Amy Jones Lewis

Josh Fisher | Janet Sinopoli | Victoria Fisher | Sarah Galasso

501 Grant Street, Suite 1075
Pittsburgh, PA 15219
Phone: 888-851-7094
Customer Service Phone: 412-690-2444

www.carnegielearning.com

Foundation Authors (2010)

William S. Hadley,
Algebra and Proportional Reasoning

Mary Lou Metz,
Data Analysis and Probability

Mary Lynn Raith,
Number and Operations

Janet Sinopoli,
Algebra

Jaclyn Snyder,
Geometry and Measurement

Acknowledgments

- The members of the Carnegie Learning Production Team—Sara Kozelnik, Sara Schmidt Boldon, Laura Norris, Mary Travis, Jaana Bykonich, Michelle Rohm, and Bob Dreas
- The members of Carnegie Learning Cognitive Scientist Team—John Connelly, Bob Hausmann, and Martina Pavelko—for their insight in learning science and collaboration on MATHia Software.
- **Primary Design:** Abbe Eckstein
- **Design Support:** Madison Kalo, Douglas Fuchs, and Heather Greenwood
- **Production Vendors:** Paul Leveno, BizeeWorks, LLC, Lumina Datamatics, LTD, and Trivium Education Services

Credits: Art and Photo Credits follow the Index.

ISBN: 978-1-68459-752-9

Teacher Implementation Guide

Printed in the United States of America

1 2 3 4 5 6 7 8 9 B&B 25 24 23 22 21

Cover Design by Anne Milliron and Moncur (thinkmoncur.com)

Welcome

You are the most important ingredient of learning.

That's why we're committed to giving you resources and services that help you work your magic.

For more than 20 years, we've partnered with teachers around the country to put the latest cognitive science research on how to best support student learning into action. We're focused on being a true partner every step of the way, so you never have to face these challenges alone.

Let us help you bring your classroom vision to life.

GEOMETRY • TEACHER IMPLEMENTATION GUIDE

Welcome FM–3
Guiding Principles FM–4
Introduction to Blended Learning FM–5
Content Organization FM–6
Connections to Improve Focus FM–8
Geometry Standards Overview FM–9
Teacher Resource Overview FM–11
Geometry Table of Contents FM–12
Three Phases of the Instructional Approach FM–30
Learning Together + Learning Individually FM–31
Implementing MATHbook FM–32
Implementing MATHia FM–34
Research-Based Strategies FM–36
Comprehensive Assessment FM–38
Planning Resources FM–42
Support for All Students FM–44
Skills Practice FM–46
Getting Ready for Geometry FM–48
A Meeting of the Minds FM–49

Guiding Principles

All Students Are Capable Learners

Perspective matters

- **Environment and culture are important.**
  Foster a community that recognizes diverse ways of thinking, including those that are disparate from our own.
- **Students enter class with varying degrees of experience and mathematical success.**
  Recognize students' strengths while ensuring that everyone has access to mathematical learning opportunities through a variety of access points.
- **Students need to learn how to best benefit from instruction.**
  Incorporate student interactions that develop their ability to reason and reflect.

Learning by Doing™

Production matters

- **Students must engage in the learning process.**
  Present opportunities for students to produce work artifacts and make their reasoning visible.
- **Students need to experience both investigation and explicit instruction.**
  Sequence tasks that interleave problem-solving and worked examples in thoughtful ways. New skills should develop when relevant to solve problems.
- **Students need to connect and integrate concrete and abstract representations of concepts.**
  Relate experiences with procedures, language, or algebraic notation. Formal tools should serve to generalize and communicate experiences.

Learning Through Assessment

Knowledge emerges over time

- **Students need to develop the ability to evaluate themselves, make judgments about their performance, and improve over time.**
  Utilize a system that provides students with multiple opportunities to demonstrate knowledge and reflect on their own learning.
- **Assessments provide insights throughout the learning experience so teachers can make real-time adjustments and plan next steps.**
  Embed ongoing formative assessment and provide learning insights that drive the instructional process. Empower teachers with a cadre of analog and AI-powered digital tools.

Education Is a Human Endeavor

Collaboration is key

- **Students learn through listening, speaking, reading, and writing.**
  Promote thinking and mathematical discourse. Equip teachers with tools and professional learning to sharpen their skills as facilitators.
- **Students learn through mistakes.**
  Present problem-solving opportunities to identify and remediate misconceptions in real-time.
- **Teachers drive the pace of the class. Students need time to develop proficiency in concepts and skills.**
  Facilitate a balance between time learning together and time learning individually.

Introduction to Blended Learning

Flexible Teaching. Flexible Learning.

The High School Math Solution delivers instructional resources that make learning math attainable for all students.

While delivered through separate mediums, **MATHbook** + **MATHia work in parallel** to engage students with various learning experiences they need to understand the mathematics at each grade level.

Available in English and Spanish.

Learning Together

MATHbook

Over the course of a year, you will spend approximately 60% of your instructional time teaching whole-class activities.

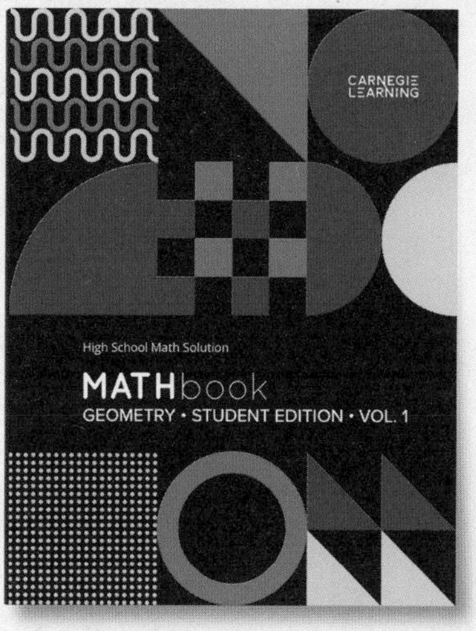

MATHbook is a consumable text that empowers students to become creators of their mathematical knowledge.

Learning Individually

MATHia

Over the course of the year, you will spend approximately 40% of your instructional time monitoring students as they work individually.

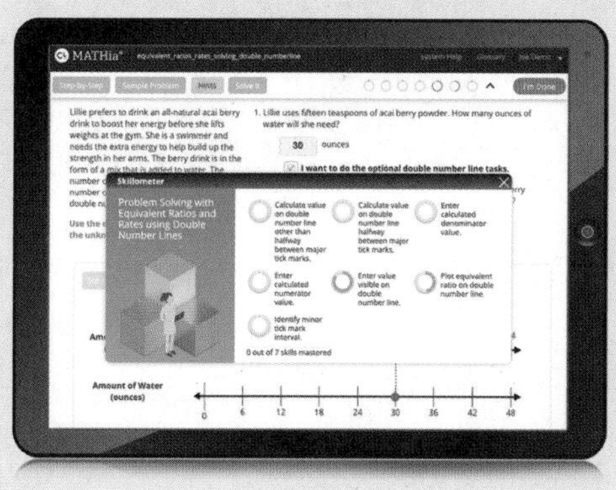

MATHia is intelligent software that provides just-in-time support and tracks student progress against fine-grained skills to deliver the right content they need to become proficient with the mathematics.

Content Organization

Each course is organized into five modules.

- Each Module contains 2–4 Topics.
- Each Topic provides a blend of **MATHbook** and **MATHia** resources to meet the grade-level standards.

Pacing

The pacing recommendations you see sum to approximately 140 instructional sessions.

1 Session ≈ 45 minutes

A session represents approximately 45 minutes of instruction. This includes time for work in:

MATHbook

≈ 107 sessions

MATHia

≈ 42 sessions

You can complete this sequence within a regular school year and can interleave approximately 30 sessions for assessments.

ALGEBRA I

MODULE 1: Searching for Patterns

TOPICS (28 SESSIONS)	
Quantities and Relationships	9
Sequences	9
Linear Regressions	10

MODULE 2: Exploring Constant Change

TOPICS (48 SESSIONS)	
Linear Functions	12
Solving Linear Equations and Inequalities	8
Systems of Equations and Inequalities	15
Functions Derived from Linear Relationships	13

GEOMETRY

MODULE 1: Reasoning with Shapes

TOPICS (37 SESSIONS)	
Using a Rectangular Coordinate System	16
Rigid Motions on a Plane	11
Congruence Through Transformations	10

MODULE 2: Establishing Proof

TOPICS (47 SESSIONS)	
Composing and Decomposing Shapes	14
Justifying Line and Angle Relationships	24
Using Congruence Theorems	9

ALGEBRA II

MODULE 1: Analyzing Structure

TOPICS (40 SESSIONS)	
Exploring and Analyzing Patterns	17
Composing and Decomposing Functions	8
Characteristics of Polynomial Functions	15

MODULE 2: Developing Structural Similarities

TOPICS (36 SESSIONS)	
Relating Factors and Zeros	10
Polynomial Models	5
Rational Functions	21

MODULE 3

Investigating Growth and Decay

TOPICS	19 SESSIONS
Introduction to Exponential Functions	9
Using Exponential Equations	10

MODULE 4

Describing Distributions

TOPICS	18 SESSIONS
One-Variable Statistics	11
Two-Variable Categorical Data	7

MODULE 5

Maximizing and Minimizing

TOPICS	39 SESSIONS
Introduction to Quadratic Functions	15
Solving Quadratic Equations	18
Applications of Quadratics	6

MODULE 3

Investigating Proportionality

TOPICS	26 SESSIONS
Similarity	15
Trigonometry	11

MODULE 4

Connecting Geometric and Algebraic Descriptions

TOPICS	19 SESSIONS
Circles and Volume	11
Conic Sections	8

MODULE 5

Making Informed Decisions

TOPICS	20 SESSIONS
Independence and Conditional Probability	9
Computing Probabilities	11

MODULE 3

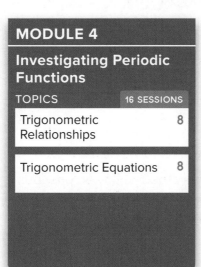

Inverting Functions

TOPICS	38 SESSIONS
Radical Functions	14
Exponential and Logarithmic Functions	9
Exponential and Logarithmic Equations	9
Applications of Growth Modeling	6

MODULE 4

Investigating Periodic Functions

TOPICS	16 SESSIONS
Trigonometric Relationships	8
Trigonometric Equations	8

MODULE 5

Relating Data and Decisions

TOPICS	17 SESSIONS
Interpreting Data in Normal Distributions	8
Making Inferences and Justifying Conclusions	9

Connections to Improve Focus

Mathematics is not a list of disconnected topics but rather a body of knowledge made up of interrelated concepts. This sequence coherently builds new understanding onto the foundations developed in prior grades or previous lessons within this course. We positioned the supporting work standards to reinforce the major work of the grade.

The Benefit in the Sequence

This course starts with **Reasoning with Shapes** on the coordinate plane as students use this familiar structure to investigate geometric figures. This sequence serves to engage students in the major work of the grade as they begin to formalize their understanding of geometric relationships

- Students use the coordinate system to quantify geometric relationships and conjecture about geometric properties.
- They integrate circles throughout the course, rather than considering a circle as an isolated geometric figure.
- They use a circle's structure to investigate side and angle relationships off the coordinate plane and complete constructions using arcs.
- Students engage in formal reasoning once they have first made sense of geometric relationships they will prove.

With a solid foundation in concrete geometric investigations, students are prepared for the work of the remaining Modules in this course.

Mixed Practice

The **Spaced Review** section provides practice of concepts from previous topics and the fluency skills important for the course.

The **End of Topic Review** section provides review practice of the concepts in the topic.

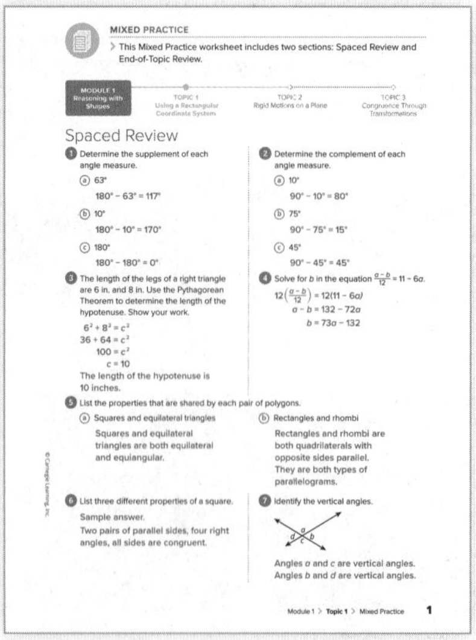

MIXED PRACTICE

> This Mixed Practice worksheet includes two sections: Spaced Review and End-of-Topic Review.

MODULE 1 Reasoning with Shapes — TOPIC 1 Using a Rectangular Coordinate System — TOPIC 2 Rigid Motions on a Plane — TOPIC 3 Congruence Through Transformations

Spaced Review

1. Determine the supplement of each angle measure.
   (a) 63° — 180° − 63° = 117°
   (b) 10° — 180° − 10° = 170°
   (c) 180° — 180° − 180° = 0°
2. Determine the complement of each angle measure.
   (a) 10° — 90° − 10° = 80°
   (b) 75° — 90° − 75° = 15°
   (c) 45° — 90° − 45° = 45°
3. The length of the legs of a right triangle are 6 in. and 8 in. Use the Pythagorean Theorem to determine the length of the hypotenuse. Show your work.
   $6^2 + 8^2 = c^2$
   $36 + 64 = c^2$
   $100 = c^2$
   $c = 10$
   The length of the hypotenuse is 10 inches.
4. Solve for b in the equation $\frac{a-b}{12} = 11 - 6a$.
   $12\left(\frac{a-b}{12}\right) = 12(11 - 6a)$
   $a - b = 132 - 72a$
   $b = 73a - 132$
5. List the properties that are shared by each pair of polygons.
   (a) Squares and equilateral triangles — Squares and equilateral triangles are both equilateral and equiangular.
   (b) Rectangles and rhombi — Rectangles and rhombi are both quadrilaterals with opposite sides parallel. They are both types of parallelograms.
6. List three different properties of a square.
   Sample answer.
   Two pairs of parallel sides, four right angles, all sides are congruent.
7. Identify the vertical angles.
   Angles a and c are vertical angles. Angles b and d are vertical angles.

© Carnegie Learning, Inc.

Module 1 > Topic 1 > Mixed Practice 1

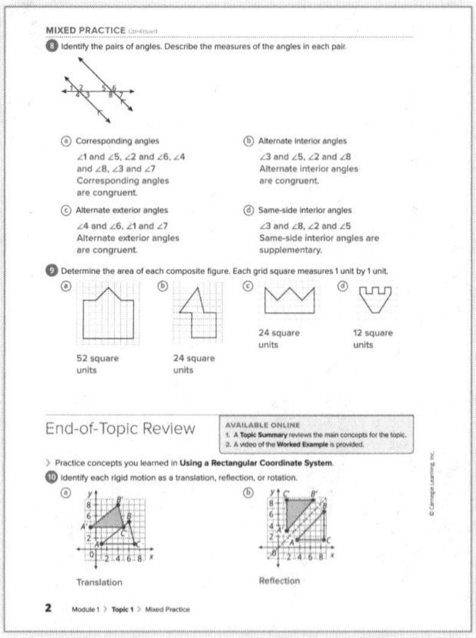

MIXED PRACTICE Continued

8. Identify the pairs of angles. Describe the measures of the angles in each pair.
   (a) Corresponding angles — ∠1 and ∠5, ∠2 and ∠6, ∠4 and ∠8, ∠3 and ∠7. Corresponding angles are congruent.
   (b) Alternate interior angles — ∠3 and ∠5, ∠2 and ∠8. Alternate interior angles are congruent.
   (c) Alternate exterior angles — ∠4 and ∠6, ∠1 and ∠7. Alternate exterior angles are congruent.
   (d) Same-side interior angles — ∠3 and ∠8, ∠2 and ∠5. Same-side interior angles are supplementary.
9. Determine the area of each composite figure. Each grid square measures 1 unit by 1 unit.
   (a) 52 square units (b) 24 square units (c) 24 square units (d) 12 square units

End-of-Topic Review

AVAILABLE ONLINE
1. A **Topic Summary** reviews the main concepts for the topic.
2. A video of the **Worked Example** is provided.

> Practice concepts you learned in **Using a Rectangular Coordinate System**.

10. Identify each rigid motion as a translation, reflection, or rotation.
    (a) Translation (b) Reflection

© Carnegie Learning, Inc.

2 Module 1 > Topic 1 > Mixed Practice

Can you or should you rearrange the topics?

Because the learning in each new topic builds on previous understandings, we highly recommend the presented sequence.

If you have questions or need more assistance, please contact our Professional Learning Team at **PL@carnegielearning.com ▶**

Geometry Standards Overview

Lesson Standards are shown in blue. **Spaced Practice Standards are shown in gray.**

		Geometry					
		Congruence	Similarity, Right Triangles, and Trigonometry	Circles	Expressing Geometric Properties with Equations	Geometric Measurement and Dimension	Modeling with Geometry
MODULE 1 Reasoning with Shapes	**TOPIC 1** Using a Rectangular Coordinate System	G.CO.1 G.CO.5 G.CO.10† G.CO.11† G.CO.12	8.G.7		G.GPE.4 G.GPE.5 G.GPE.7 A.CED.4	4.G.2 6.G.3 7.G.5 8.G.5	G.MG.2
	TOPIC 2 Rigid Motions on a Plane	G.CO.1 G.CO.2 G.CO.3 G.CO.4 G.CO.5 G.CO.12	8.G.7		8.F.1 G.GPE.5		
	TOPIC 3 Congruence Through Transformations	G.CO.6 G.CO.7 G.CO.8 G.CO.9 4.G.3 G.CO.2 G.CO.5			4.G.1 G.GPE.5		
MODULE 2 Establishing Proof	**TOPIC 1** Composing and Decomposing Shapes	G.CO.9† G.CO.10† G.CO.11† G.CO.12 G.CO.13	8.G.7	G.C.2 G.C.3	G.GPE.5 G.GPE.7	8.G.8	
	TOPIC 2 Justifying Line and Angle Relationships	G.CO.9 G.CO.10 G.CO.8 G.CO.11 G.CO.12		G.C.2 G.C.3 G.C.4 (+)			
	TOPIC 3 Using Congruence Theorems	G.CO.9 G.CO.10 G.CO.11		G.C.2			
MODULE 3 Investigating Proportionality	**TOPIC 1** Similarity	G.CO.9 G.CO.10 G.CO.12	G.SRT.1a G.SRT.1b G.SRT.2 G.SRT.3 G.SRT.4 G.SRT.5	G.C.2	G.GPE.6		
	TOPIC 2 Trigonometry		G.SRT.6 G.SRT.7 G.SRT.8 G.SRT.9 (+) G.SRT.10 (+) G.SRT.11 (+) G.SRT.3 G.SRT.4 G.SRT.5				
MODULE 4 Connecting Geometric and Algebraic Descriptions	**TOPIC 1** Circles and Volume	G.CO.9	G.SRT.6 G.SRT.8	G.C.1 G.C.5	8.EE.7b	G.GMD.1 G.GMD.3 G.GMD.4	G.MG.1 G.MG.2 G.MG.3
	TOPIC 2 Conic Sections		F.TF.8 G.SRT.5 G.SRT.6	G.C.5	G.GPE.1 G.GPE.2 G.GPE.3 (+) A.REI.7 F.IF.8	G.GMD.4	G.MG.1
MODULE 5 Making Informed Decisions	**TOPIC 1** Independence and Conditional Probability		F.TF.8 G.SRT.8		G.GPE.1 G.GPE.3		
	TOPIC 2 Computing Probabilities		G.SRT.8			G.GMD.3	

Log in to MyCL to view a Coherence Map that also shows prerequisite standards.

Geometry Standards Overview Continu

Lesson Standards are shown in blue. Spaced Practice Standards are shown in gray.

		Statistics and Probability	
		Conditional Probability and the Rules of Probability	Using Probability to Make Decisions
MODULE 1 Reasoning with Shapes	TOPIC 1 Using a Rectangular Coordinate System		
	TOPIC 2 Rigid Motions on a Plane		
	TOPIC 3 Congruence Through Transformations		
MODULE 2 Establishing Proof	TOPIC 1 Composing and Decomposing Shapes		6.SP.5c
	TOPIC 2 Justifying Line and Angle Relationships		
	TOPIC 3 Using Congruence Theorems		
MODULE 3 Investigating Proportionality	TOPIC 1 Similarity		
	TOPIC 2 Trigonometry		
MODULE 4 Connecting Geometric and Algebraic Descriptions	TOPIC 1 Circles and Volume		
	TOPIC 2 Conic Sections		
MODULE 5 Making Informed Decisions	TOPIC 1 Independence and Conditional Probability	S.CP.1 S.CP.2 S.CP.7 S.CP.8 (+)	
	TOPIC 2 Computing Probabilities	S.CP.2 S.CP.3 S.CP.4 S.CP.5 S.CP.6 S.CP.9 (+) S.CP.7	S.MD.6 (+) S.MD.7 (+) 7.SP.8

Teacher Resource Overview

Throughout this Teacher's Implementation Guide, the **Engage + Develop + Teach** navigation helps you understand the intent of each section and provides you with everything you need at point-of-use.

Three Phases of Teaching Support

ENGAGE
Read the Module Overview to appreciate the arc of the math.

+

DEVELOP
Read the **Topic Overview** and do the math to experience the content development.

+

TEACH
Read the facilitation notes and plan learning experiences.

Module Overview

- Overview of the mathematical arc of the module
  - Description of MATHbook topics and MATHia sequences
  - Aligned Skills Practice sets
- Pacing information
- Connections to Prior and Future Learning

Topic Overview

- Overview Topic content
  - Lesson descriptions
  - Aligned MATHia workspaces
  - Aligned Skills Practice problem sets
  - Pacing information
- Connections to Prior and Future Learning
- Checklist of skills students will demonstrate throughout the topic
- Assessment Overview
- Sample Topic Plan

Facilitation Notes

- Lesson overview
- Aligned standards
- Lesson Structure and Pacing Guide
- MATHia connection recommendations
- Lesson Planning and Reflection Templates
- Understanding prerequisite skills in the Review
- Essential Ideas
- Suggestions for chunking each activity
- Point-of-use facilitation tools
  - Language links (ELL Tips)
  - Student look-fors
  - Questions to support discourse
  - Pointers to differentiation strategies and common misconceptions
- Alignment of Skills Practice problem sets

The Research Shows....

"Teachers must first develop their ideas about where the curriculum program is going mathematically (curriculum vision) before deciding whether the curriculum materials will help them reach that mathematical goal (curriculum trust)."

— Drake & Sherin, 2009, p. 325

Geometry Table of Contents

On pages FM–11 through FM–28, you will see the table of contents of this course, presented at both the module and topic levels.

On each Module page, you will see:

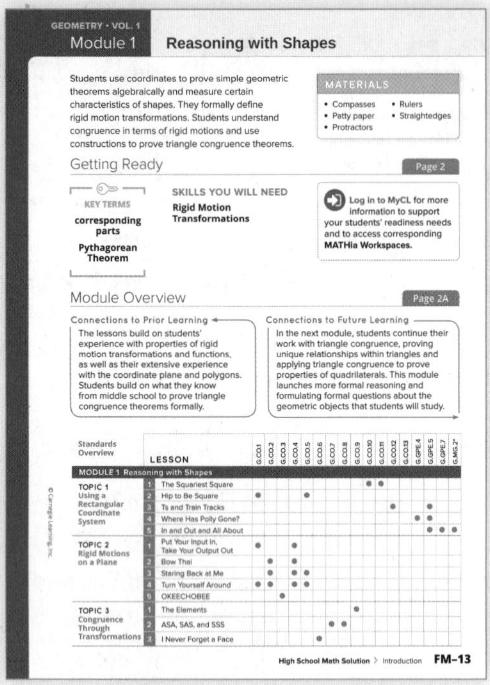

GEOMETRY • VOL. 1

Module 1 **Reasoning with Shapes**

Students use coordinates to prove simple geometric theorems algebraically and measure certain characteristics of shapes. They formally define rigid motion transformations. Students understand congruence in terms of rigid motions and use constructions to prove triangle congruence theorems.

MATERIALS
- Compasses
- Patty paper
- Protractors
- Rulers
- Straightedges

Getting Ready — Page 2

KEY TERMS
corresponding parts
Pythagorean Theorem

SKILLS YOU WILL NEED
Rigid Motion Transformations

Log in to MyCL for more information to support your students' readiness needs and to access corresponding **MATHia Workspaces.**

Module Overview — Page 2A

Connections to Prior Learning
The lessons build on students' experience with properties of rigid motion transformations and functions, as well as their extensive experience with the coordinate plane and polygons. Students build on what they know from middle school to prove triangle congruence theorems formally.

Connections to Future Learning
In the next module, students continue their work with triangle congruence, proving unique relationships within triangles and applying triangle congruence to prove properties of quadrilaterals. This module launches more formal reasoning and formulating formal questions about the geometric objects that students will study.

Standards Overview

		LESSON	G.CO.1	G.CO.2	G.CO.3	G.CO.4	G.CO.5	G.CO.6	G.CO.7	G.CO.8	G.CO.9	G.CO.10	G.CO.11	G.CO.12	G.CO.13	G.GPE.4	G.GPE.5	G.GPE.7	G.MG.2*
MODULE 1 Reasoning with Shapes																			
TOPIC 1 Using a Rectangular Coordinate System	1	The Squariest Square										●	●						
	2	Hip to Be Square	●				●												
	3	Ts and Train Tracks												●			●		
	4	Where Has Polly Gone?														●	●		
	5	In and Out and All About															●	●	●
TOPIC 2 Rigid Motions on a Plane	1	Put Your Input In, Take Your Output Out	●			●													
	2	Bow Thai		●		●													
	3	Staring Back at Me		●		●	●												
	4	Turn Yourself Around	●	●		●	●												
	5	OKEECHOBEE			●														
TOPIC 3 Congruence Through Transformations	1	The Elements									●								
	2	ASA, SAS, and SSS							●	●									
	3	I Never Forget a Face						●											

© Carnegie Learning, Inc.

High School Math Solution > Introduction FM–13

- An overview of the mathematical arc of the module.
- The materials you will need.
- Readiness skills students will need.
- The standards aligned to the lessons of the module.

On each Topic page, you will see:

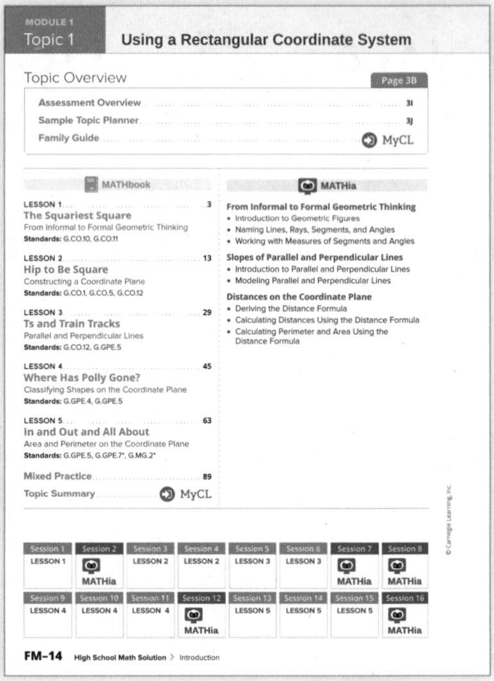

MODULE 1

Topic 1 **Using a Rectangular Coordinate System**

Topic Overview — Page 3B

Assessment Overview 3I
Sample Topic Planner 3J
Family Guide .... MyCL

MATHbook

LESSON 1 3
The Squariest Square
From Informal to Formal Geometric Thinking
Standards: G.CO.10, G.CO.11

LESSON 2 13
Hip to Be Square
Constructing a Coordinate Plane
Standards: G.CO.1, G.CO.5, G.CO.12

LESSON 3 29
Ts and Train Tracks
Parallel and Perpendicular Lines
Standards: G.CO.12, G.GPE.5

LESSON 4 45
Where Has Polly Gone?
Classifying Shapes on the Coordinate Plane
Standards: G.GPE.4, G.GPE.5

LESSON 5 63
In and Out and All About
Area and Perimeter on the Coordinate Plane
Standards: G.GPE.5, G.GPE.7*, G.MG.2*

Mixed Practice 89
Topic Summary .... MyCL

MATHia

From Informal to Formal Geometric Thinking
- Introduction to Geometric Figures
- Naming Lines, Rays, Segments, and Angles
- Working with Measures of Segments and Angles

Slopes of Parallel and Perpendicular Lines
- Introduction to Parallel and Perpendicular Lines
- Modeling Parallel and Perpendicular Lines

Distances on the Coordinate Plane
- Deriving the Distance Formula
- Calculating Distances Using the Distance Formula
- Calculating Perimeter and Area Using the Distance Formula

Session 1	Session 2	Session 3	Session 4	Session 5	Session 6	Session 7	Session 8
LESSON 1	MATHia	LESSON 2	LESSON 2	LESSON 3	LESSON 3	MATHia	MATHia
Session 9	**Session 10**	**Session 11**	**Session 12**	**Session 13**	**Session 14**	**Session 15**	**Session 16**
LESSON 4	LESSON 4	LESSON 4	MATHia	LESSON 5	LESSON 5	LESSON 5	MATHia

© Carnegie Learning, Inc.

FM–14 High School Math Solution > Introduction

- The instructional sequence of the lessons and the aligned **MATHia** workspaces.
- Pointers to topic-level resources for you, students, and families.
- A sample topic sequence that blends **MATHbook** and **MATHia**.

MATHEMATICAL COHERENCE

The High School Math Solution arc of mathematics develops coherently, building understanding by linking concepts together within and across grades, so students can learn mathematics more deeply and apply what they've learned to more complex problems going forward.

Log into MyCL, your digital access to all **Geometry** resources including:
- Language Links
- Skills Practice worksheets (editable)
- MATHia alignments
- Digital facilitation support

www.carnegielearning.com/login ▶

Module 1 Reasoning with Shapes

Students use coordinates to prove simple geometric theorems algebraically and measure certain characteristics of shapes. They formally define rigid motion transformations. Students understand congruence in terms of rigid motions and use constructions to prove triangle congruence theorems.

MATERIALS

- Compasses
- Patty paper
- Protractors
- Rulers
- Straightedges

Getting Ready

Page 2

KEY TERMS

corresponding parts

Pythagorean Theorem

SKILLS YOU WILL NEED

Rigid Motion Transformations

Log in to MyCL for more information to support your students' readiness needs and to access corresponding **MATHia Workspaces.**

Module Overview

Page 2A

Connections to Prior Learning

The lessons build on students' experience with properties of rigid motion transformations and functions, as well as their extensive experience with the coordinate plane and polygons. Students build on what they know from middle school to prove triangle congruence theorems formally.

Connections to Future Learning

In the next module, students continue their work with triangle congruence, proving unique relationships within triangles and applying triangle congruence to prove properties of quadrilaterals. This module launches more formal reasoning and formulating formal questions about the geometric objects that students will study.

Standards Overview

		LESSON	G.CO.1	G.CO.2	G.CO.3	G.CO.4	G.CO.5	G.CO.6	G.CO.7	G.CO.8	G.CO.9	G.CO.10	G.CO.11	G.CO.12	G.CO.13	G.GPE.4	G.GPE.5	G.GPE.7	G.MG.2*
MODULE 1 Reasoning with Shapes																			
TOPIC 1 Using a Rectangular Coordinate System	1	The Squariest Square										●	●						
	2	Hip to Be Square	●				●												
	3	Ts and Train Tracks												●			●		
	4	Where Has Polly Gone?														●	●		
	5	In and Out and All About															●	●	●
TOPIC 2 Rigid Motions on a Plane	1	Put Your Input In, Take Your Output Out	●			●													
	2	Bow Thai		●		●													
	3	Staring Back at Me		●		●	●												
	4	Turn Yourself Around	●	●		●	●												
	5	OKEECHOBEE			●														
TOPIC 3 Congruence Through Transformations	1	The Elements									●								
	2	ASA, SAS, and SSS							●	●									
	3	I Never Forget a Face						●											

Topic 1 Using a Rectangular Coordinate System

Topic Overview

Page 3B

Assessment Overview 3I

Sample Topic Planner 3J

Family Guide .... MyCL

MATHbook

LESSON 1 .... 3K

The Squariest Square

From Informal to Formal Geometric Thinking

Standards: G.CO.10, G.CO.11

LESSON 2 .... 13A

Hip to Be Square

Constructing a Coordinate Plane

Standards: G.CO.1, G.CO.5, G.CO.12

LESSON 3 .... 29A

Ts and Train Tracks

Parallel and Perpendicular Lines

Standards: G.CO.12, G.GPE.5

LESSON 4 .... 45A

Where Has Polly Gone?

Classifying Shapes on the Coordinate Plane

Standards: G.GPE.4, G.GPE.5

LESSON 5 .... 63A

In and Out and All About

Area and Perimeter on the Coordinate Plane

Standards: G.GPE.5, G.GPE.7, G.MG.2

Mixed Practice 89

Topic Summary .... MyCL

MATHia

From Informal to Formal Geometric Thinking

- Introduction to Geometric Figures
- Naming Lines, Rays, Segments, and Angles
- Working with Measures of Segments and Angles

Slopes of Parallel and Perpendicular Lines

- Introduction to Parallel and Perpendicular Lines
- Modeling Parallel and Perpendicular Lines

Distances on the Coordinate Plane

- Deriving the Distance Formula
- Calculating Distances Using the Distance Formula
- Calculating Perimeter and Area Using the Distance Formula

Session 1	Session 2	Session 3	Session 4	Session 5	Session 6	Session 7	Session 8
LESSON 1	MATHia	LESSON 2	LESSON 2	LESSON 3	LESSON 3	MATHia	MATHia

Session 9	Session 10	Session 11	Session 12	Session 13	Session 14	Session 15	Session 16
LESSON 4	LESSON 4	LESSON 4	MATHia	LESSON 5	LESSON 5	LESSON 5	MATHia

Rigid Motions on a Plane

Topic Overview

Page 91A

Assessment Overview 91I
Sample Topic Planner 91J
Family Guide .... MyCL

MATHbook

LESSON 1 .... 91K
Put Your Input In, Take Your Output Out
Geometric Components of Rigid Motions
Standards: G.CO.1, G.CO.4

LESSON 2 .... 103A
Bow Thai
Translations as Functions
Standards: G.CO.2, G.CO.4

LESSON 3 .... 115A
Staring Back at Me
Reflections as Functions
Standards: G.CO.2, G.CO.4, G.CO.5

LESSON 4 .... 129A
Turn Yourself Around
Rotations as Functions
Standards: G.CO.1, G.CO.2, G.CO.4, G.CO.5

LESSON 5 .... 143A
OKEECHOBEE
Reflectional and Rotational Symmetry
Standards: G.CO.3

Mixed Practice 153
Topic Summary .... MyCL

MATHia

Geometric Components of Rigid Motions
- Developing Definitions of Rigid Motions
- Exploring Rigid Motions and Dilations

Rigid Motions as Functions
- Describing a Translation
- Describing a Reflection
- Describing a Rotation
- Specifying a Sequence of Rigid Motion Transformations

Reflectional and Rotational Symmetry
- Rotations and Reflections on the Plane
- Reflectional Symmetry
- Rotational Symmetry

Session 1	Session 2	Session 3	Session 4	Session 5	Session 6	Session 7
LESSON 1	LESSON 1	LESSON 2	LESSON 2	LESSON 3	LESSON 3	MATHia

Session 8	Session 9	Session 10	Session 11
LESSON 4	LESSON 4	MATHia	LESSON 5

MODULE 1

Topic 3

Congruence Through Transformations

Topic Overview

Page 155A

Assessment Overview 155G

Sample Topic Planner 155H

Family Guide .... MyCL

MATHbook

LESSON 1 .... 155I

The Elements

Formal Reasoning in Euclidean Geometry

Standards: G.CO.9

LESSON 2 .... 171A

ASA, SAS, and SSS

Proving Triangle Congruence Theorems

Standards: G.CO.7, G.CO.8

LESSON 3 .... 185A

I Never Forget a Face

Using Triangle Congruence to Solve Problems

Standards: G.CO.6

Mixed Practice 197

Topic Summary .... MyCL

MATHia

Formal Reasoning in Euclidean Geometry

- Calculating and Justifying Angle Measures
- Calculating Angle Measures

Triangle Congruence Theorems

- Introduction to Triangle Congruence
- Using Triangle Congruence

Session 1	Session 2	Session 3	Session 4	Session 5	Session 6	Session 7
LESSON 1	LESSON 1	MATHia	LESSON 2	LESSON 2	LESSON 2	MATHia

Session 8	Session 9	Session 10
LESSON 3	LESSON 3	MATHia

Module 2 Establishing Proof

Students investigate geometric relationships and make conjectures. They prove several geometric theorems. Students use the theorems they proved to prove new theorems and verify properties, relying on identifying congruent triangles as a critical element of their deductive reasoning.

MATERIALS

- Blank paper
- Compasses
- Glue sticks
- Patty paper
- Protractors
- Rulers
- Scissors
- Straightedges

Getting Ready

Page 199

KEY TERMS

circle

Triangle Inequality Theorem

SKILLS YOU WILL NEED

Recognizing Angle Relationships

Log in to MyCL for more information to support your students' readiness needs and to access corresponding **MATHia Workspaces.**

Module Overview

Page 200A

Connections to Prior Learning

The lessons build on students' prior experience with geometric shapes and triangle congruence. Students have recognized, explored, conjectured about, and used most of the relationships that they prove in this module. They used construction tools to investigate triangles in middle school.

Connections to Future Learning

In the next module, students will use the relationships they develop here to move from congruence to the broader case of similarity, leading to trigonometry and volume formulas. Reasons for statements in proofs will be pulled from theorems in this topic to prove new theorems in the next topic.

Standards Overview

		LESSON	N.RN.2	G.CO.9	G.CO.10	G.CO.11	G.CO.12	G.CO.13	G.C.2	G.C.3	G.C.4 (+)
MODULE 2 Establishing Proof											
TOPIC 1 Composing and Decomposing Shapes	1	Running Circles Around Geometry		●					●		
	2	The Quad Squad				●					
	3	Into the Ring					●	●			
	4	Tri- Tri- Tri- and Separate Them			●						
	5	Meet Me in the Middle			●					●	
TOPIC 2 Justifying Line and Angle Relationships	1	Proof Positive		●							
	2	A Parallel Universe		●							
	3	Ins and Outs			●						
	4	Identical Twins	●	●	●						
	5	Corners in a Round Room							●	●	●
TOPIC 3 Using Congruence Theorems	1	SSS, SAS, AAS,...S.O.S.!			●						
	2	Props To You				●					
	3	Three-Chord Song							●		

Composing and Decomposing Shapes

Topic Overview

Page 201A

Assessment Overview 201I
Sample Topic Planner 201J
Family Guide .... MyCL

MATHbook

LESSON 1 .... 201K
Running Circles Around Geometry
Using Circles to Make Conjectures
Standards: G.CO.9, G.C.2

LESSON 2 .... 215A
The Quad Squad
Conjectures About Quadrilaterals
Standards: G.CO.11

LESSON 3 .... 231A
Into the Ring
Constructing an Inscribed Regular Polygon
Standards: G.CO.12, G.CO.13

LESSON 4 .... 247A
Tri- Tri- Tri- and Separate Them
Conjectures About Triangles
Standards: G.CO.10

LESSON 5 .... 261A
Meet Me in the Middle
Points of Currency
Standards: G.CO.10, G.C.3

Mixed Practice 277
Topic Summary .... MyCL

MATHia

Using Circles to Make Conjectures
- Introduction to Circles
- Exploring the Inscribed Angle Theorem
- Determining Central and Inscribed Angles in Circles

Conjectures About Quadrilaterals
- Using Circles to Draw Quadrilaterals
- Angles of an Inscribed Quadrilaterale

Points of Concurrency
- Points of Concurrency

Session 1	Session 2	Session 3	Session 4	Session 5	Session 6	Session 7
LESSON 1	LESSON 1	MATHia	LESSON 2	LESSON 2	MATHia	LESSON 3
Session 8	**Session 9**	**Session 10**	**Session 11**	**Session 12**	**Session 13**	**Session 14**
LESSON 3	LESSON 3	LESSON 4	LESSON 4	LESSON 5	LESSON 5	MATHia

Topic 2 Justifying Line and Angle Relationships

Topic Overview

Page 279A

Assessment Overview 279I
Sample Topic Planner 279J
Family Guide .... MyCL

MATHbook

LESSON 1 .... 279K
Proof Positive
Forms of Proof
Standards: G.CO.9

LESSON 2 .... 301A
A Parallel Universe
Proving Parallel Line Theorems
Standards: G.CO.9

LESSON 3 .... 321A
Ins and outs
Interior and Exterior Angles of Polygons
Standards: G.CO.10

LESSON 4 .... 335A
Identical Twins
Perpendicular Bisector and Isosceles Triangle Theorems
Standards: N.RN.2, G.CO.9, G.CO.10

LESSON 5 .... 355A
Corners in a Round Room
Angle Relationships Inside and Outside Circles
Standards: G.C.2, G.C.3, G.C.4 (+)

Mixed Practice 383
Topic Summary .... MyCL

MATHia

Forms of Proof
- Introduction to Proofs
- Completing Measure Proofs
- Connecting Steps in Angle Proofs
- Using Angle Theorems

Lines Cut by a Transversal
- Classifying Angles Formed by Transversals
- Calculating Angle Measures Formed by Transversals
- Calculating Angles Formed by Multiple Transversals

Proving Parallel Lines Theorems
- Proving Parallel Lines Theorems
- Proving the Converses of Parallel Lines Theorems

Interior and Exterior Angles of Polygons
- Proving Triangle Theorems

Proving Triangles Congruent
- Proving Triangles Congruent Using SAS and SSS
- Proving Triangles Congruent Using AAS and ASA
- Proving Theorems using Congruent Triangles

Special Right Triangles
- Introduction to Special Right Triangles
- Calculating the Lengths of Sides of Special Right Triangles

Solving Problems with Congruence
- Using Triangle Theorems

Angle Relationships Inside and Outside Circles
- Determining Interior and Exterior Angles in Circles

Session 1	Session 2	Session 3	Session 4	Session 5	Session 6	Session 7	Session 8	Session 9	Session 10	Session 11	Session 12
LESSON 1	LESSON 1	LESSON 1	MATHia	MATHia	MATHia	LESSON 2	LESSON 2	MATHia	MATHia	LESSON 3	LESSON 3

Session 13	Session 14	Session 15	Session 16	Session 17	Session 18	Session 19	Session 20	Session 21	Session 22	Session 23	Session 24
MATHia	MATHia	LESSON 4	LESSON 4	LESSON 4	MATHia	MATHia	LESSON 5	LESSON 5	LESSON 5	MATHia	MATHia

MODULE 2

Topic 3

Using Congruence Theorems

Topic Overview

Page 385A

Assessment Overview 385G

Sample Topic Planner 385H

Family Guide .... MyCL

MATHbook

LESSON 1 .... 385I

SSS, SAS, AAS, . . . S.O.S.!

Using Triangle Congruence to Determine Relationships Between Segments

Standards: G.CO.10

LESSON 2 .... 399A

Props To You

Properties of Quadrilaterals

Standards: G.CO.11

LESSON 3 .... 425A

Three-Chord Song

Relationships Between Chords

Standards: G.C.2

Mixed Practice 439

Topic Summary .... MyCL

MATHia

Extending Triangle Congruence Theorems

- Proving Triangles Congruent Using HL and HA

Properties of Quadrilaterals

- Understanding Parallelograms
- Determining Parts of Quadrilaterals and Parallelograms

Parallelogram Proofs

- Proofs About Parallelograms

Session 1	Session 2	Session 3	Session 4	Session 5	Session 6	Session 7
LESSON 1	LESSON 1	MATHia	LESSON 2	LESSON 2	LESSON 2	MATHia

Session 8	Session 9
LESSON 3	MATHia

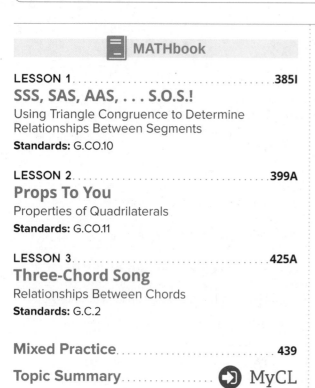

Module 3 Investigating Proportionality

Students establish triangle similarity criteria and use them to prove proportionality and solve problems. They explore side length ratios in similar right triangles to define trigonometric ratios.

MATERIALS

- Compasses
- Glue sticks
- Markers
- Mirrors
- Patty paper
- Protractors
- Rulers
- Scissors
- Straightedges
- Tape Measures

Getting Ready

Page 444

KEY TERMS

dialtion

scale factor

SKILLS YOU WILL NEED

Using Proportions to Determine Unknown Lengths

Log in to MyCL for more information to support your students' readiness needs and to access corresponding **MATHia Workspaces.**

Module Overview

Page 444A

Connections to Prior Learning

Students have extensive experience with ratios and proportional reasoning from middle school. They have drawn similar figures on the plane using a point of dilation. Students know a figure is similar to another when they can obtain the second using a sequence of transformations. They proved the Pythagorean Theorem using area models and applied it to solve for unknown side lengths.

Connections to Future Learning

In future courses, students will use trigonometric ratios to define trigonometric functions. They use these ratios to build the unit circle, which will be "unrolled" along the *x*-axis, connecting the geometric and algebraic representations of these functions. Students will then be able to model a wide variety of periodic phenomena algebraically.

Standards Overview		LESSON	G.SRT.1a	G.SRT.1b	G.SRT.2	G.SRT.3	G.SRT.4	G.SRT.5	G.SRT.6	G.SRT.7	G.SRT.8	G.SRT.9 (+)	G.SRT.10 (+)	G.SRT.11 (+)	G.GPE.1
MODULE 3 Investigating Proportionality															
TOPIC 1 Similarity	1	Big, Little, Big, Little		●	●										
	2	Similar Triangles or Not?			●	●									
	3	Keep It in Proportion	●				●								
	4	This Isn't Your Average Mean				●	●	●							
	5	Run It Up the Flagpole						●							
	6	Jack's Spare Key													●
TOPIC 2 Trigonometry	1	Three Angle Measure							●						
	2	The Tangent Ratio							●		●				
	3	The Sine Ratio							●		●				
	4	The Cosine Ratio							●		●				
	5	We Complement Each Other								●	●				
	6	A Deriving Force										●	●	●	

Similarity

Topic Overview

Page 445A

Assessment Overview 445I
Sample Topic Planner 445J
Family Guide ..... MyCL

MATHbook

LESSON 1 ..... 445K
Big, Little, Big, Little
Dilating Figures to Create Similar Figures
Standards: G.SRT.1b, G.SRT.2

LESSON 2 ..... 459A
Similar Triangles or Not?
Establishing Triangle Similarity Criteria
Standards: G.SRT.2, G.SRT.3

LESSON 3 ..... 471A
Keep It in Proportion
Theorems About Proportionality
Standards: G.SRT.1a, G.SRT.4

LESSON 4 ..... 497A
This Isn't Your Average Mean
More Similar Triangles
Standards: G.SRT.3, G.SRT.4, G.SRT.5

LESSON 5 ..... 507A
Run It Up the Flagpole
Application of Similar Triangles
Standards: G.SRT.5

LESSON 6 ..... 519A
Jack's Spare Key
Partitioning Segments in Given Ratios
Standards: G.GPE.6

Mixed Practice 533
Topic Summary ..... MyCL

MATHia

Dilating Figures to Create Similar Figures
- Understanding Similarity
- Describing a Dilation
- Specifying a Sequence of Transformations

Establishing Triangle Similarity Criteria
- Understanding the Triangle Similarity Theorems
- Identifying Similar Triangles

Theorems About Proportionality
- Proofs Using Similar Triangles

Application of Similar Triangles
- Calculating Corresponding Parts of Similar Triangles

Partitioning Segments in Given Ratios
- Partitioning Segments in Given Ratios
- Partitioning Segments Proportionally

Session 1	Session 2	Session 3	Session 4	Session 5	Session 6	Session 7	Session 8
LESSON 1	LESSON 2	LESSON 2	MATHia	LESSON 3	LESSON 3	LESSON 3	LESSON 3

Session 9	Session 10	Session 11	Session 12	Session 13	Session 14	Session 15
MATHia	LESSON 4	MATHia	LESSON 5	LESSON 5	LESSON 6	MATHia

Trigonometry

Topic Overview

Page 535A

Assessment Overview 535I
Sample Topic Planner 535J
Family Guide .... MyCL

MATHbook

LESSON 1 .... 535K
Three Angle Measure
Introduction to Trigonometry
Standards: G.SRT.6

LESSON 2 .... 547A
The Tangent Ratio
Tangent Ratio, Cotangent Ratio, and Inverse Tangent
Standards: G.SRT.6, G.SRT.8

LESSON 3 .... 563A
The Sine Ratio
Sine Ratio, Cosecant Ratio, and Inverse Sine
Standards: G.SRT.6, G.SRT.8

LESSON 4 .... 575A
The Cosine Ratio
Cosine Ratio, Secant Ratio, and Inverse Cosine
Standards: G.SRT.6, G.SRT.8

LESSON 5 .... 589A
We Complement Each Other
Complement Angle Relationships
Standards: G.SRT.7, G.SRT.8

LESSON 6 .... 599A
A Deriving Force
Deriving the Triangle Area Formula, the Law of Sines, and the Law of Cosines
Standards: 6G.SRT.9 (+), G.SRT.10 (+), G.SRT.11 (+)

Mixed Practice 613
Topic Summary .... MyCL

MATHia

Trigonometric Ratios

- Introduction to Trigonometric Ratios
- Relating Sines and Cosines of Complementary Angles
- Using One Trigonometric Ratio to Solve Problems
- Using Multiple Trigonometric Ratios to Solve Problems

Session 1	Session 2	Session 3	Session 4	Session 5	Session 6	Session 7
LESSON 1	MATHia	LESSON 2	LESSON 2	LESSON 3	LESSON 4	LESSON 5

Session 8	Session 9	Session 10	Session 11
MATHia	MATHia	LESSON 6	MATHia

GEOMETRY • VOL. 2
Module 4

Connecting Geometric and Algebraic Descriptions

Students determine arc lengths and areas of sectors and circles. They use volume formulas to solve problems. Students translate between geometric descriptions of and the equations for conic sections.

MATERIALS

- Blank paper (8.5 in. by 11 in.)
- Centimeter cubes
- Compasses
- Glue sticks
- Index cards
- Patty paper
- Pencils
- Protractors
- Scissors
- Spreadsheet technology
- Straightedges
- String

Getting Ready

Page 616

cross-section

volume

SKILLS YOU WILL NEED

Using the Distance Formula

Log in to MyCL for more information to support your students' readiness needs and to access corresponding **MATHia Workspaces.**

Module Overview

Page 616A

Connections to Prior Learning

Students have used and related the circumference and area of circles. They solved real-world and mathematical problems using area and volume formulas. They examined shapes on a coordinate plane and verified the characteristics of triangles, quadrilaterals, and composite figures algebraically.

Connections to Future Learning

Conic sections are helpful in the study of three-dimensional geometry. The conic sections studied are part of a larger family, including ellipses and hyperbolas. Students will use conic sections in higher-level mathematics courses or applications such as measuring trajectories of objects in space or electrons moving around an atom.

Standards Overview		LESSON	A.CED.2	A.REI.7	F.TF.8	G.C.1	G.C.5	G.GPE.1	G.GPE.2	G.GPE.3(+)	G.GMD.1	G.GMD.3	G.GMD.4	G.MG.1	G.MG.2	G.MG.3
MODULE 4 Connecting Geometric and Algebraic Descriptions																
TOPIC 1 Circles and Volume	1	All Circles Great and Small				●	●				●					
	2	A Slice of Pi					●				●					
	3	Do Me a Solid									●		●			
	4	Get to the Point									●	●		●	●	●
TOPIC 2 Conic Sections	1	Any Way You Slice It											●	●		
	2	X^2 Plus Y^2 Equals Radius^2						●								
	3	A Blip on the Radar	●	●				●								
	4	Sin^2 sθ Plus Cos^2 θ Equals 1^2			●											
	5	Going the Equidistance							●							

MODULE 4

Topic 1

Circles and Volume

Topic Overview

Page 617A

Assessment Overview 617G

Sample Topic Planner 617H

Family Guide .... MyCL

MATHbook

LESSON 1 .... 617I

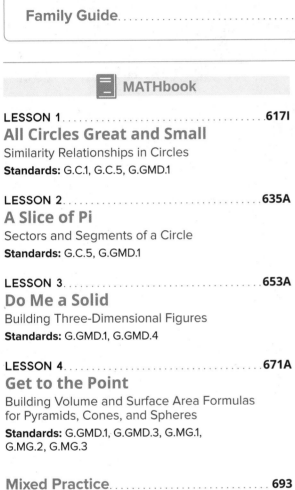

All Circles Great and Small

Similarity Relationships in Circles

Standards: G.C.1, G.C.5, G.GMD.1

LESSON 2 .... 635A

A Slice of Pi

Sectors and Segments of a Circle

Standards: G.C.5, G.GMD.1

LESSON 3 .... 653A

Do Me a Solid

Building Three-Dimensional Figures

Standards: G.GMD.1, G.GMD.4

LESSON 4 .... 671A

Get to the Point

Building Volume and Surface Area Formulas for Pyramids, Cones, and Spheres

Standards: G.GMD.1, G.GMD.3, G.MG.1, G.MG.2, G.MG.3

Mixed Practice 693

Topic Summary .... MyCL

MATHia

Similarity Relationships in Circles

- Relating Arc Length and Radius
- Determining Chords in Circles
- Calculating the Area of a Sector

Volume

- Creating Three-Dimensional Shapes from Two-Dimensional Figures
- Calculating Volume of Cylinders
- Calculating Volume of Pyramids
- Calculating Volume of Cones
- Calculating Volume of Spheres

Surface Area

- Introduction to Formulas for the Surface Area of Solids
- Calculating Surface Area of Solids

Session 1	Session 2	Session 3	Session 4	Session 5	Session 6	Session 7
LESSON 1	LESSON 2	LESSON 2	MATHia	LESSON 3	LESSON 3	MATHia

Session 8	Session 9	Session 10	Session 11
LESSON 4	LESSON 4	LESSON 4	MATHia

MODULE 4

Topic 2 Conic Sections

Topic Overview

Page 695A

Assessment Overview 695I

Sample Topic Planner 695J

Family Guide .... MyCL

MATHbook

LESSON 1 .... 695K
Any Way You Slice It
Cross-Sections
Standards: G.GMD.4, G.MG.1

LESSON 2 .... 709A
X^2 Plus Y^2 Equals Radius^2
Deriving the Equation for a Circle
Standards: G.GPE.1

LESSON 3 .... 721A
A Blip on the Radar
Determining Points on a Circle
Standards: A.CED.2, A.REI.7, G.GPE.1

LESSON 4 .... 735A
$\sin^2 \theta$ Plus $\cos^2 \theta$ Equals 1^2
The Pythagorean Identity
Standards: F.TF.8

LESSON 5 .... 743A
Going the Equidistance
Equation of a Parabola
Standards: G.GPE.2

Mixed Practice 769

Topic Summary .... MyCL

MATHia

Cross-Sections
- Visualizing Cross-Sections of Three-Dimensional Shapes

Equation of a Circle
- Deriving the Equation of a Circle
- Determining the Radius and Center of a Circle

Log in to MyCL additional content addressing G.GPE.3 (+).

Session 1	Session 2	Session 3	Session 4	Session 5	Session 6	Session 7	Session 8
LESSON 1	LESSON 2	LESSON 2	LESSON 3	MATHia	LESSON 4	LESSON 5	LESSON 5

Module 5 Making Informed Decisions

Students differentiate between independent and dependent events and calculate compound probabilities. They use permutations and combinations to solve problems.

MATERIALS

- Technology with !, *n*P*r*, and *n*C*r* capabilities (optional)

Getting Ready

Page 772

KEY TERMS

tree diagram

probability

SKILLS YOU WILL NEED

Using Two-Way Tables

Log in to MyCL for more information to support your students' readiness needs and to access corresponding **MATHia Workspaces.**

Module Overview

Page 772A

Connections to Prior Learning

This module's lessons build on the intuitive understandings of simple and compound probabilities developed in middle school. Students have used probabilities to make predictions and organized and analyzed two-variable categorical data.

Connections to Future Learning

Lessons provide both formal and intuitive strategies for determining the conditional probabilities of real-world events. Students studying engineering, economics, psychology, genetics, and medicine will reason with probability to analyze data sets and make decisions.

Standards Overview

		LESSON	S.CP.1	S.CP.2	S.CP.3	S.CP.4	S.CP.5	S.CP.6	S.CP.7	S.CP.8 (+)	S.CP.9 (+)	S.MD.6 (+)	S.MD.7 (+)
MODULE 5 Making Informed Decisions Descriptions													
TOPIC 1 Independence and Conditional Probability	1	What Are the Chances?	●										
	2	And?		●						●			
	3	Or?		●					●	●			
	4	And, Or, and More!		●					●	●			
TOPIC 2 Computing Probabilities	1	Table Talk		●		●							
	2	It All Depends			●	●	●	●					
	3	Give Me 5!									●		
	4	A Different Kind of Court Trial									●		
	5	What Do You Expect?										●	●

MODULE 5

Topic 1

Independence and Conditional Probability

Topic Overview

Page 773A

Assessment Overview 773G

Sample Topic Planner 773H

Family Guide .... MyCL

MATHbook

LESSON 1 .... 773I

What Are the Chances?

Compound Sample Spaces

Standards: S.CP.1

LESSON 2 .... 789A

And?

Compound Probability with *And*

Standards: S.CP.2, S.CP.8 (+)

LESSON 3 .... 803A

Or?

Compound Probability with *Or*

Standards: S.CP.2, S.CP.7, S.CP.8 (+)

LESSON 4 .... 817A

And, Or, and More!

Calculating Compound Probability

Standards: S.CP.2, S.CP.7, S.CP.8 (+)

Mixed Practice 829

Topic Summary .... MyCL

MATHia

Independence and Conditional Probability

- Independent Events

Session 1	Session 2	Session 3	Session 4	Session 5	Session 6	Session 7
LESSON 1	LESSON 1	LESSON 2	LESSON 2	MATHia	LESSON 3	LESSON 3

Session 8	Session 9
LESSON 4	LESSON 4

MODULE 5

Topic 2 Computing Probabilities

Topic Overview

Page 831A

Assessment Overview 831I

Sample Topic Planner 831J

Family Guide .... MyCL

MATHbook

LESSON 1 .... 831K

Table Talk

Compound Probability for Data Displayed in Two-Way Tables

Standards: S.CP.2, S.CP.4

LESSON 2 .... 845A

It All Depends

Conditional Probability

Standards: S.CP.3, S.CP.4, S.CP.5, S.CP.6

LESSON 3 .... 857A

Give Me 5!

Permutations and Combinations

Standards: S.CP.9 (+)

LESSON 4 .... 879A

A Different Kind of Court Trial

Independent Trials

Standards: S.CP.9 (+)

LESSON 5 .... 893A

What Do You Expect?

Expected Value

Standards: S.MD.6 (+), S.MD.7 (+)

Mixed Practice 907

Topic Summary .... MyCL

MATHia

Computing Probabilities

- Understanding Frequency Tables
- Calculating Compound Probabilities from Two-Way Tables
- Conditional Probability
- Recognizing Concepts of Conditional Probability

Session 1	Session 2	Session 3	Session 4	Session 5	Session 6	Session 7
LESSON 1	MATHia	LESSON 2	LESSON 2	MATHia	LESSON 3	LESSON 3

Session 8	Session 9	Session 10	Session 11
LESSON 4	LESSON 4	LESSON 5	LESSON 5

Three Phases of the Instructional Approach

This instructional approach is a culmination of the collective knowledge of our researchers, instructional designers, cognitive learning scientists, and master practitioners. It is based on a scientific understanding of how people learn, as well as an understanding of how to apply the science to the classroom.

Engage

Activate student thinking by tapping into prior knowledge and real-world experiences. Provide an introduction that generates curiosity and plants the seeds for deeper learning.

Develop

Build a deep understanding of mathematics through a variety of activities. Students encounter real-world problems, sorting activities, worked examples, and peer analysis—in an environment where collaboration, conversations, and questioning are routine practices.

Demonstrate

Reflect on and evaluate what was learned. Ongoing formative assessment underlies the entire learning experience, driving real-time adjustments, next steps, insights, and measurements.

Learning Together + Learning Individually

MATHbook

NAVIGATING EACH LESSON

Each lesson has the same structure allowing you to track your progress.

Lesson trackers show your progress.

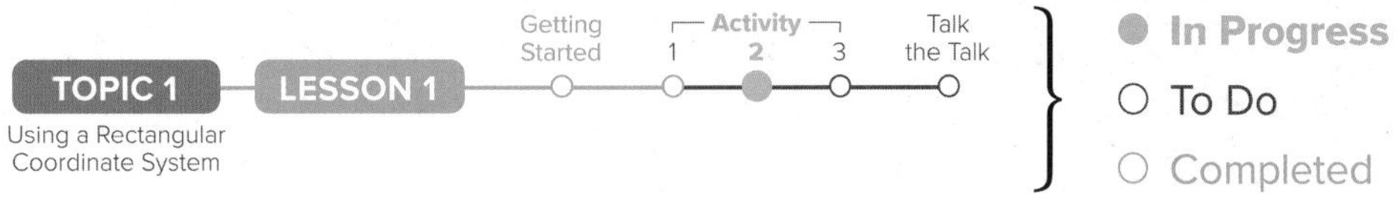

Icons guide you through the lesson.

GETTING STARTED + **ACTIVITIES** + **TALK THE TALK**

MATHia CONNECTION

In the workspaces listed, students will practice with the concepts and skills they are developing in the activity.

MATHia

NAVIGATING EACH WORKSPACE

Workspaces aligned at the lesson level support benchmarking through self-paced MATHia.

Concept Builders focus on developing an understanding of math concepts. Students will learn using explore tools, animations, classification tools, and worked examples.

Progress Meter

Mastery Workspaces provide personalized instruction as students learn and practice with skills and concepts. MATHia will automatically adjust the number of problems students require to master the skills of that workspace.

Skillometer

Implementing MATHbook

LESSON STRUCTURE AND PACING GUIDE

You will see specific instructional strategies for each activity type. By understanding the instructional sequence, you have the FLEXIBILITY to plan out your pedagogical moves in a way that works for your specific classroom.

Engage

INSTRUCTIONAL STRATEGIES

Connect to prior knowledge
Build off intuition
Establish a situation

Develop

INSTRUCTIONAL STRATEGIES

Investigation
Classification
Worked example
Peer analysis
Real-world problem solving
Mathematical problem solving

Pacing Approximates

1 – 3 Sessions	≈ 5 – 10 Minutes	≈ 15 – 30 Minutes Each
LESSON OVERVIEW	GETTING STARTED	ACTIVITIES

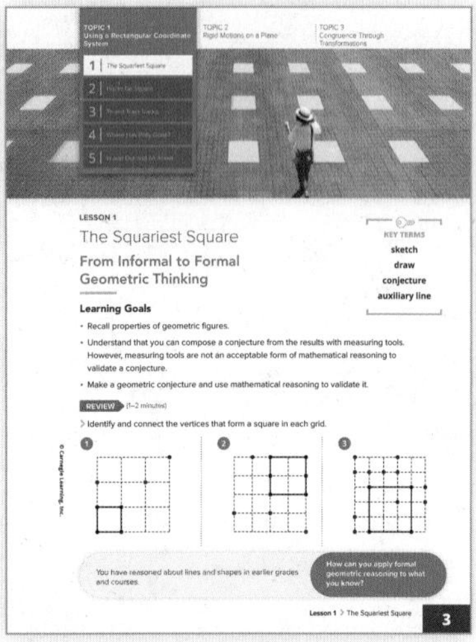
LESSON 1
The Squariest Square
From Informal to Formal Geometric Thinking
KEY TERMS
sketch
draw
conjecture
auxiliary line
Learning Goals
• Recall properties of geometric figures.
• Understand that you can compose a conjecture from the results with measuring tools. However, measuring tools are not an acceptable form of mathematical reasoning to validate a conjecture.
• Make a geometric conjecture and use mathematical reasoning to validate it.
REVIEW (1–2 minutes)
Identify and connect the vertices that form a square in each grid.
You have reasoned about lines and shapes in earlier grades and courses.
How can you apply formal geometric reasoning to what you know?
Lesson 1 > The Squariest Square 3

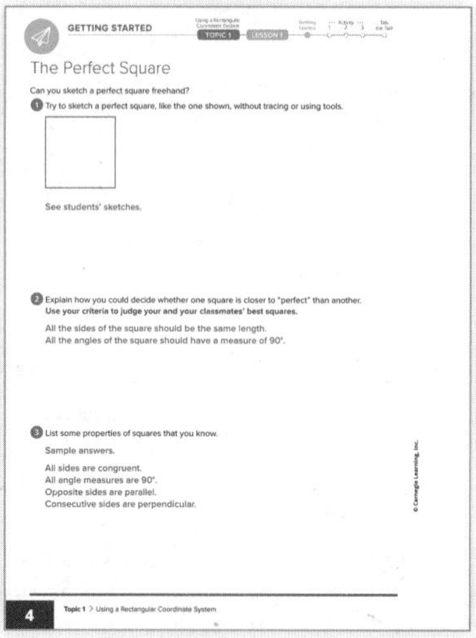
GETTING STARTED
The Perfect Square
Can you sketch a perfect square freehand?
1 Try to sketch a perfect square, like the one shown, without tracing or using tools.
See students' sketches.
2 Explain how you could decide whether one square is closer to "perfect" than another. Use your criteria to judge your and your classmates' best squares.
All the sides of the square should be the same length.
All the angles of the square should have a measure of 90°.
3 List some properties of squares that you know.
Sample answers.
All sides are congruent.
All angle measures are 90°.
Opposite sides are parallel.
Consecutive sides are perpendicular.
4 Topic 1 > Using a Rectangular Coordinate System

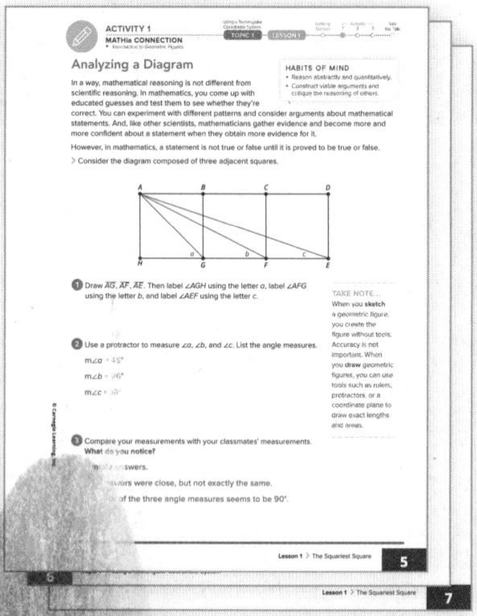
ACTIVITY 1
MATHia CONNECTION
Analyzing a Diagram
HABITS OF MIND
In a way, mathematical reasoning is not different from scientific reasoning. In mathematics, you come up with educated guesses and test them to see whether they're correct. You can experiment with different patterns and consider arguments about mathematical statements. And, like other scientists, mathematicians gather evidence and become more and more confident about a statement when they obtain more evidence for it.
However, in mathematics, a statement is not true or false until it is proved to be true or false.
Consider the diagram composed of three adjacent squares.
1 Draw $\overline{AG}$, $\overline{AF}$, $\overline{AE}$. Then label ∠AGH using the letter a, label ∠AFG using the letter b, and label ∠AEF using the letter c.
2 Use a protractor to measure ∠a, ∠b, and ∠c. List the angle measures.
3 Compare your measurements with your classmates' measurements. What do you notice?
Lesson 1 > The Squariest Square 5

How to engage with students to guide their mathematical development.

Establishing Mathematical Goals to Focus Learning

- Create a classroom climate of collaboration and establish the learning process as a partnership between you and your students.
- Communicate continuously with students about learning goals to encourage self-monitoring of their learning.

Activating Student Thinking

- Tap into students' prior knowledge and real-world experiences.
- Pay attention to the strategies students use, for these strategies reveal underlying thought processes and present opportunities for connections through the lesson.

Aligning Teaching to Learning

- Support student-to-student discourse as well as whole-class conversations that elicit and use evidence of student thinking.
- Encourage productive struggle by allowing students time to engage with and persevere through mathematics.

Demonstrate

INSTRUCTIONAL STRATEGIES

Exit ticket procedures
Exit ticket application
Generalization
Graphic organizer
Writing task
Presentation

≈ 5 – 10 Minutes

Practice-Content Connections

WITHIN EACH LESSON . . .

Activities within each lesson denote a practice or pair of practices to help students develop the habits of mind.

LOOK FOR...

HABITS OF MIND

On Page FM–67 to see how they are visible throughout each lesson.

TALK THE TALK

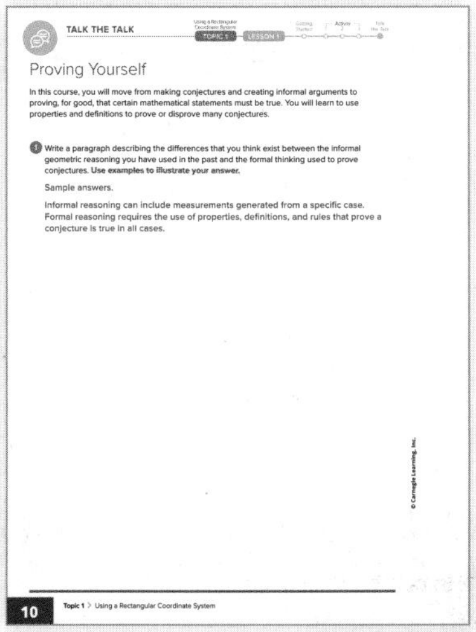
TALK THE TALK

Proving Yourself

In this course, you will move from making conjectures and creating informal arguments to proving, for good, that certain mathematical statements must be true. You will learn to use properties and definitions to prove or disprove many conjectures.

1 Write a paragraph describing the differences that you think exist between the informal geometric reasoning you have used in the past and the formal thinking used to prove conjectures. Use examples to illustrate your answer.

Sample answers.

Informal reasoning can include measurements generated from a specific case. Formal reasoning requires the use of properties, definitions, and rules that prove a conjecture is true in all cases.

10 Topic 1 > Using a Rectangular Coordinate System

ASSIGNMENT

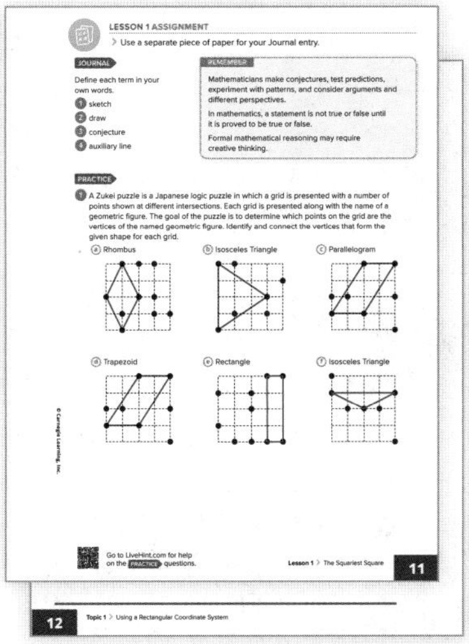
LESSON 1 ASSIGNMENT

> Use a separate piece of paper for your Journal entry.

JOURNAL

Define each term in your own words.

1 sketch
2 draw
3 conjecture
4 auxiliary line

REMEMBER

Mathematicians make conjectures, test predictions, experiment with patterns, and consider arguments and different perspectives.

In mathematics, a statement is not true or false until it is proved to be true or false.

Formal mathematical reasoning may require creative thinking.

PRACTICE

1 A Zukei puzzle is a Japanese logic puzzle in which a grid is presented with a number of points shown at different intersections. Each grid is presented along with the name of a geometric figure. The goal of the puzzle is to determine which points on the grid are the vertices of the named geometric figure. Identify and connect the vertices that form the given shape for each grid.

a Rhombus b Isosceles Triangle c Parallelogram
d Trapezoid e Rectangle f Isosceles Triangle

Go to LiveHint.com for help on the PRACTICE questions.

Lesson 1 > The Squarest Square 11

12 Topic 1 > Using a Rectangular Coordinate System

MIXED PRACTICE

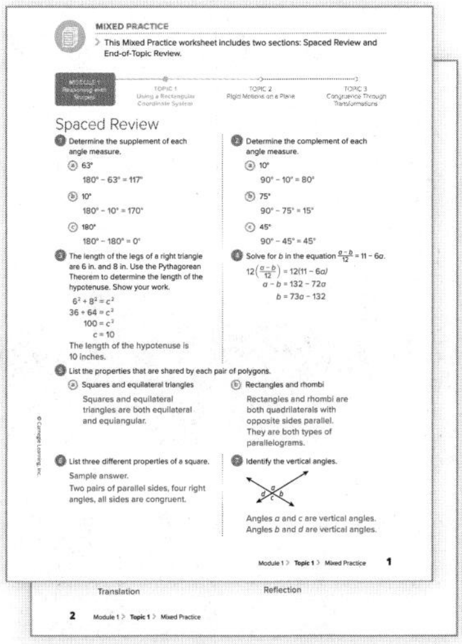
MIXED PRACTICE

> This Mixed Practice worksheet includes two sections: Spaced Review and End-of-Topic Review.

Spaced Review

1 Determine the supplement of each angle measure.
a 63° 180° − 63° = 117°
b 10° 180° − 10° = 170°
c 180° 180° − 180° = 0°

2 Determine the complement of each angle measure.
a 10° 90° − 10° = 80°
b 75° 90° − 75° = 15°
c 45° 90° − 45° = 45°

3 The length of the legs of a right triangle are 6 in. and 8 in. Use the Pythagorean Theorem to determine the length of the hypotenuse. Show your work.
$6^2 + 8^2 = c^2$
$36 + 64 = c^2$
$100 = c^2$
$c = 10$
The length of the hypotenuse is 10 inches.

5 List the properties that are shared by each pair of polygons.
a Squares and equilateral triangles
Squares and equilateral triangles are both equilateral and equiangular.
b Rectangles and rhombi
Rectangles and rhombi are both quadrilaterals with opposite sides parallel. They are both types of parallelograms.

6 List three different properties of a square.
Sample answer.
Two pairs of parallel sides, four right angles, all sides are congruent.

7 Identify the vertical angles.
Angles a and c are vertical angles. Angles b and d are vertical angles.

Module 1 > Topic 1 > Mixed Practice 1

Translation Reflection

2 Module 1 > Topic 1 > Mixed Practice

How to engage with students to guide their mathematical development.

Promoting Self-Reflection

- Encourage students to take responsibility for their own learning and self-assess.
- Listen and review their answers, explanations, and provide feedback to help them advance their understanding.

Reflection and Practice

Reflect on and practice the new concepts of the lesson.

LiveHint™

Students can go to **LiveHint.com** for hints on the **practice questions**.

Building Fluency

Spaced practice aligned to concepts and skills from previous lessons builds fluency.

Implementing MATHia

MATHia works alongside **MATHbook** to ensure students have time to develop the concepts and skills of the course. The work students do in **MATHia** continuously supports their work in **MATHbook**, even when their software pace is ahead of or behind the aligned lessons.

Engage

INSTRUCTIONAL STRATEGIES

Learning goals
Key terms
Connections

Develop and Demonstrate

INSTRUCTIONAL STRATEGIES

Animations
Classifications
Explore tools
Real-world problem solving
Worked examples

Self-Paced: Median student completion time provided at the topic level.

UNIT OVERVIEW

CONCEPT BUILDER WORKSPACES

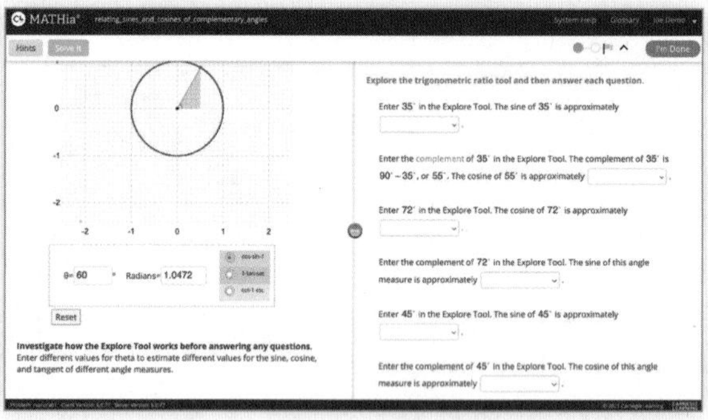

How to engage with students working individually

Establishing Mathematical Goals to Focus Learning

- Have students read the learning goals and connecting statement.
- Establish a workspace completion goal within the unit.
- Encourage self-motivation rather than compliance.

Activating Student Thinking

- Promote student responsibility for self-monitoring their learning.
- Remind them to assess their progress using the **Progress Meter**.

The **Progress Meter** shows students which step they are on in the current problem and how many problems remain in the workspace.

MATHia

Develop and Demonstrate

INSTRUCTIONAL STRATEGIES

Classifications
Equation solvers
Graphing tools
Interactive diagrams
Real-world problem solving

MASTERY WORKSPACES

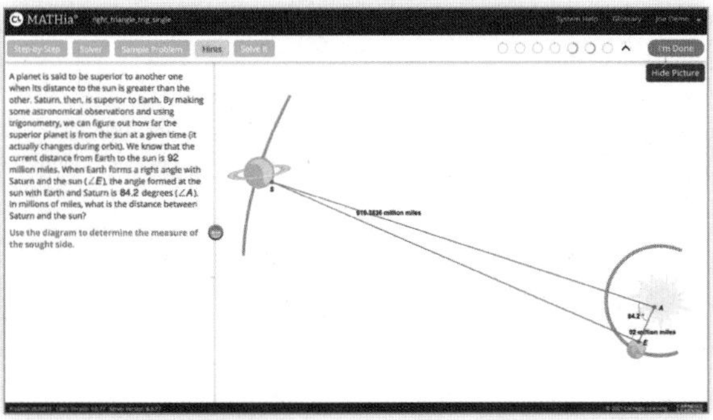

Personalizing Learning

- Encourage students to think about how each workspace connects to what they are learning in **MATHbook**.
- Remind them to assess their progress using the **Skillometer**.

The **Skillometer** shows progress rings that move from blue to green to indicate mastery. It is a predictor of how likely students are to be successful with a skill in the future. It is not a percent of correct and incorrect responses.

STUDENT SELF-HELP TOOLS

Promoting Self-Reflection

- Empower students to use the self-help tools as needed to take ownership of their learning.
- Remind students that mistakes are learning opportunities.
- Cultivate an environment where asking for help is a regular practice.

Step-by-Step

The Step-by-Step demonstrates how to use the tools in a **Mastery Workspace** by guiding students through a worked example.

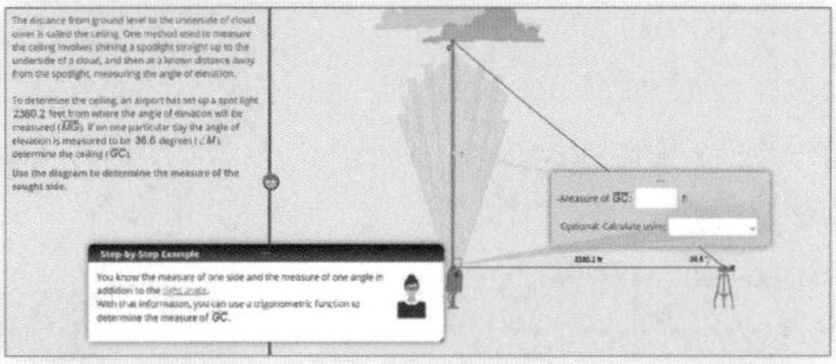

On-Demand Hints

Multi-level hints are available throughout the software to help students solve the problems they are working on.

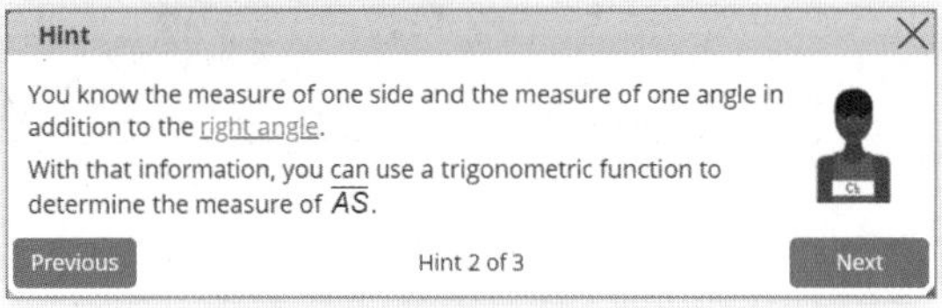

Just-in-Time Hints

When students make a common error, a Just-in-Time Hint automatically appears. These are indicated by the arrow in a red text box.

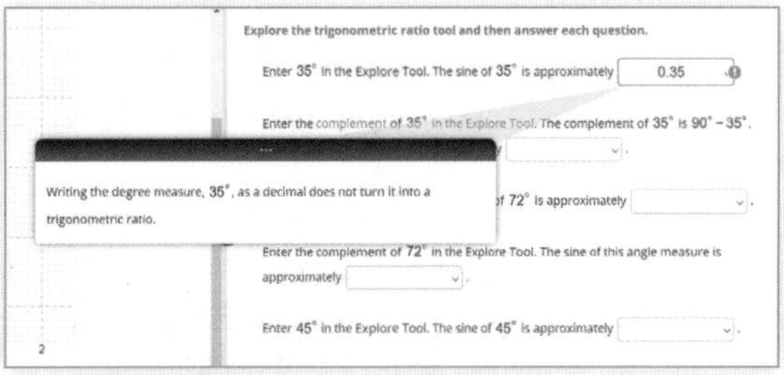

Research-Based Strategies

Founded by cognitive and computer scientists from Carnegie Mellon University and teachers from Pittsburgh Public Schools, Carnegie Learning has been deeply immersed in research from the start.

Our internal researchers collaborate with various independent research organizations, tirelessly working to understand more about how people learn and how to best facilitate learning. We supplement this information with feedback and data from our products, teachers, and students, to continuously evaluate and elevate our instructional approach and delivery.

The embedded strategies, tools, and guidance provided in these instructional resources are informed by books like Adding it Up, How People Learn, and Principles to Action.

MATHbook

Worked Examples

- Worked examples provide a means for students to view each step taken to solve the example problem.
- The questions that follow serve as a model for self-questioning and self-explanations. They represent and mimic an internal dialog about the mathematics and the strategies.
- This approach doesn't allow students to skip over the example without interacting with it, thinking about it, and responding to the questions.
- This approach will help students develop the desired habits of mind for being conscientious about the importance of steps and their order.

WORKED EXAMPLE

You can use the proportional relationship between arc length and circumference to determine the length of an arc for a circle with a radius of 10 inches and a central angle measure of 80°.

$$\frac{s}{2\pi r} = \frac{m}{360^\circ}$$
$$\frac{m\widehat{AB}}{2\pi(10)} = \frac{80^\circ}{360^\circ}$$
$$\frac{m\widehat{AB}}{20\pi} = \frac{2}{9}$$
$$m\widehat{AB} = \frac{40}{9}\pi$$

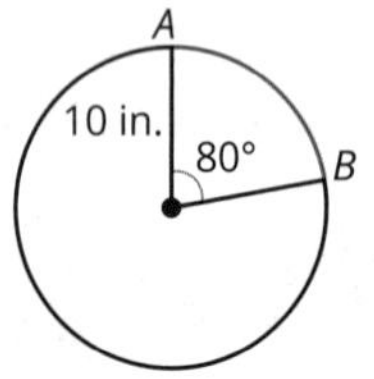

The measure of $\widehat{AB}$ is $\frac{40}{9}\pi$, or approximately 14 inches.

MATHbook

Thumbs Up/Thumbs Down

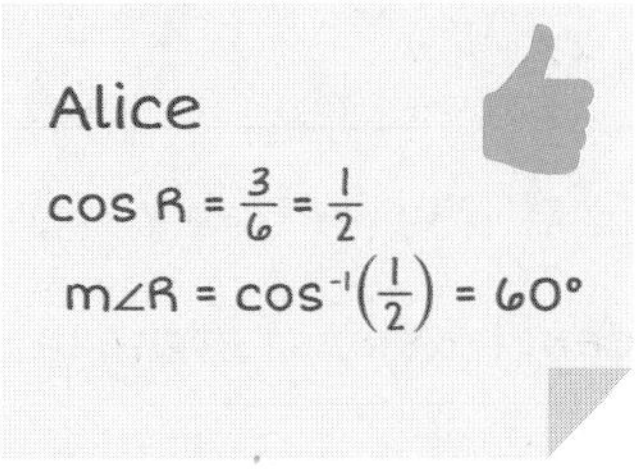
Alice
$\cos R = \frac{3}{6} = \frac{1}{2}$
$m\angle R = \cos^{-1}\left(\frac{1}{2}\right) = 60°$

- Thumbs Up problems allow students the opportunity to analyze viable methods and problem-solving strategies. We present questions to help students think more in-depth about the various strategies and analyze correct responses.
- Research shows that only providing positive examples does not eliminate some of the misconceptions students may have. Negative examples provide a way to directly address misconceptions.
- From the incorrect responses, students learn to identify and explain errors and how to make corrections.

Who's Correct?

"Who's Correct?" problems are an advanced form of correct vs. incorrect responses.

See page FM-55 in the introductory lesson **A Meeting of the Minds** to consider strategies that support students with these problem types.

The ultimate expression of ACT-R theory for math learning

MATHia

MATHia has its basis in the ACT-R (Adaptive Control of Thought – Rational) theory of human knowledge and cognitive performance, developed by John Anderson — one of the founders of Carnegie Learning (Anderson et. al., 2004; Anderson, 2007). The ACT-R theory is now recognized as the most comprehensive description of how the mind works, and has been the basis of thousands of publications; it is regularly used to model and predict important characteristics of human behavior, such as error patterns and response times, in a wide variety of studies of cognitive tasks, from natural language parsing and production to driving and flying.

As per ACT-R, MATHia treats complex problem solving as the coordination, strengthening—and eventual proceduralizing—of a large number of relatively simple "knowledge components," which represent the strategies and concepts required to master a domain. These knowledge components are collected into a "cognitive model," which allows the software to follow individual students' solution strategies, and to track the growth of knowledge for each student over time.

For more information about our extensive research, visit

www.carnegielearning.com/why/research ▶

Comprehensive Assessment

Assessment is an arc and not a one-time event. It is a regular part of the instructional cycle. Ongoing formative assessment underlies the entire learning experience, driving real-time adjustments, next steps, insights, and measurements.

CHECK READINESS › MONITOR LEARNING › MEASURE PERFORMANCE

Check Student Readiness

Module Readiness MODULE

You can collect and interpret data about student readiness at the module level.

The **MATHia** ReadyCheck Assessments gauge student readiness of concepts and skills that are prerequisite for any upcoming content. The scoring guide informs student instructional needs.

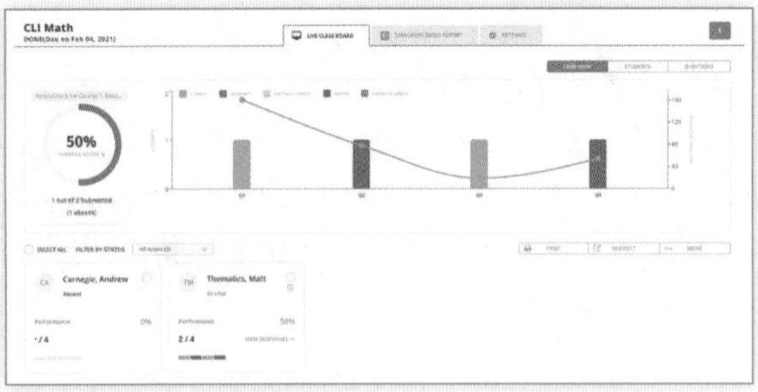

Additional **MATHia** sequences are available to address any unfinished learning.

Each **MATHbook** module begins with a resource for Getting Ready.

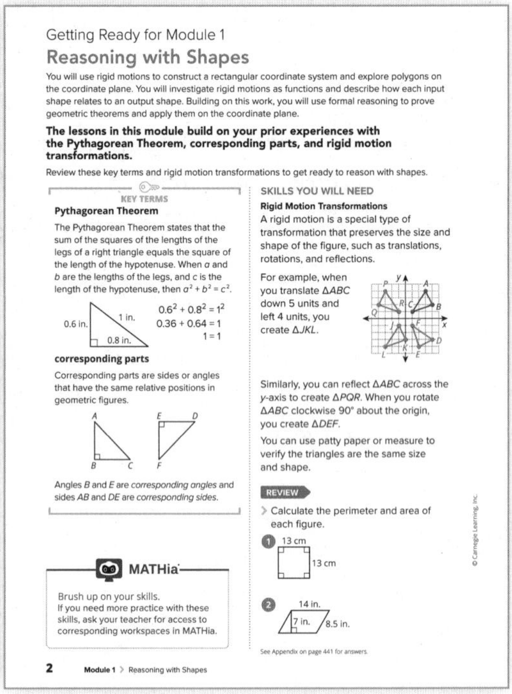
Getting Ready for Module 1

Reasoning with Shapes

You will use rigid motions to construct a rectangular coordinate system and explore polygons on the coordinate plane. You will investigate rigid motions as functions and describe how each input shape relates to an output shape. Building on this work, you will use formal reasoning to prove geometric theorems and apply them on the coordinate plane.

The lessons in this module build on your prior experiences with the Pythagorean Theorem, corresponding parts, and rigid motion transformations.

Review these key terms and rigid motion transformations to get ready to reason with shapes.

KEY TERMS

Pythagorean Theorem

The Pythagorean Theorem states that the sum of the squares of the lengths of the legs of a right triangle equals the square of the length of the hypotenuse. When a and b are the lengths of the legs, and c is the length of the hypotenuse, then $a^2 + b^2 = c^2$.

$0.6^2 + 0.8^2 = 1^2$
$0.36 + 0.64 = 1$
$1 = 1$

corresponding parts

Corresponding parts are sides or angles that have the same relative positions in geometric figures.

Angles B and E are *corresponding angles* and sides AB and DE are *corresponding sides*.

MATHia

Brush up on your skills.
If you need more practice with these skills, ask your teacher for access to corresponding workspaces in MATHia.

SKILLS YOU WILL NEED

Rigid Motion Transformations

A rigid motion is a special type of transformation that preserves the size and shape of the figure, such as translations, rotations, and reflections.

For example, when you translate ΔABC down 5 units and left 4 units, you create ΔJKL.

Similarly, you can reflect ΔABC across the y-axis to create ΔPQR. When you rotate ΔABC clockwise 90° about the origin, you create ΔDEF.

You can use patty paper or measure to verify the triangles are the same size and shape.

REVIEW

› Calculate the perimeter and area of each figure.

1. 13 cm, 13 cm
2. 14 in., 7 in., 8.5 in.

See Appendix on page 441 for answers.

© Carnegie Learning, Inc.

2 Module 1 › Reasoning with Shapes

Anticipate Learning TOPIC

As you prepare for each topic, read the **Topic Overviews** and do the math of the lesson to experience the content development. Review the **Assessment Overview** to prepare for how you will summatively assess learning.

How Does a Student Demonstrate Understanding?

Students will demonstrate an understanding of the standards in *Using a Rectangular Coordinate System* when they can:

Log in to MyCL for resources that support **student meta-cognition**.

TOPIC 1

Recognize that slopes of perpendicular lines are negative reciprocals.	✓
Determine the equation of a line parallel or perpendicular to a given line that passes through a given point.	✓
Prove the slope criteria for parallel and perpendicular lines and use them to solve problems.	✓

Teacher Resources:
- Topic Overviews
- Sample Topic Planner
- Assessment Overview

Student Resources:
- I-Can Statements

Monitor Student Learning

MATHbook SESSION

To set the stage for learning, Lesson Overviews provide Learning Goals and Review questions. Most importantly, you will see a statement that connects to prior knowledge and a question that anticipates new learning.

You have learned about constant ratios in similar triangles, given a specific reference angle.

How can you use the ratio of the opposite side length to the adjacent side length to solve for unknown measurements?

REVIEW (1–2 minutes)

> Use a calculator to compute each. Round your answers to the nearest hundredth.

1. $\frac{\sqrt{3}}{3}$

   0.58

IN THIS REVIEW
Students calculate the decimal equivalents of radicals. They will use this skill in **ACTIVITY 1 Connecting Slope and Tangent.**

As you facilitate lessons, use the Questions to Support Discourse to assess students' sense-making and reasoning, to gauge what they know, and generate evidence of student learning.

Questions to Support Discourse

	Questions	TYPE
2	• What is the relationship between the side opposite $\angle A$ and the side adjacent to $\angle B$? What about the side adjacent to $\angle A$ and the side opposite $\angle B$?	Gathering
	• Why is the ratio for $\sin\angle A$ equal to the ratio for $\cos\angle B$? • Why is the ratio for $\csc\angle A$ equal to the ratio for $\sec\angle B$? • Why is the ratio for $\tan\angle A$ equal to the ratio for $\cot\angle B$?	Seeing structure

---

As students self-reflect during the Talk the Talk, you can interpret how well they have demonstrated the learning outcomes and prepare for what's next.

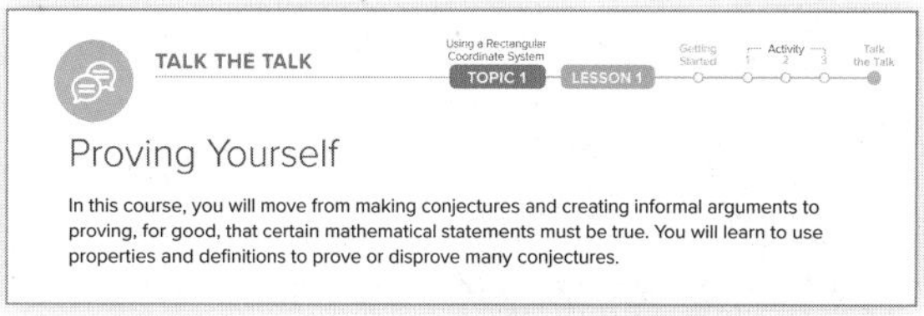

TALK THE TALK
Using a Rectangular Coordinate System
TOPIC 1
LESSON 1
Getting Started
Activity
Talk the Talk
Proving Yourself
In this course, you will move from making conjectures and creating informal arguments to proving, for good, that certain mathematical statements must be true. You will learn to use properties and definitions to prove or disprove many conjectures.

MATHia SESSION

As students work through MATHia, monitor **LiveLab** for real-time recommendations on how to support student progress.

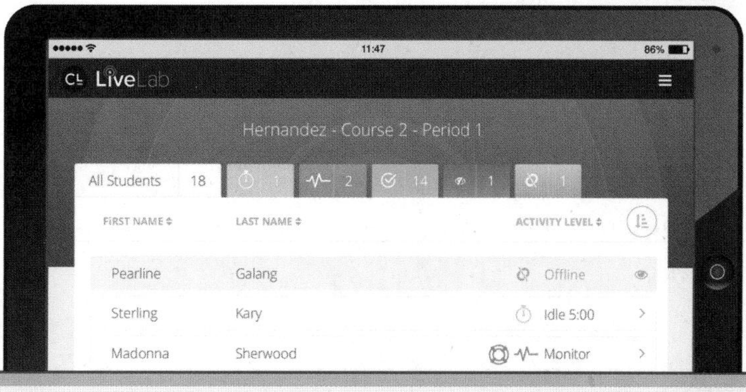

Comprehensive Assessment Continued

These instructional tools provide guidance, and support for you to collect, interpret, and act on data about student progress towards learning the appropriate mathematical content for this course.

Measure Student Performance

MATHia's progress monitoring and formative assessment capture student growth as they learn, and provides you real-time and actionable insights.

Progress Monitoring in MATHia

Skills Report

The Skills Report monitors skill proficiency in mastery workspaces.

It provides detailed information about each student's skill mastery progress organized by module, unit, and workspace.

Use this report to group students and identify skills that need additional support or remediation.

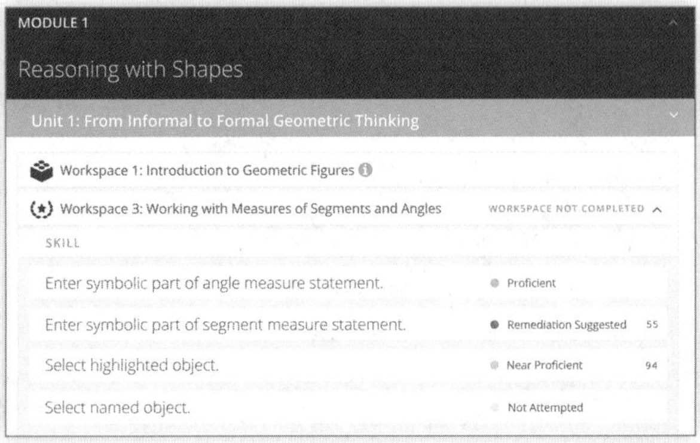

Standards Reports

The Standards Report provides an easy view of student proficiency on specific standards.

TAKE NOTE . . .

Each report has two views:
Class View and Student View.

Other reports available include:
Progress Report, Session Report, and Leadership Reports for Administrators.

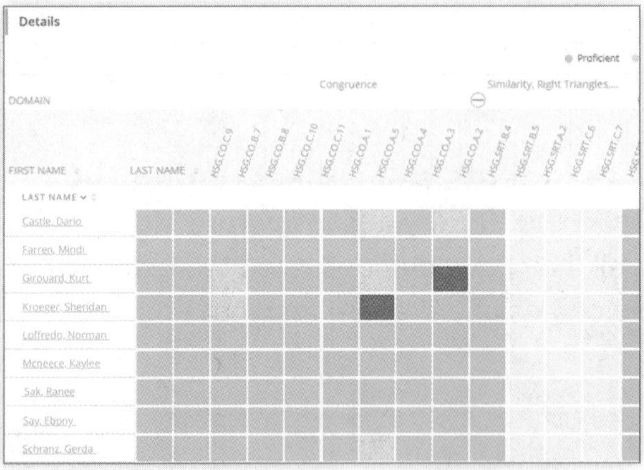

Predictive Analytics

Predictive data and insights assist you in monitoring student progress and predicting their end-of-year outcomes.

These insights allow you to proactively plan instruction that caters to individual student needs.

All summative assessments are available online in MyCL and via Edulastic.

Summative Assessments in MATHbook

Pre-Test and Post-Test

The Pre-Test and Post-Test are parallel forms. Use these assessments when you want to measure growth over the topic.

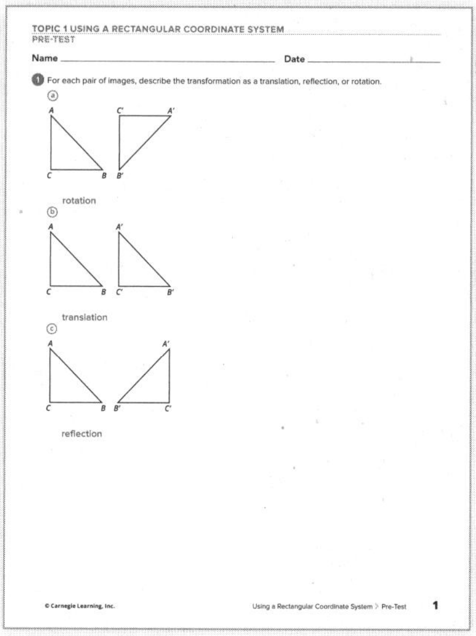

TOPIC 1 USING A RECTANGULAR COORDINATE SYSTEM
PRE-TEST

Name ______________________ Date ______________

1. For each pair of images, describe the transformation as a translation, reflection, or rotation.

a. rotation

b. translation

c. reflection

© Carnegie Learning, Inc. Using a Rectangular Coordinate System > Pre-Test 1

End of Topic Test

End of Topic Test Form A and Form B are parallel assessments. Items include short-answer and open-ended questions.

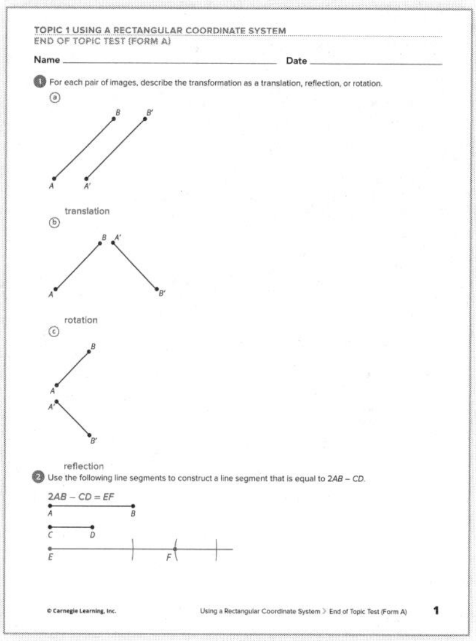

TOPIC 1 USING A RECTANGULAR COORDINATE SYSTEM
END OF TOPIC TEST (FORM A)

Name ______________________ Date ______________

1. For each pair of images, describe the transformation as a translation, reflection, or rotation.

a. translation

b. rotation

c. reflection

2. Use the following line segments to construct a line segment that is equal to 2AB – CD.

2AB – CD = EF

© Carnegie Learning, Inc. Using a Rectangular Coordinate System > End of Topic Test (Form A) 1

Standardized Test

Multiple choice questions help students prepare for standardized tests. Items include multiple choice and multiple select.

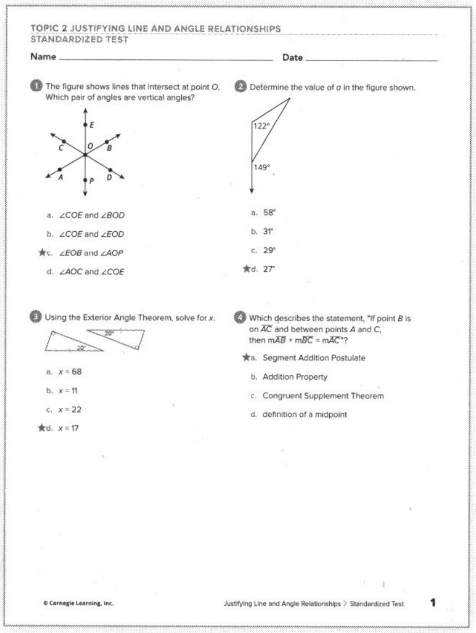

TOPIC 2 JUSTIFYING LINE AND ANGLE RELATIONSHIPS
STANDARDIZED TEST

Name ______________________ Date ______________

1. The figure shows lines that intersect at point O. Which pair of angles are vertical angles?

a. ∠COE and ∠BOD
b. ∠COE and ∠EOD
★c. ∠EOB and ∠AOP
d. ∠AOC and ∠COE

2. Determine the value of a in the figure shown.

a. 58°
b. 31°
c. 29°
★d. 27°

3. Using the Exterior Angle Theorem, solve for x.

a. x = 68
b. x = 11
c. x = 22
★d. x = 17

4. Which describes the statement, "If point B is on $\overline{AC}$ and between points A and C, then $m\overline{AB} + m\overline{BC} = m\overline{AC}$"?

★a. Segment Addition Postulate
b. Addition Property
c. Congruent Supplement Theorem
d. definition of a midpoint

© Carnegie Learning, Inc. Justifying Line and Angle Relationships > Standardized Test 1

Performance Tasks

Each topic includes an open-ended task and a rubric that gives students an opportunity to creatively demonstrate what they learned.

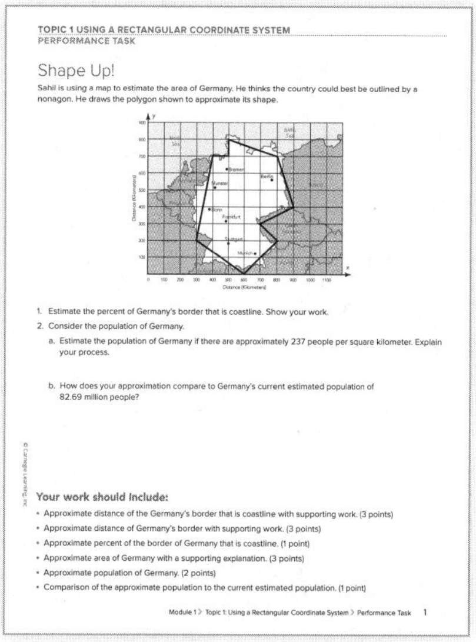

TOPIC 1 USING A RECTANGULAR COORDINATE SYSTEM
PERFORMANCE TASK

Shape Up!

Sahil is using a map to estimate the area of Germany. He thinks the country could best be outlined by a nonagon. He draws the polygon shown to approximate its shape.

1. Estimate the percent of Germany's border that is coastline. Show your work.
2. Consider the population of Germany.
   a. Estimate the population of Germany if there are approximately 237 people per square kilometer. Explain your process.
   b. How does your approximation compare to Germany's current estimated population of 82.69 million people?

Your work should include:

- Approximate distance of the Germany's border that is coastline with supporting work. (3 points)
- Approximate distance of Germany's border with supporting work. (3 points)
- Approximate percent of the border of Germany that is coastline. (1 point)
- Approximate area of Germany with a supporting explanation. (3 points)
- Approximate population of Germany. (2 points)
- Comparison of the approximate population to the current estimated population. (1 point)

Module 1 > Topic 1: Using a Rectangular Coordinate System > Performance Task 1

Need a link out to the **Reports Handbook**? Log in to **www.carnegielearning.com ▶**

Planning Resources

WITHIN THE TEACHER'S IMPLEMENTATION GUIDE . . .

You have access to tools that support your planning process.

LOOK FOR . . .

- Pacing support at the course, module, topic, and lesson levels
- Topic Planner
- Lesson Planner
- Lesson-level facilitation notes
- MyPL videos

MyPL™

The power of the **Carnegie Learning Professional Learning Team**—right at your fingertips.

- Hundreds of easily searchable videos created by a team of Master Math Practictioners
- Tools to save and share videos with colleagues
- 24/7 access to classroom strategies, implementation support, and more

To prioritize activities as you plan, pay attention to the activities denoted with an asterisk.

These activities highlight a key term of concept that is essential to the learning goals of the lesson.

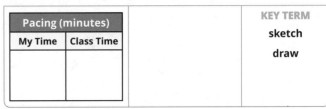

ACTIVITY 1 Analyzing a Diagram ✪

Pacing (minutes)			KEY TERM
My Time	Class Time		sketch draw

Use the **Connect the learning** section in each **MATHbook** lesson overview to connect the classroom activities with students' progress through **MATHia**.

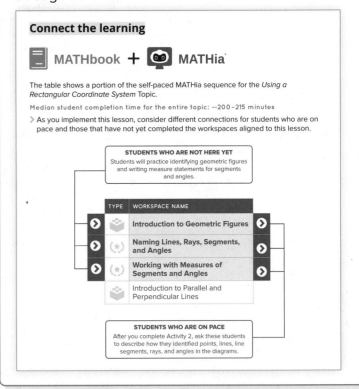

Connect the learning

MATHbook + MATHia

The table shows a portion of the self-paced MATHia sequence for the *Using a Rectangular Coordinate System* Topic.

Median student completion time for the entire topic: ~200–215 minutes

> As you implement this lesson, consider different connections for students who are on pace and those that have not yet completed the workspaces aligned to this lesson.

STUDENTS WHO ARE NOT HERE YET
Students will practice identifying geometric figures and writing measure statements for segments and angles.

TYPE	WORKSPACE NAME
	Introduction to Geometric Figures
(★)	**Naming Lines, Rays, Segments, and Angles**
(★)	**Working with Measures of Segments and Angles**
	Introduction to Parallel and Perpendicular Lines

STUDENTS WHO ARE ON PACE
After you complete Activity 2, ask these students to describe how they identified points, lines, line segments, rays, and angles in the diagrams.

Family Support

Each topic includes a **Family Guide**—guidance for parents and guardians to support their student as they are learning.

Each Family Guide includes:

- A mathematical overview
- The aligned **MATHia** sequence
- Learning tips
- Key terms

Point-of-Use Facilitation Tools

You can **adapt** each lesson for a variety of learners.

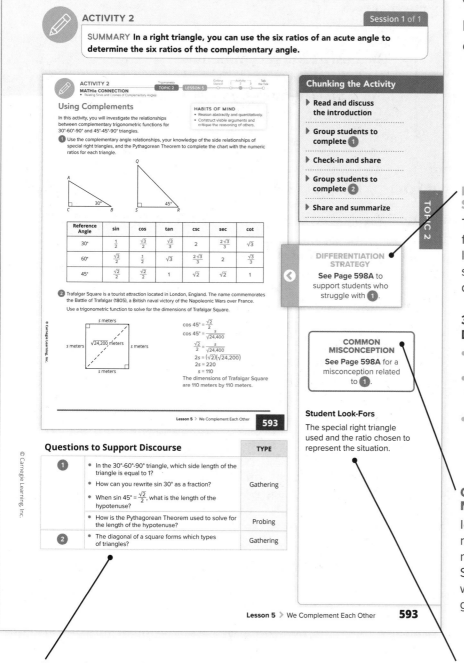

ACTIVITY 2

Session 1 of 1

SUMMARY **In a right triangle, you can use the six ratios of an acute angle to determine the six ratios of the complementary angle.**

ACTIVITY 2
MATHia CONNECTION
• Relating Sines and Cosines of Complementary Angles

Trigonometry TOPIC 2 LESSON 5 — Getting Started · Activity 1 2 3 · Talk the Talk

Using Complements

In this activity, you will investigate the relationships between complementary trigonometric functions for 30°-60°-90° and 45°-45°-90° triangles.

HABITS OF MIND
• Reason abstractly and quantitatively.
• Construct viable arguments and critique the reasoning of others.

1 Use the complementary angle relationships, your knowledge of the side relationships of special right triangles, and the Pythagorean Theorem to complete the chart with the numeric ratios for each triangle.

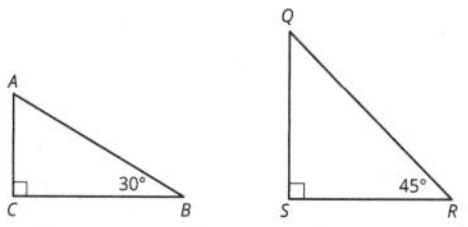

Reference Angle	sin	cos	tan	csc	sec	cot
30°	$\frac{1}{2}$	$\frac{\sqrt{3}}{2}$	$\frac{\sqrt{3}}{3}$	2	$\frac{2\sqrt{3}}{3}$	$\sqrt{3}$
60°	$\frac{\sqrt{3}}{2}$	$\frac{1}{2}$	$\sqrt{3}$	$\frac{2\sqrt{3}}{3}$	2	$\frac{\sqrt{3}}{3}$
45°	$\frac{\sqrt{2}}{2}$	$\frac{\sqrt{2}}{2}$	1	$\sqrt{2}$	$\sqrt{2}$	1

2 Trafalgar Square is a tourist attraction located in London, England. The name commemorates the Battle of Trafalgar (1805), a British naval victory of the Napoleonic Wars over France.

Use a trigonometric function to solve for the dimensions of Trafalgar Square.

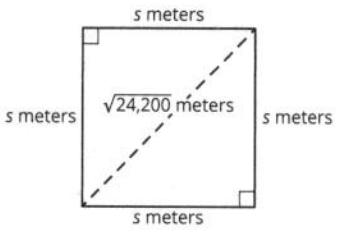

$\cos 45° = \frac{\sqrt{2}}{2}$

$\cos 45° = \frac{s}{\sqrt{24{,}400}}$

$\frac{\sqrt{2}}{2} = \frac{s}{\sqrt{24{,}400}}$

$2s = (\sqrt{2})(\sqrt{24{,}200})$

$2s = 220$

$s = 110$

The dimensions of Trafalgar Square are 110 meters by 110 meters.

Chunking the Activity

- Read and discuss the introduction
- Group students to complete 1
- Check-in and share
- Group students to complete 2
- Share and summarize

TOPIC 2

DIFFERENTIATION STRATEGY
See Page 598A to support students who struggle with 1.

COMMON MISCONCEPTION
See Page 598A for a misconception related to 1.

Student Look-Fors

The special right triangle used and the ratio chosen to represent the situation.

Questions to Support Discourse

		TYPE
1	• In the 30°-60°-90° triangle, which side length of the triangle is equal to 1? • How can you rewrite sin 30° as a fraction? • When $\sin 45° = \frac{\sqrt{2}}{2}$, what is the length of the hypotenuse?	Gathering
	• How is the Pythagorean Theorem used to solve for the length of the hypotenuse?	Probing
2	• The diagonal of a square forms which types of triangles?	Gathering

DIFFERENTIATION STRATEGIES

These strategies provide flexibility within the lesson to allow for varying student acquisition and demonstration of learning.

3 Types of Differentiation Strategies:

- Assisting All Students
- Supporting Students who Struggle
- Challenging Advanced Learners

COMMON MISCONCEPTIONS

Identify mathematical relationships that students may overgeneralize. Suggestions provide ways to address the given misconception.

Questions to Support Discourse

The overarching questioning strategies throughout each lesson promote analysis and higher-order thinking skills.

Use these questions during facilitation to gather information, probe thinking, make the mathematical structures explicit, and encourage reflection and justification as students are working together or when they are sharing responses as a class.

Student Look-Fors

These notes provide specific language, strategies, or errors to look and listen for as you circulate and monitor students working in pairs or groups.

Supporting for All Students

Everyone is an English language learner. Whether it's learning the language itself or the specialized, academic language of mathematics, students consistently use various strategies to make sense of the world.

Students learn through all 4 domains of language:

- Listening
- Reading
- Speaking
- Writing

The design and recommended implementation of MATHbook and MATHia provides you with the structure to address all 4 domains.

Strategies to Support Language Development

Best practices recommend to specifically teach academic language and to use cuing.

Academic Language	See **page FM-66** for strategies to support acquisition of academic language.
Setting the Stage Setting the Stage	Each lesson overview provides guidance to help students anticipate how the new information will connect to previous learning.
Language Links LANGUAGE LINK	Point-of-use language links provide suggestions to support language acquisition for a broader range of academic and contextual terms.
Glossary A – Z	This resource provides written definitions as well as visual examples. A Glossary is in MATHbook and **MATHia** and is available in both English and Spanish.
Google Translate	While working in **MATHia**, students can use **Google Translate** to read problems in their native language. Students can also use the **Text-to-Speech** feature in **MATHia** to hear the problems read aloud.

Strategies to Support Productive Skills

- The write-in nature of MATHbook allows students to highlight, annotate, and even write words in their native language.
- Graphic organizers provide opportunities to synthesize and display relationships between concepts and terms.

Strategies to Support Interactions

- Grouping students provides structured opportunities for ELL to practice speaking English.
- Pairing an ELL with more proficient English speakers allows opportunities to communicate their thinking in a low-stress way.

Strategies to Support Social-Emotional Learning

"SEL is the process through which all young people and adults acquire and apply the knowledge, skills, and attitudes to develop healthy identities, manage emotions and achieve personal and collective goals, feel and show empathy for others, establish and maintain supportive relationships, and make responsible and caring decisions."

— Collaborative for Academic, Social, and Emotional Learning (CASEL)

The CASEL 5 areas of competence:

- Self-awareness
- Self-management
- Social awareness
- Relationship skills
- Responsible decision-making

The development of these instructional materials, the intended implementation, and professional development support have always strived to incorporate tenets that support social and academic success.

The incorporation of social-emotional learning prompts begins in the introductory lesson, **A Meeting of the Minds**, located on **page FM-49**.

THINK ABOUT . . .
How can you connect to students' cultural, social, and geographic backgrounds and encourage them to share experiences from their lives?

Interleaved notes on lesson pages provide you with point-of-use reminders.

Student Look-Fors
Appreciating the perspective of others and empathizing with their ideas are key elements of social awareness. Continually encourage students to appreciate diversity in perspectives, backgrounds, and culture as they work together during the year.

Evidence for ESSA

Our High School Math Solution meets U.S. Department of Education standards under the **Every Student Succeeds Act (ESSA)** as a Level 1 program demonstrating "Strong Evidence" of efficacy, the highest rating available.

www.carnegielearning.com/ESSA ▶

Skills Practice

The Skills Practice workbook gives students without access to technology the opportunity to engage with problems that target each lesson's skills, concepts, and applications.

All Skills Practice problem sets are available via Edulastic.

TOPIC 2 TRIGONOMETRY
SKILLS PRACTICE

Name ______________________

PROBLEM SET 1: Exploring Trigonometric Ratios

> Determine the ratio $\frac{\text{opposite}}{\text{hypotenuse}}$ using $\angle A$ as the reference angle. Write your answers as fractions in simplest form.

1

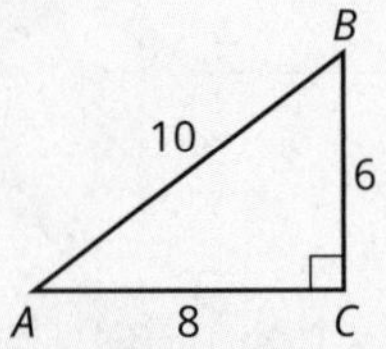

$$\frac{\textbf{opposite}}{\textbf{hypotenuse}} = \frac{3}{5}$$

WORKED EXAMPLE

The first solution is revealed to students to provide explicit guidance as they practice.

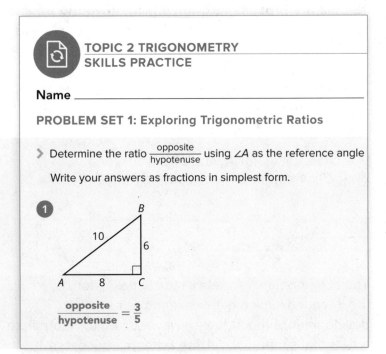

Skills Practice

You can locate Skills Practice connections at the end of each lesson's Additional Facilitation Notes.

PROBLEM SET	
1	**Exploring Trigonometric Ratios**
2	Calculating Tanget and Cotangent Ratios

Using Skills Practice for Re-Engagement

After working through **MATHbook** lessons and **MATHia** workspaces, some students may need to re-engage with specific skills.

You can use the Skills Practice problem sets to support small group remediation.

Re-Engaging with Skills Practice

- **Discuss the first problem and its solution**
- **Have students verbalize the solution strategy or process**
- **Guide students as they complete the second question**
- **Group students to complete the rest of the problem set**
- **Offer corrective feedback**

NOTES

Getting Ready for Geometry

A Meeting of the Minds

Plan to facilitate **A Meeting of the Minds** with your students to establish a community of learners.

You are about to begin an exciting journey!

You have a powerful resource to accommodate all high school students and various classroom implementations.

This **High School Math Solution** is intentionally designed to motivate and engage students, to develop a deep conceptual understanding of mathematics and fluency with procedures, and to provide you with tools to assess student understanding along the way.

These instructional materials will empower students to construct their knowledge and learn by doing. **MATHbook** and **MATHia** provide provides opportunities for "AHA" moments when students reveal connections between different concepts.

Have a great year!

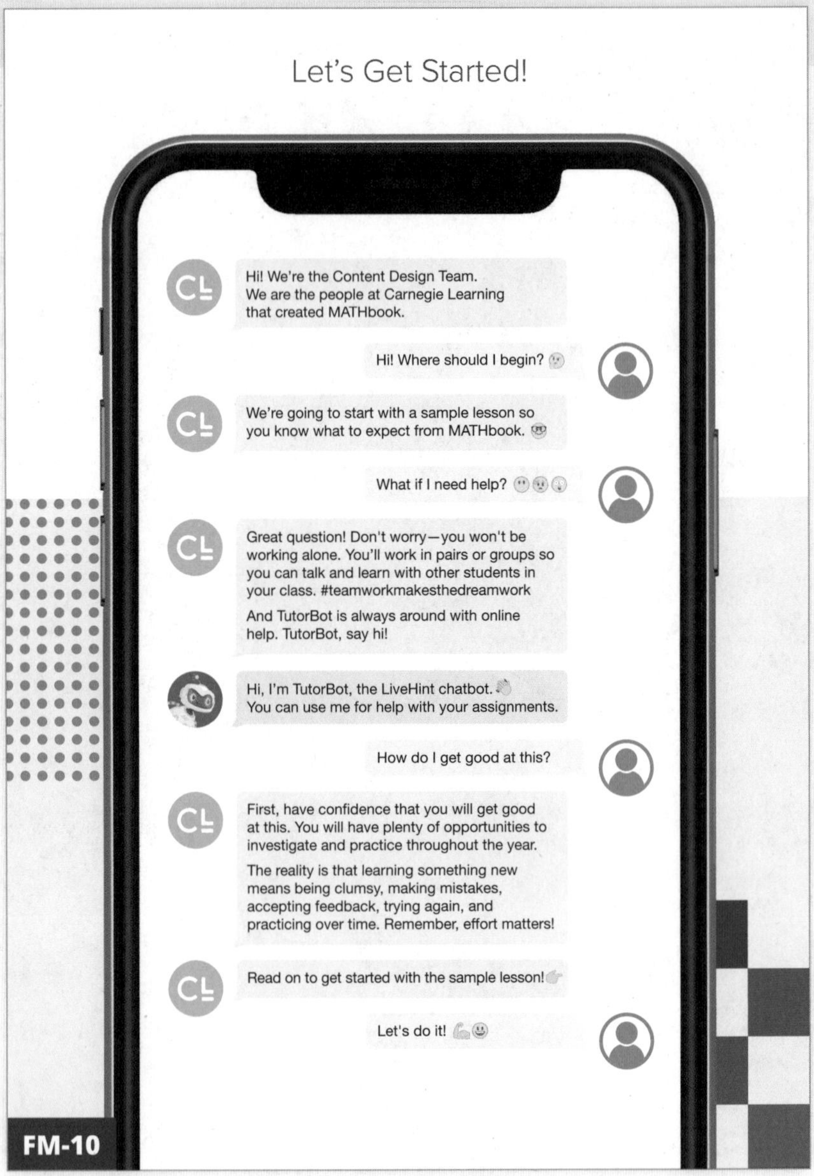

ENGAGE + DEVELOP + TEACH

at the **Module** level

at the **Topic** level

Read the facilitation notes and plan learning experiences.

MODULE 1 Reasoning With Shapes — MODULE 2 Establishing Congruence — MODULE 3 Investigating Proportionality — MODULE 4 Connecting Geometric and Algebraic Descriptions — MODULE 5 Making informed Decisions

OVERVIEW: LESSON

A Meeting of the Minds

Introduction to MATHbook and Your Learning Resources

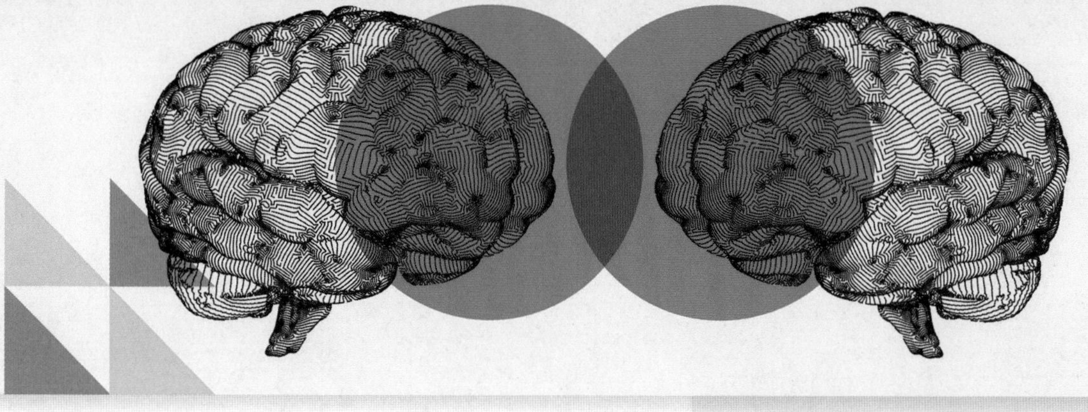

ENGAGE

- Students think about the variety of ways in which they learn.

DEVELOP

- Students preview the contents of MATHbook.
- They analyze a sample strategy to interact with the consumable text.
- Students explore the supports within MATHia and connection between MATHbook and MATHia.

DEMONSTRATE

- Students reflect on learning and set goals for the year.

Here you will see the full language of the mathematical content standards addressed in the lesson.

For this lesson, the focus is building community and familiarizing students with MATHbook and MATHia.

LESSON STRUCTURE AND PACING GUIDE 1 SESSION

✪ This activity highlights a key term or concept that is essential to the learning goals of the lesson.

Session 1

INSTRUCTIONAL SEQUENCE

ENGAGE	DEVELOP	DEVELOP
Building off intuition	Investigation Peer analysis	Worked example

✪ ✪ ✪

GETTING STARTED
You Know a Lot!

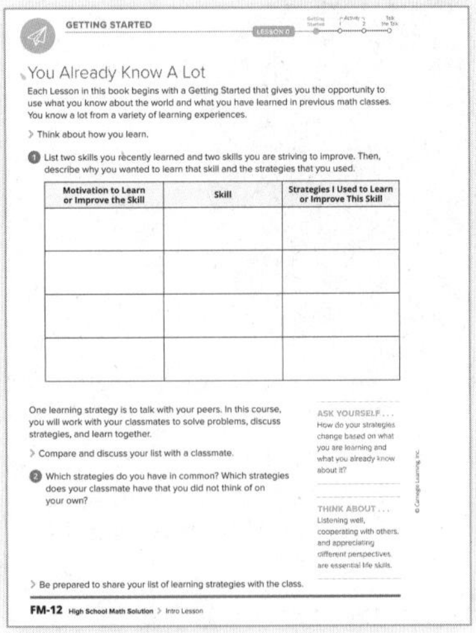
GETTING STARTED

You Already Know A Lot

Each Lesson in this book begins with a Getting Started that gives you the opportunity to use what you know about the world and what you have learned in previous math classes. You know a lot from a variety of learning experiences.

> Think about how you learn.

1 List two skills you recently learned and two skills you are striving to improve. Then, describe why you wanted to learn that skill and the strategies that you used.

Motivation to Learn or Improve the Skill	Skill	Strategies I Used to Learn or Improve This Skill

One learning strategy is to talk with your peers. In this course, you will work with your classmates to solve problems, discuss strategies, and learn together.

> Compare and discuss your list with a classmate.

2 Which strategies do you have in common? Which strategies does your classmate have that you did not think of on your own?

ASK YOURSELF . . . How do your strategies change based on what you are learning and what you already know about it?

THINK ABOUT . . . Listening well, cooperating with others, and appreciating different perspectives are essential life skills.

> Be prepared to share your list of learning strategies with the class.

FM-12 High School Math Solution > Intro Lesson

Students describe different strategies they use to learn new skills.

- They identify their motivation to learn or improve skills.
- They learn that collaboration is important to learning or improving skills.

ACTIVITY 1
Using MATHbook

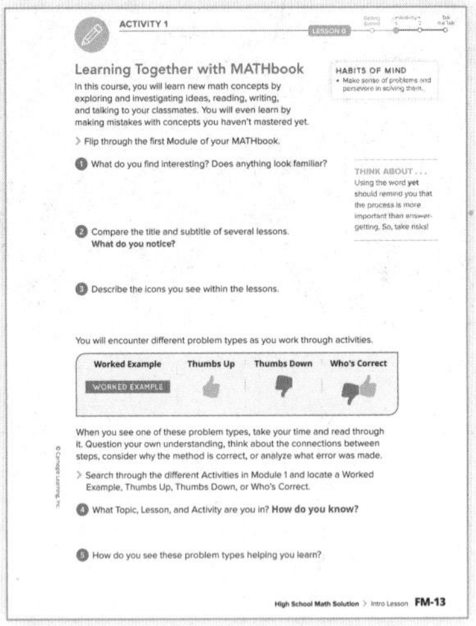
ACTIVITY 1

Learning Together with MATHbook

In this course, you will learn new math concepts by exploring and investigating ideas, reading, writing, and talking to your classmates. You will even learn by making mistakes with concepts you haven't mastered yet.

HABITS OF MIND
• Make sense of problems and persevere in solving them.

> Flip through the first Module of your MATHbook.

1 What do you find interesting? Does anything look familiar?

THINK ABOUT . . . Using the word yet should remind you that the process is more important than answer-getting. So, take risks!

2 Compare the title and subtitle of several lessons. What do you notice?

3 Describe the icons you see within the lessons.

You will encounter different problem types as you work through activities.

Worked Example | Thumbs Up | Thumbs Down | Who's Correct

When you see one of these problem types, take your time and read through it. Question your own understanding, think about the connections between steps, consider why the method is correct, or analyze what error was made.

> Search through the different Activities in Module 1 and locate a Worked Example, Thumbs Up, Thumbs Down, or Who's Correct.

4 What Topic, Lesson, and Activity are you in? How do you know?

5 How do you see these problem types helping you learn?

High School Math Solution > Intro Lesson FM-13

Students explore MATHbook identifying common elements and problem types.

- They learn about utilizing the consumable text to produce work artifacts.
- They explore the Academic Glossary and reflect on the Habits of Mind.

ACTIVITY 2
Learning Individually

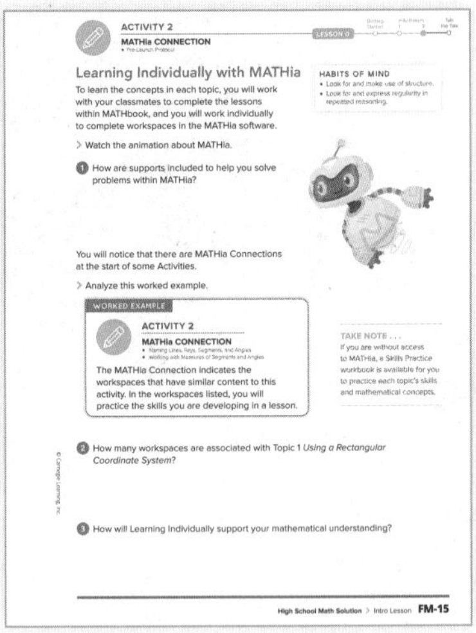
ACTIVITY 2

MATHia CONNECTION

Learning Individually with MATHia

To learn the concepts in each topic, you will work with your classmates to complete the lessons within MATHbook, and you will work individually to complete workspaces in the MATHia software.

HABITS OF MIND
• Look for and make use of structure.
• Look for and express regularity in repeated reasoning.

> Watch the animation about MATHia.

1 How are supports included to help you solve problems within MATHia?

You will notice that there are MATHia Connections at the start of some Activities.

> Analyze this worked example.

WORKED EXAMPLE

ACTIVITY 2

MATHia CONNECTION

The MATHia Connection indicates the workspaces that have similar content to this activity. In the workspaces listed, you will practice the skills you are developing in a lesson.

TAKE NOTE . . . If you are without access to MATHia, a Skills Practice workbook is available for you to practice each topic's skills and mathematical concepts.

2 How many workspaces are associated with Topic 1 *Using a Rectangular Coordinate System*?

3 How will Learning Individually support your mathematical understanding?

High School Math Solution > Intro Lesson FM-15

Students learn about the supports included in MATHia.

- They develop an understanding of the connections between MATHia and MATHbook.

Log in to MyCL for **lesson support** including:

Slides

Videos

www.carnegielearning.com/login

INSTRUCTIONAL SEQUENCE

DEMONSTRATE

Writing task

TALK THE TALK

So Give It a Shot!

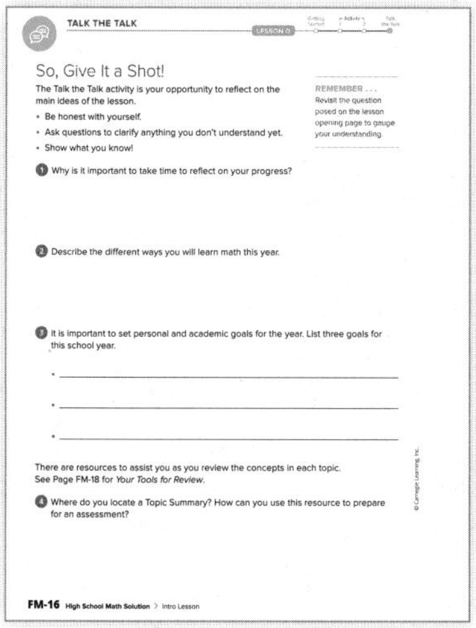
TALK THE TALK

LESSON 0

So, Give It a Shot!

The Talk the Talk activity is your opportunity to reflect on the main ideas of the lesson.

- Be honest with yourself.
- Ask questions to clarify anything you don't understand yet.
- Show what you know!

REMEMBER . . .
Revisit the question posed on the lesson opening page to gauge your understanding.

1. Why is it important to take time to reflect on your progress?

2. Describe the different ways you will learn math this year.

3. It is important to set personal and academic goals for the year. List three goals for this school year.

- ______
- ______
- ______

There are resources to assist you as you review the concepts in each topic. See Page FM-18 for *Your Tools for Review*.

4. Where do you locate a Topic Summary? How can you use this resource to prepare for an assessment?

© Carnegie Learning, Inc.

FM-16 High School Math Solution > Intro Lesson

Students set goals for the school year.

- They describe the different ways they learn.
- They describe why it is essential to reflect on their progress.

NOTES

TOPIC 1

Log in to MyCL for:

- Editable templates
- Additional planning support

Now that you have read the Lesson Overview, you are ready to plan.

Do the math

> Tear out the lesson planning template (pageFM–53) and jot down thoughts as you work through this lesson and read the Facilitation Notes.

- Anticipate student responses
- Track your time, so you can estimate how much time to spend on any activity
- Decide which differentiation and collaboration strategies you may use and how that may impact pacing

Connect the learning

MATHbook + MATHia

The table shows the self-paced MATHia sequence for the Pre-Launch Protocol.

Median student completion time: ~10 minutes

> As you implement this lesson, consider different connections for students who are on pace and those that have not yet completed the workspaces aligned to this lesson.

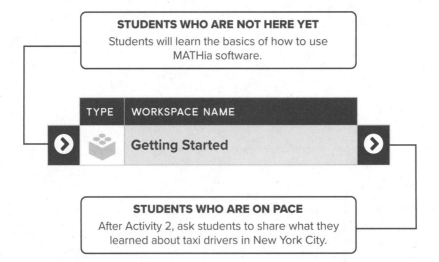

STUDENTS WHO ARE NOT HERE YET

Students will learn the basics of how to use MATHia software.

TYPE	WORKSPACE NAME
	Getting Started

STUDENTS WHO ARE ON PACE

After Activity 2, ask students to share what they learned about taxi drivers in New York City.

A Meeting of the Minds

An Introduction to MATHbook and Your Learning Resources

Session 1

GETTING STARTED You Know a Lot ✪

Pacing (minutes)	
My Time	Class Time

ACTIVITY 1 Using MATHbook ✪

Pacing (minutes)	
My Time	Class Time

KEY TERM
yet

ACTIVITY 2 Learning Individually ✪

Pacing (minutes)	
My Time	Class Time

TALK THE TALK So Give It a Shot! ✪

Pacing (minutes)	
My Time	Class Time

✪ This activity highlights a key term or concept that is essential to the learning goals of the lesson.

Log in to **MyCL** for:

- Editable templates
- Additional planning support

Reflect on your lesson

Consider the effectiveness of your lesson on student learning.

What went well?

What did not go as planned?

Anticipate how you would change the lesson next time you teach it.

How will you capitalize on the things that went well?

How will you improve things that did not go as planned?

MATERIALS

- None

INTRO LESSON

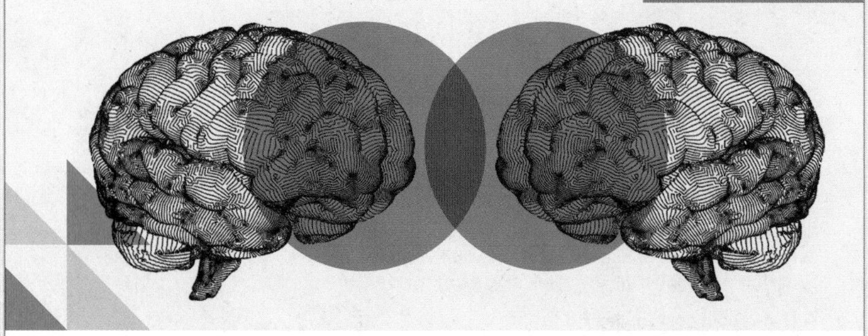

A Meeting of the Minds

An Introduction to MATHbook and Your Learning Resources

KEY TERMS
yet

Learning Goals

- Establish a community of learners.
- Preview the contents of MATHbook.
- Consider how you will interact with MATHbook to make your learning visible.
- Understand how MATHia software supports each MATHbook Topic.
- Set personal goals to take ownership of your learning.

REVIEW (1–2 minutes)

The questions in this section review a skill you will need in the lesson.
> Consider each question. Be prepared to share your strategies, conclusions, and questions.

1. Why is it helpful to review what you already know before learning something new?

When I review what I already know, then I know where a good starting place for me to learn something new is.

TAKE NOTE . . .
Each lesson opens with a statement that connects what you have learned with a question to ponder.

In previous math classes, you explored transformations, analyzed patterns and relationships, learned about functions, operations with real numbers, probability and statistics, and geometry.

How can you use MATHbook and MATHia software to meet the goals of this course?

High School Math Solution > Intro Lesson **FM-11**

Setting the Stage

- **Assign Review (optional, 1 - 2 minutes)**
- **Communicate the learning goals and key terms to look out for**
- **Tap into your students' prior learning by reading the narrative statement**
- **Provide a sense of direction by reading the question**

TOPIC 1

IN THIS REVIEW
These questions present a formative assessment opportunity, building from the Getting Ready, that reactivates students' prior knowledge. This statement will identify where in the lesson students will use this skill.

In this course, you will build on your work with transformations, linear equations, constructions, and angle relationships. You will apply proportions to explore similarity and relationships in right triangles. You will expand your work with circles, volume, and probability.

Essential Ideas

- Create a classroom of collaboration and establish the learning process as a partnership between you and your students.
- Communicate continuously with students about the learning goals of the lesson to encourage self-monitoring of their learning.
- Students learn when they are actively engaged in a task: reasoning about math, writing their solutions, justifying their strategies, and sharing knowledge with peers.
- Support productive struggle by allowing students time to engage with and persevere through mathematics.
- Listen and review student responses and explanations and provide feedback to help them improve their understanding.
- Encourage students to take responsibility for their learning and self-assess.

GETTING STARTED

SUMMARY **Learning happens in different ways, using different strategies. Math is not different. MATHbook uses a variety of strategies to support learning.**

Chunking the Activity

- **Read and discuss the introduction**
- **Have students work individually to complete 1**
- **Read and discuss the directions**
- **Group students to complete 2**
- **Share and summarize**

COMMON MISCONCEPTION

See Page FM–63 for misconceptions related to reading in MATHbook.

DIFFERENTIATION STRATEGY

See Page FM–63 to assist all students after they complete 2.

Student Look-Fors

Appreciating the perspective of others and empathizing with their ideas are key elements of social awareness. Continually encourage students to appreciate diversity in perspectives, backgrounds, and cultures as they work together during the year.

GETTING STARTED — LESSON 0 — Getting Started · Activity 1 · Activity 2 · Talk the Talk

You Already Know A Lot

Each Lesson in this book begins with a Getting Started that gives you the opportunity to use what you know about the world and what you have learned in previous math classes. You know a lot from a variety of learning experiences.

> Think about how you learn.

1. List two skills you recently learned and two skills you are striving to improve. Then, describe why you wanted to learn that skill and the strategies that you used.

Motivation to Learn or Improve the Skill	Skill	Strategies I Used to Learn or Improve This Skill
Sample answers. I want to be in the band.	I recently learned to play the tuba.	Somebody taught me and I practiced.
I watched a baking show on TV.	I recently learned to bake a cake.	I read cookbooks and watched videos.
I loved playing soccer with my friends	I want to improve my soccer skills.	I learned by trying and watching others.
I want to write a comic book.	I want to improve my drawing skills.	I practiced and got feedback.

One learning strategy is to talk with your peers. In this course, you will work with your classmates to solve problems, discuss strategies, and learn together.

> Compare and discuss your list with a classmate.

2. Which strategies do you have in common? Which strategies does your classmate have that you did not think of on your own?

ASK YOURSELF . . .
How do your strategies change based on what you are learning and what you already know about it?

THINK ABOUT . . .
Listening well, cooperating with others, and appreciating different perspectives are essential life skills.

> Be prepared to share your list of learning strategies with the class.

Questions to Support Discourse

	Question	TYPE
1	• Think of a time when you helped someone learn how to do something, what did you do?	Gathering
	• How do the strategies you use to learn skills help you persevere when solving problems?	Reflecting and justifying
2	• How did your list change as you shared with your classmates? • How did your strategies compare to your classmates'? • How long does it take you to learn something?	Probing
	• At what point are you confident in your knowledge?	Reflecting and justifying

ACTIVITY 1

SUMMARY **MATHbook helps you learn mathematical content and develop the habits of mind. You will create a variety of learning artifacts in MATHbook.**

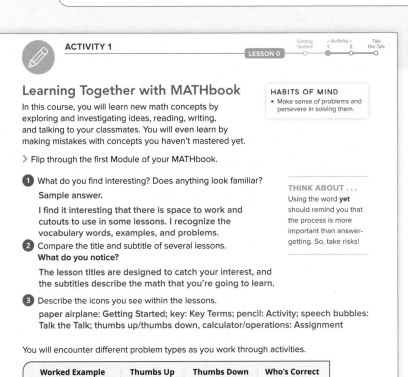

Learning Together with MATHbook

HABITS OF MIND
- Make sense of problems and persevere in solving them.

In this course, you will learn new math concepts by exploring and investigating ideas, reading, writing, and talking to your classmates. You will even learn by making mistakes with concepts you haven't mastered yet.

> Flip through the first Module of your MATHbook.

1. What do you find interesting? Does anything look familiar?
   Sample answer.
   I find it interesting that there is space to work and cutouts to use in some lessons. I recognize the vocabulary words, examples, and problems.

THINK ABOUT . . .
Using the word **yet** should remind you that the process is more important than answer-getting. So, take risks!

2. Compare the title and subtitle of several lessons. **What do you notice?**
   The lesson titles are designed to catch your interest, and the subtitles describe the math that you're going to learn.

3. Describe the icons you see within the lessons.
   paper airplane: Getting Started; key: Key Terms; pencil: Activity; speech bubbles: Talk the Talk; thumbs up/thumbs down, calculator/operations: Assignment

You will encounter different problem types as you work through activities.

Worked Example	Thumbs Up	Thumbs Down	Who's Correct
WORKED EXAMPLE			

When you see one of these problem types, take your time and read through it. Question your own understanding, think about the connections between steps, consider why the method is correct, or analyze what error was made.

> Search through the different Activities in Module 1 and locate a Worked Example, Thumbs Up, Thumbs Down, or Who's Correct.

4. What Topic, Lesson, and Activity are you in? **How do you know?**
   Sample answer. I can look at the tracker in the header, or I can look at the footer.

5. How do you see these problem types helping you learn?
   Sample answer. The Worked Examples will give me steps to follow. The other problem types will make me think about possible errors I might make in my work.

Questions to Support Discourse

		TYPE
1	• What do you notice as you look through the first module? • What are you wondering about MATHbook?	Gathering
5	• How are the worked example and thumbs up problem types similar?	Seeing structure

Chunking the Activity

- Read and discuss the introduction
- Group students to complete 1 - 5
- Check-in and share
- Group students to complete 6 and 7
- Check-in and share
- Group students to complete 8 and 9
- Check-in and share
- Complete 10 as a class

TOPIC 1

DIFFERENTIATION STRATEGY

See Page FM–63 to group students to complete the activity.

LANGUAGE LINK

While students have encountered icons for apps, games, or programs, ensure that they understand *icon* refers to the symbols used to represent features in the text, such as the pencil icon at the start of each activity.

NOTES

NOTE: Determine norms and routines students will use to access everyday supplies, such as calculators and highlighters. Build students' capacity for responsible decision-making by empowering students to take ownership of the routines.

LANGUAGE LINK

ELL TIP

A Spanish version of the Glossary is available for students in their digital resources. This is a useful tool for students and family members that read in Spanish.

DIFFERENTIATION STRATEGY

See Page FM–64 to assist all students with 9.

Student Look-Fors

Relationship skills are critical for success and are developed over time. Look for students that are interacting with their partners and applying active listening techniques. Throughout the course provide students with guidance to build their ability to communicate clearly, listen well and cooperate with others.

ACTIVITY 1 (continued)

In MATHbook, you can mark up the pages in any way that is helpful to you as you take ownership of your learning.

> Analyze a page from Brody's MATHbook.

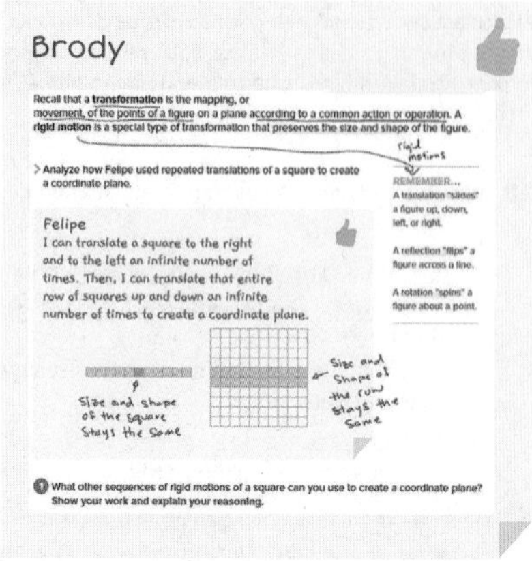

6. What strategies did Brody use to make sense of the key term and strategies?

   Sample answer.

   He used a highlighter.

   He labeled key parts of the strategies.

   He took notes in the margin.

7. Locate the term **rigid motion** in the glossary. What page is it on?

   Page G-32

Through the process of writing, you clarify your understanding and improve your communication skills. The Academic Glossary on Page FM-20 is your guide as you engage with the kind of thinking you do as you are learning the content.

DID YOU KNOW . . .
Colleges and employers highly value candidates with strong verbal communication skills.

8. Locate the phrase **explain your reasoning** in the Academic Glossary. Which of the Ask Yourself questions should Brody have asked himself?

   Sample answer.

   How should I organize my thoughts? Is my explanation logical? Does my reasoning make sense? How can I justify my answer to others?

It is not just about what mathematical content you are learning, but how you are learning it. Did you notice the Habits of Mind beside each Activity title? You can locate the full list on Page FM-19.

9. What is the Habit of Mind for this Using MATHbook activity? **How will developing this habit help you?**

   Make sense of problems and persevere in solving them.

10. How will Learning Together help you learn math?

    I can clarify my ideas by sharing with others and build from their ideas.

Questions to Support Discourse

		TYPE
6	• Why do you think it is important to interact with the text the way that Brody did?	Reflecting and justifying
7	• What are some situations where the glossary will be helpful?	Gathering
8	• Which part(s) of the academic glossary are most helpful for you?	Probing
9	• Where did you locate the Habit of Mind for this Using MATHbook activity?	Gathering
	• Why is perseverance an important habit to build?	Reflecting and justifying

ACTIVITY 2

SUMMARY **MATHia works with MATHbook to deepen understanding. MATHia includes supports to help students successfully achieve their mathematical goals.**

ACTIVITY 2

MATHia CONNECTION
- Pre-Launch Protocol

LESSON 0 — Getting Started · Activity 1 · 2 · Talk the Talk

Learning Individually with MATHia

To learn the concepts in each topic, you will work with your classmates to complete the lessons within MATHbook, and you will work individually to complete workspaces in the MATHia software.

> Watch the animation about MATHia.

HABITS OF MIND
- Look for and make use of structure.
- Look for and express regularity in repeated reasoning.

1. How are supports included to help you solve problems within MATHia?

   Sample answer.

   There are hints, step-by-step examples, and sample problems.

You will notice that there are MATHia Connections at the start of some Activities.

> Analyze this worked example.

WORKED EXAMPLE

ACTIVITY 2

MATHia CONNECTION
- Naming Lines, Rays, Segments, and Angles
- Working with Measures of Segments and Angles

The MATHia Connection indicates the workspaces that have similar content to this activity. In the workspaces listed, you will practice the skills you are developing in a lesson.

TAKE NOTE . . .
If you are without access to MATHia, a Skills Practice workbook is available for you to practice each topic's skills and mathematical concepts.

2. How many workspaces are associated with Topic 1 *Using a Rectangular Coordinate System*?

   There are 11 workspaces associated with Topic 1 *Using a Rectangular Coordinate System*.

3. How will Learning Individually support your mathematical understanding?

   Sample answer.

   I will be able to work at my pace and get the support that I need to master skill and develop my understanding of math.

Questions to Support Discourse

		TYPE
1	• What are the supports that you learned about?	Gathering
	• How will the step-by-step examples help you as you work in MATHia?	Probing
2	• How can you use the MATHia Connections to help you succeed this year?	Reflecting and justifying

Chunking the Activity

- Read and discuss the introduction and watch the animation
- Group students to complete 1
- Check-in and share
- Read and discuss the worked example
- Group students to complete 2 and 3
- Share and summarize

NOTE: Go to **www.carnegielearning.com/mathia-hs-animation** for the MATHia animation.

DIFFERENTIATION STRATEGY

See Page FM–64 to assist all students with MATHia.

COMMON MISCONCEPTION

See Page FM–64 for misconceptions related to working in MATHia.

LANGUAGE LINK

Remind all students to turn to the academic glossary and read about the term *analyze* before they analyze the worked example.

TALK THE TALK

SUMMARY **Understanding the resources and supports available in MATHbook and MATHia will help you successfully achieve your goals for the year.**

Chunking the Activity

- **Read and discuss the directions**
- **Group students to complete 1 and 2**
- **Check-in and share**
- **Have students work individually to complete 3**
- **Group students to complete 4**
- **Share and summarize**

DIFFERENTIATION STRATEGY

See Page FM–65 to support students who struggle with 3.

See Page FM–65 to assist all students in extending 3.

NOTE: Self-awareness takes time to develop. Students may come in with some self-awareness skills, but need reminders and opportunities to continue developing those skills. Frequent opportunities to reflect on progress and actions helps to build self-awareness.

Student Look-Fors

Look at the types of goals students are writing. Promote self-management by encouraging students to think about a combination of short and long term goals. Have a plan for revisiting these goals throughout the year.

TALK THE TALK — LESSON 0 — Getting Started, Activity 1, 2, Talk the Talk

So, Give It a Shot!

The Talk the Talk activity is your opportunity to reflect on the main ideas of the lesson.

- Be honest with yourself.
- Ask questions to clarify anything you don't understand yet.
- Show what you know!

REMEMBER . . .
Revisit the question posed on the lesson opening page to gauge your understanding.

1. Why is it important to take time to reflect on your progress?

   Sample answer.

   Reflection empowers me to take ownership of my own learning and thinking. Reflection builds critical thinking that I can use in future learning.

2. Describe the different ways you will learn math this year.

   Sample answer.

   I will use MATHbook to learn new mathematical concepts alongside my classmates. In MATHia, I will work individually to learn and practice skills that align to the MATHbook topics.

3. It is important to set personal and academic goals for the year. List three goals for this school year.

   - ____________________
   - ____________________
   - ____________________

There are resources to assist you as you review the concepts in each topic. See Page FM-18 for *Your Tools for Review*.

4. Where do you locate a Topic Summary? How can you use this resource to prepare for an assessment?

   The Topic Summaries are located in MyCL. I can use this resource to identify the key ideas in each lesson and to analyze a worked example to ensure my understanding.

FM-16 High School Math Solution > Intro Lesson

Questions to Support Discourse

	Question	TYPE
1	How will tracking your progress help you succeed this year?	Reflecting and justifying
2	What are the different tools that you learned about during this lesson?	Gathering
	What are some of the ways that you learn outside of math class? Will they be the same in math class?	Probing
3	Are the goals you set short term goals or long term goals?	Probing
	Why do you think it is important to have both short-term and long-term goals for the school year?	Reflecting and justifying

ASSIGNMENT

INTRO LESSON ASSIGNMENT

> Use a separate piece of paper for your Journal entry.

JOURNAL

If how you felt about learning math this year were a meme, what would the meme be? Sketch or include your meme and explain your reasoning.

REMEMBER

In this course, you will build on your work with transformations, linear equations, constructions, and angle relationships. You will apply proportions to explore similarity and relationships in right triangles. You will expand your work with circles, volume, and probability.

PRACTICE

> Share the Family Guide for Topic 1 *Using a Rectangular Coordinate System* with an adult.

1. Follow this QR code or URL to access the digital file.

   ONLINE RESOURCES FOR FAMILIES
   www.carnegielearning.com/home-connection/

2. What information does the Family Guide provide?

   Topic name, key terms, a Math Myth, questions to ask

As you complete the Practice section of each Assignment, LiveHint is your textbook assistant. LiveHint allows you to obtain real-time hints from any device on questions through the TutorBot. With LiveHint, you never have to navigate through assignments on your own.

> Go to **LiveHint.com.**

LiveHint™

3. Follow the instructions to access hints to this question.

   - First hint: ____________________
   - Second hint: ____________________
   - Third hint: ____________________

STRETCH Optional

Why do you think Module 1 is titled *Reasoning with Shapes*?

Chunking the Assignment

TOPIC 1

- Journal
- Practice 1 - 3
- Stretch (advanced learners)

JOURNAL

Sample answer.

I love math. Math helps me explore new ideas, develop critical thinking skills, and is everywhere around me.

STRETCH

Sample answer.

We will investigate shapes on the coordinate plane and explore the effects of applying rigid motions to a shape.

NOTES

A Meeting of the Minds

This resource details additional facilitation notes to fully assist you as you plan each lesson to support all students, students who struggle, and advanced learners. It provides differentiation strategies, common student misconceptions, and suggestions to extend certain activities.

GETTING STARTED
You Know a Lot

Session 1 of 1

Students learn to appreciate diversity as they reflect on strategies used to learn new skills. They begin to build foundations for collaboration as they share with their classmates.

CHUNK	AUDIENCE	ADDITIONAL SUPPORTS
As students work on the entire lesson	All Students	**COMMON MISCONCEPTION** Students often believe that reading is not a skill regularly used in math class. They need support and opportunities to build their capacity and stamina for reading in math. When planning, think about how you will scaffold the text for students. Think about breaking the text into smaller pieces to analyze, reading the text aloud to the whole class, or other strategies to support students as they read the text. Go to MyCL and MyPL for additional ideas to support reading the text.
After students complete 2	All Students	**DIFFERENTIATION STRATEGY** To encourage collaboration, select a team-building activity to do with your class at the end of this activity.

ACTIVITY 1
Using MATHbook

Session 1 of 1

Students explore MATHbook identifying common elements and problem types. They learn about utilizing the consumable text to produce work artifacts. They explore the Academic Glossary and reflect on the Habits of Mind.

CHUNK	AUDIENCE	ADDITIONAL SUPPORTS
As you group students to complete the activity	All Students	**DIFFERENTIATION STRATEGY** Use random groups for this activity and to start the school year while you learn more about your students. As the year progresses, use what you know about students, along with data from MATHia, to strategize how to group your students. You can also visit MyPL to learn more about grouping strategies and suggestions for grouping students.

CHUNK	AUDIENCE	ADDITIONAL SUPPORTS
After completing 9	All Students	**DIFFERENTIATION STRATEGY** Throughout MATHbook, students will make sense of problems and persevere in solving them. It is a focus for all lessons. Have students turn to pageFM–19 and read and discuss the top paragraph. As students encounter other habits of mind, take the opportunity to come back and ask students to reflect on what those habits of mind mean for them.

ACTIVITY 2

Session 1 of 1

Learning Individually

Students watch an animation about MATHia and learn about the supports included in MATHia. They recognize where to identify the workspaces connected to the content they are working on in the MATHbook.

CHUNK	AUDIENCE	ADDITIONAL SUPPORTS
When discussing the introduction	All Students	**COMMON MISCONCEPTION** Students often interpret Learning Individually or learning through MATHia as independent work, and they should not ask their peers for support when needed. Remind students of the importance of asking their peers for help. Create protocols such as, ask three before me (MATHia and their peers).
As students work on the activity	All Students	**DIFFERENTIATION STRATEGY** Goal setting and reflection are critical for MATHia success. Encourage students to set goals for what they will accomplish while on MATHia and reflect on their learning in a journal after each MATHia session. Go to MyCL and MyPL for additional ideas about MATHia logs or journaling.

TALK THE TALK

Session 1 of 1

So Give It a Shot

Students set goals for the school year. They describe the different ways they learn and why it is essential to reflect on their progress.

CHUNK	AUDIENCE	ADDITIONAL SUPPORTS
As students work on 3	Students who Struggle	**DIFFERENTIATION STRATEGY** • Share goals with support teachers. • Reflection and goal setting are critical elements of self-awareness and responsible decision-making. Encourage students to reflect on previous successes and struggles in math to set goals for the school year.
To extend 3	All Students	**DIFFERENTIATION STRATEGY** Give students an opportunity to create a set of class goals and norms that you will revisit throughout the year.

Your Tools for Review

MIXED PRACTICE

To maximize long-term learning, students need to practice skills distributed over multiple learning sessions. While practicing a skill or retrieving information multiple times in a short period is an important start, students need to space practice over days and weeks to retain the new knowledge.

The Mixed Practice provides spaced practice of concepts from the previous lesson and topic and the fluency skills important for the course.

The Chunking the Assignment in each lesson provides suggestions for assigning the Spaced Review questions.

TOPIC SUMMARY

Each topic contains a succinct overview of the important ideas and concepts from each topic.

These are accessible online via MyCL.

A video is available to explain each worked example.

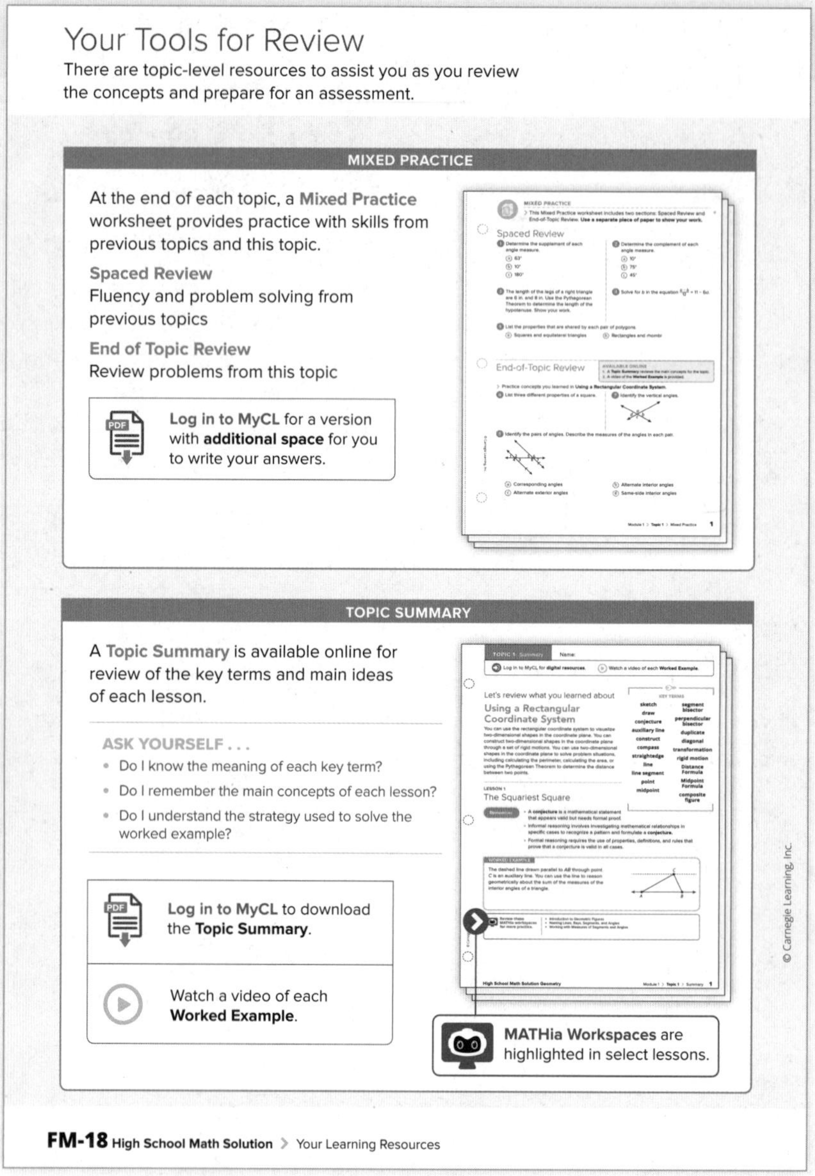
Your Tools for Review

There are topic-level resources to assist you as you review the concepts and prepare for an assessment.

MIXED PRACTICE

At the end of each topic, a **Mixed Practice** worksheet provides practice with skills from previous topics and this topic.

Spaced Review
Fluency and problem solving from previous topics

End of Topic Review
Review problems from this topic

Log in to MyCL for a version with **additional space** for you to write your answers.

TOPIC SUMMARY

A **Topic Summary** is available online for review of the key terms and main ideas of each lesson.

ASK YOURSELF . . .

- Do I know the meaning of each key term?
- Do I remember the main concepts of each lesson?
- Do I understand the strategy used to solve the worked example?

Log in to MyCL to download the **Topic Summary**.

Watch a video of each **Worked Example**.

MATHia Workspaces are highlighted in select lessons.

FM-18 High School Math Solution > Your Learning Resources

HABITS OF MIND

HABITS OF MIND

> Tear out this page and use it as a guide as you engage with the the kind of thinking you do as you are learning the content.

Mathematical Practices

The types of activities within this book require you to make sense of mathematics and to demonstrate your reasoning through problem solving, writing, discussing, and presenting.

FOR ALL LESSONS . . .

Make sense of problems and persevere in solving them.

ASK YOURSELF . . .

- What is this problem asking and what is my plan for answering it?
- What tools do I need to solve this problem?
- Does my answer make sense?

TAKE NOTE . . .
To help develop these habits of mind ask yourself the types of questions listed as you work.

Each activity denotes the practice or pair of practices intentionally being developed. With practice you can develop the habits of mind of a productive mathematical thinker.

WHEN YOU SEE . . .	ASK YOURSELF . . .	WHAT DOES THIS MEAN FOR YOU?
HABITS OF MIND • Reason abstractly and quantitatively. • Construct viable arguments and critique the reasoning of others.	• What representation can I use to solve this problem? • How can this problem be represented with symbols and numbers? • How can I explain my thinking? • How does my strategy compare to my partner's?	
HABITS OF MIND • Model with Mathematics. • Use appropriate tools strategically.	• What expression or equation could represent this situation? • What tools would help me solve this problem? • What representations best show my thinking? • How does this answer make sense in the context of the original problem?	
HABITS OF MIND • Attend to precision.	• Is my answer accurate? • Did I use the correct units or labels? • Is there a more efficient way to solve this problem? • Is there more sophisticated vocabulary that I could use in my explanation?	
HABITS OF MIND • Look for and make use of structure. • Look for and express regularity in repeated reasoning.	• What characteristics of this expression or equation are made clear through this representation? • How can I use what I know to explain why this works? • Can I develop a more efficient method? • How could this problem help me to solve another problem?	

As you facilitate each lesson, listen carefully, value diversity of thought, redirect students' questions with guiding questions, provide additional support with those struggling with a task, and hold students accountable for an end product.

When students share their work, make your expectations clear, require that students defend and talk about their solutions, and monitor student progress by checking for understanding.

Thinking and Reasoning

Each lesson provides opportunities for students to think, reason, and communicate their mathematical understanding. However, it is your responsibility as a teacher to recognize these opportunities and incorporate these practices into your daily rituals. Expertise is a long-term goal, and students must be encouraged to apply these practices to new content throughout their school careers.

At the start of each activity, you will see the habit or pair of habits that students can focus on as they engage in the mathematics and collaborate with their peers. You will see questions and directions highlighted in **blue** throughout the activity that promote these habits.

Language Acquisition

Students need to possess an understanding of the language of their text. They must learn to read for different purposes and write about what they are learning. Encourage students to become familiar with the keywords and the questions they can ask themselves when they encounter these words.

We recommend explicit instruction about your expectations of language used and how students write responses throughout the text. Encourage students to answer questions with complete sentences. Complete sentences help students reflect on how they arrived at a solution, make connections between topics, and consider what a solution means both mathematically and in context.

Ask Yourself

The Ask Yourself questions help students develop the proficiency to explain to themselves the meaning of problems.

Supporting English Language Learners

There is strong evidence backing the importance of teaching academic vocabulary to students acquiring English as a second language.

ACADEMIC GLOSSARY

There are important terms you will encounter throughout this book.

Knowing what is meant by these terms and using these terms will help you think, reason, and communicate your ideas. You will often see these phrases in highlighted questions throughout each activity.

TERM	DEFINITION	ASK YOURSELF	RELATED PHRASES
Analyze	To study or look closely for patterns. Analyzing can involve examining or breaking a concept down into smaller parts to gain a better understanding of it.	• Do I see any patterns? • Have I seen something like this before? • What happens if the shape, representation, or numbers change?	**Examine** **Evaluate** **Determine** **Observe** **Consider** **Investigate** **What do you notice?** **What do you think?** **Sort and match**
Explain Your Reasoning	To give details or describe how to determine an answer or solution. Explaining your reasoning helps justify conclusions.	• How should I organize my thoughts? • Is my explanation logical? • Does my reasoning make sense? • How can I justify my answer to others?	**Show your work** **Explain your calculation** **Justify** **Why or why not?**
Represent	To display information in various ways. Representing mathematics can be done using words, tables, graphs, or symbols.	• How should I organize my thoughts? • How do I use this model to show a concept or idea? • What does this representation tell me? • Is my representation accurate?	**Show** **Sketch** **Draw** **Create** **Plot** **Graph** **Write an equation** **Complete the table**
Estimate	To make an educated guess based on the analysis of given data. Estimating first helps inform reasoning.	• Does my reasoning make sense? • Is my solution close to my estimation?	**Predict** **Approximate** **Expect** **About how much?**
Describe	To represent or give an account of in words. Describing communicates mathematical ideas to others.	• How should I organize my thoughts? • Is my explanation logical? • Did I consider the context of the situation? • Does my reasoning make sense?	**Demonstrate** **Label** **Display** **Compare** **Determine** **Define** **What are the advantages?** **What are the disadvantages?** **What is similar?** **What is different?**

Home Connection

Encourage your students to share these pages with their parents or guardians to inform them of the types of questions that appear throughout this text.

MODULE 1

Reasoning with Shapes

TOPIC 1
Using a Rectangular Coordinate System

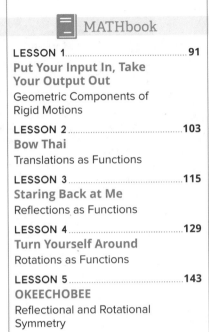

LESSON 1 3
The Squariest Square
From Informal to Formal Geometric Thinking

LESSON 2 13
Hip to Be Square
Constructing a Coordinate Plane

LESSON 3 29
Ts and Train Tracks
Parallel and Perpendicular Lines

LESSON 4 45
Where Has Polly Gone?
Classifying Shapes on the Coordinate Plane

LESSON 5 63
In and Out and All About
Area and Perimeter on the Coordinate Plane

TOPIC 2
Rigid Motions on a Plane

MATHbook

LESSON 1 91
Put Your Input In, Take Your Output Out
Geometric Components of Rigid Motions

LESSON 2 103
Bow Thai
Translations as Functions

LESSON 3 115
Staring Back at Me
Reflections as Functions

LESSON 4 129
Turn Yourself Around
Rotations as Functions

LESSON 5 143
OKEECHOBEE
Reflectional and Rotational Symmetry

TOPIC 3
Congruence Through Transformations

LESSON 1 155
The Elements
Formal Reasoning in Euclidean Geometry

LESSON 2 171
ASA, SAS, and SSS
Proving Triangle Congruence Theorems

LESSON 3 185
I Never Forget a Face
Using Triangle Congruence to Solve Problems

MATHia

From Informal to Formal Geometric Thinking
- Introduction to Geometric Figures
- Naming Lines, Rays, Segments, and Angles
- Working with Measures of Segments and Angles

Slopes of Parallel and Perpendicular Lines
- Introduction to Parallel and Perpendicular Lines
- Modeling Parallel and Perpendicular Lines

Distances on the Coordinate Plane
- Deriving the Distance Formula
- Calculating Distances Using the Distance Formula
- Calculating Perimeter and Area Using the Distance Formula

Geometric Components of Rigid Motions
- Developing Definitions of Rigid Motions
- Exploring Rigid Motions and Dilations

Rigid Motions as Functions
- Describing a Translation
- Describing a Reflection
- Describing a Rotation
- Specifying a Sequence of Rigid Motion Transformations

Reflectional and Rotational Symmetry
- Rotations and Reflections on the Plane
- Reflectional Symmetry
- Rotational Symmetry

Formal Reasoning in Euclidean Geometry
- Calculating and Justifying Angle Measures
- Calculating Angle Measures

Triangle Congruence Theorems
- Introduction to Triangle Congruence
- Using Triangle Congruence

Getting Ready for Module 1
Reasoning with Shapes

Review this content to identify student readiness with the Pythagorean Theorem, corresponding parts, and rigid motion transformations as essential understanding needed for access to **Reasoning with Shapes**.

Using the Getting Ready

- **Read and discuss the intro**
- **Review the key terms and skills you will need**
- **Ask students to complete the Review**

Log in to MyCL for more information to support your students' readiness needs and to access corresponding **MATHia Workspaces**.

ADDITIONAL KEY TERMS

line of symmetry

function

perpendicular

Getting Ready for Module 1

Reasoning with Shapes

You will use rigid motions to construct a rectangular coordinate system and explore polygons on the coordinate plane. You will investigate rigid motions as functions and describe how each input shape relates to an output shape. Building on this work, you will use formal reasoning to prove geometric theorems and apply them on the coordinate plane.

The lessons in this module build on your prior experiences with the Pythagorean Theorem, corresponding parts, and rigid motion transformations.

Review these key terms and rigid motion transformations to get ready to reason with shapes.

KEY TERMS

Pythagorean Theorem

The Pythagorean Theorem states that the sum of the squares of the lengths of the legs of a right triangle equals the square of the length of the hypotenuse. When a and b are the lengths of the legs, and c is the length of the hypotenuse, then $a^2 + b^2 = c^2$.

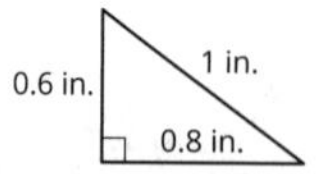

$0.6^2 + 0.8^2 = 1^2$
$0.36 + 0.64 = 1$
$1 = 1$

corresponding parts

Corresponding parts are sides or angles that have the same relative positions in geometric figures.

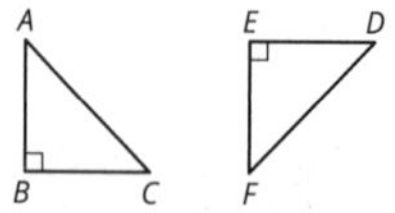

Angles B and E are *corresponding angles* and sides AB and DE are *corresponding sides.*

MATHia

Brush up on your skills.
If you need more practice with these skills, ask your teacher for access to corresponding workspaces in MATHia.

SKILLS YOU WILL NEED

Rigid Motion Transformations

A rigid motion is a special type of transformation that preserves the size and shape of the figure, such as translations, rotations, and reflections.

For example, when you translate ΔABC down 5 units and left 4 units, you create ΔJKL.

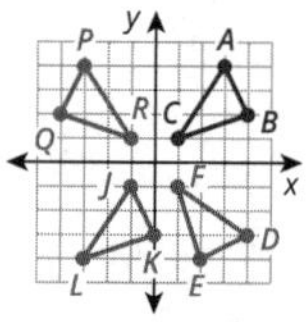

Similarly, you can reflect ΔABC across the y-axis to create ΔPQR. When you rotate ΔABC clockwise 90° about the origin, you create ΔDEF.

You can use patty paper or measure to verify the triangles are the same size and shape.

REVIEW

> Calculate the perimeter and area of each figure.

1.

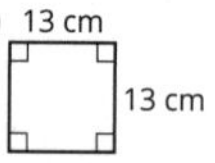

$P = 4(13) = 52$ cm
$A = 13^2 = 169$ cm^2

2.

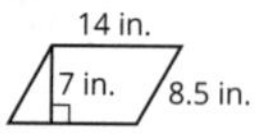

$P = 2(14) + 2(8.5) = 45$ in.
$A = 7(14) = 98$ in.

See Appendix on page 441 for answers.

Questions to Support Discourse

		TYPE
PYTHAGOREAN THEOREM	• How can you determine which sides represent a, b, and c?	Gathering
	• Does it matter which leg you represent with a and which you represent with b? Why?	Probing
	• Can you use the Pythagorean Theorem to determine the length of the legs of a right triangle? How?	Seeing structure
CORRESPONDING PARTS	• How do you know that AB and DE are corresponding sides?	Probing
	• Does the orientation of the figures change which parts are corresponding?	Seeing structure
RIGID MOTIONS	• Would $\triangle JKL$ have been in the same location had you translated $\triangle ABC$ left before being translated down? Why? • When you perform multiple rigid motion transformations on the same figure, will the resulting figure still have the same size and shape? Why?	Seeing structure

OVERVIEW: MODULE 1

Reasoning with Shapes

Where are we?

1 Session ≈ 45 minutes

MODULE 1 Reasoning with Shapes	MODULE 2 Establishing Proof	MODULE 3 Investigating Proportionality	MODULE 4 Connecting Geometric and Algebraic Descriptions	MODULE 5 Making Informed Decisions
37 Sessions	47 Sessions	26 Sessions	19 Sessions	20 Sessions

Why is this Module named **Reasoning with Shapes?**

In **Reasoning with Shapes,** students take the first steps to transition from the informal reasoning that encompassed much of their geometric studies throughout middle school to the more formal reasoning required in high school geometry. They begin to reason about the defining characteristics of shapes they are very familiar with: squares, circles, and triangles.

Students reason algebraically—connecting what they know about lines on the coordinate plane to verify simple geometric theorems. They formally define the geometric functions: translations, reflections, and rotations. Students reason about these transformations and how they can use them to determine the minimum criteria for triangle congruence. They use constructions to prove whether these geometric characteristics are true in all cases.

The geometric reasoning that students do in this module prepares them for the formal proofs that they will write in the next module.

The Research Shows....

"In fact, as one of the fundamental 'implements' of Euclidean geometry, along with the straightedge, the compass is involved and invoked in constructing midpoints of segments, right angles, regular polygons, transformations, and so on. . . . The student who remarks with surprise (as many students do), 'I never thought that you needed a circle to make a square!' experiences the lovely realization that the circle (through the compass) leaves its trace on the square."

—Developing Essential Understanding of Geometry, NCTM, pg. 43

MyCL

Go to MyPL to access the video for **Module Overview**: **Reasoning with Shapes**.

www.carnegielearning.com/mathbook-Geometry-module-1-overview

The Mathematical Arc of
Reasoning with Shapes

Students use coordinates to prove simple geometric theorems algebraically and measure certain characteristics of shapes. They formally define rigid motion transformations. Students understand congruence in terms of rigid motions and use constructions to prove triangle congruence theorems.

1 Session ≈ 45 minutes

	16 SESSIONS TOPIC 1 Using a Rectangular Coordinate System	11 SESSIONS TOPIC 2 Rigid Motions on a Plane
LEARNING TOGETHER	11 Sessions	9 Sessions
STANDARDS	G.CO.1, G.CO.5, G.CO.10†, G.CO.11†, G.CO.12, G.GPE.4, G.GPE.5, G.GPE.7, G.MG.2	G.CO.1, G.CO.2, G.CO.3, G.CO.4, G.CO.5
MATHbook Lessons aligned into Topics to drive content goals.	**Students investigate the properties of squares and use transformations of squares to construct a coordinate plane.** • They prove the slope criteria for parallel and perpendicular lines. • They develop strategies for determining the perimeters and areas of triangles, quadrilaterals, and composite figures on the coordinate plane. • They explore the effects of changes to the dimensions of a plane figure on its perimeter and area.	**Students define translations in terms of equal distances along directed line segments, reflections in terms of perpendicular lines, and rotations in terms of equal arcs around concentric circles.** • They use rigid motions to solve problems and identify a sequence of rigid motions that maps a given figure onto another. • They consider reflectional and rotational symmetry and identify lines of reflection and angles of rotation for given plane figures.
LEARNING INDIVIDUALLY	~5 Sessions	~2 Sessions
STANDARDS	G.CO.1, G.GPE.5, G.GPE.7	G.CO.3, G.CO.4, G.CO.5
MATHia Sequences aligned at the topic level to support content goals.	• Students define, identify, and name basic geometric figures. • They write measure statements for segments and angles. • They write equations of parallel and perpendicular lines. • They derive the Distance Formula from the Pythagorean Theorem. • They use the Distance Formula to determine the perimeter and area of shapes on the coordinate plane.	• Students select translations, reflections, or rotations to map a pre-image to an image. • They describe sequences of geometric transformations that map one figure onto a congruent or similar figure. • They identify rigid motions that carry figures onto themselves. • They use a diagram tool to draw the reflectional and rotational symmetries and write the corresponding functions.
	Targeted practice of each topic's skills and mathematical concepts.	
For students without access to MATHia. Skills Practice	• Students identify geometric figures. • They construct perpendicular lines and duplicate line segments. • They write equations of parallel and perpendicular lines. • They use the Distance Formula to solve problems on the coordinate plane involving shapes.	• Students create and describe transformation machines. • They complete rigid motion transformations and write functions to describe them. • They determine the center of rotations and draw the lines of symmetry. • They describe reflectional and rotational symmetry.

Log in to MyCL for additional **online resources**.

10 SESSIONS

TOPIC 3

Congruence Through Transformations

7 Sessions

G.CO.6, G.CO.7, G.CO.8, G.CO.9

Students use the definitions of congruence through rigid motions to determine the minimum criteria for triangle congruence.

- They first consider counterexamples, conditional statements, truth values, and truth tables.
- They investigate the Linear Pair and the Segment Addition Postulates.
- They then prove by construction the Side-Side-Side, Side-Angle-Side, and Angle-Side-Angle Congruence Theorems.
- They solve problems using these theorems.

~3 Sessions

G.CO.7, G.CO.8, G.CO.9, G.CO.10

- Students calculate the measure of angles and justify their reasoning.
- They write and identify triangle congruency statements and corresponding sides and angles.
- They match pairs of triangles to the theorem by which they are proven congruent.
- They use the congruence theorems to determine whether two triangles are congruent and identify the reasons for given congruency statements.

Targeted practice of each topic's skills and mathematical concepts.

- Students write conditional statements and identify each hypothesis and the conclusion.
- They use postulates to complete statements.
- They determine whether triangle pairs are congruent by SSS, SAS, or ASA.
- They state the theorem that proves the congruence of triangle pairs and write a congruence statement.

NOTES

Connection to Prior Learning

How is **Reasoning with Shapes** connected to prior learning?

Students have had extensive experiences on the coordinate plane that they will build upon to start this module and course. They have graphed lines and calculated distances using absolute value and the Pythagorean Theorem.

MATH REPRESENTATION

Determine the length of the rope securing the badminton pole to the ground.

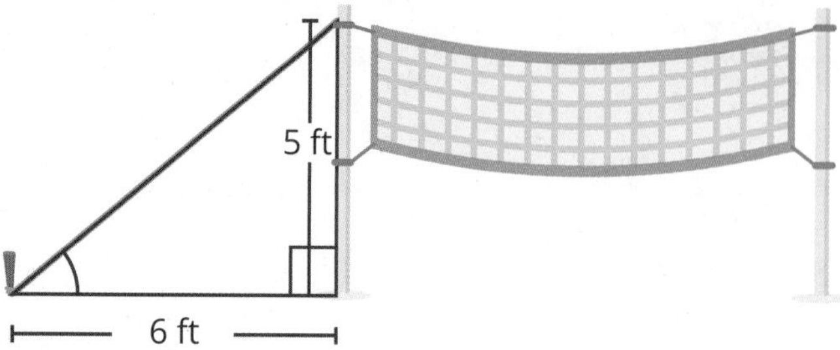

$$5^2 + 6^2 = o^2$$
$$61 = o^2$$
$$\sqrt{61} = o$$
$$7.81 \approx o$$

The rope is approximately 7.81 feet long.

Students first experienced construction tools in middle school when they investigated the number of triangles they can form given three side or angle measurements.

In grade 8, students learned that a figure is congruent to another when you can specify a sequence of rigid motion transformations that map one figure onto the other.

Connection to Future Learning

When will students use knowledge from **Reasoning with Shapes** in future learning?

Students will use constructions and the deductive reasoning that constructions require to compose and decompose figures and examine the structure of geometric relationships. They will use triangle congruence to formally prove many of these geometric relationships.

MATH REPRESENTATION

You can use Angle-Side-Angle Congruence Theorem to prove that opposite angles of a parallelogram are congruent.

Given: Parallelogram *PARG* with diagonals $\overline{PR}$ and $\overline{AG}$ intersecting at point *a* .

Prove: $\angle GPA \cong \angle ARG$

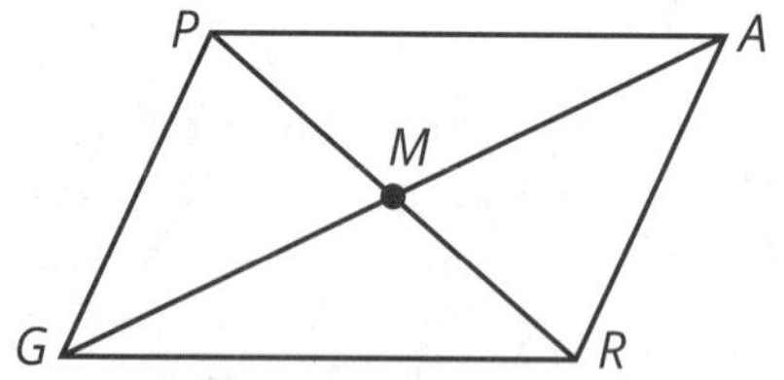

Statements	Reasons
1. Parallelogram *cNeT* with diagonals $\overline{PR}$ and $\overline{AG}$ intersesct at point *M*	1. Given
2. $\overline{PG} \parallel \overline{AR}$ and $\overline{GR} \parallel \overline{PA}$	2. Definition of a parallelogram
3. $\angle PAG \cong \angle RGA$ and $\angle PGA \cong \angle RAG$	3. Alternative Interior Angle Theorem
4. $\overline{PR} \simeq \overline{PR}$	4. Reflexive Property
5. $\Delta APG \cong \Delta GRA$	5. ASA Congruence Theorem
6. $\angle GPA \cong \angle ARG$	6. CPCTC

ENGAGE + DEVELOP + TEACH

ENGAGE at the **Module** level

DEVELOP Read the **Topic Overview** and do the math to experience the content development.

TEACH at the **Lesson** level

OVERVIEW: TOPIC 1

Using a Rectangular Coordinate System

Where are we?

1 Session ≈ 45 minutes

MODULE 1 Establishing Proof	TOPIC 1 Using a Rectangular Coordinate System	TOPIC 2 Rigid Motions on a Plane	TOPIC 3 Congruence Through Transformations
Pacing	16 Sessions	11 Sessions	10 Sessions

How are the key concepts of *Using a Rectangular Coordinate System* developed?

Students begin the course by exploring the nature of geometric reasoning. They start with informal reasoning involving measurement tools and consider more formal strategies, including analyzing additional cases, using construction tools, and adding auxiliary lines.

Next, students consider the parallel and perpendicular structure of the coordinate plane. They learn basic constructions to build a coordinate plane using transformations of a square. Students then use transformations to develop the slope criteria for parallel and perpendicular lines and write the equations for lines.

See Math Representation.

Students then derive the Distance Formula. They combine their knowledge of the Distance Formula and slopes of lines to verify parallel sides and perpendicular angles of figures, classify triangles and quadrilaterals, and compose a quadrilateral given three of the vertices. Students investigate the pattern of shapes formed when connecting midpoints.

Students then use the Distance Formula to calculate the area and perimeter of shapes on the coordinate plane. This work synthesizes their knowledge of the slope criteria, translations, and solving systems of linear equations. Students extend this knowledge to include scenarios comparing speed and time.

MATH REPRESENTATION

You can use transformations to prove that the slopes of perpendicular lines are opposite reciprocals.

Perform a 90° counterclockwise rotation of point R using point O as the center of rotation.

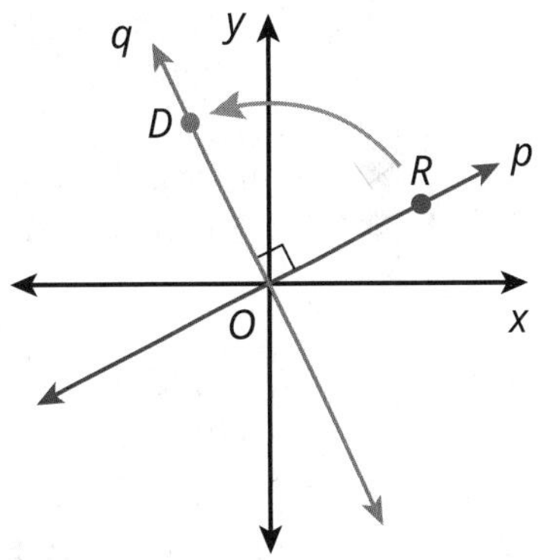

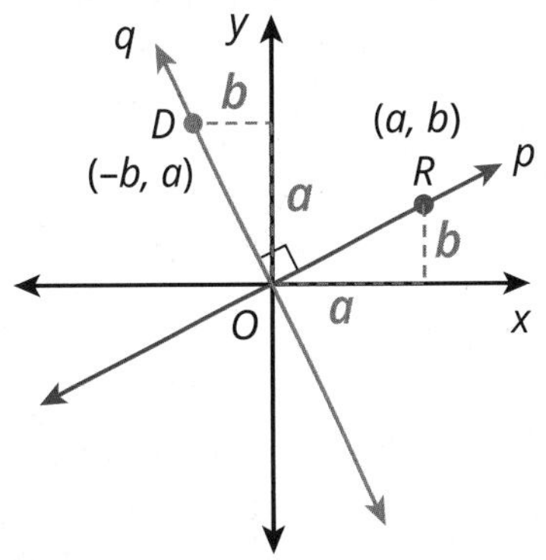

Using these slopes, you can demonstrate that the slope of line q is the opposite reciprocal of the slope of line p.

PLAN FOR 11 class sessions and ~5 MATHia sessions.

Log in to MyCL for **lesson support** including:

- Slides
- Videos

	LESSON 1	LESSON 2
	The Squariest Square From Informal to Formal Geometric Thinking	**Hip to Be Square** Constructing a Coordinate Plane
	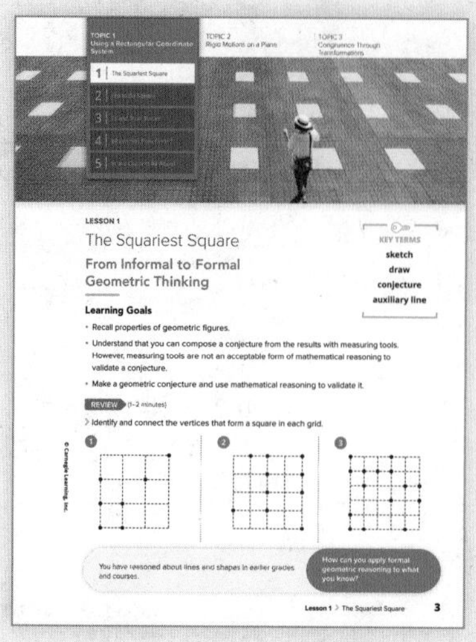	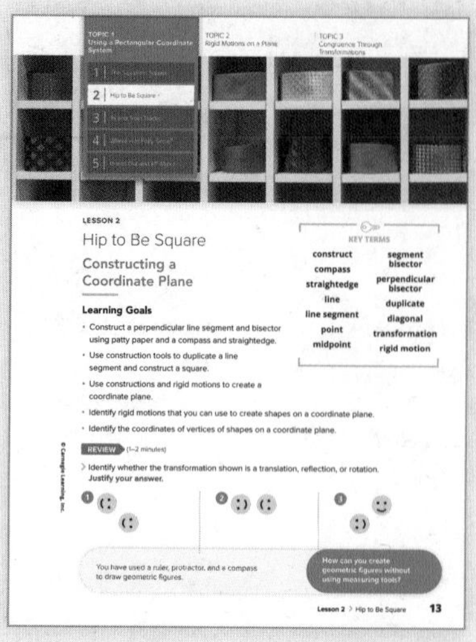
LEARNING TOGETHER	1 Session	2 Sessions
STANDARDS	G.CO.10†, G.CO.11†	G.CO.1, G.CO.5, G.CO.12
MATHbook Activities sequenced to address standards and meet content goals.	Students make a conjecture regarding the sum of angle measures in a diagram. They use informal geometric reasoning with a protractor for a specific case and then with patty paper to support their thinking. Students use formal reasoning with an enhanced diagram with auxiliary lines to determine mathematical relationships, angle measures, and side lengths. They contrast the two forms of reasoning.	Students construct perpendicular bisectors and a square. They notice relationships in the process and conjecture that any point on a perpendicular bisector is equidistant to the original segment's endpoints. Students also conjecture about the diagonals of a square. They consider translating a square to create a coordinate plane and describe the rigid motions to form shapes on a coordinate plane.
MATERIALS	• Patty paper • Protractors • Straightedges	• Compasses • Patty paper • Straightedges

LEARNING INDIVIDUALLY — Median time for students to complete MATHia for this topic is ~200 minutes.

MATHia
Workspaces aligned at the lesson level to support benchmarking through self-paced MATHia.

- Introduction to Geometric Figures
- Naming Lines, Rays, Segments, and Angles
- Working with Measures of Segments and Angles

For students without access to MATHia.

Skills Practice

Problem sets for additional practice of the lesson skills.

Lesson 1	Lesson 2
• Identifying Properties of Geometric Figures	• Constructing Perpendicular Lines

TOPIC 1

LESSON 3

Ts and Train Tracks

Parallel and Perpendicular Lines

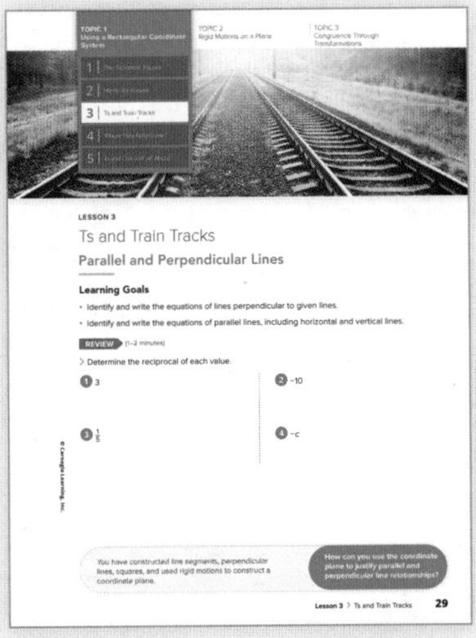
LESSON 3

Ts and Train Tracks

Parallel and Perpendicular Lines

Learning Goals

- Identify and write the equations of lines perpendicular to given lines.
- Identify and write the equations of parallel lines, including horizontal and vertical lines.

REVIEW (1–2 minutes)

> Determine the reciprocal of each value.

1 3

2 −10

4 −c

You have constructed line segments, perpendicular lines, squares, and used rigid motions to construct a coordinate plane.

How can you use the coordinate plane to justify parallel and perpendicular line relationships?

Lesson 3 > Ts and Train Tracks 29

2 Sessions

G.CO.12, G.GPE.5

Students graph parallel and perpendicular lines using rigid motions and then construct parallel lines using a translation. They make conjectures about the slopes of parallel and perpendicular lines and then demonstrate that the slopes of perpendicular lines are negative reciprocals and the slopes of parallel lines are equal. They write equations for vertical, horizontal, and perpendicular lines.

- Compasses
- Patty paper
- Straightedges

LESSON 4

Where Has Polly Gone?

Classifying Shapes on the Coordinate Plane

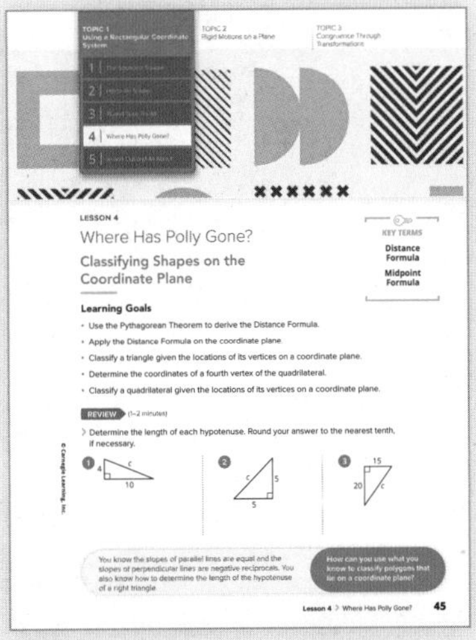
LESSON 4

Where Has Polly Gone?

Classifying Shapes on the Coordinate Plane

KEY TERMS

Distance Formula

Midpoint Formula

Learning Goals

- Use the Pythagorean Theorem to derive the Distance Formula.
- Apply the Distance Formula on the coordinate plane.
- Classify a triangle given the locations of its vertices on a coordinate plane.
- Determine the coordinates of a fourth vertex of the quadrilateral.
- Classify a quadrilateral given the locations of its vertices on a coordinate plane.

REVIEW (1–2 minutes)

> Determine the length of each hypotenuse. Round your answer to the nearest tenth, if necessary.

You know the slopes of parallel lines are equal and the slopes of perpendicular lines are negative reciprocals. You also know how to determine the length of the hypotenuse of a right triangle.

How can you use what you know to classify polygons that lie on a coordinate plane?

Lesson 4 > Where Has Polly Gone? 45

3 Sessions

G.GPE.4, G.GPE.5

Students relate the Distance Formula to the Pythagorean Theorem and calculate the distance between points. They classify quadrilaterals and triangles on the coordinate plane based on the length and slopes of their sides. Students use the converse to the Pythagorean Theorem to identify a triangle as acute, right, or obtuse. They also apply the Midpoint Formula and specify figures formed by connected midpoints.

- Straightedges

For the most up-to-date MATHia alignment, log in to MyCL.

Lesson 3:

- Introduction to Parallel and Perpendicular Lines
- Modeling Parallel and Perpendicular Lines

Lesson 4:

- Deriving the Distance Formula
- Calculating Distances Using the Distance Formula

Problem sets for additional practice of the lesson skills.

Lesson 3:

- Duplicating Line Segments
- Writing Equations of Parallel and Perpendicular Lines

Lesson 4:

- Classifying Shapes on the Coordinate Plane

PLAN FOR 11 class sessions and ~5 MATHia sessions.

In and Out and All About
Area and Perimeter on the Coordinate Plane

LESSON 5

In and Out and All About

Area and Perimeter on the Coordinate Plane

KEY TERM
composite figure

Learning Goals
- Determine the perimeter and area of rectangles, triangles, and composite figures on the coordinate plane.
- Use transformations to discover efficient strategies to determine the perimeter and area of rectangles and triangles.
- Use the Distance Formula to solve real-world problems involving perimeters of parallelograms, trapezoids, and hexagons.
- Decompose polygons—including trapezoids and hexagons—to solve real-world problems involving area.
- Calculate the area under a curve to determine distance in an acceleration model.

REVIEW (1–2 minutes)

Determine the distance between each set of points. Round your answer to the nearest tenth, if necessary.

1 (2, −3) and (−4, 1)

2 (−4.75, −8.5) and (3.25, 5.5)

You have used the Distance Formula and the slope formula to classify geometric figures on the coordinate plane.

How can you use rigid motions to determine the perimeter and area of polygons on the coordinate plane?

© Carnegie Learning, Inc.

Lesson 5 > In and Out and All About 63

Log in to MyCL for lesson support including:
- Slides
- Videos

NOTES

LEARNING TOGETHER	3 Sessions
STANDARDS	G.GPE.5, G.GPE.7, G.GPE.7, G.MG.2
MATHbook Activities sequenced to address standards and meet content goals.	Students calculate the area and perimeter of polygons on the coordinate plane. They translate figures on the coordinate plane for efficient computations and investigate how doubling a dimension affects the area. Students use algebra skills to identify and compute the height of a triangle for a given base. They also calculate the area and perimeter of composite figures to solve real-world problems.
MATERIALS	None

LEARNING INDIVIDUALLY	For the most up-to-date MATHia alignment, log in to MyCL.
MATHia Workspaces aligned at the lesson level to support benchmarking through self-paced MATHia.	• Calculating Perimeter and Area Using the Distance Formula

For students without access to MATHia.

Skills Practice

Problem sets for additional practice of the lesson skills.

- Determining Perimeter and Area of Rectangles and Triangles on the Coordinate Plane
- Determining Perimeter and Area of Other Polygons on the Coordinate Plane

Connection to Prior Learning

What is the entry point for students?

Students first began classifying shapes in elementary school. While they have not yet formalized this knowledge, they know how side lengths, angle measures, and side relationships define a figure. Students have had extensive experience with linear relationships and have calculated a line's slope using graphs and equations. They have learned graphical and algebraic methods to solve systems of linear equations.

MATH REPRESENTATION

You can calculate the slope of a linear relationship from a table of values.

STEP 1 From the table of values. Use (0, 15) as the first point and (1, 23) as the second point.

STEP 2 Label the points with the variables.

$$\begin{array}{cc} (0, 15) & (1, 23) \\ \downarrow\ \downarrow & \downarrow\ \downarrow \\ (x_1, y_1) & (x_2, y_2) \end{array}$$

STEP 3 Use the slope formula.

$$m = \frac{y_2 - y_1}{x_2 - x_1} = \frac{23 - 15}{1 - 0}$$
$$= \frac{8}{1}$$
$$= 8$$

Students have calculated the area and perimeter of triangles, quadrilaterals, and other figures. This topic adds another step to the process by providing only the figure's vertices and requiring students to use the Pythagorean Theorem to calculate side lengths before applying area or perimeter formulas.

NOTES

Connection to Future Learning

Why is *Using a Rectangular Coordinate System* important?

The coordinate plane provides a structure that allows students to analyze and classify the properties of figures algebraically. Provided with only vertices for the given shapes, students must take the initial step of calculating side lengths using the Distance Formula. Proving relationships and performing geometric measurements algebraically integrates geometry and algebra.

MATH REPRESENTATION

Gage constructed parallel lines. He reasoned that if alternate interior angles are congruent when a transversal cuts two lines, the lines are parallel.

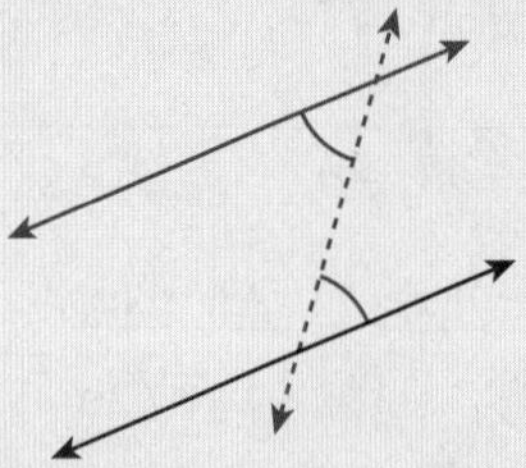

As with much of high school geometry, students formalize concepts that they investigated informally in elementary and middle school.

NOTES

Log in to MyCL for resources that support **student meta-cognition**.

TOPIC 1

How Does a Student Demonstrate Understanding?

Students will demonstrate an understanding of the standards in *Using a Rectangular Coordinate System* when they can:

Recognize that slopes of perpendicular lines are negative reciprocals.	✓
Determine the equation of a line parallel or perpendicular to a given line that passes through a given point.	✓
Prove the slope criteria for parallel and perpendicular lines and use them to solve problems.	✓
Use the Distance Formula to determine whether sides of a figure are congruent.	✓
Use the slope criteria for parallel and perpendicular lines to determine the relationship between sides of a figure.	✓
Use the Midpoint Formula to bisect the side of a figure.	✓
Write the equation for a line perpendicular to a given side of a figure that passes through the opposite vertex.	✓

HABITS OF MIND

How do the activities in *Using a Rectangular Coordinate System* promote student expertise in the mathematical practice standards?

All Carnegie Learning topics are written with the goal of creating mathematical thinkers who are active participants in class discourse, so elements of the habits of mind should be evident in all lessons. Students are expected to make sense of problems and work towards solutions, reason using concrete and abstract ideas, and communicate their thinking while providing a critical ear to the thinking of others.

Throughout *Using a Rectangular Coordinate System,* students use tools appropriately to construct basic geometric shapes accurately. They attend to precision as they use clear reasoning to classify shapes and to accurately calculate lengths and relationships of sides and perimeters and the areas of figures. Students use reasoning as they seek efficient strategies for making these calculations. They use structure as they recognize the significance of perpendicular lines through a given vertex when calculating the area of a triangle given any side as the base. They use the structure of geometric shapes to decompose composite figures into sets of non-overlapping triangles and rectangles.

Mixed Practice

At the end of each topic, a **Mixed Practice** worksheet provides practice with skills from previous topics and this topic.

Spaced Review
Fluency and problem solving from previous topics

End of Topic Review
Review problems from this topic

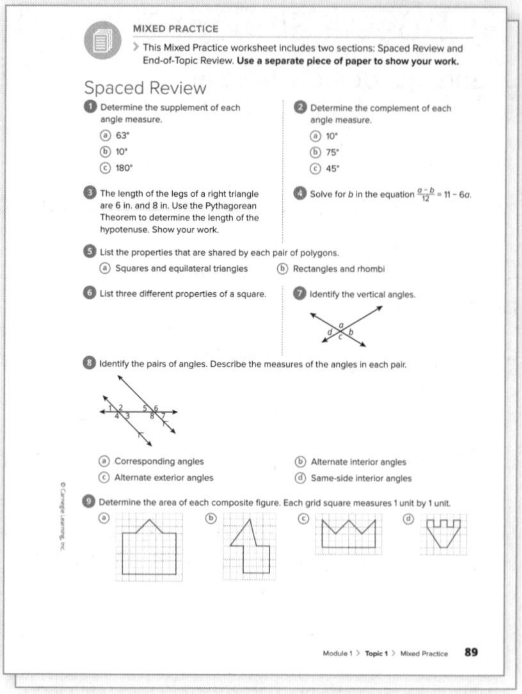
MIXED PRACTICE

> This Mixed Practice worksheet includes two sections: Spaced Review and End-of-Topic Review. **Use a separate piece of paper to show your work.**

Spaced Review

1. Determine the supplement of each angle measure.
   a. 63°
   b. 10°
   c. 180°
2. Determine the complement of each angle measure.
   a. 10°
   b. 75°
   c. 45°
3. The length of the legs of a right triangle are 6 in. and 8 in. Use the Pythagorean Theorem to determine the length of the hypotenuse. Show your work.
4. Solve for b in the equation $\frac{a-b}{12} = 11 - 6a$.
5. List the properties that are shared by each pair of polygons.
   a. Squares and equilateral triangles
   b. Rectangles and rhombi
6. List three different properties of a square.
7. Identify the vertical angles.
8. Identify the pairs of angles. Describe the measures of the angles in each pair.
   a. Corresponding angles
   b. Alternate interior angles
   c. Alternate exterior angles
   d. Same-side interior angles
9. Determine the area of each composite figure. Each grid square measures 1 unit by 1 unit.

Module 1 > Topic 1 > Mixed Practice 89

Log in to MyCL for **digital resources**.
A version with **additional space** for students to write their answers.
Downloadable and editable in Word
Editable via Edulastic

Topic Summary

Available online, a **Topic Summary** reviews the main concepts for the topic.

Essential Ideas for each lesson.

Log in to MyCL for **digital resources**.
A printable version available for download.
A video of the **Worked Example** being solved
www.carnegielearning.com/login

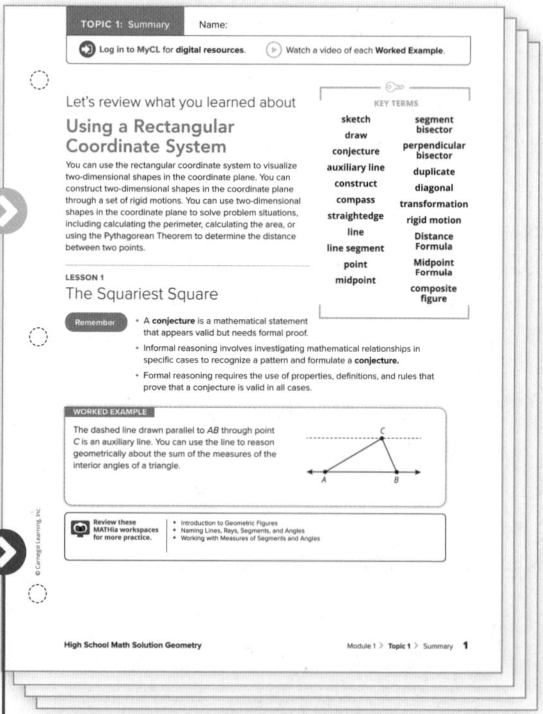
TOPIC 1: Summary Name:

Log in to MyCL for **digital resources**. Watch a video of each **Worked Example**.

Let's review what you learned about

Using a Rectangular Coordinate System

You can use the rectangular coordinate system to visualize two-dimensional shapes in the coordinate plane. You can construct two-dimensional shapes in the coordinate plane through a set of rigid motions. You can use two-dimensional shapes in the coordinate plane to solve problem situations, including calculating the perimeter, calculating the area, or using the Pythagorean Theorem to determine the distance between two points.

KEY TERMS: sketch, draw, conjecture, auxiliary line, construct, compass, straightedge, line, line segment, point, midpoint, segment bisector, perpendicular bisector, duplicate, diagonal, transformation, rigid motion, Distance Formula, Midpoint Formula, composite figure

LESSON 1
The Squariest Square

Remember
- A **conjecture** is a mathematical statement that appears valid but needs formal proof.
- Informal reasoning involves investigating mathematical relationships in specific cases to recognize a pattern and formulate a **conjecture**.
- Formal reasoning requires the use of properties, definitions, and rules that prove that a conjecture is valid in all cases.

WORKED EXAMPLE
The dashed line drawn parallel to AB through point C is an auxiliary line. You can use the line to reason geometrically about the sum of the measures of the interior angles of a triangle.

Review these MATHia workspaces for more practice.
- Introduction to Geometric Figures
- Naming Lines, Rays, Segments, and Angles
- Working with Measures of Segments and Angles

High School Math Solution Geometry Module 1 > Topic 1 > Summary 1

MATHia Workspaces are highlighted in select lessons to help you understand the connections and what you might want to review.

Assessment

Assessments aligned to this topic:

1. Pre-test
2. Post-test
3. End of Topic Test (Form A)
4. End of Topic Test (Form B)
5. Standardized Test Practice
6. Performance Task with Rubric

An **Assessment Overview** identifies the standard(s) aligned with each item on every test.

Log in to MyCL for **digital resources**.
A version with **additional space** for students to write their answers.
Downloadable and editable in Word
Editable via Edulastic

End of Topic Test	
1. G.CO.5	9. G.GPE.5, G.GPE.7
2. G.CO.12	10. G.GPE.7
3. G.CO.5, G.CO.12	11. G.GPE.7
4. G.CO.12	12. G.GPE.7
5. G.GPE.5	13. G.GPE.7
6. G.GPE.5	14. G.GPE.5, G.GPE.7
7. G.GPE.5	15. G.GPE.7
8. G.GPE.5, G.GPE.7	16. G.GPE.7

Standardized Test	
1. G.GPE.5	12. G.GPE.5
2. G.GPE.5, G.GPE.7	13. G.GPE.7
3. G.GPE.5	14. G.GPE.5, G.GPE.7
4. G.GPE.5, G.GPE.7	15. G.GPE.7
5. G.CO.12	16. G.GPE.5, G.GPE.7
6. G.CO.12	17. 6.NS.4
7. G.GPE.5	18. G.GPE.5
8. G.CO.5	19. G.GPE.7
9. G.GPE.7	20. G.CO.12
10. G.GPE.7	21. G.CO.12
11. G.GPE.7	

Family Guide

Teachers, encourage your families to log into the **Home Connection** to access a collection of resources that supports their students as they learn about *Using a Rectangular Coordinate System.*

www.carnegielearning.com/home-connection

For families with limited online access, print and send home the **Family Guide**.

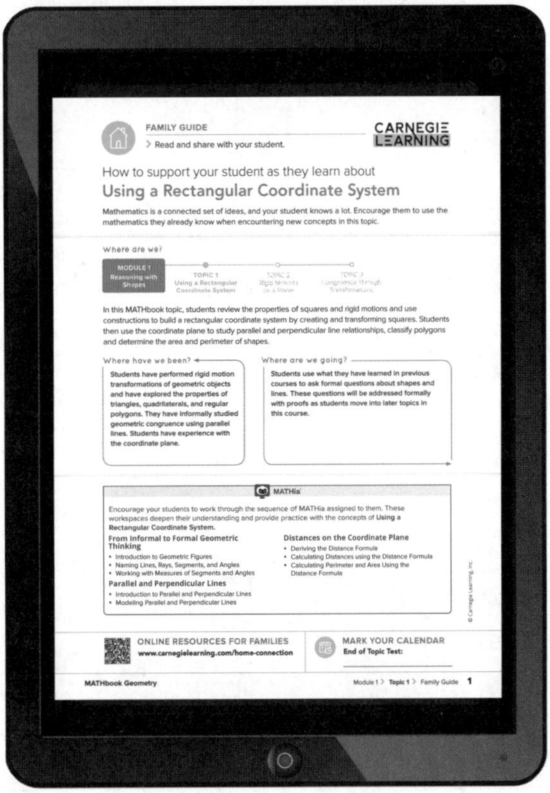

TOPIC 1

Using a Rectangular Coordinate System

Scope out MATHbook and MATHia sessions for this topic, keeping in mind your long term plan.

You can schedule MATHia sessions any time; however, if you are using Skills Practice as the alternative, schedule those sessions after a completed lesson.

Log in to MyCL for:
- Editable templates
- Alternative plans for longer sessions
- Implementations not using MATHia

1 Session ≈ 45 minutes

CORE IMPLEMENTATION PLAN with flexible access to computers/tablets.

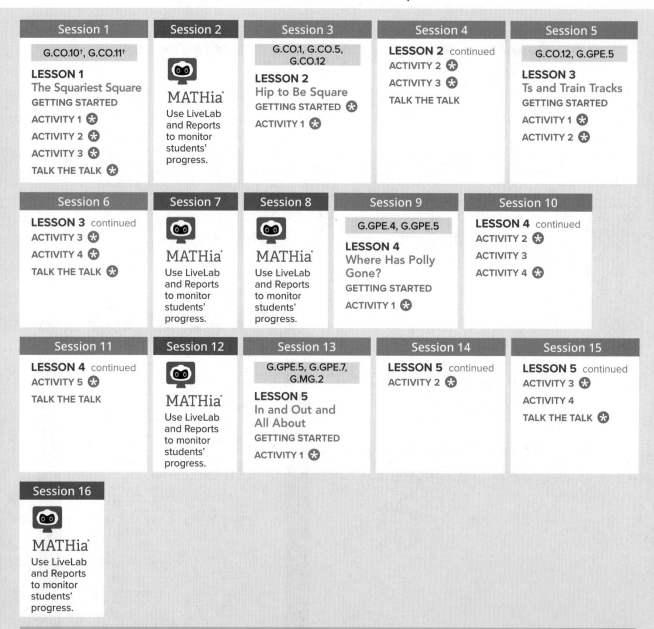

Session 1
G.CO.10†, G.CO.11†
LESSON 1
The Squariest Square
GETTING STARTED
ACTIVITY 1 ✪
ACTIVITY 2 ✪
ACTIVITY 3 ✪
TALK THE TALK ✪

Session 2
MATHia
Use LiveLab and Reports to monitor students' progress.

Session 3
G.CO.1, G.CO.5, G.CO.12
LESSON 2
Hip to Be Square
GETTING STARTED ✪
ACTIVITY 1 ✪

Session 4
LESSON 2 continued
ACTIVITY 2 ✪
ACTIVITY 3 ✪
TALK THE TALK

Session 5
G.CO.12, G.GPE.5
LESSON 3
Ts and Train Tracks
GETTING STARTED
ACTIVITY 1 ✪
ACTIVITY 2 ✪

Session 6
LESSON 3 continued
ACTIVITY 3 ✪
ACTIVITY 4 ✪
TALK THE TALK ✪

Session 7
MATHia
Use LiveLab and Reports to monitor students' progress.

Session 8
MATHia
Use LiveLab and Reports to monitor students' progress.

Session 9
G.GPE.4, G.GPE.5
LESSON 4
Where Has Polly Gone?
GETTING STARTED
ACTIVITY 1 ✪

Session 10
LESSON 4 continued
ACTIVITY 2 ✪
ACTIVITY 3
ACTIVITY 4 ✪

Session 11
LESSON 4 continued
ACTIVITY 5 ✪
TALK THE TALK

Session 12
MATHia
Use LiveLab and Reports to monitor students' progress.

Session 13
G.GPE.5, G.GPE.7, G.MG.2
LESSON 5
In and Out and All About
GETTING STARTED
ACTIVITY 1 ✪

Session 14
LESSON 5 continued
ACTIVITY 2 ✪

Session 15
LESSON 5 continued
ACTIVITY 3 ✪
ACTIVITY 4
TALK THE TALK ✪

Session 16
MATHia
Use LiveLab and Reports to monitor students' progress.

Complete End-of-Topic Review and Assess

✪ This activity highlights a key term or concept that is essential to the learning goals of the lesson.

Where are we?

TOPIC 1 Using a Rectangular Coordinate System	LESSON 1 The Squariest Square	LESSON 2 Hip to Be Square	LESSON 3 Ts and Train Tracks	LESSON 4 Where Has Polly Gone?	LESSON 5 In and Out and All About
Pacing	1 Session	2 Sessions	2 Sessions	3 Sessions	3 Sessions

OVERVIEW: LESSON 1

The Squariest Square

From Informal to Formal Geometric Thinking

ENGAGE

- Students attempt to sketch a perfect square without using any tools. They list a square's properties.

DEVELOP

- Students draw line segments to create specific angles that they measure with a protractor.
- They conjecture about the angle measures and informally reason using a protractor and patty paper.
- They use formal reasoning based on mathematical relationships to determine angle and side measures.

DEMONSTRATE

- Students contrast informal geometric reasoning and formal thinking to prove conjectures.

HIGH SCHOOL GEOMETRY

Congruence

Prove geometric theorems.

10. Prove theorems about triangles.†

11. Prove theorems about parallelograms.†

†The full intent of the standard is not met in this lesson. Students make conjectures about these theorems; they will prove them and fully meet the standard in future lessons.

LESSON STRUCTURE AND PACING GUIDE 1 SESSION

⊛ This activity highlights a key term or concept that is essential to the learning goals of the lesson.

Session 1

INSTRUCTIONAL SEQUENCE

ENGAGE Connect to prior knowledge	DEVELOP Investigation	DEVELOP Investigation

GETTING STARTED
The Perfect Square

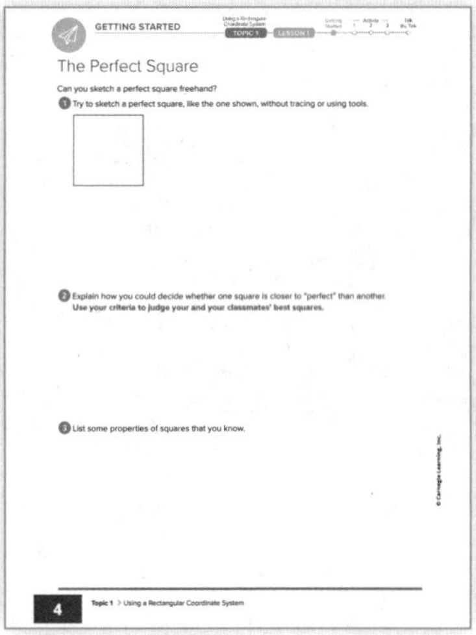

The Perfect Square

Can you sketch a perfect square freehand?

1 Try to sketch a perfect square, like the one shown, without tracing or using tools.

2 Explain how you could decide whether one square is closer to "perfect" than another. Use your criteria to judge your and your classmates' best squares.

3 List some properties of squares that you know.

Students attempt to sketch a perfect square without using any tools.

- They list a square's properties.

⊛ ACTIVITY 1
Analyzing a Diagram

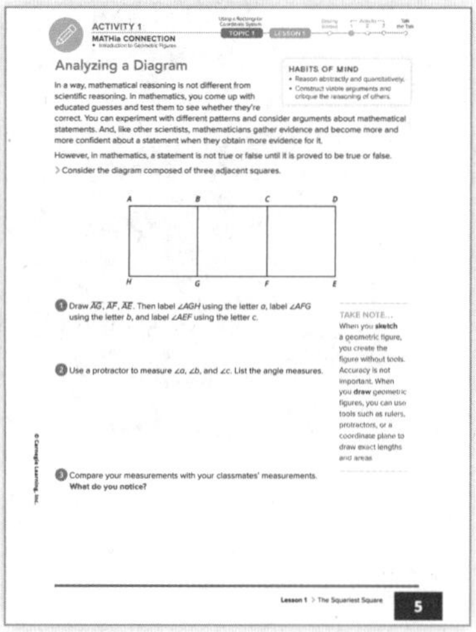

Analyzing a Diagram

In a way, mathematical reasoning is not different from scientific reasoning. In mathematics, you come up with educated guesses and test them to see whether they're correct. You can experiment with different patterns and consider arguments about mathematical statements. And, like other scientists, mathematicians gather evidence and become more and more confident about a statement when they obtain more evidence for it.

However, in mathematics, a statement is not true or false until it is proved to be true or false.

Consider the diagram composed of three adjacent squares.

1 Draw $\overline{AG}$, $\overline{AF}$, $\overline{AE}$. Then label $\angle AGH$ using the letter a, label $\angle AFG$ using the letter b, and label $\angle AEF$ using the letter c.

2 Use a protractor to measure $\angle a$, $\angle b$, and $\angle c$. List the angle measures.

3 Compare your measurements with your classmates' measurements. What do you notice?

Students learn the distinction between the terms *sketch* and *draw*.

- They draw line segments within a diagram composed of 3 squares to create specific angles.
- They use a protractor to measure the angles.

⊛ ACTIVITY 2
Making Conjectures

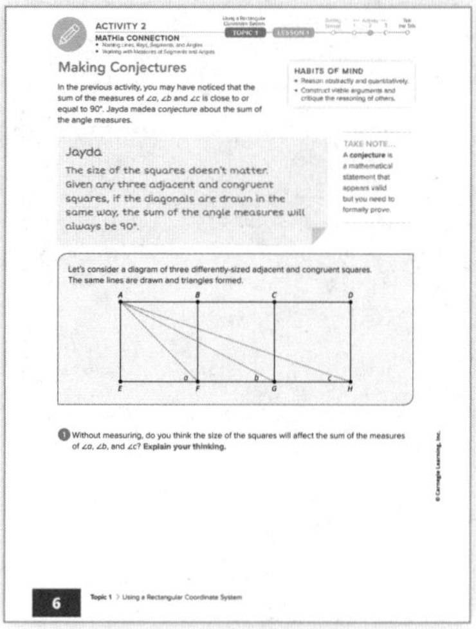

Making Conjectures

In the previous activity, you may have noticed that the sum of the measures of $\angle a$, $\angle b$ and $\angle c$ is close to or equal to 90°. Jayda made a conjecture about the sum of the angle measures.

Jayda: The size of the squares doesn't matter. Given any three adjacent and congruent squares, if the diagonals are drawn in the same way, the sum of the angle measures will always be 90°.

Let's consider a diagram of three differently-sized adjacent and congruent squares. The same lines are drawn and triangles formed.

1 Without measuring, do you think the size of the squares will affect the sum of the measures of $\angle a$, $\angle b$, and $\angle c$? Explain your thinking.

Students conjecture that the angles in the diagram sum to 90°.

- They use a protractor to determine whether their conjecture holds in a larger diagram.
- They manipulate the angles with patty paper to support their claim.

Log in to MyCL for **lesson support** including:

Slides

Videos

www.carnegielearning.com/login

INSTRUCTIONAL SEQUENCE

DEVELOP
Mathematical problem solving

DEMONSTRATE
Writing task

ACTIVITY 3
Drawing Auxiliary Lines

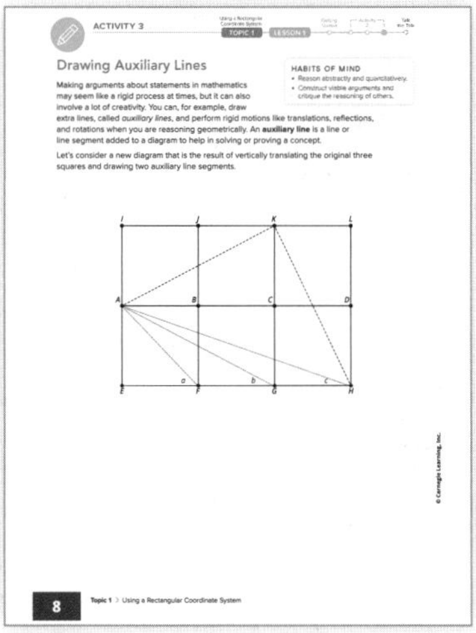

ACTIVITY 3

TOPIC 1 LESSON 1

Drawing Auxiliary Lines

HABITS OF MIND
- Reason abstractly and quantitatively.
- Construct viable arguments and critique the reasoning of others.

Making arguments about statements in mathematics may seem like a rigid process at times, but it can also involve a lot of creativity. You can, for example, draw extra lines, called *auxiliary lines*, and perform rigid motions like translations, reflections, and rotations when you are reasoning geometrically. An **auxiliary line** is a line or line segment added to a diagram to help in solving or proving a concept.

Let's consider a new diagram that is the result of vertically translating the original three squares and drawing two auxiliary line segments.

8 Topic 1 > Using a Rectangular Coordinate System

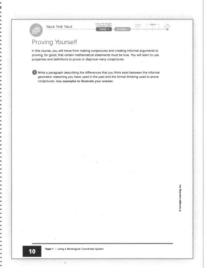

Students analyze an enhanced diagram with auxiliary lines.

- They determine mathematical relationships, angle measures, and side lengths from the diagram.

TALK THE TALK
Proving Yourself

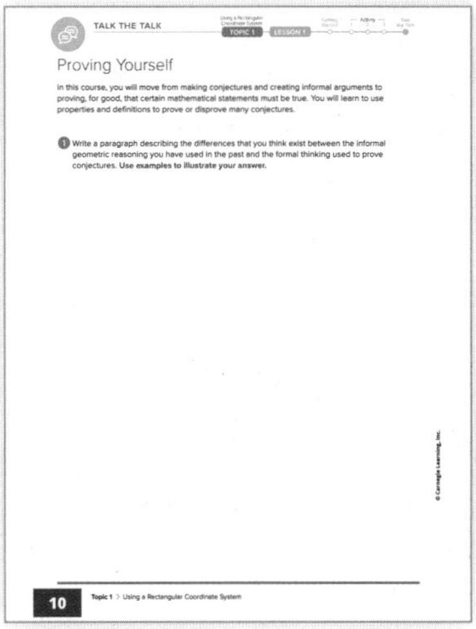

TALK THE TALK

TOPIC 1 LESSON 1

Proving Yourself

In this course, you will move from making conjectures and creating informal arguments to proving, for good, that certain mathematical statements must be true. You will learn to use properties and definitions to prove or disprove many conjectures.

1 Write a paragraph describing the differences that you think exist between the informal geometric reasoning you have used in the past and the formal thinking used to prove conjectures. **Use examples to illustrate your answer.**

10 Topic 1 > Using a Rectangular Coordinate System

Students contrast informal geometric reasoning and formal thinking to prove conjectures.

- They use examples to illustrate their reasoning.

NOTES

TOPIC 1

Log in to MyCL for:

- Editable templates
- Additional planning support

Now that you have read the Module, Topic, and Lesson Overviews, you are ready to plan.

Do the math

> Tear out the lesson planning template (page 3O) and jot down thoughts as you work through this lesson and read the Facilitation Notes.

- Anticipate student responses
- Track your time, so you can estimate how much time to spend on any activity
- Decide which differentiation and collaboration strategies you may use and how that may impact pacing

Connect the learning

MATHbook + MATHia

The table shows a portion of the self-paced MATHia sequence for the *Using a Rectangular Coordinate System* Topic.

Median student completion time for the entire topic: ~200–215 minutes

> As you implement this lesson, consider different connections for students who are on pace and those that have not yet completed the workspaces aligned to this lesson.

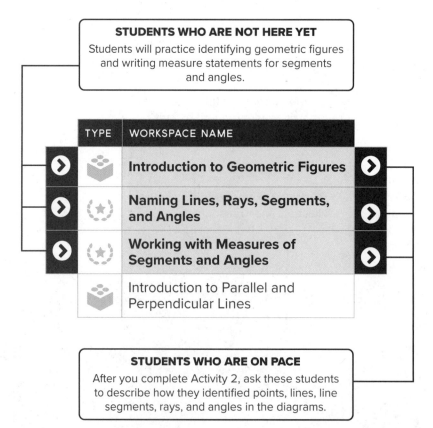

STUDENTS WHO ARE NOT HERE YET
Students will practice identifying geometric figures and writing measure statements for segments and angles.

TYPE	WORKSPACE NAME
	Introduction to Geometric Figures
	Naming Lines, Rays, Segments, and Angles
	Working with Measures of Segments and Angles
	Introduction to Parallel and Perpendicular Lines

STUDENTS WHO ARE ON PACE
After you complete Activity 2, ask these students to describe how they identified points, lines, line segments, rays, and angles in the diagrams.

The Squariest Square

From Informal to Formal Geometric Thinking

Session 1

GETTING STARTED The Perfect Square

Pacing (minutes)	
My Time	Class Time

ACTIVITY 1 Analyzing a Diagram ✪

Pacing (minutes)	
My Time	Class Time

KEY TERMS
sketch
draw

ACTIVITY 2 Making Conjectures ✪

Pacing (minutes)	
My Time	Class Time

KEY TERM
conjecture

ACTIVITY 3 Drawing Auxiliary Lines ✪

Pacing (minutes)	
My Time	Class Time

KEY TERM
auxiliary line

TALK THE TALK Proving Yourself ✪

Pacing (minutes)	
My Time	Class Time

✪ This activity highlights a key term or concept that is essential to the learning goals of the lesson.

Log in to MyCL for:
- Editable templates
- Additional planning support

Reflect on your lesson

> Consider the effectiveness of your lesson on student learning.

What went well?

What did not go as planned?

> Anticipate how you would change the lesson next time you teach it.

How will you capitalize on the things that went well?

How will you improve things that did not go as planned?

MATERIALS

- Patty paper
- Protractors
- Straightedges

Setting the Stage

TOPIC 1

- **Assign Review (optional, 1 – 2 minutes)**
- **Communicate the learning goals and key terms to look out for**
- **Tap into your students' prior learning by reading the narrative statement**
- **Provide a sense of direction by reading the question**

TOPIC 1 Using a Rectangular Coordinate System | TOPIC 2 Rigid Motions on a Plane | TOPIC 3 Congruence Through Transformations

1 | The Squariest Square
2 | Hip to Be Square
3 | Ts and Train Tracks
4 | Where Has Polly Gone?
5 | In and Out and All About

LESSON 1

The Squariest Square

From Informal to Formal Geometric Thinking

KEY TERMS
sketch
draw
conjecture
auxiliary line

Learning Goals

- Recall properties of geometric figures.
- Understand that you can compose a conjecture from the results with measuring tools. However, measuring tools are not an acceptable form of mathematical reasoning to validate a conjecture.
- Make a geometric conjecture and use mathematical reasoning to validate it.

REVIEW (1–2 minutes)

> Identify and connect the vertices that form a square in each grid.

1 2 3

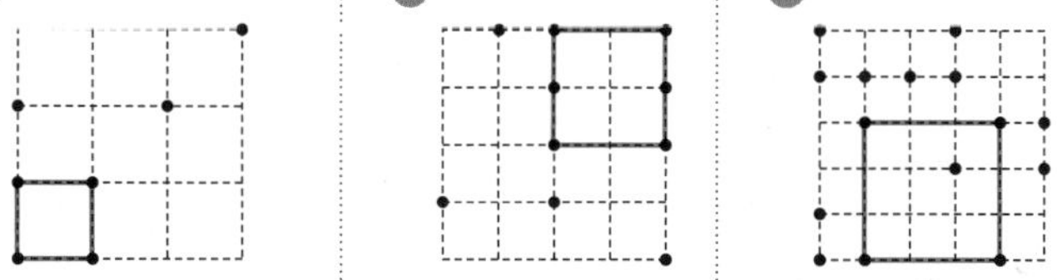

You have reasoned about lines and shapes in earlier grades and courses.

How can you apply formal geometric reasoning to what you know?

IN THIS REVIEW
Students use the properties of a square to solve problems. They will use this skill throughout the lesson.

Mathematicians make conjectures, test predictions, experiment with patterns, and consider arguments and different perspectives.

In mathematics, a statement is not true or false until it is proved to be true or false.

Formal mathematical reasoning may require creative thinking.

Essential Ideas

- A conjecture is a mathematical statement that appears valid but needs formal proof.
- Informal reasoning involves investigating mathematical relationships in specific cases to recognize a pattern and formulate a conjecture. Investigations include taking measurements and using patty paper.
- Formal reasoning requires the use of properties, definitions, and rules that prove that a conjecture is valid in all cases.

SUMMARY **A square has four congruent sides and four right angles. Its opposite sides are parallel, and its consecutive sides are perpendicular.**

Chunking the Activity

- **Read and discuss the introduction**
- **Have students work individually to complete the activity**
- **Share and summarize**

COMMON MISCONCEPTION

See Page 12A for a misconception related to 3.

DIFFERENTIATION STRATEGY

See Page 12A to challenge advanced learners to extend 3.

Student Look-Fors

- Vocabulary such as *parallel, perpendicular, right angles, congruent,* and *equal.*
- Recognition of relationships among side measures, angle measures, and between sides.

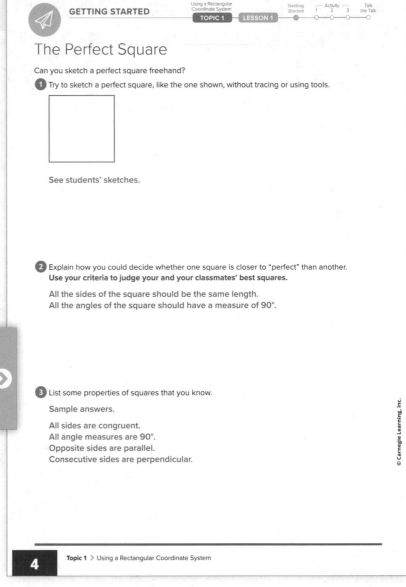

The Perfect Square

Can you sketch a perfect square freehand?

1. Try to sketch a perfect square, like the one shown, without tracing or using tools.

See students' sketches.

2. Explain how you could decide whether one square is closer to "perfect" than another. **Use your criteria to judge your and your classmates' best squares.**

All the sides of the square should be the same length.
All the angles of the square should have a measure of 90°.

3. List some properties of squares that you know.

Sample answers.

All sides are congruent.
All angle measures are 90°.
Opposite sides are parallel.
Consecutive sides are perpendicular.

Questions to Support Discourse

		TYPE
1	• What features were you trying to sketch accurately?	Probing
2	• What tools could you use to test these criteria?	Gathering
3	• What do you know about the measures of the sides of a square? The angles of a square? • What is the relationship between the opposite sides of a square? Consecutive sides of a square?	Gathering

ACTIVITY 1

Session 1 of 1

SUMMARY **You can use a square's properties to investigate relationships in diagrams. Measuring provides insight into relationships that may exist.**

ACTIVITY 1
MATHia CONNECTION
- Introduction to Geometric Figures

Using a Rectangular Coordinate System — TOPIC 1 — LESSON 1 — Getting Started — Activity 1, 2, 3 — Talk the Talk

Analyzing a Diagram

HABITS OF MIND
- Reason abstractly and quantitatively.
- Construct viable arguments and critique the reasoning of others.

In a way, mathematical reasoning is not different from scientific reasoning. In mathematics, you come up with educated guesses and test them to see whether they're correct. You can experiment with different patterns and consider arguments about mathematical statements. And, like other scientists, mathematicians gather evidence and become more and more confident about a statement when they obtain more evidence for it.

However, in mathematics, a statement is not true or false until it is proved to be true or false.

> Consider the diagram composed of three adjacent squares.

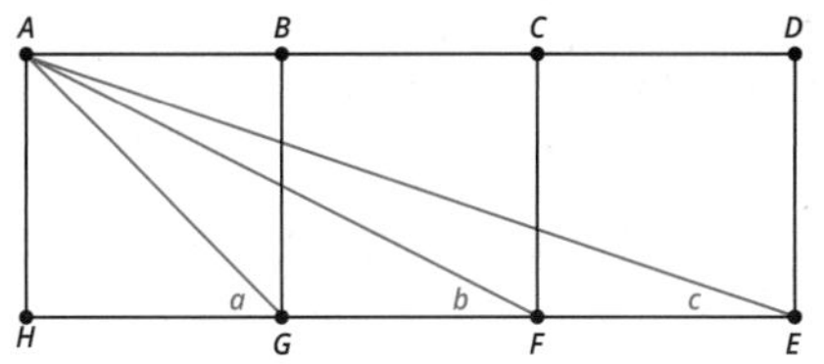

1 Draw $\overline{AG}$, $\overline{AF}$, $\overline{AE}$. Then label $\angle AGH$ using the letter a, label $\angle AFG$ using the letter b, and label $\angle AEF$ using the letter c.

2 Use a protractor to measure $\angle a$, $\angle b$, and $\angle c$. List the angle measures.

$m\angle a \approx 45°$

$m\angle b \approx 26°$

$m\angle c \approx 19°$

TAKE NOTE...
When you **sketch** a geometric figure, you create the figure without tools. Accuracy is not important. When you **draw** geometric figures, you can use tools such as rulers, protractors, or a coordinate plane to draw exact lengths and areas.

3 Compare your measurements with your classmates' measurements. **What do you notice?**

Sample answers.

Our answers were close, but not exactly the same.

The sum of the three angle measures seems to be 90°.

Questions to Support Discourse

		TYPE
1	• What does the notation $\overline{AG}$ mean? • What mathematical term describes a line segment joining two non-consecutive vertices? • Explain how to locate an angle given three letters.	Gathering
2	• Without measuring, can you tell which angle has the largest measure? Smallest measure? If so, explain your reasoning.	Probing
3	• Why aren't your answers the same?	Gathering
	• What relationship do you notice among the three angles?	Probing

Chunking the Activity

- Read and discuss the introduction
- Group students to complete 1 and 2
- Check-in and share
- Complete 3 as a class
- Read and discuss the definitions

TOPIC 1

DIFFERENTIATION STRATEGY

See Page 12B to support students who struggle with 1 and 2.

NOTE: This is the first pairing of these habits of mind.

- Reason abstractly and quantitatively
- Construct viable arguments and critique the reasoning of others

Have students refer to page FM–19 for questions to ask themselves.

LANGUAGE LINK

ELL TIP

As you encounter mathematics vocabulary from middle school throughout the lesson, ask a student to define the term for the class. Possible terms include *adjacent*, *congruent*, *diagonals*, *isosceles triangle*, and *translations*.

ACTIVITY 2

SUMMARY **Experimenting with different methods and visualizing are important tools that mathematicians use to make conjectures.**

Chunking the Activity

- **Read and discuss the introduction and definition**
- **Group students to complete 1 and 2**
- **Check-in and share**
- **Group students to complete 3**
- **Share and summarize**

Student Look-Fors

Whether students place their patty paper in the right angle of one of the squares to demonstrate that the sum is 90°.

LANGUAGE LINK

Remind students to refer to the Academic Glossary (page FM–20) to review the definition of **explain your thinking** and related phrases. Suggest they ask themselves the following questions:

- How can I justify my answer to others?
- Is my explanation logical?

MATHia CONNECTION
- Naming Lines, Rays, Segments, and Angles
- Working with Measures of Segments and Angles

Making Conjectures

In the previous activity, you may have noticed that the sum of the measures of ∠*a*, ∠*b* and ∠*c* is close to or equal to 90°. Jayda madea *conjecture* about the sum of the angle measures.

HABITS OF MIND
- Reason abstractly and quantitatively.
- Construct viable arguments and critique the reasoning of others.

> Jayda
>
> The size of the squares doesn't matter. Given any three adjacent and congruent squares, if the diagonals are drawn in the same way, the sum of the angle measures will always be 90°.

TAKE NOTE...
A **conjecture** is a mathematical statement that appears valid but you need to formally prove.

Let's consider a diagram of three differently-sized adjacent and congruent squares. The same lines are drawn and triangles formed.

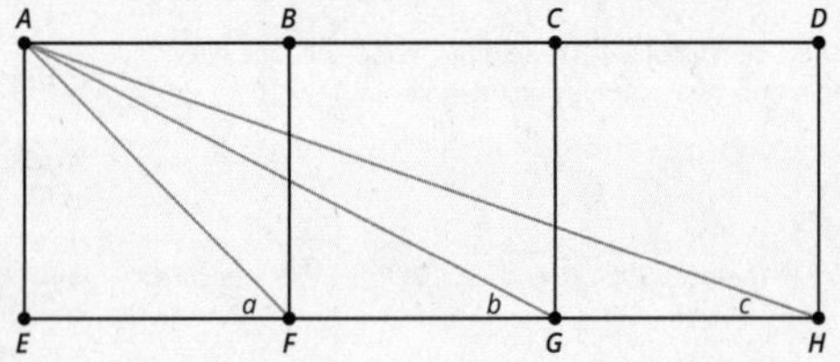

1. Without measuring, do you think the size of the squares will affect the sum of the measures of ∠*a*, ∠*b*, and ∠*c*? **Explain your thinking.**

   Sample answer.

   No, I don't think the size of the squares will affect the angle measures. All angles in a square have a measure of 90°, and the diagonal line segments drawn to form ∠*a*, ∠*b*, and ∠*c* were drawn thesame way.

Questions to Support Discourse

		TYPE
1	• Explain what a conjecture is in your own words. • How is Jayda's statement different than the conclusion you made in the previous activity?	Gathering
	• Why does the mathematical term *similar* apply to the two diagrams? • What characteristics changed in the enlarged diagram? • Why are the angle measures the same in the original and enlarged diagrams?	Seeing structure

2 Use a protractor to test your prediction on these differently-sized squares. Record your results.

m∠a ≈ 45°

m∠b ≈ 26°

m∠c ≈ 19°

My measurements were the same as the ones in the smaller diagram.

ASK YOURSELF...
Do your results support Jayda's conjecture?

There are many different ways to verify that the sum of the angle measures could be 90°. Experimenting with different methodsand visualizing are important tools that mathematicians use toapproach problems in effective ways and gain confidence in their conclusions.

3 Copy each of the angles a, b, and c from the diagram onto a different piece of patty paper. How can you manipulate the three angles to show that their sum is 90°?

Sample answer.

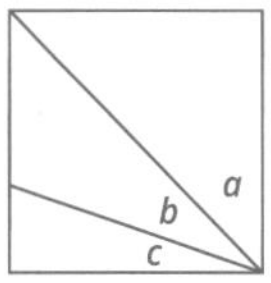

NOTES

TOPIC 1

Questions to Support Discourse

		TYPE
2	• How did your results compare to those from the previous activity? Why does that make sense?	Seeing structure
3	• Does this strategy make it clear that the angle measures sum to exactly 90°? Why not? • How did you complete this activity without knowing the measure of each angle? Explain your strategy.	Probing

SUMMARY **An auxiliary line is a line or line segment added to a diagram to help solve or prove a concept.**

Chunking the Activity

- **Read and discuss the introduction and analyze the diagram**
- **Group students to complete the activity**
- **Share and summarize**

Student Look-Fors

Identification of ΔAKH as a right triangle without any justification.

NOTE: The purpose of this activity is to use formal reasoning, compare it to informal reasoning, and review geometry terms and concepts. It is not a requirement to demonstrate that $m\angle a + m\angle b + m\angle c = 90°$ using formal proof.

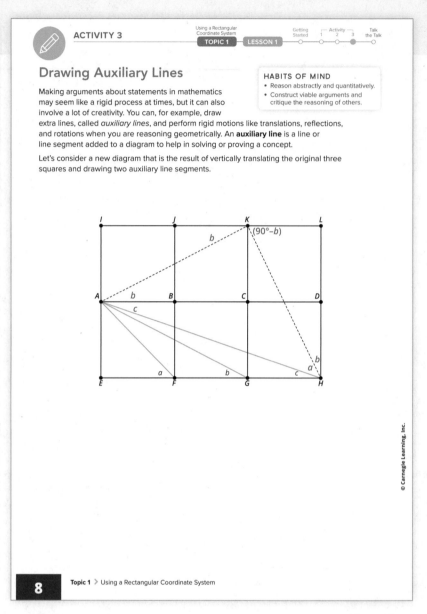

Drawing Auxiliary Lines

HABITS OF MIND
- Reason abstractly and quantitatively.
- Construct viable arguments and critique the reasoning of others.

Making arguments about statements in mathematics may seem like a rigid process at times, but it can also involve a lot of creativity. You can, for example, draw extra lines, called *auxiliary lines*, and perform rigid motions like translations, reflections, and rotations when you are reasoning geometrically. An **auxiliary line** is a line or line segment added to a diagram to help in solving or proving a concept.

Let's consider a new diagram that is the result of vertically translating the original three squares and drawing two auxiliary line segments.

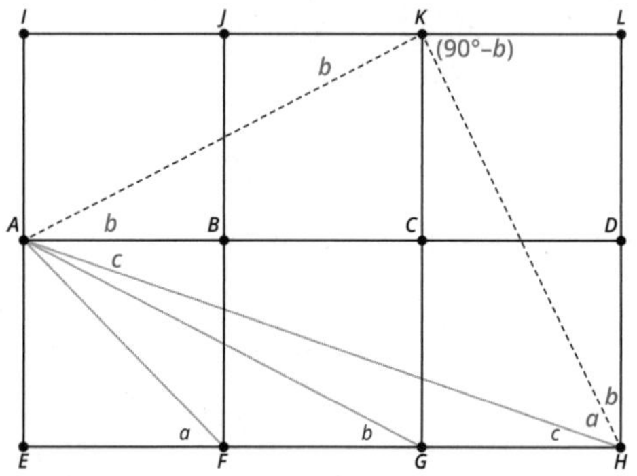

Questions to Support Discourse

		TYPE
Intro	• What does *vertically translating the original three squares* mean? • How does a figure change when you translate it? • Name the two auxiliary line segments.	Gathering

ACTIVITY 3 Continued

1 What other angle measures or side lengths can you determine using these added figures? **List all the concepts and facts you use.**

Sample answers.

Triangles *AIK*, *AEG* and *KLH* are all right triangles because each triangle has an angle that is also a corner of a square.

$\overline{AG}$ is the hypotenuse of triangle ΔAEG. $\overline{AK}$ is the hypotenuse of ΔAIK. $\overline{HK}$ is the hypotenuse of ΔKLH. Each triangle has a leg one unit in length and a leg two units in length. According to the Pythagorean Theorem, each hypotenuse would have the same length.

The $m\angle L$ is 90° and the $m\angle KHL$ is b°, so angle the $m\angle LKH$ must equal $(90 - b)$° for the angle measures to sum to 180°.

The $m\angle AKH$ is 90°. Angles *JKA*, *AKH*, and *LKH* form a straight line with a measure totaling 180°. The measures of $\angle JKA$ and $\angle LKH$ total 90°, so $\angle AKH$ must be a 90° angle.

ΔAEF, ΔAKH, and ΔAKG are isosceles triangles.

NOTES

DIFFERENTIATION STRATEGY

See Page 12C to support all students with 1.

DIFFERENTIATION STRATEGY

See Page 12C to challenge advanced learners to extend this activity.

Questions to Support Discourse

		TYPE
1	• What other right triangles do you recognize in the diagram? • Which line segment in the original diagram is the same length as $\overline{AK}$ and $\overline{KH}$? How do you know? • What other triangles are congruent to ΔAEG? How can you tell? Using this information, what other angles are congruent to $\angle b$? • Why are ΔAEH and ΔADH congruent? Using this information, which other angle is congruent to $\angle c$? • What is an isosceles triangle? What are the vertices of the isosceles triangles in the diagram?	Probing

TALK THE TALK

SUMMARY **Formal reasoning requires the use of properties, definitions, and rules that prove that a conjecture is valid in all cases.**

Chunking the Activity

- **Read and discuss the introduction**
- **Group students to complete the activity**
- **Share and summarize**

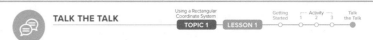

Proving Yourself

In this course, you will move from making conjectures and creating informal arguments to proving, for good, that certain mathematical statements must be true. You will learn to use properties and definitions to prove or disprove many conjectures.

1. Write a paragraph describing the differences that you think exist between the informal geometric reasoning you have used in the past and the formal thinking used to prove conjectures. **Use examples to illustrate your answer.**

   Sample answers.

   Informal reasoning can include measurements generated from a specific case. Formal reasoning requires the use of properties, definitions, and rules that prove a conjecture is true in all cases.

Questions to Support Discourse

	Questions to Support Discourse	TYPE
1	• Are measurements or reasoning with patty paper enough to prove a conjecture? Explain why not. • What is the value in taking measurements and using patty paper?	Seeing structure

ASSIGNMENT

LESSON 1 ASSIGNMENT

> Use a separate piece of paper for your Journal entry.

JOURNAL

Define each term in your own words.

1. sketch
2. draw
3. conjecture
4. auxiliary line

REMEMBER

Mathematicians make conjectures, test predictions, experiment with patterns, and consider arguments and different perspectives.

In mathematics, a statement is not true or false until it is proved to be true or false.

Formal mathematical reasoning may require creative thinking.

PRACTICE

1. A Zukei puzzle is a Japanese logic puzzle in which a grid is presented with a number of points shown at different intersections. Each grid is presented along with the name of a geometric figure. The goal of the puzzle is to determine which points on the grid are the vertices of the named geometric figure. Identify and connect the vertices that form the given shape for each grid.

(a) Rhombus

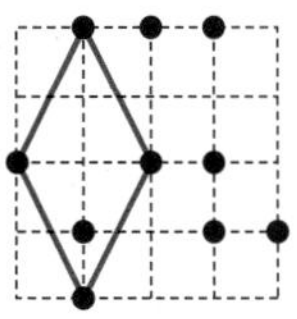

(b) Isosceles Triangle

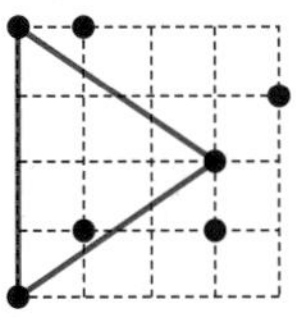

(c) Parallelogram

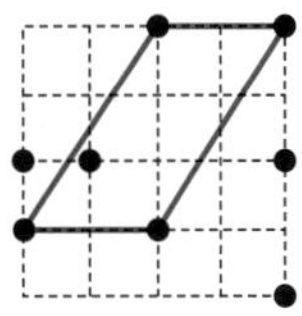

(d) Trapezoid

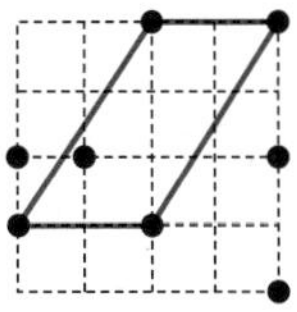

(e) Rectangle

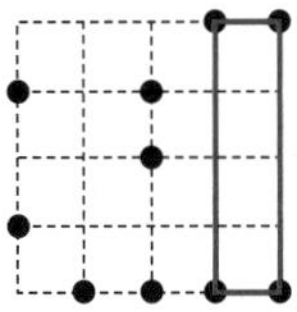

(f) Isosceles Triangle

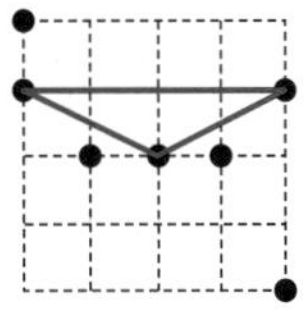

Go to LiveHint.com for help on the PRACTICE questions.

Chunking the Assignment

- Journal
- Practice 1
- Stretch (advanced learners)
- Mixed Practice (page 89) 1

TOPIC 1

JOURNAL

1. When you sketch a geometric figure, you create the figure without tools.
2. When you draw geometric figures, you can use measurement tools.
3. A conjecture is a mathematical statement that appears valid, but you have yet to prove it formally.
4. You can add auxiliary lines or segments to a diagram to help in solving or proving a concept.

Encourage students to use LiveHint.com for help with the PRACTICE questions of this assignment.

NOTES

STRETCH

One-third of the square is shaded.

Let the base of the shaded triangle have a length of 1. Vertical angles are congruent, and alternate interior angles are congruent. Thus, the two triangles shown with marked angles are similar by Angle-Angle Similarity.

Since the smaller triangle has half the base length of the larger shaded triangle, its height is also half the height of the larger triangle. The two triangles have a combined height of 1, so the height of the larger triangle is $\frac{2}{3}$. The area of the triangle then is $\frac{1}{2}(1)\left(\frac{2}{3}\right)$, or $\frac{1}{3}$ square units. The full square has an area of 1 square unit, so $\frac{1}{3}$ of the square is shaded.

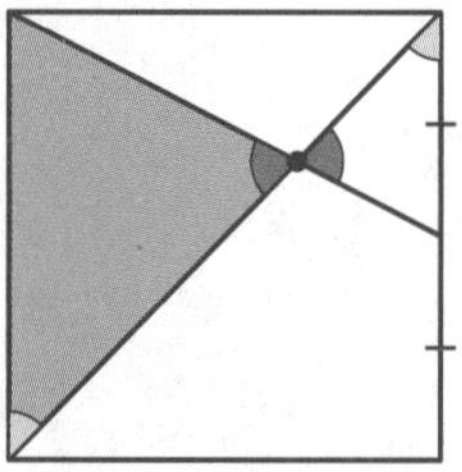

(g) Square

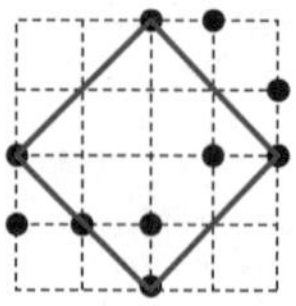

(h) Parallelogram

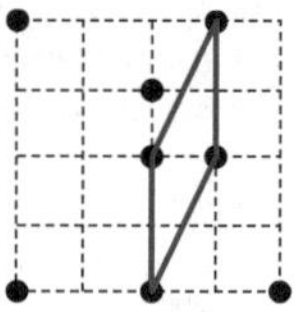

(i) Rectangle

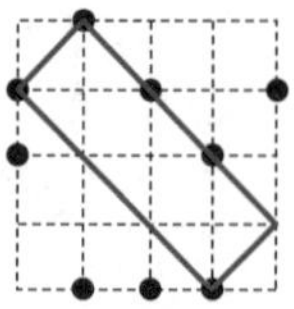

STRETCH Optional

> Determine the fractional part of the square the shaded area represents. Explain your reasoning.

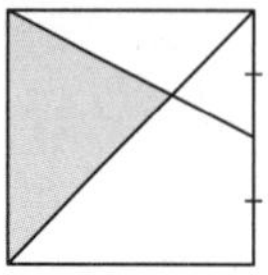

The Squariest Square

This resource details additional facilitation notes to fully assist you as you plan each lesson to support all students, students who struggle, and advanced learners. It provides differentiation strategies, common student misconceptions, and suggestions to extend certain activities.

GETTING STARTED

Session 1 of 1

The Perfect Square

Students attempt to sketch a perfect square without using any tools. They list a square's properties.

CHUNK	AUDIENCE	ADDITIONAL SUPPORTS
As students work on 3	All Students	**COMMON MISCONCEPTION** Students may have the misconception that the terms *equal* and *congruent* have the same meaning. Clarify that the term *equal* applies to numeric and algebraic expressions, and the term *congruent* applies to geometric figures. For example, • The lengths of the sides of a square are equal. • The sides of a square are congruent. • The measures of all angles are 90°. • All angles are congruent.
To extend 3	Advanced Learners	**DIFFERENTIATION STRATEGY** Encourage students to include properties related to a square's diagonals, other categories of polygons to which a square belongs, and formulas for the perimeter and area of a square.

ACTIVITY 1

Session 1 of 1

Analyzing a Diagram

Students learn the distinction between the terms *sketch* and *draw*. They draw line segments within a diagram composed of 3 squares to create specific angles. They use a protractor to measure the angles.

CHUNK	AUDIENCE	ADDITIONAL SUPPORTS
Before students begin 1 and 2	Students who Struggle	**DIFFERENTIATION STRATEGY** Review segment and angle notation as well as the use of a protractor.

ACTIVITY 3

Session 1 of 1

Drawing Auxiliary Lines

Students analyze an enhanced diagram with auxiliary lines. They determine mathematical relationships, angle measures, and side lengths from the diagram.

<table>
<tr><th>CHUNK</th><th>AUDIENCE</th><th>ADDITIONAL SUPPORTS</th></tr>
<tr><td>As students work on 1</td><td>All Students</td><td>DIFFERENTIATION STRATEGY
Suggest students use markings, labels, or the same colored pencil to identify congruent sides and angles. These markings may help them identify additional information, such as the isosceles triangle, ΔAKH, in the diagram.</td></tr>
<tr><td>To extend the activity</td><td>Advanced Learners</td><td>DIFFERENTIATION STRATEGY
Have students organize their information to demonstrate that $m\angle a + m\angle b + m\angle c = 90°$. One possible solution path:
1. Label $\angle b$ in triangles congruent to ΔAEG.
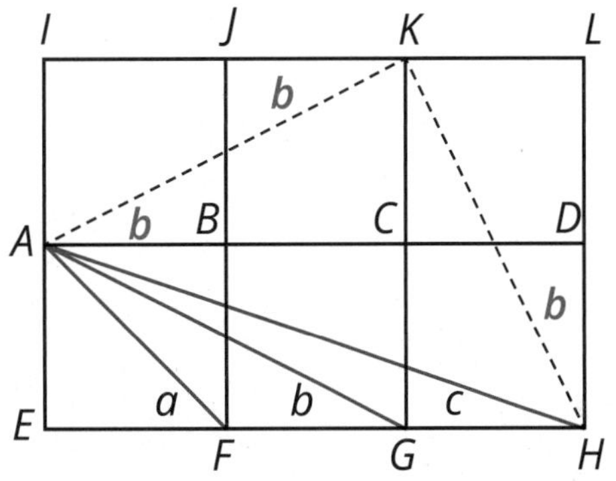

2. Label $\angle c$ in the triangle congruent to ΔAEH.
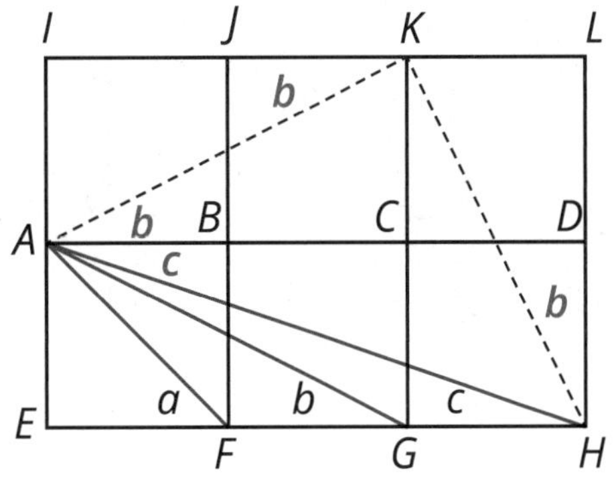
</td></tr>
</table>

CHUNK	AUDIENCE	ADDITIONAL SUPPORTS
To extend the activity	Advanced Learners	**DIFFERENTIATION STRATEGY** **continued...** **3.** ΔKLH is a right triangle. So m$\angle LKH$ is $(90 - b)°$. 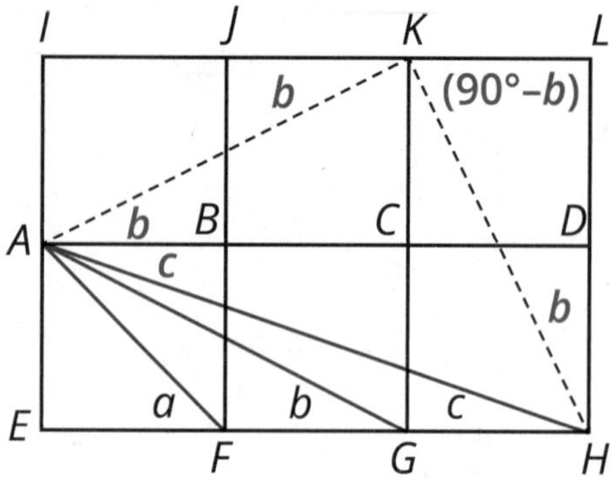 **4.** The m$\angle AKH$ = 90°, forming $\overleftrightarrow{IL}$. 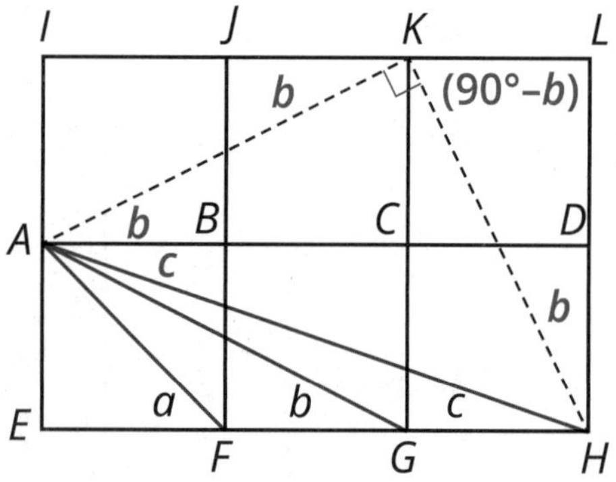 **5.** ΔAKH is a right isosceles triangle, similar to ΔAEF. Label $\angle a$ in ΔAKH. 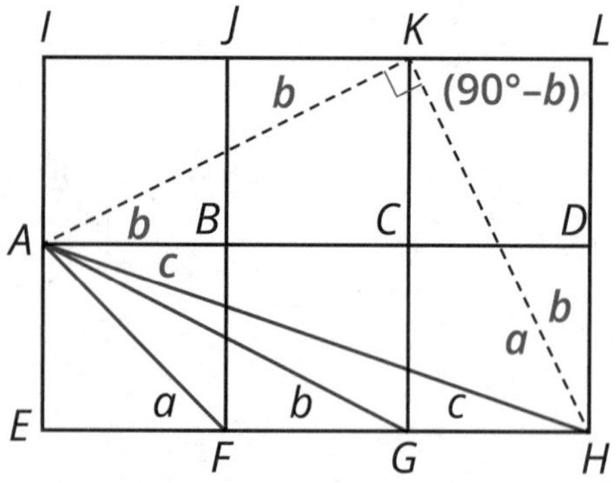 **6.** m$\angle a$ + m$\angle b$ + m$\angle c$ = m$\angle H$ m$\angle a$ + m$\angle b$ + m$\angle c$ = 90°

Practice the learning

MATHbook + Skills Practice

The table shows the targeted practice of the skills and mathematical concepts for the *Using a Rectangular Coordinate System* Topic. The highlighted Problem Set aligns with **The Squariest Square**.

PROBLEM SET	
1	**Identifying Properties of Geometric Figures**
2	Constructing Perpendicular Lines
3	Duplicating Line Segments
4	Writing Equations of Parallel and Perpendicular Lines
5	Classifying Shapes on the Coordinate Plane
6	Determining Perimeter and Area of Rectangles and Triangles on the Coordinate Plane
7	Determining Perimeter and Area of Other Polygons on the Coordinate Plane

ANYTIME AFTER ACTIVITY 3

Facilitate students as they work individually on **Problem Set 1**.

NOTES

ENGAGE + DEVELOP + TEACH

ENGAGE at the **Module** level

DEVELOP at the **Topic** level

TEACH Read the facilitation notes and plan learning experiences.

Where are we?

	TOPIC 1 Using a Rectangular Coordinate System	LESSON 1 The Squariest Square	**LESSON 2 Hip to Be Square**	LESSON 3 Ts and Train Tracks	LESSON 4 Where Has Polly Gone?	LESSON 5 In and Out and All About
Pacing		1 Session	**2 Sessions**	2 Sessions	3 Sessions	3 Sessions

OVERVIEW: LESSON 2

Hip to Be Square

Constructing a Coordinate Plane

ENGAGE

- Students learn the difference among the terms *sketch*, *draw*, and *construct*.

DEVELOP

- Students construct perpendicular bisectors and conjecture about them.
- They construct a square and conjecture about its diagonals.
- They consider translating a square to create a coordinate plane.
- Students describe the rigid motions to form shapes on a coordinate plane.

DEMONSTRATE

- Students relate the translations to the slope of a line.

HIGH SCHOOL GEOMETRY

Congruence

Experiment with transformations in the plane.

1. Know precise definitions of angle, circle, perpendicular line, parallel line, and line segment, based on the undefined notions of point, line, distance along a line, and distance around a circular arc.

5. Given a geometric figure and a rotation, reflection, or translation, draw the transformed figure using, e.g., graph paper, tracing paper, or geometry software. Specify a sequence of transformations that will carry a given figure onto another.

Make geometric constructions.

12. Make formal geometric constructions with a variety of tools and methods (compass and straightedge, string, reflective devices, paper folding, dynamic geometric software, etc.).

LESSON STRUCTURE AND PACING GUIDE 2 SESSIONS

⊛ This activity highlights a key term or concept that is essential to the learning goals of the lesson.

Session 1		Session 2
INSTRUCTIONAL SEQUENCE		
ENGAGE Connect to prior knowledge	**DEVELOP** Investigation Worked example	**DEVELOP** Worked example Investigation

⊛ GETTING STARTED
Getting Back in Shape

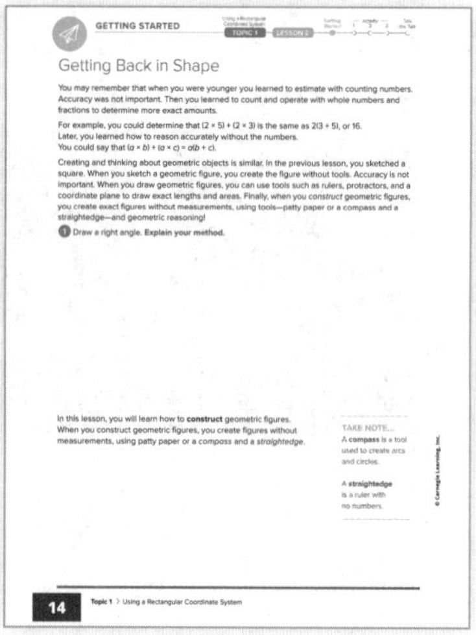
GETTING STARTED

TOPIC 1 LESSON 2

Getting Back in Shape

You may remember that when you were younger you learned to estimate with counting numbers. Accuracy was not important. Then you learned to count and operate with whole numbers and fractions to determine more exact amounts.

For example, you could determine that (2 × 5) + (2 × 3) is the same as 2(3 + 5), or 16.
Later, you learned how to reason accurately without the numbers.
You could say that $(a \times b) + (a \times c) = a(b + c)$.

Creating and thinking about geometric objects is similar. In the previous lesson, you sketched a square. When you sketch a geometric figure, you create the figure without tools. Accuracy is not important. When you draw geometric figures, you can use tools such as rulers, protractors, and a coordinate plane to draw exact lengths and areas. Finally, when you *construct* geometric figures, you create exact figures without measurements, using tools—patty paper or a compass and a straightedge—and geometric reasoning!

1 Draw a right angle. **Explain your method.**

In this lesson, you will learn how to **construct** geometric figures. When you construct geometric figures, you create figures without measurements, using patty paper or a *compass* and a *straightedge*.

TAKE NOTE...
A **compass** is a tool used to create arcs and circles.

A **straightedge** is a ruler with no numbers.

© Carnegie Learning, Inc.

14 Topic 1 > Using a Rectangular Coordinate System

Students use measuring tools to draw a right angle.

- They learn the difference between the terms *sketch*, *draw*, and *construct*.

⊛ ACTIVITY 1
Constructing a Perpendicular Line

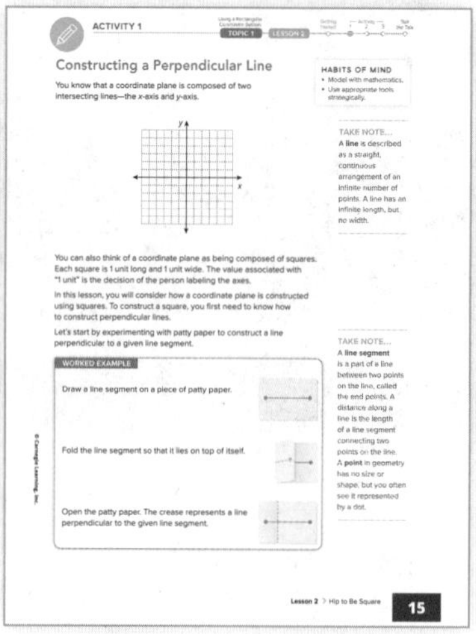
ACTIVITY 1

TOPIC 1 LESSON 2

Constructing a Perpendicular Line

You know that a coordinate plane is composed of two intersecting lines—the *x*-axis and *y*-axis.

HABITS OF MIND
- Model with mathematics.
- Use appropriate tools strategically.

TAKE NOTE...
A **line** is described as a straight, continuous arrangement of an infinite number of points. A line has an infinite length, but no width.

You can also think of a coordinate plane as being composed of squares. Each square is 1 unit long and 1 unit wide. The value associated with "1 unit" is the decision of the person labeling the axes.

In this lesson, you will consider how a coordinate plane is constructed using squares. To construct a square, you first need to know how to construct perpendicular lines.

Let's start by experimenting with patty paper to construct a line perpendicular to a given line segment.

WORKED EXAMPLE

Draw a line segment on a piece of patty paper.

Fold the line segment so that it lies on top of itself.

Open the patty paper. The crease represents a line perpendicular to the given line segment.

TAKE NOTE...
A **line segment** is a part of a line between two points on the line, called the end points. A distance along a line is the length of a line segment connecting two points on the line.
A **point** in geometry has no size or shape, but you often see it represented by a dot.

© Carnegie Learning, Inc.

Lesson 2 > Hip to Be Square 15

Students construct perpendicular lines and perpendicular bisectors.

- They conjecture that any point on a perpendicular bisector is equidistant to the original segment's endpoints.

⊛ ACTIVITY 2
Constructing a Square

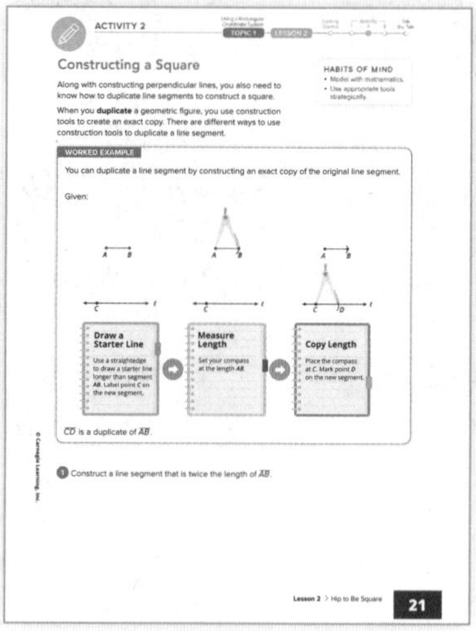
ACTIVITY 2

TOPIC 1 LESSON 2

Constructing a Square

Along with constructing perpendicular lines, you also need to know how to duplicate line segments to construct a square.

When you **duplicate** a geometric figure, you use construction tools to create an exact copy. There are different ways to use construction tools to duplicate a line segment.

HABITS OF MIND
- Model with mathematics.
- Use appropriate tools strategically.

WORKED EXAMPLE

You can duplicate a line segment by constructing an exact copy of the original line segment.

Given:

Draw a Starter Line: Use a straightedge to draw a starter line longer than segment *AB*. Label point *C* on the new segment.

Measure Length: Set your compass at the length *AB*.

Copy Length: Place the compass at *C*. Mark point *D* on the new segment.

$\overline{CD}$ is a duplicate of $\overline{AB}$.

1 Construct a line segment that is twice the length of $\overline{AB}$.

© Carnegie Learning, Inc.

Lesson 2 > Hip to Be Square 21

Students construct a square by duplicating segments and constructing perpendicular lines.

- They conjecture about a square's diagonals.

Log in to MyCL for **lesson support** including:

Slides

Videos

www.carnegielearning.com/login

NOTES

INSTRUCTIONAL SEQUENCE

DEVELOP	DEMONSTRATE
Peer analysis Real-world problem solving	Exit ticket procedures

ACTIVITY 3
Rigid Motions

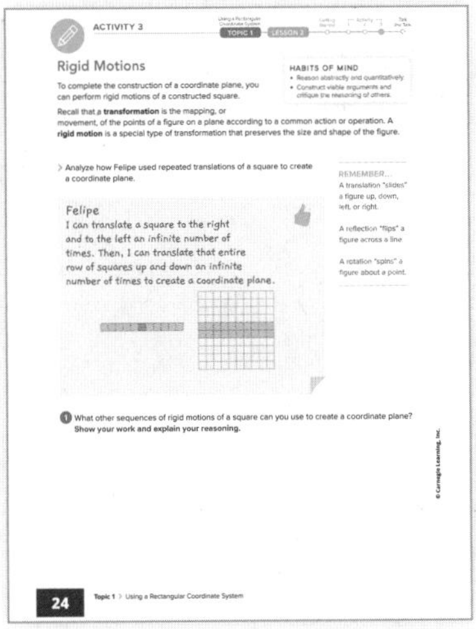

ACTIVITY 3

TOPIC 1 LESSON 2

Rigid Motions

To complete the construction of a coordinate plane, you can perform rigid motions of a constructed square.

HABITS OF MIND
- Reason abstractly and quantitatively.
- Construct viable arguments and critique the reasoning of others.

Recall that a **transformation** is the mapping, or movement, of the points of a figure on a plane according to a common action or operation. A **rigid motion** is a special type of transformation that preserves the size and shape of the figure.

> Analyze how Felipe used repeated translations of a square to create a coordinate plane.

Felipe
I can translate a square to the right and to the left an infinite number of times. Then, I can translate that entire row of squares up and down an infinite number of times to create a coordinate plane.

REMEMBER...
A translation "slides" a figure up, down, left, or right.
A reflection "flips" a figure across a line.
A rotation "spins" a figure about a point.

1 What other sequences of rigid motions of a square can you use to create a coordinate plane? **Show your work and explain your reasoning.**

© Carnegie Learning, Inc.

24 Topic 1 > Using a Rectangular Coordinate System

Students consider translating a square to create a coordinate plane.

- They describe the rigid motions to form shapes on a coordinate plane.

TALK THE TALK
Walking on a Thin Line

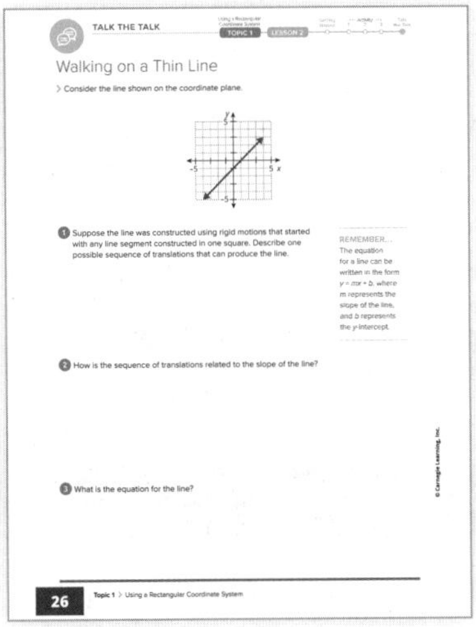

TALK THE TALK

TOPIC 1 LESSON 2

Walking on a Thin Line

> Consider the line shown on the coordinate plane.

1 Suppose the line was constructed using rigid motions that started with any line segment constructed in one square. Describe one possible sequence of translations that can produce the line.

REMEMBER...
The equation for a line can be written in the form $y = mx + b$, where m represents the slope of the line, and b represents the y-intercept.

2 How is the sequence of translations related to the slope of the line?

3 What is the equation for the line?

© Carnegie Learning, Inc.

26 Topic 1 > Using a Rectangular Coordinate System

Students describe translations of a segment to create a line.

- They relate those translations to the slope of the line.

Log in to MyCL for:

- Editable templates
- Additional planning support

Now that you have read the Module, Topic, and Lesson Overviews, you are ready to plan.

Do the math

> Tear out the lesson planning template (page 13E) and jot down thoughts as you work through this lesson and read the Facilitation Notes.

Connect the learning

MATHbook + MATHia

The table shows a portion of the self-paced MATHia sequence for the *Using a Rectangular Coordinate System* Topic.

Median student completion time for the entire topic: ~200–215 minutes

> As you implement this lesson, consider different connections for students who are on pace and those that have not yet completed the workspaces aligned to this lesson.

STUDENTS WILL CONTINUE WORKING ON SKILLS RELATED TO THIS TOPIC

TYPE	WORKSPACE NAME
	Introduction to Geometric Figures
	Naming Lines, Rays, Segments, and Angles
	Working with Measures of Segments and Angles
	Introduction to Parallel and Perpendicular Lines
	Modeling Parallel and Perpendicular Lines

Hip to Be Square

Constructing a Coordinate Plane

Session 1

GETTING STARTED Getting Back in Shape ✪

Pacing (minutes)	
My Time	Class Time

KEY TERM
construct
compass
straightedge

ACTIVITY 1 Constructing a Perpendicular Line ✪

Pacing (minutes)	
My Time	Class Time

KEY TERM
line
line segment
point
midpoint
segment bisector
perpendicular bisector

Session 2

ACTIVITY 2 Constructing a Square ✪

Pacing (minutes)	
My Time	Class Time

KEY TERM
duplicate
diagonal

ACTIVITY 3 Rigid Motions ✪

Pacing (minutes)	
My Time	Class Time

KEY TERM
transformation
rigid motion

TALK THE TALK Walking on a Thin Line

Pacing (minutes)	
My Time	Class Time

✪ This activity highlights a key term or concept that is essential to the learning goals of the lesson.

Log in to MyCL for:

- Editable templates
- Additional planning support

Reflect on your lesson

Consider the effectiveness of your lesson on student learning.

What went well?

What did not go as planned?

Anticipate how you would change the lesson next time you teach it.

How will you capitalize on the things that went well?

How will you improve things that did not go as planned?

MATERIALS

- Compasses
- Patty paper
- Straightedges

TOPIC 1 Using a Rectangular Coordinate System
TOPIC 2 Rigid Motions on a Plane
TOPIC 3 Congruence Through Transformations
1 | The Squariest Square
2 | Hip to Be Square
3 | Ts and Train Tracks
4 | Where Has Polly Gone?
5 | In and Out and All About

LESSON 2

Hip to Be Square

Constructing a Coordinate Plane

Learning Goals

- Construct a perpendicular line segment and bisector using patty paper and a compass and straightedge.
- Use construction tools to duplicate a line segment and construct a square.
- Use constructions and rigid motions to create a coordinate plane.
- Identify rigid motions that you can use to create shapes on a coordinate plane.
- Identify the coordinates of vertices of shapes on a coordinate plane.

KEY TERMS

construct	segment bisector
compass	perpendicular bisector
straightedge	duplicate
line	diagonal
line segment	transformation
point	rigid motion
midpoint	

REVIEW (1–2 minutes)

> Identify whether the transformation shown is a translation, reflection, or rotation. **Justify your answer.**

1 
translation

2 
reflection

3 
rotation or reflection

You have used a ruler, protractor, and a compass to draw geometric figures.

How can you create geometric figures without using measuring tools?

Setting the Stage

- **Assign Review (optional, 1 – 2 minutes)**
- **Communicate the learning goals and key terms to look out for**
- **Tap into your students' prior learning by reading the narrative statement**
- **Provide a sense of direction by reading the question**

TOPIC 1

IN THIS REVIEW
Students identify transformations. They will first use this skill in **ACTIVITY 3 Rigid Motions.**

A perpendicular bisector is a line, line segment, or ray that bisects a line segment and is also perpendicular to the line segment.

A translation slides a figure up, down, left, or right. A reflection flips a figure across a line. A rotation spins a figure about a point.

Essential Ideas

- When you construct geometric figures, you create exact figures using only a compass or patty paper and a straightedge.
- The midpoint of a segment is a point that divides the segment into two congruent segments.
- A segment bisector is a line, line segment, or ray that divides a line segment into two line segments of equal length.
- A perpendicular bisector is a line, line segment, or ray that bisects a line segment and is also perpendicular to the line segment.
- Any point on a perpendicular bisector is equidistant to the endpoints of the original segment it bisects.
- The diagonals of a square are congruent, bisect each other, are perpendicular to one another, and bisect the angles of the square.
- You can create a coordinate plane constructing a square and applying rigid motion transformations to the square.

SUMMARY **When you construct geometric figures, you create exact figures without measurements, using paper folding or a compass and a straightedge.**

Chunking the Activity

- **Read and discuss the introduction**
- **Group students to complete the activity**
- **Share and summarize**

Student Look-Fors

Whether students are demonstrating self-awareness.

- Showing a sense of confidence and optimism as they approach the problem
- Accurately perceiving their strengths and limitations
- Having a growth mindset

Getting Back in Shape

You may remember that when you were younger you learned to estimate with counting numbers. Accuracy was not important. Then you learned to count and operate with whole numbers and fractions to determine more exact amounts.

For example, you could determine that (2 × 5) + (2 × 3) is the same as 2(3 + 5), or 16. Later, you learned how to reason accurately without the numbers. You could say that $(a \times b) + (a \times c) = a(b + c)$.

Creating and thinking about geometric objects is similar. In the previous lesson, you sketched a square. When you sketch a geometric figure, you create the figure without tools. Accuracy is not important. When you draw geometric figures, you can use tools such as rulers, protractors, and a coordinate plane to draw exact lengths and areas. Finally, when you *construct* geometric figures, you create exact figures without measurements, using tools—patty paper or a compass and a straightedge—and geometric reasoning!

1. Draw a right angle. **Explain your method.**

   Check students' drawings.

In this lesson, you will learn how to **construct** geometric figures. When you construct geometric figures, you create figures without measurements, using patty paper or a *compass* and a *straightedge*.

TAKE NOTE...

A **compass** is a tool used to create arcs and circles.

A **straightedge** is a ruler with no numbers.

Questions to Support Discourse

		TYPE
1	• When the directions say to draw, which tools can you use? • How do you label a right angle? • What are some examples of right angles that you see in the classroom? • When the directions say to construct, which tools can you use?	Gathering
	• How do you know how long to make the rays of your right angle? • Can you think of any ways to create a right angle without using a protractor? If so, explain your strategy.	Probing

ACTIVITY 1

SUMMARY **When constructing a perpendicular bisector, a line that bisects and is perpendicular to a segment, you may recognize other relationships.**

Constructing a Perpendicular Line

HABITS OF MIND
- Model with mathematics.
- Use appropriate tools strategically.

You know that a coordinate plane is composed of two intersecting lines—the *x*-axis and *y*-axis.

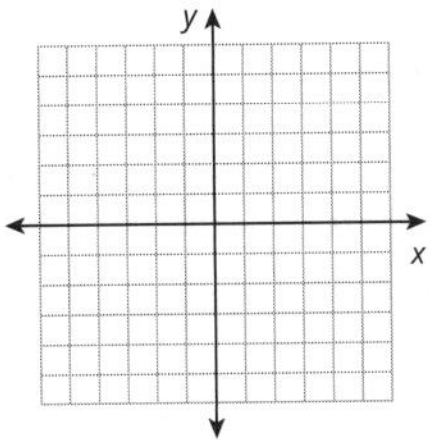

TAKE NOTE...
A **line** is described as a straight, continuous arrangement of an infinite number of points. A line has an infinite length, but no width.

You can also think of a coordinate plane as being composed of squares. Each square is 1 unit long and 1 unit wide. The value associated with "1 unit" is the decision of the person labeling the axes.

In this lesson, you will consider how a coordinate plane is constructed using squares. To construct a square, you first need to know how to construct perpendicular lines.

Let's start by experimenting with patty paper to construct a line perpendicular to a given line segment.

WORKED EXAMPLE

Draw a line segment on a piece of patty paper.

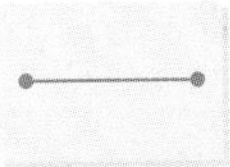

Fold the line segment so that it lies on top of itself.

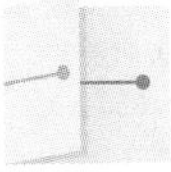

Open the patty paper. The crease represents a line perpendicular to the given line segment.

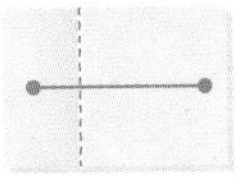

TAKE NOTE...
A **line segment** is a part of a line between two points on the line, called the end points. A distance along a line is the length of a line segment connecting two points on the line.
A **point** in geometry has no size or shape, but you often see it represented by a dot.

Questions to Support Discourse

		TYPE
Intro	• What are perpendicular lines? • Where are there perpendicular lines on the coordinate plane?	Gathering
Worked Example	• Why is it important to fold the line segment so that it lies on top of itself? • How would the crease change if you didn't fold the line segment to lie on top of itself?	Seeing structure

Chunking the Activity

- Read and discuss the introduction and worked example
- Group students to complete 1 - 3
- Check-in and share
- Read and discuss the worked example and complete 4 - 6 as a class
- Group students to analyze the worked example and complete 7 and 8
- Check-in and share
- Group students to complete 9 - 11
- Share and summarize

NOTE: This is the first pairing of these habits of mind.

- Model with mathematics
- Use appropriate tools strategically

Have students refer to page FM–19 for questions to ask themselves.

NOTES

DIFFERENTIATION STRATEGY

See Page 28A to assist all students with the strategy in **2**.

LANGUAGE LINK

ELL TIP

Discuss the meaning of the term *bisect*. The root word *sect* means to cut, as in dissect. The prefix *bi-* means two, as in a bicycle having two wheels. Therefore, the term *bisect* means to cut into two equal parts.

1 Consider $\overline{AB}$.

ⓐ Use patty paper to construct 2 different perpendicular lines through $\overline{AB}$.

Check students' patty paper.

ⓑ How can you fold the patty paper so that the perpendicular crease intersects the *midpoint* of $\overline{AB}$?

Fold the paper so that the endpoints of the line segment lie on top of each other.

TAKE NOTE...

A **midpoint** of a line segment is the point that divides the line segment into two congruent segments.

2 Thomas drew a line segment and then determined the midpoint incorrectly. **Explain what he did incorrectly and what he should have done.**

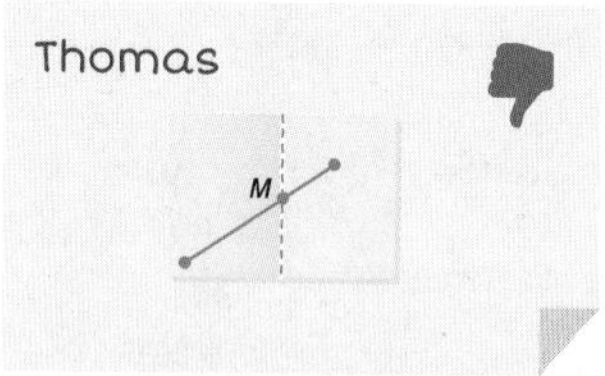

Thomas folded the patty paper by aligning the corners of the patty paper. He should have folded the patty paper so that endpoints of the line segment lie on top of one another.

A **segment bisector** is a line, line segment, or ray that divides a line segment into two line segments of equal length. The basic geometric construction used to locate a midpoint of a line segment is called bisecting a line segment.

3 Use patty paper to bisect $\overline{ST}$.

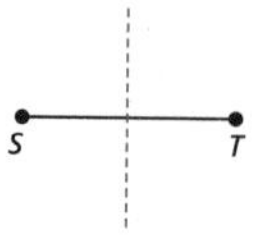

ASK YOURSELF...

How can you verify that you correctly bisected the line segment?

Check students' patty paper folds.

Questions to Support Discourse

		TYPE
1	• Why does having the endpoints lie on top of each other create a midpoint?	Seeing structure
2	• Did Thomas make a mistake by drawing the line slanted on the patty paper? • How can Thomas construct a line perpendicular to his segment?	Probing
3	• Why can't you bisect a line? • How are a midpoint and segment bisector related? How are they different? • Why is patty paper considered a construction tool, not a drawing tool?	Gathering
	• How are the steps to create a perpendicular line and a segment bisector related?	Seeing structure

You can also construct a perpendicular line through a point on a line using a compass and straightedge. To do this construction, you make use of the fact that all the radii of a circle have an equal length.

WORKED EXAMPLE

You can construct a line perpendicular to line ℓ through point *B*.

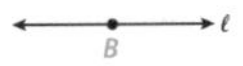

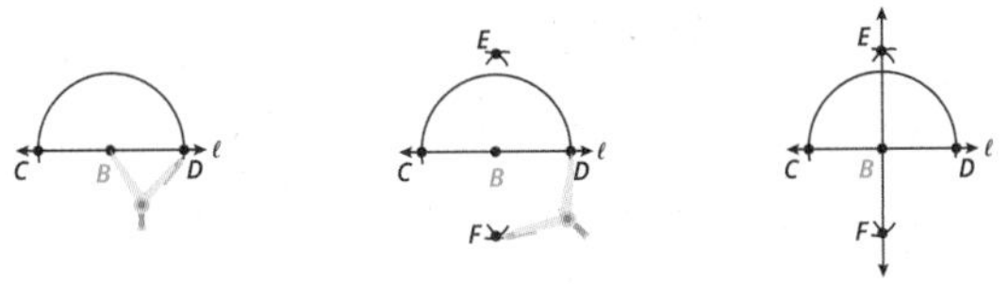

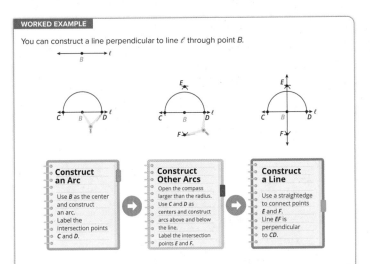

Construct an Arc
Use *B* as the center and construct an arc. Label the intersection points *C* and *D*.

Construct Other Arcs
Open the compass larger than the radius. Use *C* and *D* as centers and construct arcs above and below the line. Label the intersection points *E* and *F*.

Construct a Line
Use a straightedge to connect points *E* and *F*. Line *EF* is perpendicular to *CD*.

4 Explain why $\overleftrightarrow{EF}$ is a bisector of $\overline{CD}$.

Segments *BD* and *BC* are radii of the same circle, Circle *B*, so they are congruent.

5 Construct a line perpendicular to the given line through point *P*.

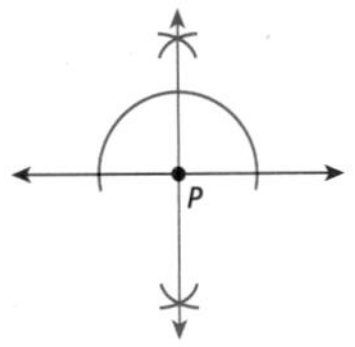

TAKE NOTE...
A **perpendicular bisector** is a line, line segment, or ray that bisects a line segment and is also perpendicular to the line segment.

NOTES

TOPIC 1

DIFFERENTIATION STRATEGY

See Page 28A to support students who struggle with the worked example.

Questions to Support Discourse

		TYPE
Worked Example	• Explain how to construct a perpendicular line in your own words. • Why do you have to open your compass larger than the radius? • How can you label the final image in the worked example so that someone else knows that line *EF* is perpendicular to line *CD*?	Probing
	• How do you know that point *B* is the midpoint of $\overline{CD}$?	Seeing structure
4	• Why does the term *perpendicular bisector* identify the line you created?	Gathering
5	• Why are a compass and straightedge construction tools, not drawing tools?	Gathering

NOTES

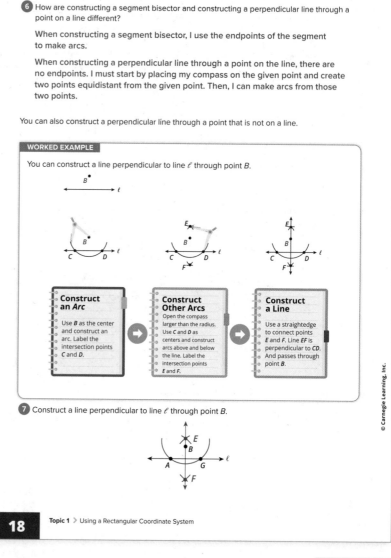

ACTIVITY 1 Continued

6 How are constructing a segment bisector and constructing a perpendicular line through a point on a line different?

When constructing a segment bisector, I use the endpoints of the segment to make arcs.

When constructing a perpendicular line through a point on the line, there are no endpoints. I must start by placing my compass on the given point and create two points equidistant from the given point. Then, I can make arcs from those two points.

You can also construct a perpendicular line through a point that is not on a line.

WORKED EXAMPLE

You can construct a line perpendicular to line ℓ through point *B*.

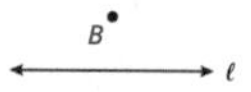

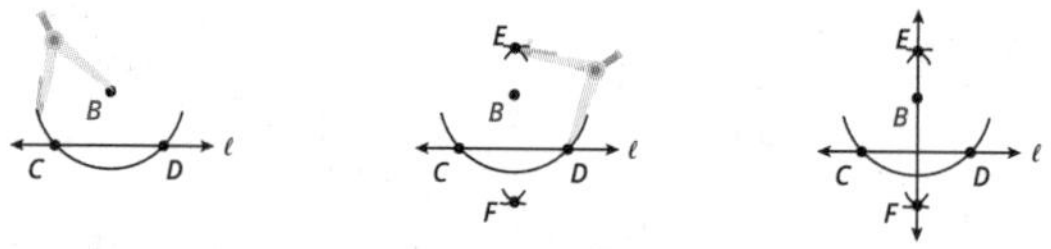

Construct an *Arc*

Use *B* as the center and construct an arc. Label the intersection points *C* and *D*.

Construct Other Arcs

Open the compass larger than the radius. Use *C* and *D* as centers and construct arcs above and below the line. Label the intersection points *E* and *F*.

Construct a Line

Use a straightedge to connect points *E* and *F*. Line *EF* is perpendicular to *CD*. And passes through point *B*.

7 Construct a line perpendicular to line ℓ through point *B*.

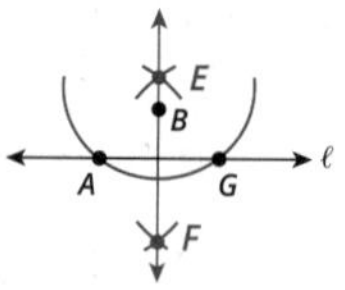

18 Topic 1 > Using a Rectangular Coordinate System

Questions to Support Discourse

		TYPE
Worked Example	• How is this problem different from the previous one? • How does the construction strategy compare to the previous one?	Gathering
	• Does it appear that the perpendicular line bisects $\overline{CD}$? How can you check?	Probing
	• How do you know that the distance from *B* to *C* is equal to the distance from *B* to *D*?	Seeing structure
7	• What effect does your original compass setting have on your construction?	Probing

ACTIVITY 1 Continued

8. Aaron is constructing the perpendicular bisector of $\overline{RS}$. His work is shown.

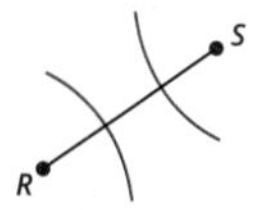

Aaron says that because the arcs do not intersect, this line segment does not have a midpoint. Kate disagrees and tells him he drew his arcs incorrectly and that he must redraw them to determine the midpoint. Who is correct? **Explain your reasoning.**

Kate is correct.
All line segments have midpoints.
If the arcs do not intersect, Aaron should set his compass so that it is open more than half the distance between the two endpoints and redraw the arcs.

9. Use construction tools to locate the perpendicular bisector of each given line segment. Label each midpoint as *M*.

ⓐ

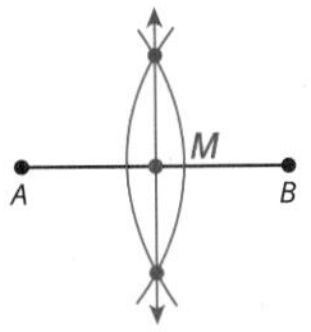

ⓑ

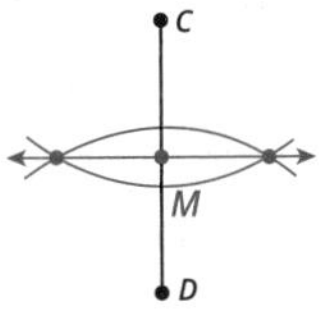

ⓒ

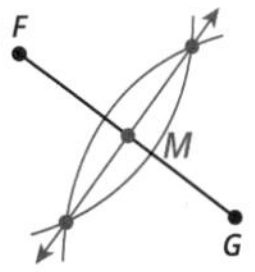

NOTES

TOPIC 1

Questions to Support Discourse

		TYPE
8	• What would cause the arcs not to intersect? • What does Aaron need to do differently?	Probing
9	• How did the different orientations affect how you constructed the perpendicular bisector?	Probing

NOTES

DIFFERENTIATION STRATEGY

See Page 28A to challenge advanced learners to extend 11.

> Consider the perpendicular bisector of line segment *AB*.

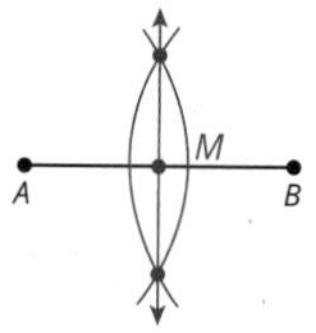

10 Choose a point on the perpendicular bisector in the image shown and label it *X*. Measure the distances from point *X* to each of the segment's endpoints. Choose another point on the perpendicular bisector and label it *Y*. Measure the distances from point *Y* to each of the segment's endpoints. **What do you notice?**

The distances from a point on the perpendicular bisector to each of the segment's endpoints are equal.

11 Make a conjecture about the distance from any point on a perpendicular bisector to the endpoints of the original segment.

Any point on a perpendicular bisector is equidistant to the endpoints of the original segment.

Questions to Support Discourse

		TYPE
10	• Which tool did you use to measure the distances? Why is using a compass a sufficient tool?	Gathering
11	• What is another way to state that conjecture? • What is the given information in your conjecture? What is the conclusion?	Gathering
	• Explain how you used informal reasoning to make your conjecture. • Why aren't your measurements enough to prove this conjecture?	Probing

ACTIVITY 2

SUMMARY **You can construct a square by duplicating segments and constructing perpendicular lines. You may recognize relationships with its diagonals.**

Constructing a Square

HABITS OF MIND
- Model with mathematics.
- Use appropriate tools strategically.

Along with constructing perpendicular lines, you also need to know how to duplicate line segments to construct a square.

When you **duplicate** a geometric figure, you use construction tools to create an exact copy. There are different ways to use construction tools to duplicate a line segment.

WORKED EXAMPLE

You can duplicate a line segment by constructing an exact copy of the original line segment.

Given:

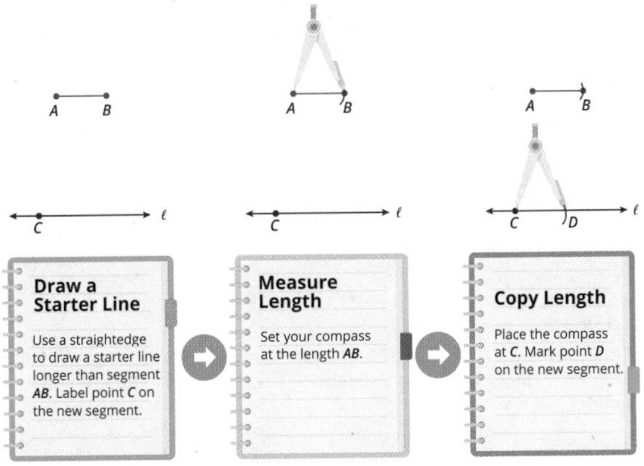

$\overline{CD}$ is a duplicate of $\overline{AB}$.

1. Construct a line segment that is twice the length of $\overline{AB}$.

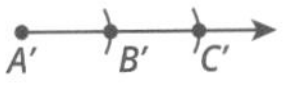

Chunking the Activity

- Read and discuss the definition and worked example
- Group students to complete 1 – 3
- Check-in and share
- Group students to complete 4 and 5
- Check-in and share
- Group students to complete 6
- Share and summarize

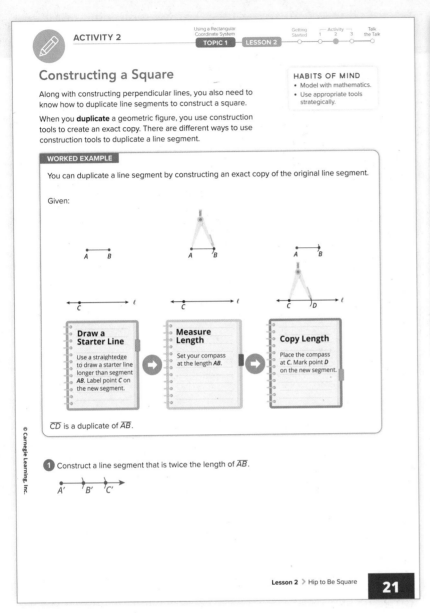

Questions to Support Discourse

		TYPE
1	• Describe the strategy you used to create the new line segment. • How can you use patty paper to verify your construction?	Probing

NOTES

ACTIVITY 2 Continued

2 Jan and Jackie each duplicated $\overline{AB}$ to create $\overline{A'B'}$.

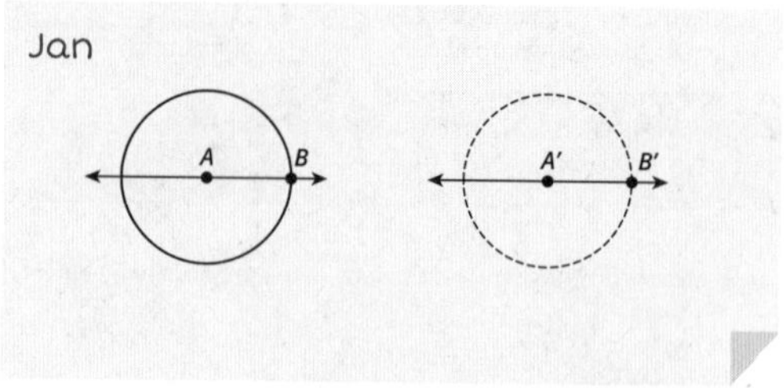

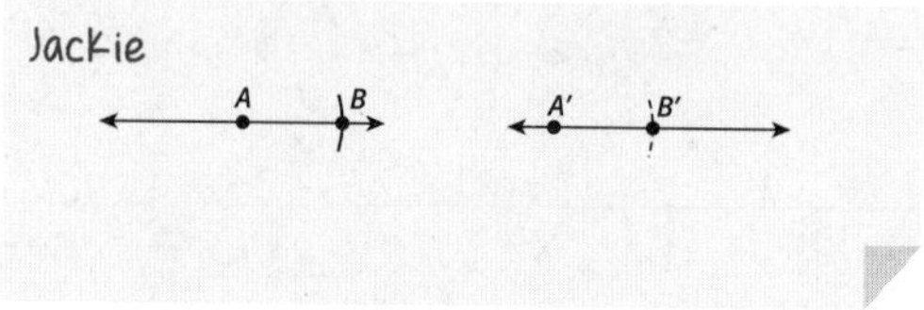

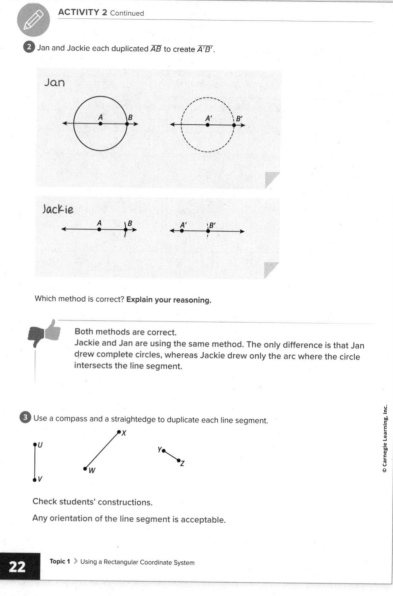

Which method is correct? **Explain your reasoning.**

Both methods are correct.
Jackie and Jan are using the same method. The only difference is that Jan drew complete circles, whereas Jackie drew only the arc where the circle intersects the line segment.

3 Use a compass and a straightedge to duplicate each line segment.

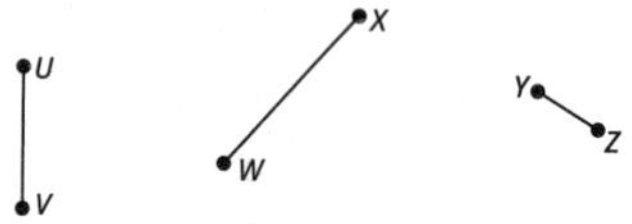

Check students' constructions.

Any orientation of the line segment is acceptable.

Questions to support discourse

		TYPE
2	• Whose method makes the most sense to you? Why?	Gathering
	• How can you modify Jan's and Jackie's methods to create a segment twice the length of $\overline{AB}$?	Probing
	• How does drawing the entire line segment help you to know that the line segments are the same length?	Seeing structure
3	• How did the different orientations affect how you constructed the duplicated line segment? • How can you use patty paper to verify your construction?	Probing

ACTIVITY 2 Continued

4 Use what you know about duplicating segments and constructing perpendicular lines to construct a Square *JKLM* with the same side length as $\overline{JK}$.

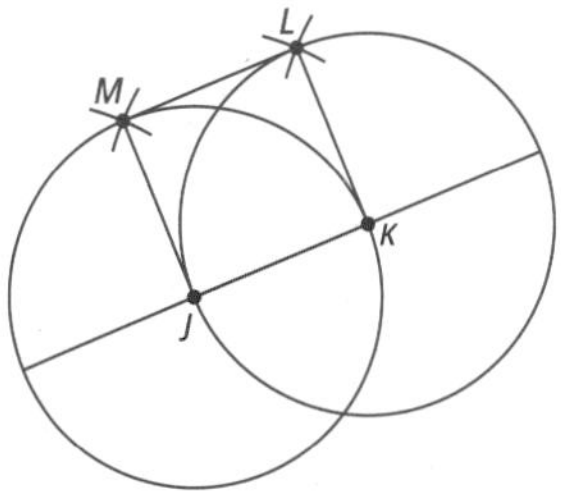

The figure should have four right angles and four congruent sides.

5 Use patty paper to verify that your figure is a square.

Students should check that all the angles are right angles and all the sides are congruent.

6 Draw the *diagonals* on your square and label the angles as shown. What do you notice about the segments and angles? **Use patty paper to justify any conjectures.**

TAKE NOTE…
A **diagonal** is a line segment joining two non-consecutive vertices of a polygon.

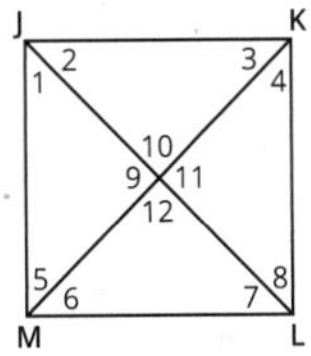

Check students' diagrams.

Sample answers.
The diagonals of a square are congruent.
The diagonals of a square bisect each other.
The diagonals of a square are perpendicular to each other.
The diagonals of a square bisect the angles at each vertex of the square.
The diagonals of a square form four congruent isosceles right triangles.

NOTES

TOPIC 1

DIFFERENTIATION STRATEGY

See Page 28B to support students who struggle with 4.

Questions to Support Discourse

		TYPE
4	• How did you construct the right angles for your square? • How did you get the first right angle you constructed to appear at point *J* or point *K* rather than at the midpoint of $\overline{JK}$? • How did you get all four side lengths to be the same?	Probing
5	• How did you use patty paper to verify that the angles are right angles? The sides are congruent?	Probing
	• What characteristics did you verify to show that the figure is a square?	Seeing structure
6	• How did you use patty paper to justify your conjecture? • What do you notice about the lengths of the diagonals? • When the diagonals intersect, do they split each other in half? What mathematical term could you use in your conjecture? • What type of angles are formed where the diagonals intersect? • What type of angles are formed where the diagonal divides each right angle of the square? • Could you say that each diagonal is a perpendicular bisector of the other? Explain what that means? How could you check? • What types of triangles do you notice?	Probing
	• Why are your responses conjectures rather than facts?	Seeing

ACTIVITY 3

SUMMARY You can use rigid motions to create a coordinate plane from a square and two-dimensional figures from line segments.

Chunking the Activity

- Read and discuss the introduction and Felipe's strategy
- Complete 1 as a class
- Group students to complete 2
- Share and summarize

LANGUAGE LINK

Remind students to refer to the Academic Glossary (page FM–20) to review the definition of **analyze** and related phrases. Suggest they ask themselves the following questions:

- Do I see any patterns?
- What happens if the shape, representation, or numbers change?

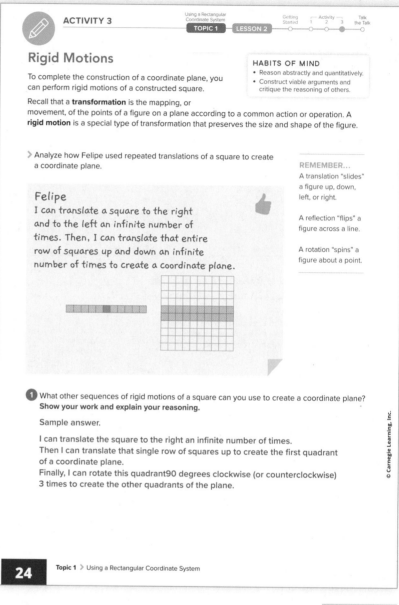

Rigid Motions

To complete the construction of a coordinate plane, you can perform rigid motions of a constructed square.

HABITS OF MIND
- Reason abstractly and quantitatively.
- Construct viable arguments and critique the reasoning of others.

Recall that a **transformation** is the mapping, or movement, of the points of a figure on a plane according to a common action or operation. A **rigid motion** is a special type of transformation that preserves the size and shape of the figure.

> Analyze how Felipe used repeated translations of a square to create a coordinate plane.

REMEMBER...
A translation "slides" a figure up, down, left, or right.

A reflection "flips" a figure across a line.

A rotation "spins" a figure about a point.

Felipe
I can translate a square to the right and to the left an infinite number of times. Then, I can translate that entire row of squares up and down an infinite number of times to create a coordinate plane.

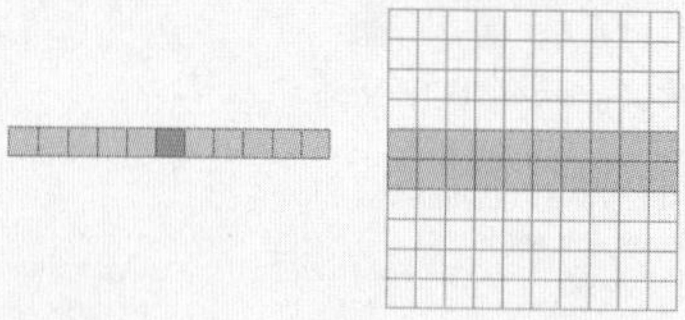

1 What other sequences of rigid motions of a square can you use to create a coordinate plane? **Show your work and explain your reasoning.**

Sample answer.

I can translate the square to the right an infinite number of times.
Then I can translate that single row of squares up to create the first quadrant of a coordinate plane.
Finally, I can rotate this quadrant90 degrees clockwise (or counterclockwise) 3 times to create the other quadrants of the plane.

Questions to Support Discourse

		TYPE
1	• What line of reflection can you use to create a coordinate plane? • Describe how Felipe created different geometric figures using repeated transformations. • What degrees of rotation would you need to create a coordinate plane?	Probing

ACTIVITY 3 Continued

2 The figures shown were each constructed using rigid motions that started with line segments constructed in one or more squares. Identify the coordinates of a figure that you can use to create the resulting shape. Then describe a sequence of transformations of that figure to produce the resulting shape.

ⓐ

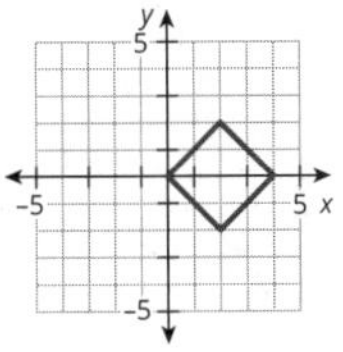

Sample answer.
- Start with the line segment with endpoints at the origin and (2, 2).
- Rotate the line segment 90° counter clockwise about the point at (2, 2).
- Then reflect the two line segments together across the x-axis.

ⓑ

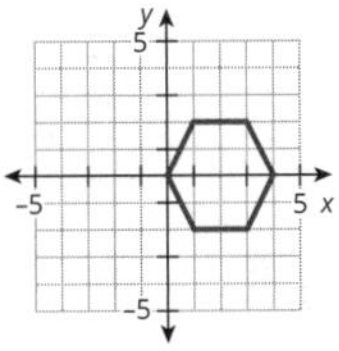

Sample answer.
- Start with the figure formed by two line segments: one with endpoints at the origin and (1, 2) and one with endpoints at (1, 2) and (2, 2).
- Reflect this figure across the vertical line $x = 2$ to create an isosceles trapezoid shape in the first quadrant.
- Then reflect the entire shape across the x-axis.

ⓒ

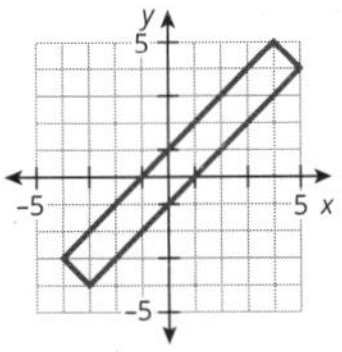

Sample answer.
- Start with the figure formed by two line segments: one with endpoints at (−4, −3) and (4, 5) and one with endpoints at (4, 5) and (5, 4).
- Rotate this figure 180° about the point at $\left(\frac{1}{2}, \frac{1}{2}\right)$.

ⓓ

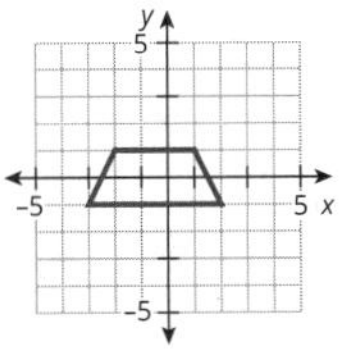

Sample answer.
- Start with the figure formed by three line segments: one with endpoints at (2, −1) and (1, 1), one with endpoints at (1, 1) and (−0.5, 1), and one with endpoints at (2, −1) and (−0.5, −1).
- Reflect this figure across the vertical line$x = −0.5$.

NOTES

NOTE: When responding to question 2, instruct students to use reflections instead of rotations if they cannot identify the angle of rotation.

COMMON MISCONCEPTION

See Page 28B for a misconception related to 2.

DIFFERENTIATION STRATEGY

See Page 28B to support students who struggle with 2.

Questions to Support Discourse

		TYPE
2	• What are the rigid motions transformations?	Gathering
	• What is another way to use transformations of a figure to produce the resulting shape? • Were you able to create the figure using a single rigid motion, or did you use a combination of rigid motions? Explain your strategy. • Explain a strategy that includes a rotation. What degree rotation did you use? • Explain a strategy that includes a reflection. What line of reflection did you use?	Probing

TALK THE TALK

SUMMARY **You can relate a sequence of translations of a line segment to the slope of a line.**

Chunking the Activity

- **Read and discuss the introduction**
- **Group students to complete the activity**
- **Share and summarize**

Student Look-Fors

Utilizing relationship skills by communicating clearly and listening well.

TALK THE TALK

Using a Rectangular Coordinate System TOPIC 1 LESSON 2 Getting Started Activity 1 2 3 Talk the Talk

Walking on a Thin Line

> Consider the line shown on the coordinate plane.

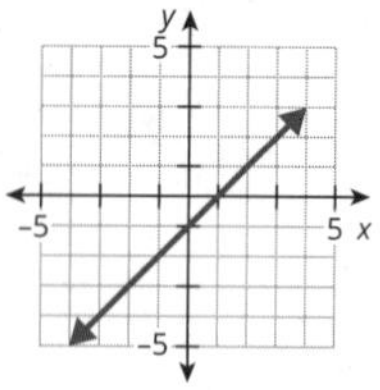

1 Suppose the line was constructed using rigid motions that started with any line segment constructed in one square. Describe one possible sequence of translations that can produce the line.

Sample answer.

Translate the line segment with endpoints at (0, −1) and (1, 0) up 1 and right 1 repeatedly and translate it down 1 and left 1 repeatedly.

REMEMBER...
The equation for a line can be written in the form $y = mx + b$, where m represents the slope of the line, and b represents the y-intercept.

2 How is the sequence of translations related to the slope of the line?

The slope of the line is 1. The slope is the ratio of translations up and to the right $\frac{+1}{+1} = 1$ or translations down and to the left $\frac{-1}{-1} = 1$.

3 What is the equation for the line?

$y = x - 1$

26 Topic 1 > Using a Rectangular Coordinate System

Questions to Support Discourse

	Questions	TYPE
1	• How did you create the portion of the line above your original segment? Why did you need two different translations? • Why did you need to do translations above and below your original segment?	Probing
2	• What is the slope of a line?	Gathering
	• How do you determine the slope of the line graphed on the coordinate plane?	Probing
	• How do your translations relate to the definition of slope?	Seeing Structure
3	• Explain how to write the equation of a line given its graph.	Probing

ASSIGNMENT

LESSON 2 ASSIGNMENT

> Use a separate piece of paper for your Journal entry.

JOURNAL

Describe the similarities and differences of a segment bisector and a perpendicular bisector.

REMEMBER

- A perpendicular bisector is a line, line segment, or ray that bisects a line segment and is also perpendicular to the line segment.
- A translation "slides" a figure up, down, left, or right. A reflection "flips" a figure across a line. A rotation "spins" a figure about a point.

PRACTICE

1. Locate the midpoint of the line segment using construction tools and label it point *M*. Then explain how you know that point *M* is the midpoint of $\overline{EF}$.

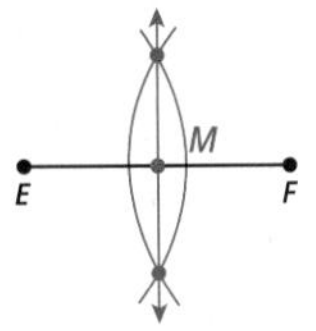

EM = *FM*

2. Construct a line perpendicular to each given line and through the given point.

(a)

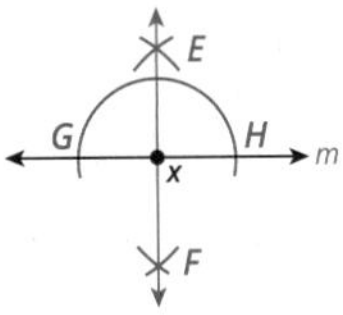

(b)

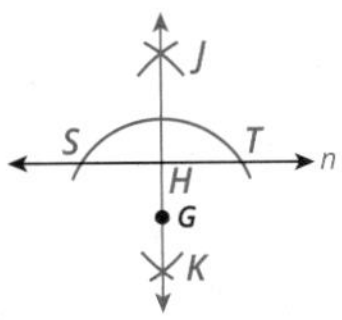

Go to LiveHint.com for help on the PRACTICE questions.

Encourage students to use LiveHint.com for help with the PRACTICE questions of this assignment.

Chunking the Assignment

SESSION 1

- Journal
- Practice 1 and 2

SESSION 2

- Practice 3
- Stretch (advanced learners)
- Mixed Practice (page 89) 2

JOURNAL

Sample answer.

Similarities:

They both divide the line segment into two line segments of equal length.

Differences:

A segment bisector does not have to form a right angle with the line segment it crosses, while a perpendicular bisector must form a right angle with the line segment it crosses.

NOTES

STRETCH

It is possible to trisect a segment with a compass and straightedge. Sample construction.

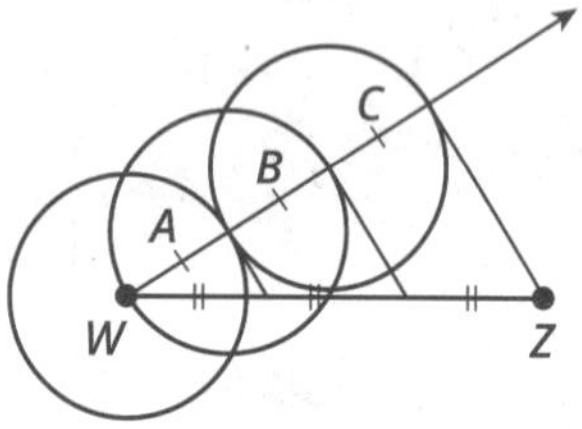

3 Construct a square with the same side length as $\overline{AB}$.

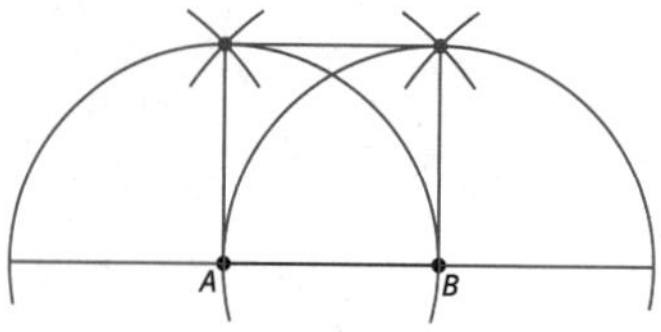

Check students' constructions.

STRETCH Optional

> Research whether it is possible to trisect a segment using only construction tools. If possible, use construction tools to trisect $\overline{WZ}$ and explain your steps. If not possible, explain why.

Hip to Be Square

This resource details additional facilitation notes to fully assist you as you plan each lesson to support all students, students who struggle, and advanced learners. It provides differentiation strategies, common student misconceptions, and suggestions to extend certain activities.

ACTIVITY 1

Session 1 of 2

Constructing a Perpendicular Line

Students construct perpendicular lines and perpendicular bisectors. They conjecture that any point on a perpendicular bisector is equidistant to the original segment's endpoints.

CHUNK	AUDIENCE	ADDITIONAL SUPPORTS
As students work on 2	All Students	**DIFFERENTIATION STRATEGY** As students read the strategy, recommend they think about the connections, annotate what was done correctly, and correct the error in the strategy. Support students by suggesting they ask themselves: • Where is the error? • Why is it an error? • How can I correct it?
As you read and discuss the worked example	Students who Struggle	**DIFFERENTIATION STRATEGY** • Model the worked example using a straightedge and compass as a student reads the directions. • Have students draw a complete circle instead of an arc or semi-circle.
To extend 11	Advanced Learners	**DIFFERENTIATION STRATEGY** Challenge students to use formal reasoning to prove their conjecture. Provide these hints: • When you draw the two distances you measured in Question 10, what type of triangle do you form on each side of the perpendicular bisector? • How might you use the two right triangles formed to show distances are equal?

ACTIVITY 2

Session 2 of 2

Constructing a Square

Students construct a square by duplicating segments and constructing perpendicular lines. They conjecture about a square's diagonals.

CHUNK	AUDIENCE	ADDITIONAL SUPPORTS
As students begin 4	Students who Struggle	**DIFFERENTIATION STRATEGY** Suggest students extend $\overline{JK}$ on both sides to construct a perpendicular bisector at Point *J* and Point *K*.

ACTIVITY 3

Session 2 of 2

Rigid Motions

Students consider translating a square to create a coordinate plane. They describe the rigid motions to form shapes on a coordinate plane.

CHUNK	AUDIENCE	ADDITIONAL SUPPORTS
As students work on 2	All Students	**COMMON MISCONCEPTION** Students may think they must transform an entire side of a shape. It may help transform a part of a side, especially to complete reflections in parts (b) and (d).
As students work on 2	Students who Struggle	**DIFFERENTIATION STRATEGY** Suggest students use patty paper to transform line segments to solve or verify their response.

Practice the learning

MATHbook + Skills Practice

The table shows the targeted practice of the skills and mathematical concepts for the *Using a Rectangular Coordinate System* Topic. The highlighted Problem Set aligns with **Hip to Be Square**.

PROBLEM SET	
1	Identifying Properties of Geometric Figures
2	**Constructing Perpendicular Lines**
3	Duplicating Line Segments
4	Writing Equations of Parallel and Perpendicular Lines
5	Classifying Shapes on the Coordinate Plane
6	Determining Perimeter and Area of Rectangles and Triangles on the Coordinate Plane
7	Determining Perimeter and Area of Other Polygons on the Coordinate Plane

ANYTIME AFTER ACTIVITY 3

Facilitate students as they work individually on **Problem Set 2**.

NOTES

ENGAGE + **DEVELOP** + **TEACH**

at the **Module** level — at the **Topic** level — Read the facilitation notes and plan learning experiences.

Where are we?

TOPIC 1 Using a Rectangular Coordinate System	LESSON 1 The Squariest Square	LESSON 2 Hip to Be Square	**LESSON 3 Ts and Train Tracks**	LESSON 4 Where Has Polly Gone?	LESSON 5 In and Out and All About
Pacing	1 Session	2 Sessions	**2 Sessions**	3 Sessions	3 Sessions

OVERVIEW: LESSON 3

Ts and Train Tracks

Parallel and Perpendicular Lines

ENGAGE

- Students make conjectures about the slopes of parallel and perpendicular lines.

DEVELOP

- Students demonstrate that the slopes of perpendicular lines are negative reciprocals.
- They describe the slope and write equations for horizontal and vertical lines.
- They write equations of perpendicular lines.

DEMONSTRATE

- Students use reasoning to justify that parallel lines have the same slope.

HIGH SCHOOL GEOMETRY

Congruence

Make geometric constructions.

12. Make formal geometric constructions with a variety of tools and methods (compass and straightedge, string, reflective devices, paper folding, dynamic geometric software, etc.).

Expressing Geometric Properties with Equations

Use coordinates to prove simple geometric theorems algebraically.

5. Prove the slope criteria for parallel and perpendicular lines and use them to solve geometric problems (e.g., find the equation of a line parallel or perpendicular to a given line that passes through a given point).

LESSON STRUCTURE AND PACING GUIDE 2 SESSIONS

⊛ This activity highlights a key term or concept that is essential to the learning goals of the lesson.

Session 1

INSTRUCTIONAL SEQUENCE

ENGAGE	DEVELOP	DEVELOP
Connect to prior knowledge	Worked example Peer analysis	Investigation Worked example

GETTING STARTED
All Aboard the Clue Train!

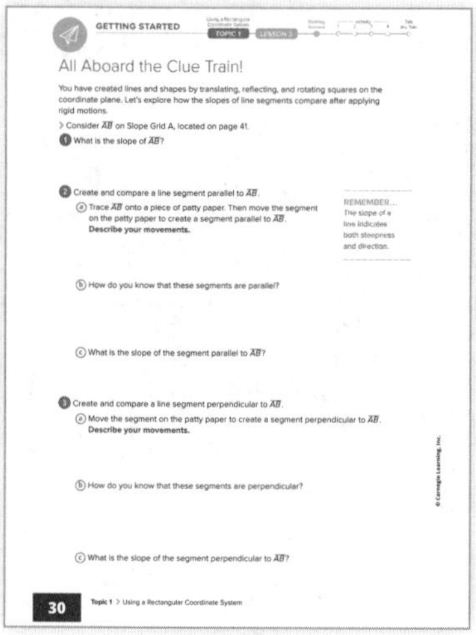
GETTING STARTED

All Aboard the Clue Train!

You have created lines and shapes by translating, reflecting, and rotating squares on the coordinate plane. Let's explore how the slopes of line segments compare after applying rigid motions.

> Consider $\overline{AB}$ on Slope Grid A, located on page 41.

1. What is the slope of $\overline{AB}$?

2. Create and compare a line segment parallel to $\overline{AB}$.
   (a) Trace $\overline{AB}$ onto a piece of patty paper. Then move the segment on the patty paper to create a segment parallel to $\overline{AB}$. **Describe your movements.**
   (b) How do you know that these segments are parallel?
   (c) What is the slope of the segment parallel to $\overline{AB}$?

REMEMBER... The slope of a line indicates both steepness and direction.

3. Create and compare a line segment perpendicular to $\overline{AB}$.
   (a) Move the segment on the patty paper to create a segment perpendicular to $\overline{AB}$. **Describe your movements.**
   (b) How do you know that these segments are perpendicular?
   (c) What is the slope of the segment perpendicular to $\overline{AB}$?

© Carnegie Learning, Inc.

30 Topic 1 > Using a Rectangular Coordinate System

Students graph parallel and perpendicular lines on a coordinate plane using rigid motions.

- They make conjectures about the slopes of parallel and perpendicular lines.

ACTIVITY 1 ⊛
Slopes of Parallel Lines

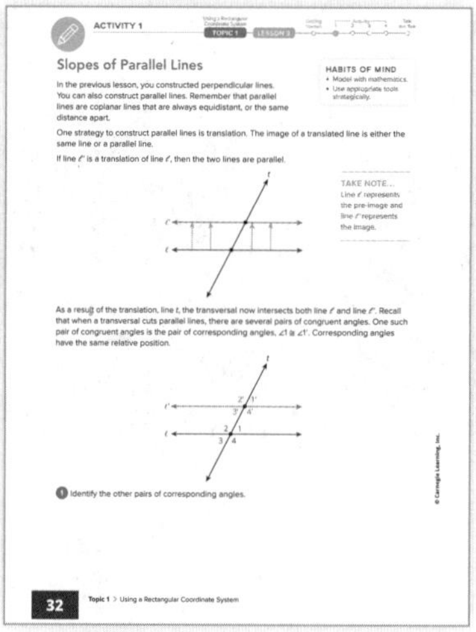
ACTIVITY 1

Slopes of Parallel Lines

HABITS OF MIND
- Model with mathematics.
- Use appropriate tools strategically.

In the previous lesson, you constructed perpendicular lines. You can also construct parallel lines. Remember that parallel lines are coplanar lines that are always equidistant, or the same distance apart.

One strategy to construct parallel lines is translation. The image of a translated line is either the same line or a parallel line.

If line ℓ' is a translation of line ℓ, then the two lines are parallel.

TAKE NOTE... Line ℓ represents the pre-image and line ℓ' represents the image.

As a result of the translation, line t, the transversal now intersects both line ℓ and line ℓ'. Recall that when a transversal cuts parallel lines, there are several pairs of congruent angles. One such pair of congruent angles is the pair of corresponding angles, $\angle 1 \cong \angle 1'$. Corresponding angles have the same relative position.

1. Identify the other pairs of corresponding angles.

© Carnegie Learning, Inc.

32 Topic 1 > Using a Rectangular Coordinate System

Students translate lines on the coordinate plane to create parallel lines.

- They compare the slopes and *y*-intercepts of parallel lines.

ACTIVITY 2 ⊛
Slopes of Perpendicular Lines

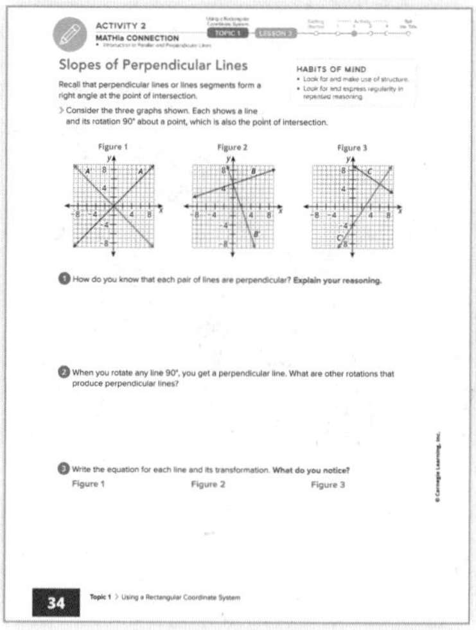
ACTIVITY 2

MATHia CONNECTION

Slopes of Perpendicular Lines

HABITS OF MIND
- Look for and make use of structure.
- Look for and express regularity in repeated reasoning.

Recall that perpendicular lines or lines segments form a right angle at the point of intersection.

> Consider the three graphs shown. Each shows a line and its rotation 90° about a point, which is also the point of intersection.

Figure 1 Figure 2 Figure 3

1. How do you know that each pair of lines are perpendicular? **Explain your reasoning.**

2. When you rotate any line 90°, you get a perpendicular line. What are other rotations that produce perpendicular lines?

3. Write the equation for each line and its transformation. **What do you notice?**
   Figure 1 Figure 2 Figure 3

© Carnegie Learning, Inc.

34 Topic 1 > Using a Rectangular Coordinate System

Students write the equations of perpendicular lines graphed on a coordinate plane.

- They demonstrate that the slopes of perpendicular lines are negative reciprocals.

Log in to MyCL for **lesson support** including:

Slides

Videos

www.carnegielearning.com/login

Session 2

INSTRUCTIONAL SEQUENCE

DEVELOP	DEVELOP	DEMONSTRATE
Mathematical problem solving	Mathematical problem solving	Generalization

TOPIC 1

ACTIVITY 3
Horizontal and Vertical Lines

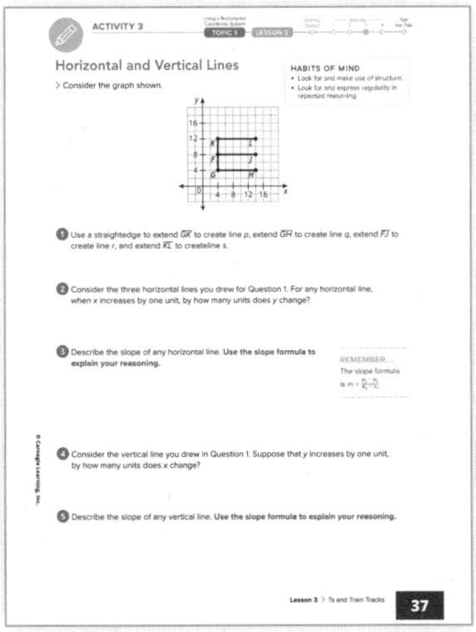
Horizontal and Vertical Lines

Students describe the slopes of horizontal and vertical lines.

- They write equations for horizontal and vertical lines.

ACTIVITY 4
Writing Equations of Perpendicular Lines

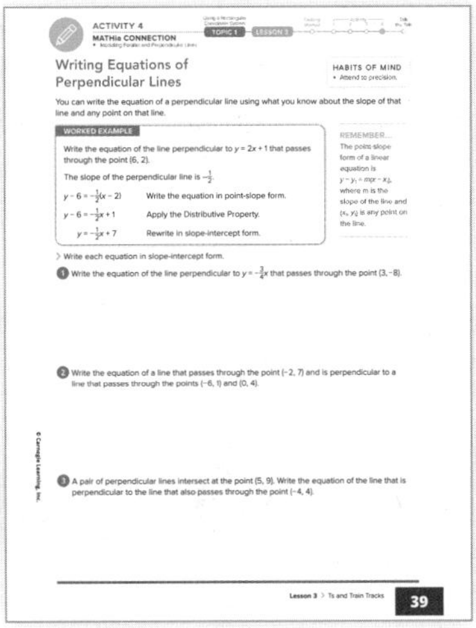
Writing Equations of Perpendicular Lines

Students write the equation of a line perpendicular to a given line that passes through a given point.

- They use the slope formula to write the equation.

TALK THE TALK
Parallels the Lesson

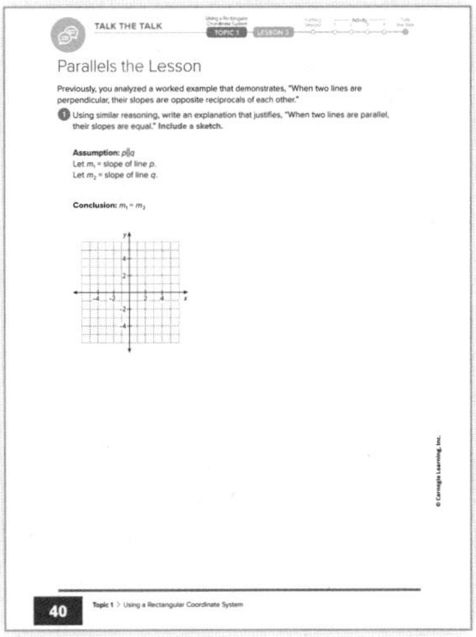
Parallels the Lesson

Students use reasoning to justify that parallel lines have the same slope.

- They include a sketch to illustrate their reasoning.

Log in to MyCL for:

- Editable templates
- Additional planning support

Now that you have read the Module, Topic, and Lesson Overviews, you are ready to plan.

Do the math

> Tear out the lesson planning template (page 29E) and jot down thoughts as you work through this lesson and read the Facilitation Notes.

Connect the learning

MATHbook + MATHia

The table shows a portion of the self-paced MATHia sequence for the *Using a Rectangular Coordinate System* Topic.

Median student completion time for the entire topic: ~200–215 minutes

> As you implement this lesson, consider different connections for students who are on pace and those that have not yet completed the workspaces aligned to this lesson.

STUDENTS WHO ARE NOT HERE YET
Students will practice writing the equations of lines parallel or perpendicular to given lines.

TYPE	WORKSPACE NAME
	Naming Lines, Rays, Segments, and Angles
	Working with Measures of Segments and Angles
	Introduction to Parallel and Perpendicular Lines
	Modeling Parallel and Perpendicular Lines
	Deriving the Distance Formula

STUDENTS WHO ARE ON PACE
After you complete Activity 4, ask these students to share how they determined the slope of each line that they wrote.

Ts and Train Tracks

Parallel and Lines

Session 1

GETTING STARTED All Aboard the Clue Train!

Pacing (minutes)	
My Time	Class Time

ACTIVITY 1 Slopes of Parallel Lines ✪

Pacing (minutes)	
My Time	Class Time

ACTIVITY 2 Slopes of Perpendicular Lines ✪

Pacing (minutes)	
My Time	Class Time

Session 2

ACTIVITY 3 Horizontal and Vertical Lines ✪

Pacing (minutes)	
My Time	Class Time

ACTIVITY 4 Writing Equations of Perpendicular Lines ✪

Pacing (minutes)	
My Time	Class Time

TALK THE TALK Parallels the Lesson ✪

Pacing (minutes)	
My Time	Class Time

✪ This activity highlights a key term or concept that is essential to the learning goals of the lesson.

Log in to MyCL for:

- Editable templates
- Additional planning support

Reflect on your lesson

> Consider the effectiveness of your lesson on student learning.

What went well?	What did not go as planned?

> Anticipate how you would change the lesson next time you teach it.

How will you capitalize on the things that went well?	How will you improve things that did not go as planned?

MATERIALS

- Compasses
- Patty paper
- Straightedges

TOPIC 1 Using a Rectangular Coordinate System | TOPIC 2 Rigid Motions on a Plane | TOPIC 3 Congruence Through Transformations

1 | The Squariest Square
2 | Hip to Be Square
3 | Ts and Train Tracks
4 | Where Has Polly Gone?
5 | In and Out and All About

LESSON 3

Ts and Train Tracks

Parallel and Perpendicular Lines

Learning Goals

- Identify and write the equations of lines perpendicular to given lines.
- Identify and write the equations of parallel lines, including horizontal and vertical lines.

REVIEW (1–2 minutes)

> Determine the reciprocal of each value.

1. 3

   $\frac{1}{3}$

2. -10

   $-\frac{1}{10}$

3. $\frac{1}{5}$

   5

4. $-c$

   $-\frac{1}{c}, c \neq 0$

You have constructed line segments, perpendicular lines, squares, and used rigid motions to construct a coordinate plane.

How can you use the coordinate plane to justify parallel and perpendicular line relationships?

Setting the Stage

- **Assign Review (optional, 1 – 2 minutes)**
- **Communicate the learning goals and key terms to look out for**
- **Tap into your students' prior learning by reading the narrative statement**
- **Provide a sense of direction by reading the question**

TOPIC 1

IN THIS REVIEW
Students write reciprocals of expressions. They will first use this skill the **GETTING STARTED All Aboard the Clue Train!**

The slopes of perpendicular lines are negative reciprocals. Any vertical line is perpendicular to any horizontal line.

Essential Ideas

- The translation of a line creates an identical line or a line parallel to the original line.
- Parallel lines have equal slopes.
- The 90° rotation of a line creates a line perpendicular to the original line.
- Perpendicular lines have slopes that are negative reciprocals of each other.
- All vertical lines have a slope of zero. All horizontal lines have an undefined slope. Vertical lines are perpendicular to horizontal lines.

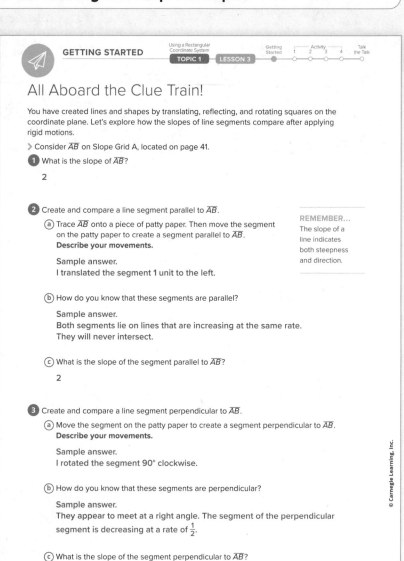

GETTING STARTED

SUMMARY **Translations create parallel lines with the same slope, while rotations of 90° create perpendicular lines with negative reciprocal slopes.**

Chunking the Activity

- **Read and discuss the introduction**
- **Group students to complete 1 - 3**
- **Check-in and share**
- **Group students to complete 4 - 7**
- **Share and summarize**

NOTE: Students have translated lines and written their equations in a previous course.

LANGUAGE LINK

Remind students to refer to the Academic Glossary (page FM–20) to review the definition of **describe** and related phrases. Suggest they ask themselves these questions:

- How should I organize my thoughts?
- Did I consider the context of the situation?

All Aboard the Clue Train!

You have created lines and shapes by translating, reflecting, and rotating squares on the coordinate plane. Let's explore how the slopes of line segments compare after applying rigid motions.

> Consider $\overline{AB}$ on Slope Grid A, located on page 41.

1. What is the slope of $\overline{AB}$?

   2

2. Create and compare a line segment parallel to $\overline{AB}$.

   (a) Trace $\overline{AB}$ onto a piece of patty paper. Then move the segment on the patty paper to create a segment parallel to $\overline{AB}$. **Describe your movements.**

   Sample answer.
   I translated the segment 1 unit to the left.

   REMEMBER...
   The slope of a line indicates both steepness and direction.

   (b) How do you know that these segments are parallel?

   Sample answer.
   Both segments lie on lines that are increasing at the same rate. They will never intersect.

   (c) What is the slope of the segment parallel to $\overline{AB}$?

   2

3. Create and compare a line segment perpendicular to $\overline{AB}$.

   (a) Move the segment on the patty paper to create a segment perpendicular to $\overline{AB}$. **Describe your movements.**

   Sample answer.
   I rotated the segment 90° clockwise.

   (b) How do you know that these segments are perpendicular?

   Sample answer.
   They appear to meet at a right angle. The segment of the perpendicular segment is decreasing at a rate of $\frac{1}{2}$.

   (c) What is the slope of the segment perpendicular to $\overline{AB}$?

   $-\frac{1}{2}$

Questions to Support Discourse

		TYPE
1	• Express the slope as a fraction.	Gathering
2	• What is another way to translate the line?	Probing
	• How is the slope for the translated segment related to the slope of the original segment?	Seeing structure
3	• If you use patty paper to verify the lines are perpendicular, explain how you created the perpendicular lines. • How did you determine the slope of the rotated segment?	Probing
	• How is the slope of the rotated segment related to the slope of the original segment?	Seeing structure

GETTING STARTED Continued

Now let's consider $\overline{CD}$ on Slope Grid B located on page 42.

4 What is the slope of $\overline{CD}$?

$\frac{1}{2}$

5 Use patty paper to create a segment parallel to $\overline{CD}$. Describe how you know that the segments are parallel. Then identify the slope of the segment parallel to $\overline{CD}$.

Sample answer.
Both segments lie on lines that are increasing at the same rate. They will never intersect.
The slope of the parallel line segment is $\frac{1}{2}$.

6 Use patty paper to create a segment perpendicular to $\overline{CD}$. Describe how you know that the segments are perpendicular. Then identify the slope of the segment perpendicular to $\overline{CD}$.

Sample answer.
I rotated $\overline{CD}$ 90° which means the segments meet at a right angle.
The segment of the perpendicular segment is decreasing at a rate of −2.
The slope of the perpendicular line segment is −2.

7 Use your investigations to write a conjecture about the relationship between the slopes of parallel and perpendicular lines.

Sample answer.
Parallel lines have the same slope.
Perpendicular lines have slopes that are opposite reciprocals of each other.

Questions to Support Discourse

		TYPE
5	• How are your responses to Questions 4 and 5 similar to your responses to Questions 1 and 2?	Probing
6	• Express the slope as a fraction.	Gathering
	• What relationship do you notice between the slope of a line and the slope of a line perpendicular to it?	Probing
7	• What is another way to state this conjecture?	Probing
	• According to your conjecture, what is the product of the slope of a line and the slope of a line perpendicular to it?	Seeing Structure

NOTES

SUMMARY **You can create parallel lines by a translation. You can construct them by creating congruent alternate interior or corresponding angles.**

Chunking the Activity

- **Read and discuss the introduction**
- **Complete 1 as a class**
- **Group students to complete 2**
- **Share and summarize**

DIFFERENTIATION STRATEGY

See Page 44A to support students who struggle with the introduction.

Slopes of Parallel Lines

HABITS OF MIND
- Model with mathematics.
- Use appropriate tools strategically.

In the previous lesson, you constructed perpendicular lines. You can also construct parallel lines. Remember that parallel lines are coplanar lines that are always equidistant, or the same distance apart.

One strategy to construct parallel lines is translation. The image of a translated line is either the same line or a parallel line.

If line ℓ' is a translation of line ℓ, then the two lines are parallel.

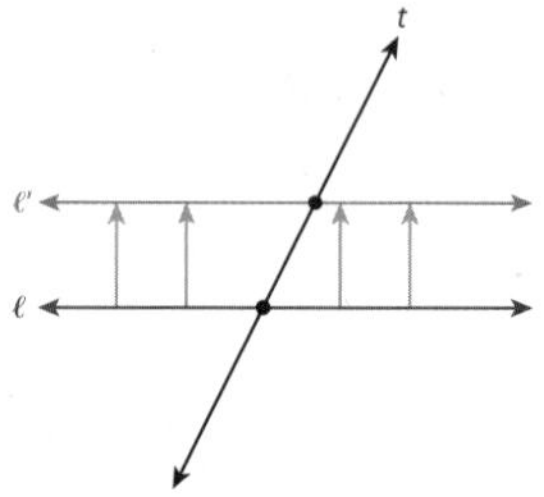

TAKE NOTE...
Line ℓ represents the pre-image and line ℓ' represents the image.

As a result of the translation, line t, the transversal now intersects both line ℓ and line ℓ'. Recall that when a transversal cuts parallel lines, there are several pairs of congruent angles. One such pair of congruent angles is the pair of corresponding angles, $\angle 1 \cong \angle 1'$. Corresponding angles have the same relative position.

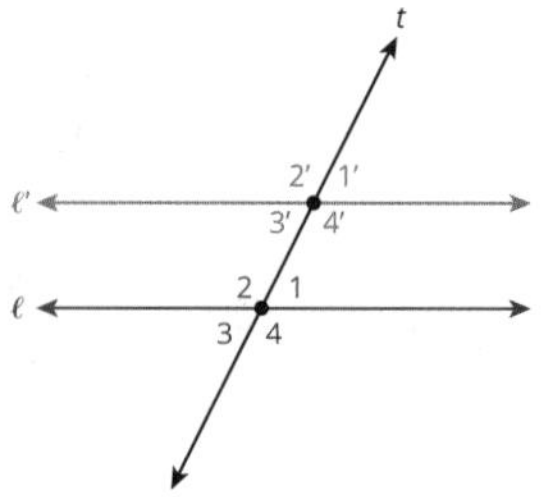

1 Identify the other pairs of corresponding angles.

$\angle 2 \cong \angle 2'$
$\angle 3 \cong \angle 3'$
$\angle 4 \cong \angle 4'$

Questions to Support Discourse

		TYPE
Intro	• What notation shows the lines are parallel? • Name another pair of corresponding angles.	Gathering
1	• What other angle relationships do you recognize? • What pairs of supplementary angles are created by parallel lines and a transversal?	Probing

ACTIVITY 1 Continued

Now, let's compare the characteristics of lines translated on a coordinate plane.

2 Consider the line $y = x$ on the coordinate plane shown.

(a) Translate the line $y = x$ up and then down to create three parallel lines.

Sample answers shown.

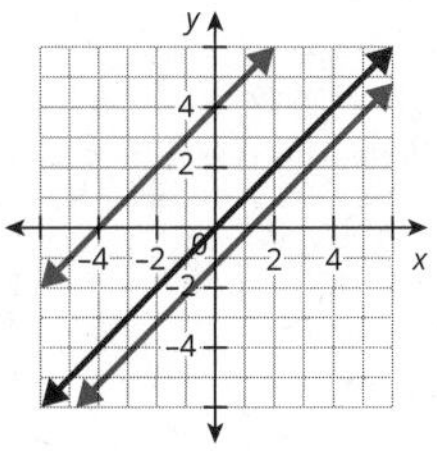

(b) Write the equations of your lines in slope-intercept form.

Sample answer.
$y = x - 1$
$y = x + 4$

REMEMBER...
The slope intercept form of a line is $y = mx + b$, where m represents the slope and b represents the y-intercept.

(c) Compare the slopes and y-intercepts of your lines. **What do you notice?**

The slopes are equal values.
The y-intercepts are different.

Questions to Support Discourse

		TYPE
2	• What is the slope-intercept form of a line? • How did you use your graph to write the equations for the lines?	Probing
	• How does a translation affect the equation for a line?	Seeing structure

NOTES

Student Look-Fors

Whether students use patty paper to translate the line.

ACTIVITY 2

SUMMARY **You can show that when two lines are perpendicular, their slopes are negative reciprocals using specific and general cases.**

Chunking the Activity

- **Read and discuss the introduction**
- **Group students to complete 1 – 3**
- **Check-in and share**
- **Read and discuss the worked example**
- **Group students to complete 4 and 5**
- **Share and summarize**

NOTE: This is the first pairing of these habits of mind.

- Look for and make use of structure
- Look for and express regularity in repeated reasoning

Have students refer to page FM–19 for questions to ask themselves.

Student Look-Fors

- The equation of each line written from the graph and a comparison of their equations.
- The equation of the first line written from the graph and the second line written by taking the negative reciprocal of the first line for its slope.

Slopes of Perpendicular Lines

HABITS OF MIND
- Look for and make use of structure.
- Look for and express regularity in repeated reasoning.

Recall that perpendicular lines or lines segments form a right angle at the point of intersection.

> Consider the three graphs shown. Each shows a line and its rotation 90° about a point, which is also the point of intersection.

Figure 1 | Figure 2 | Figure 3

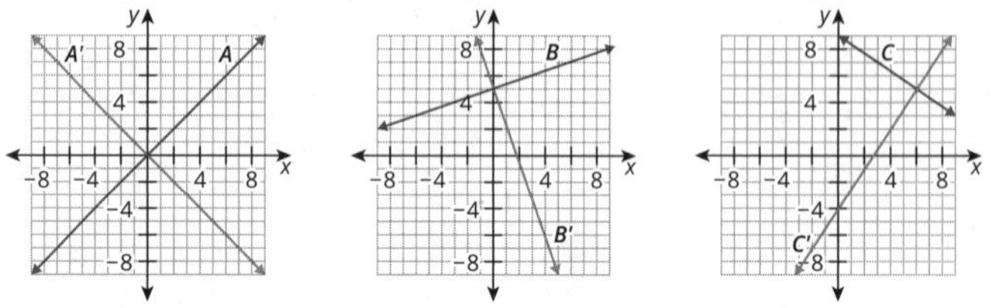

1. How do you know that each pair of lines are perpendicular? **Explain your reasoning.**

   The angle formed by the intersection of the lines measures 90°, which is a right angle. When two lines form right angles, they are perpendicular.

2. When you rotate any line 90°, you get a perpendicular line. What are other rotations that produce perpendicular lines?

   Sample answer.
   You can rotate a line counterclockwise 90° to produce perpendicular lines. You can also rotate a line 270° clockwise or counterclockwise.

3. Write the equation for each line and its transformation. **What do you notice?**

Figure 1	Figure 2	Figure 3
$A: y = x$	$B: y = \frac{1}{3}x + 5$	$C: y = -\frac{2}{3}x + 9$
$A': y = -x$	$B': y = -3x + 5$	$C': y = \frac{3}{2}x - 4$

   The slopes of each pair of perpendicular lines are reciprocals of each other with opposite signs.

Questions to Support Discourse

		TYPE
1	• Why does this specific rotation create perpendicular lines?	Probing
	• How could you use patty paper to verify that the lines are perpendicular?	Seeing structure
3	• What strategy did you use to write the equation of each line?	Probing
	• What is the relationship between the slopes? • Is there any relationship between perpendicular lines and their *y*-intercepts? • Why can't you use these equations to prove perpendicular lines have reciprocal slopes with opposite signs?	Seeing structure

ACTIVITY 2 Continued

It appears that when two lines are perpendicular, then their slopes are opposite reciprocals. Let's investigate.

> Read and analyze the worked example.

WORKED EXAMPLE

If two lines are perpendicular, then their slopes are opposite reciprocals.

Let's use the graph shown to analyze the validity of this statement.

Assumption: $p \perp q$

Let m_1 = slope of line p and let m_2 = slope of line q.

Point R lies on line p.

Conclusion: $m_1 = -\frac{1}{m_2}$

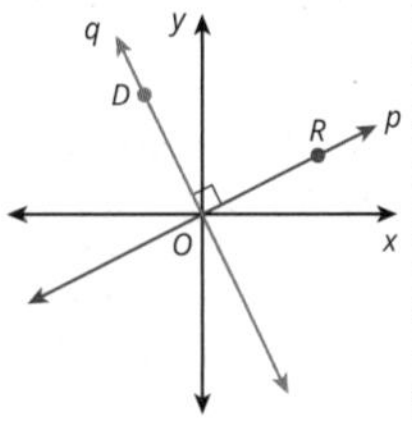

Perform a 90° counterclockwise rotation of point R using point O as the center of rotation. Since p and q are perpendicular, the image (point D) lies on line q due to a 90° rotation.

Since a 90° rotation maps the positive x-axis onto the positive y-axis and the positive y-axis onto the negative x-axis, then the coordinates of $R(a, b)$ are transformed into the coordinates of $D(-b, a)$. Graphically, you can follow the movement of lengths a and b under the rotation.

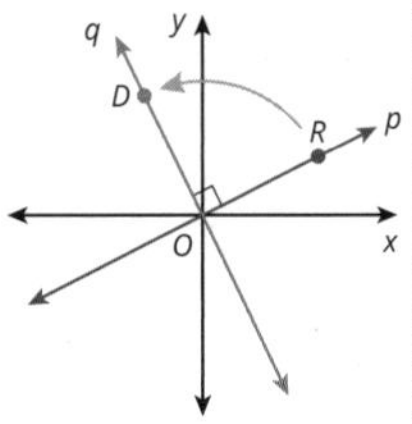

Using the graph, you can identify the slope of each line.

$p : m_1 = \frac{b}{a}$ $\qquad q : m_2 = \frac{a}{-b}$

Using these slopes, you can demonstrate that $m_1 = -\frac{1}{m_2}$.

$$\frac{b}{a} = -\frac{1}{\frac{a}{-b}}$$
$$= -1 \cdot \frac{-b}{a}$$
$$= \frac{b}{a}$$

The slope of line q is the opposite reciprocal of the slope of line p.

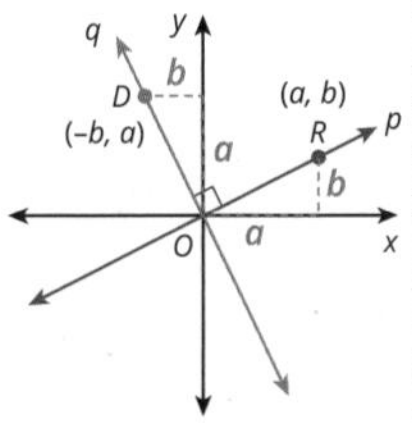

NOTES

DIFFERENTIATION STRATEGY

See Page 44A to assist all students with the worked example.

Questions to Support Discourse

		TYPE
Worked Example	• How does the Assumption statement relate to the If-Then statement? The Conclusion statement? • What is meant by *negative reciprocals*? • Explain what the conclusion $m_1 = -\frac{1}{m_2}$ means. • Does the negative sign mean the second line always has a negative slope? Explain your thinking.	Gathering
	• Explain why the coordinates of point D are $(-b, a)$. • Explain how the side lengths of each triangle were determined. • How can you use the labeled diagram to determine each slope? • Explain the steps to rewrite the complex fraction.	Probing
	• Why does the worked example demonstrate formal reasoning?	Seeing structure

NOTES

4 Verify that the product of the slopes of line p and line q is −1.

$\left(\frac{a}{b}\right)\left(\frac{b}{-a}\right) = -1$

THINK ABOUT...
The product of the slopes of perpendicular lines is −1.

5 Line j and line k are perpendicular. Given each slope of line j, determine the slope of line k.

ⓐ $m = \frac{2}{3}$

For line k, $m = -\frac{3}{2}$.

ⓑ $m = -\frac{4}{5}$

For line k, $m = \frac{5}{4}$.

ⓒ $m = -3$

For line k, $m = \frac{1}{3}$.

Questions to Support Discourse

		TYPE
4	• How did you show the slopes are negative reciprocals?	Probing
5	• How did you determine the negative reciprocal of −3?	Probing

SUMMARY **All vertical lines have a slope of zero. All horizontal lines have an undefined slope.**

Horizontal and Vertical Lines

HABITS OF MIND
- Look for and make use of structure.
- Look for and express regularity in repeated reasoning.

Consider the graph shown.

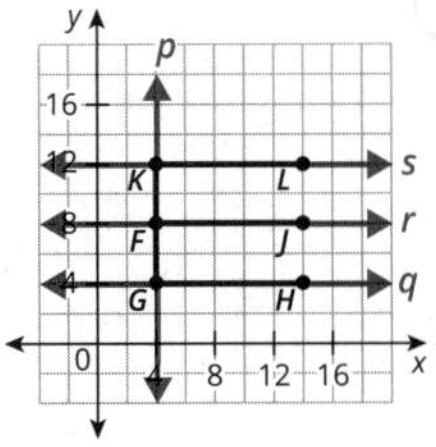

1. Use a straightedge to extend $\overline{GK}$ to create line *p*, extend $\overline{GH}$ to create line *q*, extend $\overline{FJ}$ to create line *r*, and extend $\overline{KL}$ to createline *s*.

   See graph.

2. Consider the three horizontal lines you drew for Question 1. For any horizontal line, when *x* increases by one unit, by how many units does *y* change?

   The value of *y* does not change.

3. Describe the slope of any horizontal line. **Use the slope formula to explain your reasoning.**

   The slope of any horizontal line is zero because as *x* increases, the value of *y* stays the same.
   If $y_2 - y_1 = 0$, then $m = \frac{y_2 - y_1}{x_2 - x_1} = \frac{0}{x_2 - x_1} = 0$.

REMEMBER...
The slope formula is $m = \frac{y_2 - y_1}{x_2 - x_1}$.

4. Consider the vertical line you drew in Question 1. Suppose that *y* increases by one unit, by how many units does *x* change?

   The value of *x* does not change.

5. Describe the slope of any vertical line. **Use the slope formula to explain your reasoning.**

   The slope of any vertical line is undefined because as y increases, the value of *x* stays the same.
   If $x_2 - x_1 = 0$, then $m = \frac{y_2 - y_1}{x_2 - x_1} = \frac{y_2 - y_1}{0}$, which is undefined.

Questions to Support Discourse

		TYPE
3	• Demonstrate the slope is zero using two points from a line. • Demonstrate the slope is zero using points (x_1, y_1) and (x_2, y_2).	Probing
	• If one line has a slope of zero, how do you know all the other lines have a slope of zero?	Seeing structure
5	• What is another way to demonstrate the slope is undefined?	Probing

Chunking the Activity

- Read and discuss the introduction
- Group students to complete 1 - 5
- Check-in and share
- Group students to complete 6 - 10
- Share and summarize

TOPIC 1

DIFFERENTIATION STRATEGY

See Page 44B to assist all students with the worked example.

NOTE: This is the first instance of this habit of mind.

- Attend to precision

Have students refer to page FM–19 for questions to ask themselves.

Student Look-Fors

- Reasoning from the graphs using the definition of slope or stating the flat lines have a slope of zero.
- Algebraic explanations using $m = \frac{y_2 - y_1}{x_2 - x_1}$ with coordinate pairs.

NOTES

DIFFERENTIATION STRATEGY

See Page 44B to assist all students with 8.

6 Determine whether each of the given statements is always true, sometimes true, or never true. **Explain your reasoning.**

(a) All vertical lines are parallel.

Always true

The slopes of all vertical lines are undefined, and therefore the same. So, all vertical lines are parallel.

(b) All horizontal lines are parallel.

Always true

The slopes of all horizontal lines are zero, and therefore the same. So, all horizontal lines are parallel.

7 Describe the relationship between any vertical line and any horizontal line.

Any vertical line and any horizontal line are perpendicular to each other.

8 Write an equation for a horizontal line and an equation for a vertical line that pass through the point (2, −1).

Horizontal line: $y = -1$

Vertical line: $x = 2$

THINK ABOUT...
How would a sketch help you see the relationships?

9 Write an equation for a line that is perpendicular to the line given by $x = 5$ and passes through the point (1, 0).

$y = 0$

10 Write an equation for a line that is perpendicular to the line given by $y = -2$ and passes through the point (5, 6).

$x = 5$

Questions to Support Discourse

		TYPE
8	• How do you know the form of the equation for a horizontal or vertical line? • How can you use a table of values to verify your reasoning? A graph?	Seeing structure
9 and 10	• What is the slope of the original line? What is the reciprocal of that slope? • How do you know which number from the ordered pair to use in your equation?	Probing
	• Does the relationship that perpendicular lines have negative reciprocal slopes apply to vertical and horizontal lines. Explain your thinking.	Seeing structure
	• Sketch a graph to verify your thinking.	Reflecting and justifying

SUMMARY To write the equation of a line perpendicular to a given line, you must use the negative reciprocal relationship between their slopes.

Writing Equations of Perpendicular Lines

HABITS OF MIND
• Attend to precision.

You can write the equation of a perpendicular line using what you know about the slope of that line and any point on that line.

WORKED EXAMPLE

Write the equation of the line perpendicular to $y = 2x + 1$ that passes through the point (6, 2).

The slope of the perpendicular line is $-\frac{1}{2}$.

$y - 6 = -\frac{1}{2}(x - 2)$	Write the equation in point-slope form.
$y - 6 = -\frac{1}{2}x + 1$	Apply the Distributive Property.
$y = -\frac{1}{2}x + 7$	Rewrite in slope-intercept form.

REMEMBER...
The point-slope form of a linear equation is $y - y_1 = m(x - x_1)$, where m is the slope of the line and (x_1, y_1) is any point on the line.

> Write each equation in slope-intercept form.

1. Write the equation of the line perpendicular to $y = -\frac{3}{4}x$ that passes through the point (3, −8).

$m = \frac{4}{3}$

$y + 8 = \frac{4}{3}(x - 3)$

$y + 8 = \frac{4}{3}x - 4$

$y = \frac{4}{3}x - 12$

2. Write the equation of a line that passes through the point (−2, 7) and is perpendicular to a line that passes through the points (−6, 1) and (0, 4).

The slope of the original line is $\frac{1}{2}$.

$m = \frac{1 - 4}{-6 - 0} = \frac{-3}{-6} = \frac{1}{2}$

So, the slope of the line perpendicular is −2.

$y - 7 = -2x - 4$

$y - 7 = -2(x + 2)$

$y = -2x + 3$

3. A pair of perpendicular lines intersect at the point (5, 9). Write the equation of the line that is perpendicular to the line that also passes through the point (−4, 4).

The slope of the original line is $\frac{5}{9}$.

$m = \frac{9 - 4}{5 + 4} = \frac{5}{9}$

So, the slope of the line perpendicular is $-\frac{9}{5}$.

$y - 9 = -\frac{9}{5}x + 9$

$y - 9 = -\frac{9}{5}(x - 5)$

$y = -\frac{9}{5}x + 18$

Chunking the Activity

- Read and discuss the directions
- Group students to complete the activity
- Share and summarize

DIFFERENTIATION STRATEGY

See Page 44C to support students who struggle with 2 and 3.

Questions to Support Discourse

		TYPE
1	• How did you determine the slope to use in your equation? • Did you write your equation in slope-intercept or point-slope form? Explain your process.	Probing
2	• Explain how you determined the slope of the original line? The perpendicular line?	Probing
	• How is this problem different than Question 1? • Why isn't it necessary to determine the equation of the original line to solve this problem?	Seeing structure
3	• How is knowing the point of intersection helpful?	Probing
	• How is the information given in Question 3 similar to the information given in Question 2?	Seeing structure

TALK THE TALK

SUMMARY **You can use translations to verify that when two lines are parallel, their slopes are equal.**

Chunking the Activity

- **Read and discuss the introduction**
- **Group students to complete the activity**
- **Share and summarize**

Student Look-Fors

Reference to the worked example in Activity 2 to complete this task.

Parallels the Lesson

Previously, you analyzed a worked example that demonstrates, "When two lines are perpendicular, their slopes are opposite reciprocals of each other."

1. Using similar reasoning, write an explanation that justifies, "When two lines are parallel, their slopes are equal." **Include a sketch.**

Assumption: $p \| q$
Let m_1 = slope of line p.
Let m_2 = slope of line q.

Conclusion: $m_1 = m_2$

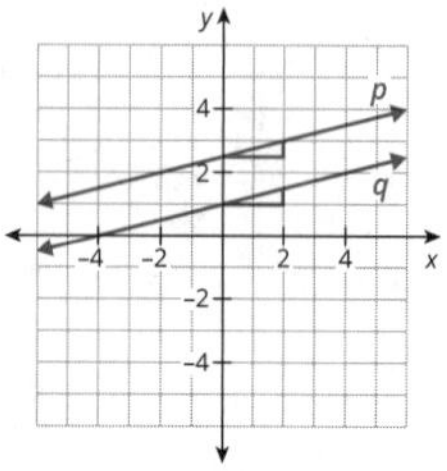

Sample answer.

A translation of line q produces line p. I can construct a right triangle on line q as shown to represent the slope of line q, m_2.
When you translate line q to produce line p, you also translate this triangle.
Since translations preserve size, shape, and orientation, line$p$ must have the same slope as line q, becausethe translated right triangle is congruent to the original.

Questions to Support Discourse

		TYPE
1	• Explain what the Assumption and Conclusion statements mean in your own words.	Gathering
	• Describe the translation applied to the original line to create the parallel line. • How did you use slope triangles in your explanation?	Probing
	• Why did you use a translation rather than a rotation in your explanation?	Seeing structure

GETTING STARTED RESOURCE

Slope Grid A

Each square on the grid represents 1 square unit.

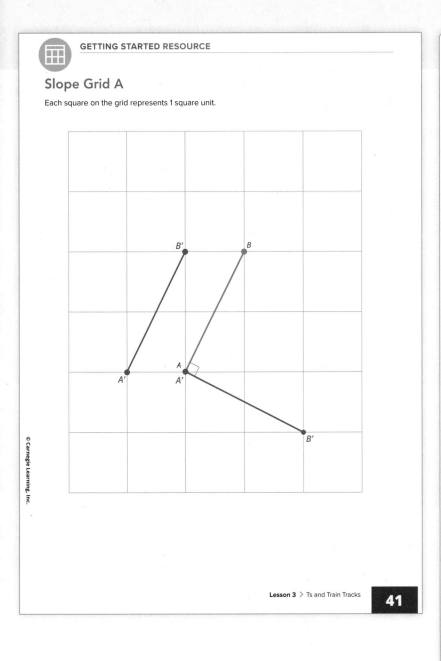

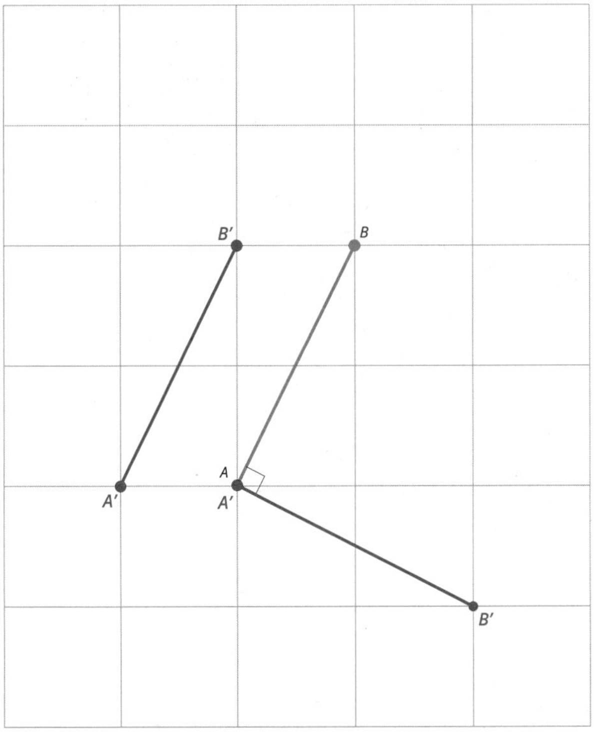

NOTES

NOTES

Slope Grid B

Each square on the grid represents 1 square unit.

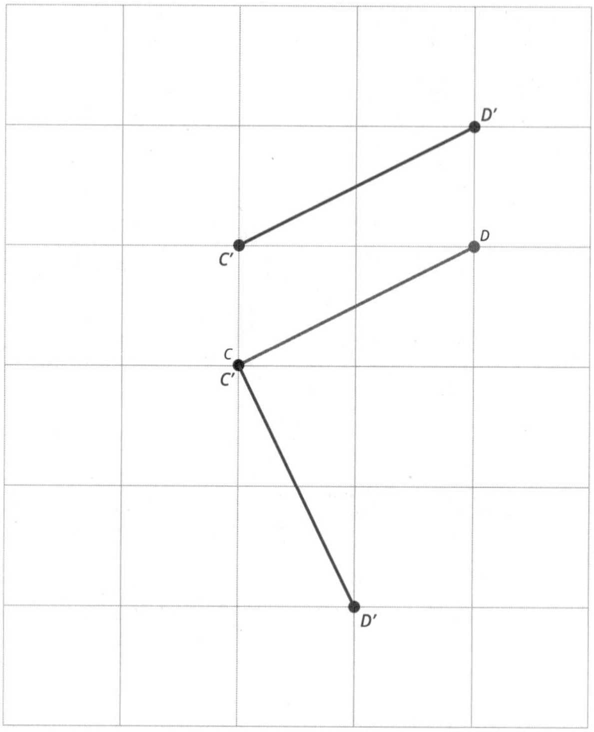

ASSIGNMENT

LESSON 3 ASSIGNMENT

Use a separate piece of paper for your Journal entry.

JOURNAL

Explain in your own words why the slope of a vertical line is undefined.

REMEMBER

The slope of parallel lines are the same.
The slopes of perpendicular lines are opposite reciprocals. Any vertical line is perpendicular to any horizontal line.

PRACTICE

Christopher is a developer and plans to build a new development. Use the grid to help Christopher create a map for his development. Each gridline represents one block.

1. Two main roads pass through the development, Moonbeam Drive and Sunshine Avenue. Are these two roads parallel to each other? Explain your reasoning.

   Yes, the two roads are parallel because they have the same slope.

   Moonbeam Dr.: $m = \frac{0-4}{20-15} = -\frac{4}{5}$

   Sunshine Ave.: $m = \frac{2-6}{7-2} = -\frac{4}{5}$

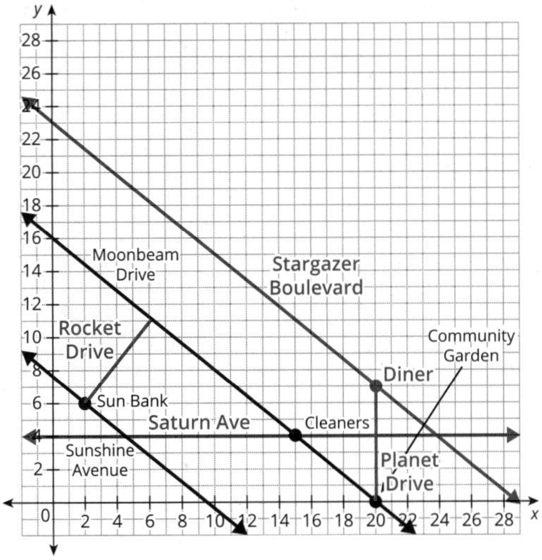

2. Christopher wants to build a road named Stargazer Boulevard that will parallel Moonbeam Drive. On this road, he will build a diner located 7 blocks north of the community garden. Determine the equation of the line that represents Stargazer Boulevard. Show your work. Then draw and label Stargazer Boulevard on the coordinate plane.

   The slope of Stargazer Blvd. is the same as the slope of Moonbeam Dr. because the two lines are parallel. The location of the diner is at (20, 7).

   $y - 7 = -\frac{4}{5}(x - 20)$

   $y = -\frac{4}{5}x + 23$

   The equation of the line representing Stargazer Blvd. is $y = -\frac{4}{5}x + 23$. See graph.

Go to LiveHint.com for help on the PRACTICE questions.

Chunking the Assignment

TOPIC 1

SESSION 1

- **Practice 1 - 3**
- **Mixed Practice (page 89) 3**

SESSION 2

- **Journal**
- **Practice 4 - 6**
- **Stretch (advanced learners)**

JOURNAL

Sample answer.

The slope of a line is the ratio of the change in *y*-values to the change in *x*-values between any two points on the line.

For a vertical line, the *x*-values do not change. Therefore, the change in *x*-values is 0. Since you cannot divide by 0, the value of the slope is undefined.

Encourage students to use LiveHint.com for help with the PRACTICE questions of this assignment.

NOTES

STRETCH

1. If you rotate ΔABC 90° counterclockwise, then the three lines of $\Delta A'B'C'$ are perpendicular to the lines of ΔABC, so the slopes of those lines are negative reciprocals. Point A' is $(-4, 7)$, Point B' is $(-2, 3)$, and Point C' is $(-5, 2)$.

Line $A'B'$:

$y - y_1 = m(x - x_1)$

$y - 7 = -2(x - (-4))$

$y = -2x - 1$

Line $B'C'$:

$y - y_1 = m(x - x_1)$

$y - 2 = \frac{1}{3}(x - (-5))$

$y = \frac{1}{3}x + \frac{11}{3}$

Line $A'C'$:

$y - y_1 = m(x - x_1)$

$y - 2 = 5(x - (-5))$

$y = 5x + 27$

LESSON 3 ASSIGNMENT Continued

3. The development will have two office buildings located at the points (8, 4) and (12, 10). Will a perpendicular line represent the shortest distance between Moonbeam Drive and the two office buildings? Why or why not?

No. A line joining the two office buildings is not perpendicular to Moonbeam Drive.

Slope of line joining two office buildings: $m = \frac{10 - 4}{12 - 8} = \frac{6}{4} = \frac{3}{2}$.

The slope of Moonbeam Drive is $-\frac{4}{5}$.

4. Christopher wants to build a road named Rocket Drive that connects Sun Bank to Moonbeam Drive. He wants this road to be as short as possible. Determine the equation of the line that represents Rocket Drive. Show your work. Then draw and label Rocket Drive on the coordinate plane.

The slope of Moonbeam Dr. is $-\frac{4}{5}$. So, I know the slope of Rocket Dr. is $\frac{5}{4}$. The coordinates of Sun Bank are (2, 6). The equation of the line representing Rocket Drive is $y = \frac{5}{4}x + \frac{7}{2}$. See graph.

$y - 6 = \frac{5}{4}(x - 2)$

$y = \frac{5}{4}x + \frac{7}{2}$

5. A straight road named Planet Drive will connect the diner and the community garden. What is the equation of the line that represents Planet Drive? Show your work. Draw and label Planet Drive on the coordinate plane.

The equation of the line representing Planet Drive is $x = 20$. See graph.

6. Christopher decides that another road to be named Saturn Avenue will go past the cleaners and be perpendicular to Planet Drive. Determine the equation of the line that represents Saturn Avenue. Show your work. Draw and label Saturn Avenue on the coordinate plane.

The slope of the line representing Saturn Avenue is 0. The line goes past the cleaners, so it passes through the point (15, 4). The equation of the line representing Saturn Avenue is $y = 4$.

STRETCH Optional

Triangle ABC is located on three lines such that the vertices occur at the points of intersection of pairs of the lines, as shown on the graph.

1. If ΔABC is rotated 90° counterclockwise around the origin to form $\Delta A'B'C'$, determine the equations of the lines that would contain $\Delta A'B'C'$. Explain your reasoning. Then draw the three lines that contain $\Delta A'BC'$ and label $\Delta A'B'C'$.

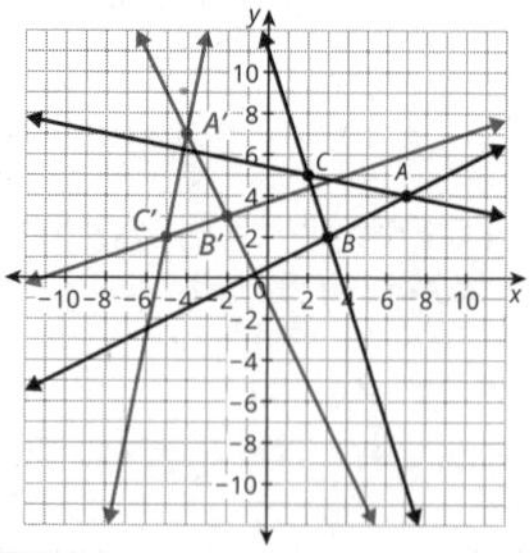

Ts and Train Tracks

This resource details additional facilitation notes to fully assist you as you plan each lesson to support all students, students who struggle, and advanced learners. It provides differentiation strategies, common student misconceptions, and suggestions to extend certain activities.

ACTIVITY 1

Session 1 of 2

Slopes of Parallel Lines

Students construct parallel lines not on the coordinate plane. They use construction tools to duplicate an angle.

CHUNK	AUDIENCE	ADDITIONAL SUPPORTS
As students read and discuss the introduction	Students who Struggle	**DIFFERENTIATION STRATEGY** Suggest students annotate this content. Have them mark each congruent angle pair listed with a different color to note its location in the diagram.

ACTIVITY 2

Session 1 of 2

Slopes of Perpendicular Lines

Students write the equations of perpendicular lines graphed on a coordinate plane. They demonstrate that the slopes of perpendicular lines are negative reciprocals.

CHUNK	AUDIENCE	ADDITIONAL SUPPORTS
As students discuss the worked example	All Students	**DIFFERENTIATION STRATEGY** Encourage students to take time to read through the worked example and annotate key ideas or steps in the process. As they think about the connections have students ask themselves: • Why is this method correct? • Have I used this method before?

ACTIVITY 3

Session 2 of 2

Horizontal and Vertical Lines

Students describe the slopes of horizontal and vertical lines. They write equations for horizontal and vertical lines.

CHUNK	AUDIENCE	ADDITIONAL SUPPORTS
As students discuss the worked example	All Students	**DIFFERENTIATION STRATEGY** Remind students that they can derive the point-slope formula from the slope formula. $m = \frac{y_2 - y_1}{x_2 - x_1}$ $y_2 - y_1 = m(x_2 - x_1)$
As students share and summarize 8	All Students	**DIFFERENTIATION STRATEGY** Students often confuse the equations for vertical and horizontal lines. Suggest a method they can use to construct the information they need rather than relying on memorization. Sketch a horizontal line and label a few points. 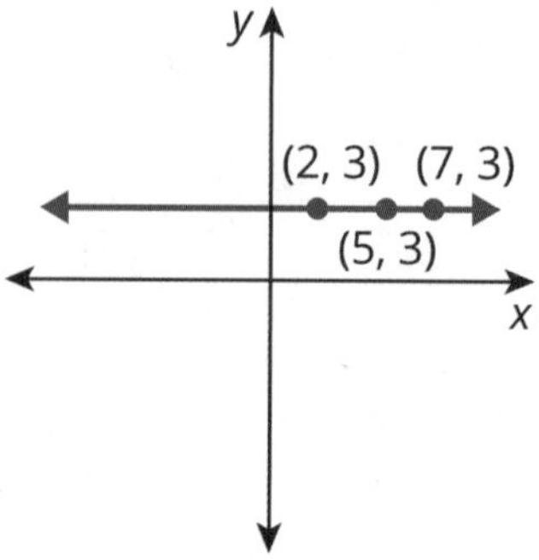 In all cases, $y = 3$. Therefore, for horizontal lines, use $y = a$, where a is any real number. Sketch a vertical line and label a few points. 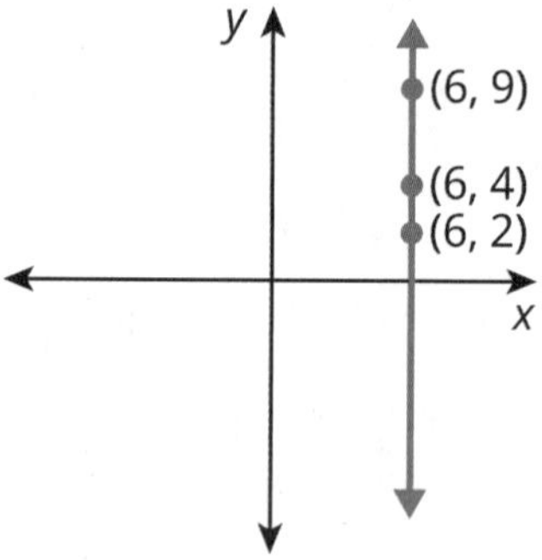 In all cases, $x = 6$. Therefore, for vertical lines, use $x = a$, where a is any real number.

ACTIVITY 4

Session 2 of 2

Writing Equations of Perpendicular Lines

Students write the equation of a line perpendicular to a given line that passes through a given point.

CHUNK	AUDIENCE	ADDITIONAL SUPPORTS
As students work on 2 and 3	Students who Struggle	**DIFFERENTIATION STRATEGY** • Modify Questions 2 and 3 to provide equations of lines rather than two points. • Suggest students organize their work by labeling their steps with "$m =$ " and "$\perp m =$."

Practice the learning

MATHbook + Skills Practice

The table shows the targeted practice of the skills and mathematical concepts for the *Using a Rectangular Coordinate System* Topic. The highlighted **Problem Set** aligns with **Ts and Train Tracks**.

PROBLEM SET	
1	Identifying Properties of Geometric Figures
2	Constructing Perpendicular Lines
3	**Duplicating Line Segments**
4	**Writing Equations of Parallel and Perpendicular Lines**
5	Classifying Shapes on the Coordinate Plane
6	Determining Perimeter and Area of Rectangles and Triangles on the Coordinate Plane
7	Determining Perimeter and Area of Other Polygons on the Coordinate Plane

ANYTIME AFTER ACTIVITY 4

Facilitate students as they work individually on **Problem Sets 3** and **4**.

ENGAGE at the **Module** level + **DEVELOP** at the **Topic** level + **TEACH** Read the facilitation notes and plan learning experiences.

Where are we?

TOPIC 1 Using a Rectangular Coordinate System	LESSON 1 The Squariest Square	LESSON 2 Hip to Be Square	LESSON 3 Ts and Train Tracks	**LESSON 4 Where Has Polly Gone?**	LESSON 5 In and Out and All About
Pacing	1 Session	2 Sessions	2 Sessions	**3 Sessions**	3 Sessions

OVERVIEW: LESSON 4

Where Has Polly Gone?

Classifying Shapes on the Coordinate Plane

ENGAGE

- Students compare characteristics of triangles and quadrilaterals in a Venn diagram.

DEVELOP

- Students use the Distance Formula to calculate the distance between two points.
- They classify triangles on the coordinate plane.
- They identify the location of a vertex for a partially-composed quadrilateral.
- They classify quadrilaterals on the coordinate plane.
- Students calculate the midpoints of a quadrilateral's sides.

DEMONSTRATE

- Students identify a vertex location of a quadrilateral using a translation.

HIGH SCHOOL GEOMETRY

Expressing Geometric Properties with Equations

Use coordinates to prove simple geometric theorems algebraically.

4. Use coordinates to prove simple geometric theorems algebraically.

5. Prove the slope criteria for parallel and perpendicular lines and use them to solve geometric problems (e.g., find the equation of a line parallel or perpendicular to a given line that passes through a given point).

LESSON STRUCTURE AND PACING GUIDE 3 SESSIONS

⊛ This activity highlights a key term or concept that is essential to the learning goals of the lesson.

Session 1		Session 2
INSTRUCTIONAL SEQUENCE		
ENGAGE Connect to prior knowledge	**DEVELOP** Classification Peer analysis	**DEVELOP** Classification Peer analysis

GETTING STARTED
You Better Shape Up

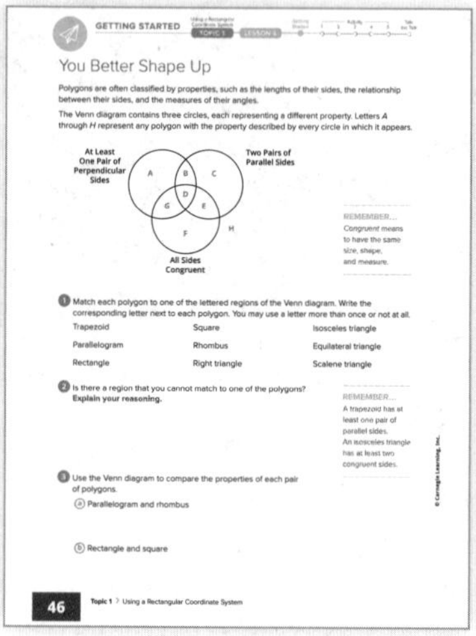
GETTING STARTED

You Better Shape Up

Polygons are often classified by properties, such as the lengths of their sides, the relationship between their sides, and the measures of their angles.

The Venn diagram contains three circles, each representing a different property. Letters *A* through *H* represent any polygon with the property described by every circle in which it appears.

At Least One Pair of Perpendicular Sides; Two Pairs of Parallel Sides; All Sides Congruent

REMEMBER... Congruent means to have the same size, shape, and measure.

1 Match each polygon to one of the lettered regions of the Venn diagram. Write the corresponding letter next to each polygon. You may use a letter more than once or not at all.

Trapezoid, Square, Isosceles triangle, Parallelogram, Rhombus, Equilateral triangle, Rectangle, Right triangle, Scalene triangle

2 Is there a region that you cannot match to one of the polygons? Explain your reasoning.

REMEMBER... A trapezoid has at least one pair of parallel sides. An isosceles triangle has at least two congruent sides.

3 Use the Venn diagram to compare the properties of each pair of polygons.

ⓐ Parallelogram and rhombus

ⓑ Rectangle and square

46 Topic 1 > Using a Rectangular Coordinate System

Students compare characteristics of triangles and quadrilaterals in a Venn diagram.

- They identify whether statements about these polygons are always, sometimes, or never true.

ACTIVITY 1
Calculating Distance on the Coordinate Plane

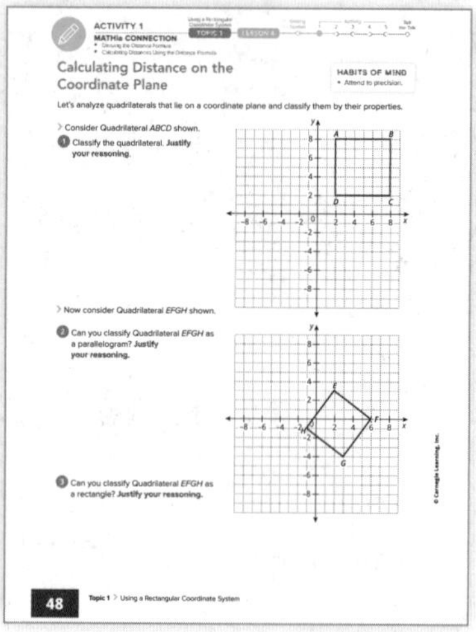
ACTIVITY 1

Calculating Distance on the Coordinate Plane

HABITS OF MIND • Attend to precision.

Let's analyze quadrilaterals that lie on a coordinate plane and classify them by their properties.

> Consider Quadrilateral *ABCD* shown.

1 Classify the quadrilateral. Justify your reasoning.

> Now consider Quadrilateral *EFGH* shown.

2 Can you classify Quadrilateral *EFGH* as a parallelogram? Justify your reasoning.

3 Can you classify Quadrilateral *EFGH* as a rectangle? Justify your reasoning.

48 Topic 1 > Using a Rectangular Coordinate System

Students identify quadrilaterals by considering their side lengths and the slopes of their sides.

- They relate the Distance Formula to the Pythagorean Theorem and calculate the distance between points.

ACTIVITY 2
Classifying Triangles on the Coordinate Plane

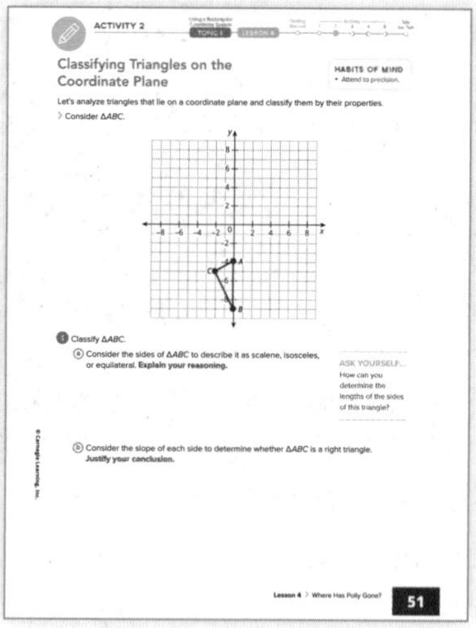
ACTIVITY 2

Classifying Triangles on the Coordinate Plane

HABITS OF MIND • Attend to precision.

Let's analyze triangles that lie on a coordinate plane and classify them by their properties.

> Consider △*ABC*.

1 Classify △*ABC*.

ⓐ Consider the sides of △*ABC* to describe it as scalene, isosceles, or equilateral. Explain your reasoning.

ASK YOURSELF... How can you determine the lengths of the sides of this triangle?

ⓑ Consider the slope of each side to determine whether △*ABC* is a right triangle. Justify your conclusion.

Lesson 4 > Where Has Polly Gone? 51

Students classify triangles by considering their side lengths and the slopes of their sides.

- They apply the converse of the Pythagorean Theorem to classify a triangle as acute, right, or obtuse.

Log in to MyCL for **lesson support** including:

Slides

Videos

www.carnegielearning.com/login

Session 3

INSTRUCTIONAL SEQUENCE

DEVELOP	DEVELOP	DEVELOP
Mathematical problem solving	Classification	Mathematical problem solving

ACTIVITY 3
Determining an Unknown Point of a Quadrilateral

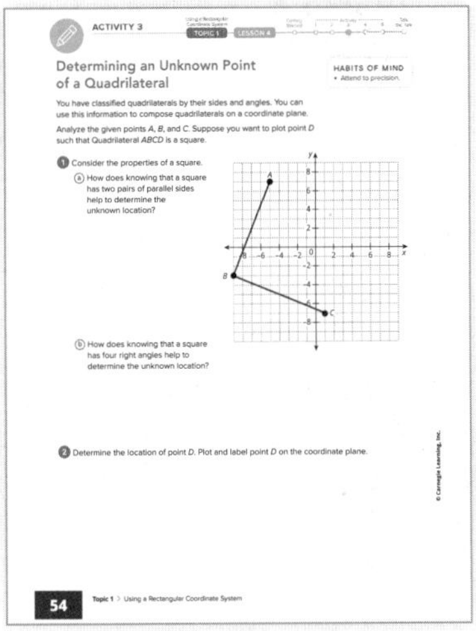

ACTIVITY 3

Determining an Unknown Point of a Quadrilateral

Students compose quadrilaterals on a coordinate plane.

- They identify the coordinate of a vertex in a partially-composed quadrilateral.

ACTIVITY 4
Classifying a Quadrilateral on the Coordinate Plane

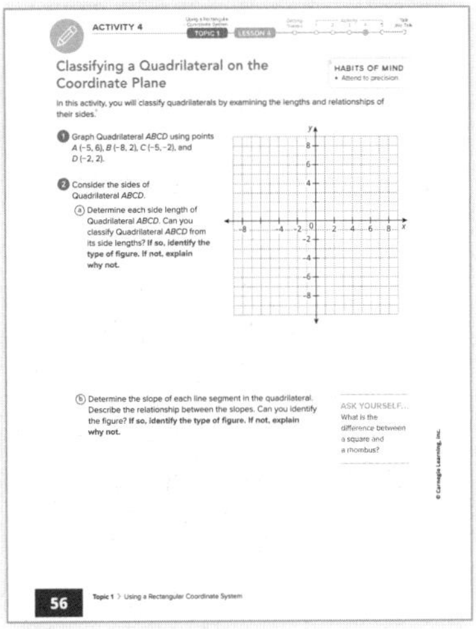

ACTIVITY 4

Classifying a Quadrilateral on the Coordinate Plane

Students classify quadrilaterals on the coordinate plane.

- They graph quadrilaterals and identify them by their side lengths and the slopes of their sides.

ACTIVITY 5
Classifying a Quadrilateral Formed by Midpoints

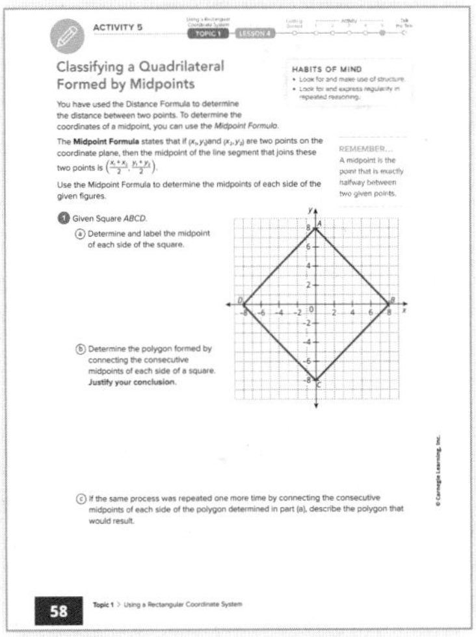

ACTIVITY 5

Classifying a Quadrilateral Formed by Midpoints

Students use the Midpoint Formula to calculate the midpoints of the sides of quadrilaterals.

- They then connect consecutive midpoints and identify the resulting quadrilateral.

TOPIC 1

Log in to MyCL for:
- Editable templates
- Additional planning support

Session 3

INSTRUCTIONAL SEQUENCE

DEMONSTRATE
Exit ticket procedures

TALK THE TALK
Look, Ma! No Gridlines!

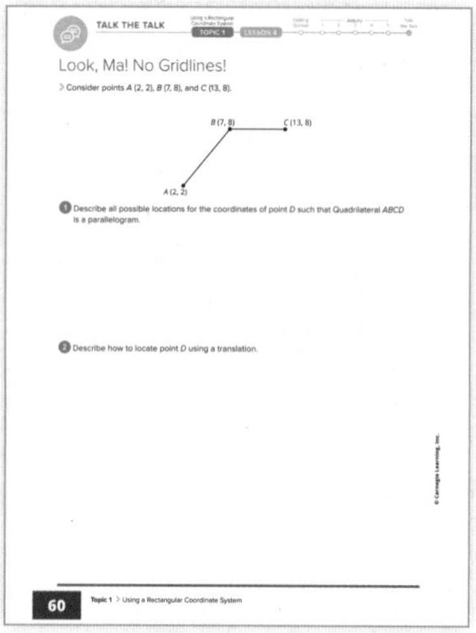
TALK THE TALK

Look, Ma! No Gridlines!

Consider points A (2, 2), B (7, 8), and C (13, 8).

1 Describe all possible locations for the coordinates of point D such that Quadrilateral $ABCD$ is a parallelogram.

2 Describe how to locate point D using a translation.

60 Topic 1 Using a Rectangular Coordinate System

Students identify the coordinate pair of a vertex of a quadrilateral without using a coordinate plane.

- They describe how to get the same result using a translation.

Now that you have read the Module, Topic, and Lesson Overviews, you are ready to plan.

Do the math

> Tear out the lesson planning template (page 45E) and jot down thoughts as you work through this lesson and read the Facilitation Notes.

Connect the learning

MATHbook + MATHia

The table shows a portion of the self-paced MATHia sequence for the *Using a Rectangular Coordinate System* Topic.

Median student completion time for the entire topic: ~200–215 minutes

> As you implement this lesson, consider different connections for students who are on pace and those that have not yet completed the workspaces aligned to this lesson.

STUDENTS WHO ARE NOT HERE YET
Students will practice using the distance formula to determine distances between points on the coordinate plane.

TYPE	WORKSPACE NAME
	Deriving the Distance Formula
	Calculating Distances Using the Distance Formula
	Calculating Perimeter and Area Using the Distance Formula

STUDENTS WHO ARE ON PACE
After you complete Activity 1, ask these students to share how they used the explore tool and the Distance Formula to solve problems.

Where Has Polly Gone?

Classifying Shapes on the Coordinate Plane

Session 1

GETTING STARTED You Better Shape Up

Pacing (minutes)	
My Time	Class Time

ACTIVITY 1 Calculating Distance on the Coordinate Plane ✪

Pacing (minutes)	
My Time	Class Time

KEY TERM
Distance Formula

Session 2

ACTIVITY 2 Classifying Triangles on the Coordinate Plane ✪

Pacing (minutes)	
My Time	Class Time

ACTIVITY 3 Determining an Unknown Point of a Quadrilateral

Pacing (minutes)	
My Time	Class Time

ACTIVITY 4 Classifying a Quadrilateral on the Coordinate Plane ✪

Pacing (minutes)	
My Time	Class Time

Session 3

ACTIVITY 5 Classifying a Quadrilateral Formed by Midpoints ✪

Pacing (minutes)	
My Time	Class Time

KEY TERM
Midpoint Formula

TALK THE TALK Look, Ma! No Gridlines!

Pacing (minutes)	
My Time	Class Time

✪ This activity highlights a key term or concept that is essential to the learning goals of the lesson.

Log in to MyCL for:
- Editable templates
- Additional planning support

Reflect on your lesson

> Consider the effectiveness of your lesson on student learning.

What went well?	What did not go as planned?

> Anticipate how you would change the lesson next time you teach it.

How will you capitalize on the things that went well?	How will you improve things that did not go as planned?

MATERIALS

- Straightedges

Setting the Stage

- **Assign Review (optional, 1 – 2 minutes)**
- **Communicate the learning goals and key terms to look out for**
- **Tap into your students' prior learning by reading the narrative statement**
- **Provide a sense of direction by reading the question**

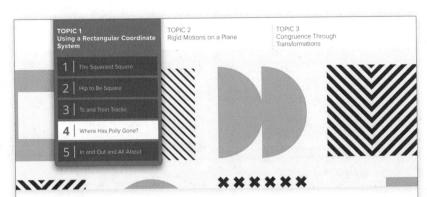

TOPIC 1 Using a Rectangular Coordinate System
TOPIC 2 Rigid Motions on a Plane
TOPIC 3 Congruence Through Transformations
1 | The Squariest Square
2 | Hip to Be Square
3 | Ts and Train Tracks
4 | Where Has Polly Gone?
5 | In and Out and All About

LESSON 4

Where Has Polly Gone?

Classifying Shapes on the Coordinate Plane

KEY TERMS

Distance Formula

Midpoint Formula

Learning Goals

- Use the Pythagorean Theorem to derive the Distance Formula.
- Apply the Distance Formula on the coordinate plane.
- Classify a triangle given the locations of its vertices on a coordinate plane.
- Determine the coordinates of a fourth vertex of the quadrilateral.
- Classify a quadrilateral given the locations of its vertices on a coordinate plane.

REVIEW (1–2 minutes)

> Determine the length of each hypotenuse. Round your answer to the nearest tenth, if necessary.

1 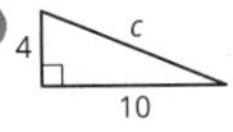

10.8

2 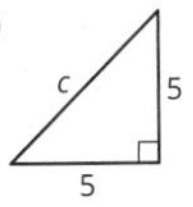

7.1

3 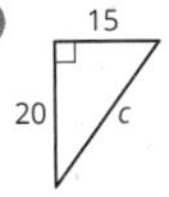

25

You know the slopes of parallel lines are equal and the slopes of perpendicular lines are negative reciprocals. You also know how to determine the length of the hypotenuse of a right triangle.

How can you use what you know to classify polygons that lie on a coordinate plane?

IN THIS **REVIEW**

Students solve for the hypotenuse of a right triangle. They first use this skill in **ACTIVITY 1 Calculating Distance on the Coordinate Plane.**

You can use the Distance Formula given by $d = \sqrt{(x_2 - x_1)^2 + (y_2 - y_1)^2}$ to determine side lengths of polygons on the coordinate plane to classify them.

Essential Ideas

- You can derive the Distance Formula from the Pythagorean Theorem.
- The Distance Formula is $d = \sqrt{(x_2 - x_1)^2 + (y_2 - y_1)^2}$, where d is the distance between points (x_1, y_1) and (x_2, y_2).
- The Midpoint Formula, $\left(\frac{x_1 + x_2}{2}, \frac{y_1 + y_2}{2}\right)$, identifies the midpoint of the line segment with endpoints (x_1, y_1) and (x_2, y_2).
- You can use the coordinates of triangles graphed on the coordinate plane to classify them according to side and angle measures.
- To classify a quadrilateral from its graph, you need to consider how its sides' lengths and slopes determine its properties.

SUMMARY **You can use a Venn diagram to compare the properties of polygons.**

Chunking the Activity

- **Read and discuss the introduction and diagram**
- **Group students to complete 1 - 2**
- **Check-in and share**
- **Group students to complete 3 - 5**
- **Share and summarize**

DIFFERENTIATION STRATEGY

See Page 62A to support students who struggle with 1.

See Page 62A to assist all students with 1.

NOTE: The High School Math Solution uses the inclusive definition of a trapezoid, defining a trapezoid as a quadrilateral with *at least* one pair of parallel sides. An isosceles trapezoid has *at least* two congruent sides.

You Better Shape Up

Polygons are often classified by properties, such as the lengths of their sides, the relationship between their sides, and the measures of their angles.

The Venn diagram contains three circles, each representing a different property. Letters *A* through *H* represent any polygon with the property described by every circle in which it appears.

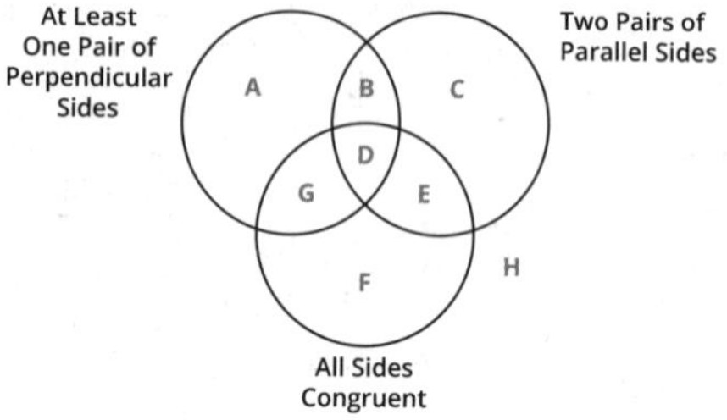

REMEMBER...
Congruent means to have the same size, shape, and measure.

1. Match each polygon to one of the lettered regions of the Venn diagram. Write the corresponding letter next to each polygon. You may use a letter more than once or not at all.

Trapezoid **H**	Square **D**	Isosceles triangle **H**
Parallelogram **C**	Rhombus **E**	Equilateral triangle **F**
Rectangle **B**	Right triangle **A**	Scalene triangle **H**

2. Is there a region that you cannot match to one of the polygons? Explain your reasoning.

   Region G does not match to a polygon in the set. The only polygon that has all sides congruent and at least one pair of perpendicular sides is a square, but it also has two pairs of parallel sides, so it belongs in Region D.

REMEMBER...
A trapezoid has at least one pair of parallel sides.
An isosceles triangle has at least two congruent sides.

3. Use the Venn diagram to compare the properties of each pair of polygons.

   (a) Parallelogram and rhombus

   A parallelogram and a rhombus both have two pairs of parallel sides, but a rhombus also has all sides congruent.

   (b) Rectangle and square

   A rectangle and a square both have two pairs of parallel sides and at least one pair of perpendicular sides, but a square also has all sides congruent.

Questions to Support Discourse

		TYPE
1	• What does Section B in the Venn diagram represent? • What is a polygon? Sketch a shape that is not a polygon.	Gathering
	• Which characteristics listed apply to this polygon? • Which section of the Venn diagram represents those characteristics?	Probing
3	• In which circles of the Venn diagram does each polygon lie? How can you use that information to compare their properties?	Probing

GETTING STARTED Continued

4 Marla and Flynn analyze the Venn diagram shown.

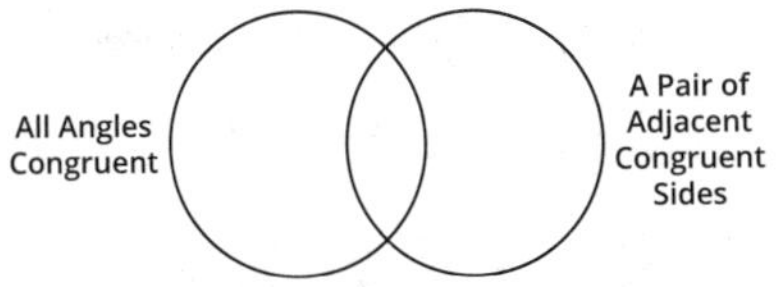

REMEMBER...
Adjacent sides are sides that share a vertex.

Marla says that the overlapping region describes a rhombus. Flynn says the overlapping region describes a square. Who's correct? **Explain your reasoning.**

Flynn is correct.
Both a rhombus and a square have a pair of adjacent congruent sides, but only a square has all angles congruent as well, since it has four right angles.

5 Determine whether each statement is always true, sometimes true, or never true.
Explain your reasoning.

(a) A rectangle is a parallelogram.

Always true. A parallelogram is a quadrilateral with two pairs of opposite sides that are parallel. All rectangles have that same property.

(b) A rhombus is a square.

Sometimes true. A rhombus has two pairs of opposite sides that are parallel and four congruent sides, but it does not have to have four congruent angles as a square does.

(c) A scalene triangle is a right triangle.

Sometimes true. A scalene triangle has three different side lengths, but one of its angles may or may not be a right angle.

(d) A parallelogram is a trapezoid.

Always true. A trapezoid is a quadrilateral with at least one pair of parallel sides. All parallelograms have that same property.

(e) A right triangle is an equilateral triangle.

Never true. An equilateral triangle has congruent angles, which each measure 60°, so it can never be a right triangle.

NOTES

DIFFERENTIATION STRATEGY

See Page 62A to assist all students with the strategy in 4.

TOPIC 1

Questions to Support Discourse

		TYPE
4	• What characteristics does the overlapping region represent?	Gathering
5	• Sketch an example of a trapezoid that is not a parallelogram. • Sketch an example of a rhombus that is a square. • Sketch an example of a rhombus that is not a square. • Sketch a scalene triangle that is a right triangle. • Sketch a scalene triangle that is not a right triangle.	Probing
	• How can you justify your responses?	Reflecting and justifying

SUMMARY **The Distance Formula is $d = \sqrt{(x_2 - x_1)^2 + (y_2 - y_1)^2}$, where d is the distance between points (x_1, y_1) and (x_2, y_2).**

Chunking the Activity

- **Read and discuss the introduction**
- **Group students to complete 1 – 5**
- **Check-in and share**
- **Read and discuss the definition**
- **Complete 6 and 7 as a class**
- **Group students to complete 8 and 9**
- **Share and summarize**

LANGUAGE LINK

Remind students to refer to the Academic Glossary (page FM–20) to review the definition of **justify** and related phrases. Suggest they ask themselves these questions:

- How can I justify my answer to others?
- Is my explanation logical?

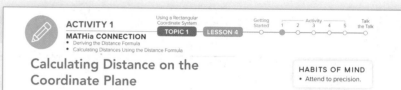

Calculating Distance on the Coordinate Plane

HABITS OF MIND
- Attend to precision.

Let's analyze quadrilaterals that lie on a coordinate plane and classify them by their properties.

> Consider Quadrilateral *ABCD* shown.

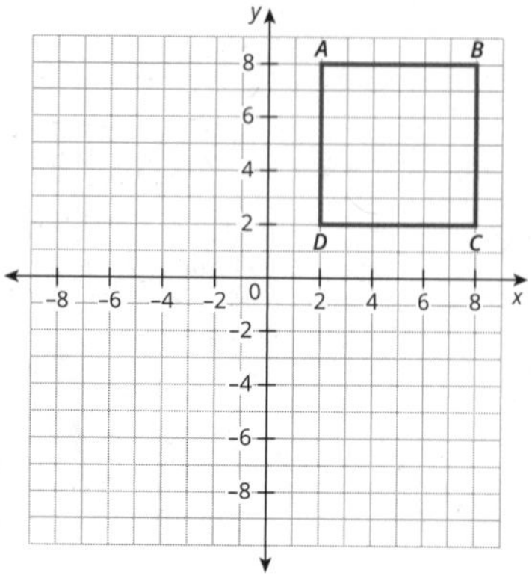

1. Classify the quadrilateral. **Justify your reasoning.**

   Quadrilateral *ABCD* is a square. Because its sides are horizontal and vertical line segments, I know they are perpendicular, so the figure has four right angles. I can use the number line on the axes to determine the distance between the vertices and conclude that the side lengths are all congruent.

> Now consider Quadrilateral *EFGH* shown.

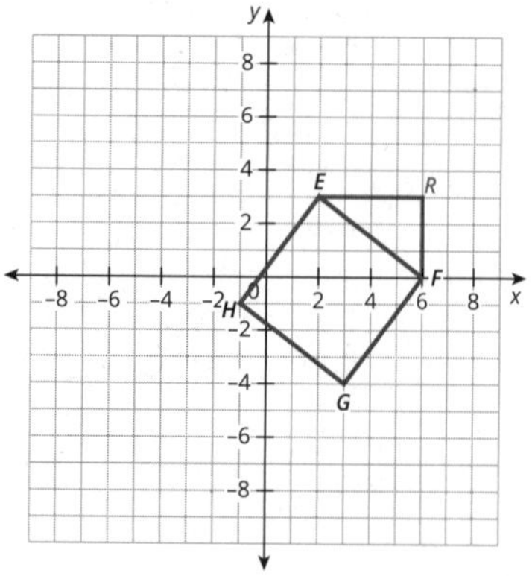

2. Can you classify Quadrilateral *EFGH* as a parallelogram? **Justify your reasoning.**

   Quadrilateral *EFGH* is a parallelogram. The slope of side *EF* is $-\frac{3}{4}$, the slope of side *FG* is $\frac{4}{3}$, the slope of side *GH* is $-\frac{3}{4}$, and the slope of side *HE* is $\frac{4}{3}$. The opposite sides of the quadrilateral have the same slope, so they are parallel to each other.

3. Can you classify Quadrilateral *EFGH* as a rectangle? **Justify your reasoning.**

   Quadrilateral *EFGH* is a rectangle. I can use the slopes I calculated in the previous question. Since the slopes of sides *EF* and *GH* are opposite reciprocals of the slopes of sides *FG* and *HE*, the sides are perpendicular to each other. Therefore, the quadrilateral has four right angles.

Questions to Support Discourse

		TYPE
1	• Which properties did you check to determine whether this polygon is a square?	Probing
2 and 3	• What relationship were you looking for among the slope values? • Why didn't you need to check the side lengths?	Probing

4 What information do you need to classify Quadrilateral *EFGH* as a square?

I need to know whether the side lengths are congruent.

5 On Quadrilateral *EFGH,* draw a Right Triangle *EFR* such that $\overline{EF}$ is the hypotenuse. Use the Pythagorean Theorem to determine the length of $\overline{EF}$.

$ER^2 + FR^2 = EF^2$

$4^2 + 3^2 = EF^2$

$16 + 9 = EF^2$

$\sqrt{25} = EF$

$EF = 5$

REMEMBER...
The Pythagorean Theorem states that the sum of the squares of the lengths of the legs of a right triangle equals the square of the length of the hypotenuse.
$a^2 + b^2 = c^2$

You can rewrite the Pythagorean Theorem as the *Distance Formula*. The **Distance Formula** states that if (x_1, y_1) and (x_2, y_2) are two points on the coordinate plane, then the distance d between (x_1, y_1) and (x_2, y_2) is calculated using the formula given.

$$d = \sqrt{(x_2 - x_1)^2 + (y_2 - y_1)^2}$$

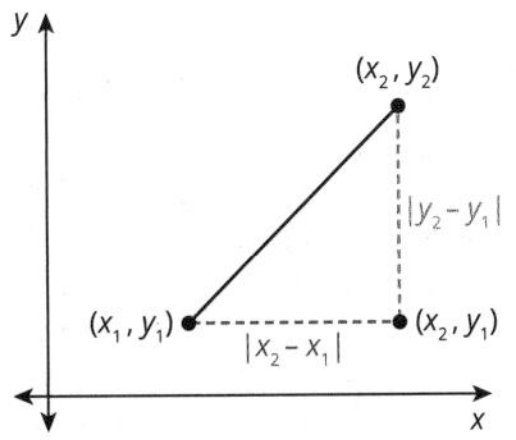

THINK ABOUT...
You use absolute value symbols because the difference represents a distance.

6 When you use the Distance Formula, does it matter which point you identify as (x_1, y_1) and which point you identify as (x_2, y_2)? **Explain your reasoning.**

No. Once I square the differences, the values are the same, so order does not matter. For example, $(3 - 5)^2 = (-2)^2 = 4$ and $(5 - 3)^2 = 2^2 = 4$.

NOTES

DIFFERENTIATION STRATEGY

See Page 62B to support students who struggle with the definition of *Distance Formula*.

Questions to Support Discourse

		TYPE
5	• How did you figure out the lengths of the legs? • Do you think all the legs are five units long? Explain your thinking.	Probing
Definition	• Which portion of the diagram is the distance we are trying to calculate?	Gathering
	• How are the dotted lines related to your procedure in Question 5? • How was the ordered pair (x_2, y_1) determined from the original two points? • What do the absolute value expressions represent? Which steps connect the absolute value expressions to the Distance Formula? • Why is using the Distance Formula equivalent to solving for *c* using the Pythagorean Theorem?	Seeing structure

NOTES

DIFFERENTIATION STRATEGY

See Page 62B to assist all students with 7.

DIFFERENTIATION STRATEGY

See Page 62B to support students who struggle with 8.

Student Look-Fors

- Sign errors
- Errors due to subtraction with an *x*-coordinate and a *y*-coordinate

7. Can you classify Quadrilateral *EFGH* as a square? **Justify your reasoning.**

Quadrilateral *EFGH* is a square.

In Question 3, I determined it was a rectangle. Also, all four sides are congruent. I already determined that side *EF* had a length of 5 units in Question 5.

$FG = \sqrt{(6-3)^2 + [0-(-4)]^2}$

$= \sqrt{3^2 + (-4)^2} = \sqrt{25} = 5$

$GH = \sqrt{[3-(-1)]^2 + [-4-(-1)]^2}$

$= \sqrt{4^2 + (-3)^2} = \sqrt{25} = 5$

$HE = \sqrt{(-1-2)^2 + (-1-3)^2}$

$= \sqrt{(-3)^2 + (-4)^2} = \sqrt{25} = 5$

8. Use the Distance Formula to calculate the distance between each pair of points. Round your answer to the nearest tenth, if necessary. **Show all your work.**

ⓐ (1, 2) and (3, 7)

$d = \sqrt{(3-1)^2 + (7-2)^2}$

$d = \sqrt{2^2 + 5^2}$

$d = \sqrt{29}$

$d \approx 5.4$

ⓑ (−6, 4) and (2, −8)

$d = \sqrt{[2-(-6)]^2 + (-8-4)^2}$

$d = \sqrt{8^2 + (-12)^2}$

$d = \sqrt{208}$

$d \approx 14.4$

ⓒ (−5, 2) and (−6, 10)

$d = \sqrt{[-6-(-5)]^2 + (10-2)^2}$

$d = \sqrt{(-1)^2 + 8^2}$

$d = \sqrt{65}$

$d \approx 8.1$

9. Calculate the distance between the points (−1, −2) and (−3, −7). Notice the similarity between this problem and Question 8, part (a).

Carlos says that the solution must be the negative of the solution of part (a). Mandy disagrees and says that the solution will be the same as the solution of part (a). Who is correct? **Explain your reasoning and state the correct solution.**

Mandy is correct.
Because you are squaring the differences, the solution will be positive. The distance between those points is also approximately 5.4. units.

Questions to Support Discourse

		TYPE
7	• Which property do you need to determine whether this rectangle is also a square? • How can you determine the side lengths? What is another way? • Explain your steps to solve for a side length.	Probing
8	• Show how you calculated the distance.	Probing
	• Does it make a difference which squared expression you write first under the radical symbol? Why not? • Why do the original squared terms include a minus sign?	Seeing structure

ACTIVITY 2

SUMMARY **You can use the coordinates of triangles graphed on the coordinate plane to classify them according to side and angle measures.**

Classifying Triangles on the Coordinate Plane

HABITS OF MIND
- Attend to precision.

Let's analyze triangles that lie on a coordinate plane and classify them by their properties.

> Consider ΔABC.

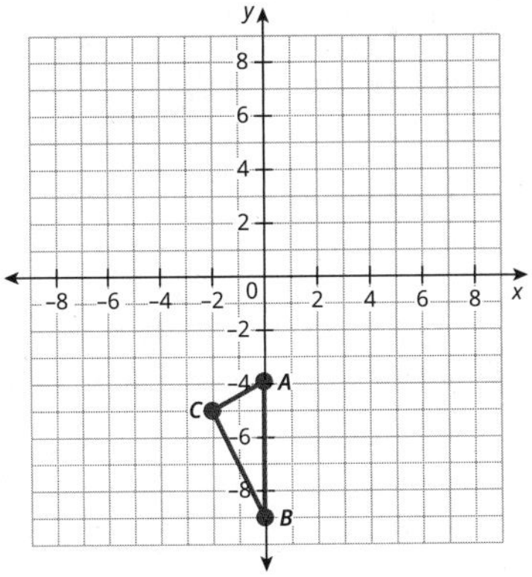

1 Classify ΔABC.

(a) Consider the sides of ΔABC to describe it as scalene, isosceles, or equilateral. **Explain your reasoning.**

Triangle *ABC* is a scalene triangle.

$AB = 5$

$BC = \sqrt{20} \approx 4.47$

$AC = \sqrt{5} \approx 2.24$

ASK YOURSELF...
How can you determine the lengths of the sides of this triangle?

(b) Consider the slope of each side to determine whether ΔABC is a right triangle. **Justify your conclusion.**

Triangle *ABC* is a right triangle.

Slope of $\overline{AB}$ is undefined.

Slope of $\overline{AC} = \frac{1}{2}$.

Slope of $\overline{BC} = -2$

The slopes of the segments that form angle *C* are opposite reciprocals of each other, so they must be perpendicular, which means they form a right angle.

Chunking the Activity

- Read and discuss the introduction
- Group students to complete 1
- Check-in and share
- Read and discuss the text and diagrams
- Group students to complete 2 - 4
- Share and summarize

DIFFERENTIATION STRATEGY

See Page 62C to assist all students with 1.

Questions to Support Discourse

		TYPE
1	• Explain how you determined the lengths of the sides of the triangle. • How did you use the lengths of the sides to classify the triangle? • How did you use the slopes of the sides of the triangle to classify the triangle?	Probing

NOTES

ⓒ Use the Converse of the Pythagorean Theorem to determine whether ΔABC is a right triangle. **Explain your reasoning.**

$$a^2 + b^2 = c^2$$

$$(\sqrt{5})^2 + (\sqrt{20})^2 = 5^2$$

$$5 + 20 = 25$$

$$25 = 25$$

Since the final equation is a true statement, ΔABC is a right triangle.

REMEMBER...
The Converse of the Pythagorean Theorem states that when the sum of the squares of the two shorter sides of a triangle equals the square of the longest side, then the triangle is a right triangle.

You can use the relationship among the sides of a triangle to determine whether the triangle is acute or obtuse. Given a, b, and c are the sides of a triangle with c as the longest side, when $c^2 < a^2 + b^2$, the triangle is acute, and when $c^2 > a^2 + b^2$, the triangle is obtuse.

Right angle | Acute angle | Obtuse angle

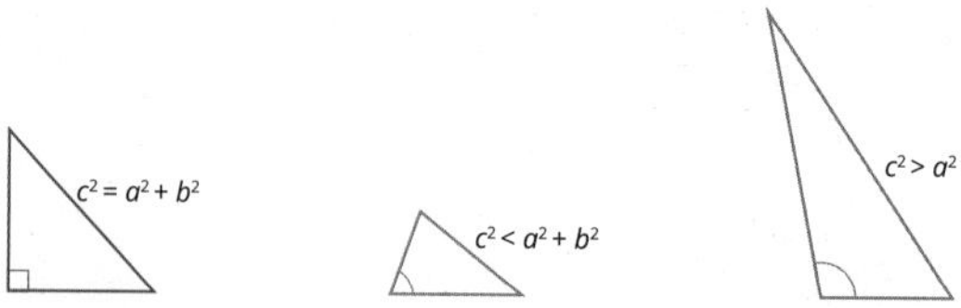

2 Determine whether each set of side lengths creates an acute, right, or obtuse triangle.

ⓐ 42 cm, 36 cm, 15 cm

Obtuse triangle

ⓑ 18.5 m, 11 m, 15 m

Acute triangle

ⓒ 4 ft, $\sqrt{65}$ ft, 7 ft

Right triangle

DIFFERENTIATION STRATEGY

See Page 62C to assist all students with **2**.

Student Look-Fors

Correct substitution of the values in the Pythagorean Theorem. The largest value is c.

Questions to Support Discourse

		TYPE
1	• Why was it a good idea to use the side lengths expressed as radicals? • Explain why $(\sqrt{5})^2 = 5$?	Probing
Diagrams	• What do the dotted lines in the diagrams represent? • Why does it make sense that when the value of c^2 is less than the sum of $a^2 + b^2$, the angle is an acute triangle?	Seeing structure
2	• How did you know that $\sqrt{65}$ is the largest value?	Gathering
	• Does it make a difference which values you substitute for a, b, and c in the Pythagorean Theorem? Explain your thinking.	Probing

ACTIVITY 2 Continued

3 Graph ΔJKL using points $J\,(-2, 4)$, $K\,(8, 4)$ and $L\,(6, -2)$.

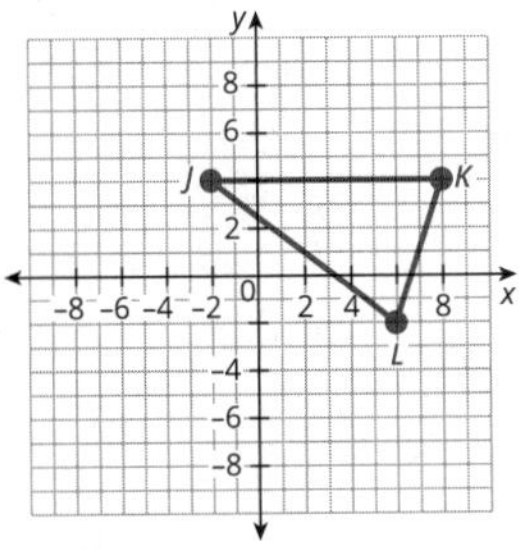

THINK ABOUT...
Are you using a straightedge to draw the triangle?

4 Classify ΔJKL.

ⓐ Consider the sides of ΔJKL. Describe the triangle as scalene, isosceles, or equilateral. **Explain your reasoning.**

Triangle JKL is isosceles because sides $\overline{JK}$ and $\overline{JL}$ are the same length.

$JK = 10$

$KL = \sqrt{40} \approx 6.32$

$JL = 10$

ⓑ Consider the angles of ΔJKL. Describe the triangle as acute, obtuse, or right. **Explain your reasoning.**

Triangle JKL is an acute triangle.

The longest sides are $\overline{JK}$ and $\overline{JL}$. Because $10^2 < 10^2 + (\sqrt{40})^2$, the triangle is acute.

Questions to Support Discourse

		TYPE
4	• What is an advantage of using the Pythagorean Theorem instead of the slope to classify a triangle?	Gathering
	• Explain how you determined the lengths of the sides of the triangle. • How did you use the lengths of the sides to classify the triangle? • What is another way you can determine that this triangle is not a right triangle?	Probing

NOTES

TOPIC 1

Student Look-Fors

Working to build relationships within the group to improve teamwork. If groups are struggling to work together effectively, consider facilitating a team-building activity.

ACTIVITY 3

SUMMARY **To compose a quadrilateral on a coordinate plane, you need to consider its properties, side lengths, and slopes to determine its vertices.**

Chunking the Activity

- Read and discuss the introduction
- Group students to complete 1 and 2
- Check-in and share
- Group students to complete 3
- Share and summarize

Student Look-Fors

Strategies to locate the vertex, such as counting units on the coordinate plane, using formulas, and translating line segments.

Determining an Unknown Point of a Quadrilateral

HABITS OF MIND
- Attend to precision.

You have classified quadrilaterals by their sides and angles. You can use this information to compose quadrilaterals on a coordinate plane.

Analyze the given points *A*, *B*, and *C*. Suppose you want to plot point *D* such that Quadrilateral *ABCD* is a square.

1. Consider the properties of a square.

   a. How does knowing that a square has two pairs of parallel sides help to determine the unknown location?

   Because each pair of opposite sides of a square are parallel, the opposite sides have the same slope. I can use the slope of $\overline{AB}$ to draw side $\overline{DC}$ and the slope of $\overline{BC}$ to draw side $\overline{AD}$. Their intersection determines the vertex, *D*.

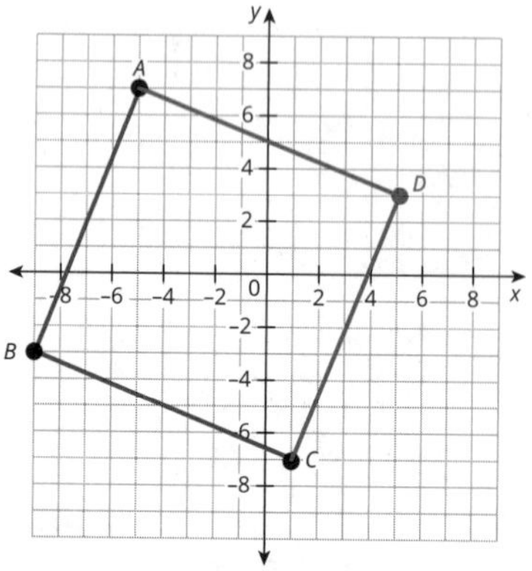

   b. How does knowing that a square has four right angles help to determine the unknown location?

   Because consecutive sides of a square are perpendicular, consecutive sides have slopes that are opposite reciprocals. I can use the slope of $\overline{AB}$ to draw consecutive side $\overline{AD}$ and the slope of $\overline{BC}$ to draw consecutive side $\overline{CD}$. Their intersection determines the vertex, *D*.

2. Determine the location of point *D*. Plot and label point *D* on the coordinate plane.

   See graph.
   The coordinates of point *D* are (5, 3).

Questions to Support Discourse

		TYPE
1	• How can you use the slope of $\overline{BA}$ to graph side $\overline{CD}$? What would be your next step? • How can you use the slope of $\overline{BC}$ to graph side $\overline{CD}$? What would be your next step? • How does your method take into account that the sides must be the same length?	Probing
	• How can you check your work using translations?	Reflecting and justifying

ACTIVITY 3 Continued

3 Use the same locations for points *A*, *B*, and *C* to identify the location of a new point *E*, such that Quadrilateral *ABCE* is a trapezoid with only one pair of parallel sides.

ⓐ Identify information that is helpful to locate point *E*. **Explain your reasoning.**

I need to decide what two sides of quadrilateral *ABCD* from Question 2 I will keep parallel, and whether I will extend or shorten a remaining side so that the other two sides are not parallel

ⓑ Describe the possible locations of point *E* such that Quadrilateral *ABCE* is a trapezoid with only one pair of parallel sides.

Point *E* can lie on $\overleftrightarrow{AD}$ anywhere to the right of point *A* except at point (5, 3).
Point *E* can lie on $\overleftrightarrow{CD}$, anywhere above point *C* except at (5, 3).

Questions to Support Discourse

		TYPE
3	• Which sides did you keep parallel? • How did you make sure the other two sides were not parallel? • What are three possible coordinate pairs for point *E*?	Probing

NOTES

Student Look-Fors

- Which sides are parallel in the trapezoid.
- Recognition of infinite solutions.
- Realization that the trapezoid cannot have vertex *E* at (5, 3).

SUMMARY **To classify a quadrilateral from its graph, consider how its sides' lengths and slopes determine its properties.**

Chunking the Activity

- **Read and discuss the introduction**
- **Group students to complete the activity**
- **Share and summarize**

COMMON MISCONCEPTION

See Page 62D for a misconception related to 2.

Classifying a Quadrilateral on the Coordinate Plane

HABITS OF MIND
- Attend to precision.

In this activity, you will classify quadrilaterals by examining the lengths and relationships of their sides.

1. Graph Quadrilateral *ABCD* using points *A* (−5, 6), *B* (−8, 2), *C* (−5, −2), and *D* (−2, 2).

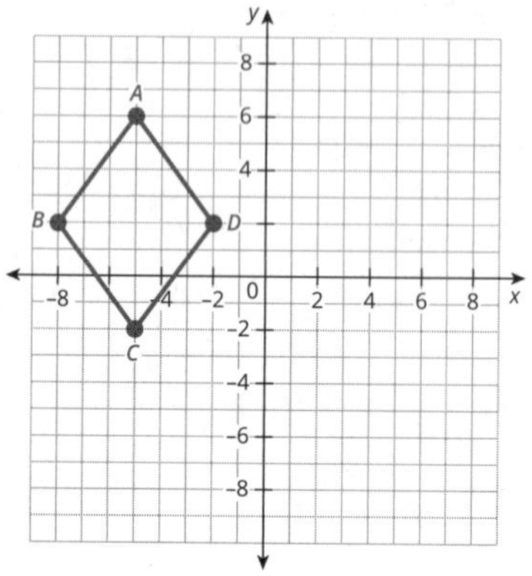

2. Consider the sides of Quadrilateral *ABCD*.

   ⓐ Determine each side length of Quadrilateral *ABCD*. Can you classify Quadrilateral *ABCD* from its side lengths? **If so, identify the type of figure. If not, explain why not.**

   All sides are 5 units in length.

   The quadrilateral is a rhombus because all four sides are the same length. It might also be a square, but I would have to know the measure of the angles.

   ⓑ Determine the slope of each line segment in the quadrilateral. Describe the relationship between the slopes. Can you identify the figure? **If so, identify the type of figure. If not, explain why not.**

   Slope of $\overline{AB} = \frac{4}{3}$

   Slope of $\overline{BC} = -\frac{4}{3}$

   Slope of $\overline{CD} = \frac{4}{3}$

   Slope of $\overline{AD} = -\frac{4}{3}$

   Opposite sides have the same slope. None of the slopes have an opposite reciprocal relationship. Quadrilateral *ABCD* is a rhombus and not a square.

ASK YOURSELF...
What is the difference between a square and a rhombus?

Questions to Support Discourse

		TYPE
2	• Which quadrilaterals have all sides the same length? • How do opposite slopes, not opposite reciprocal slopes, appear on the graph?	Gathering
	• How did you calculate the side lengths? • How could you tell the sides were all the same length without doing any calculations?	Probing
	• Do you have enough information to determine that this quadrilateral is a rhombus? A square? Explain your thinking. • What do the slopes tell you about the angles and opposite sides in this quadrilateral? • How can you verify that this figure is a rhombus but not a square?	Seeing structure

ACTIVITY 4 Continued

3 Graph Quadrilateral *ABCD* using points *A* (8, 8), *B* (3, −7), *C* (10, −6), and *D* (13, 3) Classify this quadrilateral as a trapezoid, a rhombus, a rectangle, a square, or none of these. **Explain your reasoning.**

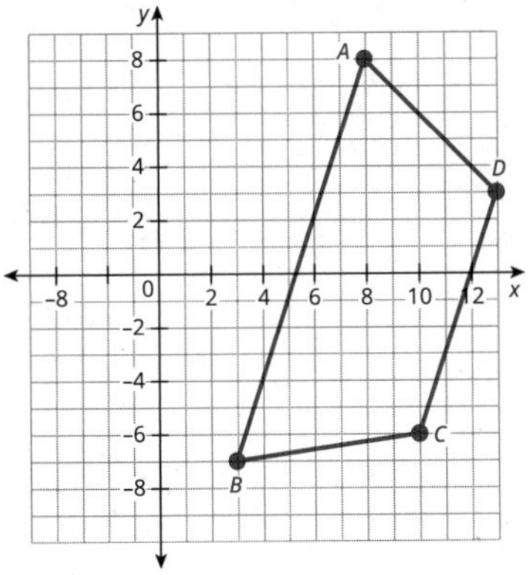

Quadrilateral *ABCD* is a trapezoid. It has one pair of parallel sides. The slope of $\overline{AB}$ and the slope of $\overline{CD}$ are 3.

THINK ABOUT...
Which types of figures can you eliminate as you determine information about the figure?

Questions to Support Discourse

		TYPE
3	• For how many segments of the quadrilateral do you need to determine the slope?	Seeing structure

NOTES

TOPIC 1

SUMMARY **The Midpoint Formula, $\left(\frac{x_1 + x_2}{2}, \frac{y_1 + y_2}{2}\right)$, identifies the midpoint of the line segment with endpoints (x_1, y_1) and (x_2, y_2).**

Chunking the Activity

- Read and discuss the introduction and definition
- Group students to complete 1
- Check-in and share
- Group students to complete 2
- Share and summarize

Classifying a Quadrilateral Formed by Midpoints

HABITS OF MIND
- Look for and make use of structure.
- Look for and express regularity in repeated reasoning.

You have used the Distance Formula to determine the distance between two points. To determine the coordinates of a midpoint, you can use the *Midpoint Formula*.

The **Midpoint Formula** states that if $(x_1, y_1)$and (x_2, y_2) are two points on the coordinate plane, then the midpoint of the line segment that joins these two points is $\left(\frac{x_1 + x_2}{2}, \frac{y_1 + y_2}{2}\right)$.

REMEMBER...
A midpoint is the point that is exactly halfway between two given points.

Use the Midpoint Formula to determine the midpoints of each side of the given figures.

1 Given Square *ABCD*.

(a) Determine and label the midpoint of each side of the square.

Midpoint of $\overline{AB}$ is (4, 4).

Midpoint of $\overline{BC}$ is (4, −4).

Midpoint of $\overline{CD}$ is (−4, −4).

Midpoint of $\overline{DA}$ is (−4, 4).

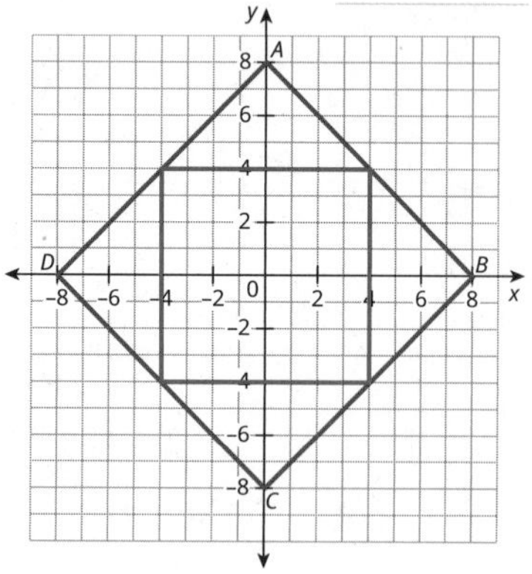

(b) Determine the polygon formed by connecting the consecutive midpoints of each side of a square. **Justify your conclusion.**

The polygon formed by connecting the consecutive midpoints of each side of a square is also a square.

Consecutive sides are perpendicular since they are horizontal and vertical lines. The measures of all 4 sides are 5 units.

(c) If the same process was repeated one more time by connecting the consecutive midpoints of each side of the polygon determined in part (a), describe the polygon that would result.

The midpoints of the sides of the secondary figure are (−4,0), (0, 4), (4,0), and (0, −4).

The resulting figure is also a square.

Questions to Support Discourse

		TYPE
Intro	• How is a midpoint related to a segment bisector? • Explain how to calculate midpoint in your own words.	Gathering
	• How is the formula for the midpoint related to the formula for the mean of two values? Why does that make sense?	Seeing structure
1	• Why do you think the resulting figure is also a square? • What do you think would happen if you continue this process?	Seeing structure

ACTIVITY 5 Continued

2 Consider the given line segment JK, where $x \neq y$.

(a) Sketch any rhombus that is not a square. Label the midpoint of each side of the rhombus.

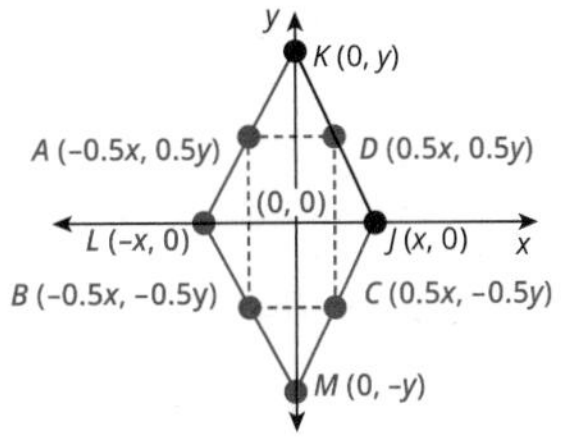

(b) Determine the polygon formed by connecting the consecutive midpoints of each side of a rhombus. **Justify your conclusion.**

The polygon formed by connecting the consecutive midpoints of each side of a rhombus is a rectangle.

Points A, B, C, and D are midpoints of each side of the given rhombus.

Let $x \neq y$.	Slope of $\overline{AB}$: $m = \frac{y}{0}$
$AB = y$	undefined
$BC = x$	Slope of $\overline{BC}$:
$CD = y$	$m = \frac{0}{-x} = 0$
$DA = x$	Slope of $\overline{CD}$: $m = \frac{y}{0}$
$AB = CD$ and $BC = DA$	undefined
	Slope of $\overline{DA}$: $m = \frac{0}{x} = 0$

Vertical lines are perpendicular to horizontal lines.

$\overline{AB} \perp \overline{BC}$

$\overline{BC} \perp \overline{CD}$

$\overline{CD} \perp \overline{DA}$

$\overline{DA} \perp \overline{AB}$

$\overline{AB} \parallel \overline{CD}$

$\overline{BC} \parallel \overline{DA}$

$ABCD$ is a rectangle because opposite sides are congruent, and all four angles are right angles.

(c) If the same process was repeated one more time by connecting the consecutive midpoints of each side of the polygon determined in part (a), describe the polygon that would result.

If you connected the consecutive midpoints of the sides of the rectangle (secondary figure), the polygon formed would be a rhombus.

NOTES

DIFFERENTIATION STRATEGY

See Page 62D to support students who struggle with 2.

See Page 62D to challenge advanced learners to extend 2.

Questions to Support Discourse

		TYPE
2	• Why do you think the resulting figure is a rectangle when you start with a rhombus but a square when you start with a square? • Why do you think connecting the midpoints of the sides of a rectangle forms a rhombus?	Seeing structure

SUMMARY The use of translations is an effective strategy when determining the endpoints of parallel segments on a coordinate plane.

Chunking the Activity

- **Read and discuss the situation**
- **Have students work individually to complete the activity**
- **Share and summarize**

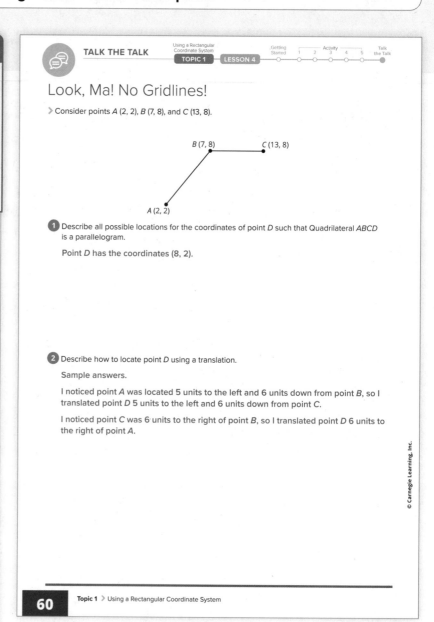

Look, Ma! No Gridlines!

> Consider points *A* (2, 2), *B* (7, 8), and *C* (13, 8).

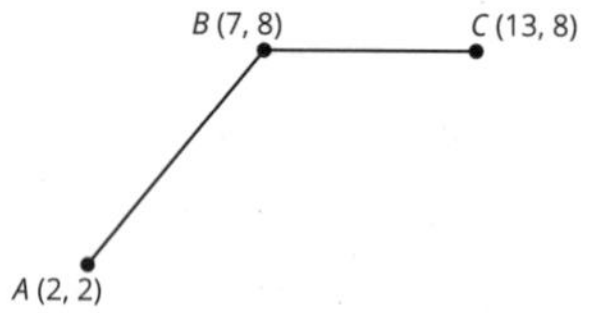

1. Describe all possible locations for the coordinates of point *D* such that Quadrilateral *ABCD* is a parallelogram.

   Point *D* has the coordinates (8, 2).

2. Describe how to locate point *D* using a translation.

   Sample answers.

   I noticed point *A* was located 5 units to the left and 6 units down from point *B*, so I translated point *D* 5 units to the left and 6 units down from point *C*.

   I noticed point *C* was 6 units to the right of point *B*, so I translated point *D* 6 units to the right of point *A*.

Questions to Support Discourse

		TYPE
1	• What are the properties of a parallelogram?	Gathering
	• How can you use the length of the segments to determine the coordinates of point *D*? • How can you use the slope of the segments to locate the fourth point?	Probing
2	• How is a translation related to your strategy?	Seeing structure

ASSIGNMENT

LESSON 4 ASSIGNMENT

> Use a separate piece of paper for your Journal entry.

JOURNAL

Describe how you can use the Distance Formula and the slope formula to classify triangles and quadrilaterals on the coordinate plane.

REMEMBER

You can use the Distance Formula given by $d = \sqrt{(x_2 - x_1)^2 + (y_2 - y_1)^2}$ to determine side lengths of polygons on the coordinate plane in order to classify them.

PRACTICE

1. The grid represents a map of Jose's neighborhood. It shows the locations of his house as well as the houses of four friends.

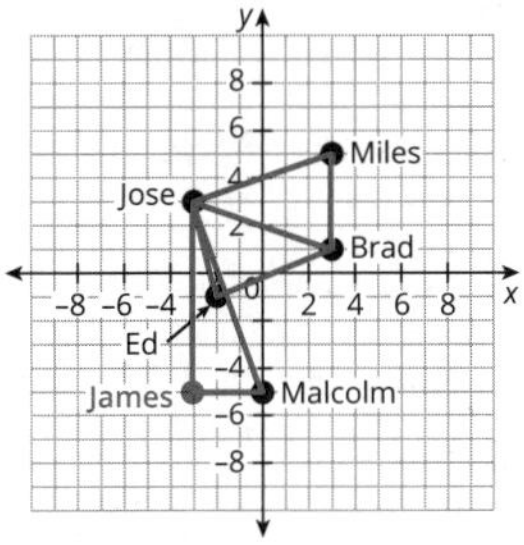

(a) Draw a triangle between the houses of Jose, Ed, and Brad. Determine whether this triangle is a scalene, isosceles, or equilateral triangle. Explain your reasoning.

The triangle is scalene. The distance between Jose and Brad $= \sqrt{40} \approx 6.32$. The distance between Jose and Ed is $d = \sqrt{17} \approx 4.12$. The distance between Brad and Ed is $\sqrt{29} \approx 5.39$.

(b) Determine whether the triangle is a right triangle. Explain your reasoning. If it is not a right triangle, determine whether it is acute or obtuse.

The triangle is acute. $(\sqrt{40})^2 < (\sqrt{29})^2 + (\sqrt{17})^2$

(c) Jose, Miles, and Brad are meeting for band rehearsal. Miles claims that the distance from Jose's house to his house is the same as the distance from Jose's house to Brad's house. Is his claim correct? Explain your answer. Which type of triangle do you form when you connect their houses?

Miles's claim is correct. The distance from Jose's to Brad's house is $\sqrt{40}$, and the distance from Jose to Miles is $\sqrt{40}$. The distance from Miles's house to Brad's house is 4. Because this triangle has two equal sides, it is an isosceles triangle.

(d) A new boy, James, moved into the neighborhood at the location (−3, −5). Plot and label James's house on the grid. Then, determine whether the triangle formed by connecting his house, Jose's house, and Malcolm's house is a right triangle.

See graph. The distance from Jose's house to James's house is 8. The triangle is a right triangle because it contains a horizontal and vertical side forming a right angle.

Go to LiveHint.com for help on the PRACTICE questions.

Encourage students to use LiveHint.com for help with the PRACTICE questions of this assignment.

Chunking the Assignment

TOPIC 1

SESSION 1

- Journal
- Stretch (advanced learners)

SESSION 2

- Practice 1 - 3

SESSION 3

- Mixed Practice (page 89) 4

JOURNAL

You can use the Distance Formula to determine the lengths of the sides of a triangle to classify it as equilateral, isosceles, or scalene.

You can use the slope formula to classify a triangle as a right triangle (slopes of consecutive sides will be opposite reciprocals). You can also use the slope formula to classify a quadrilateral as a square or rectangle (slopes of consecutive sides are opposite reciprocals) or as a parallelogram or rhombus (slopes of opposite sides are equal).

You can use the Distance Formula to determine the lengths of the sides of a quadrilateral to classify it as a rhombus or square (four equal side lengths) or a parallelogram or rectangle (opposite sides are equal).

NOTES

STRETCH

Point *B*: (−4, −1)

Point *C*: (2, −3)

2 Susan is an interior floor designer. When designing a new floor, she uses a coordinate grid to represent the room. The client wants a rectangular tile insert in the floor of the room. The coordinates for 3 of the corners of the insert are *A* (−7, −4), *B* (1, 6), and *C* (6, 2).

ⓐ Plot and label the points on a coordinate plane, then determine the coordinates of the fourth point of the rectangular tile insert. Plot this as point *D* and connect the points to form the rectangle.

The coordinates of point *D* are (−2, −8).

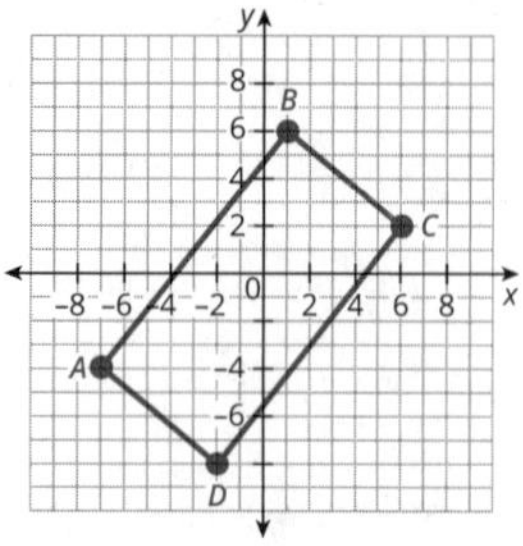

ⓑ To prove the figure you drew is a rectangle, verify that the length of opposite sides are equal.

AB and *DC* = $\sqrt{164}$.

AD and *BC* = $\sqrt{41}$.

3 A client of Susan's has asked her to create a new wood floor for his living room by laying wood strips in different directions, as shown on the coordinate grid. Determine whether Quadrilateral *ABCD* is best described as a trapezoid, a rhombus, a rectangle, or a square. Explain your reasoning.

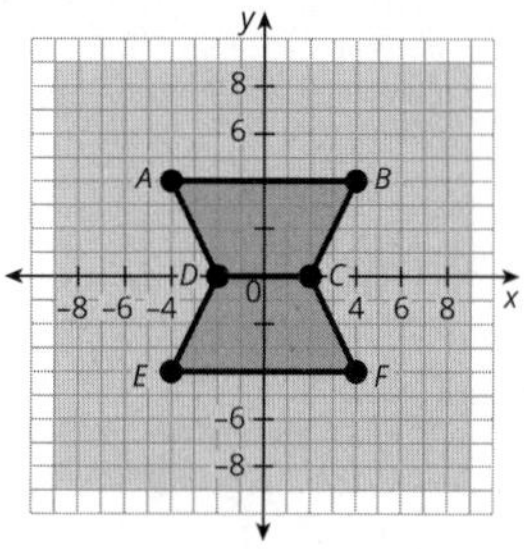

Slope of $\overline{AB}$: $m = 0$

Slope of $\overline{BC}$: $m = 2$

Slope of $\overline{CD}$: $m = 0$

Slope of $\overline{AD}$: $m = -2$

None of the slopes have opposite reciprocal relationships, so Quadrilateral *ABCD* cannot be a square or rectangle. There are only two opposite sides that are parallel, so Quadrilateral *ABCD* must be a trapezoid.

STRETCH Optional

The lines that connect points *A*, *B*, and *C* on a coordinate plane form a right triangle.

- Point *A* is at (−2, 5).
- Point *B* is 6 units down from point *A* and to the left of point *A*.
- Point *C* is located 4 units to the right of point *A* and down from point *A*.
- The angle at point *B* is a right angle.
- The slope of the line between point *B* and point *C* is $-\frac{1}{3}$.
- The distance between point *A* and point *B* is $\sqrt{40}$.

1 Determine the coordinates of point *B* and point *C*.

Where Has Polly Gone?

This resource details additional facilitation notes to fully assist you as you plan each lesson to support all students, students who struggle, and advanced learners. It provides differentiation strategies, common student misconceptions, and suggestions to extend certain activities.

GETTING STARTED

Session 1 of 1

You Better Shape Up

Students compare characteristics of triangles and quadrilaterals in a Venn diagram. They identify whether statements about these polygons are always, sometimes, or never true.

CHUNK	AUDIENCE	ADDITIONAL SUPPORTS
As students work on 1	Students who Struggle	**DIFFERENTIATION STRATEGY** Model a strategy for students to complete the Venn Diagram. For example: • Select a polygon, such as a right triangle, and ask: • Does it have at least one pair of perpendicular sides? *yes* • Does it have two pairs of parallel sides? *no* • Are all sides congruent? *no* Based on the responses, a right triangle belongs in Section A.
As students discuss 1	All Students	**DIFFERENTIATION STRATEGY** Ask students to create counterexamples for incorrect responses.
As students work on 4	All Students	**DIFFERENTIATION STRATEGY** Encourage students to take time to read through each strategy, thinking about and annotating the connections, to determine whether each strategy is correct or not. Suggest students ask themselves: • Does the reasoning make sense? • When the reasoning makes sense, what is the justification? • When the reasoning does not make sense, what error was made?

ACTIVITY 1

Session 1 of 3

Calculating Distance on the Coordinate Plane

Students identify quadrilaterals by considering their side lengths and the slopes of their sides. They relate the Distance Formula to the Pythagorean Theorem and calculate the distance between points.

CHUNK	AUDIENCE	ADDITIONAL SUPPORTS
As you read and discuss the Distance Formula	Students who Struggle	**DIFFERENTIATION STRATEGY** Provide additional scaffolding to help students make sense of the diagram. • Label the axes with x_1, x_2, y_1, and y_2 so they understand how to determine the coordinate pairs for the three vertices. • Trace over the horizontal side of the triangle with a colored pencil, and then use the same color to trace the x_1- and x_2-coordinates of its endpoints. Repeat the process with the y_1- and y_2-coordinates for the vertical side of the triangle. • Explain how to derive the algebraic expressions for the side lengths. • Write the expression of the sum of the two squares. • Explain why it's necessary to take the square root of the expression to solve for the hypotenuse (distance).
As students work on 7	All Students	**DIFFERENTIATION STRATEGY** • Students calculated *EF* in Question 5 using the Pythagorean Theorem. Have them start by recalculating *EF* using the Distance Formula and compare the steps. • Suggest they label the coordinate pairs before using the Distance Formula. $E\,(2, 3)$ $F\,(6, 0)$ x_1, y_1 x_2, y_2
As students work on 8	Students who Struggle	**DIFFERENTIATION STRATEGY** Students may prefer to use a diagram to visualize the Distance Formula notation. If so, demonstrate how they can sketch a diagram instead of using graph paper to calculate the horizontal and vertical lengths before substituting them in the Pythagorean Theorem.

ACTIVITY 2

Session 2 of 3

Classifying Triangles on the Coordinate Plane

Students classify triangles by considering their side lengths and the slopes of their sides. They apply the converse of the Pythagorean Theorem to classify a triangle as acute, right, or obtuse.

CHUNK	AUDIENCE	ADDITIONAL SUPPORTS
As students begin 1	All Students	**DIFFERENTIATION STRATEGY** Review labeling conventions. When labeling a triangle, use a capital letter for each vertex and a lower case version of the same letter for the opposite side. Have students label the sides of ΔABC with a, b, and c before completing Question 1, part (c).
As you share and summarize 1	All Students	**DIFFERENTIATION STRATEGY** Remind students to attend to precision as they express their responses to Question 1, parts (a) and (b). • AB represents a numeric value, the distance between Point A and Point B. For example, $AB = 5$. • $\overline{AB}$ represents a geometric figure, the segment between Point A and Point B. For example, the slope of $\overline{AB}$ is undefined.
As students begin 2	All Students	**DIFFERENTIATION STRATEGY** Remind students that before they use any strategy to determine whether a triangle is a right triangle, they should check that the three sides' lengths create a triangle using the Triangle Inequality Theorem. This theorem states that the sum of any two sides' lengths is greater than the third side's length.

ACTIVITY 4

Session 2 of 3

Classifying a Quadrilateral on the Coordinate Plane

Students classify quadrilaterals on the coordinate plane. They graph the quadrilaterals and identify them by their side lengths and the slopes of their sides.

CHUNK	AUDIENCE	ADDITIONAL SUPPORTS
As you share and summarize 2	All Students	**COMMON MISCONCEPTION** Students may say that they can recognize from the graph that the figure is not a square without doing math. Explain that: • Our goal is not just to answer the question but also to learn and practice formal reasoning methods. • When a graph has different scales on its *x*- and *y*-axis, the graph will be distorted, and observations may lead to inaccurate conclusions.

ACTIVITY 5

Session 3 of 3

Classifying a Quadrilateral Formed by Midpoints

Students use the Midpoint Formula to calculate the midpoints of the sides of quadrilaterals. They then connect consecutive midpoints and identify the resulting quadrilateral.

CHUNK	AUDIENCE	ADDITIONAL SUPPORTS
As students begin 2	Students who Struggle	**DIFFERENTIATION STRATEGY** Provide sample coordinate pairs for the rhombus.
To extend 2	Advanced Learners	**DIFFERENTIATION STRATEGY** Have students repeat the activity with a parallelogram and trapezoid. Then have them analyze the results based on whether the original figure was a square, rhombus, parallelogram, or trapezoid.

Practice the learning

MATHbook + Skills Practice

The table shows the targeted practice of the skills and mathematical concepts for the *Using a Rectangular Coordinate System* Topic. The highlighted Problem Set aligns with **Where Has Polly Gone?**

PROBLEM SET	
1	Identifying Properties of Geometric Figures
2	Constructing Perpendicular Lines
3	Duplicating Line Segments
4	Writing Equations of Parallel and Perpendicular Lines
5	**Classifying Shapes on the Coordinate Plane**
6	Determining Perimeter and Area of Rectangles and Triangles on the Coordinate Plane
7	Determining Perimeter and Area of Other Polygons on the Coordinate Plane

ANYTIME AFTER ACTIVITY 5

Facilitate students as they work individually on **Problem Set 5**.

NOTES

ENGAGE + DEVELOP + TEACH

at the **Module** level

at the **Topic** level

Read the facilitation notes and plan learning experiences.

Where are we?

TOPIC 1 Using a Rectangular Coordinate System	LESSON 1 The Squariest Square	LESSON 2 Hip to Be Square	LESSON 3 Ts and Train Tracks	LESSON 4 Where Has Polly Gone?	**LESSON 5 In and Out and All About**
Pacing	1 Session	2 Sessions	2 Sessions	3 Sessions	**3 Sessions**

OVERVIEW: LESSON 5

In and Out and All About

Area and Perimeter on the Coordinate Plane

ENGAGE

- Students describe ways to calculate the area of polygons drawn on a grid.

DEVELOP

- Students calculate the area and perimeter of polygons and composite figures on the coordinate plane.
- They consider how doubling a dimension of a rectangle affects its area.
- They translate figures on the coordinate plane for efficient computations.
- They determine the height of a triangle on the coordinate plane.
- Students solve real-world problems involving perimeter and area.

DEMONSTRATE

- Students estimate the area of an irregularly-shaped figure.

HIGH SCHOOL GEOMETRY

Expressing Geometric Properties with Equations

Use coordinates to prove simple geometric theorems algebraically.

5. Prove the slope criteria for parallel and perpendicular lines and use them to solve geometric problems (e.g., find the equation of a line parallel or perpendicular to a given line that passes through a given point).

7. Use coordinates to compute perimeters of polygons and areas of triangles and rectangles, e.g., using the distance formula.

Modeling with Geometry

Apply geometric concepts in modeling situations.

2. Apply concepts of density based on area and volume in modeling situations (e.g., persons per square mile, BTUs per cubic foot).

LESSON STRUCTURE AND PACING GUIDE 3 SESSIONS

✪ This activity highlights a key term or concept that is essential to the learning goals of the lesson.

Session 1

INSTRUCTIONAL SEQUENCE

ENGAGE
Connect to prior knowledge

GETTING STARTED
It's Child's Play

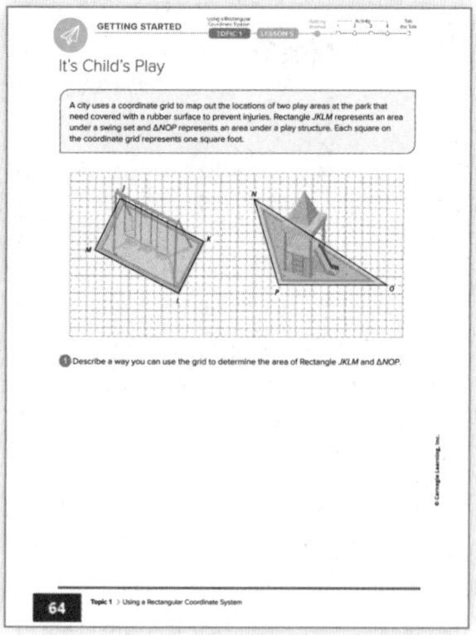

Students consider two figures on a coordinate grid.

- They describe ways to calculate the area of each figure.

DEVELOP
Peer analysis
Mathematical problem solving

✪ ACTIVITY 1
Perimeter and Area of Figures on the Coordinate Plane

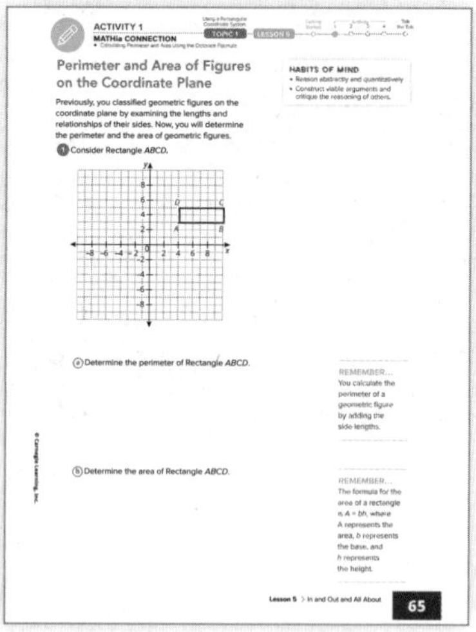

Students calculate the area and perimeter of polygons on the coordinate plane.

- They consider how doubling a dimension of a rectangle affects its area.
- They translate figures on the coordinate plane for efficient computations.

Session 2

DEVELOP
Worked example
Peer analysis

✪ ACTIVITY 2
Calculating Heights of Triangles

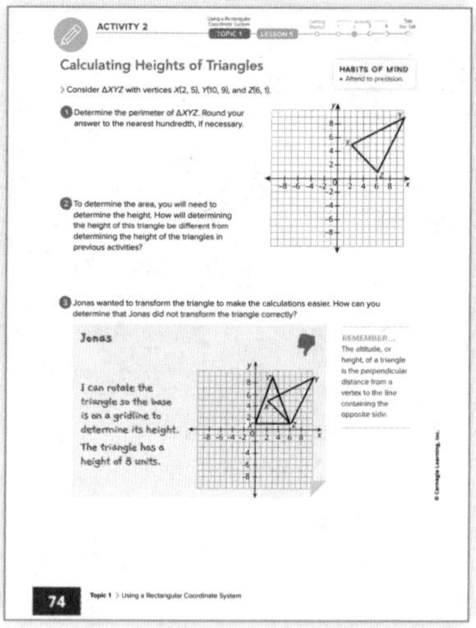

Students calculate the area of triangles on the coordinate plane.

- They use algebra to determine the height of a triangle.

Log in to MyCL for **lesson support** including:

Slides

Videos

www.carnegielearning.com/login

TOPIC 1

Session 3

INSTRUCTIONAL SEQUENCE

DEVELOP	DEVELOP	DEMONSTRATE
Real-world problem solving	Real-world problem solving	Exit ticket application

ACTIVITY 3
Perimeter and Area of a Composite Figure

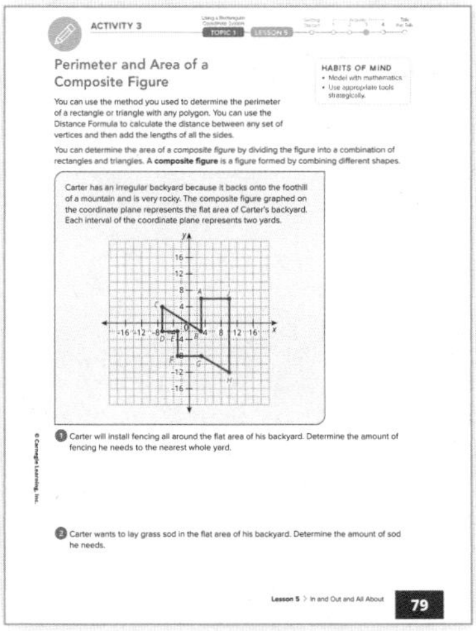

Students calculate the area of a composite figure on the coordinate plane.

- They solve a real-world problem involving perimeter and area.

ACTIVITY 4
Solving Problems with Perimeter and Area

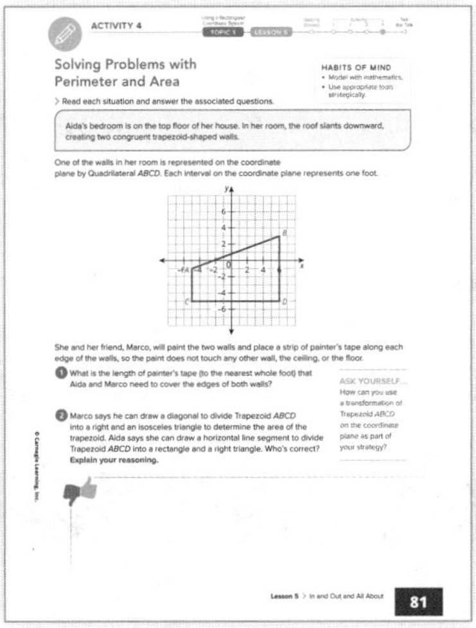

Students solve real-world problems involving perimeter and area.

- They relate distance traveled to the area under a (rate) × (time) graph.

TALK THE TALK
Vive les Maths!

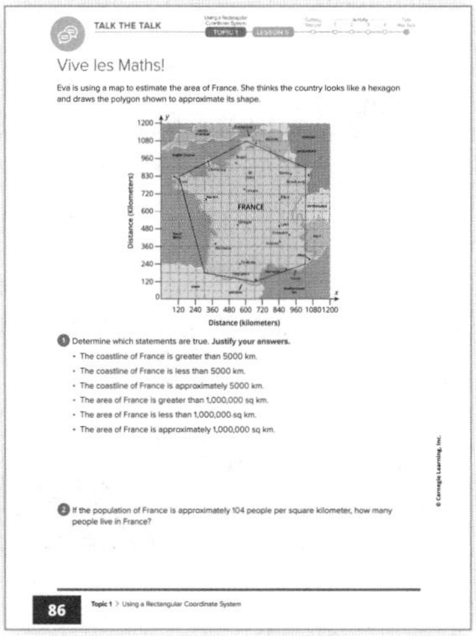

Students estimate the area of France by analyzing a map on the coordinate plane.

- They use population density to estimate France's population.

Log in to MyCL for:

- Editable templates
- Additional planning support

Now that you have read the Module, Topic, and Lesson Overviews, you are ready to plan.

Do the math

> Tear out the lesson planning template (page 63E) and jot down thoughts as you work through this lesson and read the Facilitation Notes.

Connect the learning

MATHbook + MATHia

The table shows a portion of the self-paced MATHia sequence for the *Using a Rectangular Coordinate System* Topic.

Median student completion time for the entire topic: ~200–215 minutes

> As you implement this lesson, consider different connections for students who are on pace and those that have not yet completed the workspaces aligned to this lesson.

STUDENTS WHO ARE NOT HERE YET
Students will practice using the Distance Formula to measure different shapes.

TYPE	WORKSPACE NAME
	Introduction to Parallel and Perpendicular Lines
	Modeling Parallel and Perpendicular Lines
	Deriving the Distance Formula
	Calculating Distances using the Distance Formula
	Calculating Perimeter and Area Using the Distance Formula

STUDENTS WHO ARE ON PACE
After you complete Activity 1, ask these students to share how they determined perimeters and areas of shapes in this workspace.

In and Out and All About

Area and Perimeter on the Coordinate Plane

Session 1

GETTING STARTED It's Child's Play

Pacing (minutes)	
My Time	Class Time

ACTIVITY 1 Perimeter and Area of Figures on the Coordinate Plane ✪

Pacing (minutes)	
My Time	Class Time

Session 2

ACTIVITY 2 Calculating Heights of Triangles ✪

Pacing (minutes)	
My Time	Class Time

Session 3

ACTIVITY 3 Perimeter and Area of a Composite Figure ✪

Pacing (minutes)	
My Time	Class Time

KEY TERM
composite figure

ACTIVITY 4 Solving Problems with Perimeter and Area

Pacing (minutes)	
My Time	Class Time

TALK THE TALK Vive les Maths! ✪

Pacing (minutes)	
My Time	Class Time

✪ This activity highlights a key term or concept that is essential to the learning goals of the lesson.

Log in to MyCL for:
- Editable templates
- Additional planning support

Reflect on your lesson

> Consider the effectiveness of your lesson on student learning.

What went well?

What did not go as planned?

> Anticipate how you would change the lesson next time you teach it.

How will you capitalize on the things that went well?

How will you improve things that did not go as planned?

MATERIALS

- None

1 | The Squariest Square
2 | Hip to Be Square
3 | Ts and Train Tracks
4 | Where Has Polly Gone?
5 | In and Out and All About

LESSON 5

In and Out and All About

Area and Perimeter on the Coordinate Plane

KEY TERM

composite figure

Learning Goals

- Determine the perimeter and area of rectangles, triangles, and composite figures on the coordinate plane.
- Use transformations to discover efficient strategies to determine the perimeter and area of rectangles and triangles.
- Use the Distance Formula to solve real-world problems involving perimeters of parallelograms, trapezoids, and hexagons.
- Decompose polygons—including trapezoids and hexagons—to solve real-world problems involving area.
- Calculate the area under a curve to determine distance in an acceleration model.

REVIEW (1–2 minutes)

Determine the distance between each set of points. Round your answer to the nearest tenth, if necessary.

1. (2, −3) and (−4, 1)

   7.2

2. (−4.75, −8.5) and (3.25, 5.5)

   16.1

You have used the Distance Formula and the slope formula to classify geometric figures on the coordinate plane.

How can you use rigid motions to determine the perimeter and area of polygons on the coordinate plane?

Setting the Stage

- **Assign Review (optional, 1 – 2 minutes)**
- **Communicate the learning goals and key terms to look out for**
- **Tap into your students' prior learning by reading the narrative statement**
- **Provide a sense of direction by reading the question**

IN THIS REVIEW

Students determine the distance between two points. They will first use this skill in **ACTIVITY 1 Perimeter and Area of Figures on the Coordinate Plane.**

Rigid transformations can make calculating the perimeter and area of figures on the coordinate plane more efficient.

You can think of any side of a triangle as its base, and the height of the triangle is the perpendicular distance from the base to the opposite vertex.

Essential Ideas

- Doubling a dimension of a rectangle or triangle doubles its area.
- You can translate a shape on a coordinate plane for more efficient computations.
- You can use the Distance Formula to determine the height of a triangle.
- To calculate a composite figure's area, you can decompose it into polygons with known area formulas, compute the areas, and calculate the sum.
- You can solve real-world problems with perimeter and area.
- You can estimate the area of an irregularly-shaped figure by making it resemble a polygon.

SUMMARY **You can calculate the polygon's area by counting the number of square units in its interior or using a formula.**

Chunking the Activity

- **Read and discuss the situation**
- **Group students to complete the activity**
- **Share and summarize**

Student Look-Fors

An error identifying the height of ΔNOP when using $\overline{PO}$ as the base. Students may use the length of $\overline{NP}$ as the height of the triangle rather than determining the length of a perpendicular line segment dropped from point N to an extension of $\overline{PO}$.

COMMON MISCONCEPTION

See Page 88A for a misconception related to 1.

It's Child's Play

A city uses a coordinate grid to map out the locations of two play areas at the park that need covered with a rubber surface to prevent injuries. Rectangle *JKLM* represents an area under a swing set and ΔNOP represents an area under a play structure. Each square on the coordinate grid represents one square foot.

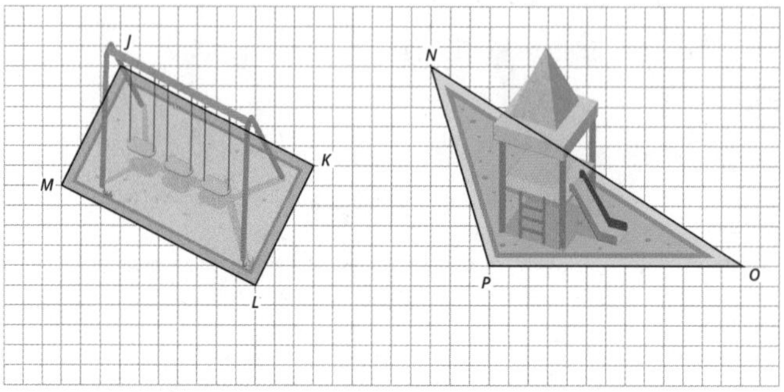

1 Describe a way you can use the grid to determine the area of Rectangle *JKLM* and ΔNOP.

Sample answers.

I can count the number of blocks inside of each shape, then convert square units to square feet.

I can use the formulas for the area of a rectangle, $A = bh$, and the area of a triangle, $A = \frac{1}{2}bh$. I can get the measurements for b and h by using the Distance Formula, where each unit represents one square foot.

Questions to Support Discourse

		TYPE
1	• What is the area formula for a triangle? • What are the units of your answer?	Gathering
	• If you were counting blocks, how did you count partial blocks? • If you used the area formula, how did you determine the base and height for the rectangular playground? • Which side(s) can you consider the base of the triangle? • If $\overline{PO}$ is the base, how do you determine the height of the triangle? • How did you calculate the measure of the base? The measure of the height?	Probing

ACTIVITY 1

Session 1 of 3

SUMMARY **Doubling a dimension of a rectangle or triangle doubles its area. You can translate a shape on a coordinate plane for efficient computations.**

ACTIVITY 1

MATHia CONNECTION

- Calculating Perimeter and Area Using the Distance Formula

Perimeter and Area of Figures on the Coordinate Plane

HABITS OF MIND
- Reason abstractly and quantitatively.
- Construct viable arguments and critique the reasoning of others.

Previously, you classified geometric figures on the coordinate plane by examining the lengths and relationships of their sides. Now, you will determine the perimeter and the area of geometric figures.

1 Consider Rectangle *ABCD*.

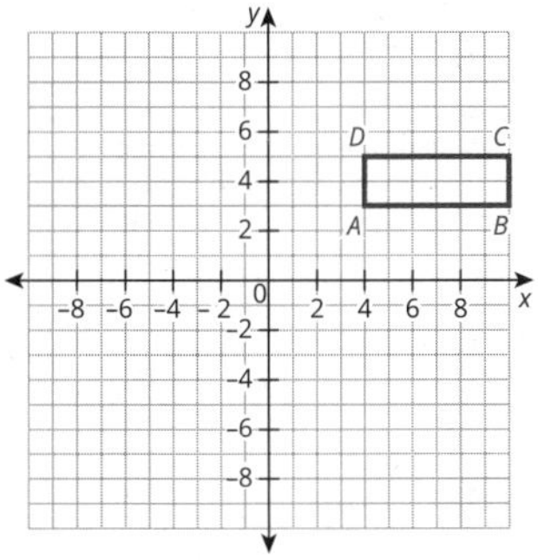

ⓐ Determine the perimeter of Rectangle *ABCD*.

The perimeter of Rectangle *ABCD* is 16 units.

REMEMBER...
You calculate the perimeter of a geometric figure by adding the side lengths.

ⓑ Determine the area of Rectangle *ABCD*.

The area of Rectangle *ABCD* is 12 square units.

REMEMBER...
The formula for the area of a rectangle is $A = bh$, where A represents the area, b represents the base, and h represents the height.

Chunking the Activity

- Read and discuss the introduction
- Group students to complete 1 – 5
- Check-in and share
- Read and discuss Shantelle's strategy
- Complete 6 and 7 as a class
- Group students to complete 8 – 10
- Check-in and share
- Group students to complete 11 – 13
- Share and summarize

DIFFERENTIATION STRATEGY

See Page 88A to support students who struggle with this activity.

Questions to Support Discourse

		TYPE
1	• Explain your strategy. What is another method? • What are the units of your answer?	Probing

NOTES

Student Look-Fors

A perimeter of 18 units or an area of 18 square units signifies that the student didn't take into account the graph's scale when solving Question 3.

DIFFERENTIATION STRATEGY

See Page 88B to assist all students with 5.

2 Horace says that he determined the area of Rectangle *ABCD* by determining the product (*CD*)(*CB*). Bernice says that Horace is incorrect because he needs to use the base of the rectangle and that the base is $\overline{AB}$, not $\overline{CD}$. Horace responded by saying that $\overline{CD}$ is one of the bases. Who's correct? **Explain your reasoning.**

Horace is correct. Line segment *CD* is one of the bases. You can consider any side of the rectangle as a base.

When you graph a rectangle along gridlines, you can determine the perimeter and area by simply counting units or square units on the coordinate plane. This is true when all coordinates are integers. If they are fractions or decimals, it presents a challenge.

> Analyze Rectangle *RSTU* on the coordinate plane shown.

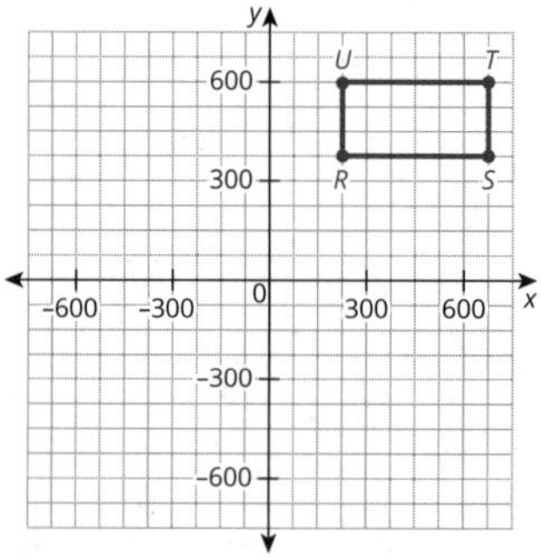

THINK ABOUT...
Notice the intervals along the axes.

3 Calculate the perimeter and area of Rectangle *RSTU*.

The perimeter of Rectangle *RSTU* is 1350 units.

The area of Rectangle *RSTU* is 101,250 square units.

4 How would doubling the height of the rectangle affect the area?

Doubling the height of the rectangle doubles the area.

5 How would doubling the length of the base of the rectangle affect the area?

Doubling the base of the rectangle doubles the area.

Questions to Support Discourse

		TYPE
3	• What are the dimensions of the rectangle?	Gathering
4	• Demonstrate this situation on the graph. • What are the dimensions of the enlarged rectangle? • Show your calculations to solve this problem.	Probing
	• If you didn't take the scale into account and got an area of 18 square units, how can you apply the scale to your answer to get the correct area?	Seeing structure
5	• How is this graph different from the previous graph?	Gathering
	• What are the dimensions of the enlarged rectangle?	Probing
	• Why do you think you get the same area regardless of what dimension you double?	Seeing structure

ACTIVITY 1 Continued

Shantelle used another strategy to determine the perimeter and area of Rectangle *RSTU*.

> Shantelle
> If I translate Rectangle RSTU to have at least one point of image R′S′T′U′ on the origin, it is easier to calculate the perimeter and area of Rectangle RSTU because one of the points will have coordinates (0,0).

6. Explain how Shantelle knows that a translation of Rectangle *RSTU* will have the same area and perimeter as the pre-image *RSTU*?

   Transformations preserve size and shape, so the two figures are congruent.

7. Translate Rectangle *RSTU* so that point *R* is at the origin.

   (a) List the coordinates of rectangle *R′S′T′U′*.

   R′(0,0), *S′*(450,0), *T′*(450,225), *U′*(0,225)

   (b) Determine the perimeter and area of Rectangle *R′S′T′U′*. **What do you notice?**

   The perimeter of Rectangle *R′S′T′U′* is 1350 units.

   The area of *R′S′T′U′* is 101,250 square units.

   The perimeter and area of Rectangle *R′S′T′U′* are equal to the perimeter and area of Rectangle *RSTU*.

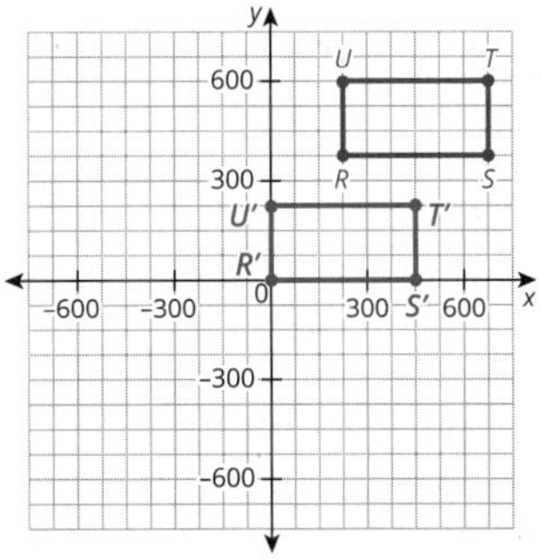

Lesson 5 > In and Out and All About 67

NOTES

TOPIC 1

DIFFERENTIATION STRATEGY

See Page 88B to assist all students with the strategy.

Questions to Support Discourse

		TYPE
7	• Describe the translations to relocate the square. • How did you determine the new coordinates?	Probing

NOTES

ACTIVITY 1 Continued

When the sides of a rectangle do not lie on the gridlines of the coordinate plane, you can use the Distance Formula to determine the lengths of the sides.

8 Consider Quadrilateral *LMNO*.

(a) Determine the perimeter and area of Quadrilateral *LMNO*. Round your answer to the nearest hundredth, if necessary.

THINK ABOUT...
Is the quadrilateral a square, a rectangle, or a rhombus?

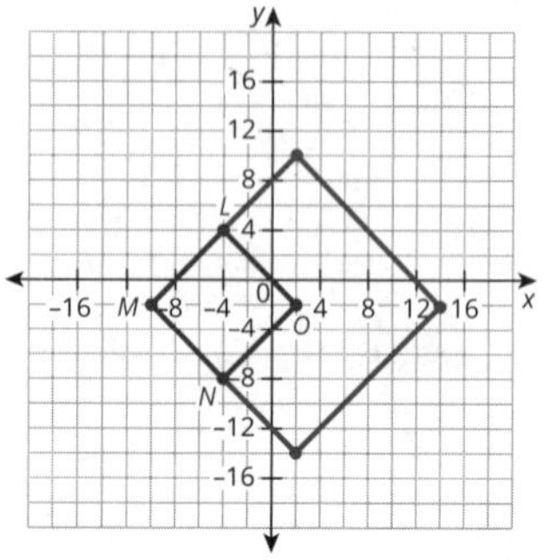

Each side of Square *LMNO* is $\sqrt{72}$ or approximately 8.49 units.

The perimeter of Square *LMNO* is approximately 33.94 units.

The area of Square *LMNO* is 72 square units.

ASK YOURSELF...
How could you translate Quadrilateral *LMNO* to make the perimeter and area calculations more efficient?

(b) Double the side lengths of Quadrilateral *LMNO*. How does the area of the new quadrilateral compare to the area of the original quadrialteral? What are the possible new coordinates?

The area of the square with doubled side lengths is four times the area of the original square.

Sample answer. See graph.

The possible new coordinates of the square are (− 10, −2), (2, 10), (14, −2), and (2, −14).

Questions to Support Discourse

		TYPE
8	• Did you use the Distance Formula or the Pythagorean Theorem to solve this problem? Why?	Gathering
	• How could you use the graph to determine that all the sides had the same length? • How did you know that this figure was a rectangle so that you could apply the formula $A = bh$? • How can you solve this problem with arithmetic?	Probing

ACTIVITY 1 Continued

9 Consider ΔDEF with vertices $D(-5,-9)$, $E(3,-1)$, and $F(3,-9)$.

(a) Determine the perimeter and area of ΔDEF. Round your answer to the nearest hundredth, if necessary.

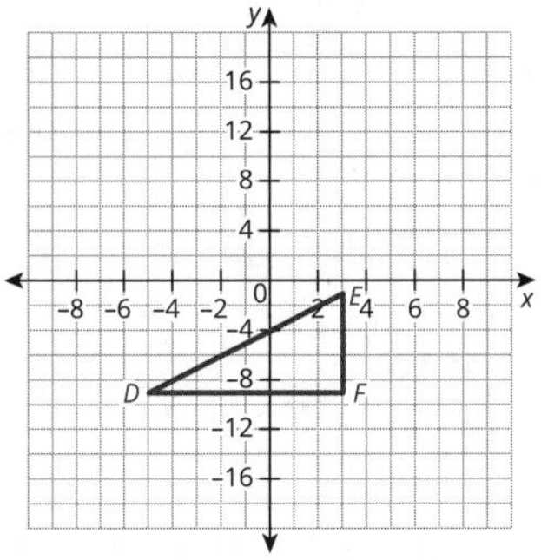

Perimeter of ΔDEF ≈ 27.31 units.

Area of ΔDEF = 32 square units.

(b) Double the height. What are the coordinates of the new triangle? How did this affect the area?

Sample answer.

Possible coordinates of the new triangle with doubled height are $D(-5,-9)$, $E'(3, 7)$, and $F(3,-9)$.

The area of the triangle doubles to 64 square units.

(c) Double the length of the base. What are the coordinates of the new triangle? How did this affect the area?

Sample answer.

Possible coordinates of the new triangle with the doubled base are $D'(-8,-9)$, $E'(8,-1)$, and $F'(8,-9)$.

The area of the triangle is doubled to 64 square units.

(d) Double the length of both the base and the height. How does this affect the area?

Doubling the base and height quadruples the area of the triangle to 128 square units.

NOTES

DIFFERENTIATION STRATEGY

See Page 90B to assist all students with 9.

TOPIC 1

Questions to Support Discourse

		TYPE
9	• Were your results what you expected? Explain your thinking?	Gathering
	• How did you calculate the perimeter? Area? • How can you solve this problem with arithmetic?	Probing
	• Is the new triangle similar to the enlarged one? How can you tell? • How can you generalize this problem using algebra?	Seeing structure

NOTES

ACTIVITY 1 Continued

10 Mr. Young gives his class ΔDEF and asks them to determine the area and perimeter. Four of his students decide first to transform the figure and then determine the perimeter and area. Here are their transformations.

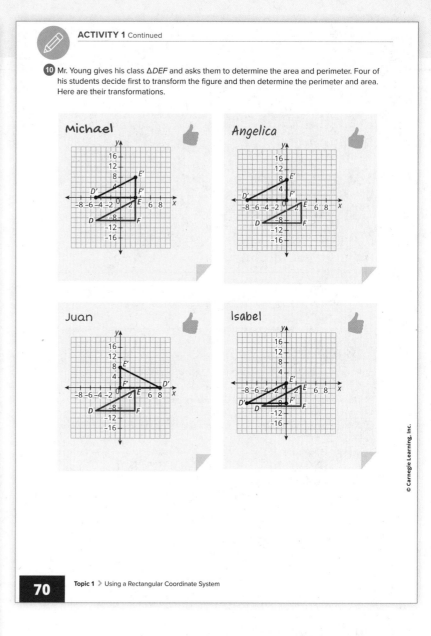

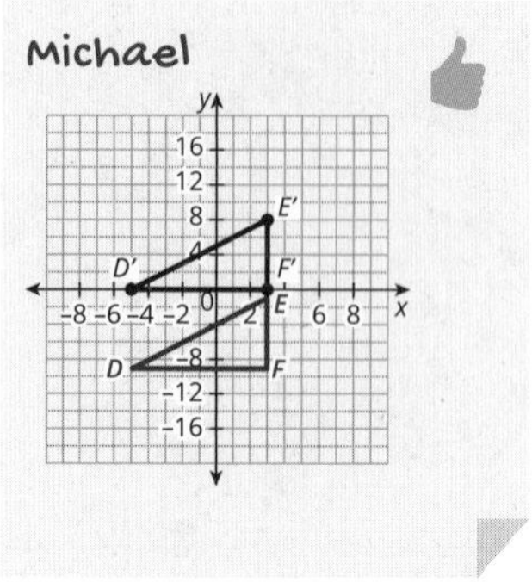

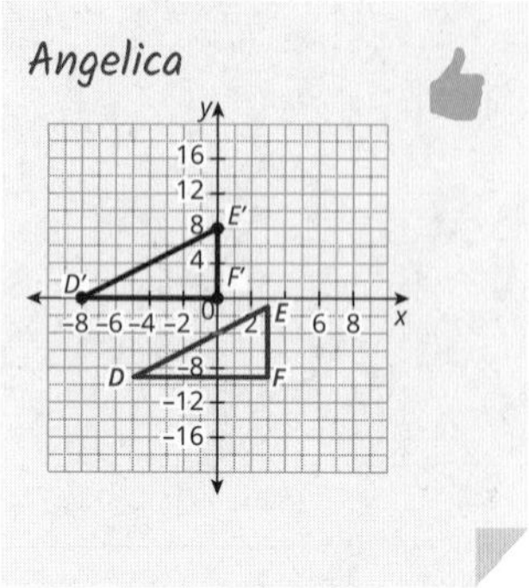

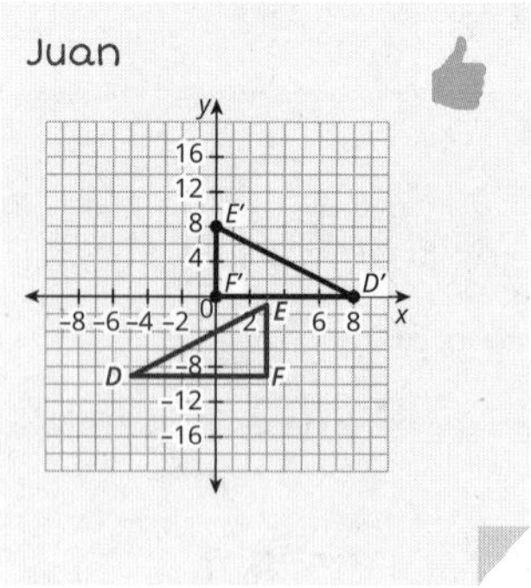

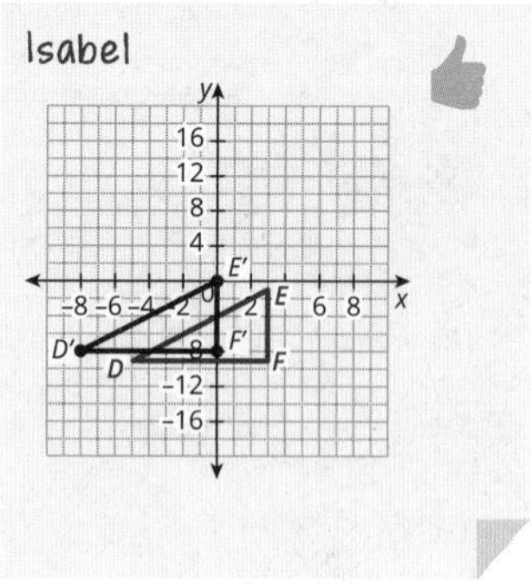

70 Topic 1 > Using a Rectangular Coordinate System

ACTIVITY 1 Continued

ⓐ Describe the transformation(s) each student made to ΔDEF.

Michael vertically translated ΔDEF up 9 units.

Angelica vertically translated ΔDEF up 9 units, then horizontally translated it to the left 3 units.

Juan vertically translated ΔDEF up 9 units, horizontally translated it to the left 3 units, and reflected it over the *y*-axis.

Isabel horizontally translated ΔDEF to the left 3 units and up 1 unit.

ⓑ Whose method do you think is most efficient? **Explain your reasoning.**

Sample answer.

Juan's method is most efficient because it transforms the triangle into Quadrant I, so all the coordinates are positive and two line segments of the triangle are on the axes.

ⓒ What do you know about the perimeter and area of all the triangles? **Explain your reasoning.**

The perimeters and areas of all the triangles are equal. Rigid motion transformations preserve size and shape, so the figures are congruent.

Consider ΔABC with vertices A (−7.5, 2), B (−5.5, 13), and C (2.5, 2).

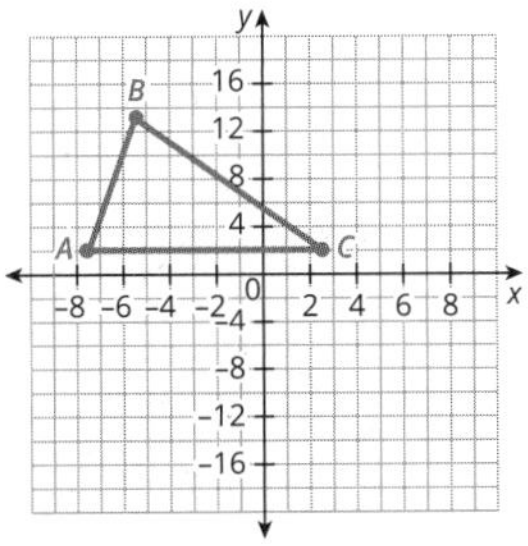

11 Determine the perimeter of ΔABC. Round your answer to the nearest hundredth, if necessary.

The perimeter of ΔABC is approximately 34.78 units

12 Consider how to determine the area of ΔABC.

ⓐ What information is needed about ΔABC to determine its area?

To determine the area of ΔABC, I need to know the measures of the base and the height.

NOTES

DIFFERENTIATION STRATEGY

See Page 88B to support students who struggle with **10** part (a).

Questions to Support Discourse

		TYPE
11	• Which student's transformation makes the most sense to you? Why? • Which student completed a transformation other than a translation? • Why do you think Juan chose a reflection?	Gathering
	• Did you transform the triangle before you completed your calculations? If so, explain your strategy.	Probing
12	• How do you know that your base and height are perpendicular?	Seeing structure

NOTES

ⓑ Arlo says that $\overline{AB}$ is the height. Trisha disagrees and says that $\overline{BC}$ can be used as the height. Randy disagrees with both of them and says that none of the line segments currently on the triangle are the height. Who is correct? **Explain your reasoning.**

Randy is correct.
The height of a triangle must be a perpendicular line from a vertex to a line containing the triangle's base. You cannot use neither $\overline{AB}$ nor $\overline{BC}$ as the height because neither of them are perpendicular to any line containing a base.

ⓒ Draw and label $\overline{BD}$ to represent the height of ΔABC. Then, determine the height of ΔABC.

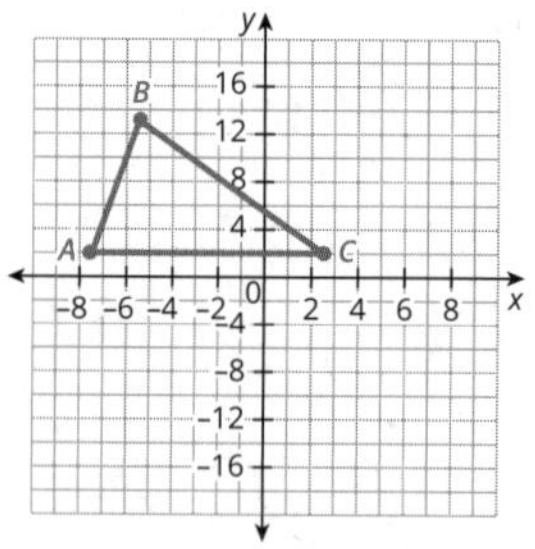

The height of ΔABC is 11 units.

ⓓ Determine the area of ΔABC.

The area of ΔABC is 55 square units.

ACTIVITY 1 Continued

13 Consider a more efficient way to determine the area and perimeter of ΔABC.

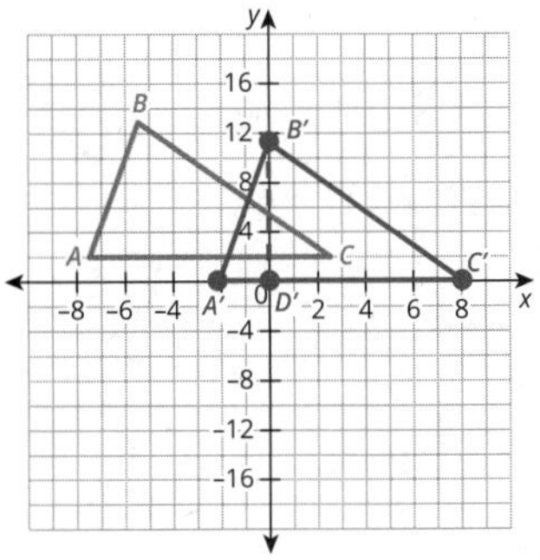

ⓐ Transform ΔABC on the coordinate plane. Label the image $A'B'C'$. **Describe the transformation(s) completed and explain your reasoning.**

Sample answer.

I vertically translated the triangle down two units so the base $\overline{AC}$ is on the *x*-axis.

I then horizontally translated the triangle to the right 5.5 units so point B is on the *y*-axis.

ⓑ Determine the perimeter and area of $\Delta A'B'C'$. Round your answer to the nearest hundredth, if necessary.

$P = \sqrt{125} + \sqrt{185} + 10 \approx 34.78$

The perimeter of triangle $A'B'C'$ is approximately 34.78 units.

$A = \frac{1}{2}(10)(11) = 55$

The area of triangle $A'B'C'$ is 55 square units.

ⓒ Compare these calculations to your previous calculations. **How did the translation change your calculations?**

Sample answer.

The calculations were somewhat simpler, but rigid motion transformations are more helpful with rectangles than triangles.

Lesson 5 > In and Out and All About 73

NOTES

Student Look-Fors

Different translations of ΔABC. For example, is $\angle A$ at the origin, or is $\overline{AC}$ along the *x*-axis with point B on the *y*-axis?

Questions to Support Discourse

		TYPE
13	• How does your transformation compare to those of your peers? • Did you see a transformation that seemed more efficient than yours? If so, explain your thinking.	Gathering

SUMMARY You can use the Distance Formula to determine the measure of a non-vertical or non-horizontal height of a triangle.

Chunking the Activity

- **Read and discuss the introduction**
- **Group students to complete 1 – 3**
- **Check-in and share**
- **Read and discuss the worked example as a class**
- **Group students to complete 4 – 6**
- **Check-in and share**
- **Group students to complete 7**
- **Check-in and share**
- **Group students to complete 8 and 9**
- **Share and summarize**

Student Look-Fors

Whether students use patty paper or the Distance Formula to determine whether Jonas transformed the triangle correctly. Encourage students to use the Distance Formula. They may not recognize the error with patty paper.

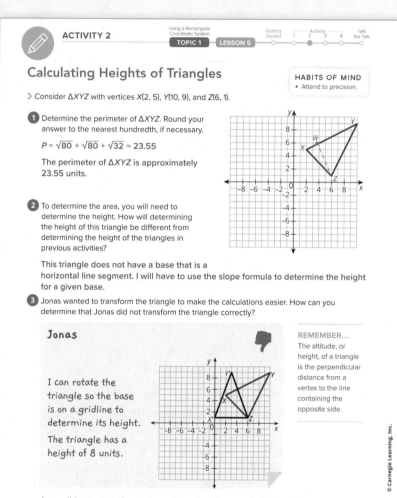

Calculating Heights of Triangles

HABITS OF MIND
- Attend to precision.

> Consider ΔXYZ with vertices $X(2, 5)$, $Y(10, 9)$, and $Z(6, 1)$.

1. Determine the perimeter of ΔXYZ. Round your answer to the nearest hundredth, if necessary.

   $P = \sqrt{80} + \sqrt{80} + \sqrt{32} \approx 23.55$

   The perimeter of ΔXYZ is approximately 23.55 units.

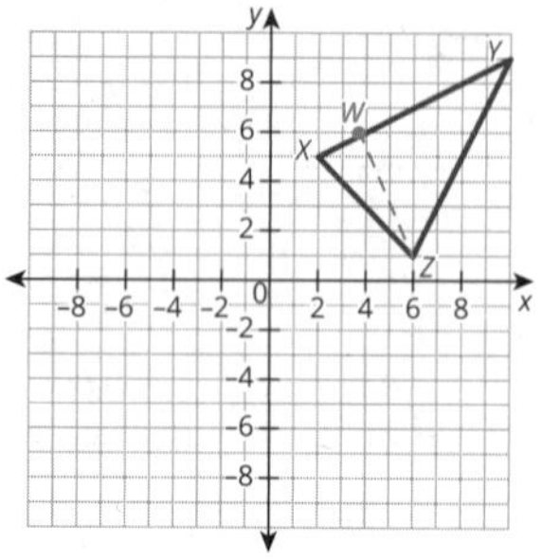

2. To determine the area, you will need to determine the height. How will determining the height of this triangle be different from determining the height of the triangles in previous activities?

   This triangle does not have a base that is a horizontal line segment. I will have to use the slope formula to determine the height for a given base.

3. Jonas wanted to transform the triangle to make the calculations easier. How can you determine that Jonas did not transform the triangle correctly?

Jonas

I can rotate the triangle so the base is on a gridline to determine its height.

The triangle has a height of 8 units.

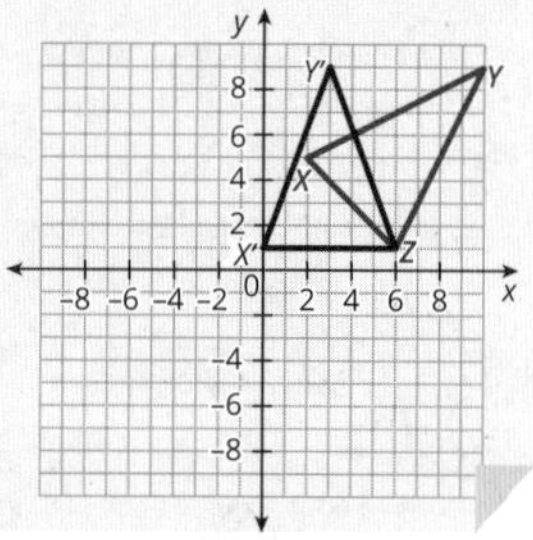

REMEMBER...
The altitude, or height, of a triangle is the perpendicular distance from a vertex to the line containing the opposite side.

Jonas did not rotate the vertices of the triangle correctly. If Jonas had performed the rotation correctly, then the image and pre-image's side lengths would be congruent, since rigid motion transformations preserve size and shape. The length of side $\overline{X'Z}$ is 6 units, and the length of $\overline{XZ}$ is $\sqrt{32}$ units, so the sides are not congruent. The lengths of sides $\overline{X'Y'}$ and $\overline{Y'Z}$ are both $\sqrt{73}$ units, but the lengths of sides $\overline{XY}$ and $\overline{YZ}$ are $\sqrt{80}$ units, so these sides are also not congruent.

Questions to Support Discourse

		TYPE
1	• What is the length of side $\overline{XY}$? Side $\overline{YZ}$? Side $\overline{XZ}$? • Which type of triangle is ΔXYZ?	Probing
3	• For which rotations could you easily identify the transformed triangle's vertices? • What are the coordinates of the vertices of $\Delta X'Y'Z$?	Gathering
	• How can you show that Jonas's work does not preserve size and shape? • How does the length of $\overline{XZ}$ compare to the length of $\overline{X'Z}$? • Is $\Delta XYZ \cong \Delta X'Y'Z$? Why not?	Probing

ACTIVITY 2 Continued

Let's use $\overline{XY}$ as the base of ΔXYZ. You can draw $\overline{ZW}$ to represent the height. Remember that the height is perpendicular to the base. To determine the length of the height, you need to locate point W, which is at the intersection of $\overline{XY}$ and $\overline{ZW}$.

REMEMBER...
The slopes of perpendicular lines are opposite reciprocals.

WORKED EXAMPLE

Calculate the slope of the base, $\overline{XY}$.

$$m = \frac{y_2 - y_1}{x_2 - x_1} = \frac{9-5}{10-2} = \frac{4}{8} = \frac{1}{2}$$

Determine the slope of the height, $\overline{ZW}$.

$$m = -2$$

You can write the equation for $\overleftrightarrow{XY}$ and $\overleftrightarrow{ZW}$ and solve the system to determine where the two lines intersect.

Determine the equations of the lines containing the base and the height.

Base $\overleftrightarrow{XY}$	Height $\overleftrightarrow{ZW}$
$X(2, 5)$, $m = \frac{1}{2}$	$Z(6, 1)$, $m = -2$
$y - y_1 = m(x - x_1)$	$y - y_1 = m(x - x_1)$
$y - 5 = \frac{1}{2}(x - 2)$	$y - 1 = -2(x - 6)$
$y = \frac{1}{2}x + 4$	$y = -2x + 13$

Solve the system of equations to determine the coordinates of the point of intersection.

$$\frac{1}{2}x + 4 = -2x + 13$$
$$\frac{5}{2}x = 9$$
$$x = \frac{18}{5}$$
$$y = -2x + 13$$
$$y = -2\left(\frac{18}{5}\right) + 13 = \frac{29}{5}$$

NOTES

DIFFERENTIATION STRATEGY

See Page 88C to assist all students with the worked example.

Questions to Support Discourse

		TYPE
Worked Example	• If $\overline{XY}$ is the base, predict where you should draw the height of the triangle. • Why do you need to calculate slope? • What information do you need to write an equation of a line? • What is the equation for the line that includes the base? The height? • What does the solution to the system of equations represent?	Probing

NOTES

ACTIVITY 2 Continued

4 Identify the coordinates of the point of intersection. Plot this point on the coordinate plane and label it point W. Draw $\overline{ZW}$ to represent the height.

The coordinates are $\left(\frac{18}{5}, \frac{29}{5}\right)$.

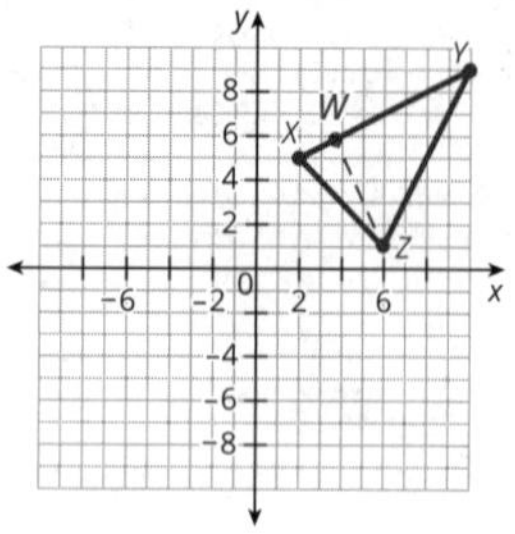

5 Determine the area of ΔXYZ.

(a) Determine the height of the triangle.

$ZW = \sqrt{\frac{144}{25} + \frac{576}{25}} = \sqrt{\frac{720}{25}}$

(b) Determine the area of the triangle.

$A = \frac{1}{2}(\sqrt{80})\left(\sqrt{\frac{720}{25}}\right) = 24$

The area of ΔXYZ is 24 square units.

You know that you can label any side of a triangle as its base.

6 Predict whether using a different side as the base will result in a different area of the triangle. **Explain your reasoning.**

Sample answer.
No. I do not think using a different side as the base will matter because the triangle's size and shape do not change.

Questions to Support Discourse

		TYPE
4	• How do you determine the coordinates of the endpoints of the line segment representing the height of the triangle?	Probing
5	• Explain how you calculated the height. • Why is it better to keep your answers in radical form when calculating the area? • Explain how you completed the operations with radicals.	Probing

ACTIVITY 2 Continued

Let's consider your prediction.

7 Triangle XYZ is on the coordinate plane. This time consider side $\overline{XZ}$ as the base.

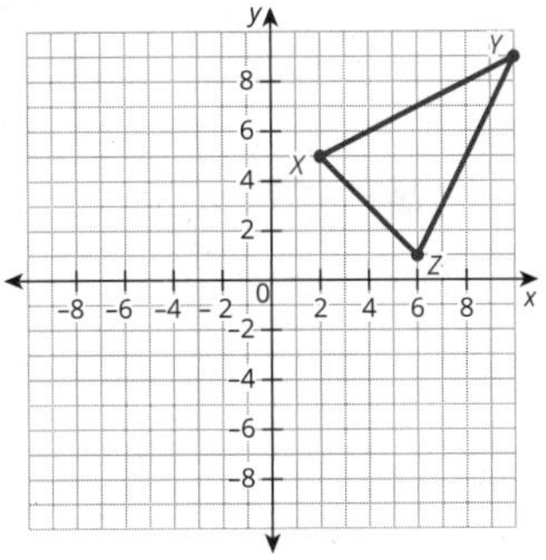

ⓐ Let point V represent the intersection point of the height, $\overline{YV}$, and the base. Determine the coordinates of point V.

Slope of $\overline{XZ} = -1$

Slope of height $\overline{YV} = 1$

Equation of base $\overline{XZ}$:

$(y - 5) = -1(x - 2)$

$y = -x + 7$

Equation of height $\overline{YV}$:

$(y - 9) = 1(x - 10)$

$y = x - 1$

Solution of the system of equations:

$x - 1 = -x + 7$

$2x = 8$

$x = 4$

$x = 4 - 1$, so $y = 3$

The coordinates of point V are (4, 3).

ⓑ Determine the height of ΔXYZ.

$YV = \sqrt{6^2 + 6^2} = \sqrt{72}$

ⓒ Determine the area of ΔXYZ.

$A = \frac{1}{2}(\sqrt{32})\sqrt{72} = 24$

The area of ΔXYZ is 24 square units.

Lesson 5 > In and Out and All About 77

Questions to Support Discourse

		TYPE
7	• Show where this height is on the graphed triangle given base $\overline{XZ}$.	Gathering
	• Why do you have to calculate slope? • What do your two equations represent? • What does the solution to the system of equations represent? • What are the endpoints of the height? • How did you calculate the measure of the height? • Which values did you substitute into the area formula?	Probing

NOTES

TOPIC 1

Student Look-Fors

Utilizing relationship skills by communicating clearly and listening well.

NOTES

Student Look-Fors

The realization that because the triangle is isosceles, the bases that have the same measure also have heights with the same measure. Question 5, part (b) and Question 8 both use

$A = \frac{1}{2}(\sqrt{80})\left(\sqrt{\frac{720}{25}}\right) = 24.$

8 Triangle XYZ is graphed on the coordinate plane. Determine the area of ΔXYZ using side $\overline{YZ}$ as the base.

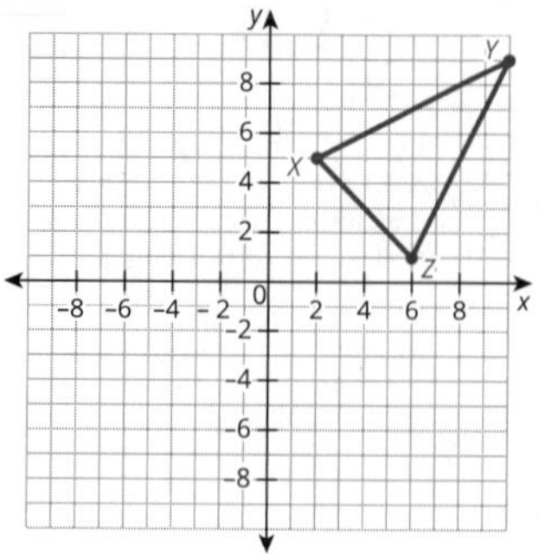

Slope of base $\overline{YZ} = 2$

Slope of height $\overline{XV} = -\frac{1}{2}$

Equation of base $\overline{YZ}$:

$(y - 1) = 2(x - 6)$

$y = 2x - 11$

Equation of height $\overline{XV}$:

$(y - 5) = \frac{1}{2}(x - 2)$

$y = -\frac{1}{2}x + 6$

Solution of the system of equations:

$2x - 11 = -\frac{1}{2}x + 6$

$\frac{5}{2}x = 17$

$x = \frac{34}{5}$

$y = 2x - 11$

$y = 2\left(\frac{34}{5}\right) - 11$

$y = \frac{13}{5}$

The coordinates of point V are $\left(\frac{34}{5}, \frac{13}{5}\right)$.

$XV = \sqrt{\frac{576}{25} + \frac{144}{25}} = \sqrt{\frac{720}{25}}$

$A = \frac{1}{2}(\sqrt{80})\left(\sqrt{\frac{720}{25}}\right) = 24$

The area of triangle XYZ is 24 square units.

9 Compare the three areas you determined for ΔXYZ. Was your prediction in Question 6 correct?

Sample answer.

Yes. My prediction was correct.
The areas are the same no matter which side of the triangle I used as a base.

Questions to Support Discourse

		TYPE
8	• Explain the basic structure of your solution strategy.	Probing
	• Why do the values you substituted into the area formula look familiar?	Seeing structure

ACTIVITY 3

SUMMARY **To calculate a composite figure's area, you can decompose it into polygons with known area formulas, compute the areas, and calculate the sum.**

Perimeter and Area of a Composite Figure

HABITS OF MIND
- Model with mathematics.
- Use appropriate tools strategically.

You can use the method you used to determine the perimeter of a rectangle or triangle with any polygon. You can use the Distance Formula to calculate the distance between any set of vertices and then add the lengths of all the sides.

You can determine the area of a *composite figure* by dividing the figure into a combination of rectangles and triangles. A **composite figure** is a figure formed by combining different shapes.

Carter has an irregular backyard because it backs onto the foothill of a mountain and is very rocky. The composite figure graphed on the coordinate plane represents the flat area of Carter's backyard. Each interval of the coordinate plane represents two yards.

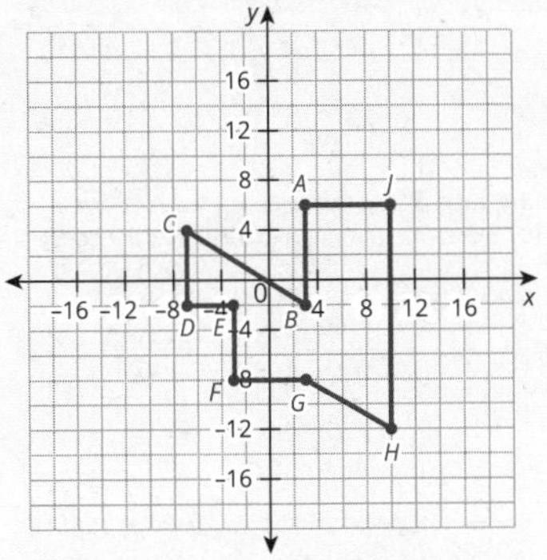

1 Carter will install fencing all around the flat area of his backyard. Determine the amount of fencing he needs to the nearest whole yard.

$P = 8 + \sqrt{136} + 6 + 4 + 6 + 6 + \sqrt{65} + 18 + 7$

≈ 74.7

Carter needs 75 yards of fencing.

2 Carter wants to lay grass sod in the flat area of his backyard. Determine the amount of sod he needs.

Carter needs 178 square yards of sod.

Questions to Support Discourse

		TYPE
1	• Do you need to use the Distance Formula to calculate the length of each of the nine sides of the composite figure? Why or why not? • Which sides require the use of the Distance Formula?	Gathering
2	• Into which shapes did you divide Carter's backyard? • Is there more than one way to divide this composite figure into familiar shapes? How? • Did you use a trapezoid? Or did you use rectangles and triangles only? • Would transforming the composite figure be helpful? Why or why not?	Probing

Chunking the Activity

- Read and discuss the definition and situation
- Group students to complete 1 and 2
- Check-in and share
- Group students to complete 3 and 4
- Share and summarize

LANGUAGE LINK

ELL TIP

Ensure that students know that *grass sod* is a section of grass torn from the surface of grassland, containing matted roots of grass. You can relocate grass sod to cover the ground where you want to grow grass.

NOTES

DIFFERENTIATION STRATEGY

See Page 88C to support students who struggle before they begin 4.

See Page 88C to assist all students with 4.

Student Look-Fors

- Correct unit conversions for square yards to square feet.
- Inclusion of the cost for the extra 10% of materials.

ACTIVITY 3 Continued

3 Compare the method you used to determine the area of sod Carter needs to your classmates' methods. If you had a different way of dividing up the composite figure, did your answers differ? **Explain why or why not.**

Sample answer.

No matter how we divided the composite figure, the total area did not change. This is because the shape of the composite figure does not change.

4 Fencing costs $5.45 per foot, and sod costs $0.62 per square foot. To allow for measurement error, Carter plans to buy an extra 10% of both materials. How much will it cost Carter to purchase these materials?

It will cost Carter **$2441.44** to purchase the materials.

Sample answer.

Fencing:
75(1.10) = 82.5 yards

82.5(3) = 247.5 feet

(247.5)($5.45) = $1348.88

Sod:
178(1.10) = 195.80 square yards

(195.80)(9) = 1762.2 feet.

(1762.2)($0.62) = $1092.56

80 Topic 1 > Using a Rectangular Coordinate System

Questions to Support Discourse

		TYPE
4	• How many extra feet of fencing does Carter want to order? • How many extra square feet of sod does Carter want to order? • How did you calculate the total cost? • When did you deal with the 10% in your calculations? • Is there a more efficient way to calculate the total cost? If so, how?	Probing

ACTIVITY 4

SUMMARY You can solve problems in context with perimeter and area, including modeling distance traveled with the area under a rate vs. time graph.

ACTIVITY 4

Solving Problems with Perimeter and Area

HABITS OF MIND
- Model with mathematics.
- Use appropriate tools strategically.

> Read each situation and answer the associated questions.

Aida's bedroom is on the top floor of her house. In her room, the roof slants downward, creating two congruent trapezoid-shaped walls.

One of the walls in her room is represented on the coordinate plane by Quadrilateral *ABCD*. Each interval on the coordinate plane represents one foot.

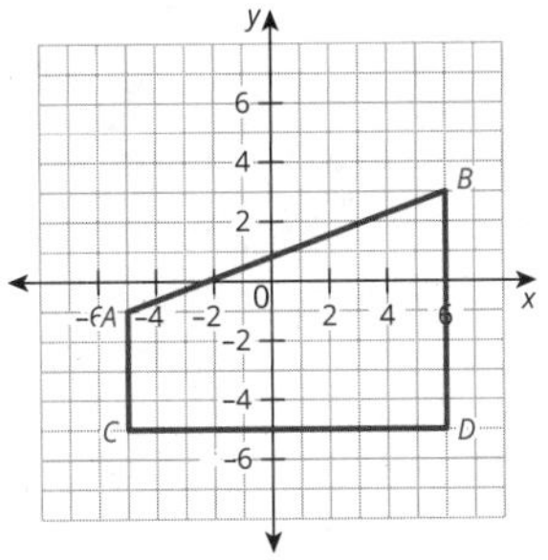

She and her friend, Marco, will paint the two walls and place a strip of painter's tape along each edge of the walls, so the paint does not touch any other wall, the ceiling, or the floor.

1. What is the length of painter's tape (to the nearest whole foot) that Aida and Marco need to cover the edges of both walls?

   69 feet

2. Marco says he can draw a diagonal to divide Trapezoid *ABCD* into a right and an isosceles triangle to determine the area of the trapezoid. Aida says she can draw a horizontal line segment to divide Trapezoid *ABCD* into a rectangle and a right triangle. Who's correct? **Explain your reasoning.**

ASK YOURSELF...
How can you use a transformation of Trapezoid *ABCD* on the coordinate plane as part of your strategy?

Both are correct.
Marco can draw diagonal *AC* and divide the trapezoid into an isosceles triangle with a base of 8 feet and a height of 11 feet and a right triangle with a height of 4 feet and a base of 11 feet.
Aida can also draw a horizontal line segment from vertex *A* to create a right triangle with a base of 11 feet and a height of 4 feet and a rectangle with a base of 11 feet and a height of 4 feet.
According to both calculations, the area of the trapezoid is 66 square feet.

Chunking the Activity

- Read and discuss the directions
- Group students to complete 1 and 2
- Check-in and share
- Group students to complete 3 - 5
- Check-in and share
- Group students to complete 6 - 10
- Share and summarize

Student Look-Fors

Whether students make a reasoned judgment after comparing and contrasting the strategies.

Questions to Support Discourse

		TYPE
1	• Is this question asking you to determine the perimeter or the area of the trapezoid? • Did you use a transformation as a strategy to solve this problem? If so, where did you place the trapezoid?	Probing
2	• Use the diagram to show Marco's thinking. • Demonstrate Aida's process.	Probing
	• Why should both sets of calculations yield the same result?	Seeing structure

NOTES

Student Look-Fors

- Errors associated with the signs used inside the radicals when substituting the values of the coordinates of the hexagon's vertices into the Distance Formula.
- Different strategies, such as using triangles and rectangles or six congruent triangles.

ACTIVITY 4 Continued

3 One gallon of paint covers approximately 400 square feet. Aida estimates she has about one-fourth of a gallon of paint remaining of the color she wants to use. Does she have enough paint for both walls? **Explain your reasoning.**

No, Aida does not have enough paint. Each wall has an area of 66 square feet, so she needs enough paint to cover 132 square feet.

One-fourth of a gallon of paint covers only 100 square feet.

> Elia and Kevin are designing a gazebo for the local park. The polygon shown on the coordinate plane represents the base of the gazebo. Each interval on the coordinate plane represents two feet.

4 The outside edge of the gazebo base requires support boards. What is the length of a board needed for the outside of the base?

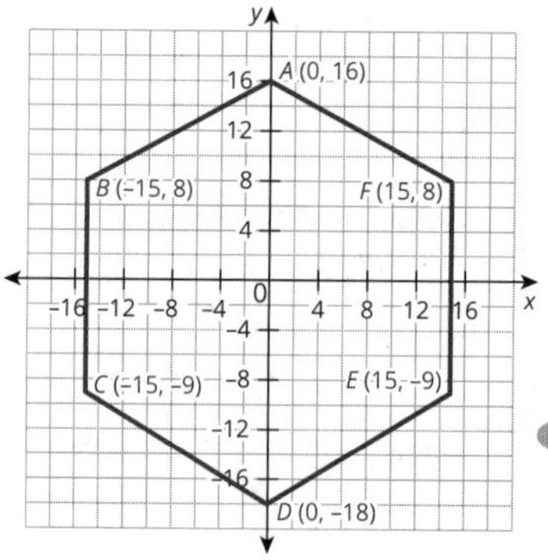

$P = 6(17) = 102$

A total of 102 feet of lumber is needed to build the outside of the base of the gazebo.

82 Topic 1 > Using a Rectangular Coordinate System

Questions to Support Discourse

		TYPE
3	• How many square feet does one-fourth of a gallon of paint cover? • What is the area of the two walls that Aida needs to paint?	Probing
4	• Is this question asking you to determine the perimeter or the area of the hexagon? • Do you need to use the Distance Formula to calculate the length of each side of the hexagon? Why or why not? • Is the hexagon equilateral? How can you tell?	Probing

ACTIVITY 4 Continued

5 How many square feet of floorboards do they need for the base of the gazebo? **Describe how you determined your answer and show your work.**

Explanations may vary.

I divided the hexagon into 4 triangles and a rectangle. I determined the area of each piece then added them together.

Area of each triangle:

$A = \frac{1}{2}bh$

$= \frac{1}{2}(15)(8)$

$= 60$

$60 \cdot 4 = 240$

$240 + 510 = 750$

Area of rectangle:

$A = bh$

$A = (30)(17) = 510$

A total of 750 square feet of floorboards is needed for the base of the gazebo.

Lesson 5 > In and Out and All About 83

Questions to Support Discourse

		TYPE
5	• How did you divide this composite figure? • What is another way to divide this composite figure into familiar shapes?	Probing

NOTES

TOPIC 1

LANGUAGE LINK

Remind students to refer to the Academic Glossary (page FM–20) to review the definition of **describe** and related phrases. Suggest they ask themselves these questions:

- How should I organize my thoughts?
- Did I consider the context of the situation?

NOTES

ACTIVITY 4 Continued

The graph shows the constant speed of a car on the highway over 2.5 hours.

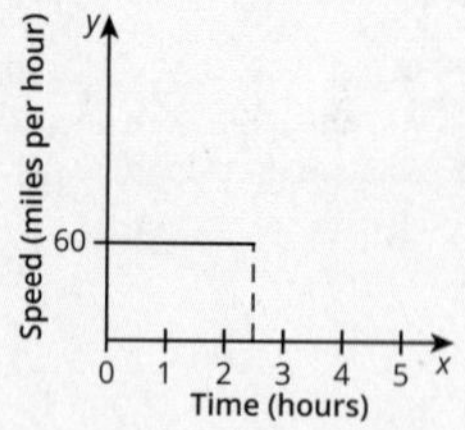

6 Describe how you could calculate the distance the car traveled in 2.5 hours using what you know about area.

Sample answer.

Distance equals rate multiplied by time.

Because the *y*-axis represents the rate and the *x*-axis represents the time, the area of the rectangle represents the distance traveled.

7 How far did the car travel in 2.5 hours?

The car traveled 150 miles.

$\frac{60 \text{ miles}}{1 \text{hour}} \times \frac{2.5 \text{ hours}}{1} = 150 \text{ miles}$

The graph you used is called a velocity-time graph. In a velocity-time graph, the area under the line or curve gives the distance.

The graph shown describes the speed and the time of a passenger jet's ascend.

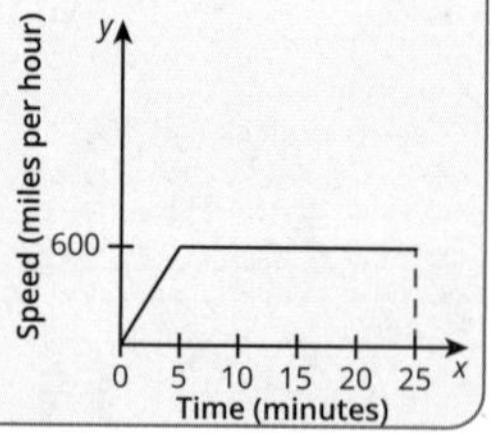

8 How can you use the graph to determine the distance the jet has traveled in 25 minutes?

I can calculate the area of the region enclosed by the graph from 0 to 25 minutes to determine the distance the jet traveled.

Questions to Support Discourse

		TYPE
6	• How do you know the speed is constant from the graph? • What is the relationship between distance, rate, and time? • What is the area of the rectangle drawn on the graph?	Probing
	• Why could you say that the area of the rectangle models the distance traveled?	Seeing structure

ACTIVITY 4 Continued

9 Determine the distance the jet has traveled:

(a) in 25 minutes.

The jet has traveled 225 miles in 25 minutes.

$\frac{1}{2}(5)(10) + (20)(10) = 225$

(b) in the first 5 minutes.

The jet has traveled 25 miles in 5 minutes.

$\frac{1}{2}(5)(10) = 25$

10 Consider the ascent of a passenger jet.

(a) Draw a velocity-time graph to model the ascent of a passenger jet using the information given.

- The jet took 7 minutes to reach a top speed of 600 miles per hour.
- The jet continued to travel at a constant speed of 600 miles per hour.
- The jet left the airport 4 hours ago.

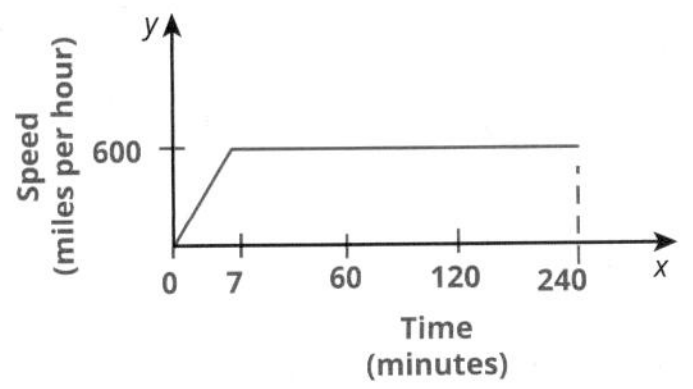

(b) How many miles has the jet traveled?

The jet traveled 2365 miles in 4 hours.

$\frac{1}{2}(7)(10) + (233)(10) = 2365$

Lesson 5 > In and Out and All About 85

NOTES

Student Look-Fors

Errors associated with the use of minutes and hours on the graph of the scenario. If students do not realize they are using two different measures of time on the same graph, their answers will be incorrect. Look for students to change minutes into hours on the *x*-axis or miles per hour into miles per minute on the *y*-axis.

TOPIC 1

Questions to Support Discourse

		TYPE
9	• Why are you able to use the area to calculate the distances? • How did you deal with the different units of time? • Explain how you calculated the area.	Probing
10	• Why did you graph a horizontal line? • Explain how you calculated the miles traveled.	Probing

SUMMARY You can estimate the area of an irregularly-shaped figure by approximating it as a polygon.

Chunking the Activity

- **Read and discuss the situation**
- **Group students to complete the activity**
- **Share and summarize**

NOTE: Encourage responsible decision making by providing an opportunity for students to reflect on their personal behavior and social interactions as they worked with their group to complete tasks.

Vive les Maths!

Eva is using a map to estimate the area of France. She thinks the country looks like a hexagon and draws the polygon shown to approximate its shape.

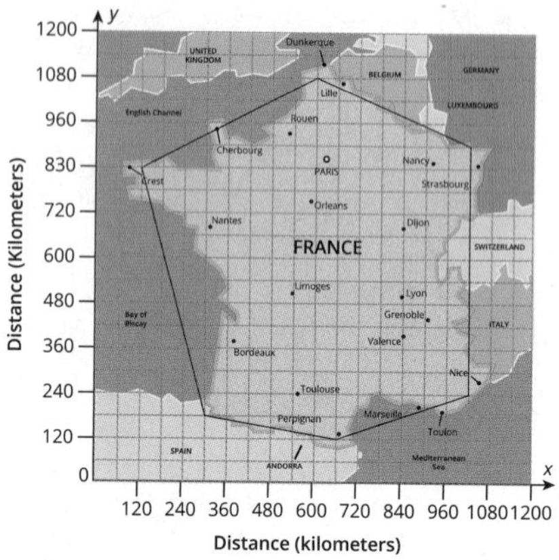

1. Determine which statements are true. **Justify your answers.**
   - The coastline of France is greater than 5000 km.
   - The coastline of France is less than 5000 km.
   - The coastline of France is approximately 5000 km.
   - The area of France is greater than 1,000,000 sq km.
   - The area of France is less than 1,000,000 sq km.
   - The area of France is approximately 1,000,000 sq km.

   The total coastlines and borders of France is less than 5000 km.
   The area of France is less than 1,000,000 square km.

   Students' explanations will vary.

2. If the population of France is approximately 104 people per square kilometer, how many people live in France?

   Approximately 666,000(104), or 69,264,000 people live in the country of France.

Questions to Support Discourse

		TYPE
1	• What polygon did you use to estimate the area of France? • What method did you use to compute the approximate length of the coastline? • What method did you use to compute the approximate area?	Probing
2	• How did you use the given information to estimate the population of France?	Probing

ASSIGNMENT

LESSON 5 ASSIGNMENT

> Use a separate piece of paper for your Journal entry.

JOURNAL

Describe how you can determine the area of a composite figure.

REMEMBER

Rigid transformations can make calculating the perimeter and area of figures on the coordinate plane more efficient.

You can think of any side of a triangle as its base. The height of the triangle is the perpendicular distance from the base to the opposite vertex.

PRACTICE

1. Olivia translates Rectangle *WXYZ* vertically up 1 unit and horizontally to the right 4 units to produce the Rectangle *W′X′Y′Z′*. Thom translates the rectangle vertically up 6 units and horizontally to the right 5 units to produce the Rectangle *W″ X″ Y″ Z″*.

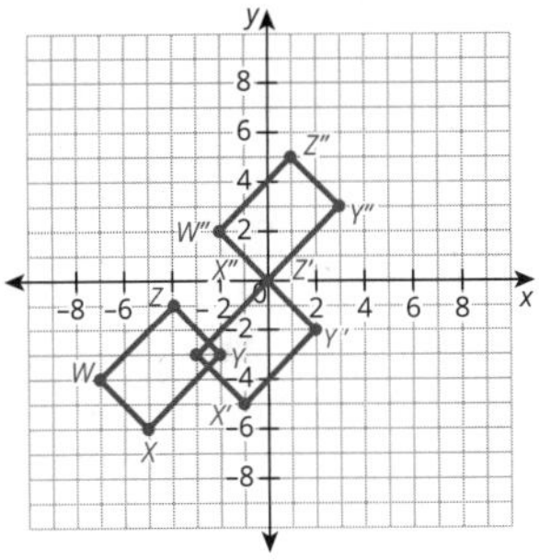

(a) Would you prefer to use Olivia's translation or Thom's translation to determine the rectangle's perimeter and area? Explain your reasoning.

Sample answer.

I prefer Thom's translation because most of the points have positive coordinates.

(b) Calculate the perimeter and area of the rectangle. Show your work.

The perimeter is approximately 14.14 units and the area is 12 square units.

Perimeter $= \sqrt{8} + \sqrt{18} + \sqrt{8} + \sqrt{18}$

$= 2\sqrt{2} + 3\sqrt{2} + 2\sqrt{2} + 3\sqrt{2}$

$= 10\sqrt{2} \approx 14.14$

Area $= (\sqrt{18})(\sqrt{8})$

$= 12$

Go to LiveHint.com for help on the PRACTICE questions.

Encourage students to use LiveHint.com for help with the PRACTICE questions of this assignment.

Chunking the Assignment

TOPIC 1

SESSION 1

- Practice 1
- Stretch (advanced learners)

SESSION 2

- Practice 2
- Mixed Practice (page 89) 5

SESSION 3

- Journal
- Practice 3

JOURNAL

Sample answer.

I can divide the composite figure into a combination of shapes, such as rectangles and triangles. I can then determine the area of each of those shapes and add the areas together to determine the area of the composite figure.

NOTES

STRETCH

The length of the base of Parallelogram *JKPR* is twice the length of the base of Parallelogram *JKLM*, and both parallelograms have the same height. Therefore, the area of Parallelogram *JKPR* is twice the area of Parallelogram *JKLM*.

2. Cisco claims that $\overline{GH}$ is the height of ΔEFG, and Beth claims that $\overline{GJ}$ is the height of ΔEFG.

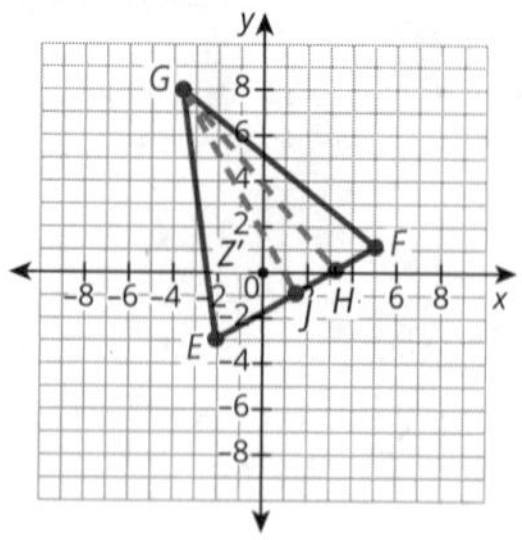

(a) Who is correct? Justify your response.

Both are correct.
Because the slopes of $\overline{EF}$ and $\overline{GJ}$ are opposite reciprocals of each other, I know that $\overline{GJ}$ must be the height.

Slope of $\overline{EF} = \frac{1}{2}$
Slope of $\overline{GJ} = -2$
Slope of $\overline{GH} = -\frac{9}{7}$.

(b) Calculate the area of ΔEFG. Show your work.

The area of ΔEFG is 50 square units.

Area $= \frac{1}{2}(\sqrt{80})(\sqrt{125}) = 50$

3. Composite Figure *ABCDEFG* is given.

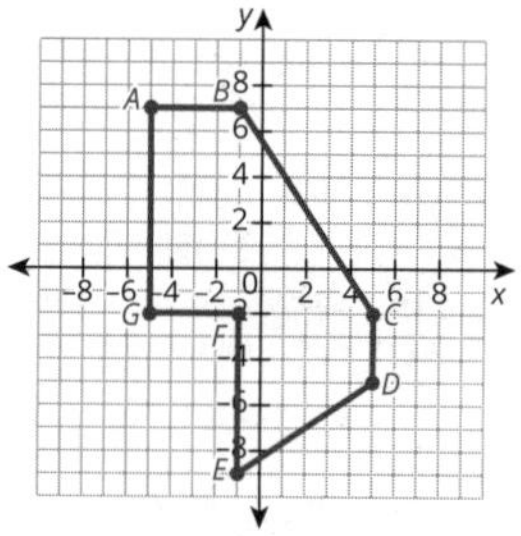

(a) Determine the perimeter of Figure *ABCDEFG*.

The perimeter of *ABCDEFG* is approximately 45.03 units.

(b) Determine the area of Figure *ABCDEFG*.

The area of *ABCDEFG* is 93 square units.

STRETCH Optional

1. Without calculating each area, determine whether or not the area of Parallelogram *JKPR* is twice that of the area of Parallelogram *JKLM*. Explain how you determined your answer.

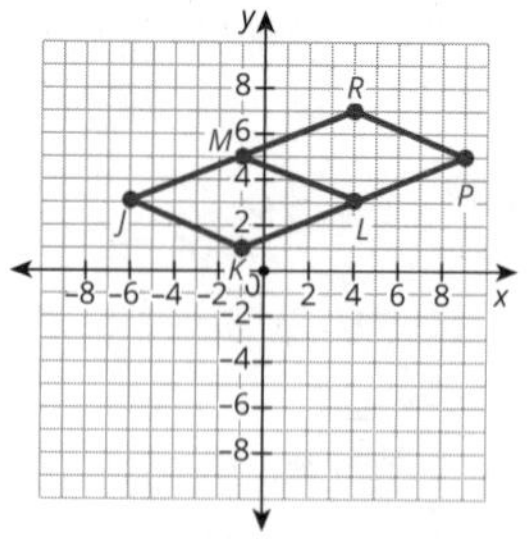

In and Out and All About

This resource details additional facilitation notes to fully assist you as you plan each lesson to support all students, students who struggle, and advanced learners. It provides differentiation strategies, common student misconceptions, and suggestions to extend certain activities.

GETTING STARTED

Session 1 of 3

It's Child's Play

Students describe ways to calculate the area of polygons drawn on a grid.

CHUNK	AUDIENCE	ADDITIONAL SUPPORTS
As you share and summarize 1	All Students	**COMMON MISCONCEPTION** Students may assume the base of a triangle must be the bottom of the triangle. For instance, in ΔNOP, they may think the base must be $\overline{PO}$. Remind students that they can use any side of a triangle as the base of the triangle. It's just not always the most efficient.

ACTIVITY 1

Session 1 of 3

Perimeter and Area of Figures on the Coordinate Plane

Students calculate the area and perimeter of polygons on the coordinate plane. They consider how doubling a dimension of a rectangle affects its area. Students translate figures on the coordinate plane for efficient computations.

CHUNK	AUDIENCE	ADDITIONAL SUPPORTS
Before starting the activity	Students who Struggle	**DIFFERENTIATION STRATEGY** Allow students to use a scale of one rather than the different scales labeled on the graphs throughout this activity.

<table>
<tr><th>CHUNK</th><th>AUDIENCE</th><th>ADDITIONAL SUPPORTS</th></tr>
<tr><td>As you share and summarize 5</td><td>All Students</td><td>

DIFFERENTIATION STRATEGY

Have students use different methods to demonstrate how doubling a dimension affects the area of a figure.

<table>
<tr><th colspan="3">Doubling the Base</th></tr>
<tr><th>Using Arithmetic</th><th>Using Geometry</th><th>Using Algebra</th></tr>
<tr><td>$b = 2(450) = 900$
$h = 225$

Area = $(900)(225)$
$= 202,500$
$\frac{202,500}{101,250} = 2$</td><td>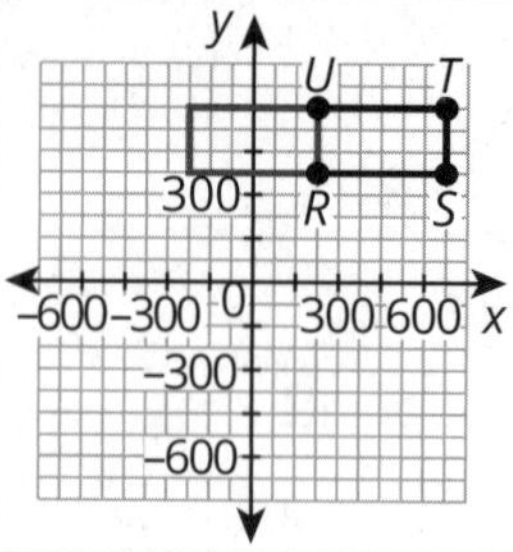
</td><td>Area = base × height
Area = $(2b)(h)$
Area = $2bh$</td></tr>
</table>

You may want to revisit these strategies when students complete Questions 9 and 10.

</td></tr>
<tr><td>As students discuss the strategy</td><td>All Students</td><td>

DIFFERENTIATION STRATEGY

Have students write the word *example* above the thumbs up strategy as an indicator that it is a correct solution to reference later. As students read through the strategy and think about the connections, suggest they ask themselves:

- Why is this method correct?
- Have I used this method before?

</td></tr>
<tr><td>As students complete 9</td><td>All Students</td><td>

DIFFERENTIATION STRATEGY

Provide students colored pencils to distinguish among the different triangles they create on the coordinate plane.

</td></tr>
<tr><td>As students work on 10</td><td>Students who Struggle</td><td>

DIFFERENTIATION STRATEGY

Provide students with patty paper to help them visualize the rigid motions.

</td></tr>
</table>

ACTIVITY 2

Session 2 of 3

Calculating Heights of Triangles

Students calculate the area of triangles on the coordinate plane. They use algebra to determine the height of a triangle.

CHUNK	AUDIENCE	ADDITIONAL SUPPORTS
Before you read and discuss the worked example	All Students	**DIFFERENTIATION STRATEGY** • Have students use paper folding to create a perpendicular bisector. • Have them interpret the text above the worked example, and use the patty paper to estimate where the height of the triangle, $\overline{ZW}$ is located given the base $\overline{XY}$. • Discuss how once students know the endpoints of the height, they can use the Distance Formula to calculate its measure.
As you read and discuss the worked example	All Students	**DIFFERENTIATION STRATEGY** • Have students number the steps and take notes in the worked example. • Provide a template with the directions on one half and blanks on the other half so that students can complete the steps with your guidance. Then, have copies of the template available for the remainder of this activity and the Talk the Talk.

ACTIVITY 3

Session 3 of 3

Perimeter and Area of a Composite Figure

Students calculate the area of a composite figure on the coordinate plane. They solve a real-world problem involving perimeter and area.

CHUNK	AUDIENCE	ADDITIONAL SUPPORTS
Before students begin 4	Students who Struggle	**DIFFERENTIATION STRATEGY** • Guide the unit conversion or provide costs in dollars per foot and dollars per square feet. • Remove the 10% from the problem situation. Calculate the cost of ordering only the materials needed to complete the job.
As students work on 4	All Students	**DIFFERENTIATION STRATEGY** Draw a square yard on the board in actual size. Divide the square yard into nine square feet to demonstrate the conversion factor and help students visualize the size.

Practice the learning

MATHbook + Skills Practice

The table shows the targeted practice of the skills and mathematical concepts for the *Using a Rectangular Coordinate System* Topic. The highlighted **Problem Set** aligns with **In and Out and All About**.

PROBLEM SET	
1	Identifying Properties of Geometric Figures
2	Constructing Perpendicular Lines
3	Duplicating Line Segments
4	Writing Equations of Parallel and Perpendicular Lines
5	Classifying Shapes on the Coordinate Plane
6	**Determining Perimeter and Area of Rectangles and Triangles on the Coordinate Plane**
7	**Determining Perimeter and Area of Other Polygons on the Coordinate Plane**

ANYTIME AFTER ACTIVITY 4

Facilitate students as they work individually on **Problem Sets 6** and **7**.

MIXED PRACTICE

Log in to MyCL to access a downloadable version with **additional space** for students to write their answers.

MIXED PRACTICE

This Mixed Practice worksheet includes two sections: Spaced Review and End-of-Topic Review. **Use a separate piece of paper to show your work.**

Spaced Review

1 Determine the supplement of each angle measure.
- ⓐ 63°
- ⓑ 10°
- ⓒ 180°

2 Determine the complement of each angle measure.
- ⓐ 10°
- ⓑ 75°
- ⓒ 45°

3 The length of the legs of a right triangle are 6 in. and 8 in. Use the Pythagorean Theorem to determine the length of the hypotenuse. Show your work.

4 Solve for b in the equation $\frac{a-b}{12} = 11 - 6a$.

5 List the properties that are shared by each pair of polygons.
- ⓐ Squares and equilateral triangles
- ⓑ Rectangles and rhombi

6 List three different properties of a square.

7 Identify the vertical angles.

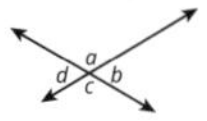

8 Identify the pairs of angles. Describe the measures of the angles in each pair.

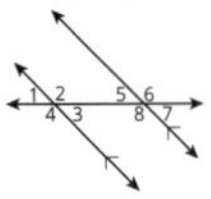

- ⓐ Corresponding angles
- ⓑ Alternate interior angles
- ⓒ Alternate exterior angles
- ⓓ Same-side interior angles

9 Determine the area of each composite figure. Each grid square measures 1 unit by 1 unit.

ⓐ ⓑ ⓒ ⓓ

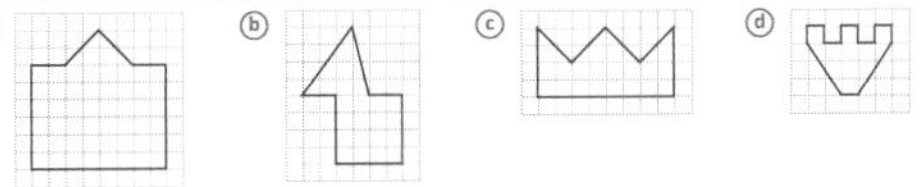

MIXED PRACTICE Continued

End-of-Topic Review

AVAILABLE ONLINE
1. A **Topic Summary** reviews the main concepts for the topic.
2. A video of the **Worked Example** is provided.

Practice concepts you learned in **Using a Rectangular Coordinate System**.

10 Identify each rigid motion as a translation, reflection, or rotation.

ⓐ

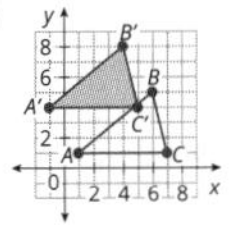

ⓑ

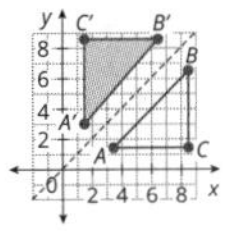

11 Write the equation of a line that passes through the point (−8, 2) and is parallel to the line $3x - 2y = 12$.

12 Write the equation of a line that passes through the point (5, −7) and is perpendicular to the line $-2x + 6y = -4$.

13 The Quadrilateral $ABCD$ has the vertices A (−5, 4), B (0, 6), C (1, 3), and D (−4, 1). Determine whether you can classify it as a parallelogram. Justify your reasoning.

14 Triangle DEF has vertices D (−2, 3), E (2, −1), and F (−5, −4). Determine whether it is scalene, isosceles, or equilateral. Explain your reasoning.

15 Figure $ABCDEFG$ is given.
- ⓐ Determine the perimeter of Figure $ABCDEFG$.
- ⓑ Determine the area of Figure $ABCDEFG$.

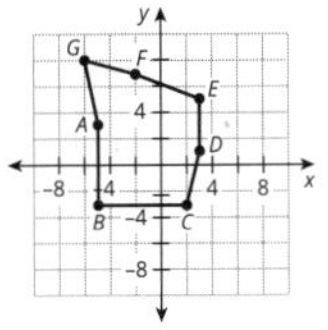

See pages 90–90B for annotated answers.

The **Spaced Review** includes fluency and problem solving from previous topics.

Aligned Standards

1 7.G.5	2 7.G.5
3 8.G.7	4 A.CED.4
5 4.G.2	6 4.G.2
7 8.G.5	8 8.G.5
9 6.G.3	

Log in to MyCL for more **End-of-Topic** review questions.

Go to **Edulastic**, and search for: G.CO.1, G.CO.5, G.CO.12, G.GPE.4, G.GPE.5, G.GPE.7, G.MG.2.

The **End-of-Topic Review** includes questions to practice the key concepts of *Using a Rectangular Coordinate System*.

Aligned Standards

10 G.CO.5	11 G.GPE.5
12 G.GPE.5	13 G.GPE.4
14 G.GPE.4	15 G.GPE.7

Answers included.

MIXED PRACTICE

This Mixed Practice worksheet includes two sections: Spaced Review and End-of-Topic Review.

MODULE 1 Reasoning with Shapes
TOPIC 1 Using a Rectangular Coordinate System
TOPIC 2 Rigid Motions on a Plane
TOPIC 3 Congruence Through Transformations

Spaced Review

1 Determine the supplement of each angle measure.

(a) 63°

$180° - 63° = 117°$

(b) 10°

$180° - 10° = 170°$

(c) 180°

$180° - 180° = 0°$

2 Determine the complement of each angle measure.

(a) 10°

$90° - 10° = 80°$

(b) 75°

$90° - 75° = 15°$

(c) 45°

$90° - 45° = 45°$

3 The length of the legs of a right triangle are 6 in. and 8 in. Use the Pythagorean Theorem to determine the length of the hypotenuse. Show your work.

$6^2 + 8^2 = c^2$
$36 + 64 = c^2$
$100 = c^2$
$c = 10$

The length of the hypotenuse is 10 inches.

4 Solve for b in the equation $\frac{a-b}{12} = 11 - 6a$.

$12\left(\frac{a-b}{12}\right) = 12(11 - 6a)$
$a - b = 132 - 72a$
$b = 73a - 132$

5 List the properties that are shared by each pair of polygons.

(a) Squares and equilateral triangles

Squares and equilateral triangles are both equilateral and equiangular.

(b) Rectangles and rhombi

Rectangles and rhombi are both quadrilaterals with opposite sides parallel. They are both types of parallelograms.

6 List three different properties of a square.

Sample answer.

Two pairs of parallel sides
Four right angles
All sides are congruent

7 Identify the vertical angles.

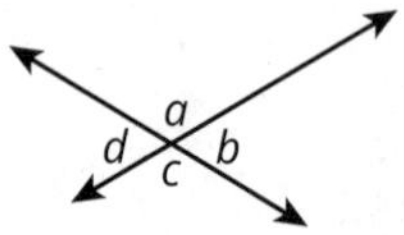

Angles a and c are vertical angles.
Angles b and d are vertical angles.

MIXED PRACTICE Continued

8 Identify the pairs of angles. Describe the measures of the angles in each pair.

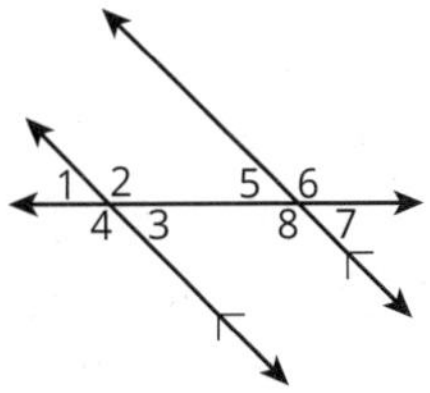

(a) Corresponding angles

∠1 and ∠5, ∠2 and ∠6, ∠4 and ∠8, ∠3 and ∠7
Corresponding angles are congruent.

(b) Alternate interior angles

∠3 and ∠5, ∠2 and ∠8
Alternate interior angles are congruent.

(c) Alternate exterior angles

∠4 and ∠6, ∠1 and ∠7
Alternate exterior angles are congruent.

(d) Same-side interior angles

∠3 and ∠8, ∠2 and ∠5
Same-side interior angles are supplementary.

9 Determine the area of each composite figure. Each grid square measures 1 unit by 1 unit.

(a)

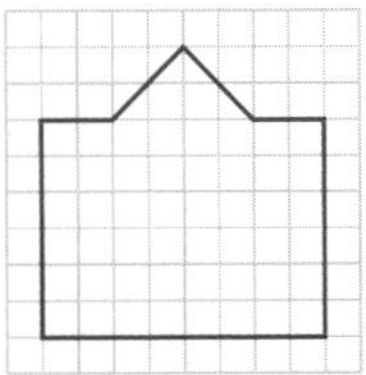

52 square units

(b)

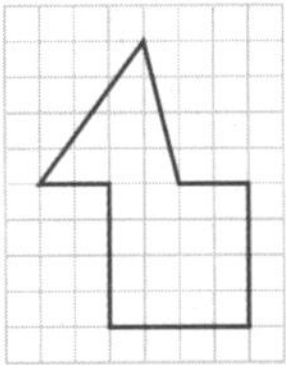

24 square units

(c)

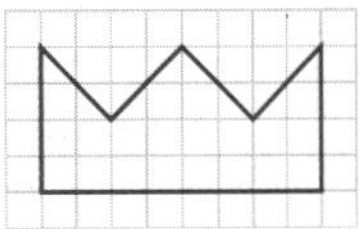

24 square units

(d)

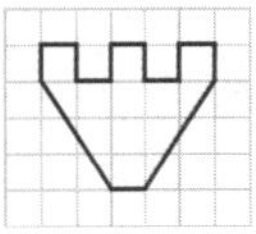

12 square units

End-of-Topic Review

AVAILABLE ONLINE

1. A **Topic Summary** reviews the main concepts for the topic.
2. A video of the **Worked Example** is provided.

> Practice concepts you learned in **Using a Rectangular Coordinate System**.

10 Identify each rigid motion as a translation, reflection, or rotation.

(a)

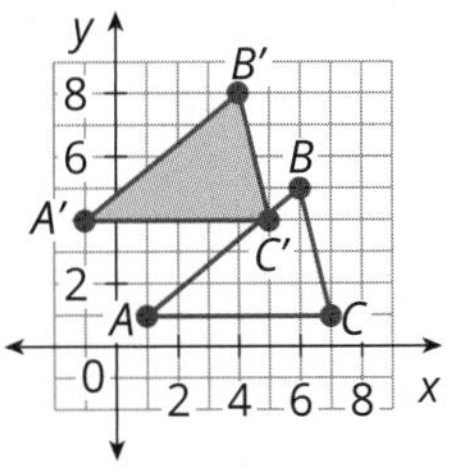

Translation

(b)

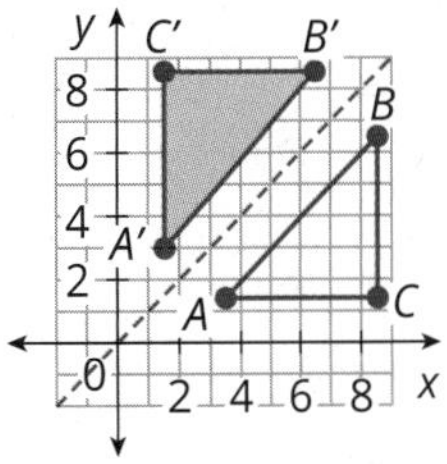

Reflection

Answers included.

MIXED PRACTICE

This Mixed Practice worksheet includes two sections: Spaced Review and End-of-Topic Review.

11 Write the equation of a line that passes through the point (−8, 2) and is parallel to the line $3x - 2y = 12$.

$$3x - 2y = 12$$
$$y = \frac{3}{2}x - 6$$
$$m = \frac{3}{2}$$
$$y - 2 = \frac{3}{2}(x + 8)$$
$$y = \frac{3}{2}x + 14$$

12 Write the equation of a line that passes through the point (5, −7) and is perpendicular to the line $-2x + 6y = -4$.

$$-2x + 6y = -4$$
$$y = \frac{1}{3}x - \frac{2}{3}$$
$$m = \frac{1}{3}$$
$$y + 7 = -3(x - 5)$$
$$y = -3x + 8$$

13 The Quadrilateral *ABCD* has the vertices *A* (–5, 4), *B* (0, 6), *C* (1, 3),and *D* (–4, 1). Determine whether you can classify it as a parallelogram. Justify your reasoning.

Yes, Quadrilateral *ABCD* is a parallelogram because the opposite sides have the same slope and are therefore parallel.
The slopes of $\overline{AB}$ and $\overline{CD}$ are $\frac{2}{5}$. The slopes of $\overline{AD}$ and $\overline{BC}$ are both $-\frac{3}{1}$.

14 Triangle *DEF* has vertices *D* (–2, 3), *E* (2, –1), and *F* (–5, –4). Determine whether it is scalene, isosceles, or equilateral. Explain your reasoning.

The triangle is isosceles.
Sides $\overline{DF}$ and $\overline{EF}$ both have lengths of $\sqrt{58}$ units.
Side $\overline{DE}$ has a length of $\sqrt{32}$ units.

15 Figure *ABCDEFG* is given.

(a) Determine the perimeter of Figure *ABCDEFG*.

28.7 units

(b) Determine the area of Figure *ABCDEFG*.

76.5 square units

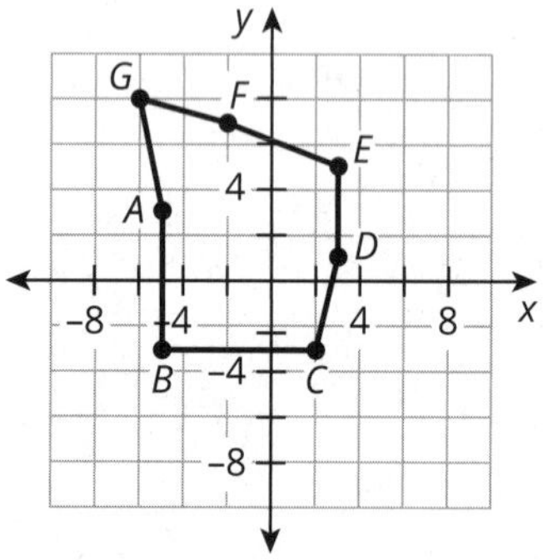

ENGAGE + **DEVELOP** + **TEACH**

ENGAGE at the **Module** level

DEVELOP: Read the **Topic Overview** and do the math to experience the content development.

TEACH at the **Lesson** level

OVERVIEW: TOPIC 2

Rigid Motions on a Plane

Where are we?

1 Session ≈ 45 minutes

MODULE 1 Establishing Proof	Using a Rectangular Coordinate System	**TOPIC 2 Rigid Motions on a Plane**	TOPIC 3 Congruence Through Transformations
Pacing	16 Sessions	**11 Sessions**	10 Sessions

How are the key concepts of ***Rigid Motions on a Plane*** developed?

Students investigate geometric transformation machines, describing how they carry each input shape to produce the output. This informal investigation shows how shapes can move on a plane and reminds students of what they know about functions.

Students then investigate how a translation maps each point of a pre-image an equal distance along parallel lines. They represent translations using function notation and differentiate translations with transformations that map points along non-parallel lines.

Students consider a reflection as a geometric function, mapping each point of a pre-image equidistant across a line of reflection. They use perpendicular bisectors to construct a line of symmetry and then use this construction to determine whether figures are reflections. Students identify translations and reflections that map one figure onto another.

Students use three concentric circles to rotate a triangle at a rotation angle of their choosing. They learn the formal definition of a rotation function and its notation. Students identify a sequence of translations, reflections, and rotations that maps one figure onto another.

See Math Representation.

Finally, students identify figures with line symmetry and rotational symmetry. They identify lines of reflection and angles of rotation that map figures onto themselves.

MATH REPRESENTATION

Consider ΔABC and point E as the center of rotation. You can rotate a figure about a point using concentric circles.

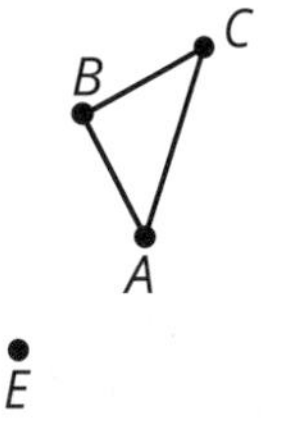

STEP 1 Use a protractor and the radius of each circle to draw 90° angles.

STEP 2 Label the new endpoints A', B', and C' respectively and use a straightedge to draw the new image.

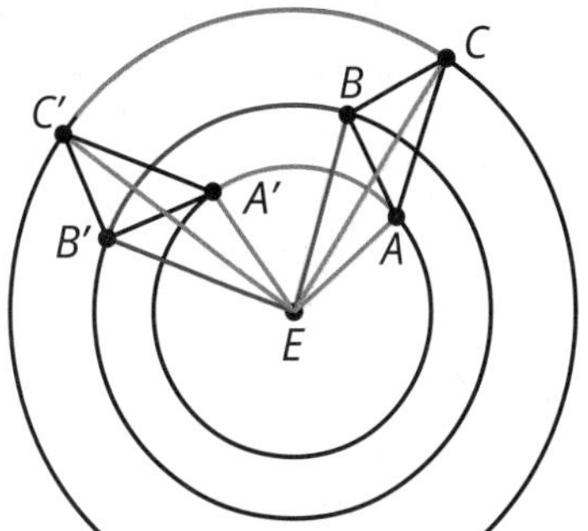

PLAN FOR 9 class sessions and ~2 MATHia sessions.

Log in to MyCL for lesson support including:

- Slides
- Videos

LESSON 1

Put Your Input In, Take Your Output Out

Geometric Components of Rigid Motions

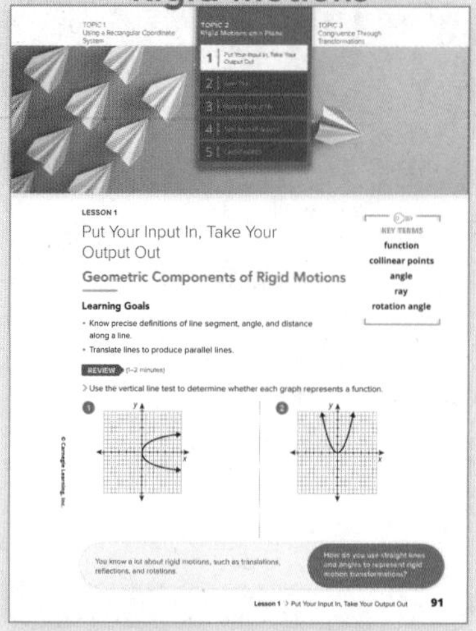
LESSON 1

Put Your Input In, Take Your Output Out

Geometric Components of Rigid Motions

Learning Goals

- Know precise definitions of line segment, angle, and distance along a line.
- Translate lines to produce parallel lines.

KEY TERMS: function, collinear points, angle, ray, rotation angle

REVIEW (1–2 minutes)

> Use the vertical line test to determine whether each graph represents a function.

Lesson 1 > Put Your Input In, Take Your Output Out 91

LESSON 2

Bow Thai

Translations as Functions

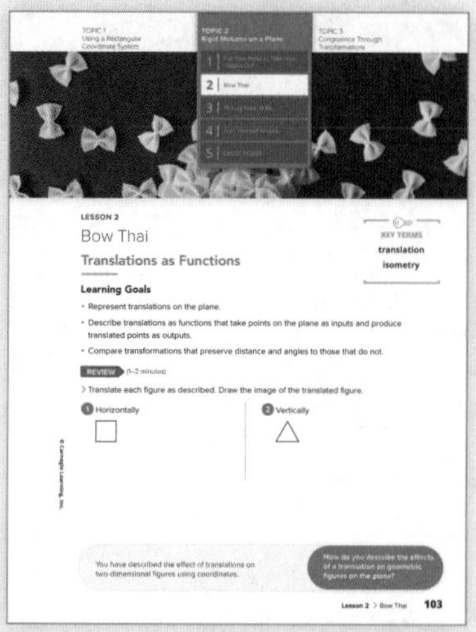
LESSON 2

Bow Thai

Translations as Functions

Learning Goals

- Represent translations on the plane.
- Describe translations as functions that take points on the plane as inputs and produce translated points as outputs.
- Compare transformations that preserve distance and angles to those that do not.

KEY TERMS: translation, isometry

REVIEW (1–2 minutes)

> Translate each figure as described. Draw the image of the translated figure.

1 Horizontally 2 Vertically

Lesson 2 > Bow Thai 103

LEARNING TOGETHER	Lesson 1: 2 Sessions	Lesson 2: 2 Sessions
STANDARDS	G.CO.1, G.CO.4	G.CO.2, G.CO.4
MATHbook Activities sequenced to address standards and meet content goals.	Students think about geometric rigid motions as functions and apply geometric rigid motions using an input-output machine. They show that translating segments maintains congruency and creates a parallel segment. Students investigate positive and negative rotation angles. They experiment with a transformation machine using patty paper to describe a sequence of transformations to create an image.	Students translate figures along parallel lines and rays sharing a common vertex and then compare the translation and dilation results. They measure a translation as a directed line segment on the coordinate plane and use function notation to describe and translate figures. Students apply transformations in a context. They compare translations described by geometric and algebraic functions.
MATERIALS	• Patty paper • Protractors (optional) • Straightedges	• Compasses • Patty paper • Straightedges

LEARNING INDIVIDUALLY — **Median time for students to complete MATHia for this topic is ~90 minutes.**

	Lesson 1	Lesson 2
MATHia Workspaces aligned at the lesson level to support benchmarking through self-paced MATHia.	• Developing Definitions of Rigid Motions • Exploring Rigid Motions and Dilations	• Describing a Translation

For students without access to MATHia. — **Problem sets for additional practice of the lesson skills.**

	Lesson 1	Lesson 2
Skills Practice	• Geometric Components of Rigid Motions	• Translation Functions

LESSON 3

Staring Back at Me

Reflections as Functions

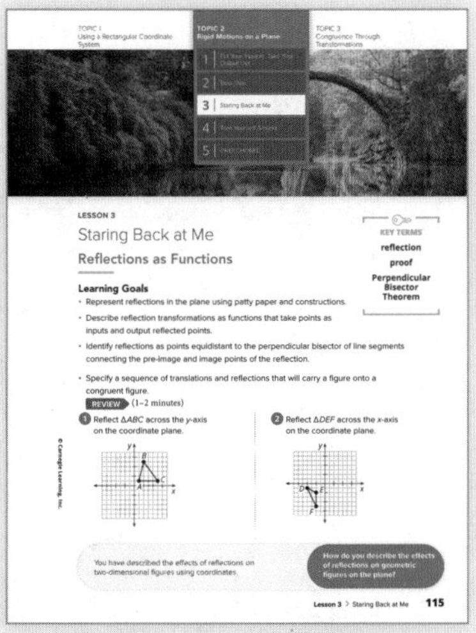

2 Sessions

G.CO.2, G.CO.4, G.CO.5

Students relate a perpendicular bisector and a line of reflection. They analyze a worked example proving the Perpendicular Bisector Theorem. Students use function notation to describe and reflect figures, and they construct lines of reflection. They identify a sequence of isometries to show that two figures are congruent. Students compare transformations on and off the coordinate plane.

- Compasses
- Patty paper
- Straightedges

LESSON 4

Turn Yourself Around

Rotations as Functions

2 Sessions

G.CO.1, G.CO.2, G.CO.4, G.CO.5

Students rotate a figure on the coordinate plane. They use a protractor and ruler to rotate a shape given a center of rotation and rotation angle. Students then reverse the process and use function notation to identify the center of rotation and rotation angle given a pre-image and image. They also sketch a sequence of isometries to show that two figures are congruent.

- Patty paper
- Protractors
- Rulers

TOPIC 2

For the most up-to-date MATHia alignment, log in to MyCL.

Lesson 3:

- Describing a Reflection

Lesson 4:

- Describing a Rotation
- Specifying a Sequence of Rigid Motion Transformations

Problem sets for additional practice of the lesson skills.

Lesson 3:

- Reflection Functions

Lesson 4:

- Rotation Functions

PLAN FOR 9 class sessions and ~2 MATHia sessions.

Log in to MyCL for lesson support including:

- Slides
- Videos

OKEECHOBEE

Reflectional and Rotational Symmetry

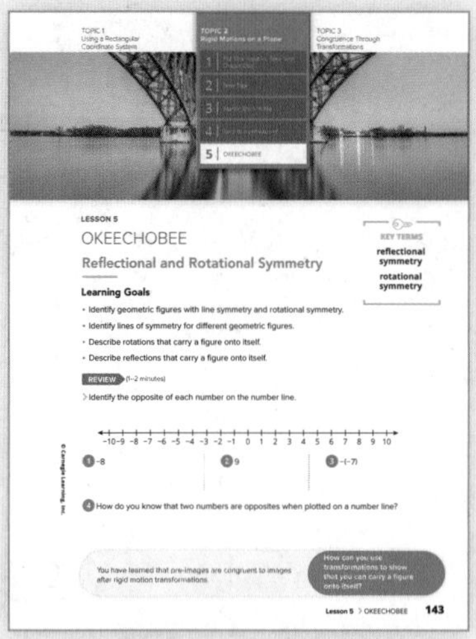
LESSON 5

OKEECHOBEE

Reflectional and Rotational Symmetry

KEY TERMS
reflectional symmetry
rotational symmetry

Learning Goals

- Identify geometric figures with line symmetry and rotational symmetry.
- Identify lines of symmetry for different geometric figures.
- Describe rotations that carry a figure onto itself.
- Describe reflections that carry a figure onto itself.

REVIEW (1–2 minutes)

Identify the opposite of each number on the number line.

1. −8
2. 9
3. −(−7)
4. How do you know that two numbers are opposites when plotted on a number line?

You have learned that pre-images are congruent to images after rigid motion transformations.

How can you use transformations to show that you can carry a figure onto itself?

© Carnegie Learning, Inc.

Lesson 5 > OKEECHOBEE 143

LEARNING TOGETHER — 1 Session

STANDARDS: G.CO.3

MATHbook

Activities sequenced to address standards and meet content goals.

Students learn the meaning of *reflectional symmetry* and *rotational symmetry*. They identify the lines of symmetry in figures and specify figures that have rotational symmetry. Students further explore rotational symmetry by considering the relationship between the rotation angles and interior angle measures of an equilateral triangle, square, and regular hexagon.

MATERIALS

- Patty paper
- Protractors

LEARNING INDIVIDUALLY — For the most up-to-date MATHia alignment, log in to MyCL.

MATHia

Workspaces aligned at the lesson level to support benchmarking through self-paced MATHia.

- Rotations and Reflections on the Plane
- Reflectional Symmetry
- Rotational Symmetry

For students without access to MATHia.

Skills Practice

Problem sets for additional practice of the lesson skills.

- Reflectional and Rotational Symmetries

NOTES

Connection to Prior Learning

What is the entry point for students?

This topic builds on students' experiences with the properties of rotations, reflections, and translations. They know that two figures are congruent when a sequence of rigid motions carries one figure onto the other. Students have described the effect of rigid motions on figures using coordinates.

MATH REPRESENTATION

Consider the point (x, y) located in the first quadrant on the coordinate plane.

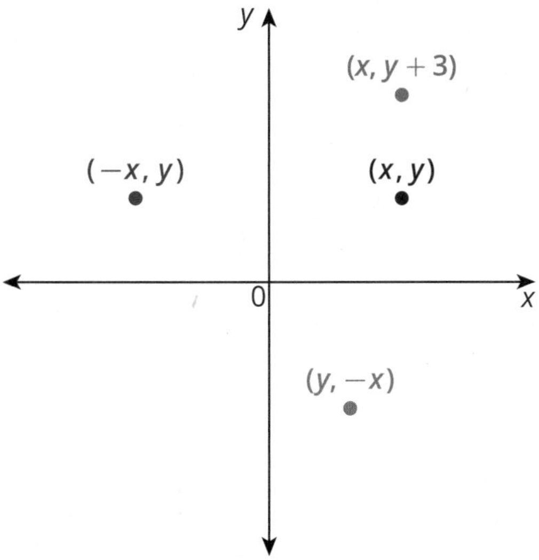

Point A represents a vertical translation of 3 units.

Point B represents a reflection across the *y*-axis.

Point C represents a rotation of 90° clockwise about the origin.

Students have learned about functions. Some have a foundation level understanding, while others have extensive experience with functions, particularly linear and exponential functions. They know that a function maps each element of the domain to exactly one element of the range.

In elementary school, students informally investigated reflectional symmetry in two-dimensional figures by folding figures and drawing lines of symmetry.

NOTES

Connection to Future Learning

Why is *Rigid Motions on a Plane* important?

Rigid Motions on a Plane begins the formal study of congruence and sets the stage for similarity and trigonometry. This topic is part of a long progression in understanding geometric and algebraic transformations.

In the next topic, students define congruent figures in terms of rigid motion transformations. They explain how the criteria for triangle congruence follow from the definition of congruence in terms of rigid motion.

MATH REPRESENTATION

You can use reflections to prove that $\Delta VAR \cong \Delta BKF$. Suppose $VA = BK$, $VR = BR$, and $AR = KF$.

STEP 1 Draw the reflection of ΔVAR across a line that maps point V onto point B. Label the image as $\Delta V'A'R'$.

STEP 2 Draw the reflection of $\Delta V'A'R'$, which maps $\overline{V'A'}$ onto $\overline{BK}$. Label the image as $\Delta V''A''R''$.

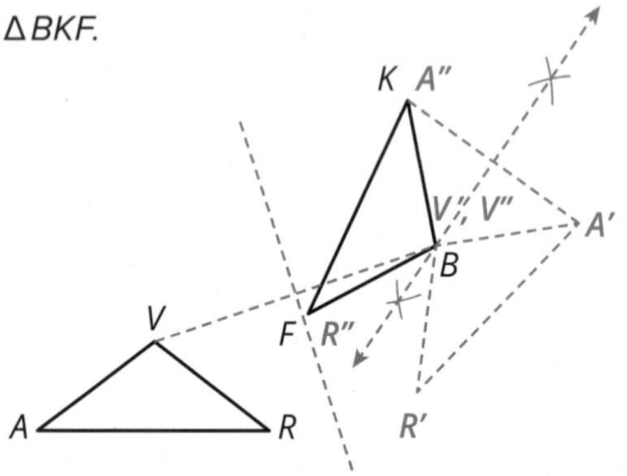

This series of reflections maps the remainder of the triangle onto each other. Knowing that two triangles have three pairs of corresponding sides proves the two triangles are congruent.

Deepening their understanding of transformations to include geometric figures on the plane extends students' ability to transform geometric figures and algebraic functions.

NOTES

Log in to MyCL for resources that support **student meta-cognition**.

How does a student demonstrate understanding?

Students will demonstrate understanding of the standards in *Rigid Motions on a Plane* when they can:

Define translations in terms of distances along parallel lines.	✓
Define reflections in terms of distances across perpendicular lines.	✓
Define rotations in terms of angles around a circle.	✓
Draw rigid motion transformations using patty paper or other construction tools.	✓
Recognize the difference between transformations that are rigid motions and those that are not.	✓
Determine the line of reflection for a given reflection.	✓
Determine the center of rotation for a given rotation.	✓
Specify a sequence of transformations that maps one figure onto another on the plane.	✓
Illustrate the rotations and reflections that carry a figure onto itself.	✓
Calculate the number of lines of symmetry and the degree of rotational symmetry of regular polygons.	✓

HABITS OF MIND

How do the activities in *Rigid Motions on a Plane* promote student expertise in the mathematical practice standards?

All Carnegie Learning topics are written with the goal of creating mathematical thinkers who are active participants in class discourse, so elements of the habits of mind should be evident in all lessons. Students are expected to make sense of problems and work towards solutions, reason using concrete and abstract ideas, and communicate their thinking while providing a critical ear to the thinking of others.

Throughout *Rigid Motions on a Plane,* students make sense of the structure of rigid motion transformations without the added scaffolding of the coordinate plane. Instead of using distances on the coordinate plane to describe these transformations, they generalize their understanding to define these transformations on a plane in terms of parallel lines, perpendicular lines, and arcs of circles. Students must attend to precision as they reason about rigid motions, pay attention to how figures move on the plane, notate these transformations accurately, and use construction tools appropriately. They are gaining expertise in constructions, which is an important proficiency as they progress through geometry.

Mixed Practice

At the end of each topic, a **Mixed Practice** worksheet provides practice with skills from previous topics and this topic.

Spaced Review
Fluency and problem solving from previous topics

End of Topic Review
Review problems from this topic

Log in to MyCL for **digital resources**.
A version with **additional space** for students to write their answers.
Downloadable and editable in Word
Editable via Edulastic

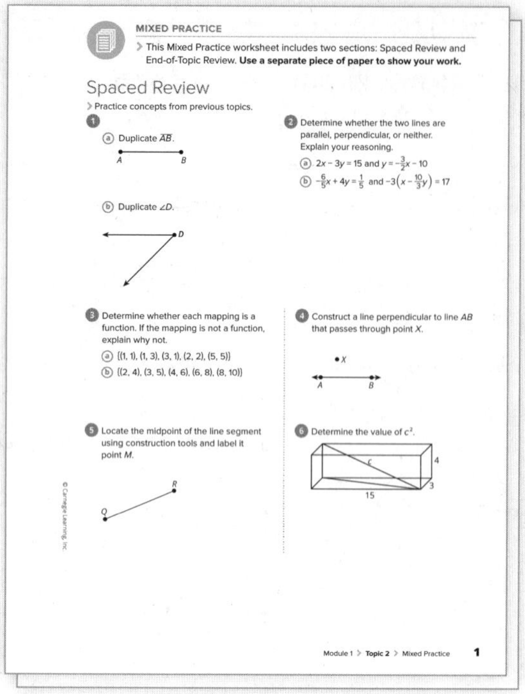
MIXED PRACTICE

> This Mixed Practice worksheet includes two sections: Spaced Review and End-of-Topic Review. **Use a separate piece of paper to show your work.**

Spaced Review

> Practice concepts from previous topics.

1 (a) Duplicate $\overline{AB}$.

(b) Duplicate $\angle D$.

2 Determine whether the two lines are parallel, perpendicular, or neither. Explain your reasoning.

(a) $2x - 3y = 15$ and $y = -\frac{3}{2}x - 10$

(b) $-\frac{6}{5}x + 4y = \frac{1}{5}$ and $-3\left(x - \frac{10}{3}y\right) = 17$

3 Determine whether each mapping is a function. If the mapping is not a function, explain why not.

(a) {(1, 1), (1, 3), (3, 1), (2, 2), (5, 5)}

(b) {(2, 4), (3, 5), (4, 6), (6, 8), (8, 10)}

4 Construct a line perpendicular to line AB that passes through point X.

5 Locate the midpoint of the line segment using construction tools and label it point M.

6 Determine the value of c^2.

© Carnegie Learning, Inc.

Module 1 > Topic 2 > Mixed Practice 1

Topic Summary

Available online, a **Topic Summary** reviews the main concepts for the topic.

Essential Ideas for each lesson.

Log in to MyCL for **digital resources**.
A printable version available for download.
A video of the **Worked Example** being solved
www.carnegielearning.com/login

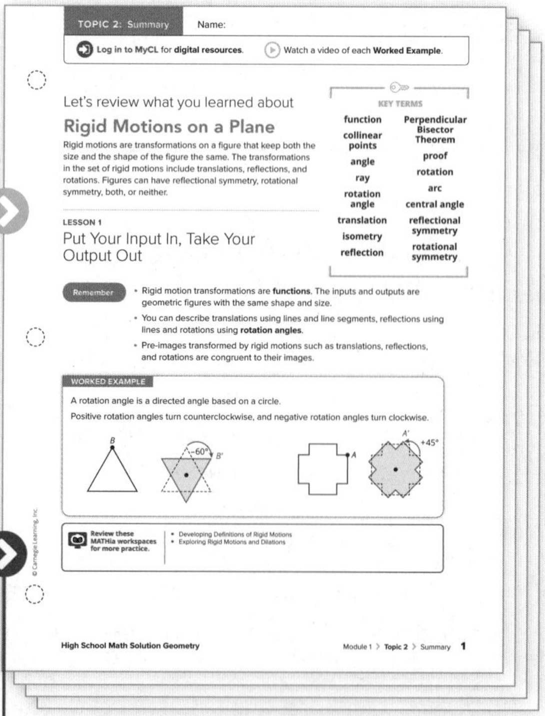
TOPIC 2: Summary Name:

Log in to MyCL for **digital resources**. Watch a video of each **Worked Example**.

Let's review what you learned about

Rigid Motions on a Plane

Rigid motions are transformations on a figure that keep both the size and the shape of the figure the same. The transformations in the set of rigid motions include translations, reflections, and rotations. Figures can have reflectional symmetry, rotational symmetry, both, or neither.

KEY TERMS: function, collinear points, angle, ray, rotation angle, translation, isometry, reflection, Perpendicular Bisector Theorem, proof, rotation, arc, central angle, reflectional symmetry, rotational symmetry

LESSON 1

Put Your Input In, Take Your Output Out

Remember

- Rigid motion transformations are **functions**. The inputs and outputs are geometric figures with the same shape and size.
- You can describe translations using lines and line segments, reflections using lines and rotations using **rotation angles**.
- Pre-images transformed by rigid motions such as translations, reflections, and rotations are congruent to their images.

WORKED EXAMPLE

A rotation angle is a directed angle based on a circle.

Positive rotation angles turn counterclockwise, and negative rotation angles turn clockwise.

Review these MATHia workspaces for more practice.
- Developing Definitions of Rigid Motions
- Exploring Rigid Motions and Dilations

© Carnegie Learning, Inc.

High School Math Solution Geometry

Module 1 > Topic 2 > Summary 1

MATHia Workspaces are highlighted in select lessons to help you understand the connections and what you might want to review.

Assessment

Assessments aligned to this topic:

1. Pre-test
2. Post-test
3. End of Topic Test (Form A)
4. End of Topic Test (Form B)
5. Standardized Test Practice
6. Performance Task with Rubric

An **Assessment Overview** identifies the standard(s) aligned with each item on every test.

Log in to MyCL for digital resources.

A version with **additional space** for students to write their answers.

Downloadable and editable in Word

Editable via Edulastic

End of Topic Test

1.	G.CO.1	7.	G.CO.4
2.	G.CO.1	8.	G.CO.5
3.	G.CO.5	9.	G.CO.2
4.	G.CO.5	10.	G.CO.3
5.	G.CO.5	11.	G.CO.3
6.	G.CO.4	12.	G.CO.3

Standardized Test

1.	G.CO.5	8.	G.CO.5	15.	G.CO.1
2.	G.CO.3	9.	G.CO.5	16.	G.CO.2
3.	G.CO.4	10.	G.CO.1	17.	G.CO.5
4.	G.CO.3	11.	G.CO.3	18.	G.CO.5
5.	G.CO.5	12.	G.CO.4	19.	G.CO.5
6.	G.CO.4	13.	G.CO.4	20.	G.CO.5
7.	G.CO.3	14.	G.CO.5		

Family Guide

Teachers, encourage your families to log into the **Home Connection** to access a collection of resources that supports their students as they learn about *Rigid Motions on a Plane.*

www.carnegielearning.com/home-connection

For families with limited online access, print and send home the **Family Guide**.

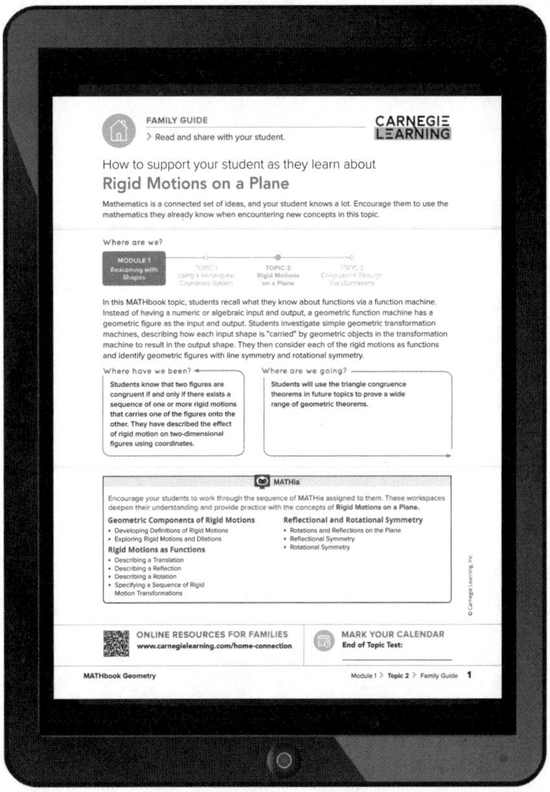

Rigid Motions on a Plane

Scope out MATHbook and MATHia sessions for this topic, keeping in mind your long term plan.

You can schedule MATHia sessions any time; however, if you are using Skills Practice as the alternative, schedule those sessions after a completed lesson.

Log in to MyCL for:

- Editable templates
- Alternative plans for longer sessions
- Implementations not using MATHia

1 Session ≈ 45 minutes

CORE IMPLEMENTATION PLAN with flexible access to computers/tablets.

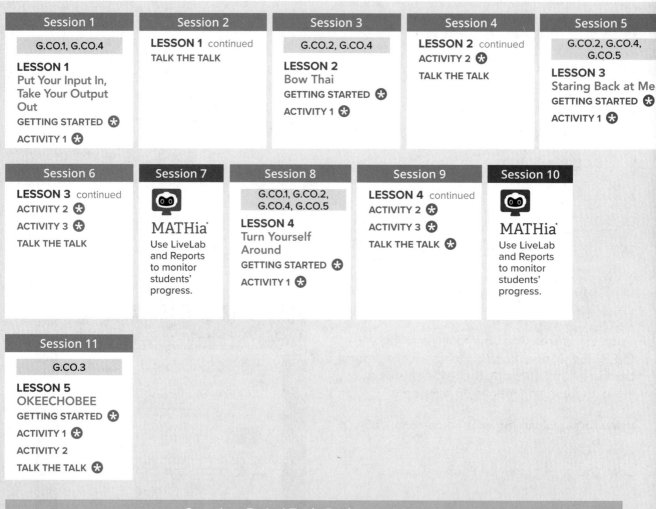

Session 1	Session 2	Session 3	Session 4	Session 5
G.CO.1, G.CO.4 **LESSON 1** Put Your Input In, Take Your Output Out GETTING STARTED ✪ ACTIVITY 1 ✪	**LESSON 1** continued TALK THE TALK	G.CO.2, G.CO.4 **LESSON 2** Bow Thai GETTING STARTED ✪ ACTIVITY 1 ✪	**LESSON 2** continued ACTIVITY 2 ✪ TALK THE TALK	G.CO.2, G.CO.4, G.CO.5 **LESSON 3** Staring Back at Me GETTING STARTED ✪ ACTIVITY 1 ✪

Session 6	Session 7	Session 8	Session 9	Session 10
LESSON 3 continued ACTIVITY 2 ✪ ACTIVITY 3 ✪ TALK THE TALK	MATHia Use LiveLab and Reports to monitor students' progress.	G.CO.1, G.CO.2, G.CO.4, G.CO.5 **LESSON 4** Turn Yourself Around GETTING STARTED ✪ ACTIVITY 1 ✪	**LESSON 4** continued ACTIVITY 2 ✪ ACTIVITY 3 ✪ TALK THE TALK ✪	MATHia Use LiveLab and Reports to monitor students' progress.

Session 11
G.CO.3 **LESSON 5** OKEECHOBEE GETTING STARTED ✪ ACTIVITY 1 ✪ ACTIVITY 2 TALK THE TALK ✪

Complete End-of-Topic Review and Assess

✪ This activity highlights a key term or concept that is essential to the learning goals of the lesson.

ENGAGE + **DEVELOP** + **TEACH**

at the **Module** level | at the **Topic** level | Read the facilitation notes and plan learning experiences.

Where are we?

TOPIC 2 Rigid Motions on a Plane	LESSON 1 Put Your Input In, Take Your Output Out	LESSON 2 Bow Thai	LESSON 3 Staring Back at Me	LESSON 4 Turn Yourself Around	LESSON 5 OKEECHOBEE
Pacing	2 Sessions	2 Sessions	2 Sessions	2 Sessions	1 Session

OVERVIEW: LESSON 1

Put Your Input In, Take Your Output Out

Geometric Components of Rigid Motions

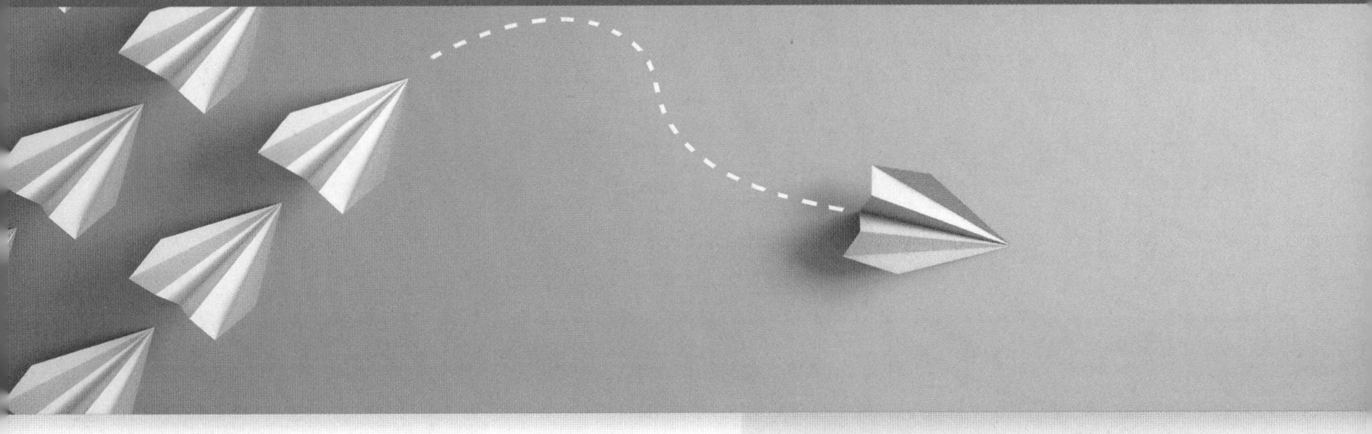

ENGAGE

- Students apply geometric rigid motions using an input-output machine.

DEVELOP

- They show that translating segments maintains congruency and creates parallel lines.

DEMONSTRATE

- Students describe a sequence of transformations to create an image.

HIGH SCHOOL GEOMETRY

Congruence

Experiment with transformations in the plane.

1. Know precise definitions of *angle, circle, perpendicular line, parallel line*, and *line segment*, based on the undefined notions of point, line, distance along a line, and distance around a circular arc.
4. Develop definitions of rotations, reflections, and translations in terms of angles, circles, perpendicular lines, parallel lines, and line segments.

LESSON STRUCTURE AND PACING GUIDE 2 SESSIONS

⊛ This activity highlights a key term or concept that is essential to the learning goals of the lesson.

Session 1		Session 2

INSTRUCTIONAL SEQUENCE

ENGAGE	DEVELOP	DEMONSTRATE
Establish a situation	Mathematical problem solving	Exit ticket application

GETTING STARTED ⊛
Transformation Machine

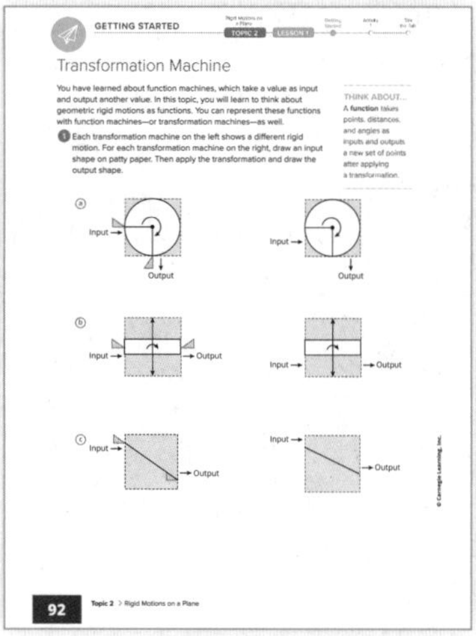

Students apply geometric rigid motions using an input-output machine.

- They describe transformation functions.

ACTIVITY 1 ⊛
Lines, Line Segments, and Angles

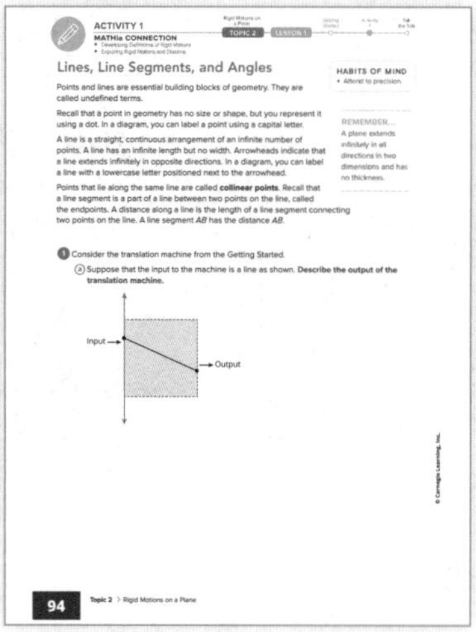

Students show that translating segments maintains congruency and creates parallel lines.

- They identify positive and negative rotation angles.

TALK THE TALK
Shake It All About

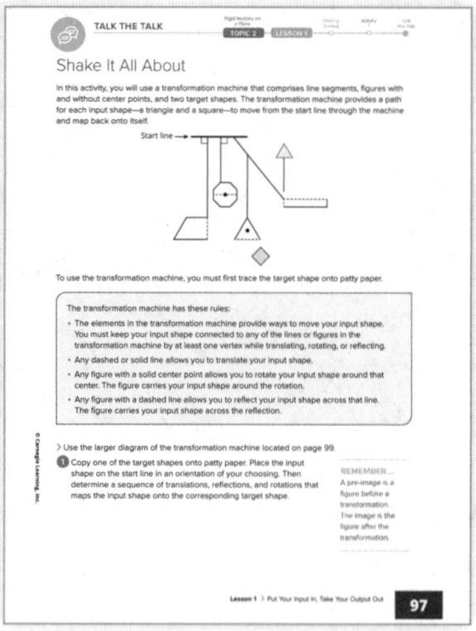

Students experiment with a transformation machine using patty paper.

- They describe the sequence of transformations to create an image.

Log in to MyCL for **lesson support** including:

Slides

Videos

www.carnegielearning.com/login

NOTES

TOPIC 2

Log in to MyCL for:

- Editable templates
- Additional planning support

Now that you have read the Module, Topic, and Lesson Overviews, you are ready to plan.

Do the math

> Tear out the lesson planning template (page 91O) and jot down thoughts as you work through this lesson and read the Facilitation Notes.

- Anticipate student responses
- Track your time, so you can estimate how much time to spend on any activity
- Decide which differentiation and collaboration strategies you may use and how that may impact pacing

Connect the learning

MATHbook + MATHia

The table shows a portion of the self-paced MATHia sequence for the *Rigid Motions on a Plane* Topic.

Median student completion time for the entire topic: ~90–120 minutes

> As you implement this lesson, consider different connections for students who are on pace and those that have not yet completed the workspaces aligned to this lesson.

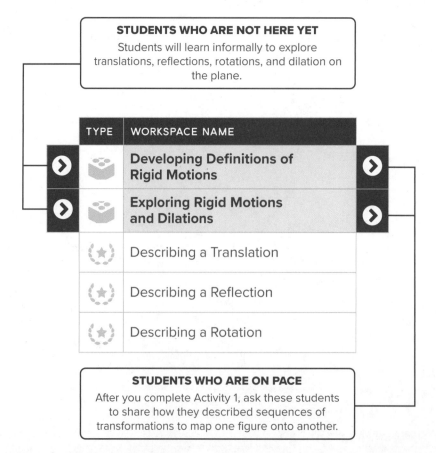

STUDENTS WHO ARE NOT HERE YET
Students will learn informally to explore translations, reflections, rotations, and dilation on the plane.

TYPE	WORKSPACE NAME
	Developing Definitions of Rigid Motions
	Exploring Rigid Motions and Dilations
	Describing a Translation
	Describing a Reflection
	Describing a Rotation

STUDENTS WHO ARE ON PACE
After you complete Activity 1, ask these students to share how they described sequences of transformations to map one figure onto another.

Put Your Input In, Take Your Output Out

Geometric Components of Rigid Motions

Session 1

GETTING STARTED Transformation Machine ✪

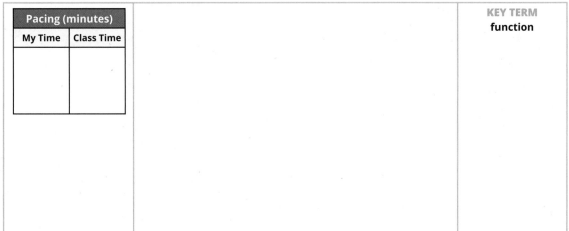

Pacing (minutes)	
My Time	Class Time

KEY TERM
function

ACTIVITY 1 Lines, Line Segments, and Angles ✪

Pacing (minutes)	
My Time	Class Time

KEY TERM
collinear points
angle
ray
rotation angle

Session 2

TALK THE TALK Shake It All About

Pacing (minutes)	
My Time	Class Time

✪ This activity highlights a key term or concept that is essential to the learning goals of the lesson.

Log in to MyCL for:
- Editable templates
- Additional planning support

Reflect on your lesson

> Consider the effectiveness of your lesson on student learning.

What went well?

What did not go as planned?

> Anticipate how you would change the lesson next time you teach it.

How will you capitalize on the things that went well?

How will you improve things that did not go as planned?

MATERIALS

- Patty paper
- Protractors (optional)
- Straightedges

TOPIC 1
Using a Rectangular Coordinate System

TOPIC 2
Rigid Motions on a Plane

TOPIC 3
Congruence Through Transformations

1 | Put Your Input In, Take Your Output Out
2 | Bow Thai
3 | Staring Back at Me
4 | Turn Yourself Around
5 | OKEECHOBEE

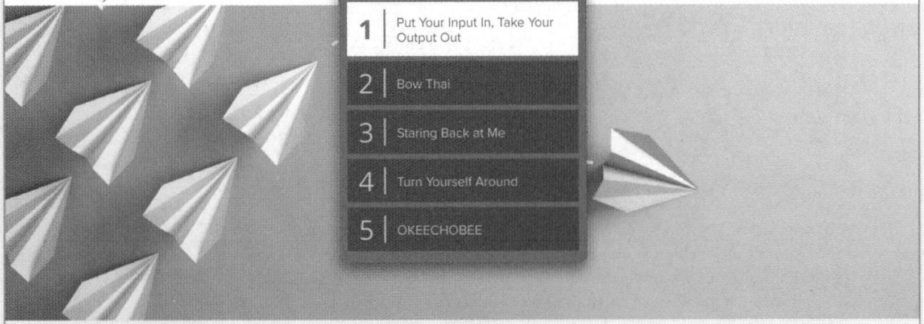

LESSON 1

Put Your Input In, Take Your Output Out

Geometric Components of Rigid Motions

KEY TERMS
function
collinear points
angle
ray
rotation angle

Learning Goals

- Know precise definitions of line segment, angle, and distance along a line.
- Translate lines to produce parallel lines.

REVIEW (1–2 minutes)

Use the vertical line test to determine whether each graph represents a function.

1 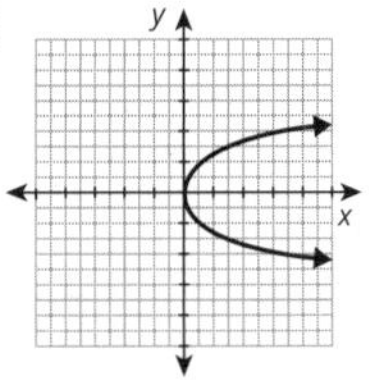

No. Some x-values correspond to more than one y-value.

2 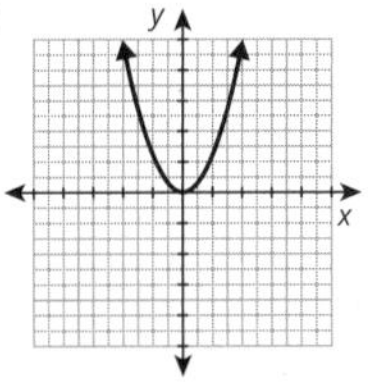

Yes. Each x-value corresponds to one and only one y-value.

You know a lot about rigid motions, such as translations, reflections, and rotations.

How do you use straight lines and angles to represent rigid motion transformations?

Setting the Stage

- **Assign Review (optional, 1 – 2 minutes)**
- **Communicate the learning goals and key terms to look out for**
- **Tap into your students' prior learning by reading the narrative statement**
- **Provide a sense of direction by reading the question**

TOPIC 2

IN THIS REVIEW
Students review the meaning of a function. They will use this skill throughout the lesson.

You can describe translations using lines and line segments. You can describe reflections using lines. You can describe rotations using rotation angles.

Pre-images transformed by rigid motions such as translations, reflections, and rotations are congruent to their images.

Essential Ideas

- Rigid motion transformations are functions. The inputs and outputs are geometric figures with the same shape and size.
- The input and output lines from a translation are parallel.
- A rotation angle is a directed angle based on a circle. Positive rotation angles turn counterclockwise, and negative rotation angles turn clockwise.
- A rotation angle describes the operation for a rotation function.
- A combination of rigid motion transformations can map a figure back onto itself.

GETTING STARTED

SUMMARY **Rigid motion transformations are functions. The inputs and outputs are geometric figures with the same shape and size.**

Chunking the Activity

- **Read and discuss the introduction**
- **Group students to complete the activity**
- **Share and summarize**

DIFFERENTIATION STRATEGY

See Page 102A to support students who struggle with 1.

Student Look-Fors

Symmetric and non-symmetric input shapes. Encourage the use of non-symmetric shapes.

LANGUAGE LINK

Provide a framework to summarize the vocabulary used in this lesson. Students will include the terms *isometry* and *dilation* in the next lesson.

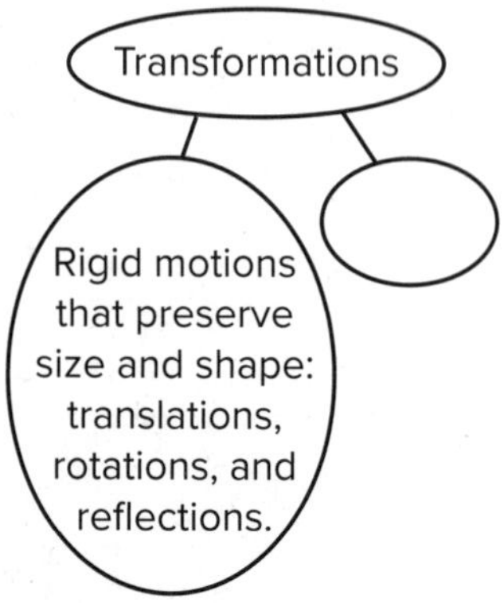

Transformation Machine

You have learned about function machines, which take a value as input and output another value. In this topic, you will learn to think about geometric rigid motions as functions. You can represent these functions with function machines—or transformation machines—as well.

THINK ABOUT...
A **function** takes points, distances, and angles as inputs and outputs a new set of points after applying a transformation.

1. Each transformation machine on the left shows a different rigid motion. For each transformation machine on the right, draw an input shape on patty paper. Then apply the transformation and draw the output shape.

(a)

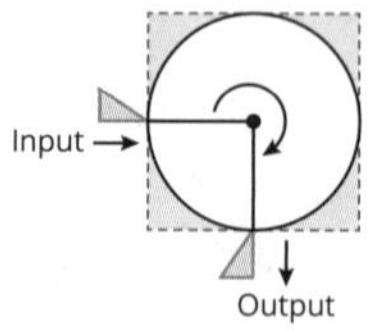

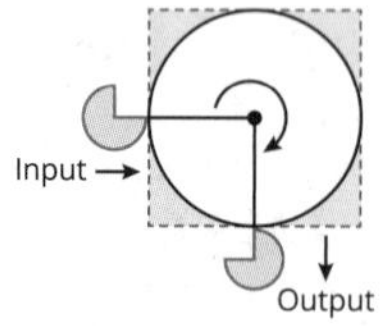

Sample answer.

(b)

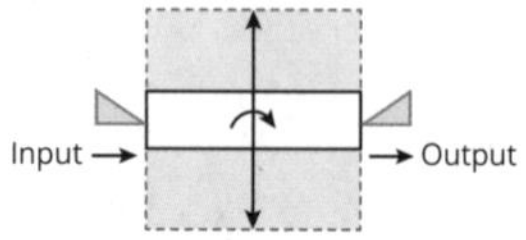

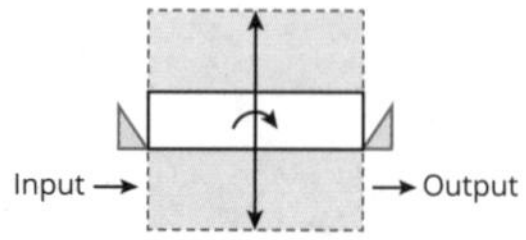

Sample answer.

(c)

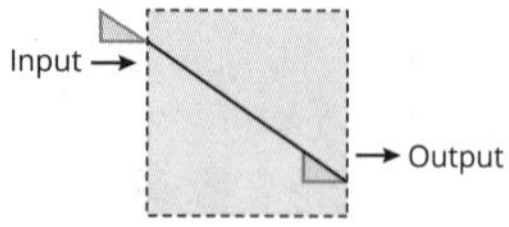

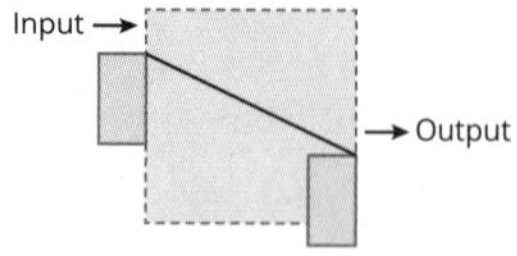

Sample answer.

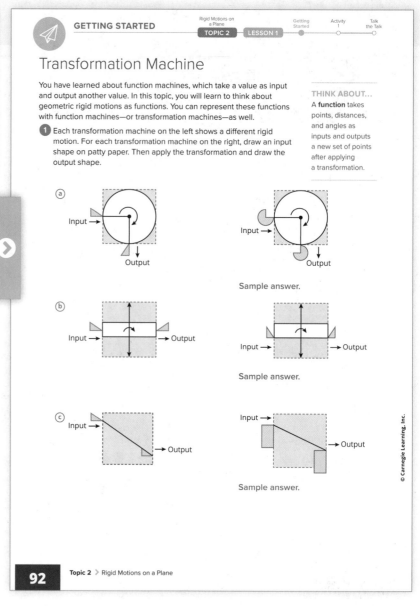

Questions to Support Discourse

		TYPE
Intro	• What makes an algebraic relation a function? • If it is a rigid motion transformation machine, which operations can it perform? • What makes a transformation a rigid motion? • What is an example of a transformation that is not a rigid motion?	Gathering
1	• Why is the output inside the transformation machine box?	Probing

GETTING STARTED Continued

2 Identify the rigid motion represented by each transformation machine.

a. Rotation
b. Reflection
c. Translation

3 Describe each transformation function. **Explain how each input shape is carried by geometric objects in the transformation machine to result in the output shape.**

The input to each function was a shape.

In the rotation, the circle carried the input shape and rotated it 270° clockwise to become the output shape.

In the reflection, the side of a rectangle carried the input shape and reflected it across a vertical line to become the output shape.

In the translation, a line segment carried the input shape to translate it along the line segment and become the output shape.

Questions to Support Discourse

		TYPE
3	• How many degrees is the clockwise rotation? • How could you describe this transformation with a counterclockwise rotation? • What is the orientation of the line of reflection?	Probing

NOTES

TOPIC 2

ACTIVITY 1

SUMMARY **The input and outline lines from a translation are parallel. A rotation angle describes the operation for a rotation function.**

Chunking the Activity

- **Read and discuss the introduction and definitions**
- **Group students to complete 1 - 3**
- **Check-in and share**
- **Read and discuss the definitions**
- **Complete 4 as a class**
- **Share and summarize**

DIFFERENTIATION STRATEGY

See Page 102A to assist all students with the introduction.

Student Look-Fors

Whether students are demonstrating proficiencies related to this habit of mind.

- Attend to precision

ACTIVITY 1

MATHia CONNECTION

- Developing Definitions of Rigid Motions
- Exploring Rigid Motions and Dilations

Lines, Line Segments, and Angles

HABITS OF MIND
- Attend to precision.

Points and lines are essential building blocks of geometry. They are called undefined terms.

Recall that a point in geometry has no size or shape, but you represent it using a dot. In a diagram, you can label a point using a capital letter.

A line is a straight, continuous arrangement of an infinite number of points. A line has an infinite length but no width. Arrowheads indicate that a line extends infinitely in opposite directions. In a diagram, you can label a line with a lowercase letter positioned next to the arrowhead.

Points that lie along the same line are called **collinear points**. Recall that a line segment is a part of a line between two points on the line, called the endpoints. A distance along a line is the length of a line segment connecting two points on the line. A line segment *AB* has the distance *AB*.

REMEMBER...
A plane extends infinitely in all directions in two dimensions and has no thickness.

1. Consider the translation machine from the Getting Started.

   a. Suppose that the input to the machine is a line as shown. **Describe the output of the translation machine.**

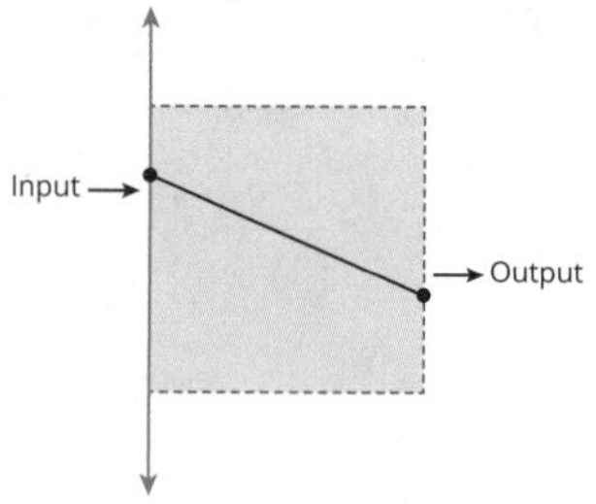

The output is a vertical line translated along the line segment.
The output line is parallel to the input line.

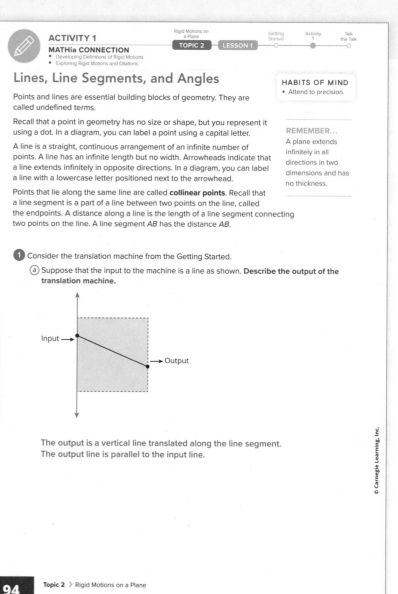

Questions to Support Discourse

		TYPE
1	• What effect does the translation have on the line? • What is the relationship between the input and output lines? • Label a point on the input line and described its position on the translated line.	Probing

ACTIVITY 1 Continued

ⓑ Suppose that the translation machine is a set of parallel line segments as shown. How does this change the output of the machine when the input is a line?

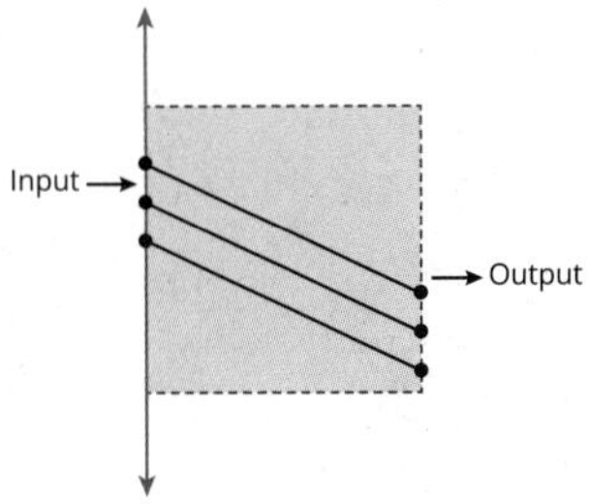

It does not change the output.

2 Identify the line segments and distances used in the translation machines in the previous activity.

The first translation machine used a line segment inside the machine.
The second translation machine used three line segments.
Each line segment represents the same distance.

3 Are the line segments in the translation machine in Question 1, part (b), congruent? **Use patty paper to justify your answer, and explain your reasoning.**

Yes. All the line segments are congruent.

REMEMBER...
Congruent line segments are line segments that have the same length. They represent equal distances.

Questions to Support Discourse

		TYPE
3	• How could you use reasoning to tell the line segments are congruent?	Reflecting and justifying

NOTES

LANGUAGE LINK

Remind students to refer to the Academic Glossary (page FM–20) to review the definition of **explain your reasoning** and related phrases. Suggest they ask themselves these questions:

- How can I justify my answer to others?
- Is my explanation logical?

NOTES

COMMON MISCONCEPTION

See Page 102A for a misconception related to the definitions.

DIFFERENTIATION STRATEGY

See Page 102A to assist all students with the diagrams.

An **angle** is a set of points consisting of a vertex point and two rays extending from the vertex point. A **ray** is a portion of a line that begins with a single point and extends infinitely in one direction.

A **rotation angle** is a directed angle based on a circle.

A positive rotation angle turns counterclockwise.

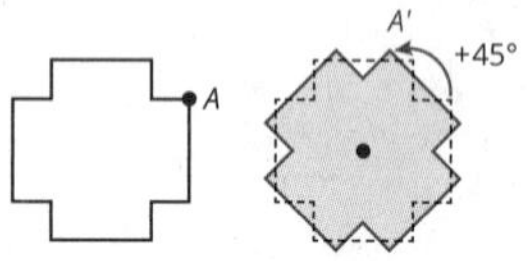

A negative rotation angle turns clockwise.

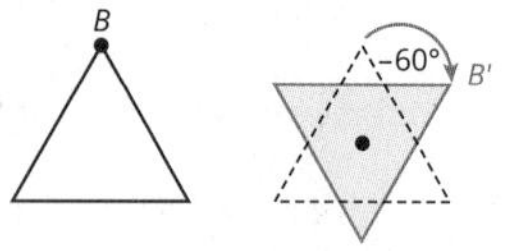

4 Identify the rotation angle used in the rotation machine in the Getting Started.

–270°

Questions to Support Discourse

		TYPE
Diagrams	• What is a negative rotation angle that would have the same results as the +45° rotation angle? • What is a positive rotation angle that would have the same results as the –60° rotation angle?	Probing
4	• How did you know the rotation angle was negative?	Gathering
	• Which benchmark angle(s) did you use to identify the 270° angle?	Probing

SUMMARY A combination of rigid motion transformations can map a figure back onto itself.

Shake It All About

In this activity, you will use a transformation machine that comprises line segments, figures with and without center points, and two target shapes. The transformation machine provides a path for each input shape—a triangle and a square—to move from the start line through the machine and map back onto itself.

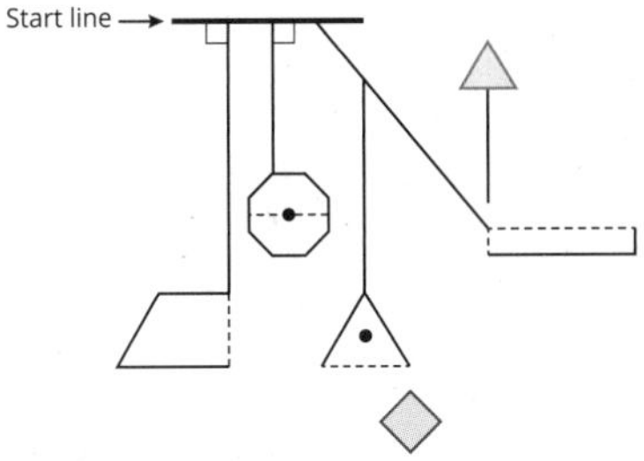

To use the transformation machine, you must first trace the target shape onto patty paper.

The transformation machine has these rules:

- The elements in the transformation machine provide ways to move your input shape. You must keep your input shape connected to any of the lines or figures in the transformation machine by at least one vertex while translating, rotating, or reflecting.
- Any dashed or solid line allows you to translate your input shape.
- Any figure with a solid center point allows you to rotate your input shape around that center. The figure carries your input shape around the rotation.
- Any figure with a dashed line allows you to reflect your input shape across that line. The figure carries your input shape across the reflection.

> Use the larger diagram of the transformation machine located on page 99.

1. Copy one of the target shapes onto patty paper. Place the input shape on the start line in an orientation of your choosing. Then determine a sequence of translations, reflections, and rotations that maps the input shape onto the corresponding target shape.

   Answers will vary.
   Check students' work.

REMEMBER...
A pre-image is a figure before a transformation. The image is the figure after the transformation.

Chunking the Activity

- Read and discuss the directions
- Group students to complete the activity
- Share and summarize

DIFFERENTIATION STRATEGY

See Page 102B to support students who struggle with the directions.

LANGUAGE LINK

ELL TIP

Ensure that students understand the meaning of *orientation* in Question 1. In this context, *orientation* means the position of an object. Explain that students can position the square and triangle any way they would like on the start line.

Questions to Support Discourse

		TYPE
Directions	• How many locations are available on the start line? • What are the two meanings of a dashed line?	Gathering
	• Explain what would happen if you started with a square at the first location on the start line. • Which transformation should you perform with the solid vertical line? • What options do you have once the figure reaches the trapezoid?	Probing

NOTES

Student Look-Fors

Using self-motivation and self-discipline to persevere in problem-solving.

2 Describe the sequence of transformations you used to transform each pre-image to each image. Label points on the transformation machine so that you can precisely describe your transformations.

NOTE: Reduced images of the transformation machines are shown only for the teacher so you can understand the solution strategies.

The triangle must start as a horizontal reflection. You can translate the triangle pre-image along the solid line to the rectangle. Then you can reflect the pre-image across the dashed line of the rectangle, and finally translate it up to the image of the triangle.

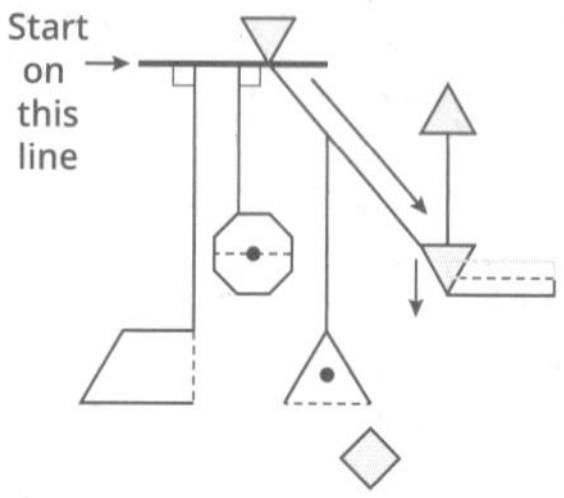

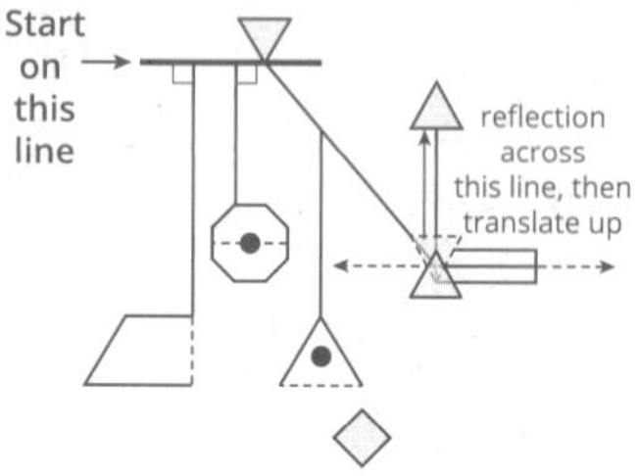

You can translate the square pre-image from its original position to the side of the triangle figure. You can then reflect the square across the dotted line of the triangle figure, and finally translate it into the final position.

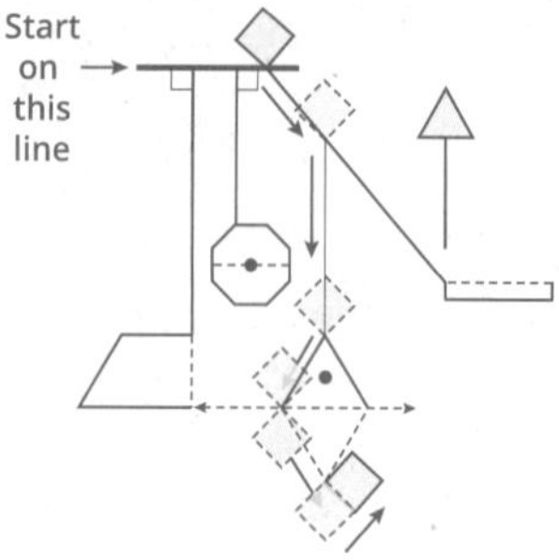

3 Consider the transformations performed on each pre-image to map it onto the image. Are the images congruent to the pre-images? **Explain why or why not.**

Yes. The images are congruent to the pre-images because they use rigid motion transformations.

Questions to Support Discourse

		TYPE
2	• Explain how an unsuccessful attempt guided you to modify your next try. • Is there another sequence of transformations that yields the same result?	Probing

TALK THE TALK RESOURCE

Function Machine

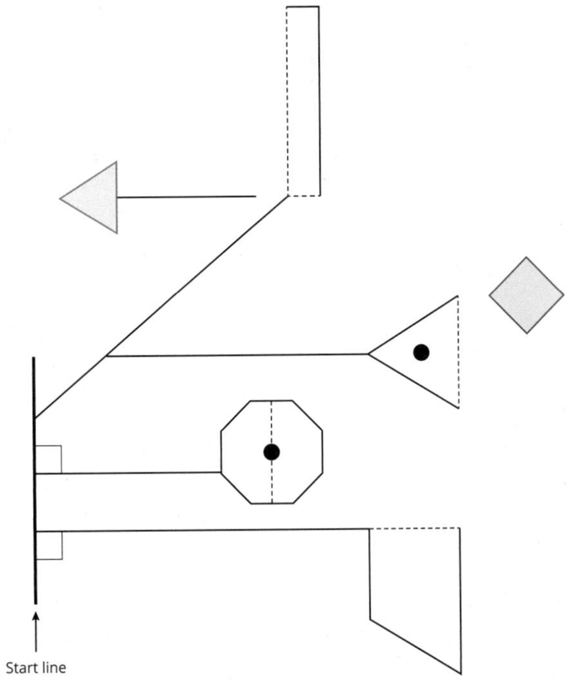

Lesson 1 > Put Your Input In, Take Your Output Out 99

NOTES

NOTES

Why is this page blank?

So you can tear out the function machine on the other side.

100 Topic 2 > Rigid Motions on a Plane

ASSIGNMENT

LESSON 1 ASSIGNMENT

> Use a separate piece of paper for your Journal entry.

REMEMBER

You can describe translations using lines and line segments. You can describe reflections using lines. You can describe rotations using rotation angles.

Pre-images transformed by rigid motions such as translations, reflections, and rotations are congruent to their images.

JOURNAL

Complete each sentence with a term from the box.

1. A(n) ____________ is a location in space.
2. A(n) ____________ is a straight continuous arrangement of an infinite number of points.
3. Points that are all located on the same line are ____________
4. A(n) ____________ is a portion of a line that includes two points and all of the collinear points between the two points.
5. A(n) ____________ is a portion of a line that begins with a single point and extends infinitely in one direction.
6. A(n) ____________ is a directed angle.
7. A(n) ____________ is a set of points consisting of a vertex point and two rays extending from the vertex point.

WORD BANK

line segment
point
collinear points
line
ray
angle
rotation angle

PRACTICE

> Create a transformation machine to perform each sequence of transformations. Describe the geometric objects you used to create each machine. Draw an example of a transformation performed by the transformation machine.

1. Translate a figure to the left, then translate it up

   Sample answer.

   The transformation machine consists of two line segments.

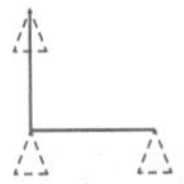

2. Translate a figure down, then reflect it across a horizontal line

   Sample answer.

   The transformation machine consists of a line segment and a line.

Go to LiveHint.com for help on the PRACTICE questions.

Encourage students to use LiveHint.com for help with the PRACTICE questions of this assignment.

Chunking the Assignment

SESSION 1

- Journal
- Mixed Practice (page 153) 1

SESSION 2

- Practice 1 - 5
- Stretch (advanced learners)

TOPIC 2

JOURNAL

1. point
2. line
3. collinear points
4. line segments
5. ray
6. rotation angle
7. angle

3. Rotate a figure clockwise 180°, then translate it to the right

Sample answer.

The transformation machine consists of an angle and a line segment.

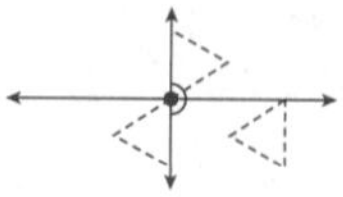

4. Reflect a figure across a vertical line, then rotate it clockwise 90°

Sample answer.

The transformation machine consists of a vertical line and an angle.

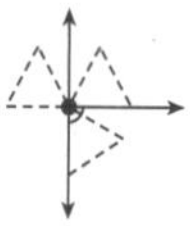

5. Translate a figure up, then reflect it across a vertical line

Sample answer.

The transformation machine consists of a line segment and a vertical line.

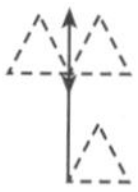

STRETCH Optional

> Determine three different transformation machines you could use to move the figure at position A to position B. Describe the geometric objects you used to create each machine. Draw an example of a transformation performed by the transformation machine.

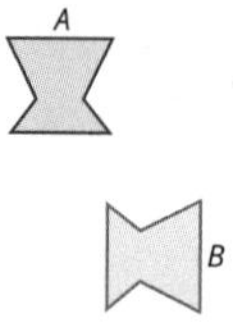

NOTES

STRETCH

Sample answers.

One transformation machine could consist of an angle that rotates the figure clockwise 90° and a line segment that translates the figure down.

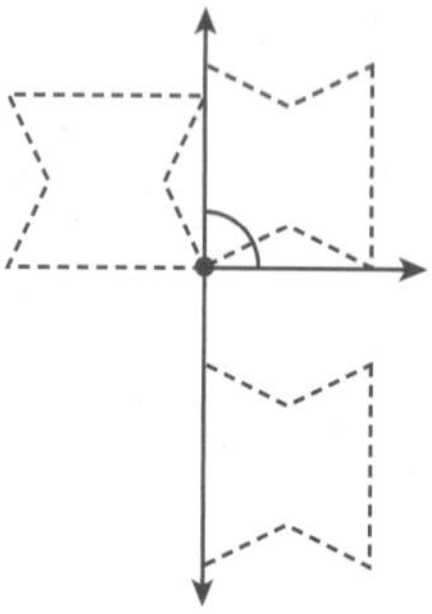

Another transformation machine could consist of an angle that rotates the figure counterclockwise 90°, a line segment that translates the figure down, and a vertical line that reflects the figure across it.

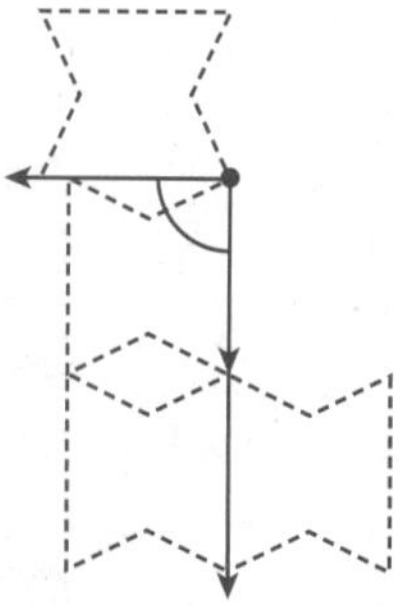

A third transformation machine could consist of a horizontal line that reflects the figure across it, a line segment that translates the figure down, and an angle that rotates the figure clockwise 90°.

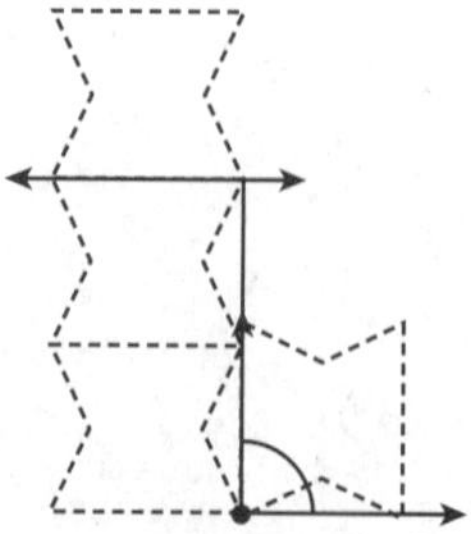

Put Your Input In, Take Your Output Out

This resource details additional facilitation notes to fully assist you as you plan each lesson to support all students, students who struggle, and advanced learners. It provides differentiation strategies, common student misconceptions, and suggestions to extend certain activities.

GETTING STARTED

Session 1 of 2

Transformation Machine

Students apply geometric rigid motions using an input-output machine. They describe transformation functions.

CHUNK	AUDIENCE	ADDITIONAL SUPPORTS
As students work on 1	Students who Struggle	**DIFFERENTIATION STRATEGY** Demonstrate the transformations in the left column as students follow along with patty paper.

ACTIVITY 1

Session 1 of 2

Lines, Line Segments, and Angles

Students show that translating segments maintains congruency and creates parallel lines. They identify positive and negative rotation angles.

CHUNK	AUDIENCE	ADDITIONAL SUPPORTS
As you read and discuss the introduction	All Students	**DIFFERENTIATION STRATEGY** Have students sketch and label diagrams of a point, line, plane, and collinear points as they read about them.
As you read and discuss the definition of *rotation angle*	All Students	**COMMON MISCONCEPTION** It may not be intuitive that positive rotation angles turn counterclockwise and negative rotation angles turn clockwise. This concept aligns with angle placement on the coordinate plane. A positive rotation angle with one ray at 0° opens up from the *x*-axis towards the *y*-axis in the first quadrant.
As you analyze the diagrams	All Students	**DIFFERENTIATION STRATEGY** Have students trace the figure onto patty paper and use a protractor to verify that the rotated angles in the diagrams are 45° and 60°.

TALK THE TALK

Session 2 of 2

Shake It All About

Students experiment with a transformation machine using patty paper. They describe the sequence of transformations to create an image.

CHUNK	AUDIENCE	ADDITIONAL SUPPORTS
As you read and discuss the directions	Students who Struggle	**DIFFERENTIATION STRATEGY** Complete one attempt as a class.

Practice the learning

MATHbook + Skills Practice

The table shows the targeted practice of the skills and mathematical concepts for the *Rigid Motions on the Plane* Topic. The highlighted Problem Set aligns with **Put Your Input In, Take Your Output Out**.

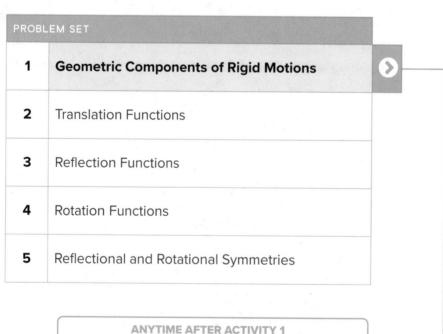

PROBLEM SET	
1	**Geometric Components of Rigid Motions**
2	Translation Functions
3	Reflection Functions
4	Rotation Functions
5	Reflectional and Rotational Symmetries

ANYTIME AFTER ACTIVITY 1
Facilitate students as they work individually on **Problem Set 1**.

ENGAGE + DEVELOP + TEACH

ENGAGE at the **Module** level + DEVELOP at the **Topic** level + TEACH Read the facilitation notes and plan learning experiences.

Where are we?

TOPIC 2 Rigid Motions on a Plane	LESSON 1 Put Your Input In, Take Your Output Out	**LESSON 2 Bow Thai**	LESSON 3 Staring Back at Me	LESSON 4 Turn Yourself Around	LESSON 5 OKEECHOBEE
Pacing	2 Sessions	**2 Sessions**	2 Sessions	2 Sessions	1 Session

OVERVIEW: LESSON 2

Bow Thai

Translations as Functions

ENGAGE

- Students translate figures along parallel lines and rays sharing a common vertex.

DEVELOP

- Students measure a translation as a directed line segment on the coordinate plane.
- They write translation functions and draw translations.
- They identify whether transformations are isometries.

DEMONSTRATE

- Students compare translations described by geometric and algebraic functions.

HIGH SCHOOL GEOMETRY

Congruence

Experiment with transformations in the plane.

2. Represent transformations in the plane using, e.g., transparencies and geometry software; describe transformations as functions that take points in the plane as inputs and give other points as outputs. Compare transformations that preserve distance and angle to those that do not.

4. Develop definitions of rotations, reflections, and translations in terms of angles, circles, perpendicular lines, parallel lines, and line segments.

LESSON STRUCTURE AND PACING GUIDE 2 SESSIONS

✪ This activity highlights a key term or concept that is essential to the learning goals of the lesson.

Session 1 | **Session 2**

INSTRUCTIONAL SEQUENCE

ENGAGE	DEVELOP	DEVELOP
Connect to prior knowledge	Worked example Peer analysis	Real-world problem solving

✪ GETTING STARTED
Universal Translator

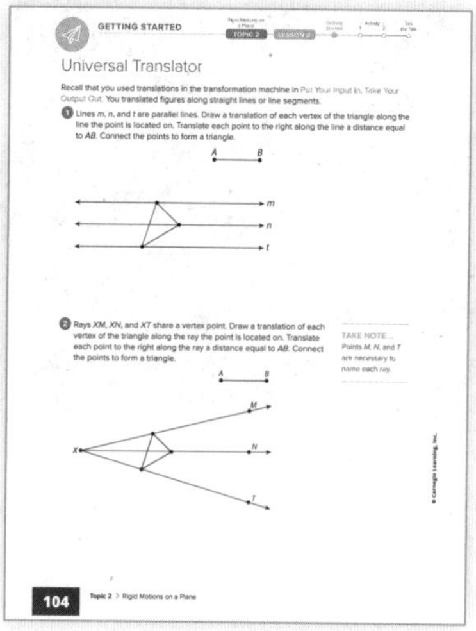
GETTING STARTED

Universal Translator

104 Topic 2 > Rigid Motions on a Plane

Students translate figures along parallel lines and rays sharing a common vertex.

- They compare the results of the translation and dilation.

✪ ACTIVITY 1
Translation Functions

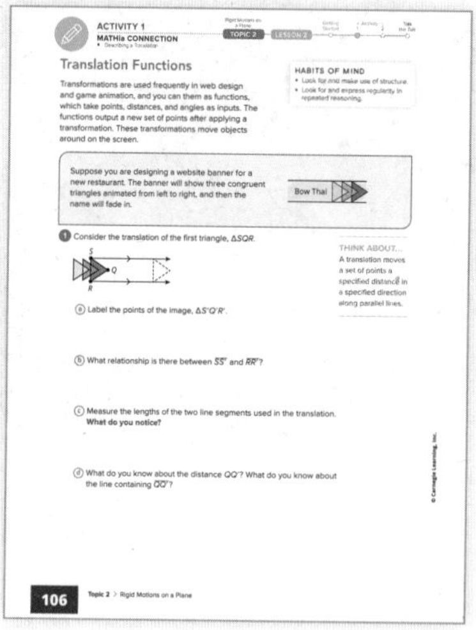
ACTIVITY 1

Translation Functions

106 Topic 2 > Rigid Motions on a Plane

Students measure a translation as a directed line segment on the coordinate plane.

- They use function notation to describe and translate figures.

✪ ACTIVITY 2
Determining Congruence Using Translations

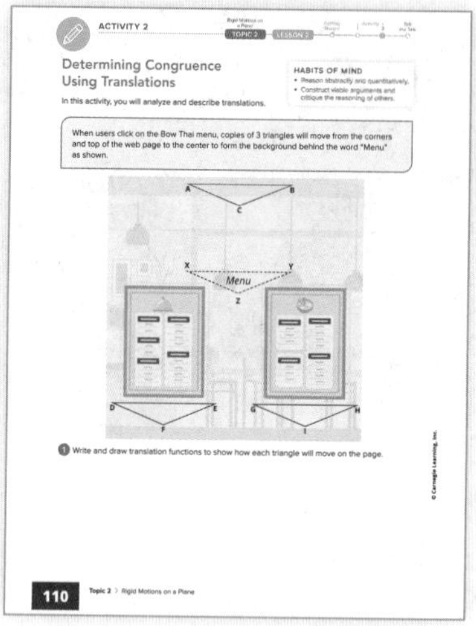
ACTIVITY 2

Determining Congruence Using Translations

110 Topic 2 > Rigid Motions on a Plane

Students write translation functions and draw translations for a real-world situation.

- They identify whether the transformations are isometries.

Log in to MyCL for **lesson support** including:

Slides

Videos

www.carnegielearning.com/login

INSTRUCTIONAL SEQUENCE

DEMONSTRATE

Writing task

TALK THE TALK

Isometries on the Menu

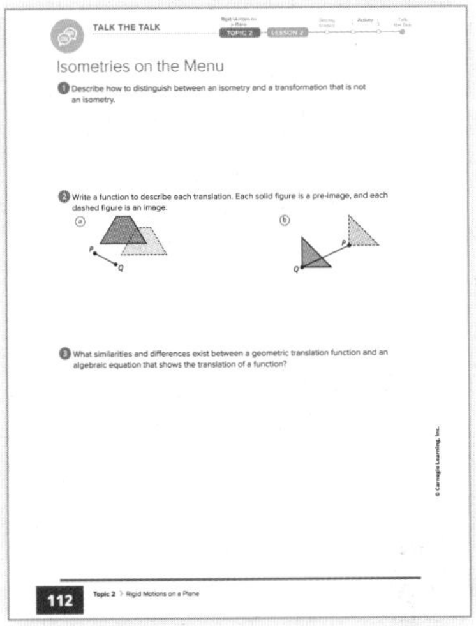
TALK THE TALK

TOPIC 2 LESSON 2

Isometries on the Menu

1 Describe how to distinguish between an isometry and a transformation that is not an isometry.

2 Write a function to describe each translation. Each solid figure is a pre-image, and each dashed figure is an image.

ⓐ

ⓑ

3 What similarities and differences exist between a geometric translation function and an algebraic equation that shows the translation of a function?

© Carnegie Learning, Inc.

112 Topic 2 > Rigid Motions on a Plane

Students distinguish between transformations that are and are not isometries.

- They compare translations described by geometric and algebraic functions.

NOTES

TOPIC 2

Log in to MyCL for:

- Editable templates
- Additional planning support

Now that you have read the Module, Topic, and Lesson Overviews, you are ready to plan.

Do the math

> Tear out the lesson planning template (page 103E) and jot down thoughts as you work through this lesson and read the Facilitation Notes.

Connect the learning

MATHbook + MATHia

The table shows a portion of the self-paced MATHia sequence for the *Rigid Motions on a Plane* Topic.

Median student completion time for the entire topic: ~90–120 minutes

> As you implement this lesson, consider different connections for students who are on pace and those that have not yet completed the workspaces aligned to this lesson.

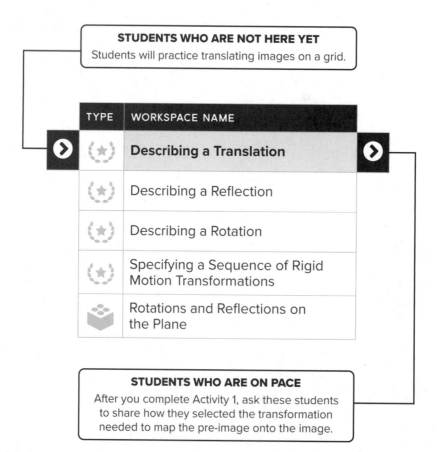

STUDENTS WHO ARE NOT HERE YET
Students will practice translating images on a grid.

TYPE	WORKSPACE NAME
	Describing a Translation
	Describing a Reflection
	Describing a Rotation
	Specifying a Sequence of Rigid Motion Transformations
	Rotations and Reflections on the Plane

STUDENTS WHO ARE ON PACE
After you complete Activity 1, ask these students to share how they selected the transformation needed to map the pre-image onto the image.

Bow Thai
Translations as Functions

Session 1

GETTING STARTED Universal Translator ✪

Pacing (minutes)	
My Time	Class Time

ACTIVITY 1 Translation Functions ✪

Pacing (minutes)	
My Time	Class Time

KEY TERM
translation
isometry

Session 2

ACTIVITY 2 Determining Congruence Using Translations ✪

Pacing (minutes)	
My Time	Class Time

TALK THE TALK Isometries on the Menu

Pacing (minutes)	
My Time	Class Time

✪ This activity highlights a key term or concept that is essential to the learning goals of the lesson.

Log in to MyCL for:

- Editable templates
- Additional planning support

Reflect on your lesson

Consider the effectiveness of your lesson on student learning.

What went well?	What did not go as planned?

Anticipate how you would change the lesson next time you teach it.

How will you capitalize on the things that went well?	How will you improve things that did not go as planned?

MATERIALS

- Compasses
- Patty paper
- Straightedges

TOPIC 1 Using a Rectangular Coordinate System

TOPIC 2 Rigid Motions on a Plane

TOPIC 3 Congruence Through Transformations

1 | Put Your Input In, Take Your Output Out
2 | Bow Thai
3 | Staring Back at Me
4 | Turn Yourself Around
5 | OKEECHOBEE

LESSON 2

Bow Thai

Translations as Functions

KEY TERMS
translation
isometry

Learning Goals

- Represent translations on the plane.
- Describe translations as functions that take points on the plane as inputs and produce translated points as outputs.
- Compare transformations that preserve distance and angles to those that do not.

REVIEW (1–2 minutes)

> Translate each figure as described. Draw the image of the translated figure.

1. Horizontally

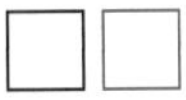

2. Vertically

You have described the effect of translations on two-dimensional figures using coordinates.

How do you describe the effects of a translation on geometric figures on the plane?

Setting the Stage

- **Assign Review (optional, 1 – 2 minutes)**
- **Communicate the learning goals and key terms to look out for**
- **Tap into your students' prior learning by reading the narrative statement**
- **Provide a sense of direction by reading the question**

TOPIC 2

IN THIS REVIEW
Students translate figures. They will use this skill throughout the lesson.

A translation is a function, T, which takes as its input a set of pre-image points and outputs a set of image points. You translate the pre-image points a distance of AB in the direction AB. For example, you can express a translation of point P as $T_{AB}(P)$ or P'.

Essential Ideas

- Translations along parallel lines congruent images.
- Translations along rays with a common endpoint produce similar images.
- A translation function represented as $T_{AB}(P) = P'$ takes as its input the location of a Point P and translates it a distance AB in the direction AB.
- Isometries preserve shape and size, creating congruent figures.
- Dilations preserve shape only, creating similar figures.

GETTING STARTED

SUMMARY **Translations along parallel lines create congruent images. Translations along rays with a common endpoint produce similar images.**

Chunking the Activity

- **Read and discuss the introduction**
- **Group students to complete 1 and 2**
- **Check-in and share**
- **Group students to complete 3 and 4**
- **Share and summarize**

DIFFERENTIATION STRATEGY

See Page 114A to challenge advanced learners to extend 2.

Student Look-Fors

- The use of patty paper or a compass and straightedge to translate the fixed distance.
- The use of mathematical vocabulary, such as *congruent, similar,* and *dilation*.

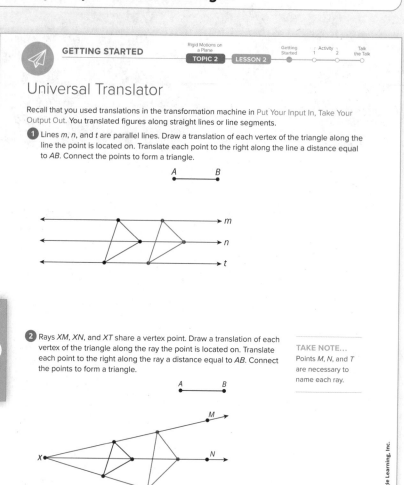

GETTING STARTED

Universal Translator

Recall that you used translations in the transformation machine in Put Your Input In, Take Your Output Out. You translated figures along straight lines or line segments.

1 Lines *m*, *n*, and *t* are parallel lines. Draw a translation of each vertex of the triangle along the line the point is located on. Translate each point to the right along the line a distance equal to *AB*. Connect the points to form a triangle.

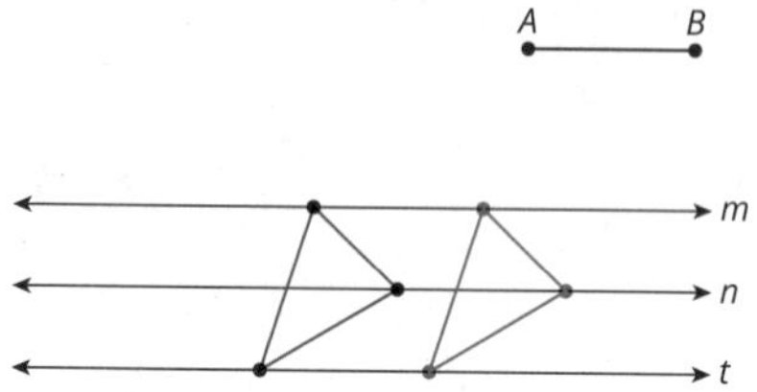

2 Rays *XM*, *XN*, and *XT* share a vertex point. Draw a translation of each vertex of the triangle along the ray the point is located on. Translate each point to the right along the ray a distance equal to *AB*. Connect the points to form a triangle.

TAKE NOTE...
Points *M*, *N*, and *T* are necessary to name each ray.

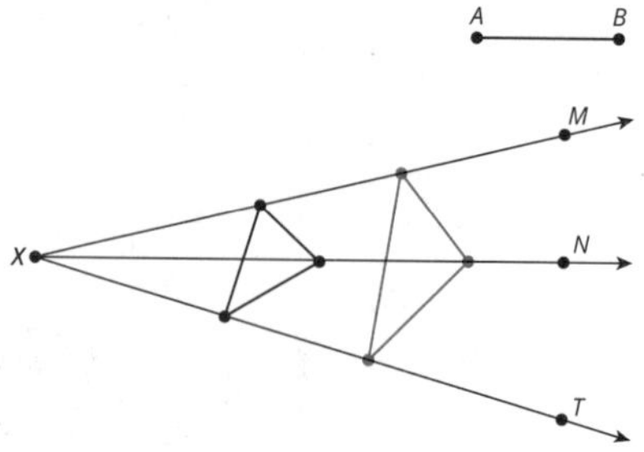

Questions to Support Discourse

		TYPE
2	• Why aren't the image and pre-image congruent? • How can you tell whether the pre-image and image are similar?	Seeing structure

GETTING STARTED Continued

3 Rays XM and XN share a vertex point, and line t is parallel to $\overrightarrow{XN}$. Draw a translation of each vertex of the triangle along the ray or line the point is located on. Translate each point to the right along the ray or line a distance equal to AB. Connect the points to form a triangle.

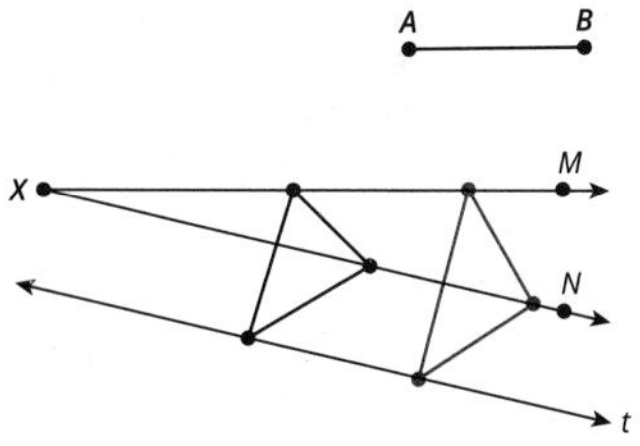

4 Compare the diagrams you created in Questions 1 through 3. Each set of three lines and/or rays makes up a transformation machine.

(a) Which transformation machine produces a translation of the triangle? **Explain your reasoning.**

The transformation machine in Question 1 produces a translation because the triangle's image is congruent to the original and in the same orientation.

(b) Which transformation machine produces a dilation of the triangle? **Explain your reasoning.**

The transformation machine in Question 2 produces a dilation because the triangle's image is proportional to the original triangle.

NOTES

LANGUAGE LINK

Revisit the framework provided in the previous lesson to summarize the difference between rigid motions and dilations.

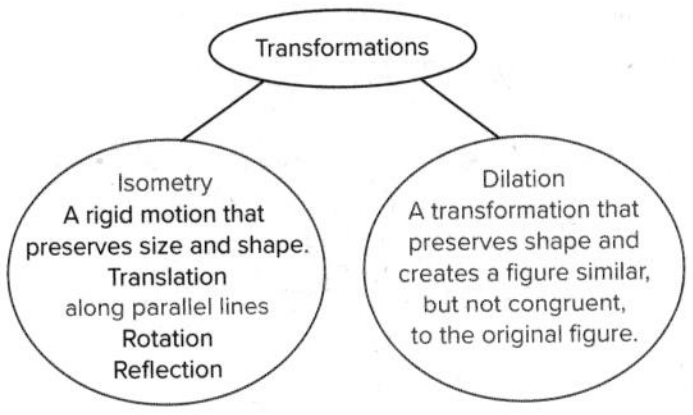

Questions to Support Discourse

		TYPE
3	• How does the image compare to the pre-image? • Why do you think the image isn't congruent or similar to the pre-image.	Seeing structure
4	• What does *dilation* mean?	Gathering

ACTIVITY 1

SUMMARY **A translation function, represented as $T_{AB}(P) = P'$, takes as its input the location of a point P and translates it a distance AB in the direction AB.**

Chunking the Activity

- Read and discuss the introduction
- Group students to complete 1
- Check-in and share
- Read and discuss the worked example
- Group students to complete 2 and 3
- Read and discuss the definitions and worked example
- Complete 4 and 5 as a class
- Group students to complete 6 – 8
- Share and summarize

Student Look-Fors

Whether students construct parallel lines or use patty paper to translate the figures.

LANGUAGE LINK

Remind students to refer to the Academic Glossary (page FM–20) to review the definition of **what do you notice** and related phrases. Suggest they ask themselves these questions:

- Do I see any patterns?
- What happens if the shape, representation, or numbers change?

Translation Functions

Transformations are used frequently in web design and game animation, and you can them as functions, which take points, distances, and angles as inputs. The functions output a new set of points after applying a transformation. These transformations move objects around on the screen.

HABITS OF MIND
- Look for and make use of structure.
- Look for and express regularity in repeated reasoning.

Suppose you are designing a website banner for a new restaurant. The banner will show three congruent triangles animated from left to right, and then the name will fade in.

1 Consider the translation of the first triangle, ΔSQR.

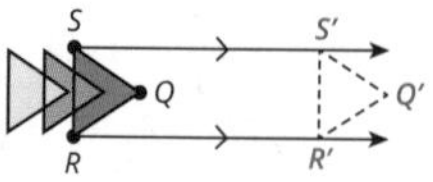

THINK ABOUT...
A translation moves a set of points a specified distance in a specified direction along parallel lines.

(a) Label the points of the image, $\Delta S'Q'R'$.

Check students' drawings.

(b) What relationship is there between $\overline{SS'}$ and $\overline{RR'}$?

The line segments are all parallel to each other.

(c) Measure the lengths of the two line segments used in the translation. **What do you notice?**

The segments are the same length.

(d) What do you know about the distance QQ'? What do you know about the line containing $\overline{QQ'}$?

QQ' is the same distance as SS' and RR'.

The line containing $\overline{QQ'}$ is parallel to the line containing $\overline{SS'}$ and $\overline{TT'}$.

Questions to Support Discourse

		TYPE
1	• How do you know $\overline{QQ'}$ is parallel to $\overline{SS'}$ and $\overline{RR'}$?	Seeing structure

ACTIVITY 1 Continued

WORKED EXAMPLE

You can measure a translation as a directed line segment.

ΔMNP was translated to produce $\Delta M'N'P'$.

- The triangle was translated a distance equal to the distance between points A and B.
- It was translated in the direction from point A to point B.

So, $\overline{AB}$ is the directed line segment used to measure this translation.

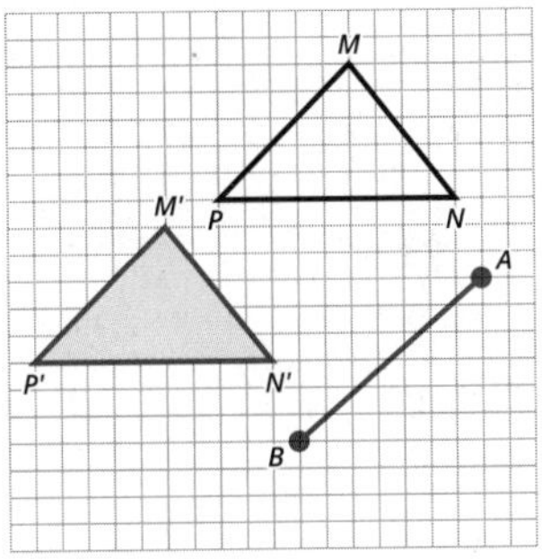

2 Suppose each grid square is 1 unit × 1 unit.

(a) What is the distance from point A to point B?

The distance $AB = \sqrt{6^2 + 7^2} \approx 9.22$ units.

(b) Compare the distance AB with the distances MM', NN', and PP'. **What do you notice?**

All the distances are equal.

(c) Can you draw another directed line segment on the grid which defines the translation of ΔMNP to $\Delta M'N'P'$? If so, draw the segment on the grid. **Explain your thinking.**

Check the placement of students' line segments.

The line segment should be parallel to $\overline{AB}$ and the same length as $\overline{AB}$.

3 Write equality and congruence statements to compare the corresponding sides and angles of the pre-image ΔMNP and the image $\Delta M'N'P'$.

$MN = M'N'$	$MP = M'P'$	$NP = N'P'$
$m\angle M = m\angle M'$	$m\angle N = m\angle N'$	$m\angle P = m\angle P'$
$\overline{MN} \cong \overline{M'N'}$	$\overline{MP} \cong \overline{M'P'}$	$\overline{NP} \cong \overline{N'P'}$
$\angle M \cong \angle M'$	$\angle N \cong \angle N'$	$\angle P \cong \angle P'$

REMEMBER...

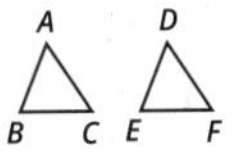

If $\Delta ABC \cong \Delta DEF$, then:
$\overline{AB} \cong \overline{DE}$
$AB = DE$
$\angle ABC \cong \angle DEF$
$m\angle ABC = m\angle DEF$

NOTES

DIFFERENTIATION STRATEGY

See Page 114A to assist all students with the worked example.

Questions to Support Discourse

		TYPE
Worked Example	• What is a directed line segment?	Gathering
	• What are the vertical and horizontal distances of the translation as noted by $\overline{AB}$?	Probing
	• How can you use the vertical and horizontal distances to check that the translation is correct?	Reflecting and justifying
2	• How did you determine the distance between points A and B?	Probing
	• Why is the distance between each pair of corresponding points equal?	Seeing structure
3	• How did you use the triangle inequality statement to make your equality and congruency statements?	Probing

NOTES

ACTIVITY 1 Continued

A **translation** is a function, *T*, which takes as its input a set of pre-image points and outputs a set of image points. The pre-image points are translated a distance of *AB* in the direction *AB*. For example, you can represent a translation of point *P* as $T_{AB}(P)$, or P'.

A translation is an example of an *isometry*. An **isometry** is a rigid motion transformation that preserves size and shape.

REMEMBER...
A function is a rule that assigns exactly one output to each input.

WORKED EXAMPLE

You can describe the distance and direction of a translation using function notation.

$T_{AB}(P) = P'$

$T_{AC}(P) = P''$

Input ↑ ↖ Output

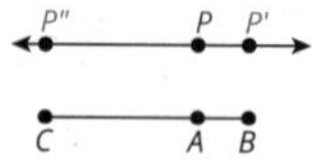

This line segment describes the distance and direction to translate point *P*. The output is described as point P'.

4 Identify the translation used to create P''.

$T_{AC}(P) = P''$

5 Consider the translation of the website banner from Question 1.

(a) Use the notation from the worked example to describe the translation of ΔSQR.

$T_{SS'}(\Delta SQR) = \Delta S'Q'R'$

$T_{QQ'}(\Delta SQR) = \Delta S'Q'R'$

$T_{RR'}(\Delta SQR) = \Delta S'Q'R'$

(b) Explain how your function represents the translation of every point of ΔSQR.

Sample answer.

Every point on ΔSQR moves a distance equal to SS' in the direction $\overline{SS'}$.

108 Topic 2 > Rigid Motions on a Plane

Questions to Support Discourse

		TYPE
Worked Example	• What does each component of the function notation represent?	Gathering
4	• How do you know whether the correct subscript is *AC* or *CA*?	Probing

ACTIVITY 1 Continued

6 Greta says that she can use the same function for every triangle in the animated web banner. Is Greta correct? **Explain your thinking, and then draw the translations to justify your answer.**

Greta is correct.
The set of 3 triangles together is translated according to the translation function given in Question 5, part (a).

7 Complete each translation using the given function.

(a) T_{AB}(Sun)

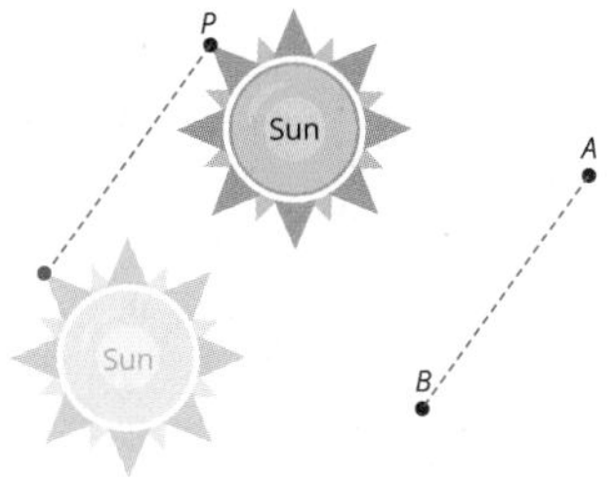

(b) $T_{L'M}$(Moon)

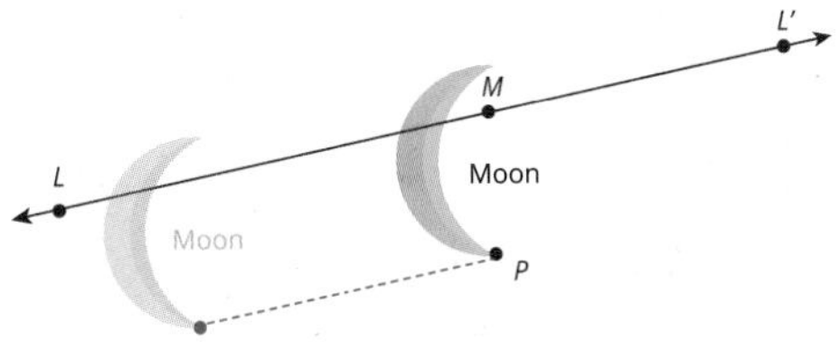

8 Explain why you can use parallel lines when describing translations.

Parallel lines determine the horizontal and vertical translations.

NOTES

DIFFERENTIATION STRATEGY

See Page 114B to support students who struggle with 7.

Questions to Support Discourse

		TYPE
7	• What is the purpose of point P? • How do you know whether the image of the sun should be above or below the pre-image? • How did you use the directed line segment to create the image? • Should the image of the moon be to the right or the left of the pre-image? How do you know?	Probing

ACTIVITY 2

SUMMARY **Isometries preserve shape and size, creating congruent figures. Dilations preserve shape only, creating similar figures.**

Chunking the Activity

- Read and discuss the situation
- Group students to complete 1 and 2
- Check-in and share
- Group students to read the situation and complete 3
- Share and summarize

NOTE: All situations provide opportunities for students to learn something new. Consider connecting to students' cultural, social, and geographic backgrounds by encouraging them to share experiences from their lives related to the mathematical content similar to the given real-world situation.

Determining Congruence Using Translations

In this activity, you will analyze and describe translations.

HABITS OF MIND
- Reason abstractly and quantitatively.
- Construct viable arguments and critique the reasoning of others.

When users click on the Bow Thai menu, copies of 3 triangles will move from the corners and top of the web page to the center to form the background behind the word "Menu" as shown.

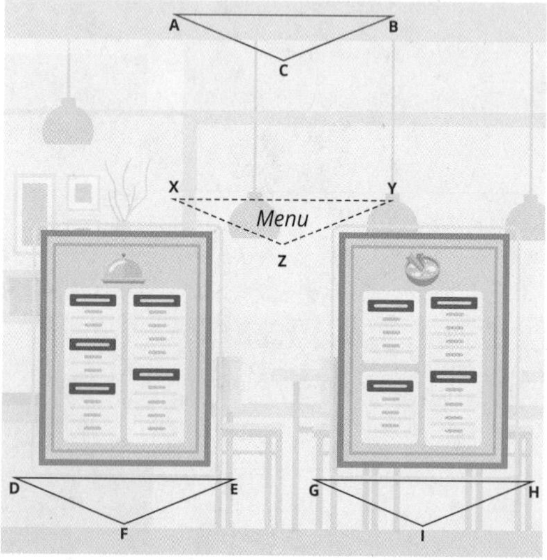

1 Write and draw translation functions to show how each triangle will move on the page.

Sample answers.

$T_{AX}(\Delta ABC) = \Delta A'B'C'$

$T_{DX}(\Delta DEF) = \Delta D'E'F'$

$T_{GX}(\Delta GHI) = \Delta G'H'I'$

Check students' drawings of the directed line segment for each translation.

Questions to Support Discourse

		TYPE
1	• How does your translation function represent the distance of the translation? The direction of the translation?	Probing

ACTIVITY 2 Continued

2 Are the triangles all congruent? **Explain why or why not.**

Sample answers.

All three triangles in the original menu are congruent, and they are all translated along parallel lines, so their translations are rigid motions that preserve size and shape.

Each triangle is congruent to ΔXYZ.

The owner of Bow Thai is thinking about using smaller triangles on the sides of the menu web page. She still wants the triangles to move and merge to form the triangle background behind the word "Menu."

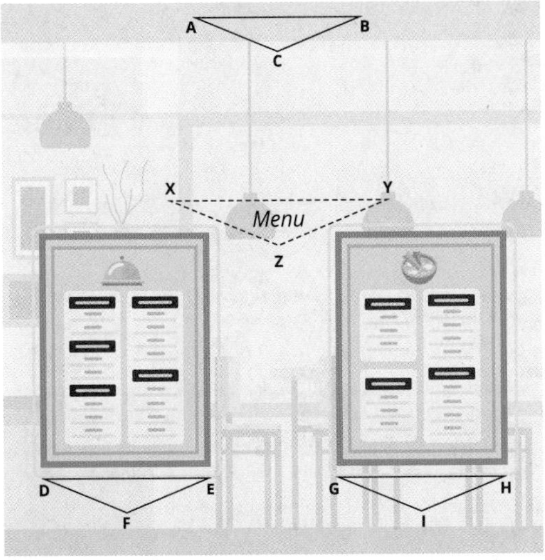

3 Are these transformations isometries? **Demonstrate why or why not and explain your process.**

The transformations are not isometries because the transformed figures have longer sides than the original figures.

Lesson 2 > Bow Thai 111

Questions to Support Discourse

		TYPE
2	• What is the connection between congruent figures, directed line segments, and parallel lines?	Probing
3	• How could you demonstrate that the background triangle is similar to the original triangle?	Seeing structure

NOTES

TOPIC 2

TALK THE TALK

SUMMARY **Geometric translation functions use a directional line segment, while algebraic equations only show horizontal and vertical translations.**

Chunking the Activity

- **Read and discuss the introduction**
- **Group students to complete the activity**
- **Share and summarize**

Student Look-Fors

Utilizing relationship skills by communicating clearly and listening well.

DIFFERENTIATION STRATEGY

See Page 114B to challenge advanced learners to extend 3.

Isometries on the Menu

1. Describe how to distinguish between an isometry and a transformation that is not an isometry.

   An isometry is a transformation that preserves both size and shape. A translation along parallel lines is an example of an isometry.
   A transformation that is not an isometry does not preserve size and shape.
   A dilation and a translation along non-parallel lines are examples of transformations that are not isometries.

2. Write a function to describe each translation. Each solid figure is a pre-image, and each dashed figure is an image.

   (a)

   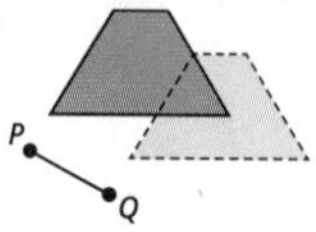

   Sample answer.

   T_{PQ}(Trapezoid) = (Trapezoid)′

   (b)

   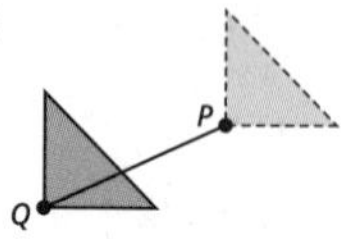

   Sample answer.

   T_{QP}(Triangle) = (Triangle)′

3. What similarities and differences exist between a geometric translation function and an algebraic equation that shows the translation of a function?

   Sample answers.

   Geometric translation functions and algebraic equations, which show the translation of a function, both represent movements on a plane.

   Geometric translation functions are described as movements that follow a directional line segment that is not limited by horizontal and vertical movements.

   Algebraic equations representing the translation of a function are limited to horizontal and vertical movements.

   Geometric translations move shapes, while algebraic equations move functions on a coordinate plane.

   Geometric translations and algebraic equations use different notation.

Questions to Support Discourse

		TYPE
1	• Are all transformations also isometries? Explain your thinking. • What is an example of a transformation that is not an isometry? • Are all rigid motions isometries? Why or why not?	Seeing structure
2	• How did you know what order to write the subscripts? • How did you represent the trapezoid or triangle in your function?	Probing
3	• How do you explain how to move a figure using a geometric function? An algebraic equation? • Compare the notation used for the inputs and outputs.	Seeing structure

ASSIGNMENT

LESSON 2 ASSIGNMENT

> Use a separate piece of paper for your Journal entry.

JOURNAL

Determine whether each statement is true or false. If the statement is false, rewrite it so that it becomes a true statement.

REMEMBER

A translation is a function, T, which takes as its input a set of pre-image points and outputs a set of image points. You translate the pre-image points a distance of AB in the direction AB. For example, you can express a translation of point P as $T_{AB}(P)$ or P'.

1. A translation function along parallel lines is a type of geometric transformation that is non-rigid.
2. Isometries includes geometric transformations such as translations, rotations, and reflections.
3. A transformation is an isometry when it does not preserve size and shape.
4. A dilation is a non-rigid geometric transformation.

PRACTICE

1. Write a function to describe each translation. Each solid figure is a pre-image, and each dashed figure is an image.

ⓐ
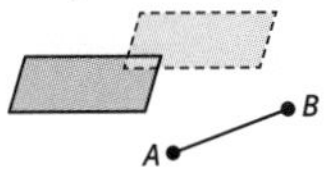

T_{AB}(Parallelogram) = Parallelogram′

ⓑ
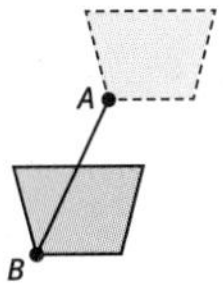

T_{BA}(Trapezoid) = Trapezoid′

ⓒ
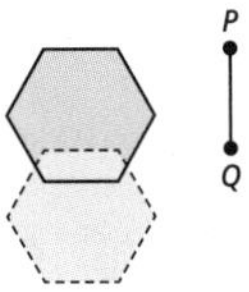

T_{PQ}(Hexagon) = Hexagon′

ⓓ
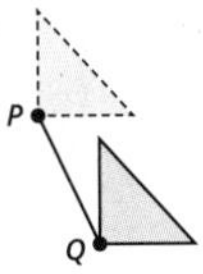

T_{QP}(Triangle) = Triangle′

Go to LiveHint.com for help on the PRACTICE questions.

Encourage students to use LiveHint.com for help with the PRACTICE questions of this assignment.

Chunking the Assignment

SESSION 1

- Journal
- Practice 1 and 2
- Stretch (advanced learners)

SESSION 2

- Mixed Practice (page 153) 2

TOPIC 2

JOURNAL

1. False
   A translation function along parallel lines is a type of geometric transformation that is rigid.
2. True
3. False
   A transformation is an isometry if it does preserve size and shape.
4. True

NOTES

STRETCH

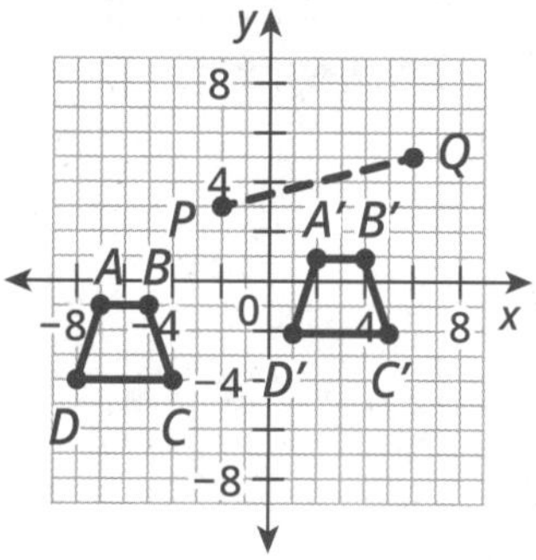

Each point of the trapezoid moved a total distance of $\sqrt{85}$ along a line with a slope of $\frac{2}{9}$.

2 Complete each translation given the function.

a) T_{AB}(Rectangle) = Rectangle′

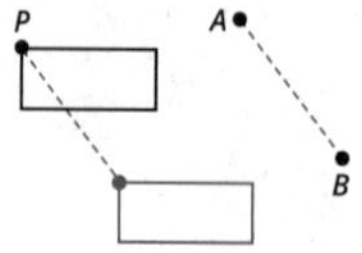

b) $T_{L'M}$(Triangle) = Triangle′

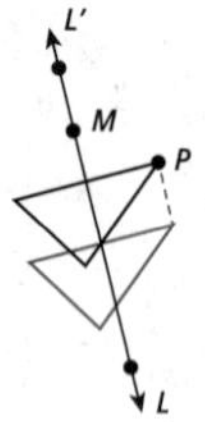

c) T_{BA}(Trapezoid) = Trapezoid′

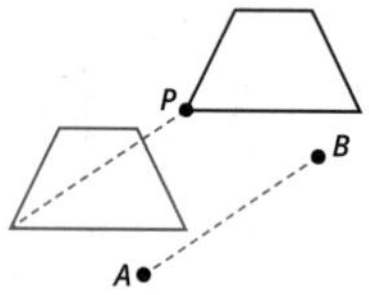

d) $T_{L'M}$(Parallelogram) = Parallelogram′

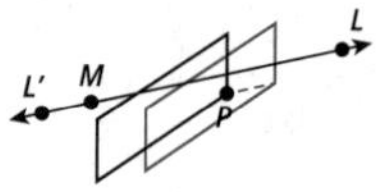

STRETCH Optional

1 A translation function for a trapezoid is given as T_{PQ}(Trapezoid $ABCD$) = Trapezoid $A'B'C'D'$. Trapezoid $ABCD$ has vertices A (−7, −1), B (−5, −1), C (−4, −4), and D (−8, −4). If P is at (−2, 3) and Q is located at (7, 5), determine the vertices of the translated trapezoid $A'B'C'D'$.

a) Draw points P and Q and trapezoids $ABCD$ and $A'B'C'D'$ on a coordinate plane. Include a dashed line between points P and Q.

b) Determine the distance traveled by each point of the trapezoid and the slope of the line along which the points moved.

Bow Thai

This resource details additional facilitation notes to fully assist you as you plan each lesson to support all students, students who struggle, and advanced learners. It provides differentiation strategies, common student misconceptions, and suggestions to extend certain activities.

GETTING STARTED

Session 1 of 2

Universal Translator

Students translate figures along parallel lines and rays sharing a common vertex. They compare the results of the translation and dilation.

CHUNK	AUDIENCE	ADDITIONAL SUPPORTS
To extend 2	Advanced Learners	**DIFFERENTIATION STRATEGY** Have students complete another translation that is the distance *AB* to the left of the pre-image and describe the effects.

ACTIVITY 1

Session 1 of 2

Translation Functions

Students measure a translation as a directed line segment on the coordinate plane. They use function notation to describe and translate figures.

CHUNK	AUDIENCE	ADDITIONAL SUPPORTS
As students discuss the worked example	All Students	**DIFFERENTIATION STRATEGY** Encourage students to take time to read through the worked example and annotate key ideas or steps in the process. As they think about the connections have students ask themselves: • Why is this method correct? • Have I used this method before?

CHUNK	AUDIENCE	ADDITIONAL SUPPORTS
As students work on 7	Students who Struggle	**DIFFERENTIATION STRATEGY** Demonstrate how to use patty paper to translate the sun, then have students duplicate the process to translate the moon. • Connect points *A* and *B* to identify the directed line segment. • Use a straightedge to extend the line segment beyond point *B*. • Trace the entire diagram, including the sun and points *P*, *A*, and *B* on patty paper. • Slide the entire diagram along the extended line until point *A* lies on point *B*.

TALK THE TALK

Session 2 of 2

Isometries on the Menu

Students distinguish between transformations that are and are not isometries. They compare translations described by geometric and algebraic functions.

CHUNK	AUDIENCE	ADDITIONAL SUPPORTS
As students complete 3	Advanced Learners	**DIFFERENTIATION STRATEGY** Ask students to model the translation of a line segment using a geometric translation function and an algebraic equation.

Practice the learning

MATHbook + Skills Practice

The table shows the targeted practice of the skills and mathematical concepts for the *Rigid Motions on the Plane* Topic. The highlighted Problem Set aligns with **Bow Thai**.

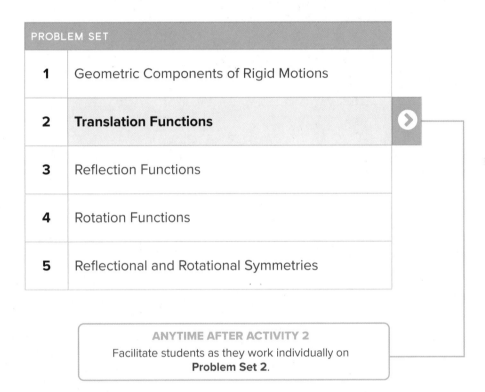

PROBLEM SET	
1	Geometric Components of Rigid Motions
2	**Translation Functions**
3	Reflection Functions
4	Rotation Functions
5	Reflectional and Rotational Symmetries

ANYTIME AFTER ACTIVITY 2

Facilitate students as they work individually on **Problem Set 2**.

TOPIC 2

NOTES

ENGAGE at the **Module** level + **DEVELOP** at the **Topic** level + **TEACH** Read the facilitation notes and plan learning experiences.

Where are we?

TOPIC 2 Rigid Motions on a Plane	LESSON 1 Put Your Input In, Take Your Output Out	LESSON 2 Bow Thai	**LESSON 3 Staring Back at Me**	LESSON 4 Turn Yourself Around	LESSON 5 OKEECHOBEE
Pacing	2 Sessions	2 Sessions	**2 Sessions**	2 Sessions	1 Session

OVERVIEW: LESSON 3

Staring Back at Me

Reflections as Functions

ENGAGE

- Students show that the perpendicular bisector is the line of reflection between a segment's endpoints.

DEVELOP

- Students recognize that the line of reflection is the perpendicular bisector of all segments connecting reflection points.
- They construct lines of reflection.
- They analyze a worked example proving the Perpendicular Bisector Theorem.
- Students learn that they can map one congruent line segment onto another using at most two reflections.

DEMONSTRATE

- Students compare geometric and algebraic reflection functions.

HIGH SCHOOL GEOMETRY

Congruence

Experiment with transformations in the plane.

2. Represent transformations in the plane using, e.g., transparencies and geometry software; describe transformations as functions that take points in the plane as inputs and give other points as outputs. Compare transformations that preserve distance and angle to those that do not.
4. Develop definitions of rotations, reflections, and translations in terms of angles, circles, perpendicular lines, parallel lines, and line segments.
5. Given a geometric figure and a rotation, reflection, or translation, draw the transformed figure using, e.g., graph paper, tracing paper, or geometry software. Specify a sequence of transformations that will carry a given figure onto another.

LESSON STRUCTURE AND PACING GUIDE 2 SESSIONS

✪ This activity highlights a key term or concept that is essential to the learning goals of the lesson.

Session 1		Session 2
INSTRUCTIONAL SEQUENCE		
ENGAGE Connect to prior knowledge	**DEVELOP** Mathematical problem solving Worked example	**DEVELOP** Worked example Mathematical problem solving

✪ GETTING STARTED
Reflecting on Bisecting

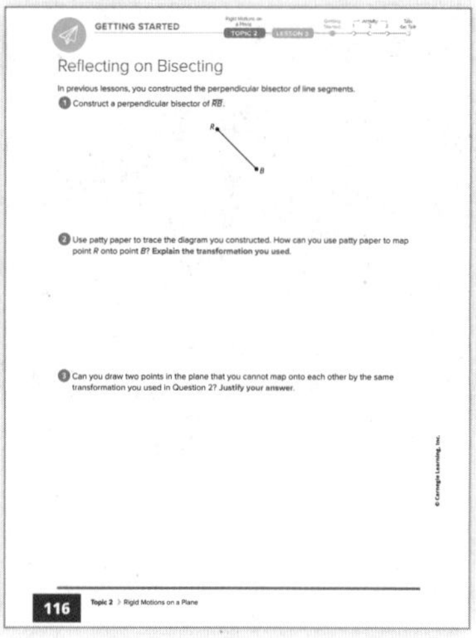
GETTING STARTED

Reflecting on Bisecting

In previous lessons, you constructed the perpendicular bisector of line segments.

1 Construct a perpendicular bisector of $\overline{RB}$.

2 Use patty paper to trace the diagram you constructed. How can you use patty paper to map point R onto point B? Explain the transformation you used.

3 Can you draw two points in the plane that you cannot map onto each other by the same transformation you used in Question 2? Justify your answer.

116 Topic 2 > Rigid Motions on a Plane

Students construct the perpendicular bisector of a line segment.

- They show that the perpendicular bisector is the line of reflection between a segment's endpoints.

✪ ACTIVITY 1
Reflection Functions

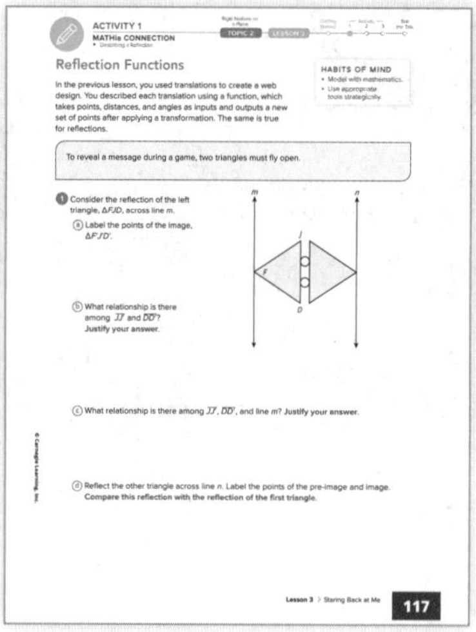
ACTIVITY 1

MATHia CONNECTION

Reflection Functions

In the previous lesson, you used translations to create a web design. You described each translation using a function, which takes points, distances, and angles as inputs and outputs a new set of points after applying a transformation. The same is true for reflections.

HABITS OF MIND

To reveal a message during a game, two triangles must fly open.

1 Consider the reflection of the left triangle, $\triangle FJD$, across line m.

a Label the points of the image, $\triangle F'J'D'$.

b What relationship is there among $\overline{JJ'}$ and $\overline{DD'}$? Justify your answer.

c What relationship is there among $\overline{JJ'}$, $\overline{DD'}$, and line m? Justify your answer.

d Reflect the other triangle across line n. Label the points of the pre-image and image. Compare this reflection with the reflection of the first triangle.

Lesson 3 > Staring Back at Me 117

Students recognize that the line of reflection is the perpendicular bisector of all segments connecting reflection points.

- They use appropriate notation to complete reflections.
- They construct lines of reflection.

✪ ACTIVITY 2
Perpendicular Bisector Theorem

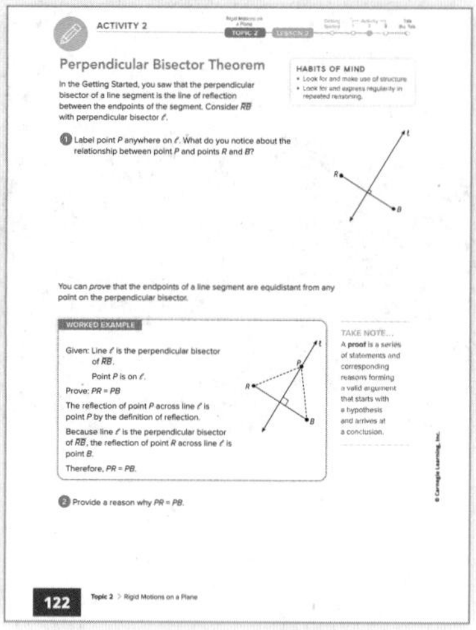
ACTIVITY 2

Perpendicular Bisector Theorem

In the Getting Started, you saw that the perpendicular bisector of a line segment is the line of reflection between the endpoints of the segment. Consider $\overline{RB}$ with perpendicular bisector ℓ.

HABITS OF MIND

1 Label point P anywhere on ℓ. What do you notice about the relationship between point P and points R and B?

You can prove that the endpoints of a line segment are equidistant from any point on the perpendicular bisector.

WORKED EXAMPLE

Given: Line ℓ is the perpendicular bisector of $\overline{RB}$.

Point P is on ℓ.

Prove: PR = PB

The reflection of point P across line ℓ is point P by the definition of reflection.

Because line ℓ is the perpendicular bisector of $\overline{RB}$, the reflection of point R across line ℓ is point B.

Therefore, PR = PB.

TAKE NOTE... A proof is a series of statements and corresponding reasons forming a valid argument that starts with a hypothesis and arrives at a conclusion.

2 Provide a reason why PR = PB.

122 Topic 2 > Rigid Motions on a Plane

Students analyze a worked example proving the Perpendicular Bisector Theorem.

- They investigate the relationship between two points equidistant from a third point.

Log in to MyCL for **lesson support** including:

Slides

Videos

www.carnegielearning.com/login

NOTES

INSTRUCTIONAL SEQUENCE

DEVELOP	DEMONSTRATE
Peer analysis Mathematical problem solving	Writing task

ACTIVITY 3
Sequences of Isometries Using Translations and Reflections

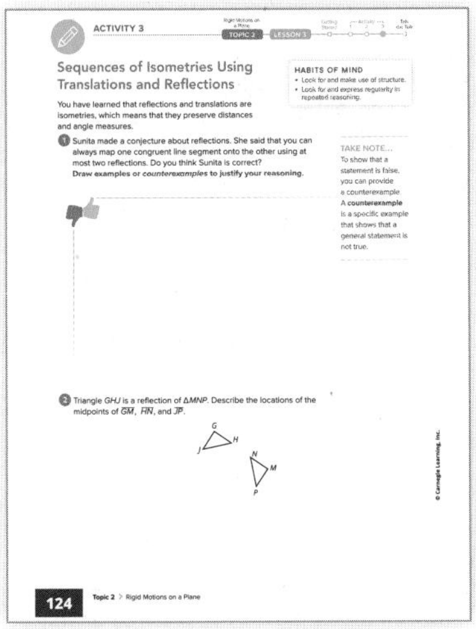

ACTIVITY 3 · Rigid Motions on a Plane · TOPIC 2 · LESSON 3

Sequences of Isometries Using Translations and Reflections

HABITS OF MIND
- Look for and make use of structure.
- Look for and express regularity in repeated reasoning.

You have learned that reflections and translations are isometries, which means that they preserve distances and angle measures.

1. Sunita made a conjecture about reflections. She said that you can always map one congruent line segment onto the other using at most two reflections. Do you think Sunita is correct? **Draw examples or *counterexamples* to justify your reasoning.**

TAKE NOTE... To show that a statement is false, you can provide a counterexample. A **counterexample** is a specific example that shows that a general statement is not true.

2. Triangle GHJ is a reflection of ΔMNP. Describe the locations of the midpoints of $\overline{GM}$, $\overline{HN}$, and $\overline{JP}$.

© Carnegie Learning, Inc.

124 Topic 2 > Rigid Motions on a Plane

Students learn that they can map one congruent line segment onto another using at most two reflections.

- They describe sequences of isometries to show that two figures are congruent.

TALK THE TALK
But We're Off the Grid

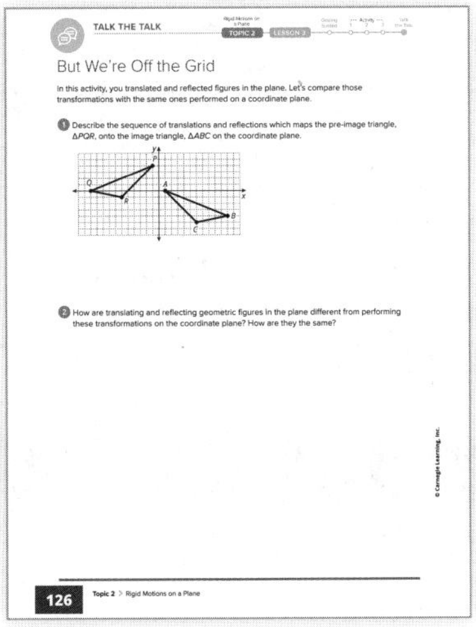

TALK THE TALK · Rigid Motions on a Plane · TOPIC 2 · LESSON 3

But We're Off the Grid

In this activity, you translated and reflected figures in the plane. Let's compare those transformations with the same ones performed on a coordinate plane.

1. Describe the sequence of translations and reflections which maps the pre-image triangle, ΔPQR, onto the image triangle, ΔABC on the coordinate plane.

2. How are translating and reflecting geometric figures in the plane different from performing these transformations on the coordinate plane? How are they the same?

© Carnegie Learning, Inc.

126 Topic 2 > Rigid Motions on a Plane

Students map one triangle onto another on the coordinate plane.

- They compare transformations on and off the plane.
- They compare geometric and algebraic reflection functions.

TOPIC 2

Log in to MyCL for:
- Editable templates
- Additional planning support

Now that you have read the Module, Topic, and Lesson Overviews, you are ready to plan.

Do the math

> Tear out the lesson planning template (page 115E) and jot down thoughts as you work through this lesson and read the Facilitation Notes.

Connect the learning

MATHbook + MATHia

The table shows a portion of the self-paced MATHia sequence for the *Rigid Motions on a Plane* Topic.

Median student completion time for the entire topic: ~90–120 minutes

> As you implement this lesson, consider different connections for students who are on pace and those that have not yet completed the workspaces aligned to this lesson.

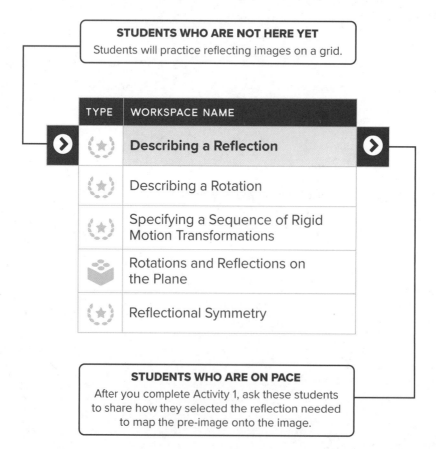

STUDENTS WHO ARE NOT HERE YET
Students will practice reflecting images on a grid.

TYPE	WORKSPACE NAME
★	**Describing a Reflection**
★	Describing a Rotation
★	Specifying a Sequence of Rigid Motion Transformations
■	Rotations and Reflections on the Plane
★	Reflectional Symmetry

STUDENTS WHO ARE ON PACE
After you complete Activity 1, ask these students to share how they selected the reflection needed to map the pre-image onto the image.

Staring Back at Me
Reflections as Functions

Session 1

GETTING STARTED Reflecting on Bisecting ✪

Pacing (minutes)	
My Time	Class Time

ACTIVITY 1 Reflection Functions ✪

Pacing (minutes)	
My Time	Class Time

KEY TERM
reflection

Session 2

ACTIVITY 2 Perpendicular Bisector Theorem ✪

Pacing (minutes)	
My Time	Class Time

KEY TERM
proof
Perpendicular Bisector Theorem

ACTIVITY 3 Sequences of Isometries Using Translations and Reflections ✪

Pacing (minutes)	
My Time	Class Time

TALK THE TALK But We're Off the Grid

Pacing (minutes)	
My Time	Class Time

✪ This activity highlights a key term or concept that is essential to the learning goals of the lesson.

Log in to MyCL for:
- Editable templates
- Additional planning support

Reflect on your lesson

> Consider the effectiveness of your lesson on student learning.

What went well?

What did not go as planned?

> Anticipate how you would change the lesson next time you teach it.

How will you capitalize on the things that went well?

How will you improve things that did not go as planned?

MATERIALS

- Compasses
- Patty paper
- Straightedges

TOPIC 1
Using a Rectangular Coordinate System

TOPIC 2
Rigid Motions on a Plane
1 | Put Your Input In, Take Your Output Out
2 | Bow Thai
3 | Staring Back at Me
4 | Turn Yourself Around
5 | OKEECHOBEE

TOPIC 3
Congruence Through Transformations

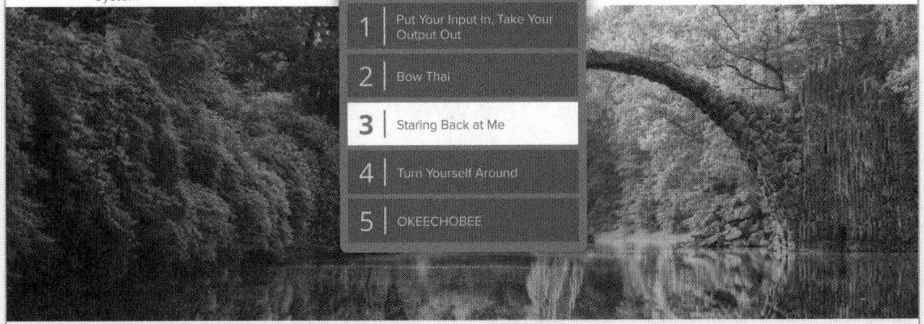

LESSON 3

Staring Back at Me

Reflections as Functions

KEY TERMS

reflection
proof
Perpendicular Bisector Theorem

Learning Goals

- Represent reflections in the plane using patty paper and constructions.
- Describe reflection transformations as functions that take points as inputs and output reflected points.
- Identify reflections as points equidistant to the perpendicular bisector of line segments connecting the pre-image and image points of the reflection.
- Specify a sequence of translations and reflections that will carry a figure onto a congruent figure.

REVIEW (1–2 minutes)

1 Reflect ΔABC across the y-axis on the coordinate plane.

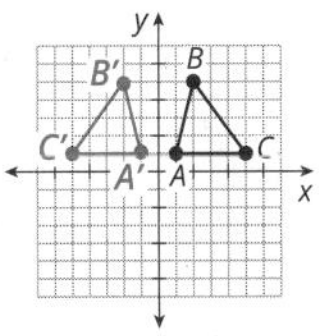

2 Reflect ΔDEF across the x-axis on the coordinate plane.

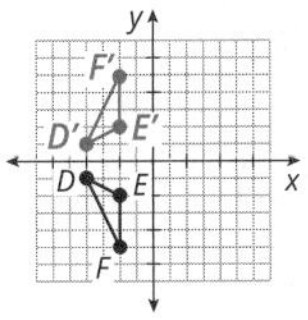

You have described the effects of reflections on two-dimensional figures using coordinates.

How do you describe the effects of reflections on geometric figures on the plane?

Setting the Stage

- **Assign Review (optional, 1 – 2 minutes)**
- **Communicate the learning goals and key terms to look out for**
- **Tap into your students' prior learning by reading the narrative statement**
- **Provide a sense of direction by reading the question**

IN THIS REVIEW
Students identify coordinates of an image after a reflection across an axis. They will use this skill in the **TALK THE TALK But We're Off the Grid.**

A reflection is a function, R_ℓ, which takes as its input, P, the location of a point with respect to some line of reflection ℓ and outputs $R_\ell(P)$, or the opposite of the location of P with respect to the line of reflection.

Any point that is equidistant from two other points lies on the perpendicular bisector between the two points.

Essential Ideas

- The Perpendicular Bisector Theorem states that any point on the perpendicular bisector of a segment is equidistant from the endpoints of that segment.
- The line of reflection is the perpendicular bisector of each segment connecting a point and its corresponding reflected point.
- You can use a sequence of translations and reflections to show that two figures are congruent.

SUMMARY **The perpendicular bisector of a line segment is a line of reflection between the segment's two endpoints.**

Chunking the Activity

- **Read and discuss the introduction**
- **Group students to complete the activity**
- **Share and summarize**

LANGUAGE LINK

Remind students to refer to the Academic Glossary (page FM–20) to review the definition of **explain**, **justify**, and related phrases. Suggest they ask themselves these questions:

- How can I justify my answer to others?
- Is my explanation logical?

Reflecting on Bisecting

In previous lessons, you constructed the perpendicular bisector of line segments.

1. Construct a perpendicular bisector of $\overline{RB}$.

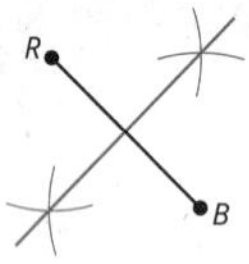

2. Use patty paper to trace the diagram you constructed. How can you use patty paper to map point *R* onto point *B*? **Explain the transformation you used.**

   I can fold the patty paper along the perpendicular bisector to map point *B* onto point *R*. Points *B* and *R* are reflections of each other across the line containing the perpendicular bisector.

3. Can you draw two points in the plane that you cannot map onto each other by the same transformation you used in Question 2? **Justify your answer.**

   This is impossible.
   Any two points in the plane are reflections of each other across some line.

Questions to Support Discourse

		TYPE
1	• Explain your steps to construct a perpendicular bisector.	Probing
2	• Which type of transformation does folding the patty paper model? • What does it mean that your crease appears where the perpendicular bisector lies? • What is the relationship between each point's distance to the perpendicular bisector?	Seeing structure

SUMMARY The line of reflection is the perpendicular bisector of each segment connecting a point and its corresponding reflected point.

Reflection Functions

HABITS OF MIND
- Model with mathematics.
- Use appropriate tools strategically.

In the previous lesson, you used translations to create a web design. You described each translation using a function, which takes points, distances, and angles as inputs and outputs a new set of points after applying a transformation. The same is true for reflections.

To reveal a message during a game, two triangles must fly open.

1 Consider the reflection of the left triangle, ΔFJD, across line m.

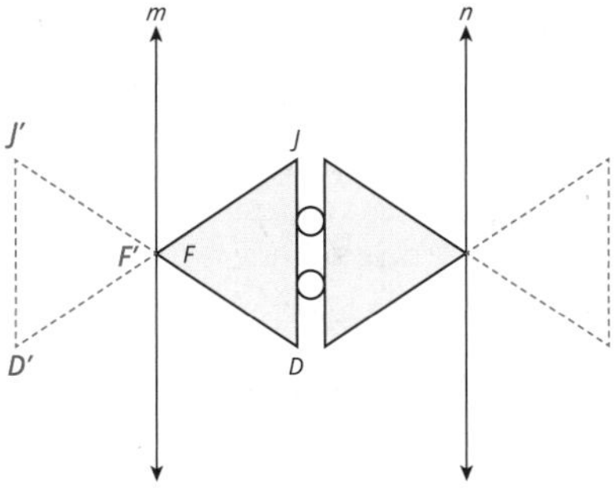

ⓐ Label the points of the image, $\Delta F'J'D'$.

Check students' drawings.

ⓑ What relationship is there among $\overline{JJ'}$ and $\overline{DD'}$? **Justify your answer.**

The line segments are parallel to each other.

ⓒ What relationship is there among $\overline{JJ'}$, $\overline{DD'}$, and line m? **Justify your answer.**

The points on line m are midpoints of the line segments. Line m is perpendicular to the line segments. So, line m is the perpendicular bisector of the segments connecting the pre-image and image points of the reflection.

ⓓ Reflect the other triangle across line n. Label the points of the pre-image and image. **Compare this reflection with the reflection of the first triangle.**

The line segments connecting this pre-image and image are also parallel to one another and are perpendicular to the line of reflection.

Questions to Support Discourse

		TYPE
1	• What do you notice about the location of point F and the location of point F'?	Gathering
	• How do you know $\overline{JJ'}$ and $\overline{DD'}$ are parallel? • How do you know that line m and line n are perpendicular bisectors of the segments joining the reflected points?	Seeing structure

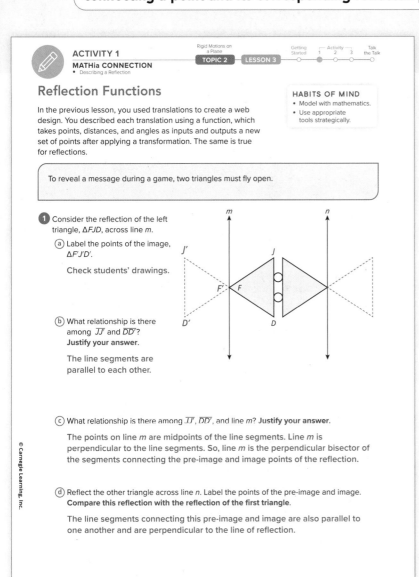

Chunking the Activity

- Read and discuss the introduction
- Group students to complete 1 and 2
- Check-in and share
- Read and discuss the definition
- Group students to complete 3 – 5
- Check-in and share
- Read and discuss the worked example
- Group students to complete 6 and 7
- Share and summarize

Student Look-Fors

Whether students are demonstrating proficiencies related to these habits of mind.

- Model with mathematics
- Use appropriate tools strategically

NOTES

COMMON MISCONCEPTION

See Page 128A for a misconception related to 4.

2 Write equality and congruence statements to compare the corresponding sides of the pre-image and the image.

$FJ = F'J'$	$\overline{FJ} \cong \overline{F'J'}$
$JD = J'D'$	$\overline{JD} \cong \overline{J'D'}$
$DF = D'F'$	$\overline{DF} \cong \overline{D'F'}$

A **reflection** is a function that takes as its input the location of a point and outputs the opposite of that location with respect to some line of reflection.

TAKE NOTE...
A reflection is an isometry.

You can write a reflection function in the form $R_\ell(P)$, where ℓ represents the line of reflection and P represents the location of the point.

3 Consider the reflections from Question 1.

(a) Write a function of the form $R_\ell(P)$ to describe the reflection of ΔFJD.

$R_m(\Delta FJD) = \Delta F'J'D'$

(b) Explain how your function represents the reflection of every point of ΔFJD.

Every point of $\Delta F'J'D'$ is a reflection across line m of the original corresponding point.

4 Describe the relationship between corresponding points of a reflection and the line of reflection.

The corresponding points of the pre-image and image in a reflection are equidistant from the line of reflection.

Questions to Support Discourse

		TYPE
Definition	• What does "the opposite of the location of p with respect to the line of reflection" mean?	Gathering
	• When would "the opposite of the location of p with respect to the line of reflection" mean that the image's location is to the left of the pre-image? Above the pre-image?	Seeing structure
3	• What does each component of the function represent?	Probing
	• Compare the reflection notation to the translation notation.	Seeing structure

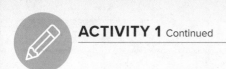

ACTIVITY 1 Continued

5 Complete each reflection using the given function.

ⓐ $R_m(STUV)$

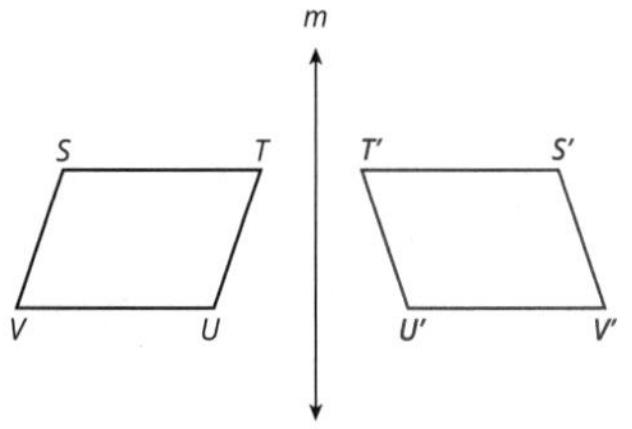

REMEMBER...
The notation $R_\ell(PQRS)$ means a reflection of points P, Q, R, and S across line ℓ.

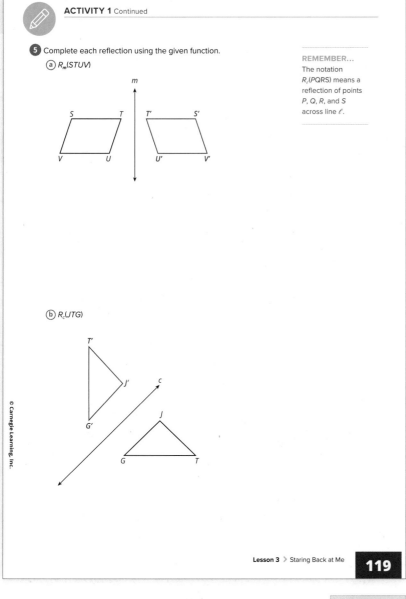

ⓑ $R_c(JTG)$

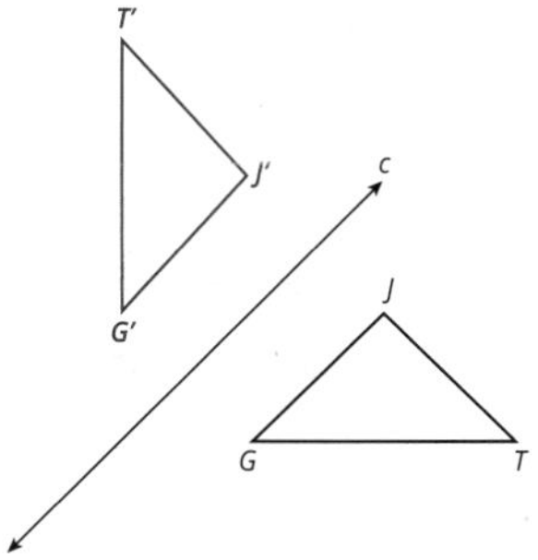

NOTES

TOPIC 2

Questions to Support Discourse

		TYPE
5	• How can you reflect the image using patty paper? A compass and straightedge?	Probing

NOTES

DIFFERENTIATION STRATEGY

See Page 128A to assist all students with the worked example.

It is possible to construct the line of reflection when given two figures that are reflections of one another.

WORKED EXAMPLE

You can identify the line of reflection between two figures.

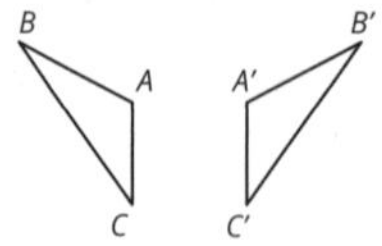

STEP 1 Label the vertices.

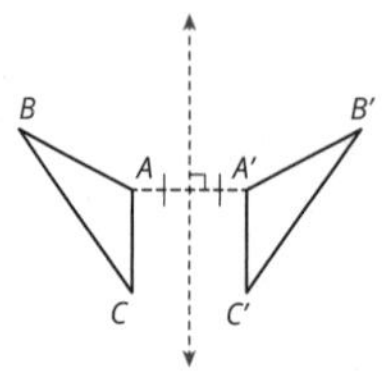

STEP 2 Connect two corresponding points. Construct the perpendicular bisector of the line segment connecting them.

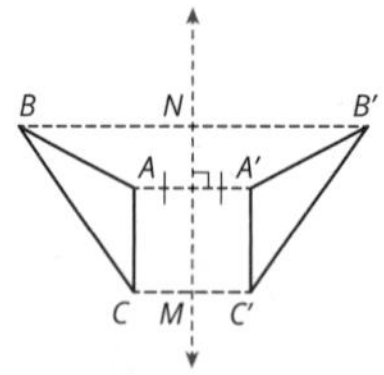

STEP 3 Connect remaining corresponding points.
Label the intersection of each line segment with the perpendicular bisector.

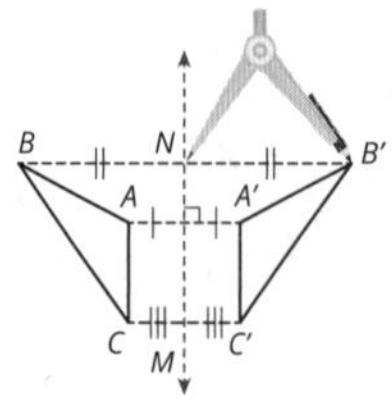

STEP 4 Use a compass to determine whether each intersection point is the midpoint of the line segment connecting corresponding vertices.

- If that is the case, the perpendicular bisector is the line of reflection.
- If not, the figures are not reflections of one another.

$\overline{CM} \cong \overline{C'M}$
$\overline{BN} \cong \overline{B'N}$
$\overleftrightarrow{MN}$ is the line of reflection.

Questions to Support Discourse

		TYPE
Worked Example	• What relationship do you notice as you connect corresponding points in this diagram? • Why don't you have to create a perpendicular bisector for each pair of corresponding points in this example?	Seeing structure

ACTIVITY 1 Continued

6 Determine whether the figures are reflections of one another. If so, identify the line of reflection.

ⓐ

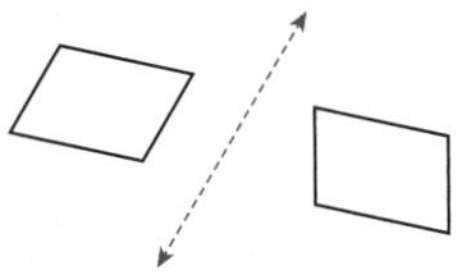

The figures are reflections of one another.

ⓑ

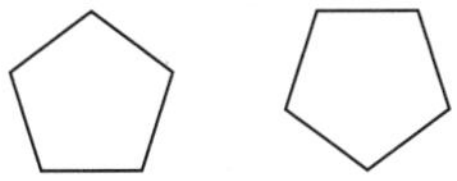

The pentagons are not reflections of one another.

ⓒ

The triangles are not reflections of one another.

7 How do you know whether two figures are not reflections of one another?

Two figures are not reflections of one another if the perpendicular bisector of one pair of corresponding vertices is not also the perpendicular of each pair of corresponding vertices.

Lesson 3 > Staring Back at Me 121

Questions to Support Discourse

		TYPE
6	• Explain how you determined whether the figures are reflections of one another. • What is an easier way to check instead of constructing a perpendicular bisector for each pair of corresponding vertices?	Probing

NOTES

TOPIC 2

SUMMARY The Perpendicular Bisector Theorem states that any point on the perpendicular bisector of a segment is equidistant from the segment's endpoints.

Chunking the Activity

- **Read and discuss the introduction**
- **Complete 1 as a class**
- **Read and discuss the definition and worked example**
- **Complete 2 as a class**
- **Read and discuss the theorem**
- **Group students to complete 3**
- **Share and summarize**

Student Look-Fors

Whether students are annotating the worked example and making connections.

Perpendicular Bisector Theorem

HABITS OF MIND

- Look for and make use of structure.
- Look for and express regularity in repeated reasoning.

In the Getting Started, you saw that the perpendicular bisector of a line segment is the line of reflection between the endpoints of the segment. Consider $\overline{RB}$ with perpendicular bisector ℓ.

1 Label point P anywhere on ℓ. What do you notice about the relationship between point P and points R and B?

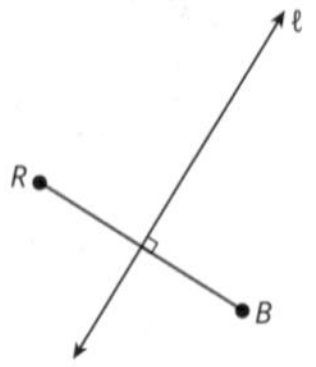

Answers may vary.

Sample answer.

Point P appears to be the same distance from points R and B.

You can *prove* that the endpoints of a line segment are equidistant from any point on the perpendicular bisector.

WORKED EXAMPLE

Given: Line ℓ is the perpendicular bisector of $\overline{RB}$.

Point P is on ℓ.

Prove: $PR = PB$

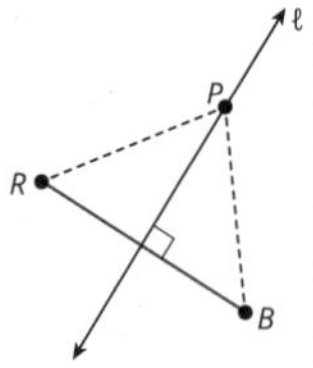

The reflection of point P across line ℓ is point P by the definition of reflection.

Because line ℓ is the perpendicular bisector of $\overline{RB}$, the reflection of point R across line ℓ is point B.

Therefore, $PR = PB$.

TAKE NOTE...

A **proof** is a series of statements and corresponding reasons forming a valid argument that starts with a hypothesis and arrives at a conclusion.

2 Provide a reason why $PR = PB$.

$\overline{PR}$ is a reflection across line ℓ of $\overline{PB}$, and rigid motions preserve size.

Questions to Support Discourse

		TYPE
1	• How can you use a compass or patty paper to show that *PR* equals *PB* for your specific case?	Reflecting and justifying
Worked Example	• How is this proof different from your reasoning in Question 1?	Seeing structure
2	• What mathematical terms did you use in your reasoning?	Reflecting and justifying

ACTIVITY 2 Continued

Because the relationship was proven true, you can now refer to it as a theorem.

THEOREM

PERPENDICULAR BISECTOR THEOREM

Any point on the perpendicular bisector of a segment is equidistant from the endpoints of that segment.

REMEMBER...

A theorem is a statement you can demonstrate to be true by accepted mathematical operations and arguments.

Let's consider the relationship between endpoints of a line segment and any point on the perpendicular bisector from another perspective.

Suppose you have two points that are equidistant from a third point. You can show that the third point lies on the perpendicular bisector of the segment connecting the points.

3 Consider point Q, which is equidistant from points A and B.

ⓐ Draw $\overrightarrow{QP}$ so that it bisects $\angle BQA$. This makes $\angle BQP$ and $\angle PQA$ congruent angles. Label the intersection of $\overrightarrow{QP}$ and $\overline{AB}$ as point C.

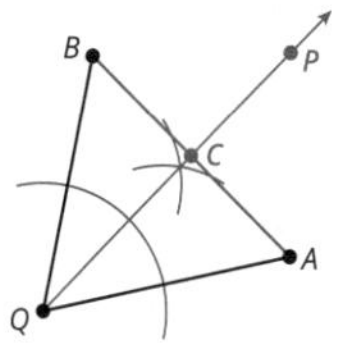

ⓑ Describe the location of $\overline{QB'}$ when $\overline{QB}$ is reflected across $\overrightarrow{QP}$. What does this tell you about the distances BC and CA? **Explain your thinking.**

$\overline{QB'}$ will lie on top of $\overline{QA}$, with point Q aligning with itself, and point B' lying on top of point A.

The distances BC and CA are equal.

ⓒ Explain how you know that $\overrightarrow{QP}$ is a perpendicular bisector of $\overline{AB}$.

Points A and B are equidistant from point C and also equidistant from point Q. Therefore, points C and Q must lie on the perpendicular bisector. Because points Q, C, and P lie on the same ray, $\overrightarrow{QP}$ is a perpendicular bisector.

NOTES

DIFFERENTIATION STRATEGY

See Page 128A to challenge advanced learners to extend 3.

TOPIC 2

Questions to Support Discourse

		TYPE
3	• Do you think you would have gotten the same result if you bisected $\angle Q$ without constructing the perpendicular bisector? Explain your thinking.	Seeing structure
	• How can you use the Perpendicular Bisector Theorem to respond to this question?	Reflecting and justifying

ACTIVITY 3

SUMMARY You can use a sequence of translations and reflections to show that two figures are congruent.

Chunking the Activity

- **Read and discuss the introduction**
- **Group students to complete 1 and 2**
- **Check-in and share**
- **Group students to complete 3 and 4**
- **Share and summarize**

LANGUAGE LINK

ELL TIP

Ensure students understand the meaning of *counterexample* in the directions. Define *counter* as to go against or follow the opposite direction. A counterexample is an example that disproves a statement. Provide an example, such as "All triangles are isosceles." Discuss why a scalene triangle is a counterexample.

Student Look-Fors

Different strategies to respond to Question 2.

- Students may identify all the midpoints first, then realize they are collinear and lie on the perpendicular bisector.
- Students may draw a perpendicular bisector first and then identify each midpoint as the intersection of the line segment connecting two corresponding points and the perpendicular bisector.

Sequences of Isometries Using Translations and Reflections

HABITS OF MIND
- Look for and make use of structure.
- Look for and express regularity in repeated reasoning.

You have learned that reflections and translations are isometries, which means that they preserve distances and angle measures.

TAKE NOTE...
To show that a statement is false, you can provide a counterexample. A **counterexample** is a specific example that shows that a general statement is not true.

1 Sunita made a conjecture about reflections. She said that you can always map one congruent line segment onto the other using at most two reflections. Do you think Sunita is correct?
Draw examples or *counterexamples* to justify your reasoning.

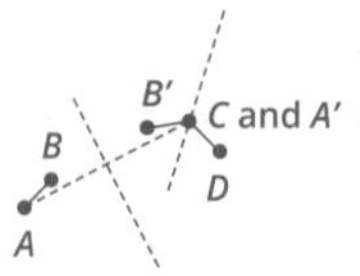

Sunita is correct.
Given $\overline{AB} \cong \overline{CD}$ when you reflect $\overline{AB}$ across a line to map point A to point C, $\overline{A'B'} \cong \overline{CD}$. Then another reflection across a line through C maps $\overline{A'B'}$ to $\overline{CD}$.

2 Triangle GHJ is a reflection of ΔMNP. Describe the locations of the midpoints of $\overline{GM}$, $\overline{HN}$, and $\overline{JP}$.

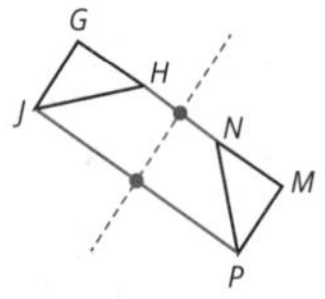

The midpoints of $\overline{GM}$, $\overline{HN}$, and $\overline{JP}$ all lie on the perpendicular bisector, or the line of reflection for the two triangles.

Questions to Support Discourse

		TYPE
1	• What is a way to generalize your steps to show Sunita is correct? • How might the segments appear if only one reflection is required?	Probing
2	• How could you determine the midpoints using patty paper? A compass and straightedge?	Probing
	• Are the midpoints always collinear? Why?	Seeing structure

ACTIVITY 3 Continued

3 Describe and sketch the sequence of translations and reflections that shows that the two figures in each pair are congruent. Images are shown with dashed lines.

(a)

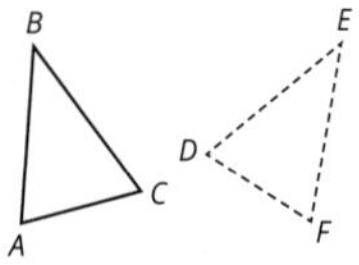

Reflect △*ABC* across a vertical line and then translate it up.

(b)

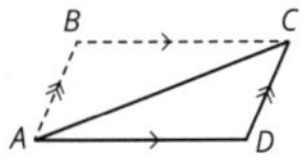

Reflect △*ADC* across a horizontal and a vertical line and then translate it.

TAKE NOTE...
Sides that have the same number of arrowhead markings are parallel to one another.

4 Miguel was investigating a transformation of △*ABC* to △*A′B′C′* and discovered that the midpoints of the segments connecting corresponding points were collinear, but the line was not a perpendicular bisector of each segment. He thought that this must not be a reflection.

Lina disagreed. She said that you can translate first to show that the midpoints lie on a perpendicular bisector. Who is correct? **Explain your reasoning.**

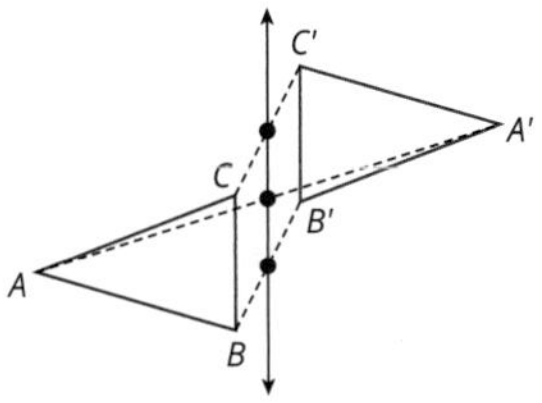

Lina is correct.
Sometimes a sequence of transformations is required to map a figure onto itself. In this case, a translation up was also required.

NOTES

DIFFERENTIATION STRATEGY
See Page 128B to support students who struggle with 3 part (b).

DIFFERENTIATION STRATEGY
See Page 128B to assist all students with the strategies in 4.

TOPIC 2

Questions to Support Discourse

		TYPE
3	• Which transformations did you use? • Where did you place the line of reflection? • Does the order of the transformations make a difference? Why or why not?	Probing
4	• Which type of translation is Lina suggesting?	Probing

TALK THE TALK

SUMMARY **Geometric functions use any line of reflection, while algebraic equations show horizontal and vertical reflections only.**

Chunking the Activity

- **Read and discuss the introduction**
- **Group students to complete the activity**
- **Share and summarize**

Student Look-Fors

Demonstrating organizational skills by making lists, outlining steps, or using other organizational strategies while solving problems.

But We're Off the Grid

In this activity, you translated and reflected figures in the plane. Let's compare those transformations with the same ones performed on a coordinate plane.

1. Describe the sequence of translations and reflections which maps the pre-image triangle, ΔPQR, onto the image triangle, ΔABC on the coordinate plane.

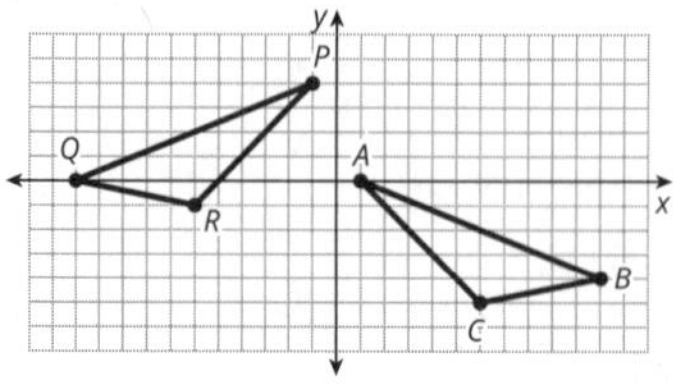

I can reflect ΔPQR across the y-axis and then translate the triangle down 4 units.

2. How are translating and reflecting geometric figures in the plane different from performing these transformations on the coordinate plane? How are they the same?

Sample answer.

Translating and reflecting on the plane and on a coordinate plane both produce the desired results.

When reflecting on a plane and on a coordinate plane, you must identify a line of reflection.

When translating on the coordinate plane, you can quantify the movements by units on the grid.

When translating on the plane, the movements are identified by directed line segments.

Questions to Support Discourse

		TYPE
1	• Which transformations did you use? • Where did you place the line of reflection? • What is another sequence of transformations that would work?	Probing
2	• Do you prefer transforming figures on or off the coordinate plane? Why?	Gathering
3	• Do you have more flexibility describing reflections on or off the coordinate plane? Why? • How does the coordinate pair (2, 5) change when you reflect it across the x-axis? The y-axis?	Seeing structure

ASSIGNMENT

LESSON 3 ASSIGNMENT

> Use a separate piece of paper for your Journal entry.

JOURNAL

Explain why a reflection of a figure is an isometry.

REMEMBER

A reflection is a function, R_ℓ, which takes as its input, P, the location of a point with respect to some line of reflection ℓ and outputs $R_\ell(P)$, or the opposite of the location of P with respect to the line of reflection.

Any point that is equidistant from two other points lies on the perpendicular bisector between the two points.

PRACTICE

1. Complete each reflection, given the function.

   a. $R_m(ABCD)$

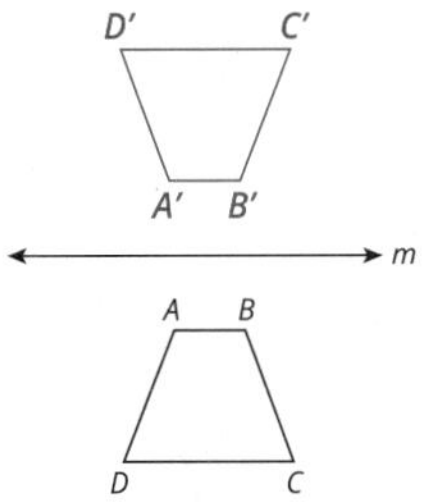

   b. $R_p(JKL)$

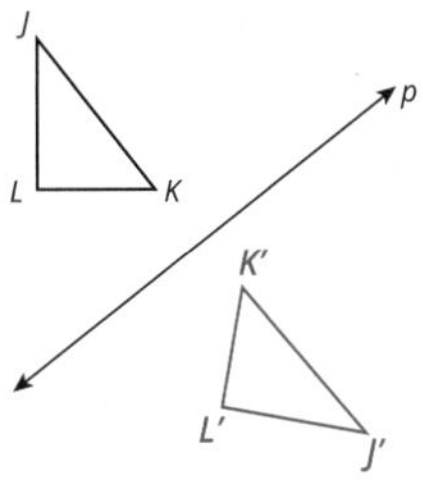

   c. $R_b(QRSTU)$

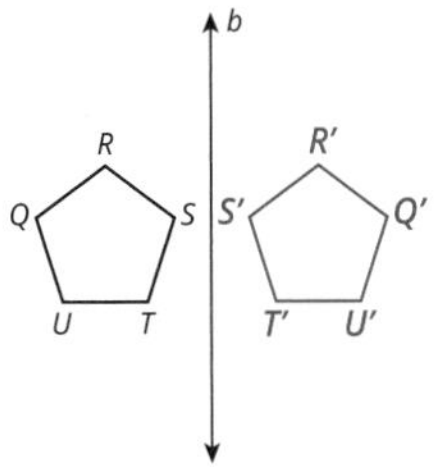

   d. $R_k(ABCD)$

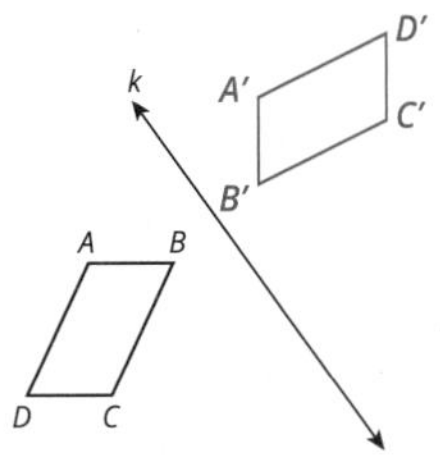

Go to LiveHint.com for help on the PRACTICE questions.

Encourage students to use LiveHint.com for help with the PRACTICE questions of this assignment.

Chunking the Assignment

SESSION 1

- Journal
- Practice 1
- Stretch (advanced learners)

SESSION 2

- Practice 2
- Mixed Practice (page 153) 3

JOURNAL

A reflection is an isometry because the location of the reflected points are opposite of the original locations of the points with respect to the line. The distances between the figure's points stay the same, so the figure's size and shape stay the same, making it an isometry.

NOTES

LESSON 3 ASSIGNMENT Continued

2 Describe the sequence of translations and reflections that show that the two figures in each pair are congruent. Images are shown with dashed lines.

ⓐ

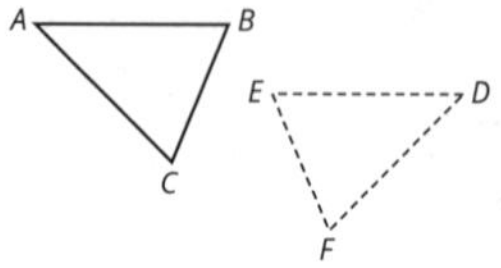

Reflect Triangle *ABC* across a vertical line and then translate it.

ⓑ

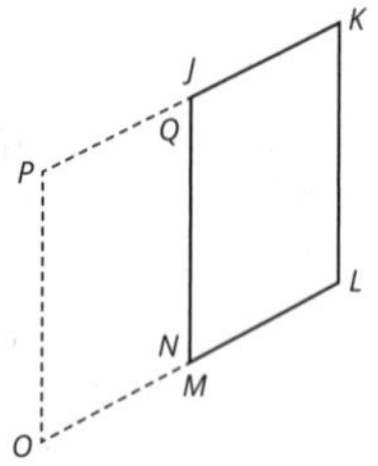

Reflect Parallelogram *JKLM* across a horizontal and vertical line and then translate it.

ⓒ

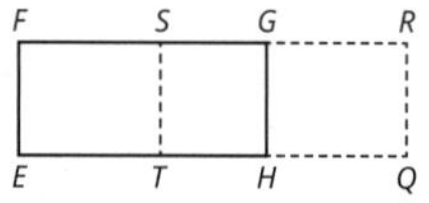

Reflect Rectangle *EFGH* across a vertical line and then translate it.

ⓓ

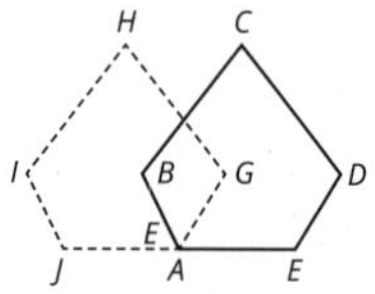

Reflect Pentagon *ABCDE* across a vertical line and then translate it.

STRETCH Optional

> Describe the sequence of translations and reflections to each figure so that the word APPLE is shown in between the two lines with the figures in the same positions.

STRETCH

Sample answer.

The first figure is a reflection across a horizontal line and then translated up. The second figure is a reflection across a horizontal and vertical line and a translation to the left and then up. The third figure is a reflection across a vertical line, and a translation left. The fourth figure is a reflection across a horizontal and vertical line and a translation to the left and then up. The fifth figure is a reflection across a vertical line and a translation to the left.

Staring Back at Me

This resource details additional facilitation notes to fully assist you as you plan each lesson to support all students, students who struggle, and advanced learners. It provides differentiation strategies, common student misconceptions, and suggestions to extend certain activities.

ACTIVITY 1
Reflection Functions

Session 1 of 2

Students recognize that the line of reflection is the perpendicular bisector of all segments connecting reflection points. They use appropriate notation to complete reflections and construct lines of reflection.

CHUNK	AUDIENCE	ADDITIONAL SUPPORTS
As students share and summarize 4	All Students	**COMMON MISCONCEPTION** Students may confuse the equalities in two situations regarding perpendicular bisectors. Discuss each statement and have students sketch a diagram to illustrate it. • When you construct the perpendicular bisector of a line segment, any point on the perpendicular bisector is equidistant to the segment's endpoints. • When you construct the perpendicular bisector as a line of reflection for a figure and its image, each point (pre-image) and its image are equidistant from the perpendicular bisector.
As students analyzed the worked example	All Students	**DIFFERENTIATION STRATEGY** Suggest students use colored pencils to re-enact the steps in the worked example.

ACTIVITY 2
Perpendicular Bisector Theorem

Session 1 of 2

Students analyze a worked example proving the Perpendicular Bisector Theorem. They investigate the relationship between two points equidistant from a third point.

CHUNK	AUDIENCE	ADDITIONAL SUPPORTS
To extend 3	Advanced Learners	**DIFFERENTIATION STRATEGY** Have students connect points *A* and *B* and investigate relationships in the resulting isosceles triangle.

ACTIVITY 3

Session 2 of 2

Sequences of Isometries Using Translations and Reflections

Students learn that they can map one congruent line segment onto another using at most two reflections. They describe sequences of isometries to show that two figures are congruent.

CHUNK	AUDIENCE	ADDITIONAL SUPPORTS
work on 3 part (b)	Students who struggle	**DIFFERENTIATION STRATEGY** Tell students that it takes two reflections and one translation, and then let students determine how to complete those transformations to map one triangle onto the other.
As students work on 4	All Students	**DIFFERENTIATION STRATEGY** Encourage students to take time to read through each strategy, thinking about and annotating the connections, to determine whether each strategy is correct or not. Suggest students ask themselves: • Does the reasoning make sense? • When the reasoning makes sense, what is the justification? • When the reasoning does not make sense, what error was made?

Practice the learning

MATHbook + Skills Practice

The table shows the targeted practice of the skills and mathematical concepts for the *Rigid Motions on a Plane* Topic. The highlighted **Problem Set** aligns with **Staring Back at Me.**

PROBLEM SET	
1	Geometric Components of Rigid Motions
2	Translation Functions
3	**Reflection Functions**
4	Rotation Functions
5	Reflectional and Rotational Symmetries

ANYTIME AFTER ACTIVITY 3
Facilitate students as they work individually on **Problem Set 3**.

TOPIC 2

NOTES

ENGAGE + DEVELOP + TEACH

at the **Module** level

at the **Topic** level

Read the facilitation notes and plan learning experiences.

Where are we?

TOPIC 2 Rigid Motions on a Plane	LESSON 1 Put Your Input In, Take Your Output Out	LESSON 2 Bow Thai	LESSON 3 Staring Back at Me	**LESSON 4 Turn Yourself Around**	LESSON 5 OKEECHOBEE
Pacing	3 Sessions	2 Sessions	2 Sessions	**2 Sessions**	1 Session

OVERVIEW: LESSON 4

Turn Yourself Around

Rotations as Functions

ENGAGE

- Students rotate a figure on the coordinate plane.

DEVELOP

- Students rotate a figure on the plane given a center of rotation and angle of rotation.
- They use function notation to represent a rotation.
- They identify the center of rotation and angle of rotation given a pre-image and image.
- Students describe a sequence of isometries to show that two figures are congruent.

DEMONSTRATE

- Students summarize what they have learned about translations, reflections, and rotations.

HIGH SCHOOL GEOMETRY

Congruence

Experiment with transformations in the plane.

1. Know precise definitions of angle, circle, perpendicular line, parallel line, and line segment, based on the undefined notions of point, line, distance along a line, and distance around a circular arc.
2. Represent transformations in the plane using, e.g., transparencies and geometry software; describe transformations as functions that take points in the plane as inputs and give other points as outputs. Compare transformations that preserve distance and angle to those that do not.
4. Develop definitions of rotations, reflections, and translations in terms of angles, circles, perpendicular lines, parallel lines, and line segments.
5. Given a geometric figure and a rotation, reflection, or translation, draw the transformed figure using, e.g., graph paper, tracing paper, or geometry software. Specify a sequence of transformations that will carry a given figure onto another.

LESSON STRUCTURE AND PACING GUIDE 2 SESSIONS

✪ This activity highlights a key term or concept that is essential to the learning goals of the lesson.

Session 1		Session 2
INSTRUCTIONAL SEQUENCE		
ENGAGE Establish a situation	**DEVELOP** Worked example Mathematical problem solving	**DEVELOP** Peer analysis Mathematical problem solving

GETTING STARTED
The Hook

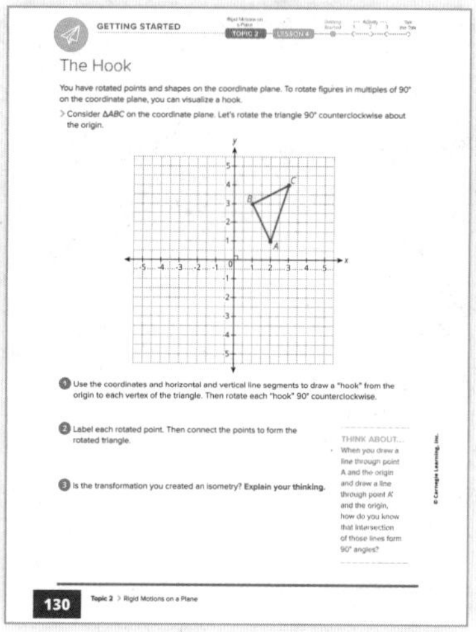

Students rotate a figure on the coordinate plane.

- They determine that the rotation is an isometry.

ACTIVITY 1
Rotation Functions

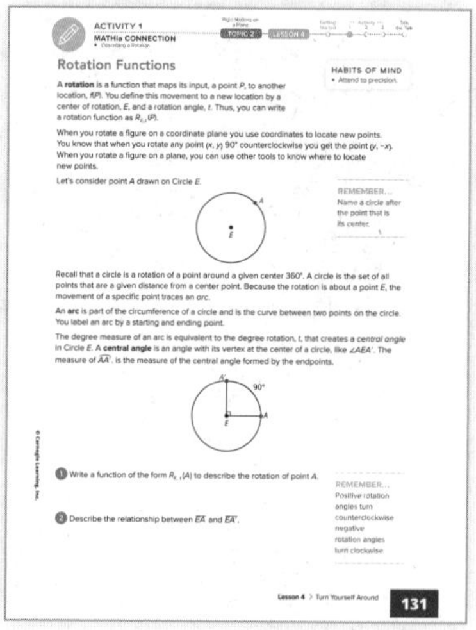

Students use a protractor and ruler to rotate a figure given a center of rotation and the angle of rotation.

- They create these rotations on the plane.

ACTIVITY 2
Determining the Center of Rotation

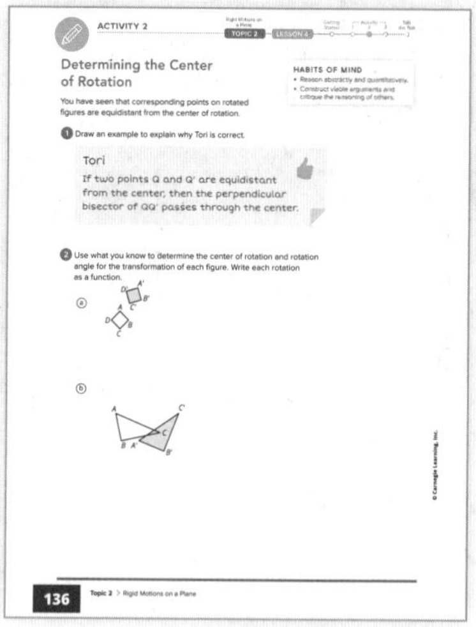

Students identify the center of rotation and angle of rotation given a pre-image and image.

- They write each rotation as a function.

Log in to MyCL for **lesson support** including:

Slides

Videos

www.carnegielearning.com/login

INSTRUCTIONAL SEQUENCE

DEVELOP
Mathematical problem solving

DEMONSTRATE
Graphic organizer

ACTIVITY 3
Sequences of Isometries

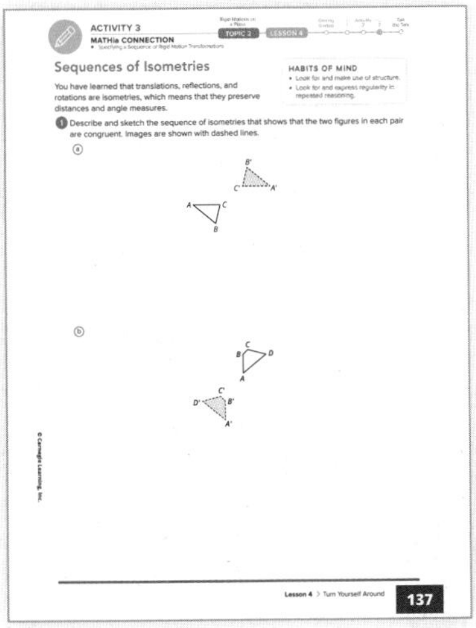
ACTIVITY 3
MATHia CONNECTION
TOPIC 2 LESSON 4

Sequences of Isometries

HABITS OF MIND
- Look for and make use of structure.
- Look for and express regularity in repeated reasoning.

You have learned that translations, reflections, and rotations are isometries, which means that they preserve distances and angle measures.

1 Describe and sketch the sequence of isometries that shows that the two figures in each pair are congruent. Images are shown with dashed lines.

(a)

(b)

© Carnegie Learning, Inc.

Lesson 4 > Turn Yourself Around 137

Students describe a sequence of isometries to show that two figures are congruent.

- They sketch their intermediate steps to validate their thinking.

TALK THE TALK
That's What It's All About!

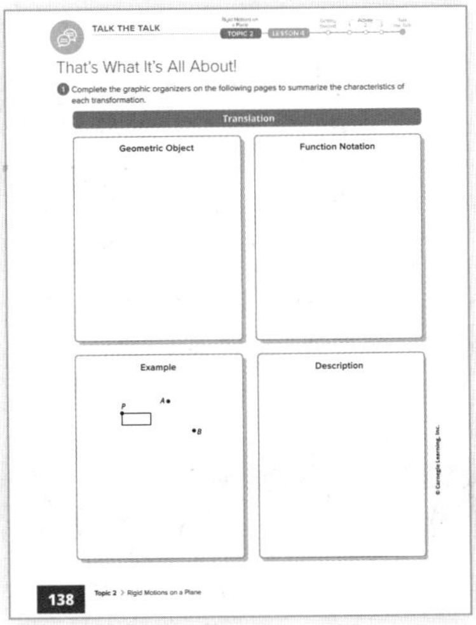
TALK THE TALK
TOPIC 2 LESSON 4

That's What It's All About!

1 Complete the graphic organizers on the following pages to summarize the characteristics of each transformation.

Translation

Geometric Object	Function Notation
Example	Description

© Carnegie Learning, Inc.

138 Topic 2 > Rigid Motions on a Plane

Students summarize what they have learned about translations, reflections, and rotations.

- They describe each transformation, use function notation, and provide an example.

NOTES

TOPIC 2

Log in to MyCL for:

- Editable templates
- Additional planning support

Now that you have read the Module, Topic, and Lesson Overviews, you are ready to plan.

Do the math

> Tear out the lesson planning template (page 129E) and jot down thoughts as you work through this lesson and read the Facilitation Notes.

Connect the learning

MATHbook + MATHia

The table shows a portion of the self-paced MATHia sequence for the *Rigid Motions on a Plane* Topic.

Median student completion time for the entire topic: ~90–120 minutes

> As you implement this lesson, consider different connections for students who are on pace and those that have not yet completed the workspaces aligned to this lesson.

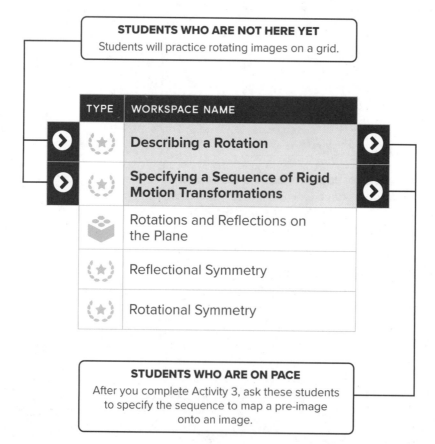

STUDENTS WHO ARE NOT HERE YET
Students will practice rotating images on a grid.

TYPE	WORKSPACE NAME
	Describing a Rotation
	Specifying a Sequence of Rigid Motion Transformations
	Rotations and Reflections on the Plane
	Reflectional Symmetry
	Rotational Symmetry

STUDENTS WHO ARE ON PACE
After you complete Activity 3, ask these students to specify the sequence to map a pre-image onto an image.

Turn Yourself Around
Rotations as Functions

Session 1

GETTING STARTED The Hook ✪

Pacing (minutes)	
My Time	Class Time

ACTIVITY 1 Rotation Functions ✪

Pacing (minutes)	
My Time	Class Time

KEY TERM
rotation
arc
central angle

TOPIC 2

Session 2

ACTIVITY 2 Determining the Center of Rotation ✪

Pacing (minutes)	
My Time	Class Time

ACTIVITY 3 Sequences of Isometries ✪

Pacing (minutes)	
My Time	Class Time

TALK THE TALK That's What It's All About! ✪

Pacing (minutes)	
My Time	Class Time

✪ This activity highlights a key term or concept that is essential to the learning goals of the lesson.

Log in to MyCL for:

- Editable templates
- Additional planning support

Reflect on your lesson

> Consider the effectiveness of your lesson on student learning.

What went well?	What did not go as planned?

> Anticipate how you would change the lesson next time you teach it.

How will you capitalize on the things that went well?	How will you improve things that did not go as planned?

TOPIC 1 Using a Rectangular Coordinate System

TOPIC 2 Rigid Motions on a Plane

TOPIC 3 Congruence Through Transformations

1 | Put Your Input In, Take Your Output Out
2 | Bow Thai
3 | Staring Back at Me
4 | Turn Yourself Around
5 | OKEECHOBEE

LESSON 4

Turn Yourself Around

Rotations as Functions

KEY TERM

- rotation
- arc
- central angle

Learning Goals

- Represent rotations in the plane.
- Describe rotation transformations as functions that take points as inputs and output rotated points.
- Specify a sequence of translations, reflections, and rotations that will carry a figure onto a congruent figure.

REVIEW (1–2 minutes)

> Consider the point (x, y) located in the first quadrant. Rotate the point (x, y) as described to plot and label a new point.

1. Rotation about the origin 90° counterclockwise
   $(-y, x)$
2. Rotation about the origin 90° clockwise
   $(y, -x)$
3. Rotation about the origin 180°
   $(-y, -x)$

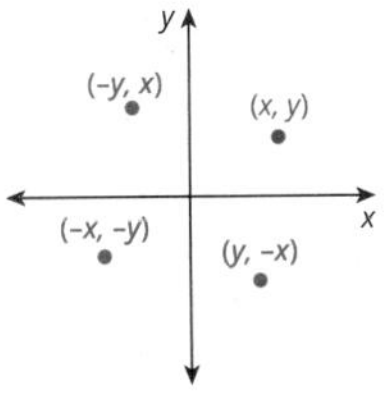

You have described the effects of rotations on two-dimensional figures using coordinates.

How can you use circles to define and describe rotations on the plane?

MATERIALS

- Patty paper
- Protractors
- Rulers

Setting the Stage

- **Assign Review (optional, 1 – 2 minutes)**
- **Communicate the learning goals and key terms to look out for**
- **Tap into your students' prior learning by reading the narrative statement**
- **Provide a sense of direction by reading the question**

TOPIC 2

IN THIS REVIEW
Students identify central angles. They will use this skill in **ACTIVITY 1 Rotation Functions.**

A rotation is a function that maps its input, a point P, to another location, $f(P)$. You define this movement to a new location is defined by a center of rotation, E, and a rotation angle, t. You can write a rotation function as $R_{E,t}(P)$.

Essential Ideas

- A rotation is an isometry.
- A rotation is a function defined by a center of rotation and a rotation angle.
- A rotation is a function, $R_{E,t}(P) = P'$, that maps its input, a point P, to another location, P'. A center of rotation, E, and a rotation angle, t, defines this movement to a new location.
- The center of rotation of a pre-image and image is the intersection of the perpendicular bisectors of segments connecting corresponding vertices.

GETTING STARTED

SUMMARY **You can rotate figures on the coordinate plane by relocating each vertex and then connecting the vertices. A rotation is an isometry.**

Chunking the Activity

- **Read and discuss the introduction**
- **Group students to complete the activity**
- **Share and summarize**

LANGUAGE LINK

Remind students to refer to the Academic Glossary (page FM–20) to review the definition of **explain your thinking** and related phrases. Suggest they ask themselves these questions:

- How can I justify my answer to others?
- Is my explanation logical?

The Hook

You have rotated points and shapes on the coordinate plane. To rotate figures in multiples of 90° on the coordinate plane, you can visualize a hook.

> Consider ΔABC on the coordinate plane. Let's rotate the triangle 90° counterclockwise about the origin.

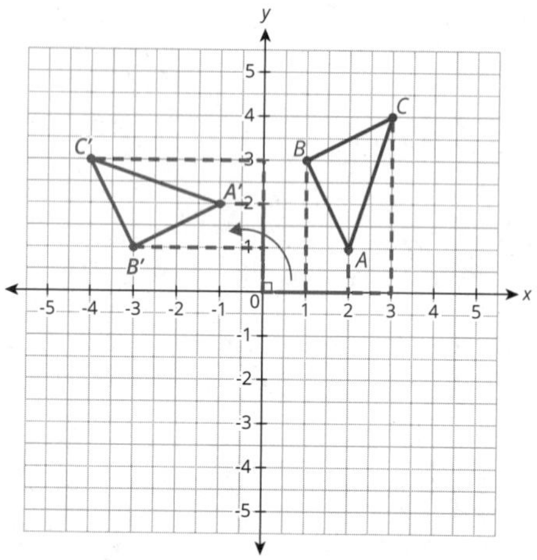

1. Use the coordinates and horizontal and vertical line segments to draw a "hook" from the origin to each vertex of the triangle. Then rotate each "hook" 90° counterclockwise.

2. Label each rotated point. Then connect the points to form the rotated triangle.

3. Is the transformation you created an isometry? **Explain your thinking.**

   The transformation is an isometry because $\Delta ABC \cong \Delta A'B'C'$.

   The triangles are congruent because the corresponding sides and angles of the triangles are congruent.

THINK ABOUT...
When you draw a line through point A and the origin and draw a line through point A' and the origin, how do you know that intersection of those lines form 90° angles?

Questions to Support Discourse

		TYPE
1	• Explain how you used a hook to determine the new position of a vertex. • How would you modify your process for a 180° rotation? • Would your process be any different for a 45° rotation?	Probing
3	• Which other transformations are isometries?	Gathering

ACTIVITY 1

SUMMARY **A rotation is a function defined by a center of rotation and a rotation angle.**

Rotation Functions

HABITS OF MIND
• Attend to precision.

A **rotation** is a function that maps its input, a point *P*, to another location, *f*(*P*). You define this movement to a new location by a center of rotation, *E*, and a rotation angle, *t*. Thus, you can write a rotation function as $R_{E,\,t}(P)$.

When you rotate a figure on a coordinate plane you use coordinates to locate new points. You know that when you rotate any point (*x*, *y*) 90° counterclockwise you get the point (*y*, −*x*). When you rotate a figure on a plane, you can use other tools to know where to locate new points.

Let's consider point *A* drawn on Circle *E*.

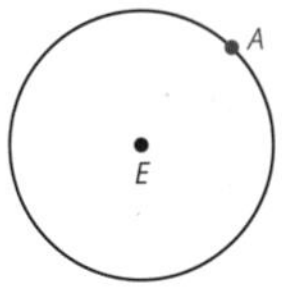

REMEMBER...
Name a circle after the point that is its center.

Recall that a circle is a rotation of a point around a given center 360°. A circle is the set of all points that are a given distance from a center point. Because the rotation is about a point *E*, the movement of a specific point traces an *arc*.

An **arc** is part of the circumference of a circle and is the curve between two points on the circle. You label an arc by a starting and ending point.

The degree measure of an arc is equivalent to the degree rotation, *t*, that creates a *central angle* in Circle *E*. A **central angle** is an angle with its vertex at the center of a circle, like ∠*AEA*′. The measure of $\overset{\frown}{AA'}$. is the measure of the central angle formed by the endpoints.

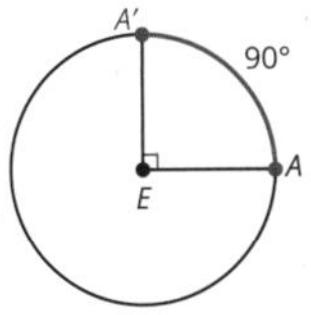

1. Write a function of the form $R_{E,\,t}(A)$ to describe the rotation of point *A*.

   $R_{E,\,90}(A) = A'$

2. Describe the relationship between $\overline{EA}$ and $\overline{EA'}$.

   The line segments are radii of the circle; all radii of a circle are congruent.
   $\overline{EA} \cong \overline{EA'}$

REMEMBER...
Positive rotation angles turn counterclockwise negative rotation angles turn clockwise.

Chunking the Activity

- Read and discuss the introduction
- Group students to complete 1 – 3
- Check-in and share
- Read and discuss the worked example
- Group students to complete 4 – 7
- Read and discuss the worked example
- Group students to complete 8

Questions to Support Discourse

		TYPE
1	• How can you tell the difference between the rotation and reflection notation? • What information do you need to perform a rotation? • What do the subscripts in the notation represent?	Probing
2	• How do you know when to use an equal sign and when to use a congruence symbol?	Gathering

NOTES

3 Rotate each point on Circle E as described. Then write a function to describe the rotation.

(a) Rotate point B 90° counterclockwise.

$R_{E,\ 90}(B) = B'$

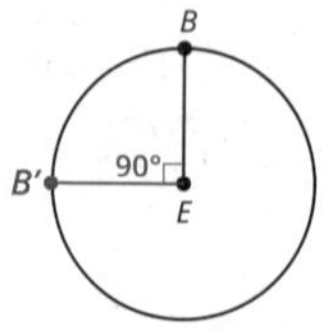

(b) Rotate point C 180° counterclockwise.

$R_{E,\ 180}(C) = C'$

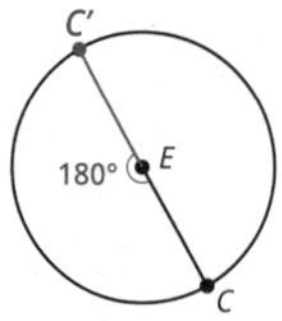

(c) Rotate point D 65° clockwise.

$R_{E,\ -65}(D) = D'$

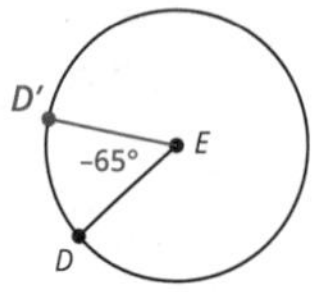

Questions to Support Discourse

		TYPE
3	• Interpret the notation.	Gathering
	• How do you know in which direction to draw the angle of rotation?	Probing
	• How can you check your work?	Reflecting and justifying

ACTIVITY 1 Continued

Let's reconsider ΔABC from the Getting Started now drawn on a plane. How can you rotate the triangle 90° counterclockwise about point E?

WORKED EXAMPLE

Consider ΔABC and point E as the center of rotation. You can rotate a figure about a point using concentric circles.

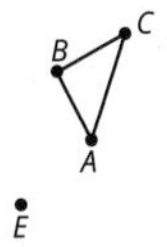

STEP 1 Draw line segments from the center of rotation to each endpoint of the figure. Then draw three concentric circles.

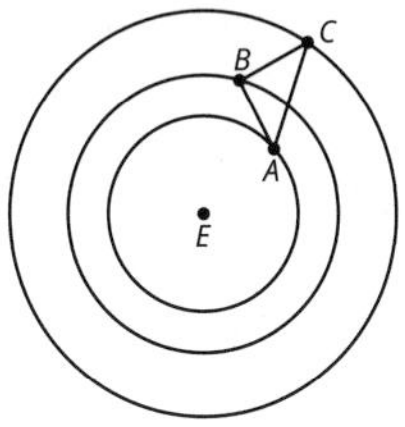

STEP 2 Use a protractor and the radius of each circle to draw 90° angles.

STEP 3 Label the new endpoints A', B', and C' respectively and use a straight edge to draw the new image.

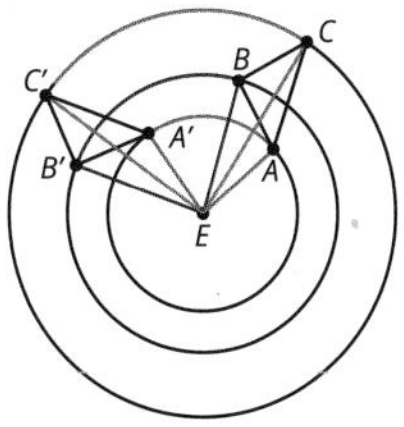

4 Write a function of the form $R_{E,\,t}(\Delta ABC)$ to describe the rotation of ΔABC.

$R_{E,\,90}(\Delta ABC) = \Delta A'B'C'$

5 Explain how your function represents the rotation of every point of ΔABC.

When the vertices are connected to make the sides of the triangle, every point of each side is rotated t about point E.

NOTES

DIFFERENTIATION STRATEGY

See Page 142A to assist all students with the worked example.

TOPIC 2

NOTES

ACTIVITY 1 Continued

6 Do the arcs you created all have the same measure? **Explain your answer.**

Sample answer.

All points do not travel the same distance as the triangle rotates. However, all points travel along an arc of the same degree measure as they move around their respective concentric circle.

7 Write equality and congruence statements to compare the corresponding sides of the pre-image and the image.

$AB = A'B'$	$\overline{AB} \cong \overline{A'B'}$
$BC = B'C'$	$\overline{BC} = \overline{B'C'}$
$CA = C'A'$	$\overline{CA} \cong \overline{C'A'}$

It is possible to apply the rotation function to a figure without drawing full circles.

WORKED EXAMPLE

Rotate $\overline{JN}$ 40°, using point A as the center of rotation.

$R_{A,\ 40}(\overline{JN})$

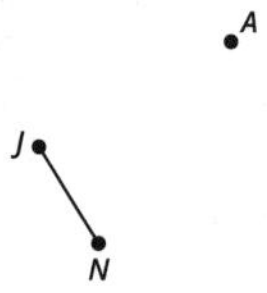

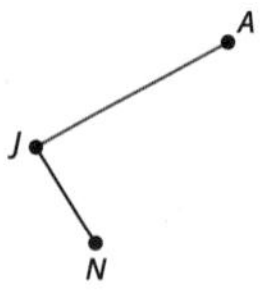

STEP 1 Draw a line segment from the center of rotation, A, to one endpoint of the line segment.

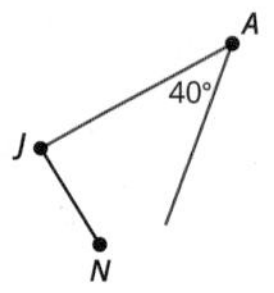

STEP 2 Using a protractor, draw a 40° angle. Use the center of rotation, A, as the vertex and the line segment drawn, $\overline{AJ}$ as one side of the angle. Since the angle measure is positive, place the angle in the counterclockwise direction of the line segment drawn.

Questions to Support Discourse

		TYPE
Worked Example	• Why is the 40° angle drawn at point A? • The length of the rays of an angle has no impact on the size of the angle. Why do the lengths of each side of the angle matter for this procedure? • Why do you have to repeat the procedure for the other vertex? • How do you know whether to draw the angle above or below $\overline{NA}$?	Probing

ACTIVITY 1 Continued

WORKED EXAMPLE

continued...

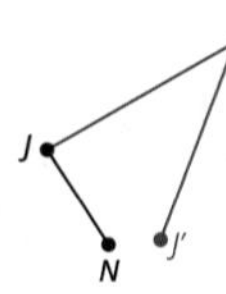

STEP 3 Use a ruler or compass to extend the side of the angle so that it is the same length as $\overline{AJ}$. Label the other endpoint J'.

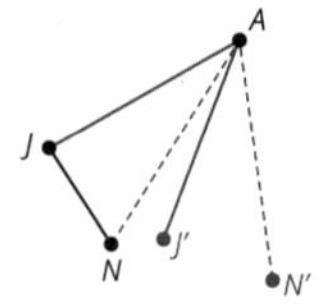

STEP 4 Repeat steps 1, 2, and 3 using the other endpoint of the original line segment.

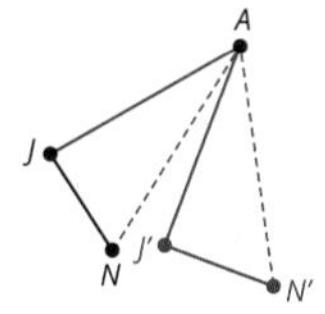

STEP 5 Connect endpoints J' and N'.

$R_{A,\ 40}(JN) = J'N'$

$\overline{J'N'}$ is the result of a 40° rotation of $\overline{JN}$ about point A.

8 Complete each rotation using the given function.

ⓐ $R_{E,\ 75}(\overline{VH})$

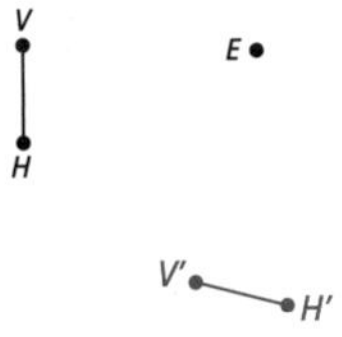

ⓑ $R_{Q,\ -30}(\overline{MN})$

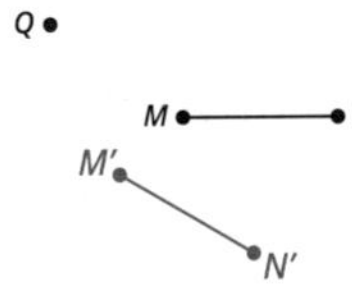

REMEMBER...

When you construct, you use only a compass and straight edge. Here you are drawing, so you can use those tools and measuring tools, such as a protractor and ruler.

NOTES

TOPIC 2

ACTIVITY 2

SUMMARY **The center of rotation of a pre-image and image is the intersection of the perpendicular bisectors to segments connecting corresponding vertices.**

Chunking the Activity

- **Read and discuss the introduction**
- **Group students to complete 1**
- **Check-in and share**
- **Group students to complete 2**
- **Share and summarize**

DIFFERENTIATION STRATEGY

See Page 142A to support students who struggle with 1.

Student Look-Fors

Whether students are demonstrating proficiencies related to these habits of mind.

- Reason abstractly and quantitatively
- Construct viable arguments and critique the reasoning of others

Determining the Center of Rotation

HABITS OF MIND
- Reason abstractly and quantitatively.
- Construct viable arguments and critique the reasoning of others.

You have seen that corresponding points on rotated figures are equidistant from the center of rotation.

1. Draw an example to explain why Tori is correct.

> Tori
> If two points Q and Q′ are equidistant from the center, then the perpendicular bisector of QQ′ passes through the center.

Sample answer.

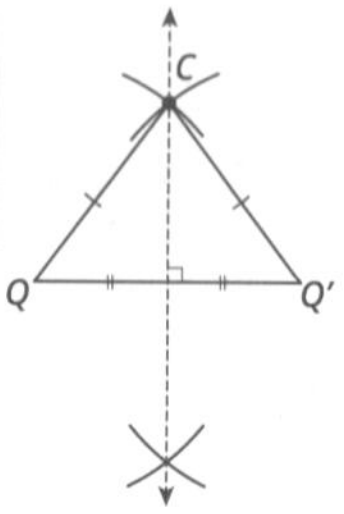

2. Use what you know to determine the center of rotation and rotation angle for the transformation of each figure. Write each rotation as a function.

(a)

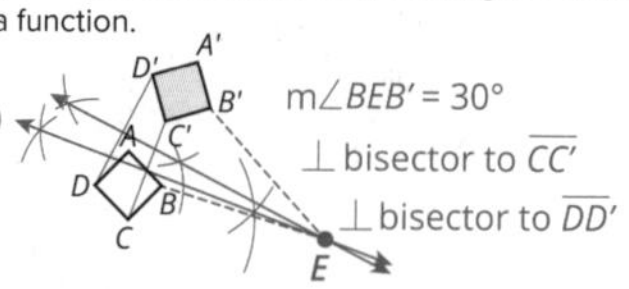

$R_{E,\,-30}(ABCD) = A'B'C'D'$

(b)

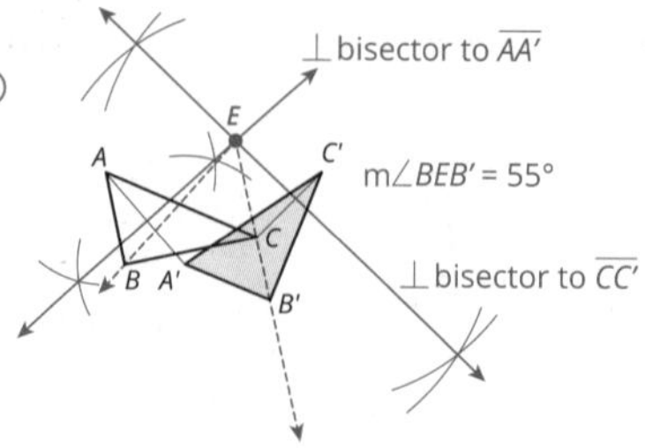

$R_{E,\,55}(\Delta ABC) = \Delta A'B'C'$

Questions to Support Discourse

		TYPE
Intro	• How did you show that corresponding points on rotated figures are equidistant from the center in the last activity?	Probing
1	• What does the perpendicular bisector have to do with rotating figures? • Why should the phrase "two points equidistant from the center" remind you of a perpendicular bisector?	Seeing structure
3	• How many perpendicular bisectors did you have to construct to determine the center of rotation? • How did you determine the rotation angle?	Probing
	• How did Tori's statement help you develop your strategy to determine the center of rotation and rotation angle?	Seeing structure

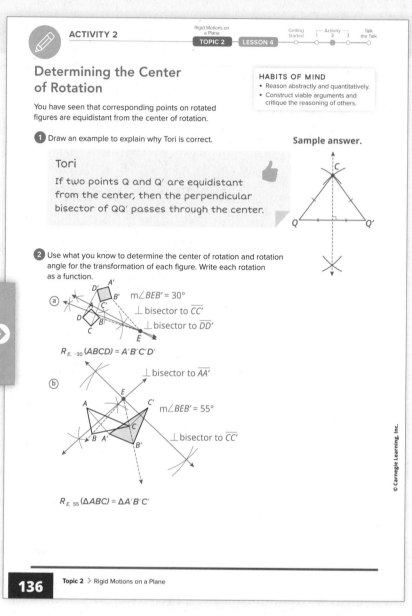

ACTIVITY 3

SUMMARY **You can use a sequence of isometries to show that two plane figures are congruent.**

ACTIVITY 3

MATHia CONNECTION
- Specifying a Sequence of Rigid Motion Transformations

Sequences of Isometries

HABITS OF MIND
- Look for and make use of structure.
- Look for and express regularity in repeated reasoning.

You have learned that translations, reflections, and rotations are isometries, which means that they preserve distances and angle measures.

1 Describe and sketch the sequence of isometries that shows that the two figures in each pair are congruent. Images are shown with dashed lines.

(a)

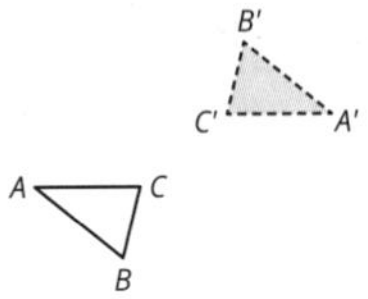

Sample answer.

You can reflect ΔABC across a horizontal line and reflect it across a vertical line to demonstrate the figures are congruent.

(b)

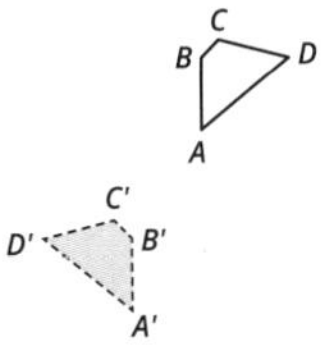

Sample answer.

You can reflect quadrilateral *ABCD* reflected across a vertical line and then translate it down to demonstrate the figures are congruent.

Chunking the Activity

- **Read and discuss the introduction**
- **Group students to complete the activity**
- **Share and summarize**

DIFFERENTIATION STRATEGY

See Page 142B to support students who struggle with 1.

See Page 142B to challenge advanced learners to extend 1 part (b).

Questions to Support Discourse

	Questions	TYPE
1	• How can you tell when you need more than one transformation? • How can you tell when a sequence of transformations includes a rotation? A reflection? • How did you determine the line of reflection? • Is there another sequence of isometries that would move the pre-image to the image? If so, describe the sequence of moves.	Probing

TALK THE TALK

SUMMARY **Translations require a directed line segment, reflections require a line of reflection, and rotations require a center and angle of rotation.**

Chunking the Activity

- **Read and discuss the directions**
- **Group students to complete the activity**
- **Share and summarize**

DIFFERENTIATION STRATEGY

See Page 142B for an alternative grouping strategy for the activity.

That's What It's All About!

1 Complete the graphic organizers on the following pages to summarize the characteristics of each transformation.

Translation

Geometric Object	Function Notation
Any figure on a plane, such as a point, line, angle, or polygon.	$T_{AB}(P) = P'$ where AB is a directed line segment.

Example

$T_{AB}(P) = P'$

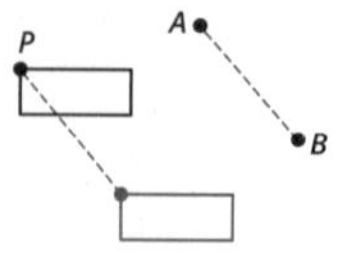

Description

Each point in the pre-image is translated the distance and direction of AB to create the image.

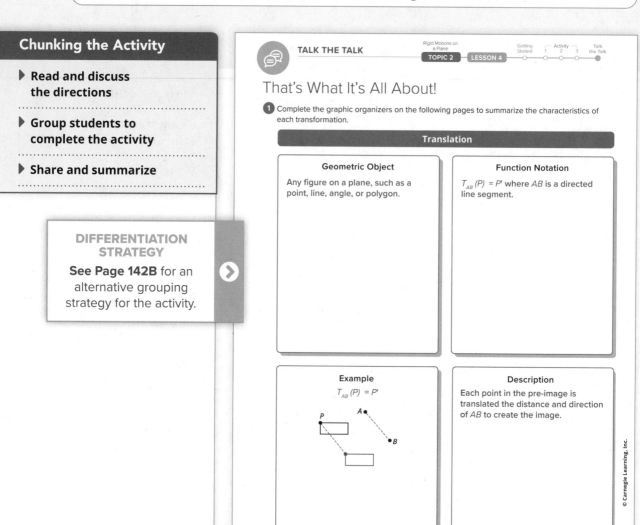

Questions to Support Discourse

		TYPE
1	• What do translations, reflections, and rotations have in common? • What information do you need to know to perform a translation? Reflection? Rotation? • How is the required information provided in the function notation?	Seeing structure

TALK THE TALK

TALK THE TALK Continued

Reflection

Geometric Object

Any figure on a plane, such as a point, line, angle, or polygon.

Function Notation

$R_{\ell}(P) = P'$ where ℓ is a line of reflection.

Example

$R_c(GJT) = \Delta G'J'T'$

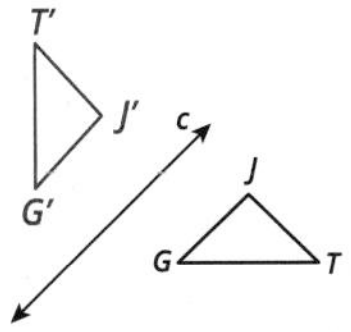

Description

Each point in the pre-image is reflected to the opposite location with respect to the line of reflection.
The line segment formed by corresponding points is perpendicular to the line of reflection.
Corresponding points are equidistant from the line of reflection.

NOTES

NOTES

TALK THE TALK Continued

Rotation

Geometric Object	Function Notation
Any figure on a plane, such as a point, line, angle, or polygon.	$R_{E,t}(P) = P'$ where E is the center of rotation and t is the angle of rotation.

Example

$R_{A,40}(JN) = (J'N')$

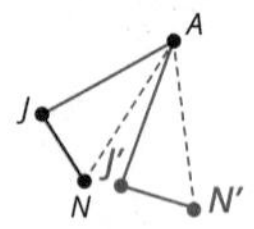

Description

Each point of JN is rotated 40° counterclockwise around point A to create $J'N'$.

ASSIGNMENT

LESSON 4 ASSIGNMENT

> Use a separate piece of paper for your Journal entry.

JOURNAL

Complete each definition.

1. A function that rotates points around a center point through an angle is called a __________.
2. Concentric circles are circles with a common __________.

REMEMBER

A rotation is a function that maps its input, a point P, to another location, $f(P)$. You define this movement to a new location by a center of rotation, E, and a rotation angle, t. You can write a rotation function as $R_{E,\,t}(P)$.

PRACTICE

1. Complete each rotation given the function.

ⓐ $R_{D,\,45}(\overline{AB})$

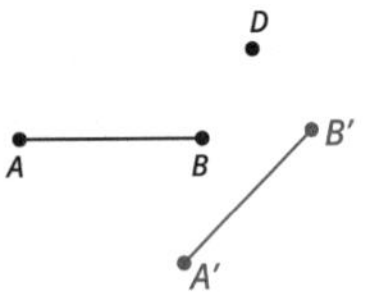

ⓑ $R_{X,\,-25}(\overline{MV})$

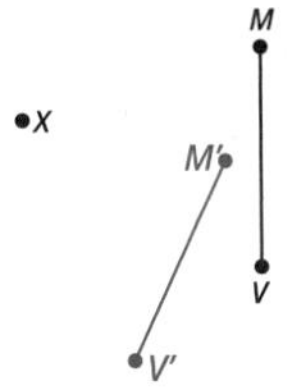

ⓒ $R_{A,\,125}(\overline{QR})$

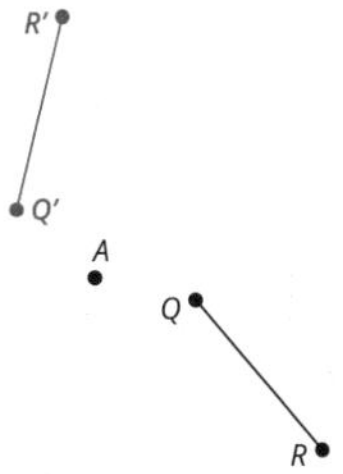

ⓓ $R_{C,\,80}(\overline{TY})$

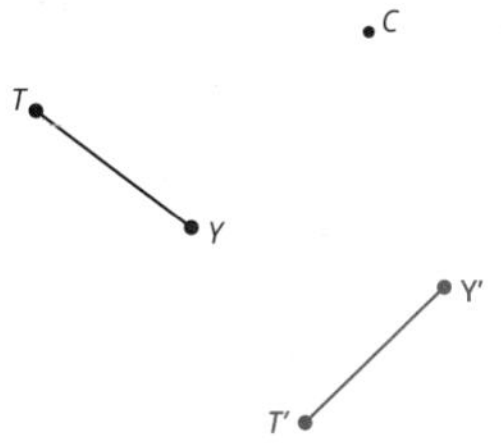

Go to LiveHint.com for help on the PRACTICE questions.

Encourage students to use LiveHint.com for help with the PRACTICE questions of this assignment.

Chunking the Assignment

SESSION 1

- Journal
- Practice 1
- Stretch (advanced learners)

SESSION 2

- Practice 2

SESSION 3

- Mixed Practice (page 153) 4 and 5

TOPIC 2

JOURNAL

1. rotation function
2. center

NOTES

STRETCH

Sample answer.
First reflect Trapezoid *ABCD* across a horizontal line that passes through $\overline{DC}$.

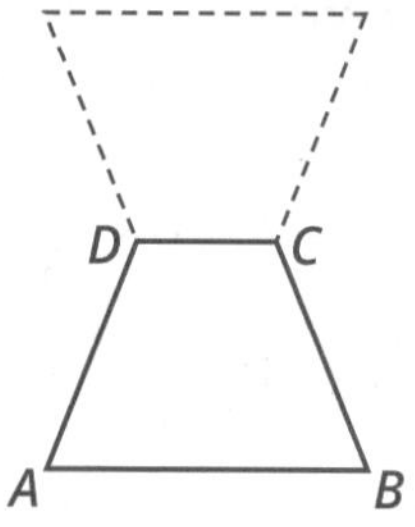

Next, rotate the reflected trapezoid 72° counterclockwise about point *D*.

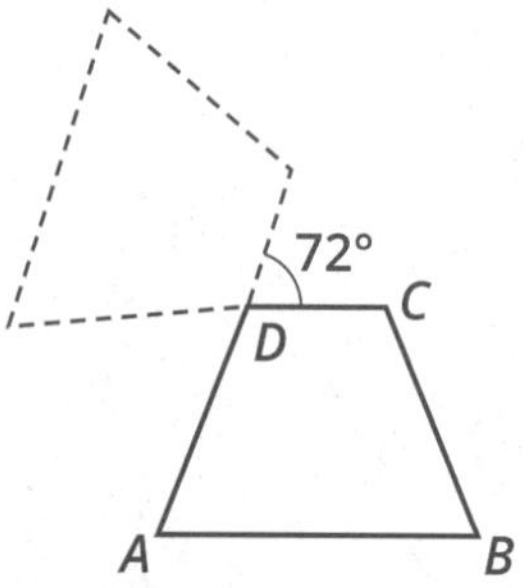

Lastly, translate the reflected and rotated trapezoid down along a line that passes through $\overline{AD}$.

2 Use what you know to determine the center of rotation and rotation angle for the transformation of each figure. Write each rotation as a function.

ⓐ

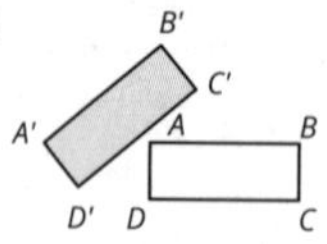

Sample answer.

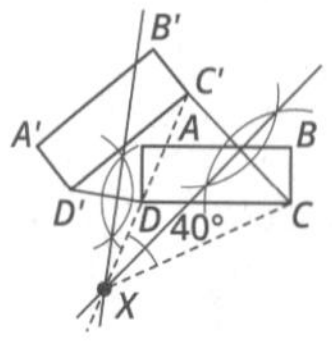

$R_{X,\ 40}(ABCD)$

ⓑ

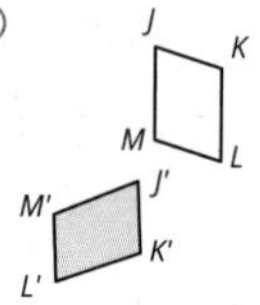

Sample answer.

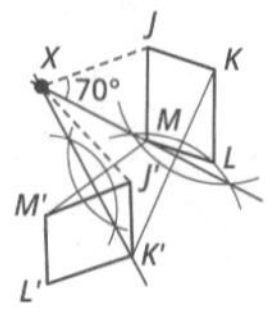

$R_{X,\ -70}(JKLM)$

STRETCH Optional

> Determine and draw the sequence of transformations that you could use to transform Trapezoid *ABCD* into Trapezoid *A′B′C′D′*. Include the lines and points that the figure is reflected on, translated on, or rotated about. Also include the rotation angle.

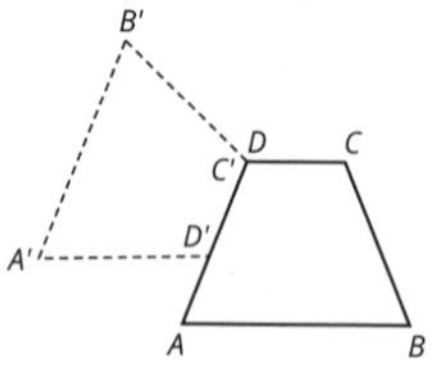

Turn Yourself Around

This resource details additional facilitation notes to fully assist you as you plan each lesson to support all students, students who struggle, and advanced learners. It provides differentiation strategies, common student misconceptions, and suggestions to extend certain activities.

ACTIVITY 1

Session 1 of 2

Rotation Functions

Students use a protractor and ruler to rotate a figure given a center of rotation and angle of rotation. They create these rotations on the plane.

CHUNK	AUDIENCE	ADDITIONAL SUPPORTS
As students analyze the worked example	All students	**DIFFERENTIATION STRATEGY** Have students re-enact the steps with patty paper alongside the directions.

ACTIVITY 2

Session 2 of 2

Determining the Center of Rotation

Students identify the center of rotation and angle of rotation given a pre-image and image. They write each rotation as a function.

CHUNK	AUDIENCE	ADDITIONAL SUPPORTS
As students work on 1	Students who Struggle	**DIFFERENTIATION STRATEGY** Suggest they use the diagram in the worked example in Activity 1 to demonstrate Tori's thinking.

ACTIVITY 3

Session 2 of 2

Sequences of Isometries

Students describe a sequence of isometries to show that two figures are congruent. They sketch their intermediate steps to validate their thinking.

CHUNK	AUDIENCE	ADDITIONAL SUPPORTS
As students work on 1	Students who Struggle	**DIFFERENTIATION STRATEGY** Suggest students use colored pencils to outline corresponding sides. This may help them to recognize the types of isometries required to move the pre-image to the image.
To extend 1 part (b)	Advanced Learners	**DIFFERENTIATION STRATEGY** Have students investigate whether a single rotation or a sequence of isometries that include a rotation would move the pre-image trapezoid onto the image trapezoid.

TALK THE TALK

Session 2 of 2

That's What It's All About!

Students summarize what they have learned about translations, reflections, and rotations on graphic organizers. They describe each transformation, use function notation, and provide an example.

CHUNK	AUDIENCE	ADDITIONAL SUPPORTS
As an alternative grouping strategy for the activity	All Students	**DIFFERENTIATION STRATEGY** Assign each group of students one of the three graphic organizers to complete. Have each group present their information and demonstrate their transformation to the class while the rest of the class completes the graphic organizer based on the group's presentation.

Practice the learning

MATHbook + Skills Practice

The table shows the targeted practice of the skills and mathematical concepts for the *Rigid Motions on the Plane* Topic. The highlighted **Problem Set** aligns with **Turn Yourself Around**.

PROBLEM SET	
1	Geometric Components of Rigid Motions
2	Translation Functions
3	Reflection Functions
4	**Rotation Functions**
5	Reflectional and Rotational Symmetries

ANYTIME AFTER ACTIVITY 3

Facilitate students as they work individually on **Problem Set 4**.

NOTES

ENGAGE at the **Module** level + **DEVELOP** at the **Topic** level + **TEACH** Read the facilitation notes and plan learning experiences.

Where are we?

TOPIC 2 Rigid Motions on a Plane	LESSON 1 Put Your Input In, Take Your Output Out	LESSON 2 Bow Thai	LESSON 3 Staring Back at Me	LESSON 4 Turn Yourself Around	LESSON 5 OKEECHOBEE
Pacing	3 Sessions	2 Sessions	2 Sessions	2 Sessions	1 Session

OVERVIEW: LESSON 5

OKEECHOBEE

Reflectional and Rotational Symmetry

ENGAGE

- Students investigate the properties of shapes by folding and rotating them.

DEVELOP

- Students identify figures that have reflectional and rotational symmetry.
- They identify lines of symmetry in figures.
- They identify reflectional and rotational symmetry in alphabet letters.

DEMONSTRATE

- Students relate the angle of rotation and the interior angle measures of regular polygons.

HIGH SCHOOL GEOMETRY

Congruence

Experiment with transformations in the plane.

3. Given a rectangle, parallelogram, trapezoid, or regular polygon, describe the rotations and reflections that carry it onto itself.

LESSON STRUCTURE AND PACING GUIDE 1 SESSION

This activity highlights a key term or concept that is essential to the learning goals of the lesson.

Session 1

INSTRUCTIONAL SEQUENCE

ENGAGE	DEVELOP	DEVELOP
Establish a situation	Classification Peer analysis	Classification

GETTING STARTED
WOW MOM

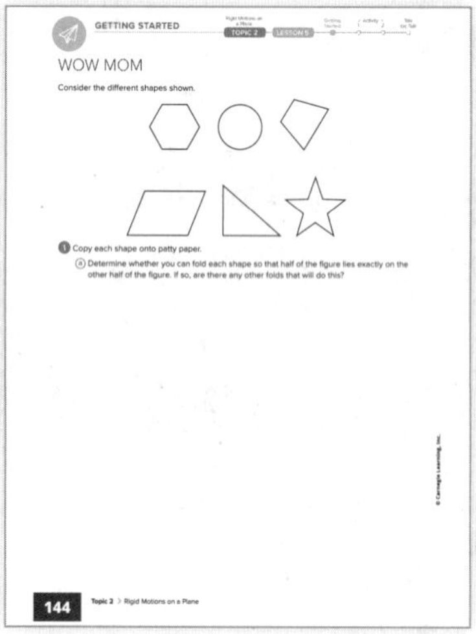
GETTING STARTED

WOW MOM

Consider the different shapes shown.

1 Copy each shape onto patty paper.

(a) Determine whether you can fold each shape so that half of the figure lies exactly on the other half of the figure. If so, are there any other folds that will do this?

© Carnegie Learning, Inc.

144 Topic 2 > Rigid Motions on a Plane

Students fold shapes so that one half lies on the other half.

- They rotate shapes so that the resulting figure is the same as the original figure's position.

ACTIVITY 1
Reflectional and Rotational Symmetries

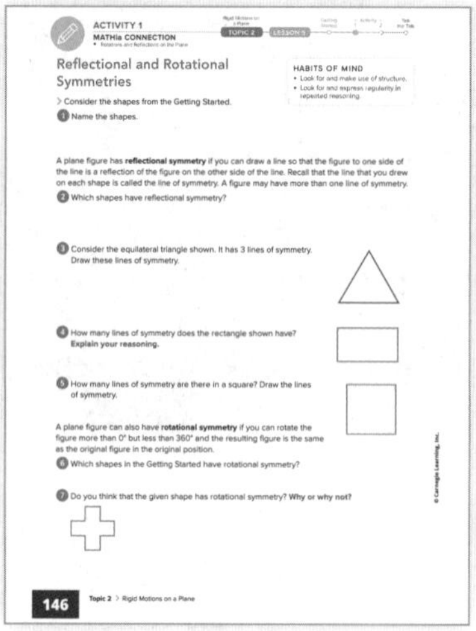
ACTIVITY 1

MATHia CONNECTION

Reflectional and Rotational Symmetries

HABITS OF MIND
- Look for and make use of structure.
- Look for and express regularity in repeated reasoning.

> Consider the shapes from the Getting Started.

1 Name the shapes.

A plane figure has **reflectional symmetry** if you can draw a line so that the figure to one side of the line is a reflection of the figure on the other side of the line. Recall that the line that you drew on each shape is called the line of symmetry. A figure may have more than one line of symmetry.

2 Which shapes have reflectional symmetry?

3 Consider the equilateral triangle shown. It has 3 lines of symmetry. Draw these lines of symmetry.

4 How many lines of symmetry does the rectangle shown have? **Explain your reasoning.**

5 How many lines of symmetry are there in a square? Draw the lines of symmetry.

A plane figure can also have **rotational symmetry** if you can rotate the figure more than 0° but less than 360° and the resulting figure is the same as the original figure in the original position.

6 Which shapes in the Getting Started have rotational symmetry?

7 Do you think that the given shape has rotational symmetry? **Why or why not?**

© Carnegie Learning, Inc.

146 Topic 2 > Rigid Motions on a Plane

Students learn about reflectional and rotational symmetry.

- They identify the lines of symmetry in figures.
- They identify figures that have rotational symmetry.

ACTIVITY 2
Identifying Symmetry

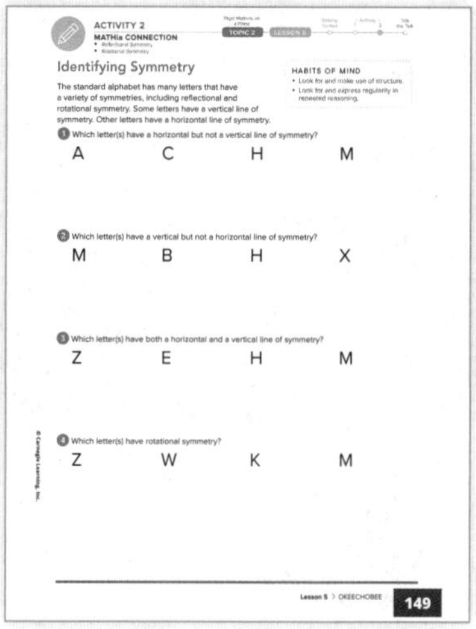
ACTIVITY 2

MATHia CONNECTION

Identifying Symmetry

HABITS OF MIND
- Look for and make use of structure.
- Look for and express regularity in repeated reasoning.

The standard alphabet has many letters that have a variety of symmetries, including reflectional and rotational symmetry. Some letters have a vertical line of symmetry. Other letters have a horizontal line of symmetry.

1 Which letter(s) have a horizontal but not a vertical line of symmetry?

A C H M

2 Which letter(s) have a vertical but not a horizontal line of symmetry?

M B H X

3 Which letter(s) have both a horizontal and a vertical line of symmetry?

Z E H M

4 Which letter(s) have rotational symmetry?

Z W K M

© Carnegie Learning, Inc.

Lesson 5 > OKEECHOBEE 149

Students identify letters of the alphabet that have horizontal and vertical lines of symmetry.

- They identify letters that have rotational symmetry.

Log in to MyCL for **lesson support** including:

Slides

Videos

www.carnegielearning.com/login

INSTRUCTIONAL SEQUENCE

DEMONSTRATE
Exit ticket application

TALK THE TALK
CHECK

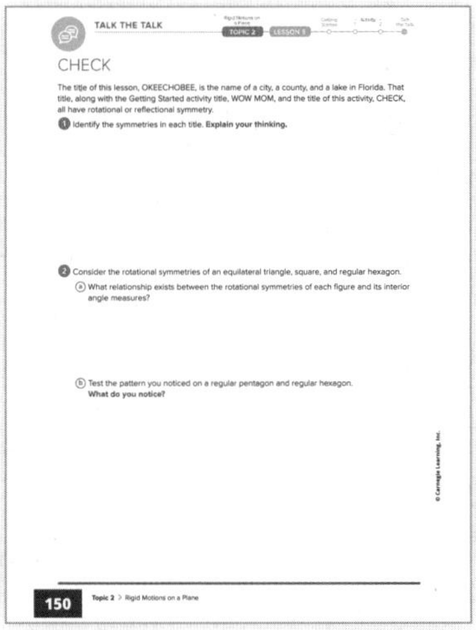
TALK THE TALK

TOPIC 2 LESSON 5

CHECK

The title of this lesson, OKEECHOBEE, is the name of a city, a county, and a lake in Florida. That title, along with the Getting Started activity title, WOW MOM, and the title of this activity, CHECK, all have rotational or reflectional symmetry.

1. Identify the symmetries in each title. **Explain your thinking.**

2. Consider the rotational symmetries of an equilateral triangle, square, and regular hexagon.
   a. What relationship exists between the rotational symmetries of each figure and its interior angle measures?
   b. Test the pattern you noticed on a regular pentagon and regular hexagon. **What do you notice?**

© Carnegie Learning, Inc.

150 Topic 2 > Rigid Motions on a Plane

Students consider the rotational symmetry of an equilateral triangle, square, and regular hexagon.

- They relate the angle of rotation and the interior angle measures of these figures.

NOTES

TOPIC 2

Now that you have read the Module, Topic, and Lesson Overviews, you are ready to plan.

Log in to MyCL for:

- Editable templates
- Additional planning support

Do the math

> Tear out the lesson planning template (page 143E) and jot down thoughts as you work through this lesson and read the Facilitation Notes.

Connect the learning

MATHbook + MATHia

The table shows a portion of the self-paced MATHia sequence for the *Rigid Motions on a Plane* Topic.

Median student completion time for the entire topic: ~90–120 minutes

> As you implement this lesson, consider different connections for students who are on pace and those that have not yet completed the workspaces aligned to this lesson.

STUDENTS WHO ARE NOT HERE YET
Students will practice drawing the reflectional or rotational symmetries of figures.

TYPE	WORKSPACE NAME
	Describing a Reflection
	Describing a Rotation
	Specifying a Sequence of Rigid Motion Transformations
	Reflectional Symmetry
	Rotational Symmetry

STUDENTS WHO ARE ON PACE
After you complete Activity 2, ask these students to share how they determined where to draw the line of reflection or center of rotation.

OKEECHOBEE

Reflectional and Rotational Symmetry

Session 1

GETTING STARTED WOW MOM ✪

Pacing (minutes)	
My Time	Class Time

ACTIVITY 1 Reflectional and Rotational Symmetries ✪

Pacing (minutes)	
My Time	Class Time

KEY TERM

reflectional symmetry

rotational symmetry

ACTIVITY 2 Identifying Symmetry

Pacing (minutes)	
My Time	Class Time

TALK THE TALK CHECK ✪

Pacing (minutes)	
My Time	Class Time

✪ This activity highlights a key term or concept that is essential to the learning goals of the lesson.

Log in to MyCL for:
- Editable templates
- Additional planning support

Reflect on your lesson

> Consider the effectiveness of your lesson on student learning.

What went well?

What did not go as planned?

> Anticipate how you would change the lesson next time you teach it.

How will you capitalize on the things that went well?

How will you improve things that did not go as planned?

MATERIALS

- Patty paper
- Protractors

TOPIC 1 Using a Rectangular Coordinate System | **TOPIC 2 Rigid Motions on a Plane** | TOPIC 3 Congruence Through Transformations

1 | Put Your Input In, Take Your Output Out
2 | Bow Thai
3 | Staring Back at Me
4 | Turn Yourself Around
5 | OKEECHOBEE

LESSON 5

OKEECHOBEE

Reflectional and Rotational Symmetry

KEY TERMS

- reflectional symmetry
- rotational symmetry

Learning Goals

- Identify geometric figures with line symmetry and rotational symmetry.
- Identify lines of symmetry for different geometric figures.
- Describe rotations that carry a figure onto itself.
- Describe reflections that carry a figure onto itself.

REVIEW (1–2 minutes)

> Identify the opposite of each number on the number line.

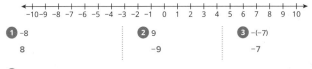

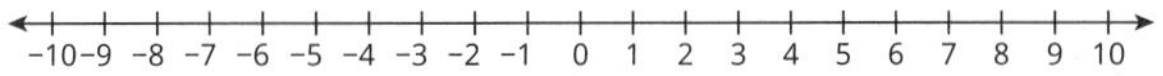

1. −8
   8
2. 9
   −9
3. −(−7)
   −7
4. How do you know that two numbers are opposites when plotted on a number line?
   The distance from 0 to each point is the same.

You have learned that pre-images are congruent to images after rigid motion transformations.

How can you use transformations to show that you can carry a figure onto itself?

Setting the Stage

- **Assign Review (optional, 1 – 2 minutes)**
- **Communicate the learning goals and key terms to look out for**
- **Tap into your students' prior learning by reading the narrative statement**
- **Provide a sense of direction by reading the question**

TOPIC 2

IN THIS REVIEW
Students identify reflections on a number line. They will use this skill throughout the lesson.

A plane figure has reflectional symmetry if you can draw a line so that the figure to one side of the line reflects the figure on the other side. A plane figure has rotational symmetry if you can rotate the figure more than 0° and less than 360° and the resulting figure is the same as the original figure.

There is a sequence of reflections or rotations that can carry any plane figure onto itself.

Essential Ideas

- A plane figure has reflectional symmetry if you can draw a line so that the figure to one side of the line reflects the figure on the other side.
- A plane figure has rotational symmetry if you can rotate the figure more than 0° and less than 360° and the resulting figure is the same as the original figure.
- A figure may have horizontal symmetry, vertical symmetry, and rotational symmetry.
- A regular polygon of n-sides has n lines of symmetry.
- A regular polygon with n sides has a rotation angle of $\frac{360°}{n}$. This angle measure is the supplement of its interior angle measure.

SUMMARY **You can explore the characteristics of shapes by folding and rotating them.**

Chunking the Activity

- **Read and discuss the introduction**
- **Group students to complete 1 part (a)**
- **Check-in and share**
- **Group students to complete 1 part (b)**
- **Share and summarize**

COMMON MISCONCEPTION

See Page 152A for a misconception related to 1 part (a).

DIFFERENTIATION STRATEGY

See Page 152A to challenge advanced learners to extend 1 part (a).

WOW MOM

Consider the different shapes shown.

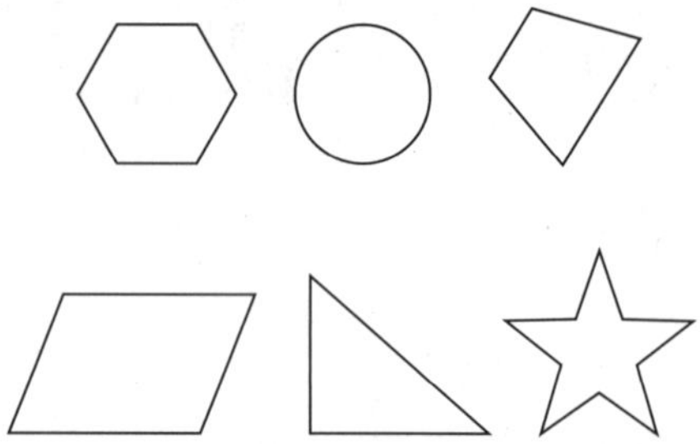

1 Copy each shape onto patty paper.

(a) Determine whether you can fold each shape so that half of the figure lies exactly on the other half of the figure. If so, are there any other folds that will do this?

You can fold the regular hexagon, circle, isosceles trapezoid, and star so that one half of the figure lies exactly on the other half of the figure. This is not possible for the parallelogram and scalene right triangle.

There are six possible folds for the regular hexagon.

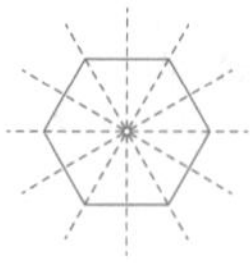

There are an infinite number of folds for the circle.

There is only one possible fold for the isosceles trapezoid.

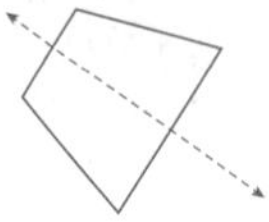

There are five possible folds for the star.

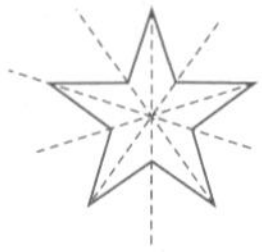

Questions to Support Discourse

		TYPE
1	• Explain the six different folds for the hexagon.	Probing
	• Which characteristics of the figure determine whether there are possible folds so that half of the figure lies exactly on the other half of the figure? • How is the number of folds related to the sides and angles? • Do you think there are any parallelograms where there would be folds that place half of the figure exactly on the other half of the figure? Which ones?	Seeing structure

GETTING STARTED Continued

ⓑ Determine whether you can rotate each figure so that it looks exactly like it did before the rotation. If so, are there other rotations that will do this?

You can rotate each figure 360° so that it looks exactly like it did before the rotation.

There are other rotations between 0° and 360° that will do this for the hexagon, circle, parallelogram, and star.

There are a total of 6 possible rotations for the hexagon.

There are an infinite number of rotations for the circle.

There are a total of two possible rotations for the parallelogram.

There are a total of 5 possible rotations for the star.

Lesson 5 > OKEECHOBEE 145

NOTES

TOPIC 2

Questions to Support Discourse

		TYPE
1	• How can you tell whether other rotations between 0° and 360° have this same effect?	Probing

SUMMARY **Reflectional symmetry and rotational symmetry are properties of figures that can be carried onto themselves by reflections and rotations.**

Chunking the Activity

- **Read and discuss the introduction**
- **Group students to complete 1 – 5**
- **Check-in and share**
- **Read and discuss the definitions**
- **Group students to complete 6 – 8**
- **Check-in and share**
- **Group students to complete 9**
- **Share and summarize**

Reflectional and Rotational Symmetries

HABITS OF MIND
- Look for and make use of structure.
- Look for and express regularity in repeated reasoning.

> Consider the shapes from the Getting Started.

1 Name the shapes.

Regular hexagon, Circle, Isosceles trapezoid, Parallelogram, Scalene right triangle, Star

A plane figure has **reflectional symmetry** if you can draw a line so that the figure to one side of the line is a reflection of the figure on the other side of the line. Recall that the line that you drew on each shape is called the line of symmetry. A figure may have more than one line of symmetry.

2 Which shapes have reflectional symmetry?

You can fold the regular hexagon, circle, isosceles trapezoid, and star so that one half of the figure lies exactly on the other half of the figure.

3 Consider the equilateral triangle shown. It has 3 lines of symmetry. Draw these lines of symmetry.

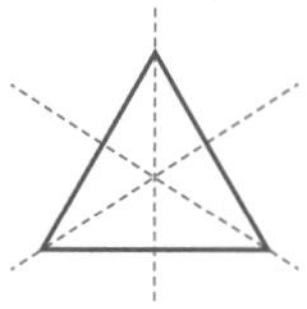

4 How many lines of symmetry does the rectangle shown have? **Explain your reasoning.**

The rectangle has 2 lines of symmetry.

5 How many lines of symmetry are there in a square? Draw the lines of symmetry.

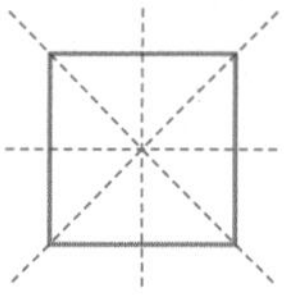

A square has 4 lines of symmetry.

A plane figure can also have **rotational symmetry** if you can rotate the figure more than 0° but less than 360° and the resulting figure is the same as the original figure in the original position.

6 Which shapes in the Getting Started have rotational symmetry?

The regular hexagon, circle, parallelogram, and star have rotational symmetry.

7 Do you think that the given shape has rotational symmetry? **Why or why not?**

Yes. The shape has rotational symmetry. You can rotate it 90°, 180°, and 270° to match itself exactly.

DIFFERENTIATION STRATEGY

See Page 152A to challenge advanced learners to extend 6.

LANGUAGE LINK

Compare the terms *line of symmetry* and *line of reflection*. A figure is symmetric about a line if the reflection of every point through that line is another point on the figure.

Questions to Support Discourse

		TYPE
2	• How is this question related to the Getting Started activity?	Probing
4	• Do lines of symmetry always pass through the vertices of the figure?	Probing
5	• Why do squares have more lines of reflection than rectangles that are not squares? • What pattern do you notice among your responses to Question 3, this question, and the regular hexagon from the Getting Started?	Seeing structure
6	• How is rotational symmetry related to the sides and angles of a figure?	Seeing structure

ACTIVITY 1 Continued

8 Can a shape have both reflectional and rotational symmetry? **Explain your reasoning.**

Yes. A shape can haveboth reflectional androtational symmetry.We have shown that regular hexagons, circles, and the star have both reflectional and rotational symmetry in this activity.

You have also identified transformations that carry a figure onto itself. Reflectional and rotational symmetry are properties of figures that can be carried onto themselves by reflections and rotations.

9 Consider the 4 shapes shown.

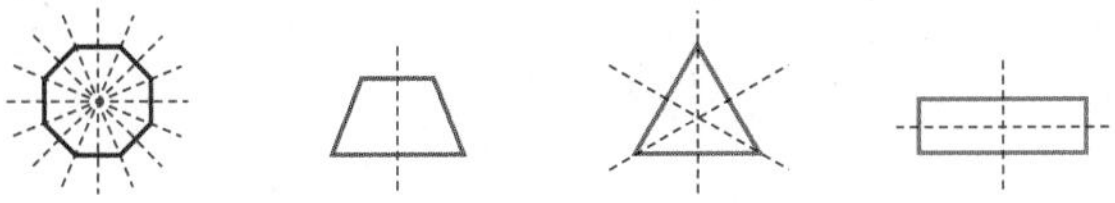

(a) Describe the reflections and rotations that can carry each figure onto itself.

The regular octagon has 8 lines of reflection. It also has 7 angles of rotation: 45°, 90°, 135°, 180°, 225°, 270°, and 360°.

The isosceles trapezoid has 1 line of reflection: the perpendicular bisector of the parallel sides. It does not have any rotational symmetry.

The equilateral triangle has 3 lines of reflection. It also has 2 angles of rotation: 120° and 240°.

The rectangle has 2 lines of symmetry. It also has 1 angle of rotation: 180°.

THINK ABOUT...
For reflections, identify the line of reflection. For rotations, describe the rotation angle and center of rotation.

Questions to Support Discourse

		TYPE
9	• What are the interior angle measures of this figure?	Gathering
	• How did you determine the rotation angles? • Once you know the smallest rotation angle, how do you get the other ones?	Probing
	• What relationship do you notice between the interior angle measures and the rotations that carry the figure onto itself? • What pattern do you notice regarding the number of lines of reflection and the number of rotation angles? Why do you think that happens?	Seeing structure

NOTES

LANGUAGE LINK

Remind students to refer to the Academic Glossary (page FM–20) to review the definition of **explain your reasoning** and related phrases. Suggest they ask themselves these questions:

- How can I justify my answer to others?
- Is my explanation logical?

Lesson 5 > OKEECHOBEE 147

NOTES

Student Look-Fors

Whether students make a reasoned judgment after comparing and contrasting the strategies.

(b) Clark says that the horizontal line of symmetry in the rectangle means that a reflection across that line carries the figure onto itself. He also says that it means that a 180° rotation will carry the figure onto itself. Is Clark correct? Does his reasoning apply to other figures? **Explain your thinking using the shapes from the Getting Started.**

Clark is correct about the rectangle. However, his reasoning does not apply to every shape. For example, the isosceles trapezoid has one line of symmetry which carries the figure onto itself. It does not indicate anything about the figure's rotational symmetry, because an isosceles trapezoid has no rotational symmetry. Clark seems to be confusing the fact that a line is an angle with a measure of 180° with an angle of rotation of 180°.

ACTIVITY 2

SUMMARY **A figure may have horizontal reflectional symmetry, vertical reflectional symmetry, and rotational symmetry.**

ACTIVITY 2

MATHia CONNECTION
- Reflectional Symmetry
- Rotational Symmetry

Identifying Symmetry

HABITS OF MIND
- Look for and make use of structure.
- Look for and express regularity in repeated reasoning.

The standard alphabet has many letters that have a variety of symmetries, including reflectional and rotational symmetry. Some letters have a vertical line of symmetry. Other letters have a horizontal line of symmetry.

1. Which letter(s) have a horizontal but not a vertical line of symmetry?

A C H M

C

2. Which letter(s) have a vertical but not a horizontal line of symmetry?

M B H X

M

3. Which letter(s) have both a horizontal and a vertical line of symmetry?

Z E H M

H

4. Which letter(s) have rotational symmetry?

Z W K M

Z

Chunking the Activity

- **Read and discuss the introduction**
- **Group students to complete the activity**
- **Share and summarize**

Student Look-Fors

Whether students are demonstrating proficiencies related to these habits of mind.

- Look for and make use of structure
- Look for and express regularity in repeated reasoning

DIFFERENTIATION STRATEGY

See Page 152B to challenge advanced learners to extend the activity.

Questions to Support Discourse

		TYPE
1 - 3	• How do you test for a horizontal line of symmetry? A vertical line of symmetry?	Probing
	• What's the difference between testing to see whether a letter has a vertical line of symmetry and reflecting a letter across a vertical line of reflection?	Seeing structure
4	• How do you test for rotational symmetry?	Probing

TALK THE TALK

SUMMARY **A regular polygon with n sides has a rotation angle of $\frac{360°}{n}$. This angle measure is the supplement of its interior angle measure.**

Chunking the Activity

- **Read and discuss the introduction**
- **Group students to complete the activity**
- **Share and summarize**

DIFFERENTIATION STRATEGY

See Page 152C to challenge advanced learners to extend the activity.

NOTE: Encourage responsible decision-making by providing an opportunity for students to reflect on their personal behavior and social interactions as they worked with their group to complete tasks.

CHECK

The title of this lesson, OKEECHOBEE, is the name of a city, a county, and a lake in Florida. That title, along with the Getting Started activity title, WOW MOM, and the title of this activity, CHECK, all have rotational or reflectional symmetry.

1. Identify the symmetries in each title. **Explain your thinking.**

   The title OKEECHOBEE has a horizontal line of symmetry through the middle of the word since each letter has a horizontal line of symmetry through its center.

   The title WOW MOM has rotational symmetry. You can rotate it 180° to match itself exactly.

   The title CHECK has a horizontal line of symmetry through the middle of the word.

2. Consider the rotational symmetries of an equilateral triangle, square, and regular hexagon.

   (a) What relationship exists between the rotational symmetries of each figure and its interior angle measures?

   The measure of the angle of rotation of a regular polygon with n sides is $\frac{360°}{n}$, which is the supplement of the measure of each of its interior angles.

   (b) Test the pattern you noticed on a regular pentagon and regular hexagon. **What do you notice?**

   The pattern is the same.
   The measure of each interior angle of a regular pentagon is 108° and the measureof the angle of rotation is 72°.
   The measure of each interior angle of a regular hexagon is 120° and the measure of the angle of rotation is 60°. In each case, the sum of the measure of an interior angle and the angle of rotation is 180°.

Questions to Support Discourse

		TYPE
1	• Which letters in your name have reflectional or rotational symmetry?	Probing
2	• What are the rotational symmetries for an equilateral triangle? • What are the measures of the interior angles of an equilateral triangle? • Show that the relationship you noticed exists for all three regular polygons.	Probing
	• Why does this relationship make sense?	Seeing structure

ASSIGNMENT

LESSON 5 ASSIGNMENT

> Use a separate piece of paper for your Journal entry.

JOURNAL

Explain the difference between reflectional symmetry and rotational symmetry in your own words.

REMEMBER

A plane figure has reflectional symmetry when you can draw a line so that the figure to one side of the line reflects the figure on the other side. A plane figure has rotational symmetry when you can rotate the figure more than 0° and less than 360°, and the resulting figure is the same as the original figure.

There is a sequence of reflections or rotations that can carry any plane figure onto itself.

PRACTICE

1. Determine how many lines of symmetry each figure has. Then draw all lines of symmetry for each figure.

(a) Regular hexagon

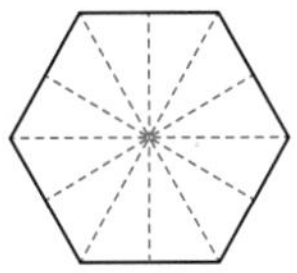

A regular hexagon has six lines of symmetry.

(b) Isosceles right triangle

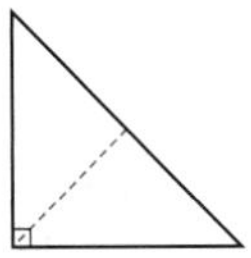

An isosceles right triangle has one line of symmetry.

(c) Rhombus

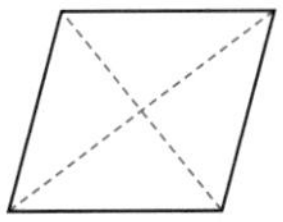

A rhombus has two lines of symmetry.

(d) Regular pentagon

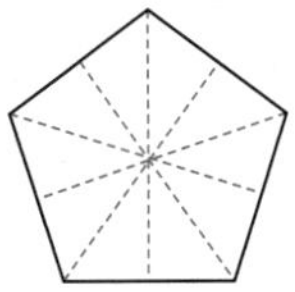

A regular pentagon has five lines of symmetry.

Go to LiveHint.com for help on the PRACTICE questions.

Encourage students to use LiveHint.com for help with the PRACTICE questions of this assignment.

Chunking the Assignment

SESSION 1

- Journal
- Practice 1 - 3
- Stretch (advanced learners)
- Mixed Practice (page 153) 6

JOURNAL

Sample answer.

Reflectional symmetry means that there is a line that you can draw through a figure such that the figure looks exactly the same on one side of the line as it does on the other side of the line. Rotational symmetry involves turning the entire figure around a point between 0° and 360° and getting the original figure in the same position.

2 Identify a sequence of transformations that will carry each given pre-image onto the image shown with dashed lines.

ⓐ

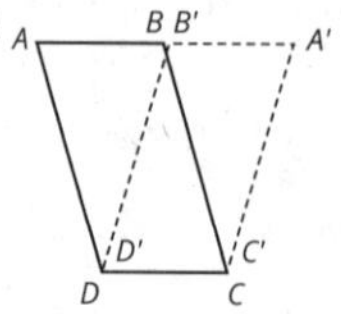

Sample answer.

You can reflect Parallelogram *ABCD* can be reflected across the vertical line that passes through Point *C* and then translated to the left.

ⓑ

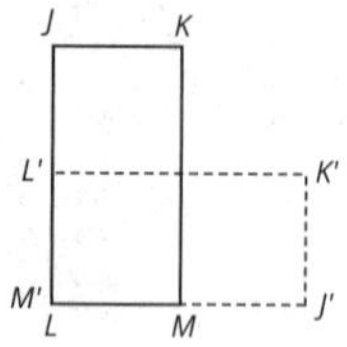

Sample answer.

You can reflect Rectangle *JKLM* can be reflected across the horizontal line that passes through Point *M* and then rotated counter clockwise 90° about point *L*.

3 Describe the sequence of rotations and reflections that can carry each figure onto itself. Use the figure's reflectional and rotational symmetry, if any, to justify your answer.

ⓐ

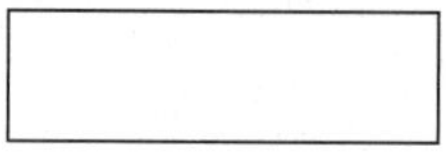

A rotation of 180° carries the rectangle onto itself. A reflection across a line connecting the midpoints of either pair of parallel sides carries the rectangle onto itself.

ⓑ

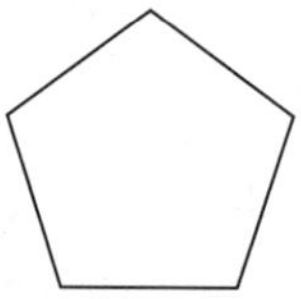

A rotation of 72° carries the pentagon onto itself. A reflection across any line from a vertex to the midpoint of the opposite side carries the pentagon onto itself.

STRETCH Optional

> Graph the figure with vertices at *A* (2, 6), *B* (5, 6), *C* (5, 3), *D* (−2, −1). Determine the equation(s) for all lines of symmetry for the figure. Draw the line(s) of symmetry using a dashed line.

NOTES

STRETCH

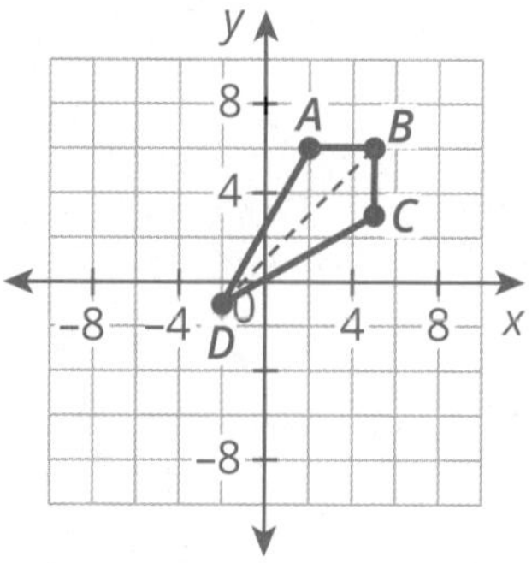

There is one line of symmetry represented by the equation $y = x + 1$.

OKEECHOBEE

This resource details additional facilitation notes to fully assist you as you plan each lesson to support all students, students who struggle, and advanced learners. It provides differentiation strategies, common student misconceptions, and suggestions to extend certain activities.

GETTING STARTED

Session 1 of 1

WOW MOM

Students fold shapes so that one half lies on the other half. They rotate shapes so that the resulting figure is the same as the original figure's position.

CHUNK	AUDIENCE	ADDITIONAL SUPPORTS
As students work on 1 part (a)	All Students	**COMMON MISCONCEPTION** Students may assume that only polygons, not circles, can have lines of reflection. Use this question to address the misconception.
To extend 1 part (a)	Advanced Learners	**DIFFERENTIATION STRATEGY** Have students investigate the relationship between the fold that maps half of the isosceles trapezoid exactly onto the other half of the isosceles trapezoid. The fold is the perpendicular bisector of both parallel sides of the trapezoid.

ACTIVITY 1

Session 1 of 1

Reflectional and Rotational Symmetries

Students learn about reflectional and rotational symmetry. They identify the lines of symmetry in figures with reflectional symmetry. Students also identify figures that have rotational symmetry.

CHUNK	AUDIENCE	ADDITIONAL SUPPORTS
To extend 6	Advanced Learners	**DIFFERENTIATION STRATEGY** Have students explore the relationship between the number of sides of a regular polygon and the measures of the angles of rotation. Students should conclude that a regular polygon of *n*-sides will have an angle of rotation of $\frac{360°}{n}$ and its multiples. Students will explore this relationship and connect it to the measure of the interior angles of a regular polygon in the Talk the Talk at the end of this lesson.

TOPIC 2

ACTIVITY 2

Session 1 of 1

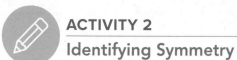

Identifying Symmetry

Students identify letters of the alphabet that have horizontal and vertical lines of symmetry. They also identify letters that have rotational symmetry.

CHUNK	AUDIENCE	ADDITIONAL SUPPORTS
To extend the activity	Advanced Learners	**DIFFERENTIATION STRATEGY** Present students with the entire alphabet and ask them to complete a Venn diagram to identify the different types of symmetry. 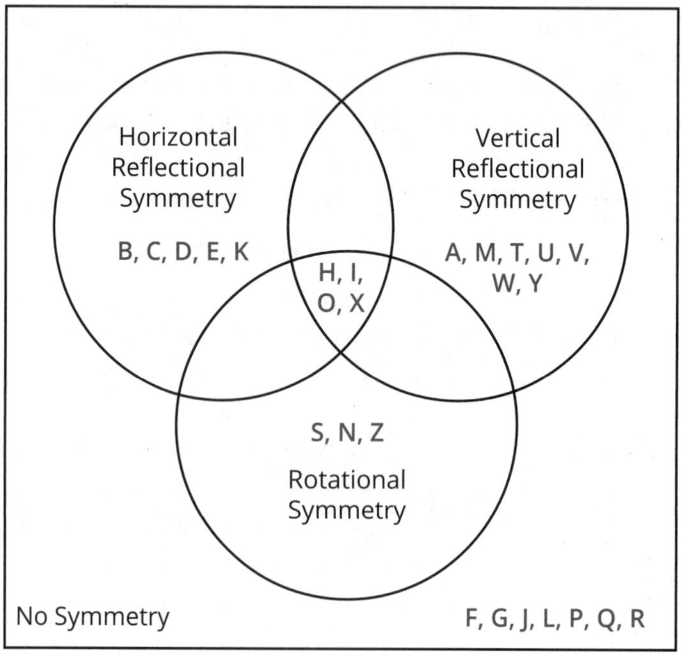

TALK THE TALK

Session 1 of 1

CHECK

Students consider the rotational symmetry of an equilateral triangle, square, and regular hexagon. They relate the angle of rotation and the interior angle measures of these figures.

CHUNK	AUDIENCE	ADDITIONAL SUPPORTS
To extend the activity	Advanced Learners	**DIFFERENTIATION STRATEGY** Have students investigate palindromes. • A palindrome is a word or sentence that reads the same forward and backward, like MOM, WOW, and RACECAR. Names like LIL, HANNAH, and BOB are also palindromes. Have students list a few palindromes and identify the symmetries of each palindrome. • A palindrome is also a number that reads the same forward and backward. Have students investigate how many three-digit and four-digit palindromes exist. Then ask students to create a formula to determine the number of palindromes that exist for any *n*-digit number. Note that 0220 is considered a four-digit palindrome.

Practice the learning

MATHbook + Skills Practice

The table shows the targeted practice of the skills and mathematical concepts for the *Rigid Motions on the Plane* Topic. The highlighted Problem Set aligns with **OKEECHOBEE**.

PROBLEM SET	
1	Geometric Components of Rigid Motions
2	Translation Functions
3	Reflection Functions
4	Rotation Functions
5	**Reflectional and Rotational Symmetries**

ANYTIME AFTER ACTIVITY 5
Facilitate students as they work individually on **Problem Set 5**.

MIXED PRACTICE

Log in to MyCL to access a downloadable version with **additional space** for students to write their answers.

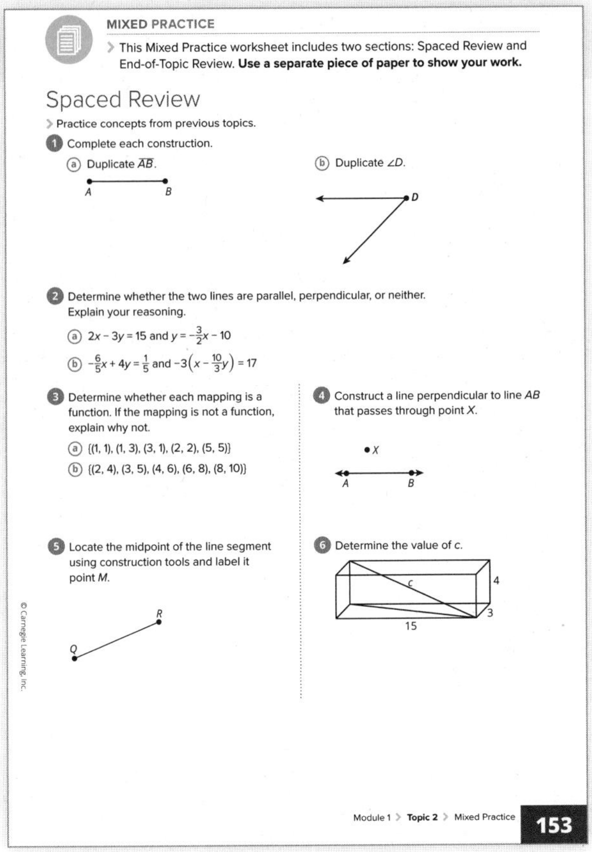

MIXED PRACTICE

> This Mixed Practice worksheet includes two sections: Spaced Review and End-of-Topic Review. **Use a separate piece of paper to show your work.**

Spaced Review

> Practice concepts from previous topics.

1. Complete each construction.
   ⓐ Duplicate $\overline{AB}$.
   ⓑ Duplicate $\angle D$.

2. Determine whether the two lines are parallel, perpendicular, or neither. Explain your reasoning.
   ⓐ $2x - 3y = 15$ and $y = -\frac{3}{2}x - 10$
   ⓑ $-\frac{6}{5}x + 4y = \frac{1}{5}$ and $-3\left(x - \frac{10}{3}y\right) = 17$

3. Determine whether each mapping is a function. If the mapping is not a function, explain why not.
   ⓐ {(1, 1), (1, 3), (3, 1), (2, 2), (5, 5)}
   ⓑ {(2, 4), (3, 5), (4, 6), (6, 8), (8, 10)}

4. Construct a line perpendicular to line *AB* that passes through point *X*.

5. Locate the midpoint of the line segment using construction tools and label it point *M*.

6. Determine the value of *c*.

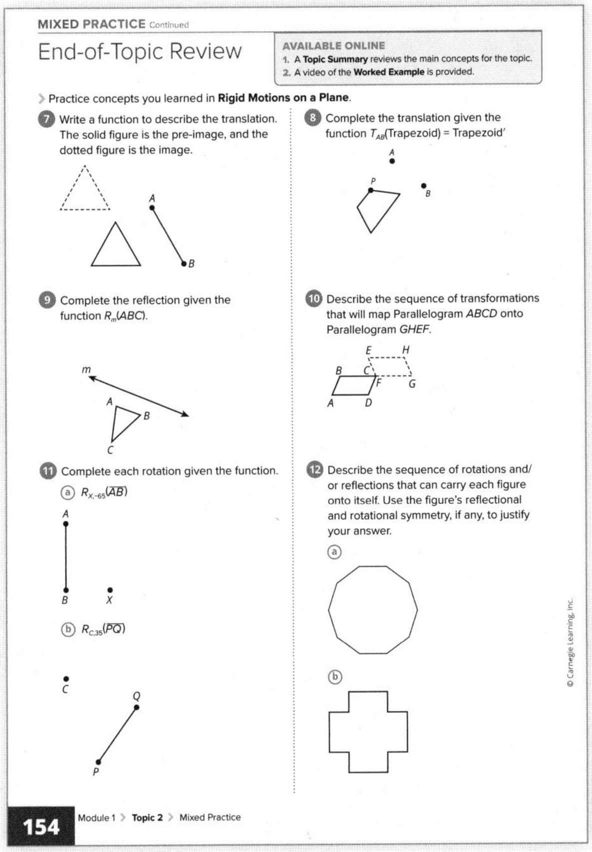

MIXED PRACTICE Continued

End-of-Topic Review

AVAILABLE ONLINE
1. A **Topic Summary** reviews the main concepts for the topic.
2. A video of the **Worked Example** is provided.

> Practice concepts you learned in **Rigid Motions on a Plane**.

7. Write a function to describe the translation. The solid figure is the pre-image, and the dotted figure is the image.

8. Complete the translation given the function T_{AB}(Trapezoid) = Trapezoid′

9. Complete the reflection given the function $R_m(ABC)$.

10. Describe the sequence of transformations that will map Parallelogram *ABCD* onto Parallelogram *GHEF*.

11. Complete each rotation given the function.
    ⓐ $R_{X,-65}(\overline{AB})$
    ⓑ $R_{C,35}(\overline{PQ})$

12. Describe the sequence of rotations and/or reflections that can carry each figure onto itself. Use the figure's reflectional and rotational symmetry, if any, to justify your answer.
    ⓐ
    ⓑ

See pages 154–154B for annotated answers.

The **Spaced Review** includes fluency and problem solving from previous topics.

Aligned Standards

1 G.CO.12	2 G.GPE.5
3 8.F.1	4 G.CO.12
5 G.CO.12	6 8.G.7

TOPIC 2

Log in to MyCL for more **End-of-Topic** review questions.

Go to **Edulastic**, and search for: G.CO.1, G.CO.2, G.CO.3, G.CO.4, G.CO.5.

The **End-of-Topic Review** includes questions to practice the key concepts of *Rigid Motions on a Plane*.

Aligned Standards

7 G.CO.2	8 G.CO.5
9 G.CO.5	10 G.CO.5
11 G.CO.5	12 G.CO.3

Answers included.

MIXED PRACTICE

> This Mixed Practice worksheet includes two sections: Spaced Review and End-of-Topic Review.

MODULE 1 Reasoning with Shapes — TOPIC 1 Using a Rectangular Coordinate System — **TOPIC 2 Rigid Motions on a Plane** — TOPIC 3 Congruence Through Transformations

Spaced Review

> Practice concepts from previous topics.

1 Complete each construction.

(a) Duplicate $\overline{AB}$.

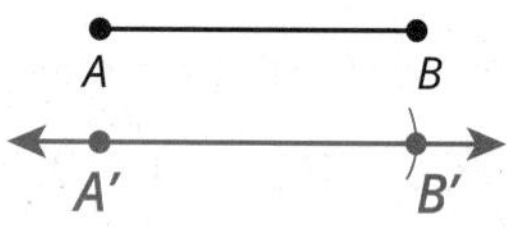

$\overline{A'B'} \cong \overline{AB}$

(b) Duplicate $\angle D$.

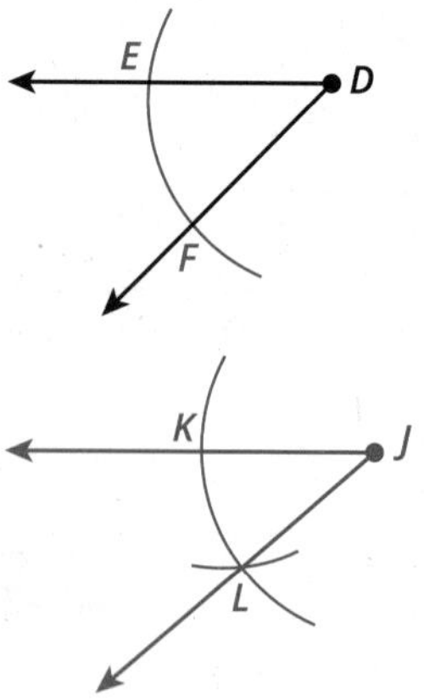

$\angle EDF \cong \angle KJL$

2 Determine whether the two lines are parallel, perpendicular, or neither. Explain your reasoning.

(a) $2x - 3y = 15$ and $y = -\frac{3}{2}x - 10$

The lines are perpendicular because their slopes are negative reciprocals. The slope of the first line is $\frac{2}{3}$ and the slope of the second line is $-\frac{3}{2}$.

(b) $-\frac{6}{5}x + 4y = \frac{1}{5}$ and $-3\left(x - \frac{10}{3}y\right) = 17$

The lines are parallel because their slopes are the same. The slope of each line is $\frac{3}{10}$.

Answers included.

MIXED PRACTICE Continued

3 Determine whether each mapping is a function. If the mapping is not a function, explain why not.

(a) {(1, 1), (1, 3), (3, 1), (2, 2), (5, 5)}

This mapping is not a function. A single x-value (1) is mapped to two different y-values (1 and 3).

(b) {(2, 4), (3, 5), (4, 6), (6, 8), (8, 10)}

This mapping is a function.

4 Construct a line perpendicular to line AB that passes through point X.

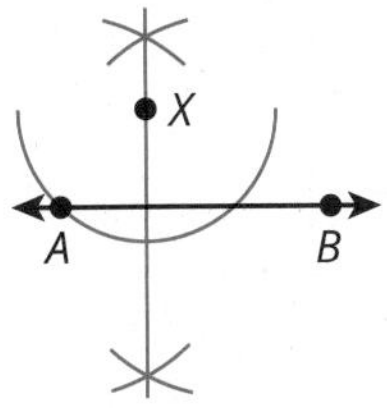

5 Locate the midpoint of the line segment using construction tools and label it point M.

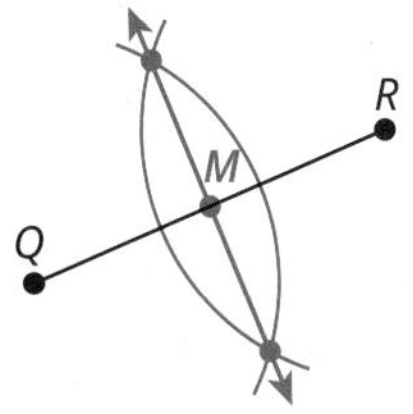

6 Determine the value of c.

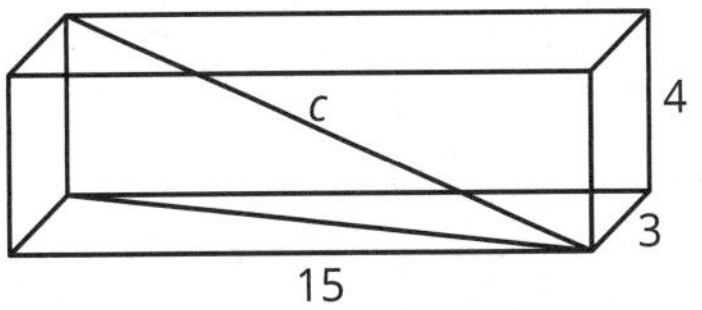

$15^2 + 3^2 = 225 + 9 = 234$

The length of the diagonal of the base is $\sqrt{234}$.

$c^2 = (\sqrt{234})^2 + 4^2$

$c^2 = 234 + 16$

$c^2 = 250$

$c \approx 15.81$

End-of-Topic Review

AVAILABLE ONLINE

1. A **Topic Summary** reviews the main concepts for the topic.
2. A video of the **Worked Example** is provided.

> Practice concepts you learned in **Rigid Motions on a Plane**.

7 Write a function to describe the translation. The solid figure is the pre-image, and the dotted figure is the image.

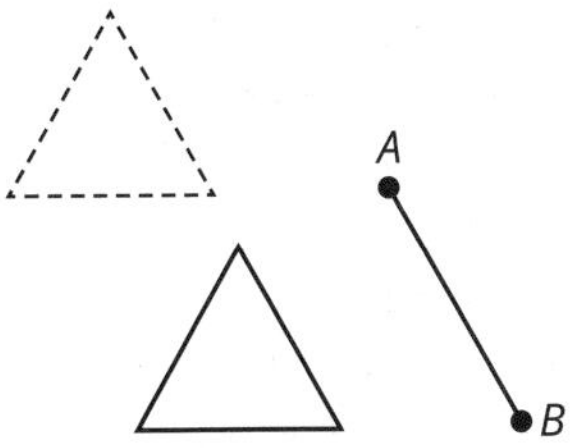

Sample answer.

T_{BA}(Triangle) = Triangle′

8 Complete the translation given the function T_{AB}(Trapezoid) = Trapezoid′

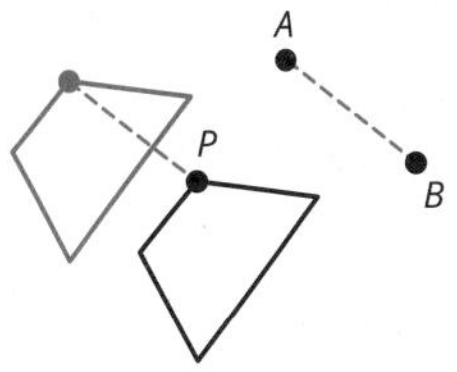

TOPIC 2

Answers included.

MIXED PRACTICE

> This Mixed Practice worksheet includes two sections: Spaced Review and End-of-Topic Review.

9 Complete the reflection given the function $R_m(ABC)$.

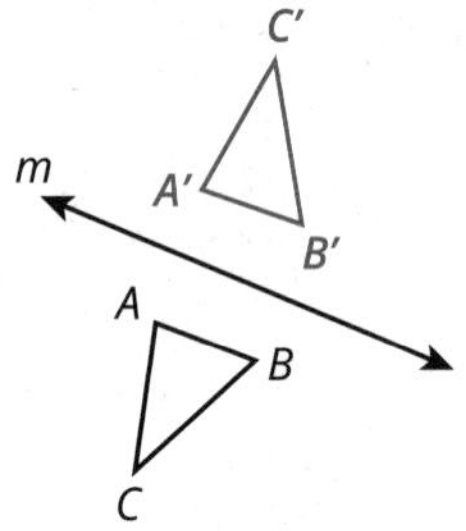

10 Describe the sequence of transformations that will map Parallelogram *ABCD* onto Parallelogram *GHEF*.

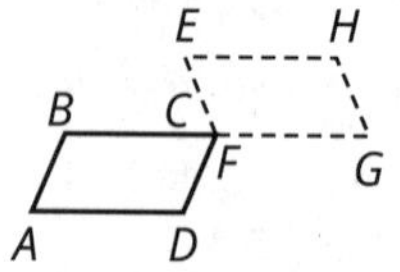

Sample answer.

Reflect Parallelogram *ABCD* across a horizontal line that contains side *BC* and then translate it right.

11 Complete each rotation given the function.

(a) $R_{X,-65}(\overline{AB})$

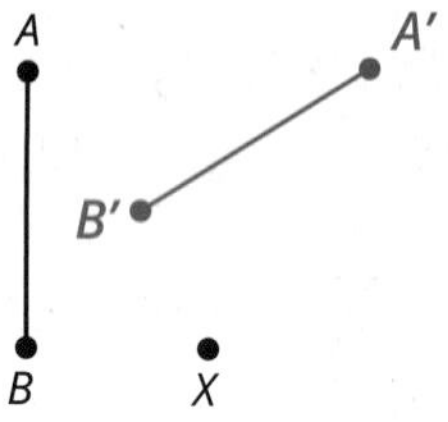

(b) $R_{C,35}(\overline{PQ})$

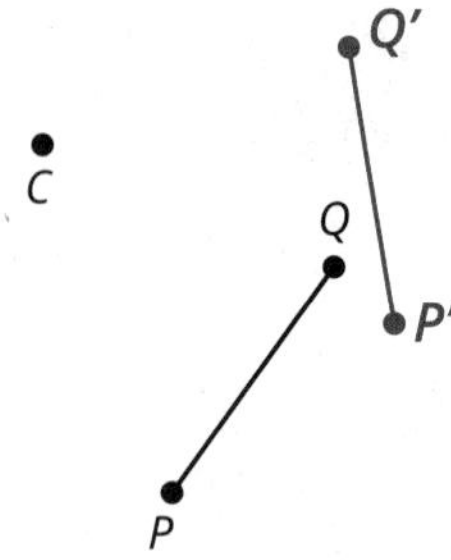

12 Describe the sequence of rotations and/or reflections that can carry each figure onto itself. Use the figure's reflectional and rotational symmetry, if any, to justify your answer.

(a)

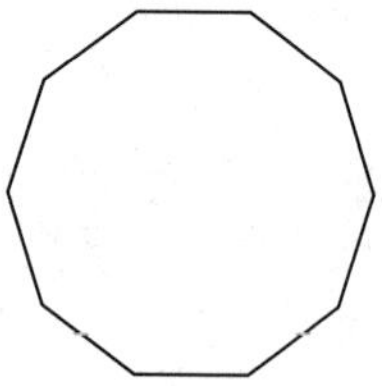

A rotation of 36° carries the figure onto itself. A reflection across a horizontal line through the center, a vertical line through the center, lines connecting the opposite vertices, and lines connecting the midpoints of opposite sides each carry the figure onto itself.

(b)

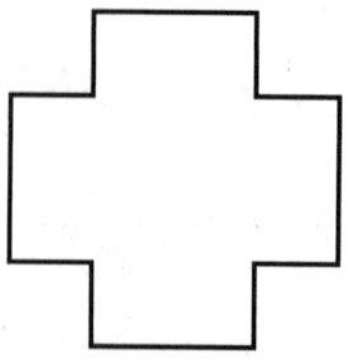

A rotation of 90° carries the figure onto itself. A reflection across a horizontal and vertical line carry the figure onto itself, and a reflection across diagonal lines through the center of the figure carries the figure onto itself.

OVERVIEW: TOPIC 3

Congruence Through Transformations

Where are we? 1 Session ≈ 45 minutes

MODULE 1 Establishing Proof	Using a Rectangular Coordinate System	TOPIC 2 Rigid Motions on a Plane	TOPIC 3 Congruence Through Transformations
Pacing	16 Sessions	11 Sessions	10 Sessions

How are the key concepts of *Congruence Through Transformations* developed?

In this topic, students use formal reasoning, rigid motions, and constructions to prove geometric theorems. They first consider conditional statements and their truth values. Students learn that a truth table summarizes all possible truth values for a conditional statement, using the notation $p \rightarrow r$. They analyze the Linear Pair Postulate, the Segment Addition Postulate, and the Angle Addition Postulate.

Given two triangles, students investigate the minimum number of measurements required to determine whether two triangles are congruent. They analyze a proof that it takes at most two reflections to map a segment onto itself, which they will use in future proofs.

See Math Representation.

Students prove the Side-Side-Side, Side-Angle-Side, and Angle-Side-Angle Congruence Theorems by construction. They write equality and congruence statements for all corresponding side and angle relationships. As a counterexample, students consider why knowing that three angles or two sides and a non-included angle aren't sufficient to know whether the triangles are congruent.

Finally, students use the triangle congruence theorems to determine whether triangles are congruent or to specify the additional information needed in given diagrams to determine whether triangles are congruent.

MATH REPRESENTATION

Consider two triangles that have two angles and an included side congruent.

In $\triangle FGH$ and $\triangle PQR$, $\overline{FG} \cong \overline{PQ}$, $\angle G \cong \angle Q$ and $\angle F \cong \angle P$. You can use rigid motions to prove that $\triangle FGH \cong \triangle PQR$.

You can map side FG onto side PQ in at most two reflections. A final reflection maps the two triangles onto each other.

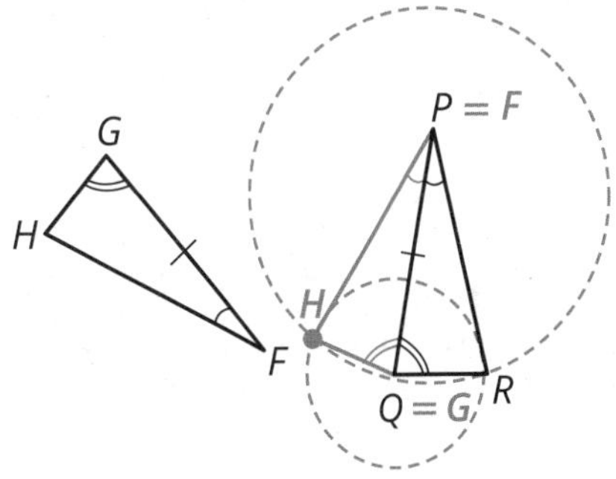

TOPIC 3

OVERVIEW: TOPIC 3

PLAN FOR 7 class sessions and ~3 MATHia sessions.

Log in to MyCL for **lesson support** including:

- Slides
- Videos

LESSON 1

The Elements

Formal Reasoning in Euclidean Geometry

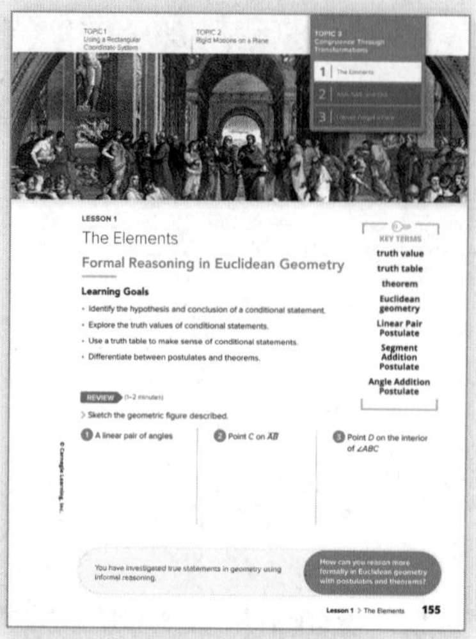
LESSON 1
The Elements
Formal Reasoning in Euclidean Geometry
Learning Goals
- Identify the hypothesis and conclusion of a conditional statement.
- Explore the truth values of conditional statements.
- Use a truth table to make sense of conditional statements.
- Differentiate between postulates and theorems.

KEY TERMS: truth value, truth table, theorem, Euclidean geometry, Linear Pair Postulate, Segment Addition Postulate, Angle Addition Postulate

REVIEW (1–2 minutes)
Sketch the geometric figure described.
1. A linear pair of angles
2. Point C on AB
3. Point D on the interior of ∠ABC

Lesson 1 > The Elements 155

LESSON 2

ASA, SAS, and SSS

Proving Triangle Congruence Theorems

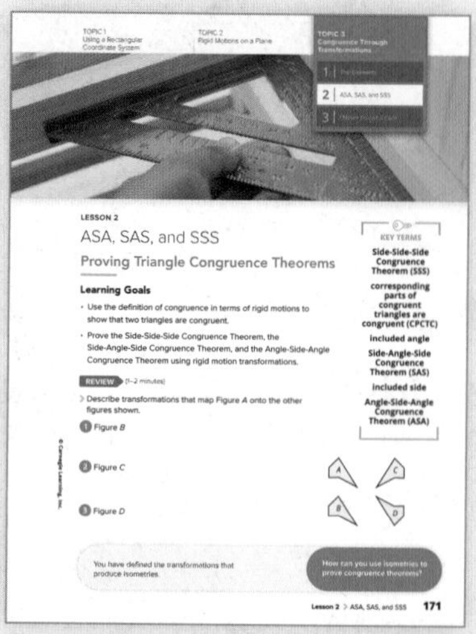
LESSON 2
ASA, SAS, and SSS
Proving Triangle Congruence Theorems
Learning Goals
- Use the definition of congruence in terms of rigid motions to show that two triangles are congruent.
- Prove the Side-Side-Side Congruence Theorem, the Side-Angle-Side Congruence Theorem, and the Angle-Side-Angle Congruence Theorem using rigid motion transformations.

KEY TERMS: Side-Side-Side Congruence Theorem (SSS), corresponding parts of congruent triangles are congruent (CPCTC), included angle, Side-Angle-Side Congruence Theorem (SAS), included side, Angle-Side-Angle Congruence Theorem (ASA)

REVIEW (1–2 minutes)
Describe transformations that map Figure A onto the other figures shown.
1. Figure B
2. Figure C
3. Figure D

Lesson 2 > ASA, SAS, and SSS 171

LEARNING TOGETHER

	Lesson 1: The Elements	Lesson 2: ASA, SAS, and SSS
Sessions	2 Sessions	3 Sessions
STANDARDS	G.CO.9	G.CO.7, G.CO.8
MATHbook Activities sequenced to address standards and meet content goals.	Students learn that a counterexample is a specific example that shows a general statement is not true. They analyze conditional statements expressed as "If, then" and create truth tables for geometry-based conditional statements. Students recognize that Euclidean geometry is a system of postulates and theorems. They apply the Linear Pair, Segment Addition, and Angle Addition Postulates.	Students analyze a worked example that proves you can map a segment onto itself in at most two reflections. They then use reflections to prove the Side-Side-Side, Side-Angle-Side, and Angle-Side-Angle Congruence Theorems for triangles. Students use *corresponding parts of congruent triangles are congruent* (CPCTC) reasoning to write congruence statements.
MATERIALS	None	• Compasses • Patty paper • Protractors • Rulers • Straightedges

LEARNING INDIVIDUALLY

Median time for students to complete MATHia for this topic is ~100 minutes.

	Lesson 1	Lesson 2
MATHia Workspaces aligned at the lesson level to support benchmarking through self-paced MATHia.	• Calculating and Justifying Angle Measures • Calculating Angle Measures	• Introduction to Triangle Congruence

For students without access to MATHia.

Problem sets for additional practice of the lesson skills.

	Lesson 1	Lesson 2
Skills Practice	• Conditional Statements, Truth Tables, and Postulates	• Triangle Congruence Theorems

I Never Forget a Face

Using Triangle Congruence to Solve Problems

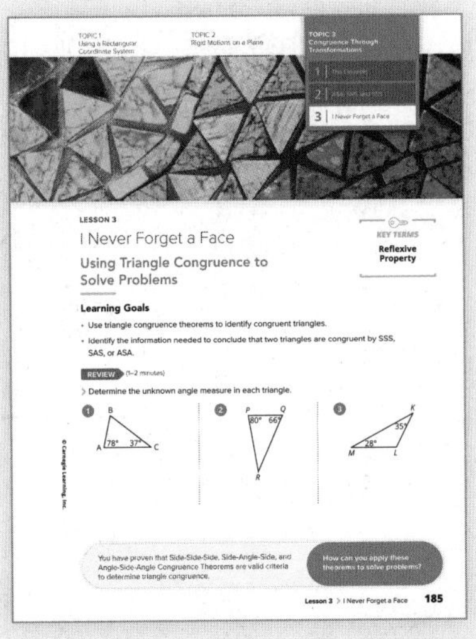
TOPIC 1 Using a Rectangular Coordinate System
TOPIC 2 Rigid Motions on a Plane
TOPIC 3 Congruence Through Transformations
3 | I Never Forget a Face

LESSON 3

I Never Forget a Face

Using Triangle Congruence to Solve Problems

KEY TERMS

Reflexive Property

Learning Goals

- Use triangle congruence theorems to identify congruent triangles.
- Identify the information needed to conclude that two triangles are congruent by SSS, SAS, or ASA.

REVIEW (1–2 minutes)

> Determine the unknown angle measure in each triangle.

You have proven that Side-Side-Side, Side-Angle-Side, and Angle-Side-Angle Congruence Theorems are valid criteria to determine triangle congruence.

How can you apply these theorems to solve problems?

Lesson 3 > I Never Forget a Face 185

2 Sessions

G.CO.6

Students use congruent triangles to solve an indirect measurement problem. They prove pairs of triangles within complex diagrams are congruent using the Side-Side-Side, Side-Angle-Side, and Angle-Side-Angle Congruence Theorems for triangles. Students also prove triangles are congruent using a coordinate plane for measures and transformations. They use all three rigid motions to create a design.

- Compasses
- Patty paper
- Straightedges

For the most up-to-date MATHia alignment, log in to MyCL.

- Using Triangle Congruence

Problem sets for additional practice of the lesson skills.

- Triangle Congruence Problems

Theorems proved in *Congruence Through Transformations:*

- Side-Side-Side Congruence Theorem (SSS)
- Side-Angle-Side Congruence Theorem (SAS)
- Angle-Side-Angle Congruence Theorem (ASA)

TOPIC 2

Connection to Prior Learning

What is the entry point for students?

In middle school, students constructed triangles from three measures of angles or sides, noticing when the conditions determine a unique triangle, more than one triangle, or no triangle. Through that hands-on exploration, they developed an intuition regarding the minimum criteria for determining whether triangles are congruent.

MATH REPRESENTATION

Given two sides and the angle between them, the included angle, of a triangle, you can construct a triangle using a compass and straightedge.

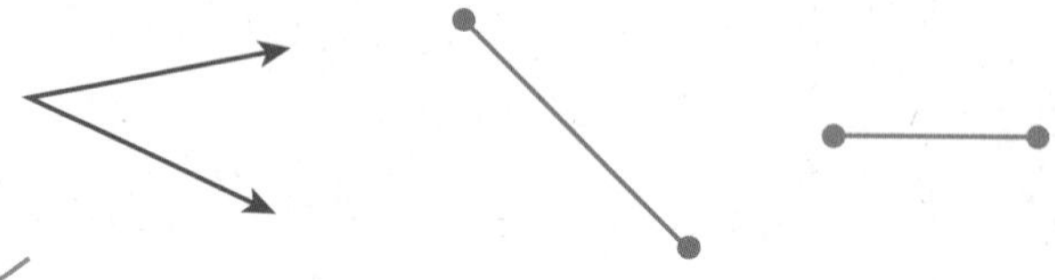

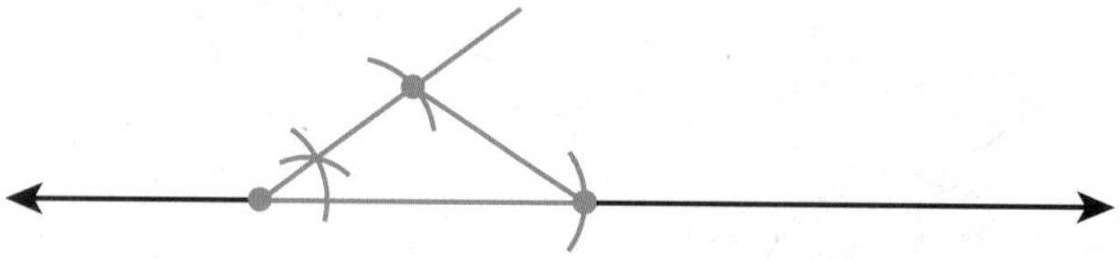

There is only 1 unique triangle that you can create given these side and angle measurements.

Connection to Future Learning

Why is *Congruence Through Transformations* important?

Proof is the linchpin of high school geometry. Students will develop deductive reasoning skills as they prove conjectures that they have made through investigation. They will use the triangle congruence theorems in many upcoming proofs. Proving these properties and relationships true in every case allows students to have sound reasoning to solve increasingly complex geometric problems.

MATH REPRESENTATION

Analyze the proof of the converse of the Perpendicular Bisector Theorem.

Given: Points *Q* and *R* are equidistant from point *P*.

You can draw an auxilliary line segment, $\overline{QR}$, to form an isosceles triangle, ΔRPQ,

Construct the midpoint of $\overline{QR}$, point *M*. You can draw another auxiliary line segment, $\overline{PM}$, connecting the midpoint with point *P*.

The two triangles, ΔPQM and ΔPRM, are congruent triangles by SSS Congruence.

This means that $\angle PMQ$ and $\angle PMR$ are congruent by CPCTC. And since these two angles are congruent and form a linear pair, they are both 90° angles.

Thus, point *P* lies on the perpendicular bisector of $\overline{QR}$.

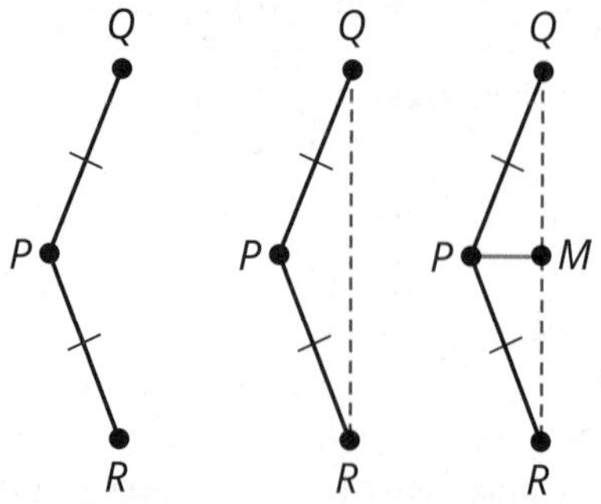

How does a student demonstrate understanding?

Students will demonstrate an understanding of the standards in *Congruence Through Transformations* when they can:

Log in to MyCL for resources that support **student meta-cognition**.

Identify corresponding sides and corresponding angles of congruent triangles.	✓
Explain that in a pair of congruent triangles, corresponding sides are congruent and corresponding angles are congruent.	✓
Define rigid motions as reflections, rotations, and translations, all of which preserve distances and angle measures.	✓
Define congruent figures as figures that have the same shape and size and describe a sequence of rigid motions that maps one onto the other.	✓
List the sufficient criteria to prove triangles are congruent.	✓
Map a triangle with one of the sufficient criteria onto the original triangle and show that corresponding sides and angles are congruent.	✓

HABITS OF MIND

How do the activities in *Congruence Through Transformations* promote student expertise in the mathematical practice standards?

All Carnegie Learning topics are written with the goal of creating mathematical thinkers who are active participants in class discourse, so elements of the habits of mind should be evident in all lessons. Students are expected to make sense of problems and work towards solutions, reason using concrete and abstract ideas, and communicate their thinking while providing a critical ear to the thinking of others.

Throughout *Congruence Through Transformations*, students use deductive reasoning to analyze and write proofs of the triangle congruence theorems. They analyze conditional statements to determine their truth values. Students attend to precision as they make accurate constructions and write proofs with clear deductive reasoning. As they connect rigid motion to congruence, students see the structure in geometric figures and relationships between parts of figures.

Mixed Practice

At the end of each topic, a **Mixed Practice** worksheet provides practice with skills from previous topics and this topic.

Spaced Review
Fluency and problem solving from previous topics

End of Topic Review
Review problems from this topic

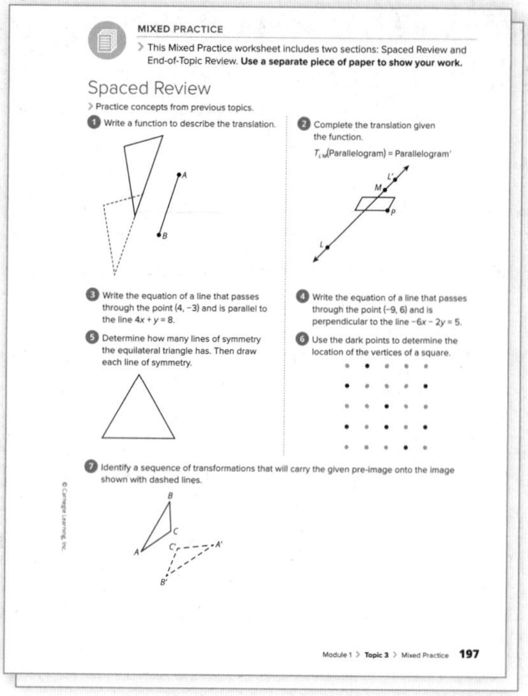
MIXED PRACTICE

This Mixed Practice worksheet includes two sections: Spaced Review and End-of-Topic Review. **Use a separate piece of paper to show your work.**

Spaced Review

Practice concepts from previous topics.

1. Write a function to describe the translation.
2. Complete the translation given the function.
3. Write the equation of a line that passes through the point (4, −3) and is parallel to the line $4x + y = 8$.
4. Write the equation of a line that passes through the point (−9, 6) and is perpendicular to the line $-6x - 2y = 5$.
5. Determine how many lines of symmetry the equilateral triangle has. Then draw each line of symmetry.
6. Use the dark points to determine the location of the vertices of a square.
7. Identify a sequence of transformations that will carry the given pre-image onto the image shown with dashed lines.

Module 1 > Topic 3 > Mixed Practice 197

Log in to MyCL for digital resources.

- A version with **additional space** for students to write their answers.
- Downloadable and editable in Word
- Editable via Edulastic

Topic Summary

Available online, a **Topic Summary** reviews the main concepts for the topic.

Essential Ideas for each lesson.

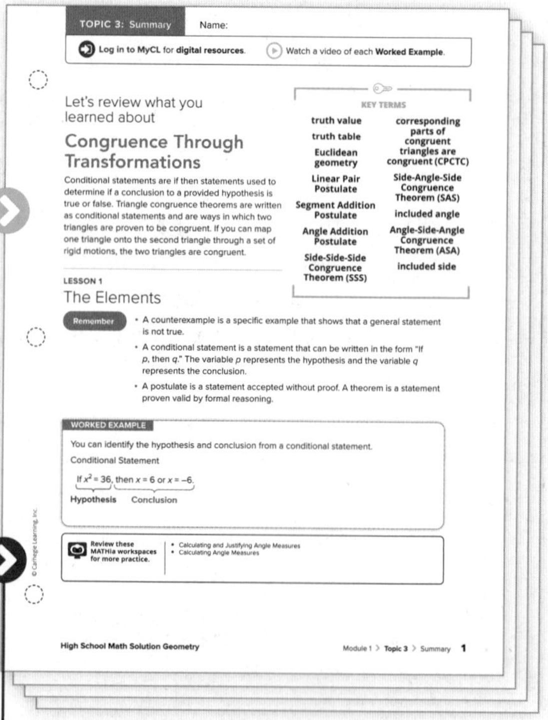
TOPIC 3: Summary Name:

Log in to MyCL for **digital resources**. Watch a video of each **Worked Example**.

Let's review what you learned about

Congruence Through Transformations

Conditional statements are if then statements used to determine if a conclusion to a provided hypothesis is true or false. Triangle congruence theorems are written as conditional statements and are ways in which two triangles are proven to be congruent. If you can map one triangle onto the second triangle through a set of rigid motions, the two triangles are congruent.

KEY TERMS: truth value, truth table, Euclidean geometry, Linear Pair Postulate, Segment Addition Postulate, Angle Addition Postulate, Side-Side-Side Congruence Theorem (SSS), corresponding parts of congruent triangles are congruent (CPCTC), Side-Angle-Side Congruence Theorem (SAS), included angle, Angle-Side-Angle Congruence Theorem (ASA), included side

LESSON 1

The Elements

Remember

- A counterexample is a specific example that shows that a general statement is not true.
- A conditional statement is a statement that can be written in the form "If p, then q." The variable p represents the hypothesis and the variable q represents the conclusion.
- A postulate is a statement accepted without proof. A theorem is a statement proven valid by formal reasoning.

WORKED EXAMPLE

You can identify the hypothesis and conclusion from a conditional statement.

Conditional Statement

If $x^2 = 36$, then $x = 6$ or $x = -6$.

Hypothesis Conclusion

Review these MATHia workspaces for more practice. • Calculating and Justifying Angle Measures • Calculating Angle Measures

High School Math Solution Geometry Module 1 > Topic 3 > Summary 1

Log in to MyCL for digital resources.

- A printable version available for download.
- A video of the **Worked Example** being solved

www.carnegielearning.com/login

MATHia Workspaces are highlighted in select lessons to help you understand the connections and what you might want to review.

Assessment

Assessments aligned to this topic:

1. Pre-test
2. Post-test
3. End of Topic Test (Form A)
4. End of Topic Test (Form B)
5. Standardized Test Practice
6. Performance Task with Rubric

An **Assessment Overview** identifies the standard(s) aligned with each item on every test.

Log in to MyCL for digital resources.

- A version with **additional space** for students to write their answers.
- Downloadable and editable in Word
- Editable via Edulastic

End of Topic Test			Standardized Test		
1. G.CO.9	8. G.CO.8	15. G.CO.6	1. G.CO.9	8. G.CO.9	15. G.CO.7
2. G.CO.9	9. G.CO.8	16. G.CO.6	2. G.CO.8	9. G.CO.8	16. G.CO.8
3. G.CO.9	10. G.CO.8		3. G.CO.9	10. G.CO.8	17. G.CO.8
4. G.CO.9	11. G.CO.8		4. G.CO.6	11. G.CO.8	18. G.CO.8
5. G.CO.9	12. G.CO.8		5. G.CO.9	12. G.CO.8	19. G.CO.9
6. G.CO.9	13. G.CO.8		6. G.CO.8	13. G.CO.8	20. G.CO.6
7. G.CO.7	14. G.CO.8		7. G.CO.9	14. G.CO.8	

Family Guide

Teachers, encourage your families to log into the **Home Connection** to access a collection of resources that supports their students as they learn about *Congruence Through Transformations.*

www.carnegielearning.com/home-connection

For families with limited online access, print and send home the **Family Guide**.

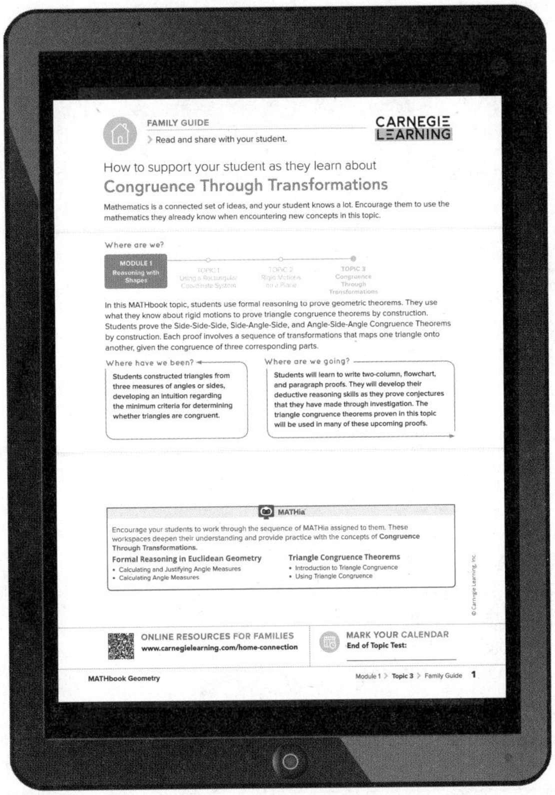

Congruence Through Transformations

Scope out MATHbook and MATHia sessions for this topic, keeping in mind your long term plan.

You can schedule MATHia sessions any time; however, if you are using Skills Practice as the alternative, schedule those sessions after a completed lesson.

Log in to MyCL for:

- Editable templates
- Alternative plans for longer sessions
- Implementations not using MATHia

1 Session ≈ 45 minutes

CORE IMPLEMENTATION PLAN with flexible access to computers/tablets.

Session 1	Session 2	Session 3	Session 4	Session 5
G.CO.9 **LESSON 1** The Elements GETTING STARTED ACTIVITY 1 ⊛ ACTIVITY 2 ⊛	**LESSON 1** continued ACTIVITY 3 ⊛ TALK THE TALK	MATHia Use LiveLab and Reports to monitor students' progress.	G.CO.7, G.CO.8 **LESSON 2** ASA, SAS, and SSS GETTING STARTED ACTIVITY 1 ⊛	**LESSON 2** continued ACTIVITY 2 ⊛ ACTIVITY 3 ⊛

Session 6	Session 7	Session 8	Session 9	Session 10
LESSON 2 continued ACTIVITY 4 ⊛ ACTIVITY 5 TALK THE TALK ⊛	MATHia Use LiveLab and Reports to monitor students' progress.	G.CO.6 **LESSON 3** I Never Forget a Face GETTING STARTED ACTIVITY 1 ⊛	**LESSON 3** continued ACTIVITY 2 ⊛ TALK THE TALK	MATHia Use LiveLab and Reports to monitor students' progress.

Complete End-of-Topic Review and Assess

⊛ This activity highlights a key term or concept that is essential to the learning goals of the lesson.

ENGAGE at the **Module** level + **DEVELOP** at the **Topic** level + **TEACH** Read the facilitation notes and plan learning experiences.

Where are we?

TOPIC 3 Congruence Through Transformations	LESSON 1 The Elements	LESSON 2 ASA, SAS, and SSS	LESSON 3 I Never Forget a Face
Pacing	2 Sessions	3 Sessions	2 Sessions

OVERVIEW: LESSON 1

The Elements

Formal Reasoning in Euclidean Geometry

ENGAGE

- Students learn that a counterexample is a specific example that shows that a general statement is not true.

DEVELOP

- Students analyze and create a truth table for geometry-based conditional statements.
- They learn that postulates and theorems are systematically built upon to develop Euclidean geometry.
- They apply the Linear Pair Postulate, the Segment Addition Postulate, and the Angle Addition Postulate.

DEMONSTRATE

- Students explain the logic of conditional statements, truth values, and truth tables.

HIGH SCHOOL GEOMETRY

Congruence

Prove geometric theorems.

9. Prove theorems about lines and angles.

LESSON STRUCTURE AND PACING GUIDE 2 SESSIONS

⊛ This activity highlights a key term or concept that is essential to the learning goals of the lesson.

Session 1

INSTRUCTIONAL SEQUENCE

ENGAGE	DEVELOP	DEVELOP
Build off intuition	Mathematical problem solving	Worked example Peer analysis

GETTING STARTED
If..., Then...

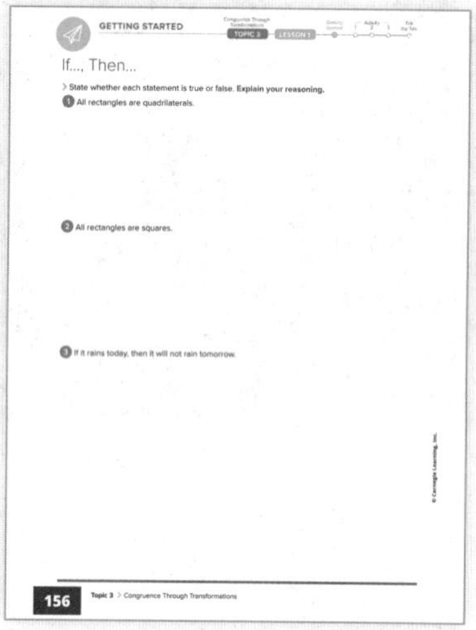
GETTING STARTED

TOPIC 3 LESSON 1

If..., Then...

> State whether each statement is true or false. **Explain your reasoning.**

1. All rectangles are quadrilaterals.
2. All rectangles are squares.
3. If it rains today, then it will not rain tomorrow.

© Carnegie Learning, Inc.

156 Topic 3 > Congruence Through Transformations

Students decide whether statements are true or false.

- They provide reasoning for their responses.

ACTIVITY 1 ⊛
Counterexamples

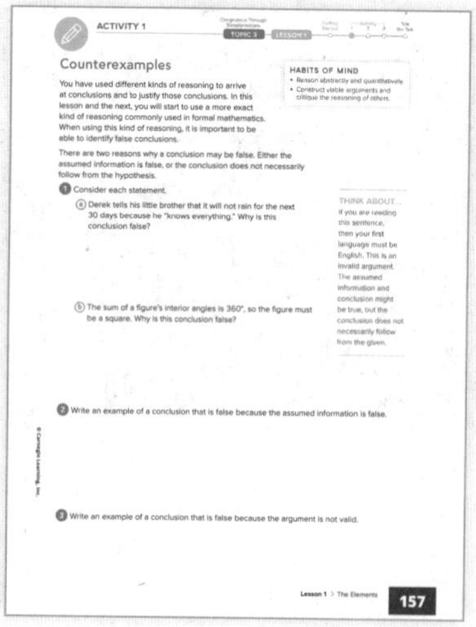
ACTIVITY 1

TOPIC 3 LESSON 1

Counterexamples

HABITS OF MIND
- Reason abstractly and quantitatively.
- Construct viable arguments and critique the reasoning of others.

You have used different kinds of reasoning to arrive at conclusions and to justify those conclusions. In this lesson and the next, you will start to use a more exact kind of reasoning commonly used in formal mathematics. When using this kind of reasoning, it is important to be able to identify false conclusions.

There are two reasons why a conclusion may be false. Either the assumed information is false, or the conclusion does not necessarily follow from the hypothesis.

1. Consider each statement.
   a. Derek tells his little brother that it will not rain for the next 30 days because he "knows everything." Why is this conclusion false?
   b. The sum of a figure's interior angles is 360°, so the figure must be a square. Why is this conclusion false?

THINK ABOUT... If you are reading this sentence, then your first language must be English. This is an invalid argument. The assumed information and conclusion might be true, but the conclusion does not necessarily follow from the given.

2. Write an example of a conclusion that is false because the assumed information is false.
3. Write an example of a conclusion that is false because the argument is not valid.

© Carnegie Learning, Inc.

Lesson 1 > The Elements 157

Students explore two reasons why a conclusion may be false.

- They learn that a counterexample is a specific example that shows that a general statement is not true.

ACTIVITY 2 ⊛
Conditional Statements and Truth Tables

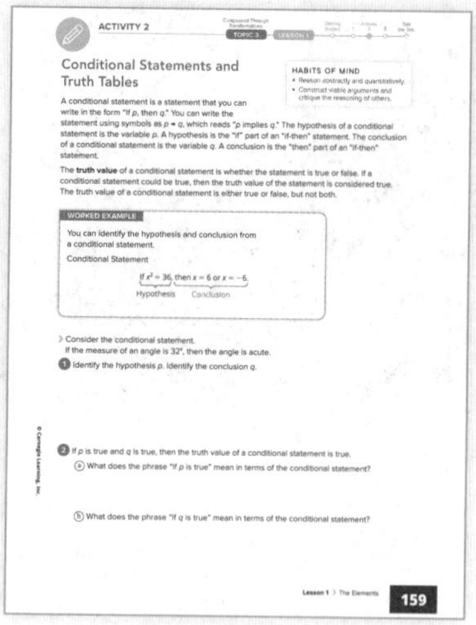
ACTIVITY 2

TOPIC 3 LESSON 1

Conditional Statements and Truth Tables

HABITS OF MIND
- Reason abstractly and quantitatively.
- Construct viable arguments and critique the reasoning of others.

A conditional statement is a statement that you can write in the form "If p, then q." You can write the statement using symbols as $p \rightarrow q$, which reads "p implies q." The hypothesis of a conditional statement is the variable p. A hypothesis is the "if" part of an "if-then" statement. The conclusion of a conditional statement is the variable q. A conclusion is the "then" part of an "if-then" statement.

The **truth value** of a conditional statement is whether the statement is true or false. If a conditional statement could be true, then the truth value of the statement is considered true. The truth value of a conditional statement is either true or false, but not both.

WORKED EXAMPLE

You can identify the hypothesis and conclusion from a conditional statement.

Conditional Statement

If $x^2 = 36$, then $x = 6$ or $x = -6$.

Hypothesis Conclusion

> Consider the conditional statement.
If the measure of an angle is 32°, then the angle is acute.

1. Identify the hypothesis p. Identify the conclusion q.
2. If p is true and q is true, then the truth value of a conditional statement is true.
   a. What does the phrase "If p is true" mean in terms of the conditional statement?
   b. What does the phrase "If q is true" mean in terms of the conditional statement?

© Carnegie Learning, Inc.

Lesson 1 > The Elements 159

Students analyze conditional statements expressed as "If *p*, then *q*."

- They analyze and create a truth table for geometric conditional statements.

Log in to MyCL for **lesson support** including:

Slides

Videos

www.carnegielearning.com/login

Session 2

INSTRUCTIONAL SEQUENCE

DEVELOP	DEMONSTRATE
Mathematical problem solving	Writing task

ACTIVITY 3
Postulates and Theorems

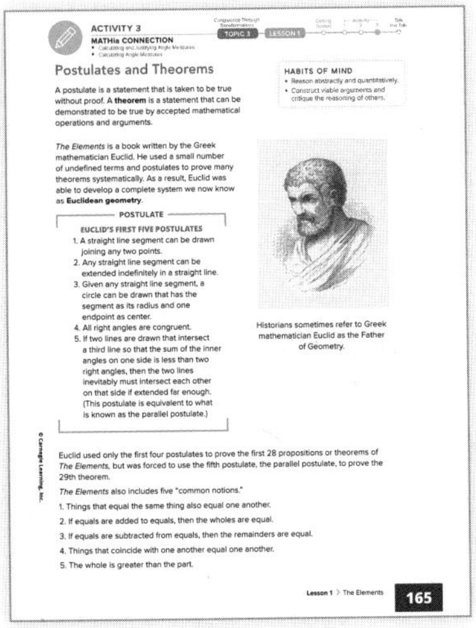
ACTIVITY 3

MATHia CONNECTION

- Calculating and Justifying Angle Measures
- Calculating Angle Measures

TOPIC 3 LESSON 1

Postulates and Theorems

A postulate is a statement that is taken to be true without proof. A **theorem** is a statement that can be demonstrated to be true by accepted mathematical operations and arguments.

The Elements is a book written by the Greek mathematician Euclid. He used a small number of undefined terms and postulates to prove many theorems systematically. As a result, Euclid was able to develop a complete system we now know as **Euclidean geometry**.

HABITS OF MIND

- Reason abstractly and quantitatively.
- Construct viable arguments and critique the reasoning of others.

POSTULATE

EUCLID'S FIRST FIVE POSTULATES

1. A straight line segment can be drawn joining any two points.
2. Any straight line segment can be extended indefinitely in a straight line.
3. Given any straight line segment, a circle can be drawn that has the segment as its radius and one endpoint as center.
4. All right angles are congruent.
5. If two lines are drawn that intersect a third line so that the sum of the inner angles on one side is less than two right angles, then the two lines inevitably must intersect each other on that side if extended far enough. (This postulate is equivalent to what is known as the parallel postulate.)

Historians sometimes refer to Greek mathematician Euclid as the Father of Geometry.

Euclid used only the first four postulates to prove the first 28 propositions or theorems of *The Elements*, but was forced to use the fifth postulate, the parallel postulate, to prove the 29th theorem.

The Elements also includes five "common notions."

1. Things that equal the same thing also equal one another.
2. If equals are added to equals, then the wholes are equal.
3. If equals are subtracted from equals, then the remainders are equal.
4. Things that coincide with one another equal one another.
5. The whole is greater than the part.

© Carnegie Learning, Inc.

Lesson 1 > The Elements 165

Students learn that postulates and theorems are systematically built upon to develop Euclidean geometry.

- They apply the Linear Pair Postulate, the Segment Addition Postulate, and the Angle Addition Postulate.

TALK THE TALK
While You Were Away...

TALK THE TALK

TOPIC 3 LESSON 1

While You Were Away...

> Write a short note to a friend explaining conditional statements, truth values, and truth tables. Include definitions of all terms and examples that are easy to understand.

© Carnegie Learning, Inc.

168 Topic 3 > Congruence Through Transformations

Students explain the logic of conditional statements, truth values, and truth tables.

- They create examples to make sense of this form of reasoning.

NOTES

TOPIC 3

Log in to MyCL for:

- Editable templates
- Additional planning support

Now that you have read the Module, Topic, and Lesson Overviews, you are ready to plan.

Do the math

Tear out the lesson planning template (page 155M) and jot down thoughts as you work through this lesson and read the Facilitation Notes.

- Anticipate student responses
- Track your time, so you can estimate how much time to spend on any activity
- Decide which differentiation and collaboration strategies you may use and how that may impact pacing

Connect the learning

MATHbook + MATHia

The table shows the self-paced MATHia sequence for the *Congruence Through Transformations* Topic.

Median student completion time: ~90–110 minutes

As you implement this lesson, consider different connections for students who are on pace and those that have not yet completed the workspaces aligned to this lesson.

STUDENTS WHO ARE NOT HERE YET
Students practice calculating and justifying angle measures in diagrams.

TYPE	WORKSPACE NAME
	Calculating and Justifying Angle Measures
	Calculating Angle Measures
	Introduction to Triangle Congruence
	Using Triangle Congruence

STUDENTS WHO ARE ON PACE
After you complete Activity 3, ask these students to share how they determined their strategy to calculate the angle measures.

The Elements
Formal Reasoning in Euclidean Geometry

Session 1

GETTING STARTED If..., Then...

Pacing (minutes)	
My Time	Class Time

ACTIVITY 1 Counterexamples ✪

Pacing (minutes)	
My Time	Class Time

ACTIVITY 2 Conditional Statements and Truth Tables ✪

Pacing (minutes)	
My Time	Class Time

KEY TERM
truth value
truth table

Session 2

ACTIVITY 3 Postulates and Theorems ✪

Pacing (minutes)	
My Time	Class Time

KEY TERM
theorem
Euclidean geometry
Linear Pair Postulate
Segment Addition Postulate
Angle Addition Postulate

TALK THE TALK While You Were Away...

Pacing (minutes)	
My Time	Class Time

✪ This activity highlights a key term or concept that is essential to the learning goals of the lesson.

Log in to MyCL for:
- Editable templates
- Additional planning support

Reflect on your lesson

> Consider the effectiveness of your lesson on student learning.

What went well?

What did not go as planned?

> Anticipate how you would change the lesson next time you teach it.

How will you capitalize on the things that went well?

How will you improve things that did not go as planned?

MATERIALS

- None

TOPIC 1 Using a Rectangular Coordinate System
TOPIC 2 Rigid Motions on a Plane
TOPIC 3 Congruence Through Transformations
1 | The Elements
2 | ASA, SAS, and SSS
3 | I Never Forget a Face

LESSON 1

The Elements

Formal Reasoning in Euclidean Geometry

Learning Goals

- Identify the hypothesis and conclusion of a conditional statement.
- Explore the truth values of conditional statements.
- Use a truth table to make sense of conditional statements.
- Differentiate between postulates and theorems.

KEY TERMS

- truth value
- truth table
- theorem
- Euclidean geometry
- Linear Pair Postulate
- Segment Addition Postulate
- Angle Addition Postulate

REVIEW (1–2 minutes)

> Sketch the geometric figure described.

1. A linear pair of angles

Sample answer.

2. Point C on $\overline{AB}$

Sample answer.

3. Point D on the interior of $\angle ABC$

Sample answer.

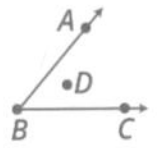

You have investigated true statements in geometry using informal reasoning.

How can you reason more formally in Euclidean geometry with postulates and theorems?

Setting the Stage

- **Assign Review (optional, 1 – 2 minutes)**
- **Communicate the learning goals and key terms to look out for**
- **Tap into your students' prior learning by reading the narrative statement**
- **Provide a sense of direction by reading the question**

IN THIS **REVIEW**
Students sketch geometric figures. They will use this skill in **ACTIVITY 3 Postulates and Theorems.**

TOPIC 3

A conditional statement is a statement in the form "if p, then q." You read the expression $p \rightarrow q$ as "p implies q." The variable p represents the hypothesis, and the variable q represents the conclusion.

You can accept a postulate without proof, but you must prove that a theorem is true.

Essential Ideas

- A counterexample is a specific example that shows that a general statement is not true. No amount of examples can prove a statement is true.
- A conditional statement is a statement that you can write in the form "If p, then q." The variable p represents the hypothesis, and the variable q represents the conclusion.
- The truth value of a conditional statement identifies whether the statement is true or false.
- The truth value is true when both p and q are true and whenever p is false. The truth value is false when p is true and q is false.
- A truth table is a table that summarizes all possible truth values for a conditional statement.
- A postulate is a statement accepted without proof. A theorem is a statement proven valid by formal reasoning.

GETTING STARTED

SUMMARY **Geometric reasoning involves determining whether statements are true or false and justifying your answer.**

Chunking the Activity

- **Read and discuss the directions**
- **Group students to complete the activity**
- **Share and summarize**

If..., Then...

State whether each statement is true or false. **Explain your reasoning.**

1. All rectangles are quadrilaterals.

   True

   All rectangles have four sides, so all rectangles are quadrilaterals.

2. All rectangles are squares.

   False

   Not all rectangles have equal side lengths, so not all rectangles are squares.

3. If it rains today, then it will not rain tomorrow.

   False

   It can rain for more than one day in a row, so if it rains today, it still could rain tomorrow.

Questions to Support Discourse

		TYPE
1	• Are rectangles a subset of quadrilaterals, or are quadrilaterals a subset of rectangles?	Gathering
2	• What is an example of a rectangle that is a square? Is not a square? • How does the word *all* influence your decision?	Probing
3	• How is this question's structure different than the others? • Does the *if-then* imply that the statement following *then* must always occur?	Gathering

ACTIVITY 1

SUMMARY **A counterexample is a specific example that shows that a general statement is not true. No amount of examples can prove a statement is true.**

Counterexamples

You have used different kinds of reasoning to arrive at conclusions and to justify those conclusions. In this lesson and the next, you will start to use a more exact kind of reasoning commonly used in formal mathematics. When using this kind of reasoning, it is important to be able to identify false conclusions.

HABITS OF MIND
- Reason abstractly and quantitatively.
- Construct viable arguments and critique the reasoning of others.

There are two reasons why a conclusion may be false. Either the assumed information is false, or the conclusion does not necessarily follow from the hypothesis.

1 Consider each statement.

(a) Derek tells his little brother that it will not rain for the next 30 days because he "knows everything." Why is this conclusion false?

The conclusion is false because the assumed information is false. No one knows everything.

(b) The sum of a figure's interior angles is 360°, so the figure must be a square. Why is this conclusion false?

The conclusion is false because the argument is not valid. The figure doesn't have to be a square. It could be any type of quadrilateral.

THINK ABOUT...
If you are reading this sentence, then your first language must be English. This is an invalid argument. The assumed information and conclusion might be true, but the conclusion does not necessarily follow from the given.

2 Write an example of a conclusion that is false because the assumed information is false.

Sample answer.

All kids like broccoli. Max is a kid. So, Max likes broccoli.

3 Write an example of a conclusion that is false because the argument is not valid.

Sample answer.

Kayleigh doesn't like apples. An apple is a green fruit. So, Kayleigh doesn't like any green fruit.

Questions to Support Discourse

		TYPE
Intro	• Does the *assumed information* refer to the hypothesis or the conclusion? • What is meant by *the conclusion does not necessarily follow from the hypothesis?*	Gathering
1	• What part of this statement is the hypothesis? How can you tell?	Seeing structure
2	• What would be a valid or true conclusion?	Probing
3	• What is a false assumption based on life in general? In mathematics?	Probing

Chunking the Activity

- **Read and discuss the introduction**
- **Group students to complete the activity**
- **Share and summarize**

LANGUAGE LINK

ELL TIP

Discuss the meaning of the prefix *counter-*. Use the terms *clockwise* and *counterclockwise* to help students realize that the prefix *counter-* means the opposite. Therefore, a counterexample is an example that proves the opposite or demonstrates a statement is false.

NOTES

COMMON MISCONCEPTION

See Page 170A for a misconception related to 4.

4 Provide a counterexample for each statement to demonstrate that they are not true.

REMEMBER...
A counterexample is a specific example that shows that a general statement is not true.

(a) All prime numbers are odd.

The only counterexample is 2, which is a prime number that is even.

(b) The sum of the measures of two acute angles is always greater than 90°.

Sample answer.

Two angles that each measure 35° are acute angles, but the sum of their measures is 70°, which is less than 90°.

Questions to Support Discourse

		TYPE
4	• Why is this conclusion false when you can come up with examples where it is true?	Probing

ACTIVITY 2

SUMMARY **You can write a conditional statement in the form "If *p*, then *q*." A truth value identifies whether the statement is true or false.**

Conditional Statements and Truth Tables

HABITS OF MIND
- Reason abstractly and quantitatively.
- Construct viable arguments and critique the reasoning of others.

A conditional statement is a statement that you can write in the form "If *p*, then *q*." You can write the statement using symbols as $p \rightarrow q$, which reads "*p* implies *q*." The hypothesis of a conditional statement is the variable *p*. A hypothesis is the "if" part of an "if-then" statement. The conclusion of a conditional statement is the variable *q*. A conclusion is the "then" part of an "if-then" statement.

The **truth value** of a conditional statement is whether the statement is true or false. If a conditional statement could be true, then the truth value of the statement is considered true. The truth value of a conditional statement is either true or false, but not both.

WORKED EXAMPLE

You can identify the hypothesis and conclusion from a conditional statement.

Conditional Statement

If $x^2 = 36$, then $x = 6$ or $x = -6$.

Hypothesis: $x^2 = 36$ — Conclusion: $x = 6$ or $x = -6$

> Consider the conditional statement.
If the measure of an angle is 32°, then the angle is acute.

1. Identify the hypothesis *p*. Identify the conclusion *q*.

   The hypothesis is "the measure of an angle is 32°."

   The conclusion is "the angle is acute."

2. If *p* is true and *q* is true, then the truth value of a conditional statement is true.

   (a) What does the phrase "If *p* is true" mean in terms of the conditional statement?

   "If *p* is true" means that the measure of the angle is 32°.

   (b) What does the phrase "If *q* is true" mean in terms of the conditional statement?

   "If *q* is true" means that the angle is acute.

Chunking the Activity

- Read and discuss the introduction and worked example
- Group students to complete 1 - 3
- Check-in and share
- Group students to complete 4 and 5
- Check-in and share
- Read and discuss the definition and worked example
- Group students to complete 6 and 7
- Share and summarize

DIFFERENTIATION STRATEGY

See Page 170A to assist all students with the introduction.

Questions to Support Discourse

		TYPE
Intro	• Is a truth value a number? • What are the two possible truth values? • Is the truth value based on the hypotenuse, conclusion, or the entire conditional statement?	Gathering

NOTES

ⓒ Explain why the truth value of the conditional statement is true if both p and q are true.

The truth value of the conditional statement is true because, by definition, an acute angle is an angle whose measure is less than 90°. An angle whose measure is 32° has a measure less than 90° and must be an acute angle.

3 If p is true and q is false, then the truth value of a conditional statement is false.

ⓐ What does the phrase "If p is true" mean in terms of the conditional statement?

"If p is true" means that the measure of the angle is 32°.

ⓑ What does the phrase "If q is false" mean in terms of the conditional statement?

"If q is false" means that the angle is not acute.

THINK ABOUT...

Continue to use this conditional statement to respond to Questions 3 through 5.

If the measure of an angle is 32°, then the angle is acute.

ⓒ Explain why the truth value of the conditional statement is false if p is true and q is false.

The truth value of the conditional statement is false because, by definition, an acute angle is an angle whose measure is less than 90°. The angle is 32°, so the statement that the angle is not acute is a false statement.

4 If p is false and q is true, then the truth value of a conditional statement is true.

ⓐ What does the phrase "If p is false" mean in terms of the conditional statement?

"If p is false" means that the measure of the angle is not 32°.

ⓑ What does the phrase "If q is true" mean in terms of the conditional statement?

"If q is true" means that the angle is acute.

Questions to Support Discourse

		TYPE
3	• Explain why "q is false" means the angle is not acute rather than the angle is obtuse. • If the angle is not acute, what other types of angle could it be?	Probing
	• How can you generalize the results from Questions 2 and 3 using the fact that p is true in both cases? • What are the other two possibilities for p and q to consider?	Seeing structure
4	• Because p is false, what are possible measures of the angle? • Which possible angle measures make the conclusion true? All of them? Some of them?	Probing
	• Explain why the term *could* in the definition of a truth value justifies that the truth value is true.	Reflecting and justifying

ACTIVITY 2 Continued

ⓒ Explain why the truth value of the conditional statement is true if p is false and q is true.

The truth value of the conditional statement is true because, by definition, an acute angle is an angle whose measure is less than 90°. The angle could be less than 90°, so the statement that the angle is acute could be a true statement.

THINK ABOUT...

If p is false and q is true, the truth value is always true. Can you think of other examples that show this?

5 If p is false and q is false, then the truth value of a conditional statement is true.

ⓐ What does the phrase "If p is false" mean in terms of the conditional statement?

"If p is false" means that the measure of the angle is not 32°.

ⓑ What does the phrase "If q is false" mean in terms of the conditional statement?

"If q is false" means that the angle is not acute.

ⓒ Explain why the truth value of the conditional statement is true if both p and q are false.

The truth value of the conditional statement is true because, by definition, an acute angle is an angle whose measure is less than 90°. The angle could be greater than 90°, so the statement that the angle is not acute could be a true statement.

Questions to Support Discourse

		TYPE
5	• What is an angle measure that makes this conditional statement true? Explain your thinking.	Probing
	• How can you generalize the results from Questions 4 and 5 using the fact that p is false in both cases?	Gathering

NOTES

NOTES

COMMON MISCONCEPTION

See Page 170A for a misconception related to the worked example.

ACTIVITY 2 Continued

A **truth table** is a table that summarizes all possible truth values for a conditional statement $p \rightarrow q$. The first two columns of a truth table represent all possible truth values for the variables p and q. The last column represents the truth value of the conditional statement $p \rightarrow q$.

WORKED EXAMPLE

The truth values for the conditional statement "If the measure of an angle is 32°, then the angle is acute" are shown.

The truth value of the conditional statement $p \rightarrow q$ is determined by the truth value of p and the truth value of q.

- If p is **true** and q is **true**, then $p \rightarrow q$ is **true**.
- If p is **true** and q is **false**, then $p \rightarrow q$ is **false**.
- If p is **false** and q is **true**, then $p \rightarrow q$ is **true**.
- If p is **false** and q is **false**, then $p \rightarrow q$ is **true**.

p	q	$p \rightarrow q$
the measure of an angle is 32°	**the angle is acute**	**If the measure of an angle is 32°, then the angle is acute.**
T	T	T
T	F	F
F	T	T
F	F	T

6 Consider the conditional statement. If m$\overline{AB}$ = 6 inches and m$\overline{BC}$ = 6 inches, then $\overline{AB} \cong \overline{BC}$.

ⓐ What is the hypothesis p?

m$\overline{AB}$ = 6 inches and m$\overline{BC}$ = 6 inches

ⓑ What is the conclusion q?

$\overline{AB} \cong \overline{BC}$

ⓒ If both p and q are true, what does that mean? What is the truth value of the conditional statement if both p and q are true?

If both p and q are true, this means m$\overline{AB}$ = 6 inches and m$\overline{BC}$ = 6 inches; therefore, $\overline{AB} \cong \overline{BC}$. The truth value of the conditional statement is true.

162 Topic 3 > Congruence Through Transformations

Questions to Support Discourse

		TYPE
Worked Example	• Choose a row in the table and interpret its meaning.	Gathering

ACTIVITY 2 Continued

(d) If p is true and q is false, what does that mean? What is the truth value of the conditional statement if p is true and q is false?

If p is true and q is false, this means $m\overline{AB} = 6$ inches and $m\overline{BC} = 6$ inches.

Therefore, $\overline{AB} \ncong \overline{BC}$. The truth value of the conditional statement is false.

(e) If p is false and q is true, what does that mean? What is the truth value of the conditional statement if p is false and q is true?

If p is false and q is true, this means $m\overline{AB} \neq 6$ inches or $m\overline{BC} \neq 6$ inches.

Therefore, $\overline{AB} \cong \overline{BC}$. The truth value of the conditional statement is true. This statement could be true if both $m\overline{AB}$ and $m\overline{BC}$ equal the same value, but not 6 inches.

(f) If both p and q are false, what does that mean? What is the truth value of the conditional statement if both p and q are false?

If both p and q are false, $m\overline{AB} \neq 6$ inches or $m\overline{BC} \neq 6$ inches.

Therefore, $\overline{AB} \ncong \overline{BC}$. The truth value of the conditional statement is true. This statement could be true if $m\overline{AB}$ and $m\overline{BC}$ do not equal the same value.

(g) Summarize your answers to parts (a) through (f) by completing a truth table for the conditional statement.

p	q	$p \rightarrow q$
$m\overline{AB} = 6$ inches and $m\overline{BC} = 6$ inches	$\overline{AB} \cong \overline{BC}$	$m\overline{AB} = 6$ inches and $m\overline{BC} = 6$ inches, then $\overline{AB} \cong \overline{BC}$
T	T	T
T	F	F
F	T	T
F	F	T

NOTES

TOPIC 3

Questions to Support Discourse

		TYPE
6	• When there are two components to p, like in parts (e) and (f), what are the different ways you can make the hypothesis false? • What is an example to support a true truth value?	Probing
	• Why don't you need to check for a false truth value? • If you can create a true or false statement, why is the truth value true? • How do your answers to the truth table in part (g) compare to the one in the worked example? • Do you think all truth tables will be the same? Explain your thinking.	Seeing structure

NOTES

Student Look-Fors

Recognizing the importance of developing critical thinking skills.

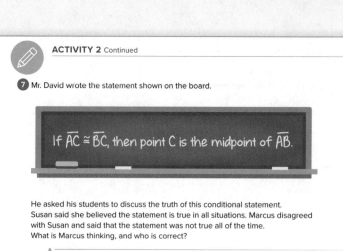

7 Mr. David wrote the statement shown on the board.

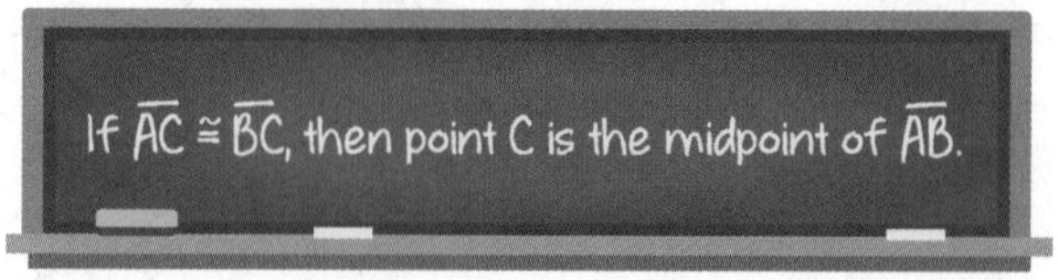

If $\overline{AC} \cong \overline{BC}$, then point C is the midpoint of $\overline{AB}$.

He asked his students to discuss the truth of this conditional statement. Susan said she believed the statement is true in all situations. Marcus disagreed with Susan and said that the statement was not true all of the time. What is Marcus thinking, and who is correct?

Marcus is correct.
If point C is not on $\overline{AB}$, the hypothesis may be true, but the conclusion is false as shown. Point C can lie anywhere on the perpendicular bisector of $\overline{AB}$.

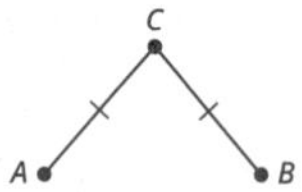

Questions to Support Discourse		TYPE
7	• Provide a diagram as a counterexample to Susan's thinking.	Probing

ACTIVITY 3

SUMMARY **A postulate is a statement accepted without proof. A theorem is a statement proven valid by formal reasoning.**

ACTIVITY 3

MATHia CONNECTION
- Calculating and Justifying Angle Measures
- Calculating Angle Measures

Postulates and Theorems

HABITS OF MIND
- Reason abstractly and quantitatively.
- Construct viable arguments and critique the reasoning of others.

A postulate is a statement that is taken to be true without proof. A **theorem** is a statement that can be demonstrated to be true by accepted mathematical operations and arguments.

The Elements is a book written by the Greek mathematician Euclid. He used a small number of undefined terms and postulates to prove many theorems systematically. As a result, Euclid was able to develop a complete system we now know as **Euclidean geometry**.

POSTULATE

EUCLID'S FIRST FIVE POSTULATES
1. A straight line segment can be drawn joining any two points.
2. Any straight line segment can be extended indefinitely in a straight line.
3. Given any straight line segment, a circle can be drawn that has the segment as its radius and one endpoint as center.
4. All right angles are congruent.
5. If two lines are drawn that intersect a third line so that the sum of the inner angles on one side is less than two right angles, then the two lines inevitably must intersect each other on that side if extended far enough. (This postulate is equivalent to what is known as the parallel postulate.)

Historians sometimes refer to Greek mathematician Euclid as the Father of Geometry.

Euclid used only the first four postulates to prove the first 28 propositions or theorems of *The Elements,* but was forced to use the fifth postulate, the parallel postulate, to prove the 29th theorem.

The Elements also includes five "common notions."

1. Things that equal the same thing also equal one another.
2. If equals are added to equals, then the wholes are equal.
3. If equals are subtracted from equals, then the remainders are equal.
4. Things that coincide with one another equal one another.
5. The whole is greater than the part.

Questions to Support Discourse

		TYPE
Intro	• What is the difference between a postulate and a theorem? • Why does it make sense that you can accept these postulates without proof? • Why should the word *congruent* replace *equal* in the common notions?	Gathering
	• How could you use line segments to illustrate the meaning of the common notions?	Probing
	• How do Euclid's common notions about geometric figures relate to numbers and properties to solve equations?	Seeing structure

Chunking the Activity

- **Read and discuss the introduction**
- **Group students to complete the activity**
- **Share and summarize**

DIFFERENTIATION STRATEGY

See Page 170B to assist all students with the introduction.

LANGUAGE LINK

ELL TIP

Ensure that students understand the meaning of *coincide*.

When solving systems of equations, students encountered the graphical solution of a system with infinitely many solutions as a pair of lines that lay one on top of the other, known as coincident lines. "Things that coincide with one another" are geometric figures that lay one on top of the other.

NOTES

Student Look-Fors

- Appropriate use of math terms, such as *adjacent*, *vertex*, and *rays*.
- Linear pairs drawn in different orientations.

ACTIVITY 3 Continued

You have already used the three undefined terms *point, line,* and *plane* to define related terms such as *line segment* and *angle*. Now consider these three fundamental postulates.

- The Linear Pair Postulate
- The Segment Addition Postulate
- The Angle Addition Postulate

You will use these postulates to make various conjectures. If you can prove your conjectures, then the conjectures will become theorems. You can then use these theorems to make even more conjectures, which may also become theorems. Mathematicians use this process to create new mathematical ideas.

POSTULATE

LINEAR PAIR POSTULATE

If two angles form a linear pair, then the angles are supplementary.

1. Use the Linear Pair Postulate to complete each representation.

   (a) Draw and label a linear pair.

   Sample answer.

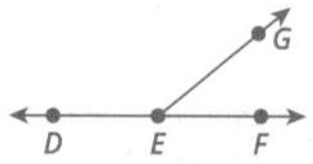

   (b) Use your labeled drawing and the Linear Pair Postulate to write the hypothesis.

   Angles *DEG* and *GEF* form a linear pair.

   (c) Use your labeled drawing and the Linear Pair Postulate to write the conclusion.

   Angles *DEG* and *GEF* are supplementary angles.

   (d) Use your conclusion and the definition of supplementary angles to write a statement about the measures of the angles in your figure.

   $m\angle DEG + m\angle GEF = 180°$

166 Topic 3 > Congruence Through Transformations

Questions to Support Discourse

	Questions	TYPE
1	• How do labels make it easier to discuss mathematical diagrams?	Gathering
	• Sketch an example of a linear pair that does not form a horizontal line. • If two angles are supplementary, do they form a linear pair? Explain your thinking.	Probing

ACTIVITY 3 Continued

POSTULATE

SEGMENT ADDITION POSTULATE

If point *B* is on $\overline{AC}$ and between points *A* and *C*, then $AB + BC = AC$.

2 Use the Segment Addition Postulate to complete each representation.

(a) Draw and label collinear points *D*, *E*, and *F* with point *E* between points *D* and *F*.

Sample answer.

(b) Use your labeled drawing and the Segment Addition Postulate to write the hypothesis.

Point *E* is on $\overline{DF}$ and between points *D* and *F*.

(c) Use your labeled drawing and the Segment Addition Postulate to write the conclusion.

$DE + EF = DF$

(d) Write your conclusion using measure notation.

$m\overline{DE} + m\overline{EF} = m\overline{DF}$

POSTULATE

ANGLE ADDITION POSTULATE

If point *D* lies in the interior of $\angle ABC$, then $m\angle ABD + m\angle DBC = m\angle ABC$.

3 Use the Angle Addition Postulate to complete each representation.

(a) Draw and label $\angle DEF$ with $\overrightarrow{EG}$ drawn in the interior of $\angle DEF$.

Sample answer.

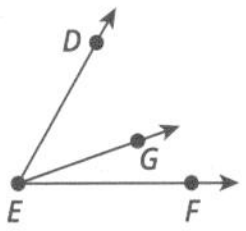

(b) Use your labeled drawing and the Angle Addition Postulate to write the hypothesis.

Point G lies in the interior of $\angle DEF$.

(c) Use your labeled drawing and the Angle Addition Postulate to write the conclusion.

$m\angle DEG + m\angle GEF = m\angle DEF$

NOTES

Student Look-Fors

- Confusion why the letters *D*, *E*, and *F* are used rather than *A*, *B*, and *C*. The postulate is a general statement to describe a situation.

Questions to Support Discourse

		TYPE
2	• According to the postulate, does point *E* have to be the midpoint? Why not?	Gathering
3	• How are the Segment Addition Postulate and Angle Addition Postulate related? • How can you apply this postulate to subtracting angles?	Seeing structure

TALK THE TALK

SUMMARY **A truth value is true when both *p* and *q* are true and whenever *p* is false. A truth value is false when *p* is true and *q* is false.**

Chunking the Activity

- Read and discuss the directions
- Group students to complete the activity
- Share and summarize

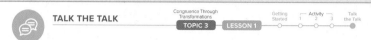

While You Were Away...

> Write a short note to a friend explaining conditional statements, truth values, and truth tables. Include definitions of all terms and examples that are easy to understand.

Sample answer.

A conditional statement is an "If *p*, then *q*" statement. The hypothesis is *p*, and the conclusion is *q*. For example, if the two numbers are 2 and 6, then the product is 12.

The truth value of a conditional statement is whether the statement is true or false, based upon whether *p* is true or false and *q* is true or false. There are four combinations.

1. If *p* is true, and *q* is true, then the conditional statement is true.
   If the two numbers are 2 and 6, then the product is 12 is a true statement.
2. If *p* is true, and *q* is false, then the conditional statement is false.
   If the two numbers are 2 and 6, then the product is not 12 is a false statement.
3. If *p* is false, and *q* is true, then the conditional statement is true.
   If the two numbers are not 2 and 6, then the product is 12 could be a true statement.

   This is true because the two numbers could be other values that have a product of 12, such as 3 and 4.
4. If *p* is false, and *q* is false, then the conditional statement is true.
   If the two numbers are not 2 and 6, then the product is not 12 could be a true statement.

   This is true because the two numbers could be other values that do not have a product of 12, such as 3 and 5 that have a product of 15.

   A truth table is a table that summarizes all possible truth values for a conditional statement.

Questions to Support Discourse

		TYPE
1	• What are the features of a conditional statement? • What are the two possible truth values? Gathering • Is the truth value based on the hypotenuse, conclusion, or the entire conditional statement?	
	• If the hypothesis is true, how do you determine the truth value of the conditional statement? • If the hypothesis is false, how do you determine the truth value of the conditional statement? • Why is the truth value of a conditional statement always true when the hypothesis is false? • Are all truth tables similar? How so? Why does this happen?	Seeing structure

ASSIGNMENT

LESSON 1 ASSIGNMENT

> Use a separate piece of paper for your Journal entry.

JOURNAL

Describe each postulate in your own words.

1. Linear Pair Postulate
2. Segment Addition Postulate
3. Angle Addition Postulate

REMEMBER

A conditional statement is a statement in the form "if p, then q." You read the expression $p \rightarrow q$, as "p implies q." The variable p represents the hypothesis, and the variable q represents the conclusion.

You can accept a postulate without proof, but you must prove that a theorem is true.

PRACTICE

1. Complete a truth table for the conditional statements.

(a) If ∠1 and ∠2 are vertical angles, then ∠1 ≅ ∠2.

p	q	$p \rightarrow q$
∠1 and ∠2 are vertical angles.	**∠1 ≅ ∠2**	**If ∠1 and ∠2 are vertical angles, then ∠1 ≅ ∠2.**
T	T	T
T	F	F
F	T	T
F	F	T

(b) If m∠1 = 100°, then ∠1 is an obtuse angle.

p	q	$p \rightarrow q$
m∠1 = 100°	**∠1 is an obtuse angle.**	**If m∠1 = 100°, then ∠1 is an obtuse angle.**
T	T	T
T	F	F
F	T	T
F	F	T

Go to LiveHint.com for help on the PRACTICE questions.

Encourage students to use LiveHint.com for help with the PRACTICE questions of this assignment.

Chunking the Assignment

SESSION 1

- Practice 1
- Stretch (advanced learners)
- Mixed Practice (page 197) 1 and 2

SESSION 2

- Journal
- Practice 2

JOURNAL

1. If two angles form a straight line, then the angles form a linear pair.
2. If a point B is between two other points A and C on a line segment, then $AB + BC = AC$.
3. If a point D lies in the interior of $\angle ABC$, then $m\angle ABD + m\angle DBC = m\angle ABC$.

TOPIC 3

ⓒ If a shape is a square, then the shape has four equal sides.

p	q	$p \rightarrow q$
A shape is a square.	**The shape has four equal sides.**	**If a shape is a square, then the shape has four equal sides.**
T	T	T
T	F	F
F	T	T
F	F	T

2 Write the postulate that confirms each statement.

ⓐ Angles *GFH* and *KFH* are supplementary angles.

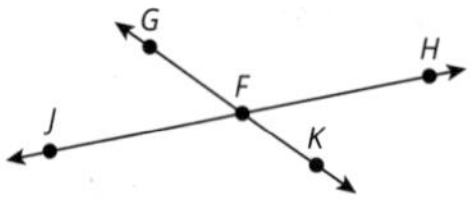

Linear Pair Postulate

ⓑ $m\overline{RS} + m\overline{ST} = m\overline{RT}$

Segment Addition Postulate

ⓒ $m\angle WXZ + m\angle ZXY = m\angle WXY$

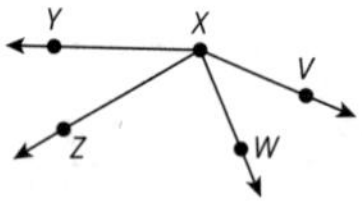

Angle Addition Postulate

ⓓ $m\angle 1 + m\angle 2 = 180°$

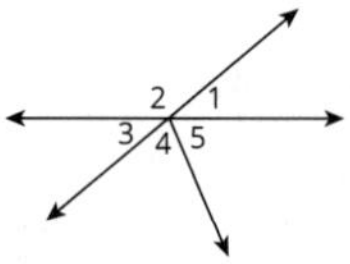

Linear Pair Postulate

STRETCH Optional

> Let the variable p represent the statement "the figure is a square" and let the variable q represent the statement "the figure is a quadrilateral."

1 Complete a truth table for the statements, then determine if conditional statements are commutative, that is $p \rightarrow q$ is the same as $q \rightarrow p$, by completing a truth table for $q \rightarrow p$.

NOTES

STRETCH

1. No, the truth tables do not match up, so conditional statements are not commutative, and $p \rightarrow q$ is not the same as $q \rightarrow p$.

p	q	$p \rightarrow q$
The figure is a square.	The figure is a quadrilateral.	If a figure is a square, then the figure is a quadrilateral.
T	T	T
T	F	F
F	T	T
F	F	T

p	q	$q \rightarrow p$
The figure is a quadrilateral.	The figure is a square.	If a figure is a quadrilateral, then the figure is a square.
T	T	T
T	F	T
F	T	F
F	F	T

The Elements

This resource details additional facilitation notes to fully assist you as you plan each lesson to support all students, students who struggle, and advanced learners. It provides differentiation strategies, common student misconceptions, and suggestions to extend certain activities.

ACTIVITY 1 — Counterexamples

Session 1 of 2

Students explore two reasons why a conclusion may be false. They learn that a counterexample is a specific example that shows that a general statement is not true.

CHUNK	AUDIENCE	ADDITIONAL SUPPORTS
As students share and summarize 4	All Students	**COMMON MISCONCEPTION** Students may assume that because they can use one counterexample to demonstrate a statement is false, they can use several examples to show that a statement is true. Explain that no number of examples is sufficient to prove that a statement is true. Instead, more formal reasoning is required.

ACTIVITY 2 — Conditional Statements and Truth Tables

Session 1 of 2

Students analyze conditional statements expressed as "If p, then q." They analyze and create a truth table for geometry-based conditional statements.

CHUNK	AUDIENCE	ADDITIONAL SUPPORTS
As students discuss the introduction	All Students	**DIFFERENTIATION STRATEGY** Have students highlight the term *could* in the statement, "If a conditional statement *could* be true, then the truth value of the statement is considered true." The importance of this word will become apparent as they respond to questions in this activity. Direct students to this statement as they respond to Questions 4 and 5 when p is false.
As students analyze the worked example	All Students	**COMMON MISCONCEPTION** Students sometimes try to relate the truth table results with the sign rules for integer multiplication. Have them use their reasoning in Question 4 to clarify this misconception.

ACTIVITY 3
Postulates and Theorems

Session 2 of 2

Students learn that postulates and theorems are systematically built upon to develop Euclidean geometry. They apply the Linear Pair Postulate, the Segment Addition Postulate, and the Angle Addition Postulate.

CHUNK	AUDIENCE	ADDITIONAL SUPPORTS
As you read and discuss the introduction	All Students	**DIFFERENTIATION STRATEGY** Have students illustrate the meaning of each postulate. For the fifth postulate, suggest they start with two parallel lines and a perpendicular transversal, then modify their diagram based on the given constraint.

Practice the learning

MATHbook + Skills Practice

The table shows the targeted practice of the skills and mathematical concepts for the *Congruence Through Transformations* Topic. The highlighted Problem Set aligns with **The Elements**.

PROBLEM SET	
1	**Conditional Statements, Truth Tables, and Postulates**
2	Triangle Congruence Theorems
3	Triangle Congruence Problems

ANYTIME AFTER ACTIVITY 3
Facilitate students as they work individually on **Problem Set 1**.

ENGAGE + DEVELOP + TEACH

at the **Module** level — at the **Topic** level — Read the facilitation notes and plan learning experiences.

Where are we?

TOPIC 3 Congruence Through Transformations	LESSON 1 The Elements	**LESSON 2 ASA, SAS, and SSS**	LESSON 3 I Never Forget a Face
Pacing	2 Sessions	**3 Sessions**	2 Sessions

OVERVIEW: LESSON 2

ASA, SAS, and SSS

Proving Triangle Congruence Theorems

ENGAGE

- Students consider the minimum criteria to determine whether two triangles are congruent.

DEVELOP

- Students interpret notation for congruent segments and angles and write congruence statements.
- They analyze a worked example that proves you can map a segment onto itself in at most two reflections.
- They prove the Side-Side-Side Congruence Theorem and the Angle-Side-Angle Congruence Theorem for triangles.
- They analyze a worked example that proves the Side-Angle-Side Congruence Theorem.
- Students investigate non-examples of congruence theorems.

DEMONSTRATE

- Students summarize the triangle congruence theorems.

HIGH SCHOOL GEOMETRY

Congruence

Understand congruence in terms of rigid motions.

7. Use the definition of congruence in terms of rigid motions to show that two triangles are congruent if and only if corresponding pairs of sides and corresponding pairs of angles are congruent.
8. Explain how the criteria for triangle congruence (ASA, SAS, and SSS) follow from the definition of congruence in terms of rigid motions.

LESSON STRUCTURE AND PACING GUIDE 3 SESSIONS

⊛ This activity highlights a key term or concept that is essential to the learning goals of the lesson.

Session 1		Session 2
INSTRUCTIONAL SEQUENCE		
ENGAGE Connect to prior knowledge	**DEVELOP** Worked example Mathematical problem solving	**DEVELOP** Mathematical problem solving

GETTING STARTED
Necessary Conditions

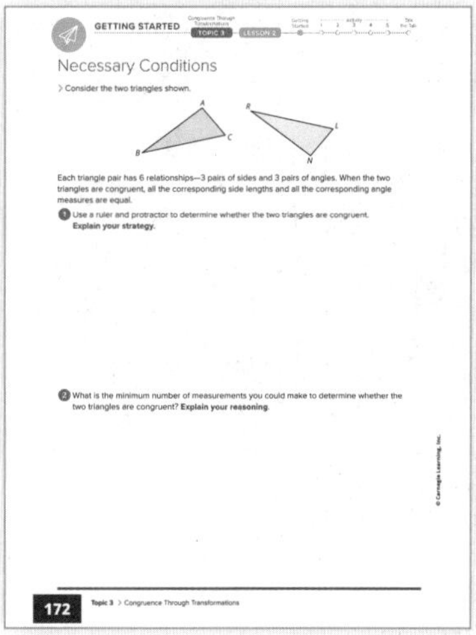

Students use measuring tools to determine whether two triangles are congruent.

- They consider the minimum criteria to determine whether two triangles are congruent.

⊛ ACTIVITY 1
Congruent Line Segments by Reflection

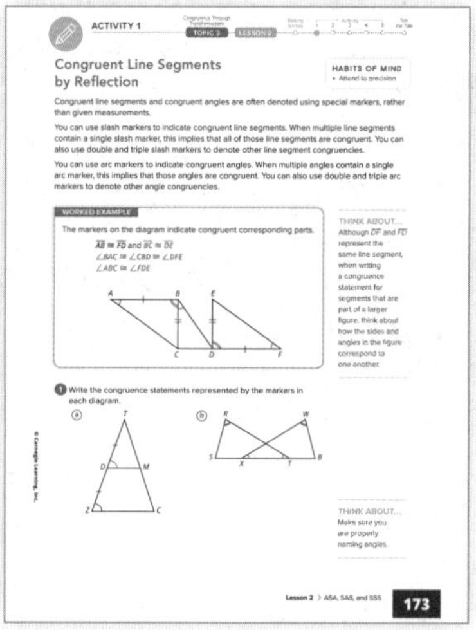

Students interpret notation for congruent segments and angles.

- They analyze a worked example that proves you can map a segment onto itself in at most two reflections.

⊛ ACTIVITY 2
Side-Side-Side Congruence

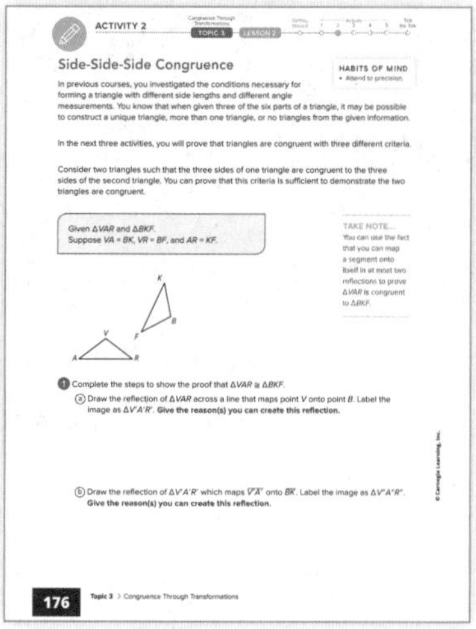

Students use reflections to prove the Side-Side-Side Congruence Theorem for triangles.

- They use corresponding parts of congruent triangles are congruent (CPCTC) reasoning to write congruence statements.

Log in to MyCL for **lesson support** including:

Slides

Videos

www.carnegielearning.com/login

Session 3

INSTRUCTIONAL SEQUENCE

DEVELOP	DEVELOP	DEVELOP
Worked example Mathematical problem solving	**Mathematical problem solving**	**Mathematical problem solving**

ACTIVITY 3
Side-Angle-Side Congruence

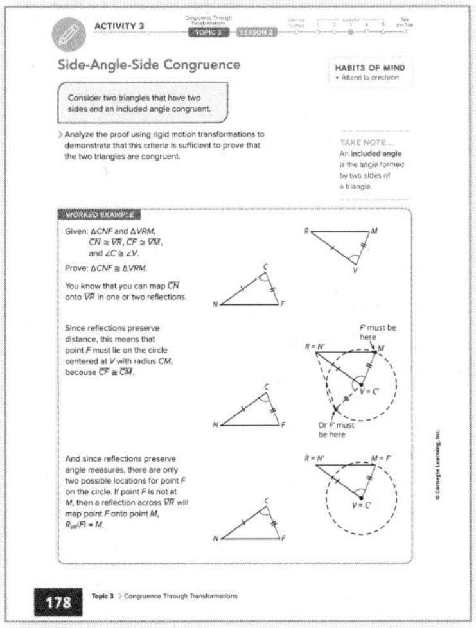

Students analyze a worked example that proves the Side-Angle-Side (SAS) Congruence Theorem.

- They prove two triangles are congruent using the SAS Theorem.

ACTIVITY 4
Angle-Side-Angle Congruence

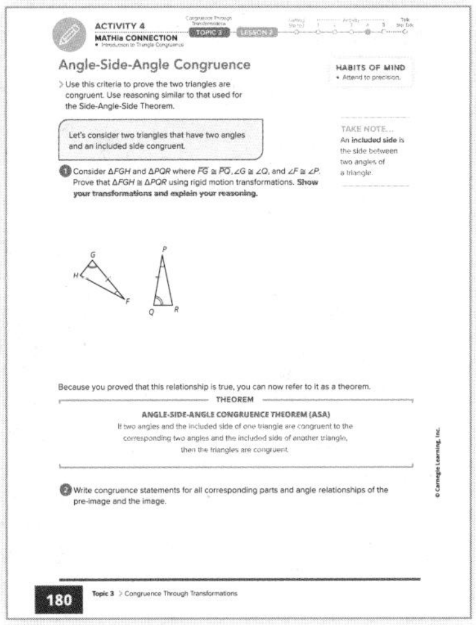

Students prove the Angle-Side-Angle Congruence Theorem using reflections.

- They write congruence statements for corresponding parts.

ACTIVITY 5
Non-Examples of Congruence Theorems

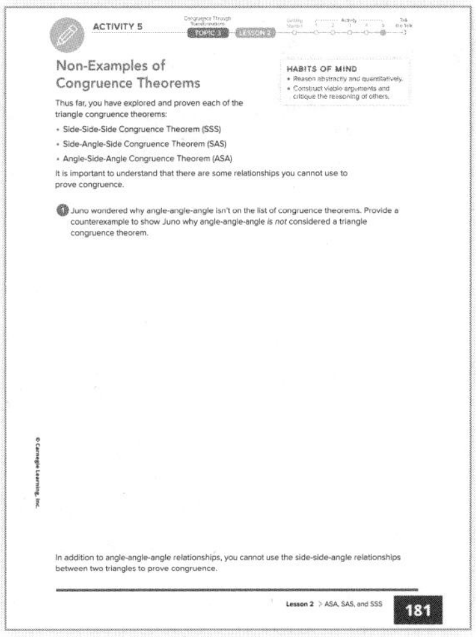

Students investigate non-examples of congruence theorems.

- They show that Angle-Angle-Angle or Side-Side-Angle congruence does not define unique triangles.

TOPIC 3

Log in to MyCL for:

- Editable templates
- Additional planning support

Session 3

INSTRUCTIONAL SEQUENCE

DEVELOP
Graphic organizer

TALK THE TALK
The Right Combination

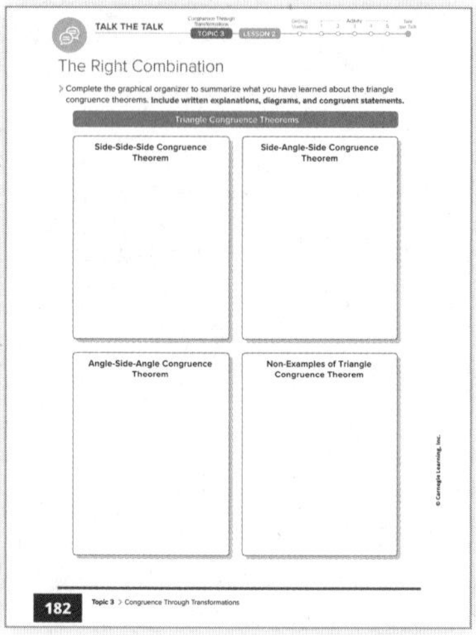
TALK THE TALK

The Right Combination

Complete the graphical organizer to summarize what you have learned about the triangle congruence theorems. Include written explanations, diagrams, and congruent statements.

Triangle Congruence Theorems

Side-Side-Side Congruence Theorem	Side-Angle-Side Congruence Theorem
Angle-Side-Angle Congruence Theorem	Non-Examples of Triangle Congruence Theorem

182 Topic 3 > Congruence Through Transformations

Students complete a graphic organizer that summarizes the triangle congruence theorems.

- They explain the theorems using diagrams, written explanations, and congruence statements.

Now that you have read the Module, Topic, and Lesson Overviews, you are ready to plan.

Do the math

Tear out the lesson planning template (page 171E) and jot down thoughts as you work through this lesson and read the Facilitation Notes.

Connect the learning

MATHbook + MATHia

The table shows the self-paced MATHia sequence for the *Congruence Through Transformations* Topic.

Median student completion time: ~90–110 minutes

As you implement this lesson, consider different connections for students who are on pace and those that have not yet completed the workspaces aligned to this lesson.

STUDENTS WHO ARE NOT HERE YET
Students practice writing and identifying triangle congruency statements and corresponding sides and angles, given a diagram of congruent triangles or a triangle congruency statement.

TYPE	WORKSPACE NAME
	Calculating and Justifying Angle Measures
	Calculating Angle Measures
	Introduction to Triangle Congruence
	Using Triangle Congruence

STUDENTS WHO ARE ON PACE
After you complete Activity 4, ask these students to share how they sorted pairs of triangles to the theorem by which they are proven congruent.

ASA, SAS, and SSS

Proving Triangle Congruence Theorems

Session 1

GETTING STARTED Necessary Conditions

Pacing (minutes)	
My Time	Class Time

ACTIVITY 1 Congruent Line Segments by Reflection ✪

Pacing (minutes)	
My Time	Class Time

Session 2

ACTIVITY 2 Side-Side-Side Congruence ✪

Pacing (minutes)	
My Time	Class Time

KEY TERM

Side-Side-Side Congruence Theorem (SSS)

Corresponding parts of congruent triangles are congruent (CPCTC)

ACTIVITY 3 Side-Angle-Side Congruence ✪

Pacing (minutes)	
My Time	Class Time

KEY TERM

included angle

Side-Angle-Side Congruence Theorem (SAS)

Session 3

ACTIVITY 4 Angle-Side-Angle Congruence ✪

Pacing (minutes)	
My Time	Class Time

KEY TERM

included side

Angle-Side-Angle Congruence Theorem (ASA)

ACTIVITY 5 Non-Examples of Congruence Theorems

Pacing (minutes)	
My Time	Class Time

TALK THE TALK The Right Combination ✪

Pacing (minutes)	
My Time	Class Time

✪ This activity highlights a key term or concept that is essential to the learning goals of the lesson.

Log in to MyCL for:

- Editable templates
- Additional planning support

Reflect on your lesson

Consider the effectiveness of your lesson on student learning.

What went well?	What did not go as planned?

Anticipate how you would change the lesson next time you teach it.

How will you capitalize on the things that went well?	How will you improve things that did not go as planned?

MATERIALS

- Compasses
- Patty Paper
- Protractors
- Rulers
- Straightedges

TOPIC 1
Using a Rectangular Coordinate System

TOPIC 2
Rigid Motions on a Plane

TOPIC 3
Congruence Through Transformations

1 | The Elements
2 | ASA, SAS, and SSS
3 | I Never Forget a Face

LESSON 2

ASA, SAS, and SSS

Proving Triangle Congruence Theorems

Learning Goals

- Use the definition of congruence in terms of rigid motions to show that two triangles are congruent.
- Prove the Side-Side-Side Congruence Theorem, the Side-Angle-Side Congruence Theorem, and the Angle-Side-Angle Congruence Theorem using rigid motion transformations.

KEY TERMS

- Side-Side-Side Congruence Theorem (SSS)
- corresponding parts of congruent triangles are congruent (CPCTC)
- included angle
- Side-Angle-Side Congruence Theorem (SAS)
- included side
- Angle-Side-Angle Congruence Theorem (ASA)

REVIEW (1–2 minutes)

> Describe transformations that map Figure *A* onto the other figures shown.

1. Figure *B*

   Translate Figure *A* down onto Figure *B*.

2. Figure *C*

   Reflect Figure *A* across a vertical line of reflection between Figures *A* and *C*.

3. Figure *D*

   Rotate Figure *A* counterclockwise 180° onto Figure *D*.

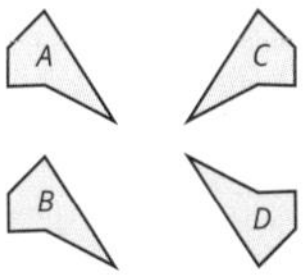

You have defined the transformations that produce isometries.

How can you use isometries to prove congruence theorems?

Setting the Stage

- **Assign Review (optional, 1 – 2 minutes)**
- **Communicate the learning goals and key terms to look out for**
- **Tap into your students' prior learning by reading the narrative statement**
- **Provide a sense of direction by reading the question**

IN THIS REVIEW
Students describe transformations to map one figure onto another. They will use this skill in **ACTIVITY 1 Congruent Line Segments by Reflection.**

You can use the SSS, SAS, and ASA Congruence Theorems to prove that triangle pairs are congruent.

TOPIC 3

Essential Ideas

- It is possible to conclude two triangles are congruent using fewer than six pairs of corresponding parts.
- If three sides of one triangle are congruent to the corresponding sides of another triangle, then the triangles are congruent.
- If two triangles have two corresponding sides and their included angles congruent, then the triangles are congruent.
- If two triangles have two corresponding angles and their included sides congruent, then the triangles are congruent.
- Corresponding parts of congruent triangles are congruent, CPCTC, which means that when two triangles are congruent, each part of one triangle is congruent to the other triangle's corresponding part.

SUMMARY **It is possible to conclude two triangles are congruent using fewer than six pairs of corresponding parts.**

Chunking the Activity

- **Read and discuss the introduction**
- **Group students to complete the activity**
- **Share and summarize**

Student Look-Fors

- Comments regarding middle school experiences where students determined whether they could construct a unique triangle from a combination of three measures of angles and sides.
- The realization that when two triangles have two pairs of congruent angles, then the third angle pair is also congruent.

Necessary Conditions

> Consider the two triangles shown.

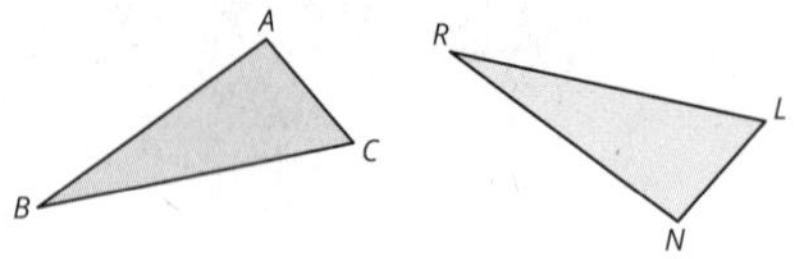

Each triangle pair has 6 relationships—3 pairs of sides and 3 pairs of angles. When the two triangles are congruent, all the corresponding side lengths and all the corresponding angle measures are equal.

1. Use a ruler and protractor to determine whether the two triangles are congruent. **Explain your strategy.**

   Sample answer.

   I measured all three pairs of corresponding angles, and each pair of angles was congruent. I measured all three pairs of corresponding sides, and each pair of sides was congruent.

2. What is the minimum number of measurements you could make to determine whether the two triangles are congruent? **Explain your reasoning.**

   Answers will vary.

   Student answers may range between comparing 3 to 6 pairs of corresponding parts, requiring 6 to 12 measurements.

Questions to Support Discourse

		TYPE
1	• Which side of ΔRNL is congruent to side $\overline{AB}$? Side $\overline{AC}$? Side $\overline{BC}$? • Which angle of ΔRNL is congruent to $\angle A$? $\angle B$? $\angle C$?	Probing
2	• Was there a point in your measuring where you recognized that the remaining sides and angles would have to be congruent as well? If so, when?	Probing

ACTIVITY 1

SUMMARY You can prove a conjecture using known facts and constructions in a logical order.

Congruent Line Segments by Reflection

HABITS OF MIND
- Attend to precision.

Congruent line segments and congruent angles are often denoted using special markers, rather than given measurements.

You can use slash markers to indicate congruent line segments. When multiple line segments contain a single slash marker, this implies that all of those line segments are congruent. You can also use double and triple slash markers to denote other line segment congruencies.

You can use arc markers to indicate congruent angles. When multiple angles contain a single arc marker, this implies that those angles are congruent. You can also use double and triple arc markers to denote other angle congruencies.

WORKED EXAMPLE

The markers on the diagram indicate congruent corresponding parts.

$\overline{AB} \cong \overline{FD}$ and $\overline{BC} \cong \overline{DE}$

$\angle BAC \cong \angle CBD \cong \angle DFE$

$\angle ABC \cong \angle FDE$

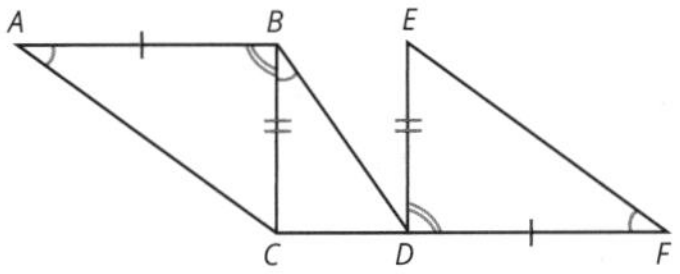

THINK ABOUT... Although $\overline{DF}$ and $\overline{FD}$ represent the same line segment, when writing a congruence statement for segments that are part of a larger figure, think about how the sides and angles in the figure correspond to one another.

1 Write the congruence statements represented by the markers in each diagram.

(a)

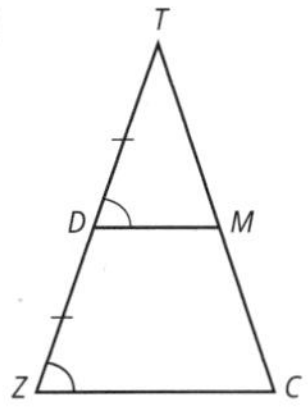

$\angle TDM \cong \angle TZC$

$\overline{TD} \cong \overline{DZ}$

(b)

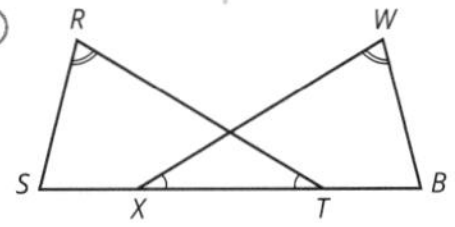

$\angle R \cong \angle W$

$\angle WXB \cong \angle RTS$

THINK ABOUT... Make sure you are properly naming angles.

Chunking the Activity

- Read and discuss the introduction and worked example
- Group students to complete 1
- Check-in and share
- Read and discuss the text and worked example
- Group students to complete 2 and 3
- Share and summarize

DIFFERENTIATION STRATEGY

See Page 184A to assist all students with the worked example.

DIFFERENTIATION STRATEGY

See Page 184A to assist all students to extend 1.

Questions to Support Discourse

		TYPE
Worked Example	• Why does it make sense to write the congruence statement as $\overline{AB} \cong \overline{FD}$ rather than $\overline{AB} \cong \overline{DF}$? • How do the corresponding parts of the triangles help you determine the order to name the endpoints of the line segments?	Seeing structure
1	• Why can you identify $\angle R$ with one letter, but you must use three letters to identify $\angle RTS$?	Seeing structure

NOTES

DIFFERENTIATION STRATEGY

See Page 184A to assist all students with the worked example.

NOTE: Students explored this concept with a conjecture in Lesson 3 of the previous topic.

ACTIVITY 1 Continued

In previous lessons, you learned that:

1. Isometries preserve distances and angle measures.
2. You can reflect any point in the plane across a line to map onto another point in the plane.
3. A point is equidistant from two other points if and only if it lies on their perpendicular bisector.

You can use these facts to prove a conjecture that you have explored. Prove that you can always map one congruent line segment onto the other using at most two reflections.

REMEMBER...
A proof is a series of statements and corresponding reasons forming a valid argument that starts with a hypothesis and arrives at a conclusion.

WORKED EXAMPLE

Prove that you can map segment onto itself in at most two reflections.

Suppose that $\overline{AB} \cong \overline{CD}$.

Since you can reflect any point in the plane across a line to map onto another point in the plane, you know that point C is a reflection of point A across line m.

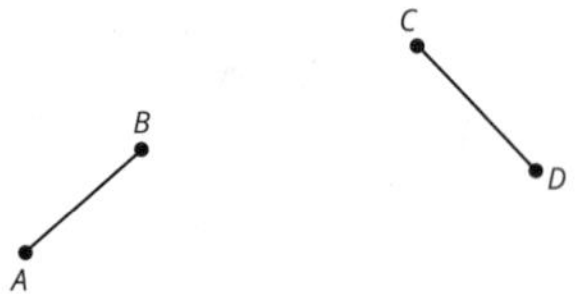

Reflect $\overline{AB}$ across line m, $R_m(\overline{AB})$.

Reflections preserve distances, so you know that $\overline{CB'} \cong \overline{CD}$, because $\overline{AB} \cong \overline{CD}$ and $\overline{AB} \cong \overline{CB'}$. Thus, point C is equidistant from point B' and from point D.

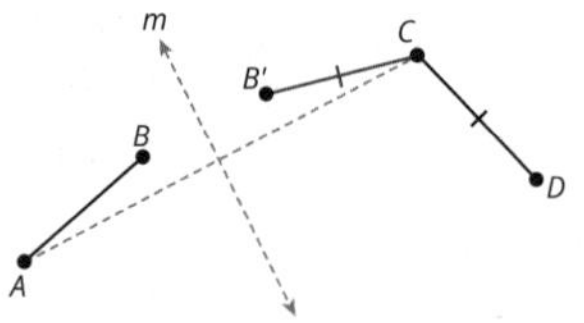

Since a point is equidistant from two other points if and only if it lies on their perpendicular bisector, this means that point C lies on the perpendicular bisector of $\overline{B'D}$ (line n).

Thus, one last reflection across the perpendicular bisector maps $\overline{CB'}$ onto $\overline{CD}$, $R_n(\overline{CB'}) \rightarrow (\overline{CD})$.

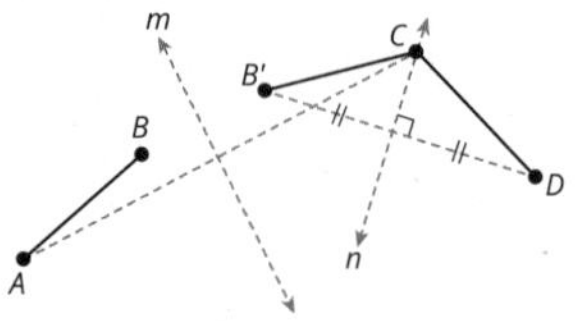

174 Topic 3 > Congruence Through Transformations

Questions to Support Discourse

		TYPE
Worked Example	• How was the position of line m determined? • Why does the line n have to pass through Point C? • How were the three facts listed before the worked example used in the proof?	Probing

ACTIVITY 1 Continued

2 The proof in the worked example shows two reflections. Create an example in which $\overline{AB}$ maps onto $\overline{CD}$ in just one reflection. **Explain your example.**

Sample answers.

$\overline{CD}$ and $\overline{AB}$ could be opposite sides of a square, such that point A and point C are consecutive vertices. The line of reflection would be the line connecting the midpoints of sides $\overline{AC}$ and $\overline{BD}$.

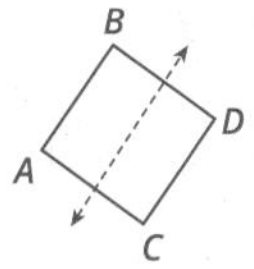

$\overline{CD}$ could be the same length as $\overline{AB}$, and point C and point A could be at the same location.

The line of reflection would be the angle bisector of $\angle DAB$ or $\angle DCB$.

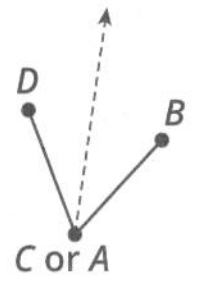

$\overline{CD}$ could be the same length as $\overline{AB}$, and point B and point D could be at the same location.

The line of reflection would be the angle bisector of $\angle ABC$ or $\angle ADC$.

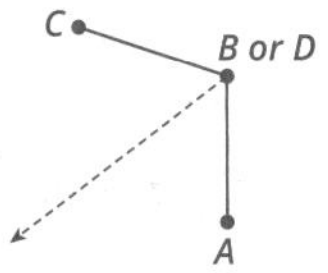

3 Use the worked example to explain why you do not need more than two reflections to map a line segment onto a congruent line segment in the plane.

One reflection is needed to map an endpoint of one segment onto the endpoint of the other segment. The second reflection maps the entire segment onto the congruent line segment.

Lesson 2 > ASA, SAS, and SSS 175

Questions to Support Discourse

		TYPE
2	• How could you use a figure with symmetry to complete this task? • How could you use two segments with a common vertex to eliminate one reflection?	Probing

NOTES

TOPIC 3

ACTIVITY 2

SUMMARY If three sides of one triangle are congruent to the corresponding sides of another triangle, then the triangles are congruent.

Chunking the Activity

- **Read and discuss the introduction**
- **Complete 1 as a class**
- **Check-in and share**
- **Group students to complete 2**
- **Read and discuss the theorem**
- **Group students to complete 3**
- **Share and summarize**

DIFFERENTIATION STRATEGY

See Page 184B to support students who struggle with 1.

Student Look-Fors

Utilizing relationship skills by communicating clearly and listening well.

Side-Side-Side Congruence

HABITS OF MIND
- Attend to precision.

In previous courses, you investigated the conditions necessary for forming a triangle with different side lengths and different angle measurements. You know that when given three of the six parts of a triangle, it may be possible to construct a unique triangle, more than one triangle, or no triangles from the given information.

In the next three activities, you will prove that triangles are congruent with three different criteria.

Consider two triangles such that the three sides of one triangle are congruent to the three sides of the second triangle. You can prove that this criteria is sufficient to demonstrate the two triangles are congruent.

Given ΔVAR and ΔBKF.
Suppose $VA = BK$, $VR = BF$, and $AR = KF$.

TAKE NOTE...
You can use the fact that you can map a segment onto itself in at most two reflections to prove ΔVAR is congruent to ΔBKF.

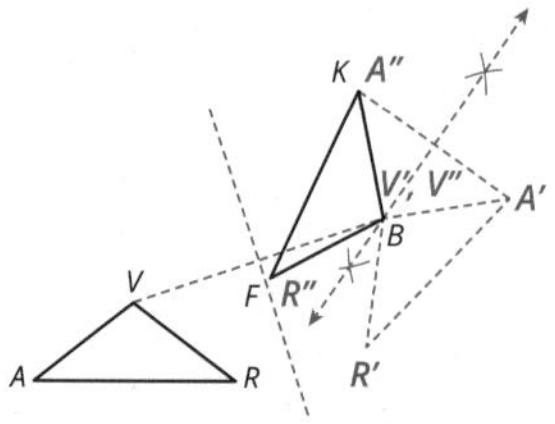

1 Complete the steps to show the proof that $\Delta VAR \cong \Delta BKF$.

(a) Draw the reflection of ΔVAR across a line that maps point V onto point B. Label the image as $\Delta V'A'R'$. **Give the reason(s) you can create this reflection.**

You can reflect any point in the plane across a line to map onto another point in the plane. In this case, V is mapped onto B.

(b) Draw the reflection of $\Delta V'A'R'$ which maps $\overline{V'A'}$ onto $\overline{BK}$. Label the image as $\Delta V''A''R''$. **Give the reason(s) you can create this reflection.**

See figure above.
You can map a segment onto itself in at most two reflections.

Questions to Support Discourse

		TYPE
Intro	• Which minimal criteria are we going to investigate in this activity?	Gathering
	• Will any three side lengths form a triangle? Provide examples and non-examples.	Probing
1	• Why do you need to map point V onto point B in part (a)? • How did you reflect the triangle? • Which reason did you select from the original three facts provided? • Why did your subsequent reflection in part (b) involve mapping segments instead of points?	Probing

ACTIVITY 2 Continued

2 Summarize the proof you completed in Question 1. Explain how knowing that the three corresponding sides of two triangles proves that the two triangles are congruent.

Sample answer.

One side of ΔVAR is mapped onto its corresponding side in ΔBFK through two reflections. This series of reflections, which preserves distance and angle measures, also maps the remainder of the triangle, its other two pairs of corresponding sides and three angles, onto each other. Knowing that two triangles have three pairs of corresponding sides proves the two triangles are congruent.

Because you proved that this relationship is true, you can now refer to it as a theorem.

REMEMBER...
You can use any theorem in the future as a reason in other proofs.

THEOREM

SIDE-SIDE-SIDE CONGRUENCE THEOREM (SSS)

If three sides of one triangle are congruent to the corresponding sides of another triangle, then the triangles are congruent.

If two triangles are congruent, then each part of one triangle is congruent to the corresponding part of the other triangle. **Corresponding parts of congruent triangles are congruent**, abbreviated as **CPCTC**, is often used as a reason in proofs. CPCTC states that corresponding angles and sides in two congruent triangles are congruent.

You can only use this reason after you have proven that the triangles are congruent.

3 Write congruence statements for all corresponding side and angle relationships of the pre-image and the image.

$VA = BK$	$\overline{VA} \cong \overline{BK}$	$\angle V \cong \angle B$
$VR = BF$	$\overline{VR} \cong \overline{BF}$	$\angle A \cong \angle K$
$AR = KF$	$\overline{AR} \cong \overline{KF}$	$\angle R \cong \angle F$
$m\angle V = m\angle B$		
$m\angle A = m\angle K$		
$m\angle R = m\angle F$		

Lesson 2 > ASA, SAS, and SSS 177

NOTES

DIFFERENTIATION STRATEGY

See Page 184B to support students who struggle with 3.

TOPIC 3

Questions to Support Discourse

		TYPE
2	• What do isometries have to do with your reasoning?	Seeing structure
Theorem	• Why don't you have to prove that the three pairs of corresponding angles are congruent?	Seeing structure
3	• How can you determine the angle and side congruencies from the diagram? From the triangle congruence statement?	Probing

SUMMARY **If two triangles have two corresponding sides and their included angles congruent, then the triangles are congruent.**

Chunking the Activity

- **Read and discuss the introduction and worked example**
- **Complete 1 as a class**
- **Read and discuss the theorem**
- **Group students to complete 2 and 3**
- **Share and summarize**

DIFFERENTIATION STRATEGY

See Page 184B to assist all students with the worked example.

Side-Angle-Side Congruence

HABITS OF MIND
- Attend to precision.

Consider two triangles that have two sides and an included angle congruent.

> Analyze the proof using rigid motion transformations to demonstrate that this criteria is sufficient to prove that the two triangles are congruent.

TAKE NOTE...
An **included angle** is the angle formed by two sides of a triangle.

WORKED EXAMPLE

Given: ΔCNF and ΔVRM,
$\overline{CN} \cong \overline{VR}$, $\overline{CF} \cong \overline{VM}$,
and $\angle C \cong \angle V$.

Prove: $\Delta CNF \cong \Delta VRM$.

You know that you can map $\overline{CN}$ onto $\overline{VR}$ in one or two reflections.

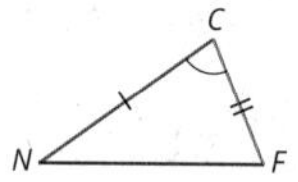

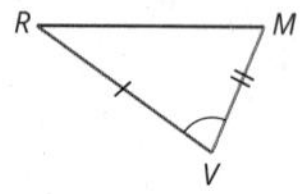

Since reflections preserve distance, this means that point F must lie on the circle centered at V with radius CM, because $\overline{CF} \cong \overline{CM}$.

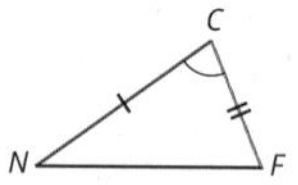

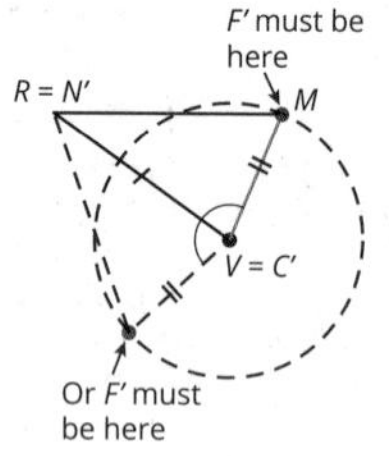

And since reflections preserve angle measures, there are only two possible locations for point F on the circle. If point F is not at M, then a reflection across $\overline{VR}$ will map point F onto point M, $R_{\overline{VR}}(F) \rightarrow M$.

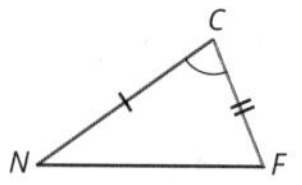

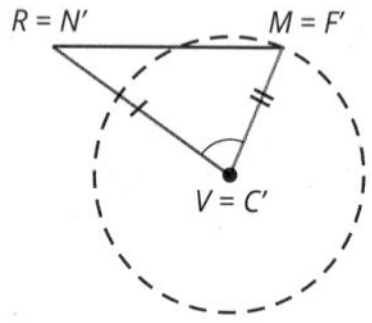

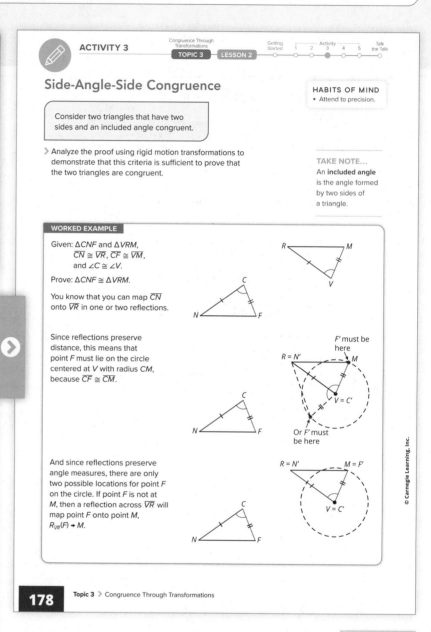

Questions to Support Discourse

		TYPE
Worked Example	• What is the purpose of the circle in the diagram? • Explain how the diagram models the reflection notation.	Probing
	• Why is using reflections a valid strategy in proofs?	Seeing structure

ACTIVITY 3 Continued

1 Explain the final steps in the worked example.

(a) Why are there only two locations that point F' could lie in relation to points V and R?

The congruent corresponding angle measures tell us that point F' can be at only 2 places on the circle—as a reflection across side VR.

(b) Why will a reflection across $\overline{VR}$ map point F' onto point M?

Point M and point F are equidistant from point V, so V lies on the perpendicular bisector of $\overline{MF'}$.

Because you proved that this relationship is true, you may now refer to it as a theorem.

THEOREM

SIDE-ANGLE-SIDE CONGRUENCE THEOREM (SAS)

If two sides and the included angle of one triangle are congruent to the corresponding two sides and the included angle of a second triangle, then the triangles are congruent.

2 Consider the diagram shown where $\overline{AB} \cong \overline{DE}$, $\overline{AC} \cong \overline{DF}$, and $\angle A \cong \angle D$.

Prove $\Delta ABC \cong \Delta DEF$ using rigid motion transformations. **Explain your steps.**

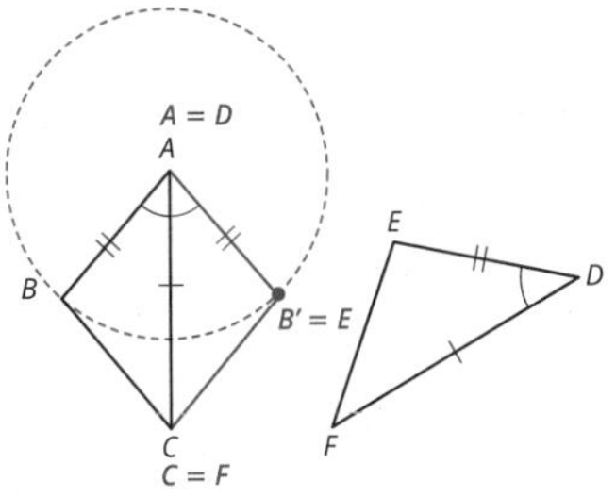

$\overline{AC}$ maps onto $\overline{DF}$ in one or two reflections. Reflections preserve distance, so point B must be on a circle centered at point D with a radius of AE, because $\overline{AB} \cong \overline{AE}$.

Reflections preserve angle measure, so there are only two possible locations for point B' to be on the circle. If point B' is not at point E, then a reflection across $\overline{DF}$ will map point B' onto point E, $R_{\overline{DF}}(B) = E$.

3 Write congruence statements for all corresponding parts and angle relationships of the pre-image and the image.

$\overline{AB} \cong \overline{DE}$	$\angle A \cong \angle D$
$\overline{AC} \cong \overline{DF}$	$\angle B \cong \angle E$
$\overline{BC} \cong \overline{EF}$	$\angle C \cong \angle F$

Questions to Support Discourse

		TYPE
Theorem	• Why does the theorem include the phrase *included angle* instead of *angle*?	Gathering
3	• How do you know that all six pairs of corresponding parts are congruent?	Seeing structure

NOTES

COMMON MISCONCEPTION

See Page 184B for a misconception related to 1.

ACTIVITY 4

SUMMARY **If two triangles have two corresponding angles and their included sides congruent, then the triangles are congruent.**

Chunking the Activity

- **Read and discuss the introduction**
- **Complete 1 as a class**
- **Read and discuss the theorem**
- **Group students to complete 2**
- **Share and summarize**

Angle-Side-Angle Congruence

> Use this criteria to prove the two triangles are congruent. Use reasoning similar to that used for the Side-Angle-Side Theorem.

HABITS OF MIND
- Attend to precision.

Let's consider two triangles that have two angles and an included side congruent.

TAKE NOTE...
An **included side** is the side between two angles of a triangle.

1 Consider ΔFGH and ΔPQR where $\overline{FG} \cong \overline{PQ}$, $\angle G \cong \angle Q$, and $\angle F \cong \angle P$. Prove that $\Delta FGH \cong \Delta PQR$ using rigid motion transformations. **Show your transformations and explain your reasoning.**

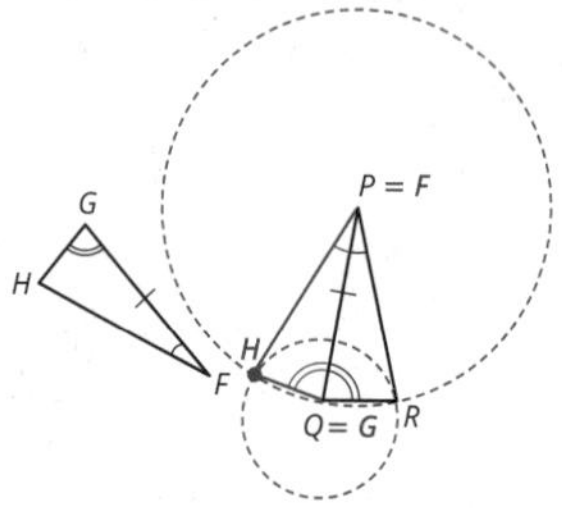

You can map side *FG* onto side *PQ* in at most two reflections. A final reflection maps the two triangles onto each other.

Because you proved that this relationship is true, you can now refer to it as a theorem.

THEOREM

ANGLE-SIDE-ANGLE CONGRUENCE THEOREM (ASA)

If two angles and the included side of one triangle are congruent to the corresponding two angles and the included side of another triangle, then the triangles are congruent.

2 Write congruence statements for all corresponding parts and angle relationships of the pre-image and the image.

$\angle H \cong \angle R$ $\quad$ $\overline{HG} \cong \overline{RQ}$

$\angle G \cong \angle Q$ $\quad$ $\overline{HF} \cong \overline{RP}$

$\angle F \cong \angle P$ $\quad$ $\overline{GF} \cong \overline{QP}$

Questions to Support Discourse

		TYPE
1	• How can you map $\overline{FG}$ onto $\overline{PQ}$ in two reflections? • How does your strategy compare to the previous two proofs?	Probing
Theorem	• Could you also refer to this theorem by SAA or AAS? Why not?	Gathering
2	• Is it easier to write the congruence statements from the triangle congruence statement or the diagram? Why?	Gathering
	• How do you know that all six pairs of corresponding parts are congruent?	Reflecting and justifying

ACTIVITY 5

SUMMARY **The congruence conjectures AAA and SSA are not valid because you can create counterexamples to disprove them.**

Non-Examples of Congruence Theorems

HABITS OF MIND
- Reason abstractly and quantitatively.
- Construct viable arguments and critique the reasoning of others.

Thus far, you have explored and proven each of the triangle congruence theorems:

- Side-Side-Side Congruence Theorem (SSS)
- Side-Angle-Side Congruence Theorem (SAS)
- Angle-Side-Angle Congruence Theorem (ASA)

It is important to understand that there are some relationships you cannot use to prove congruence.

1. Juno wondered why angle-angle-angle isn't on the list of congruence theorems. Provide a counterexample to show Juno why angle-angle-angle *is not* considered a triangle congruence theorem.

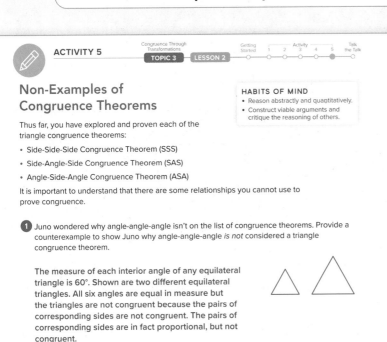

The measure of each interior angle of any equilateral triangle is 60°. Shown are two different equilateral triangles. All six angles are equal in measure but the triangles are not congruent because the pairs of corresponding sides are not congruent. The pairs of corresponding sides are in fact proportional, but not congruent.

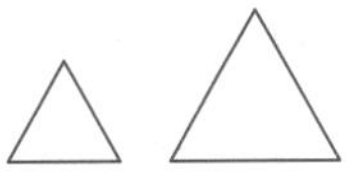

In addition to angle-angle-angle relationships, you cannot use the side-side-angle relationships between two triangles to prove congruence.

Chunking the Activity

- Read and discuss the introduction
- Group students to complete 1
- Check-in and share
- Complete 2 as a class
- Share and summarize

Questions to Support Discourse

		TYPE
1	• How many different triangles can you form using the same SSA criteria? • Why does it help to use a circle to create two triangles with the same criteria?	Probing
	• What relationship exists between the two triangles you formed using AAA? • Why does creating two different triangles with this same criteria disprove your conjecture?	Seeing structure
	• How many counterexamples are necessary to disprove any conjecture? • How many examples are necessary to prove a conjecture?	Reflecting and justifying

TALK THE TALK

SUMMARY **You can prove two triangles are congruent using the SSS, SAS, and ASA Theorems. You cannot prove triangles are congruent using AAA and SSA.**

Chunking the Activity

- **Read and discuss the directions**
- **Group students to complete the activity**
- **Share and summarize**

Student Look-Fors

Diagrams with labels, explanations in words, and congruence statements.

The Right Combination

Complete the graphical organizer to summarize what you have learned about the triangle congruence theorems. **Include written explanations, diagrams, and congruent statements.**

Triangle Congruence Theorems

Side-Side-Side Congruence Theorem

When the three sides of one triangle are congruent to the corresponding three sides of another triangle, then the triangles are congruent.

Check students' drawings and congruent statements.

Side-Angle-Side Congruence Theorem

When the two sides and the included angle of one triangle are congruent to the corresponding two sides and included angle of another triangle, then the triangles are congruent.

Check students' drawings and congruent statements.

Angle-Side-Angle Congruence Theorem

When two angles and the included side of one triangle are congruent to the corresponding two angles and included side of another triangle, then the triangle are congruent.

Check students' drawings and congruent statements.

Non-Examples of Triangle Congruence Theorem

You can not use angle-angle-angle or side-side-angle relationships to prove triangle congruence.

Questions to Support Discourse

		TYPE
Graphic Organizer	• Which are the different minimal criteria to prove that two triangles are congruent?	Gathering
	• State the theorem in your own words. • How did you use diagrams and mathematical notation to describe this theorem?	Probing
	• What general method did you use to prove these theorems? • Once you prove two triangles are congruent, how do you know that all corresponding sides and angles of the two triangles are congruent?	Reflecting and justifying

ASSIGNMENT

LESSON 2 ASSIGNMENT

> Use a separate piece of paper for your Journal entry.

JOURNAL

Explain how you can list the six pairs of corresponding parts of congruent triangles by using the triangle congruence statement rather than a diagram.

REMEMBER

The SSS Congruence Theorem states that if three sides of one triangle are congruent to the corresponding sides of another triangle, then the triangles are congruent.

The SAS Congruence Theorem states that if two sides and the included angle of one triangle are congruent to the corresponding two sides and included angle of another triangle, then the triangles are congruent.

The ASA Congruence Theorem states that if two angles and the included side of one triangle are congruent to the corresponding angles and included side of another triangle, then the triangles are congruent.

PRACTICE

1. Draw two triangles that correspond with each congruence statement. Then list the six pairs of congruent corresponding parts.

ⓐ $\Delta CGB \cong \Delta JMV$

Sample answer.

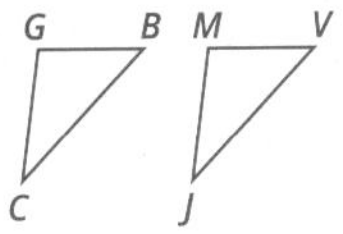

$\angle C \cong \angle J$, $\angle G \cong \angle M$,
$\angle B \cong \angle V$, $\overline{CG} \cong \overline{JM}$,
$\overline{GB} \cong \overline{MV}$, $\overline{CB} \cong \overline{JV}$

ⓑ $\Delta LBR \cong \Delta MDS$

Sample answer.

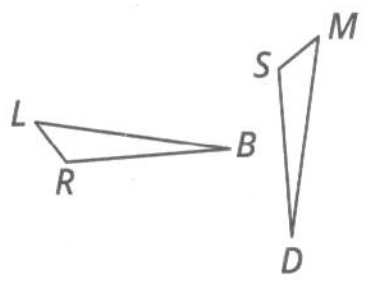

$\angle L \cong \angle M$, $\angle B \cong \angle D$,
$\angle R \cong \angle S$, $\overline{LB} \cong \overline{MD}$,
$\overline{BR} \cong \overline{DS}$, $\overline{RL} \cong \overline{SM}$

Go to LiveHint.com for help on the PRACTICE questions.

Encourage students to use LiveHint.com for help with the PRACTICE questions of this assignment.

Chunking the Assignment

SESSION 1

- Mixed Practice (page 197) 3 - 5

SESSION 2

- Journal
- Practice 1
- Stretch (advanced learners)

SESSION 3

- Practice 2

JOURNAL

If given a congruence statement, each letter represents an angle. The first letter of each triangle represents a pair of congruent angles, as do the second letters and the third letters. For example, for $\Delta ABC \cong \Delta XYZ$, $\angle A \cong \angle X$, $\angle B \cong \angle Y$, and $\angle C \cong \angle Z$.

If given a congruence statement, each pair of letters represents a side. The order of the letters matters. To get three different pairs of sides, use the first two letters, the second and third letters, and the first and last letters. For example, for $\Delta ABC \cong \Delta XYZ$, $\overline{AB} \cong \overline{XY}$, $\overline{BC} \cong \overline{YZ}$, and $\overline{AC} \cong \overline{XZ}$.

NOTES

2 For each figure, use rigid motions to verify that the triangles are congruent. State the congruence theorem that you used.

(a) Given: Parallelogram $ABCD$ with and $\overline{AB} \parallel \overline{CD}$
Verify that $\Delta ABD \cong \Delta DCA$.

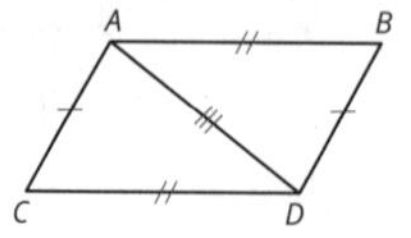

$\overline{AD} \cong \overline{DA}$

So, using SSS, I know that all three corresponding sides of the triangles are congruent.

(b) Given: $\overline{EI} \cong \overline{GH}$, $\overline{EH} \cong \overline{GI}$
Verify that $\Delta EHI \cong \Delta GIH$.

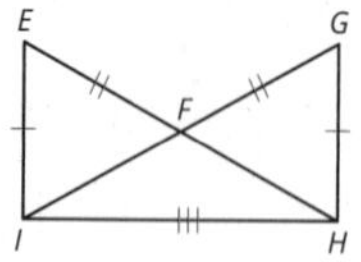

$\overline{IH} \cong \overline{HI}$

So, using SSS, I know that all three corresponding sides of the triangles are congruent.

(c) Given: $\overline{TR}$ intersects $\overline{NP}$, $\overline{TU} \cong \overline{RU}$, and $\overline{NU} \cong \overline{PU}$

Verify that $\Delta TUN \cong \Delta RUP$.

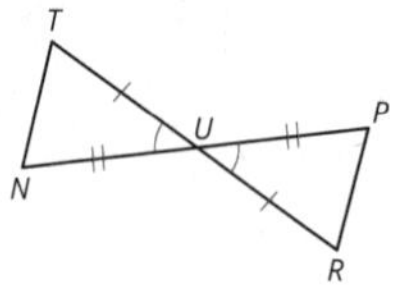

Using rotations, I can show that $\angle TUN \cong \angle PUR$.

So, using SAS, I know that the corresponding two sides and included angle of the two triangles are congruent.

STRETCH Optional

Use rigid motion and the congruence theorems to verify that $\Delta CAD \cong \Delta BAE$ in the given figure.

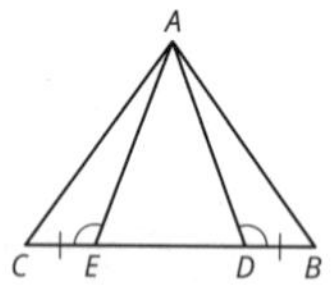

STRETCH

Statement	Reasoning
1. $\overline{CE} \cong \overline{DB}$	1. This is true because on the diagram, both of the line segments have a single slash marker, which indicates that the line segments are congruent.
2. $\angle AEC \cong \angle ADB$	2. This is true because on the diagram, both of the angles have a single arc marker, which indicates that the angles are congruent.
3. $m\angle AEC + m\angle AEB = 180°$	3. Two angles form a linear pair, which means they are supplementary angles. Supplementary angles have a sum of 180°.
4. $m\angle ADB + m\angle ADC = 180°$	4. Two angles form a linear pair, which means they are supplementary angles. Supplementary angles have a sum of 180°.
5. $\angle AEB \cong \angle ADC$	5. Both angles are supplements to angles that are congruent, so they must be congruent.
6. $\overline{AE} \cong \overline{AD}$	6. The two bottom angles inside triangle *AED* are the same, so triangle *AED* is an isosceles triangle and the sides opposite the congruent angles are congruent.
7. $\overline{ED} \cong \overline{ED}$	7. A line segment is congruent to itself.
8. $\overline{CD} \cong \overline{EB}$	8. The line segments are the same length because they are comprised of $\overline{ED}$ plus either $\overline{CE}$ or $\overline{DB}$, which are congruent, so the sum for each line segment is the same.
9. $\triangle CAD \cong \triangle BAE$	9. Because $\overline{AE} \cong \overline{AD}$, $\angle AEB \cong \angle ADC$, and $\overline{CD} \cong \overline{EB}$, $\triangle CAD \cong \triangle BAE$ are congruent to each other by the Side-Angle-Side Congruence Theorem.

ASA, SAS, and SSS

This resource details additional facilitation notes to fully assist you as you plan each lesson to support all students, students who struggle, and advanced learners. It provides differentiation strategies, common student misconceptions, and suggestions to extend certain activities.

ACTIVITY 1

Session 1 of 3

Congruent Line Segments by Reflection

Students interpret notation for congruent segments and angles. They analyze a worked example that proves you can map a segment onto itself in at most two reflections.

CHUNK	AUDIENCE	ADDITIONAL SUPPORTS
As students analyze the first worked example	All Students	**DIFFERENTIATION STRATEGY** Suggest students use colored pencils to trace congruent sides and mark congruent angles. Besides helping them understand the new notation, some students may benefit by making this a standard practice in interpreting labeled diagrams.
To extend 1	All Students	**DIFFERENTIATION STRATEGY** Demonstrate strategies to analyze diagrams. • Use Question 1, part (a) to demonstrate how to decompose figures. Decompose the diagram into two triangles, ΔRST and ΔWBX. • Discuss why $\angle S \cong \angle B$, and how this may not have been as apparent without decomposing the diagram. When two angles of one triangle are congruent to two angles of a second triangle, then the third angle pair is also congruent. • Use Question 1, part (b) to demonstrate how to extend diagrams. Have students extend $\overline{DM}$, $\overline{ZC}$, and $\overline{TZ}$. • Discuss why $\overline{DM}$ is parallel to $\overline{ZC}$. Because corresponding angles are congruent, the lines are parallel. • Use notation to label the parallel lines.
As students analyze the second worked example	All Students	**DIFFERENTIATION STRATEGY** Have students use patty paper to complete the reflections and summarize their procedure before analyzing the worked example.

TOPIC 3

ACTIVITY 2

Session 2 of 3

Side-Side-Side Congruence

Students use reflections to prove the Side-Side-Side Congruence Theorem for triangles. They use corresponding parts of congruent triangles are congruent (CPCTC) reasoning to write congruence statements.

CHUNK	AUDIENCE	ADDITIONAL SUPPORTS
As an alternative implementation strategy for 1	Students who Struggle	**DIFFERENTIATION STRATEGY** Allow students to complete the constructions using patty paper.
As students work on 3	Students who Struggle	**DIFFERENTIATION STRATEGY** Demonstrate how to use each letter's placement in the triangle congruence statement to write congruence statements for corresponding parts.

ACTIVITY 3

Session 2 of 3

Side-Angle-Side Congruence

Students analyze a worked example that proves the Side-Angle-Side (SAS) Congruence Theorem. They prove two triangles are congruent using the SAS Theorem.

CHUNK	AUDIENCE	ADDITIONAL SUPPORTS
As students analyze the worked example	All Students	**DIFFERENTIATION STRATEGY** Students may have a better understanding of the proof by seeing it unfold in stages. Perform each construction step and ask students why it is necessary and valid. Use colored pencils to emphasize corresponding parts.
As students share and summarize 1	All Students	**COMMON MISCONCEPTION** Students may be confused that $\overline{VR}$ is a perpendicular bisector because there are not any right angles in the diagram. That is because the points M, V, and F' are not collinear. Connect points F' and M, so students see that $\overline{VR}$ is the perpendicular bisector of $\overline{FM}$.

Practice the learning

MATHbook + Skills Practice

The table shows the targeted practice of the skills and mathematical concepts for the *Congruence Through Transformations* Topic. The highlighted Problem Set aligns with **ASA, SAS, and SSS**.

PROBLEM SET	
1	Conditional Statements, Truth Tables, and Postulates
2	**Triangle Congruence Theorems**
3	Triangle Congruence Problems

ANYTIME AFTER ACTIVITY 5

Facilitate students as they work individually on **Problem Set 2**.

TOPIC 3

NOTES

ENGAGE + DEVELOP + TEACH

ENGAGE at the **Module** level

DEVELOP at the **Topic** level

TEACH: Read the facilitation notes and plan learning experiences.

Where are we?

TOPIC 3 Congruence Through Transformations	LESSON 1 The Elements	LESSON 2 ASA, SAS, and SSS	LESSON 3 I Never Forget a Face
Pacing	2 Sessions	3 Sessions	2 Sessions

OVERVIEW: LESSON 3

I Never Forget a Face

Using Triangle Congruence to Solve Problems

ENGAGE

- Students explain how to use congruent triangles to measure a bridge's length indirectly.

DEVELOP

- They determine whether pairs of triangles within complex diagrams are congruent.
- They establish whether triangles are congruent using a coordinate plane for measures or transformations.

DEMONSTRATE

- Students create a design using a single geometric figure and all three rigid motions.

HIGH SCHOOL GEOMETRY

Congruence

Understand congruence in terms of rigid motions.

6. Use geometric descriptions of rigid motions to transform figures and to predict the effect of a given rigid motion on a given figure; given two figures, use the definition of congruence in terms of rigid motions to decide if they are congruent.

LESSON STRUCTURE AND PACING GUIDE 2 SESSIONS

✪ This activity highlights a key term or concept that is essential to the learning goals of the lesson.

Session 1		Session 2
INSTRUCTIONAL SEQUENCE		
ENGAGE Connect to prior knowledge	**DEVELOP** Peer analysis Mathematical problem solving	**DEVELOP** Mathematical problem solving
GETTING STARTED A Bridge Too Far	✪ **ACTIVITY 1** Using SSS, SAS, and ASA	✪ **ACTIVITY 2** SSS, SAS, and ASA on the Coordinate Plane

GETTING STARTED
A Bridge Too Far

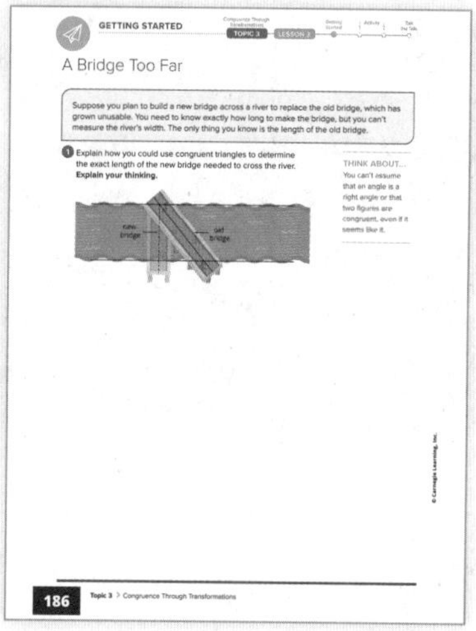
GETTING STARTED

A Bridge Too Far

Suppose you plan to build a new bridge across a river to replace the old bridge, which has grown unusable. You need to know exactly how long to make the bridge, but you can't measure the river's width. The only thing you know is the length of the old bridge.

1 Explain how you could use congruent triangles to determine the exact length of the new bridge needed to cross the river. Explain your thinking.

THINK ABOUT... You can't assume that an angle is a right angle or that two figures are congruent, even if it seems like it.

186 Topic 3 > Congruence Through Transformations

Students explain how they can indirectly measure the length of a bridge.

- They use congruent triangles in their strategy.

ACTIVITY 1
Using SSS, SAS, and ASA

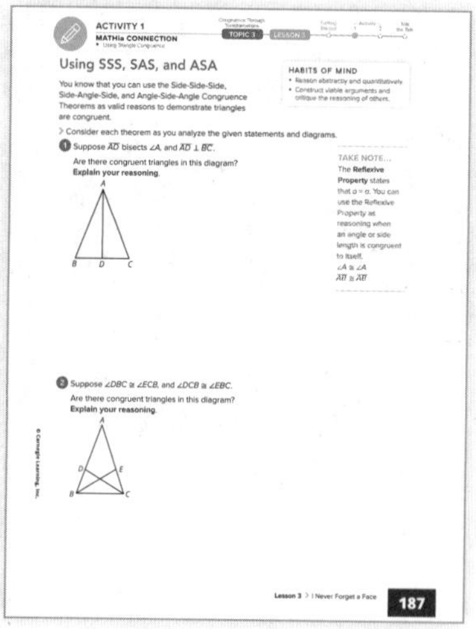
ACTIVITY 1

MATHia CONNECTION

Using SSS, SAS, and ASA

You know that you can use the Side-Side-Side, Side-Angle-Side, and Angle-Side-Angle Congruence Theorems as valid reasons to demonstrate triangles are congruent.

> Consider each theorem as you analyze the given statements and diagrams.

1 Suppose $\overline{AD}$ bisects ∠A, and $\overline{AD} \perp \overline{BC}$.

Are there congruent triangles in this diagram? Explain your reasoning.

2 Suppose ∠DBC ≅ ∠ECB, and ∠DCB ≅ ∠EBC.

Are there congruent triangles in this diagram? Explain your reasoning.

Lesson 3 > I Never Forget a Face 187

Students determine whether pairs of triangles within complex diagrams are congruent.

- They identify the information required to prove triangles are congruent using a specific theorem.

ACTIVITY 2
SSS, SAS, and ASA on the Coordinate Plane

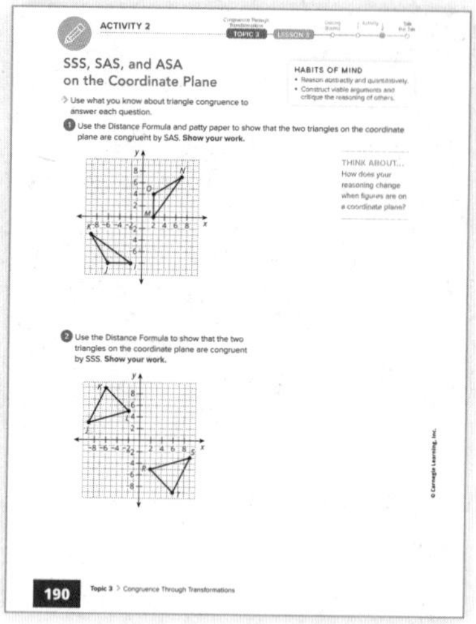
ACTIVITY 2

SSS, SAS, and ASA on the Coordinate Plane

> Use what you know about triangle congruence to answer each question.

1 Use the Distance Formula and patty paper to show that the two triangles on the coordinate plane are congruent by SAS. Show your work.

2 Use the Distance Formula to show that the two triangles on the coordinate plane are congruent by SSS. Show your work.

190 Topic 3 > Congruence Through Transformations

Students determine whether triangles are congruent using a coordinate plane for measures.

- They then use transformations on the plane to describe how to prove triangles are congruent.

Log in to MyCL for **lesson support** including:

Slides

Videos

www.carnegielearning.com/login

INSTRUCTIONAL SEQUENCE

DEMONSTRATE

Exit ticket application

TALK THE TALK

A Transformational Arteest

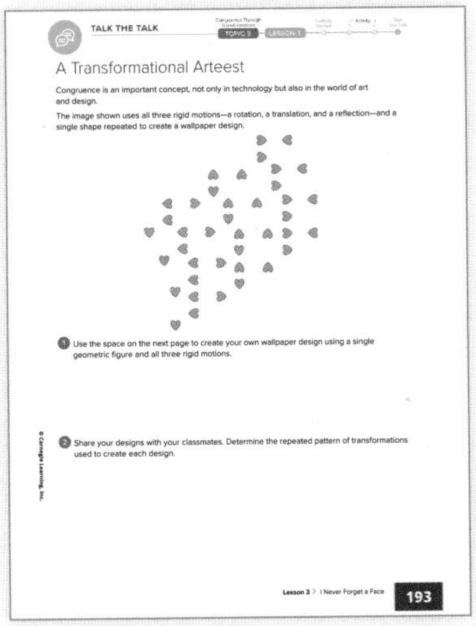
TALK THE TALK

TOPIC 3 LESSON 3

A Transformational Arteest

Congruence is an important concept, not only in technology but also in the world of art and design.

The image shown uses all three rigid motions—a rotation, a translation, and a reflection—and a single shape repeated to create a wallpaper design.

1. Use the space on the next page to create your own wallpaper design using a single geometric figure and all three rigid motions.

2. Share your designs with your classmates. Determine the repeated pattern of transformations used to create each design.

© Carnegie Learning, Inc.

Lesson 3 > I Never Forget a Face 193

Students create their own design using a single geometric figure and all three rigid motions

- They identify the repeated pattern of transformations used to create their classmates' designs.

NOTES

TOPIC 3

Now that you have read the Module, Topic, and Lesson Overviews, you are ready to plan.

Log in to MyCL for:

- Editable templates
- Additional planning support

Do the math

> Tear out the lesson planning template (page 185E) and jot down thoughts as you work through this lesson and read the Facilitation Notes.

Connect the learning

MATHbook + MATHia

The table shows the self-paced MATHia sequence for the *Congruence Through Transformations* Topic.

Median student completion time: ~90–110 minutes

> As you implement this lesson, consider different connections for students who are on pace and those that have not yet completed the workspaces aligned to this lesson.

STUDENTS WHO ARE NOT HERE YET

Students practice using SSS, SAS, AAS, and AAS congruence theorems to determine whether two triangles are congruent.

TYPE	WORKSPACE NAME
	Calculating and Justifying Angle Measures
	Calculating Angle Measures
	Introduction to Triangle Congruence
	Using Triangle Congruence

STUDENTS WHO ARE ON PACE

After you complete Activity 1, ask these students to share how they justified their reasoning for using different congruency statements.

I Never Forget a Face

Using Triangle Congruence to Solve Problems

Session 1

GETTING STARTED A Bridge Too Far

Pacing (minutes)	
My Time	Class Time

ACTIVITY 1 Using SSS, SAS, and ASA ✪

Pacing (minutes)	
My Time	Class Time

KEY TERM
Reflexive Property

Session 2

ACTIVITY 2 SSS, SAS, and ASA on the Coordinate Plane ✪

Pacing (minutes)	
My Time	Class Time

TALK THE TALK A Transformational Arteest

Pacing (minutes)	
My Time	Class Time

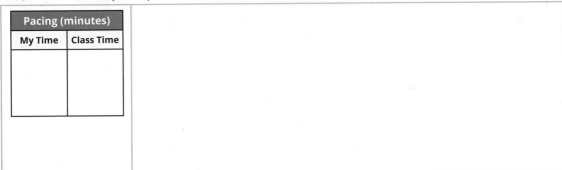

✪ This activity highlights a key term or concept that is essential to the learning goals of the lesson.

Log in to MyCL for:
- Editable templates
- Additional planning support

Reflect on your lesson

> Consider the effectiveness of your lesson on student learning.

What went well?	What did not go as planned?

> Anticipate how you would change the lesson next time you teach it.

How will you capitalize on the things that went well?	How will you improve things that did not go as planned?

MATERIALS

- Compasses
- Patty paper
- Straightedges

TOPIC 1
Using a Rectangular Coordinate System

TOPIC 2
Rigid Motions on a Plane

TOPIC 3
Congruence Through Transformations

1 | The Elements
2 | ASA, SAS, and SSS
3 | I Never Forget a Face

LESSON 3

I Never Forget a Face

Using Triangle Congruence to Solve Problems

KEY TERMS

Reflexive Property

Learning Goals

- Use triangle congruence theorems to identify congruent triangles.
- Identify the information needed to conclude that two triangles are congruent by SSS, SAS, or ASA.

REVIEW (1–2 minutes)

> Determine the unknown angle measure in each triangle.

1

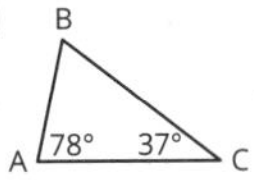

65°

2

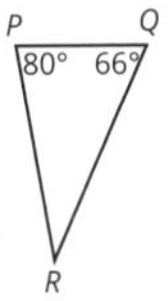

34°

3

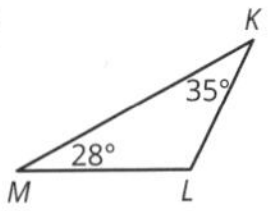

117°

You have proven that Side-Side-Side, Side-Angle-Side, and Angle-Side-Angle Congruence Theorems are valid criteria to determine triangle congruence.

How can you apply these theorems to solve problems?

Setting the Stage

- **Assign Review (optional, 1 – 2 minutes)**
- **Communicate the learning goals and key terms to look out for**
- **Tap into your students' prior learning by reading the narrative statement**
- **Provide a sense of direction by reading the question**

IN THIS REVIEW
Students use the fact that the angles of a triangle sum to 180° to solve problems. They will use this skill in **ACTIVITY 1 Using SSS, SAS, and ASA.**

You can apply the SSS, SAS, and ASA criteria for triangle congruence on and off the coordinate plane to solve real-world and mathematical problems.

TOPIC 3

Essential Ideas

- You can use the SSS, SAS, and ASA Congruence Theorems to prove triangles are congruent on and off the coordinate plane.
- You can apply the SSS, SAS, and ASA Congruence Theorems to solve real-world problems when you cannot directly measure distances.
- Congruent parts of triangles may appear in a diagram as vertical angles or as a shared side or angle of two triangles.
- You can use rigid motions on the coordinate plane to prove triangles are congruent.
- You can apply rigid motion transformations to create repeating geometric design patterns.

GETTING STARTED

SUMMARY **You can apply triangle congruence theorems to determine distances that you cannot directly measure.**

Chunking the Activity

- **Read and discuss the introduction**
- **Group students to complete the activity**
- **Share and summarize.**

DIFFERENTIATION STRATEGY

See Page 196A to support students who struggle with the activity.

Student Look-Fors

- Whether or not students construct the congruent triangle on land.
- Attempts to use drawing tools. Students should use construction tools only.

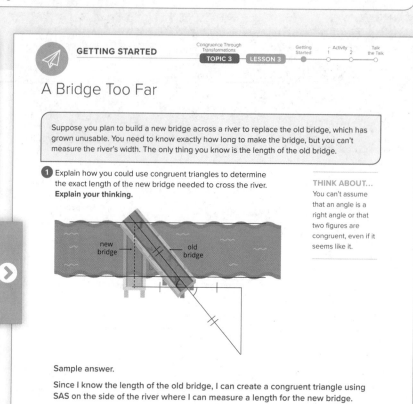

A Bridge Too Far

Suppose you plan to build a new bridge across a river to replace the old bridge, which has grown unusable. You need to know exactly how long to make the bridge, but you can't measure the river's width. The only thing you know is the length of the old bridge.

1. Explain how you could use congruent triangles to determine the exact length of the new bridge needed to cross the river. **Explain your thinking.**

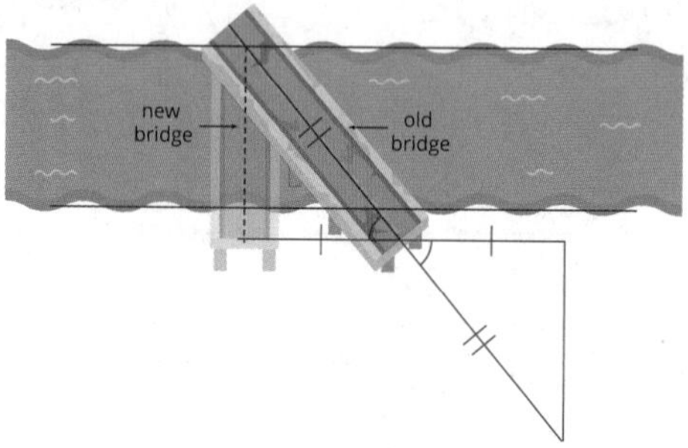

THINK ABOUT...
You can't assume that an angle is a right angle or that two figures are congruent, even if it seems like it.

Sample answer.

Since I know the length of the old bridge, I can create a congruent triangle using SAS on the side of the river where I can measure a length for the new bridge.

Questions to Support Discourse

		TYPE
1	• Why can't you measure the river's width?	Gathering
	• How can you duplicate the triangle formed by the old bridge, new bridge, and riverbank on land? • What side lengths of the original triangle do you know or can duplicate? • Describe what parts of the context represent SAS.	Probing
	• What three parts of the original triangle did you use to create a congruent triangle? • How did you use CPCTC in your explanation? • How do you know the two triangles have congruent angles? • Which congruence theorem tells you that you have created a congruent triangle?	Seeing structure

ACTIVITY 1

SUMMARY Congruent parts of triangles may appear in a diagram as vertical angles or as a shared side or angle of two triangles.

Using SSS, SAS, and ASA

HABITS OF MIND
- Reason abstractly and quantitatively.
- Construct viable arguments and critique the reasoning of others.

You know that you can use the Side-Side-Side, Side-Angle-Side, and Angle-Side-Angle Congruence Theorems as valid reasons to demonstrate triangles are congruent.

> Consider each theorem as you analyze the given statements and diagrams.

1. Suppose $\overline{AD}$ bisects $\angle A$, and $\overline{AD} \perp \overline{BC}$.

   Are there congruent triangles in this diagram? **Explain your reasoning.**

   Yes, $\Delta ABD \cong \Delta ACD$ by ASA Congruence Theorem.

   Angles *BAD* and *CAD* are congruent because $\angle A$ is bisected.

   Side $\overline{AD}$ is congruent to itself (Reflexive Property).

   Angles *ADB* and *ADC* are congruent because they are right angles.

TAKE NOTE...
The **Reflexive Property** states that $a = a$. You can use the Reflexive Property as reasoning when an angle or side length is congruent to itself.
$\angle A \cong \angle A$
$\overline{AB} \cong \overline{AB}$

2. Suppose $\angle DBC \cong \angle ECB$, and $\angle DCB \cong \angle EBC$.

   Are there congruent triangles in this diagram? **Explain your reasoning.**

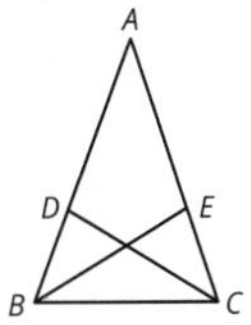

   Yes, $\Delta DBC \cong \Delta ECB$ by ASA Congruence Theorem.

   It is given that $\angle DBC \cong \angle ECB$.

   Segment *BC* is a side of both triangles.

   It is given that $\angle DCB \cong \angle EBC$.

Chunking the Activity

- Read and discuss the introduction
- Group students to complete 1 – 3
- Check-in and share
- Group students to complete 4 – 6
- Share and summarize

DIFFERENTIATION STRATEGY
See Page 196B to assist all students with 2.

Questions to Support Discourse

		TYPE
1	• Which two congruent angles form when $\overline{AD}$ bisects $\angle A$? • What congruency is determined by $\overline{AD} \perp \overline{BC}$? Why? • What is another way to state the triangle congruency statement?	Probing
	• What mathematical property supports $\overline{AD} \cong \overline{AD}$?	Seeing structure
2	• Which triangle has $\angle DCB$ as an interior angle? • Which triangle has $\angle EBC$ as an interior angle? • What side or angle do ΔDCB and ΔEBC have in common?	Probing

NOTES

COMMON MISCONCEPTION

See Page 196B for a misconception related to 3.

DIFFERENTIATION STRATEGY

See Page 196B to assist all students with 4 and 5.

3 Suppose $\overline{AB} \cong \overline{DF}$, $\angle A \cong \angle D$, and $\overline{BE} \cong \overline{FC}$.

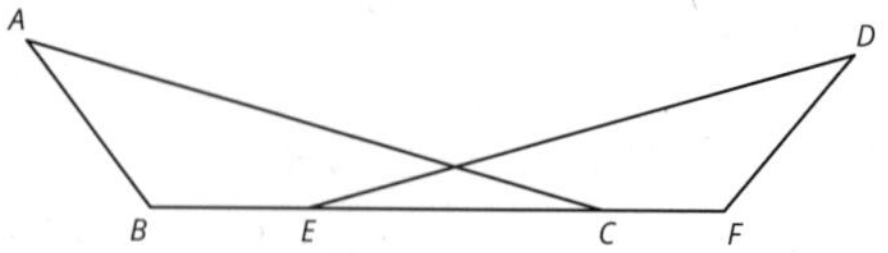

Are there congruent triangles in this diagram? **Explain your reasoning.**

No. There is not enough information to determine that ΔABC is congruent to ΔDFE because $\angle A$ and $\angle D$ are not the included angles.

4 Suppose $\overline{AC} \cong \overline{DB}$, $\overline{AB} \perp \overline{BC}$ and $\overline{DC} \perp \overline{CB}$.

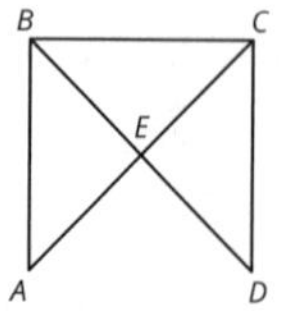

(a) What information would you need to conclude ΔCAB is congruent to ΔBDC using the ASA Congruence Theorem?

Sample answer.

I would need to know that $\angle BCA \cong \angle CBD$ to use the ASA Congruence Theorem.

(b) What information would you need to conclude ΔABE is congruent to ΔDCE using the ASA Congruence Theorem?

Sample answer.

I would need to know that $\overline{AE} \cong \overline{DE}$ and $\overline{BE} \cong \overline{CE}$.

5 Suppose $\overline{AB} \cong \overline{AC}$.

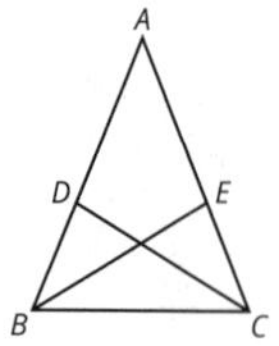

(a) What additional information would you need to conclude that ΔABE is congruent to ΔACD using the ASA Congruence Theorem?

Sample answer.

I would need to know that $\angle ABE \cong \angle ACD$ to use the ASA Congruence Theorem.

(b) What additional information would you need to conclude that ΔABE is congruent to ΔACD using the SSS Congruence Theorem?

Sample answer.

I would need to know that $\overline{AE} \cong \overline{AD}$ and $\overline{BE} \cong \overline{CD}$ to use the SSS Congruence Theorem.

Questions to Support Discourse

		TYPE
3	• Which three parts can you verify are congruent? • How do you know $\overline{BC} \cong \overline{FE}$? • Why can't you prove that these triangles are congruent?	Probing
4	• How are the two perpendicular statements helpful? • Which corresponding parts do you know are congruent in the diagram? • Is there another set of congruent parts that you could use to prove congruent triangles using ASA? If so, what are they?	Probing
5	• Which corresponding parts do you know are congruent in the diagram?	Probing

ACTIVITY 1 Continued

(c) What additional information would you need to conclude that ΔABE is congruent to ΔACD using the SAS Congruence Theorem?

Sample answer.

I would need to know that $\overline{AE} \cong \overline{AD}$ to use the SAS Congruence Theorem.

6 Simone says that since ΔABC and ΔDCB have two pairs of congruent corresponding sides and congruent corresponding angles, then the triangles are congruent by SAS. Is Simone correct? **Explain your reasoning.**

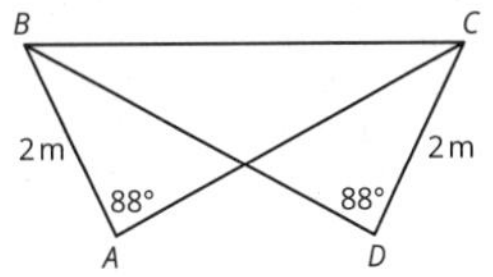

Simone is not correct.
The congruent angles are not formed by two pairs of congruent sides, so they are not the included angles. There is not enough information to determine if the triangles are congruent by SAS or SSS.

Questions to Support Discourse

		TYPE
6	• What is the other pair of corresponding sides Simone uses for SAS? • Use the diagram to explain to Simone the error in her thinking. • What additional information would Simone need to prove these triangles congruent by SAS?	Probing

NOTES

Student Look-Fors

Whether students are modeling appropriate social awareness.

- Listening to the perspectives of others
- Empathizing with others' experiences
- Respecting others

ACTIVITY 2

SUMMARY **You can use rigid motions on the coordinate plane to prove triangles are congruent.**

Chunking the Activity

- **Read and discuss the directions**
- **Group students to complete 1 and 2**
- **Check-in and share**
- **Group students to complete 3 - 5**
- **Share and summarize**

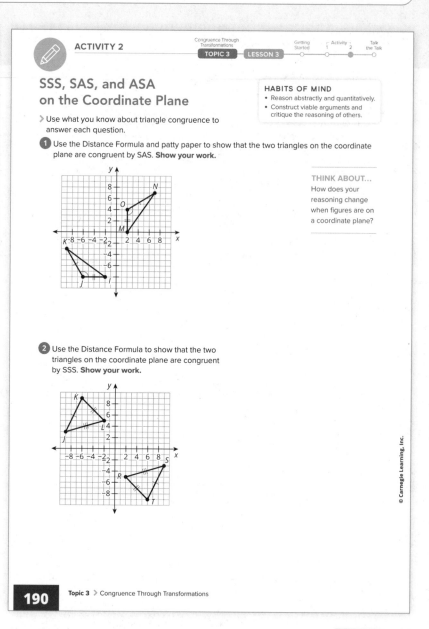

SSS, SAS, and ASA on the Coordinate Plane

HABITS OF MIND
- Reason abstractly and quantitatively.
- Construct viable arguments and critique the reasoning of others.

> Use what you know about triangle congruence to answer each question.

1. Use the Distance Formula and patty paper to show that the two triangles on the coordinate plane are congruent by SAS. **Show your work.**

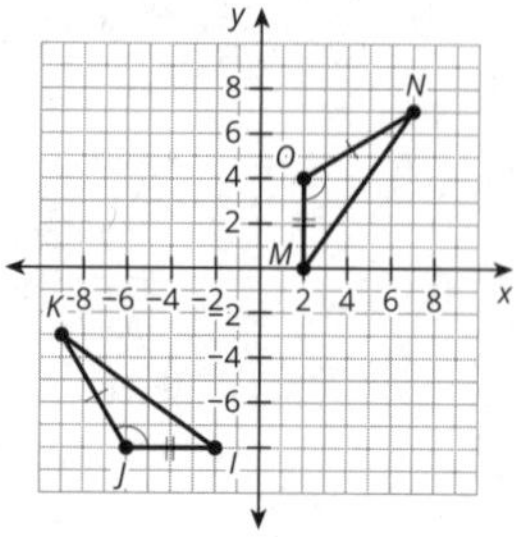

THINK ABOUT...
How does your reasoning change when figures are on a coordinate plane?

2. Use the Distance Formula to show that the two triangles on the coordinate plane are congruent by SSS. **Show your work.**

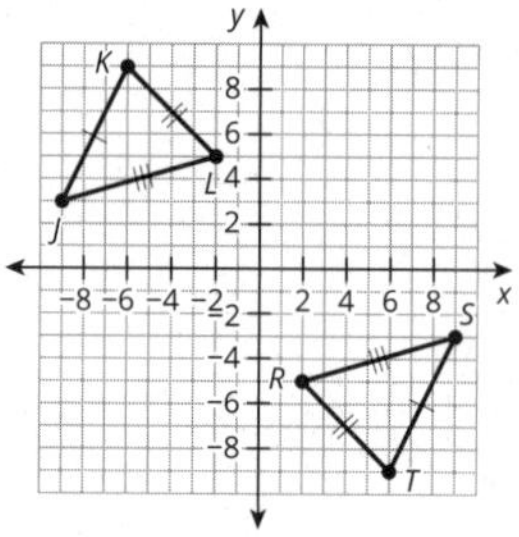

Questions to Support Discourse

	Questions to Support Discourse	TYPE
1	• When using SAS, how do you know which angle is the included angle? • How can you determine that two sides are congruent using the coordinate plane without patty paper or the distance formula? Explain your thinking.	Probing

ACTIVITY 2 Continued

3 Emerson wants to translate ΔABC and then reflect it across the y-axis to form a new triangle in Quadrant II. She uses what she knows about transformations to determine the vertices of $\Delta A'B'C'$ before performing the transformations.

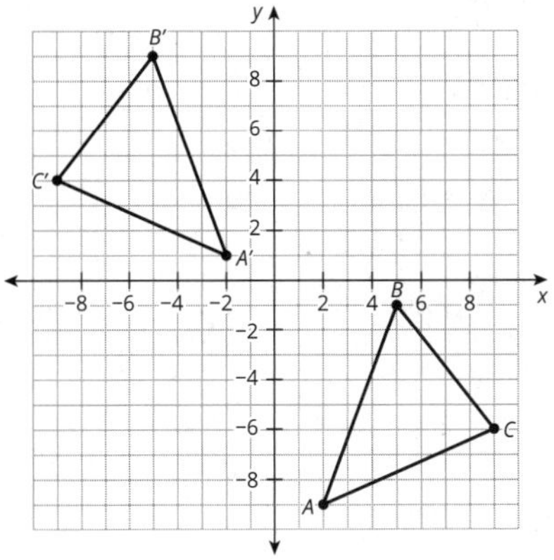

ⓐ Describe how Emerson can use the ASA Congruence Theorem to determine whether she transformed ΔABC, such that the image is congruent to the pre-image.

Emerson can determine the measure of two corresponding angles in both triangles and the length of the included sides.

If the angles are congruent and the sides are congruent, then the triangles are congruent by the ASA Congruence Theorem.

ⓑ Did Emerson perform the transformations on ΔABC so that the image is congruent to the pre-image? **Explain your reasoning**.

Yes. Emerson performed the transformations on ΔABC so that the image and pre-image are congruent. I know that the triangles are congruent by the ASA Congruence Theorem.

Questions to Support Discourse

		TYPE
3	• Which three parts of the triangles did you use to prove the triangles are congruent?	Probing
	• Why do you know the triangles are congruent by the transformations Emerson made?	Reflecting and justifying

NOTES

DIFFERENTIATION STRATEGY

See Page 196B to challenge advanced learners to extend 3.

NOTES

4 Describe how to prove the given triangles are congruent. Use the key terms *included angle* and *Side-Angle-Side Congruence Theorem* in your answer.

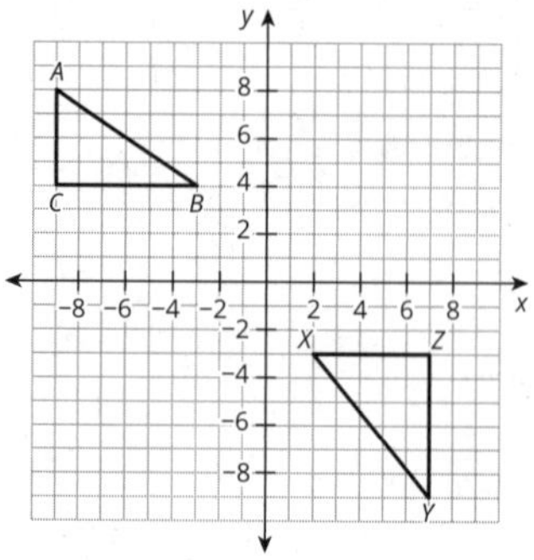

Sides $\overline{AC}$ and $\overline{XZ}$ are congruent because they each have measures of 4 units.
Sides $\overline{CB}$ and $\overline{ZY}$ are congruent because they each have measures of 6 units.
The included angles *C* and *Z* are congruent because they are both right angles.
Using the Side-Angle-Side Congruence Theorem, $\Delta ABC \cong \Delta XYZ$.

5 Describe how to prove the given triangles are congruent. Use the key terms *included side* and *Angle-Side-Angle Congruence Theorem* in your answer.

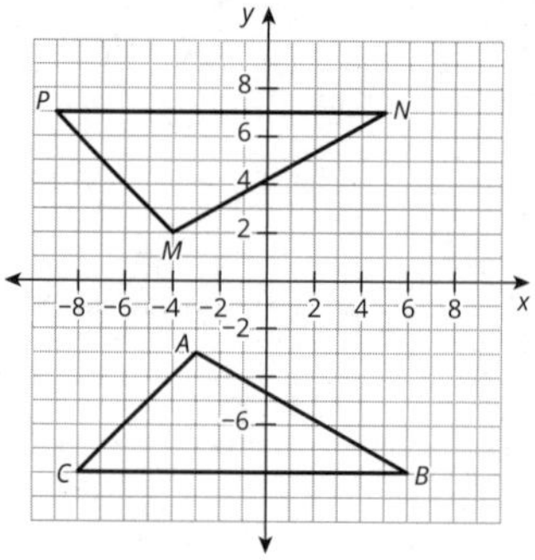

Angles *P* and *C* are congruent.
Angles *N* and *B* are congruent.
The included sides $\overline{PN}$ and $\overline{CB}$ are congruent.
Using the Angle-Side-Angle Congruence Theorem, $\Delta PMN \cong \Delta CAB$.

Questions to Support Discourse

		TYPE
4	• How did you determine side and angle measures using the coordinate plane? • What is a sequence of transformations to map ΔABC onto ΔXYZ? What is another way?	Probing
	• Why can you use rigid motions to determine that triangles are congruent?	Seeing structure
5	• What transformations did you use to map ΔMNP onto ΔABC? • Does the order of the transformations make a difference? Why or why not?	Probing

TALK THE TALK

SUMMARY You can apply rigid motion transformations to create repeating geometric design patterns.

A Transformational Arteest

Congruence is an important concept, not only in technology but also in the world of art and design.

The image shown uses all three rigid motions—a rotation, a translation, and a reflection—and a single shape repeated to create a wallpaper design.

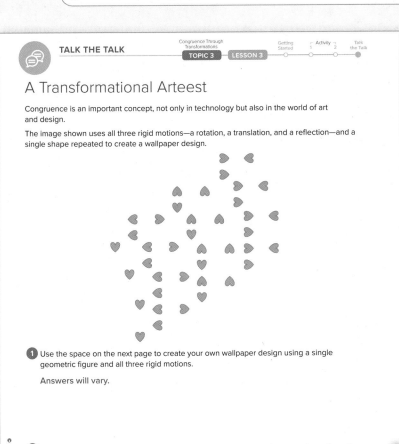

1. Use the space on the next page to create your own wallpaper design using a single geometric figure and all three rigid motions.

   Answers will vary.

2. Share your designs with your classmates. Determine the repeated pattern of transformations used to create each design.

   Answers will vary.

Chunking the Activity

- Read and discuss the directions
- Group students to complete 1
- Check-in and share
- Group students to complete 2
- Share and summarize

DIFFERENTIATION STRATEGY

See Page 196C to assist all students to extend 2.

NOTE: Before beginning the next module, take a moment to build students' capacity for self-management by having them review and reflect on their goals set during **A Meeting of the Minds.**

Questions to Support Discourse

		TYPE
Intro	• Identify a section of the design and show how it is repeated several times for this wallpaper.	Probing
1	• Does your geometric shape have any reflectional or rotational symmetry? If so, describe it. • Once you created a set with all three types of transformations, what type of transformation did you use to repeat it?	Probing
2	• Was it easier to compose or decompose a design? Explain your thinking.	Gathering
	• Explain your steps to figure out how your classmates created their designs. • How many geometric figures were in the section you identified before it started repeating?	Probing
	• Is your repeated pattern solution the same as how your classmate created it? If not, explain why you both could be correct.	Seeing structure

NOTES

TALK THE TALK Continued

> Create your own wallpaper design.

194 Topic 3 > Congruence Through Transformations

ASSIGNMENT

LESSON 3 ASSIGNMENT

> Use a separate piece of paper for your Journal entry.

JOURNAL

Explain in your own words how to determine which congruence theorem to use to identify congruent triangles.

REMEMBER

You can apply the SSS, SAS, and ASA criteria for triangle congruence on and off the coordinate plane to solve real-world and mathematical problems.

PRACTICE

1. State the theorem that proves the triangles are congruent. Then write a congruence statement.

(a)

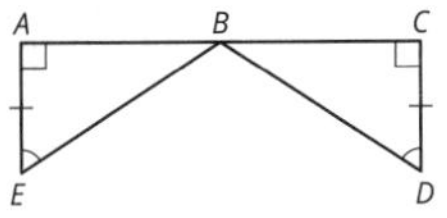

ASA Congruence Theorem
$\triangle ABE \cong \triangle CBD$

(b)

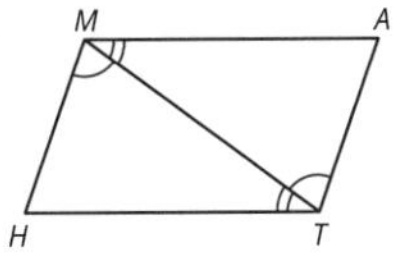

ASA Congruence Theorem
$\triangle HMT \cong \triangle ATM$

(c)

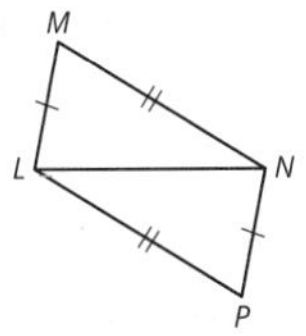

SSS Congruence Theorem
$\triangle LMN \cong \triangle NPL$

(d)

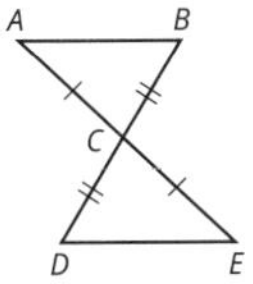

SAS Congruence Theorem
$\triangle ABC \cong \triangle EDC$

Go to LiveHint.com for help on the PRACTICE questions.

Encourage students to use LiveHint.com for help with the PRACTICE questions of this assignment.

Chunking the Assignment

SESSION 1

- Journal
- Practice 1 and 2
- Stretch (advanced learners)

SESSION 2

- Mixed Practice (page 197) 6 and 7

JOURNAL

Sample answer.

It is necessary to determine which parts of the triangles you can show to be congruent. If you can show that the triangles have three congruent sides, use the SSS Congruence Theorem. If you can show that the triangles have two congruent sides and the angle between the sides for both triangles is the same, use the SAS Congruence Theorem. If you can show that the triangles have two congruent angles and the side between the angles for both triangles is the same, use the ASA Congruence Theorem.

NOTES

STRETCH

Sample answer.

Side *AB* and side *DA* of triangles *ABB′* and *DAA′* are congruent because they are both sides of a square and squares have congruent sides. ∠*A* and ∠*D* are congruent; since they are the corners of the square, they are both right angles. ∠*AA′D* ≅ ∠*BAX* because they are alternate interior angles. The three angles of Δ*DAA*' add up to 180°, m∠*AA′D* + 90°+m∠*DAA′* = 180°. The three angles of Δ*ABX* add up to 180°, m∠*BAX* + 90°+m∠*ABB′* = 180°. Setting the two sums equal, m∠*AA′D* + 90°+m∠*DA A′* = m∠*BAX* + 90°+m∠*ABB′*. Since ∠*AA′D* ≅ ∠*BAX*, then m∠*DAA′* = m∠*ABB′*. So ∠*DAA′* ≅ ∠*ABB′*, $\overline{AB} \cong \overline{DA}$, and ∠*A* ≅ ∠*D*. Therefore by *SAS*, Δ*ABB′* ≅ Δ*DAA′*.

2. Determine the information that is needed to use the indicated theorem to show that the triangles are congruent.

(a) Δ*FJG* ≅ Δ*HJG* by SAS

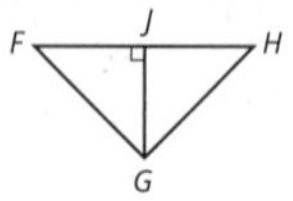

$\overline{FJ} \cong \overline{HJ}$

(b) Δ*VWX* ≅ Δ*ZYX* by ASA

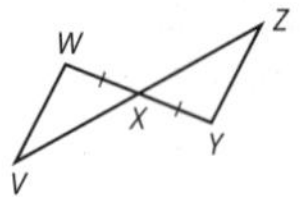

∠*W* ≅ ∠*Y*

(c) Δ*KJL* ≅ Δ*KTS* by SAS

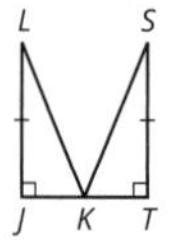

$\overline{KJ} \cong \overline{KT}$

(d) Δ*DEF* ≅ Δ*DGF* by ASA

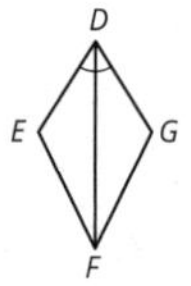

∠*DFE* ≅ ∠*DFG*

STRETCH Optional

> Figure *ABCD* is a square. Line segments *AA′* and *BB′* are perpendicular to each other.

1. Determine how you can prove that Δ*ABB′* ≅ Δ*DAA′* using either SAS, SSS, or ASA.

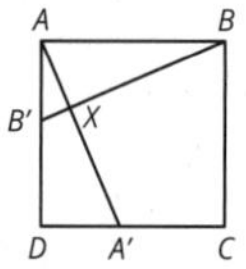

I Never Forget a Face

This resource details additional facilitation notes to fully assist you as you plan each lesson to support all students, students who struggle, and advanced learners. It provides differentiation strategies, common student misconceptions, and suggestions to extend certain activities.

GETTING STARTED

Session 1 of 3

A Bridge Too Far

Students explain how they can indirectly measure the length of a bridge. They use congruent triangles in their strategy.

CHUNK	AUDIENCE	ADDITIONAL SUPPORTS
As students work on the activity	Students who Struggle	**DIFFERENTIATION STRATEGY** Provide additional scaffolding. • Discuss strategies for reconstructing the triangle formed by the bridges and the lower river bank. • Review vertical angles and ask how students can use them to construct a triangle congruent to the original one.

ACTIVITY 1

Session 1 of 3

Using SSS, SAS, and ASA

Students determine whether pairs of triangles within complex diagrams are congruent. They identify the information required to prove triangles are congruent using a specific theorem.

CHUNK	AUDIENCE	ADDITIONAL SUPPORTS
As students work on 2	All Students	**DIFFERENTIATION STRATEGY** • Suggest students sketch the pair of triangles they plan to prove congruent separate from the diagram. For example, in Question 2, draw ΔDBC and ΔECB. 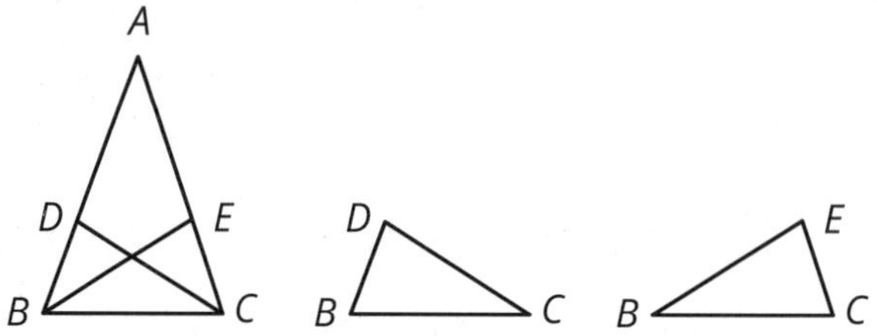 • Have students draw arc markers in the same color to mark congruent angles. Have them trace the entire side and use slash marks of the same color to label congruent sides.
As students share and summarize 3	All Students	**COMMON MISCONCEPTION** Students may not realize that the order of the parts of the triangle makes a difference. For example, they may think that if two sides and an angle are congruent, they can always use SAS. Use Question 3 to explain that the congruent sides have to form the angle.
As students work on 4 and 5	All Students	**DIFFERENTIATION STRATEGY** Suggest students trace the diagram on patty paper to have a clean copy to analyze each part of the question.

ACTIVITY 2

Session 2 of 3

SSS, SAS, and ASA on the Coordinate Plane

Students determine whether triangles are congruent using a coordinate plane for measures. They then use transformations on the plane to describe how to prove triangles are congruent.

CHUNK	AUDIENCE	ADDITIONAL SUPPORTS
To extend 3	Advanced Learners	**DIFFERENTIATION STRATEGY** Ask students to use function notation to describe the sequence of transformations to prove congruent triangles.

TALK THE TALK

Session 3 of 3

A Transformational Arteest

Students create a design using a single geometric figure and all three rigid motions. They identify the repeated pattern of transformations used to create their classmates' designs.

CHUNK	AUDIENCE	ADDITIONAL SUPPORTS
As students complete 2	All students	**DIFFERENTIATION STRATEGY** Have students decompose geometric patterns on actual wallpaper and clothing designs. Ask them to identify the transformations to create the designs.

Practice the learning

MATHbook + Skills Practice

The table shows the targeted practice of the skills and mathematical concepts for the *Congruence Through Transformations* Topic. The highlighted Problem Set aligns with **I Never Forget a Face**.

PROBLEM SET	
1	Conditional Statements, Truth Tables, and Postulates
2	Triangle Congruence Theorems
3	**Triangle Congruence Problems**

ANYTIME AFTER ACTIVITY 2

Facilitate students as they work individually on **Problem Set 3**.

TOPIC 3

NOTES

MIXED PRACTICE

Log in to MyCL to access a downloadable version with **additional space** for students to write their answers.

MIXED PRACTICE

> This Mixed Practice worksheet includes two sections: Spaced Review and End-of-Topic Review. **Use a separate piece of paper to show your work.**

Spaced Review

> Practice concepts from previous topics.

1. Write a function to describe the translation.

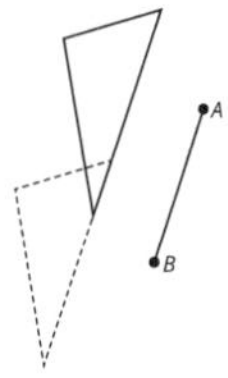

2. Complete the translation given the function.

$T_{L'M}$(Parallelogram) = Parallelogram'

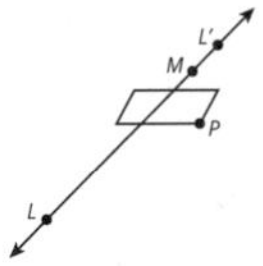

3. Write the equation of a line that passes through the point (4, −3) and is parallel to the line $4x + y = 8$.

4. Write the equation of a line that passes through the point (−9, 6) and is perpendicular to the line $-6x - 2y = 5$.

5. Determine how many lines of symmetry the equilateral triangle has. Then draw each line of symmetry.

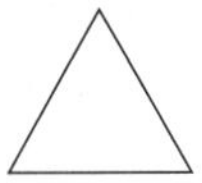

6. Use the dark points to determine the location of the vertices of a square.

7. Identify a sequence of transformations that will carry the given pre-image onto the image shown with dashed lines.

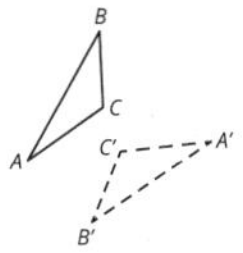

See pages 198–198B for annotated answers.

The **Spaced Review** includes fluency and problem solving from previous topics.

Aligned Standards

1 G.CO.2	2 G.CO.5
3 G.GPE.5	4 G.GPE.5
5 4.G.3	6 4.G.1
7 G.CO.5	

Log in to MyCL for more **End-of-Topic** review questions.

Go to **Edulastic**, and search for: G.CO.6, G.CO.7, G.CO.8, G.CO.9.

MIXED PRACTICE Continued

End-of-Topic Review

AVAILABLE ONLINE
1. A **Topic Summary** reviews the main concepts for the topic.
2. A video of the **Worked Example** is provided.

> Practice concepts you learned in **Congruence Through Transformations**.

8. Write the postulate that confirms the statement.

$m\angle BCD + m\angle DCE = m\angle BCE$

9. Write a conjecture about corresponding angles. Draw an example to test your conjecture.

10. Draw two triangles that correspond with the congruence statement $\Delta MTA \cong \Delta BGC$. Then list the six pairs of congruent corresponding parts.

11. For each figure shown, determine whether there is enough information to conclude that the triangles are congruent. If so, state the theorem you used.

ⓐ Given: $\angle MOP \cong \angle MON$
Is $\Delta POM \cong \Delta NOM$?

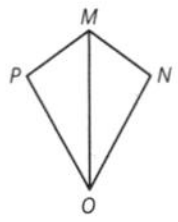

ⓑ Given: $\angle EAB \cong \angle DCB$
Point B bisects $\overline{AD}$.
Is $\Delta ABE \cong \Delta CBD$?

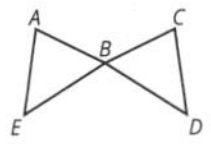

12. Complete a truth table for the conditional statement.

If $\angle A$ and $\angle B$ are supplementary angles, then $m\angle A + m\angle B = 180°$.

13. Determine whether each pair of triangles is congruent. If so, state whether they are congruent by SSS, SAS, or ASA. If not, explain why.

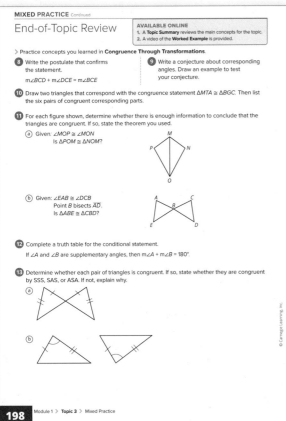

ⓐ

ⓑ

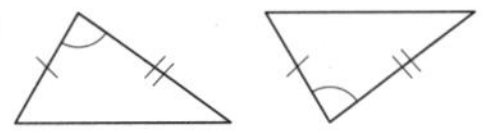

The **End-of-Topic Review** includes questions to practice the key concepts of *Congruence Through Transformations.*

Aligned Standards

8 G.CO.9	9 G.CO.9
10 G.CO.7	11 G.CO.8
12 G.CO.9	13 G.CO.8

MIXED PRACTICE

> This Mixed Practice worksheet includes two sections: Spaced Review and End-of-Topic Review.

MODULE 1 **Reasoning with Shapes**

TOPIC 1 Using a Rectangular Coordinate System

TOPIC 2 Rigid Motions on a Plane

TOPIC 3 Congruence Through Transformations

Spaced Review

> Practice concepts from previous topics.

1 Write a function to describe the translation.

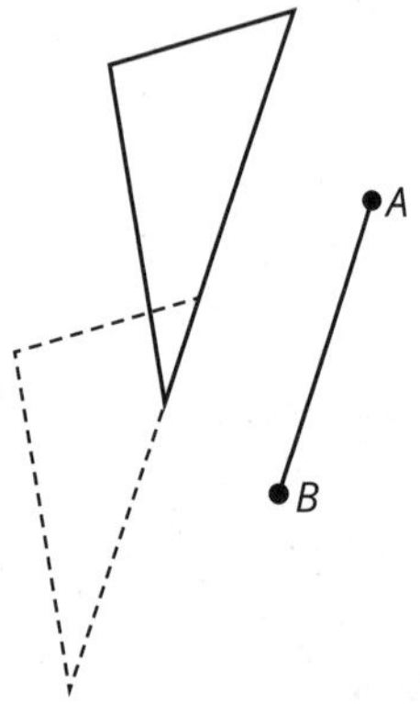

T_{AB}(Triangle) = Triangle′

2 Complete the translation given the function.

$T_{L'M}$(Parallelogram) = Parallelogram′

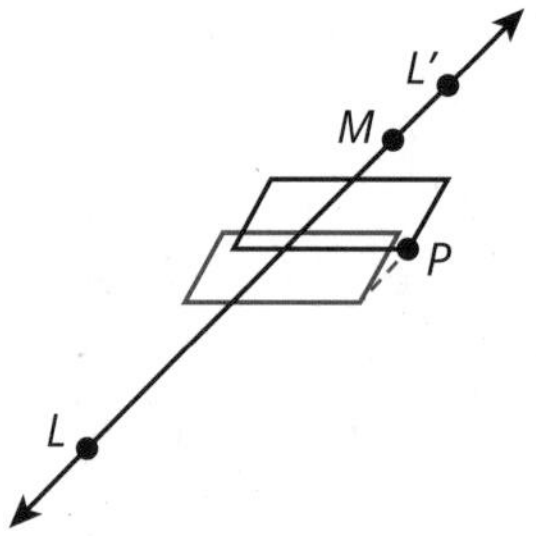

3 Write the equation of a line that passes through the point (4, −3) and is parallel to the line $4x + y = 8$.

$4x + y = 8$

$y = -4x + 8$

$m = -4$

$y + 3 = -4(x - 4)$

$y = -4x + 13$

4 Write the equation of a line that passes through the point (−9, 6) and is perpendicular to the line $-6x - 2y = 5$.

$6x - 2y = 5$

$y = 3x - \frac{5}{2}$

$m = 3$

$y - 6 = -\frac{1}{3}(x + 9)$

$y = -\frac{1}{3}x + 9$

5 Determine how many lines of symmetry the equilateral triangle has. Then draw each line of symmetry.

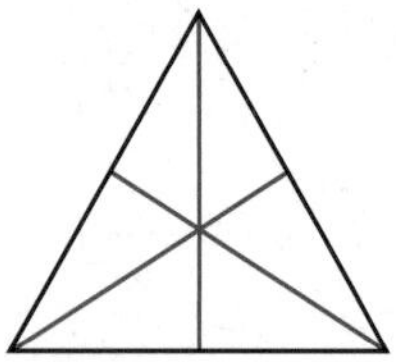

An equilateral triangle has three lines of symmetry.

6 Use the dark points to determine the location of the vertices of a square.

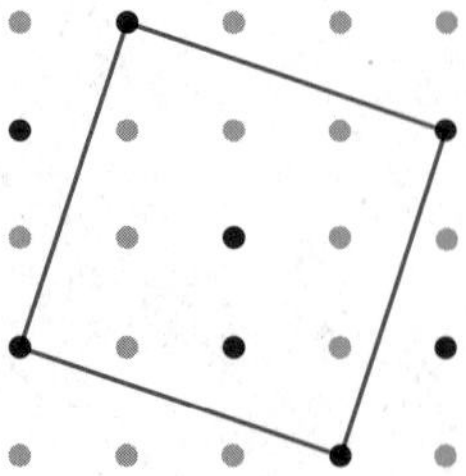

Answers included.

MIXED PRACTICE Continued

7 Identify a sequence of transformations that will carry the given pre-image onto the image shown with dashed lines.

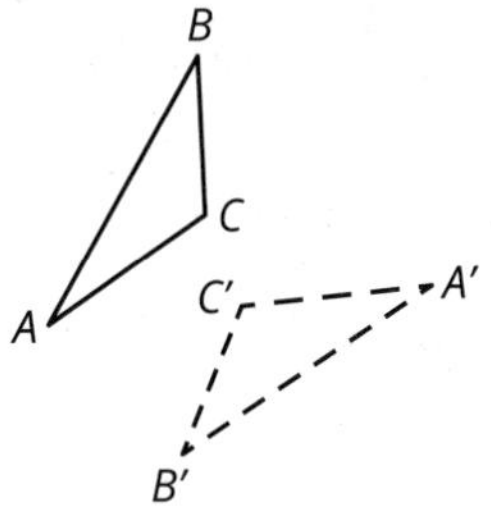

Sample answer.

I can reflect ΔABC across the vertical line that passes through Point C, then reflect across a horizontal line that passes through point C, and finally translate to get $\Delta A'B'C'$.

End-of-Topic Review

AVAILABLE ONLINE

1. A **Topic Summary** reviews the main concepts for the topic.
2. A video of the **Worked Example** is provided.

> Practice concepts you learned in **Congruence Through Transformations**.

8 Write the postulate that confirms the statement.

$m\angle BCD + m\angle DCE = m\angle BCE$

Angle Addition Postulate

9 Write a conjecture about corresponding angles. Draw an example to test your conjecture.

Sample answer.

Corresponding angles are congruent.

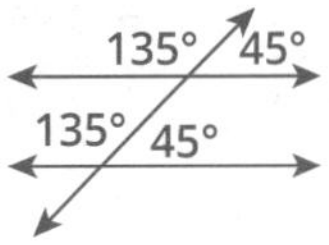

10 Draw two triangles that correspond with the congruence statement $\Delta MTA \cong \Delta BGC$. Then list the six pairs of congruent corresponding parts.

Sample answer.

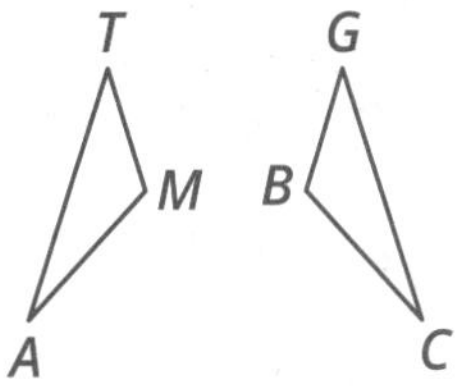

$\angle A \cong \angle C$, $\angle T \cong \angle G$, $\angle M \cong \angle B$, $\overline{AT} \cong \overline{CG}$, $\overline{TM} \cong \overline{GB}$, $\overline{MA} \cong \overline{BC}$

TOPIC 3

Answers included.

MIXED PRACTICE

> This Mixed Practice worksheet includes two sections: Spaced Review and End-of-Topic Review.

11 For each figure shown, determine whether there is enough information to conclude that the triangles are congruent. If so, state the theorem you used.

(a) Given: $\angle MOP \cong \angle MON$
Is $\Delta POM \cong \Delta NOM$?

There is not enough information to conclude that the triangles are congruent.

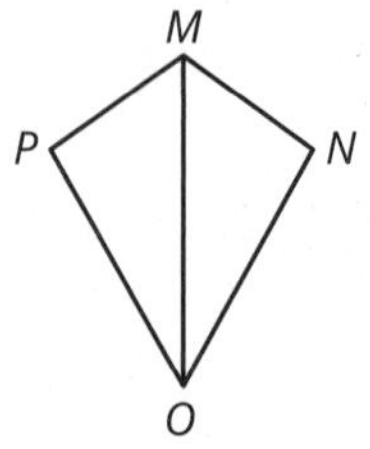

(b) Given: $\angle EAB \cong \angle DCB$
Point B bisects $\overline{AD}$.
Is $\Delta ABE \cong \Delta CBD$?

The triangles are congruent by the ASA congruence Theorem.

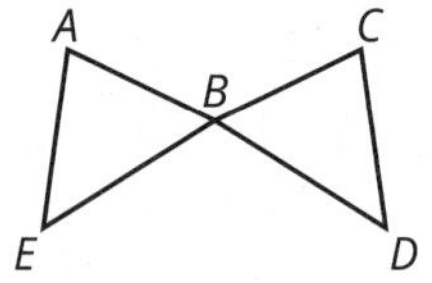

12 Complete a truth table for the conditional statement.

If $\angle A$ and $\angle B$ are supplementary angles, then $m\angle A + m\angle B = 180°$.

p	q	$p \rightarrow q$
$\angle A$ and $\angle B$ are supplementary angles.	$m\angle A + m\angle B = 180°$	If $\angle A$ and $\angle B$ are supplementary angles, then $m\angle A + m\angle B = 180°$.
T	T	T
T	F	F
F	T	T
F	F	T

13 Determine whether each pair of triangles is congruent. If so, state whether they are congruent by SSS, SAS, or ASA. If not, explain why.

(a)

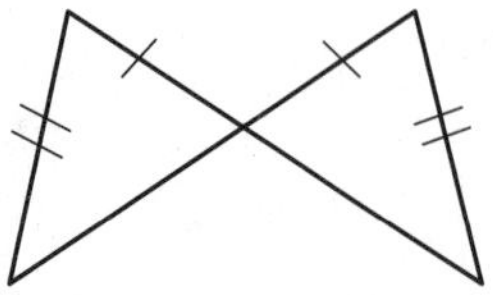

The two triangles are not necessarily congruent.

(b)

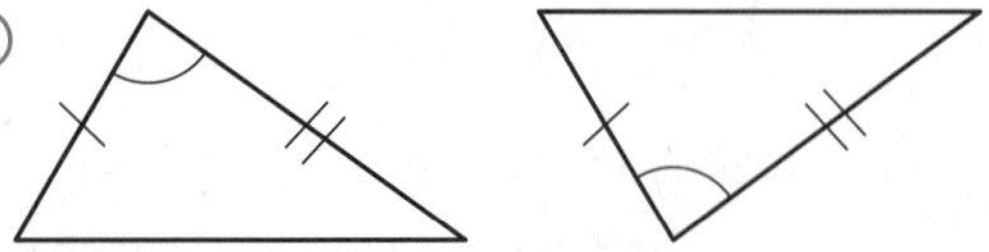

The two triangles are congruent by SAS.

MODULE 2

Establishing Proof

TOPIC 1
Composing and Decomposing Shapes

LESSON 1 201
Running Circles Around Geometry
Using Circles to Make Conjectures

LESSON 2 215
The Quad Squad
Conjectures About Quadrilaterals

LESSON 3 231
Into the Ring
Constructing an Inscribed Regular Polygon

LESSON 4 247
Tri- Tri- Tri- and Separate Them
Conjectures About Triangles

LESSON 5 261
Meet Me in the Middle
Points of Concurrency

Using Circles to Make Conjectures
- Introduction to Circles
- Exploring the Inscribed Angle Theorem
- Determining Central and Inscribed Angles in Circles

Conjectures About Quadrilaterals
- Using Circles to Draw Quadrilaterals
- Angles of an Inscribed Quadrilateral

Points of Concurrency
- Points of Concurrency

TOPIC 2
Justifying Line and Angle Relationships

MATHbook

LESSON 1 279
Proof Positive
Forms of Proof

LESSON 2 301
A Parallel Universe
Proving Parallel Line Theorems

LESSON 3 321
Ins and Outs
Interior and Exterior Angles of Polygons

LESSON 4 335
Identical Twins
Perpendicular Bisector and Isosceles Triangle Theorems

LESSON 5 355
Corners in a Round Room
Angle Relationships Inside and Outside Circles

MATHia

Forms of Proof
- Introduction to Proofs
- Completing Measure Proofs
- Connecting Steps in Angle Proofs
- Using Angle Theorems

Lines Cut by a Transversal
- Classifying Angles Formed by Transversals
- Calculating Angle Measures Formed by Transversals
- Calculating Angles Formed by Multiple Transversals

Proving Parallel Lines Theorems
- Proving Parallel Lines Theorems
- Proving the Converses of Parallel Lines Theorems

Interior and Exterior Angles of Polygons
- Proving Triangle Theorems

Proving Triangles Congruent
- Proving Triangles Congruent Using SAS and SSS
- Proving Triangles Congruent Using AAS and ASA
- Proving Theorems Using Congruent Triangles

Special Right Triangles
- Introduction to Special Right Triangles
- Calculating the Lengths of Sides of Special Right Triangles

Solving Problems with Congruence
- Using Triangle Theorems

Angle Relationships Inside and Outside Circles
- Determining Interior and Exterior Angles in Circles

TOPIC 3
Using Congruence Theorems

LESSON 1 385
SSS, SAS, AAS, ...S.O.S.!
Using Triangle Congruence to Determine Relationships Between Segments

LESSON 2 399
Props to You
Properties of Quadrilaterals

LESSON 3 425
Three-Chord Song
Relationships Between Chords

Extending Triangle Congruence Theorems
- Proving Triangles Congruent Using HL and HA

Properties of Quadrilaterals
- Understanding Parallelograms
- Determining Parts of Quadrilaterals and Parallelograms

Parallelogram Proofs
- Proofs About Parallelograms

Getting Ready for Module 2
Establishing Proof

Review this content to identify student readiness in circles, Triangle Inequality Theorem, and recognizing angle relationships as essential understanding needed for access to Establishing Proof.

Using the Getting Ready

- **Read and discuss the intro**
- **Review the key terms and skills you will need**
- **Ask students to complete the Review**

Log in to MyCL for more information to support your students' readiness needs and to access corresponding **MATHia Workspaces.**

ADDITIONAL KEY TERMS

linear pair

supplementary angles

Exterior Angle Theorem

Triangle Sum Theorem

Getting Ready for Module 2

Establishing Proof

You will use your knowledge of circles to conjecture about quadrilaterals and triangles. You will expand your understanding of line and angle relationships as you develop strategies to write formal proofs. You will continue working with proofs to validate your conjectures about triangles, quadrilaterals, and angles formed in circles.

The lessons in this module build on your prior experiences with circles, the Triangle Inequality Theorem, and angle relationships.

Review these key terms and angle relationships to get ready to establish proof.

KEY TERMS

circle

A circle is a collection of points on the same plane equidistant from the same point, called the *center*. You name circles by their center point.

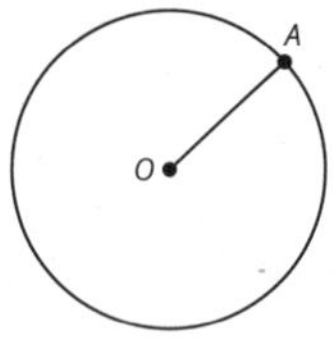

In the Circle, O is the center and $\overline{OA}$ is the radius. Segment OA is congruent to all other radii of Circle O.

Triangle Inequality Theorem

The Triangle Inequality Theorem states that the sum of the lengths of any two sides of a triangle is greater than the length of the third side.

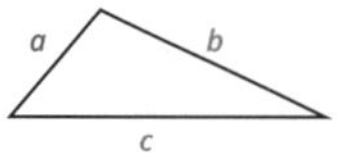

$a + b > c$

$a + c > b$

$b + c > a$

SKILLS YOU WILL NEED

Recognizing Angle Relationships

When a transversal cuts parallel lines, special angle relationships are formed.

Consider parallel lines m and ℓ and transversal t.

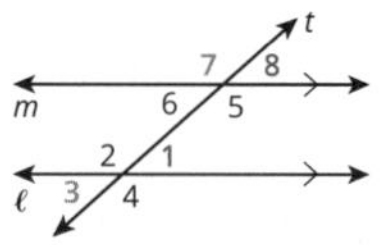

Angles in the same relative position, such as $\angle 1$ and $\angle 8$, are *corresponding angles* and are congruent.

Other congruent pairs of angles include *alternate interior angles*, such as $\angle 1$ and $\angle 6$, and *alternate exterior angles*, such as $\angle 3$ and $\angle 8$.

Same side interior angles, like $\angle 1$ and $\angle 5$, and *same sides exterior angles*, like $\angle 3$ and $\angle 7$, are supplementary.

REVIEW

> Determine the unknown angle measures.

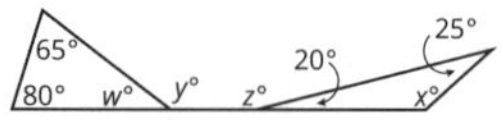

$w = 180° - (80° + 65°) = 35°$
$x = 180° - (20° + 25°) = 135°$
$y = 80° + 65° = 145°$
$z = 180° - 20° = 160°$

See Appendix on page 441 for answers.

MATHia

Brush up on your skills.
If you need more practice with these skills, ask your teacher for access to corresponding workspaces in MATHia.

Questions to Support Discourse

		TYPE
CIRCLE	• Why are all radii congruent? • Are all diameters also congruent? Explain your reasoning.	Reflecting and justifying
TRIANGLE INEQUALITY THEOREM	• What would you need to do to determine whether side lengths of 8 cm, 7 cm, and 15 cm would form a triangle?	Gathering
	• What happens when the sum of two side lengths of a triangle is less than the length of the third side?	Seeing structure
ANGLE PAIRS	• What are other special angle pairs that exist in the diagram? How are their measures related?	Gathering

ENGAGE
Read the Module Overview to appreciate the arc of the math.

\+ **DEVELOP** at the **Topic** level \+ **TEACH** at the **Lesson** level

OVERVIEW: MODULE 2

Establishing Proof

Where are we? 1 Session ≈ 45 minutes

MODULE 1 Reasoning with Shapes	**MODULE 2 Establishing Proof**	MODULE 3 Investigating Proportionality	MODULE 4 Connecting Geometric and Algebraic Descriptions	MODULE 5 Making Informed Decisions
37 Sessions	**47 Sessions**	26 Sessions	19 Sessions	20 Sessions

Why is this Module named **Establishing Proof**?

Throughout their elementary school math education, students visualize geometric shapes and relationships. As they transition to middle school, students begin analyzing geometric shapes—recognizing names and identifying properties.

Throughout the first two modules of this course, the goal is for students to move from analysis to abstraction, where they define properties and relationships precisely and construct informal arguments as to whether these properties and relationships are true in all cases.

As students work through **Establishing Proof,** their reasoning formalizes, and they learn to construct formal proofs. Throughout the rest of this course, students will use the reasoning developed in this module to discover new congruence relationships and use deduction to prove whether these congruence relationships are true in all cases.

The Research Shows....

"Proofs are stories that convince suitably qualified others that a certain statement is true. If I present you with a proof, and you have the appropriate background knowledge and ability, you can—usually with some time and effort—as a result of reading my story, become convinced that what I claim is true. But if you take that as your working definition of proof, you have to acknowledge it is fundamentally about communication, not truth."

—Keith Devlin, "What is a proof, really?" 2014

MyCL

Go to MyPL to access the video for **Module Overview: Establishing Proof**.

www.carnegielearning.com/mathbook-Geometry-module-2-overview

The Mathematical Arc of
Establishing Proof

Students investigate geometric relationships and make conjectures. They prove several geometric theorems. Students use the theorems they proved to prove new theorems and verify properties, relying on identifying congruent triangles as a critical element of their deductive reasoning.

1 Session ≈ 45 minutes	14 SESSIONS TOPIC 1 **Composing and Decomposing Shapes**	24 SESSIONS TOPIC 2 **Justifying Line and Angle Relationships**
LEARNING TOGETHER	11 Sessions	13 Sessions
STANDARDS	G.CO.9, G.CO.10[†], G.CO.11[†], G.CO.12, G.CO.13, G.C.2, G.C.3	N.RN.2, G.CO.9, G.CO.10, G.C.2, G.C.3, G.C.4 (+)
MATHbook Lessons aligned into Topics to drive content goals.	**Students investigate and conjecture about geometric figures.** • They use circles and their defining characteristics as the template upon which to construct lines, angles, triangles, and quadrilaterals. • They use reasoning to conjecture about the relationships they notice, preparing them for formal proof in future topics.	**Students engage in formal geometric reasoning.** • They learn how to write formal proofs. • They prove foundational theorems and theorems related to angle pairs formed by a transversal. • They prove conjectures about the angles on the interior and exterior of polygons and then focus on conjectures about the relationships between sides and angles in triangles. • They prove theorems about angle relationships formed by chords and lines inside and outside of circles.
LEARNING INDIVIDUALLY	~3 Sessions	~11 Sessions
STANDARDS	G.CO.11, G.C.1, G.C.2, G.C.3,	G.CO.1, G.CO.9, G.CO.10, G.SRT.4, G.SRT.5, G.C.2
MATHia Sequences aligned at the topic level to support content goals.	• Students identify parts of circles. • They explore the Inscribed Angle Theorem and calculate the measure of inscribed and central angles. • They draw quadrilaterals using circles and determine angle measures in inscribed quadrilaterals. • They learn about of points of concurrency by watching an animation and analyzing a table summarizing each point.	• Students analyze proofs before completing various proofs. • They use theorems to solve problems with congruence. • They classify angles and calculate angle measures formed by transversals. • They calculate the lengths of special right triangles. • They use angle measures inside and outside of circles to solve problems.
	Targeted practice of each topic's skills and mathematical concepts.	
For students without access to MATHia. Skills Practice	• Students identify parts of circles. • They construct quadrilaterals, triangles, angle bisectors, and duplicate angles. • They conjecture about the properties of quadrilaterals and angle measures in triangles. • They draw points of concurrency.	• Students identify reasons and statements to complete proofs. • They use the angle relationships formed from parallel lines to solve problems. • They solve problems involving the interior and exterior angles of polygons and circles. • They determine unknown measures of isosceles and special right triangles.

Log in to MyCL for additional online resources.

9 SESSIONS

TOPIC 3
Using Congruence Theorems

6 Sessions

G.CO.10, G.CO.11, G.C.2

Students use the theorems they proved in the previous topic to prove additional theorems.
- They prove congruence theorems specific to right triangles.
- They prove the properties of quadrilaterals.
- They prove theorems about relationships between chords of congruent circles.

~3 Sessions

G.CO.10, G.CO.11

- Students prove triangle congruent using the HL and HA Congruence Theorems.
- They use the properties of quadrilaterals to solve problems.
- They prove theorems about parallelograms.

Targeted practice of each topic's skills and mathematical concepts.

- Students solve problems using right triangle congruence theorems.
- They answer questions about different quadrilaterals using the properties of quadrilaterals and theorems about parallelograms.
- They solve problems using the relationship of chords in congruent circles.

NOTES

Connection to Prior Learning

How is **Establishing Proof** connected to prior learning?

In elementary and middle school, students recognized, explored, conjectured about, and used most of the relationships that they prove in this module. They have been developing formal reasoning skills through geometric constructions.

MATH REPRESENTATION

You can construct a line perpendicular to line *l* through point *B* using a compass and straightedge.

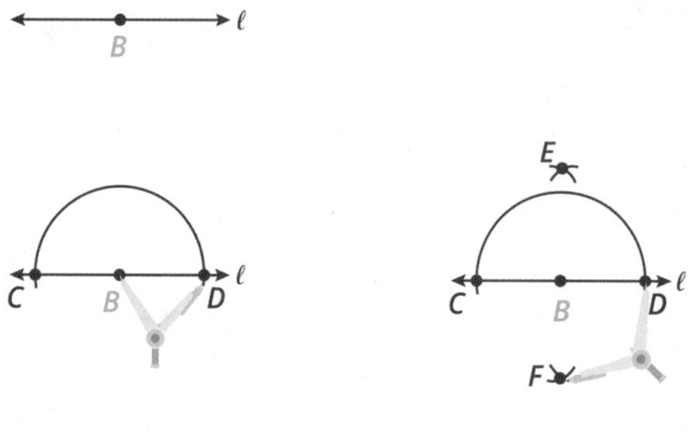

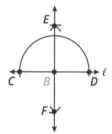

Segments *BD* and *BC* are radii of the same circle, Circle *B*, so they are congruent.

Connection to Future Learning

When will students use knowledge from **Establishing Proof** in future learning?

Students will use the relationships developed in **Establishing Proof** to move from congruence to the broader case of similarity, leading to trigonometry and volume formulas. They will use the theorems from this module as reasons for statements in proofs of the new theorems they encounter.

MATH REPRESENTATION

You can apply the Angle-Angle Similarity Theorem to verify that two triangles are similar.

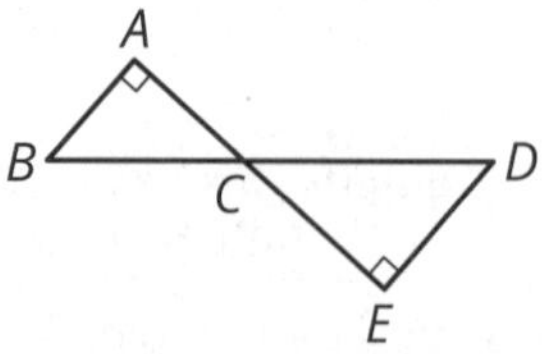

For ΔNOP and ΔRQP, you know that:

- $\angle N \cong \angle R$ because the two angles are right angles, and all right angles are congruent.
- $\angle NPO \cong \angle RPQ$ because the two angles are vertical angles, and vertical angles are congruent.

The Angle-Angle Similarity Theorem tells you that because ΔNOP and ΔRQP have two pairs of congruent angles, they are similar.

ENGAGE at the **Module** level + **DEVELOP** Read the **Topic Overview** and do the math to experience the content development. + **TEACH** at the **Lesson** level

OVERVIEW: TOPIC 1

Composing and Decomposing Shapes

Where are we?

1 Session ≈ 45 minutes

MODULE 2 Establishing Proof	TOPIC 1 Composing and Decomposing Shapes	TOPIC 2 Justifying Line and Angle Relationships	TOPIC 3 Using Congruence Theorems
Pacing	14 Sessions	24 Sessions	9 Sessions

How are the key concepts of ***Composing and Decomposing Shapes*** developed?

Students use circles to conjecture about line and angle relationships. They use diameters, secants, chords, and central angles to conjecture about vertical angles, perpendicular bisectors, arc measures, angle pairs on parallel lines, inscribed angles, and the angles formed at the intersection of a radius and a tangent.

Next, students use circles to compose quadrilaterals from their diagonals and make conjectures. Students summarize what they learned about the diagonals, angles, and sides of quadrilaterals. Finally, they explore the angle relationships of cyclic quadrilaterals.

MATH REPRESENTATIONS

You can draw Quadrilateral *BDCE* by following these steps.

- Construct the perpendicular bisector to $\overline{BC}$ through point *A* of the concentric circles.
- Use patty paper to trace $\overline{BC}$.
- Without moving the patty paper, draw the diameter $\overline{DE}$ of the inner circle so that it is not perpendicular or coincident to $\overline{BC}$.
- Connect the endpoints of the diameters to draw Quadrilateral *BDCE*.

You can classify Quadrilateral *BDCE* as a parallelogram. The diagonals bisect each other, and the opposite sides are congruent.

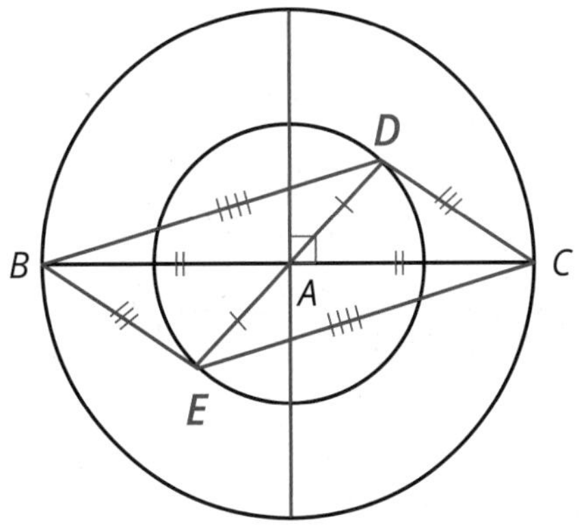

Continuing to gain familiarity with construction tools and the deductive reasoning required to precisely construct geometric figures, students inscribe a square, an equilateral triangle, and a regular hexagon in a circle.

Students now use decomposed quadrilaterals to make conjectures about triangles. They first practice writing converses of conditional statements as they begin to formalize their conjectures and consider the truth of statements and their converses.

To conclude the topic, students investigate points of concurrency by constructing the circumcenter, incenter, centroid, and orthocenter in acute, obtuse, right, and equilateral triangles.

PLAN FOR 11 class sessions and ~3 MATHia sessions.

Log in to MyCL for **lesson support** including:

- Slides
- Videos

LESSON 1

Running Circles Around Geometry

Using Circles to Make Conjectures

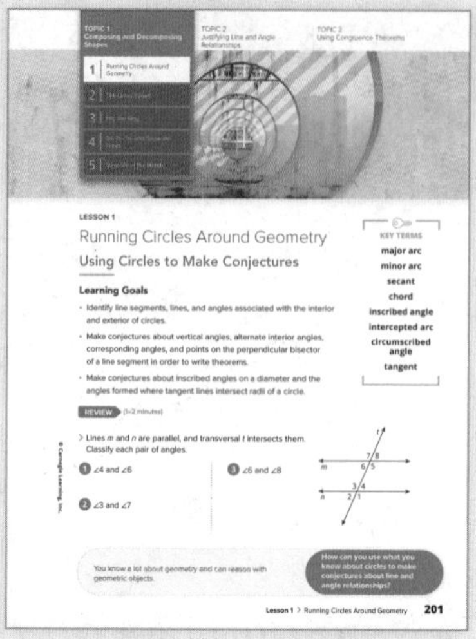

LESSON 1

Running Circles Around Geometry

Using Circles to Make Conjectures

Learning Goals

- Identify line segments, lines, and angles associated with the interior and exterior of circles.
- Make conjectures about vertical angles, alternate interior angles, corresponding angles, and points on the perpendicular bisector of a line segment in order to write theorems.
- Make conjectures about inscribed angles on a diameter and the angles formed where tangent lines intersect radii of a circle.

KEY TERMS: major arc, minor arc, secant, chord, inscribed angle, intercepted arc, circumscribed angle, tangent

REVIEW (1–2 minutes)

Lines m and n are parallel, and transversal t intersects them. Classify each pair of angles.

1. ∠4 and ∠6
2. ∠3 and ∠7
3. ∠6 and ∠8

You know a lot about geometry and can reason with geometric objects.

How can you use what you know about circles to make conjectures about line and angle relationships?

Lesson 1 > Running Circles Around Geometry 201

LEARNING TOGETHER: 2 Sessions

STANDARDS: G.CO.9†, G.C.2

MATHbook — Activities sequenced to address standards and meet content goals.

Students conjecture about line and angle relationships using circles. They construct a circle, perpendicular bisector of a diameter, and chord to identify circle parts. They then conjecture about angle relationships given parallel lines intersected by a transversal. Students critique conjectures about inscribed and central angles.

MATERIALS

- Compasses
- Protractors
- Rulers
- Straightedges

LESSON 2

The Quad Squad

Conjectures About Quadrilaterals

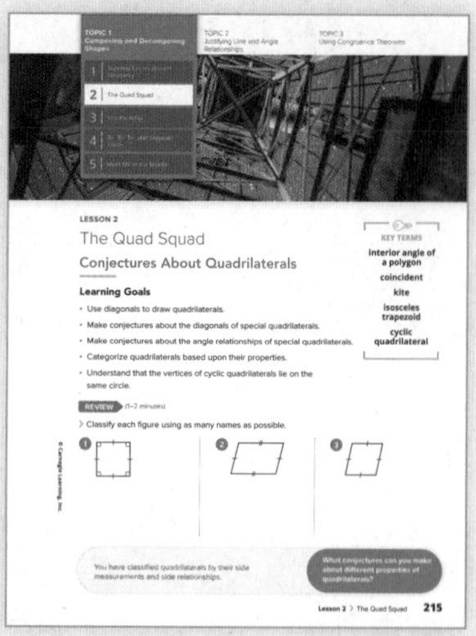

LESSON 2

The Quad Squad

Conjectures About Quadrilaterals

Learning Goals

- Use diagonals to draw quadrilaterals.
- Make conjectures about the diagonals of special quadrilaterals.
- Make conjectures about the angle relationships of special quadrilaterals.
- Categorize quadrilaterals based upon their properties.
- Understand that the vertices of cyclic quadrilaterals lie on the same circle.

KEY TERMS: interior angle of a polygon, coincident, kite, isosceles trapezoid, cyclic quadrilateral

REVIEW (1–2 minutes)

Classify each figure using as many names as possible.

You have classified quadrilaterals by their side measurements and side relationships.

What conjectures can you make about different properties of quadrilaterals?

Lesson 2 > The Quad Squad 215

LEARNING TOGETHER: 2 Sessions

STANDARDS: G.CO.11†

Students make a conjecture about the diagonals of convex and concave quadrilaterals. They construct and identify quadrilaterals inscribed in a single circle and concentric circles using perpendicular and non-perpendicular diagonals. Students consider side, angle, and diagonal relationships for various quadrilaterals. They explore and conjecture about angle relationships in cyclic quadrilaterals.

MATERIALS

- Compasses
- Patty paper
- Protractors
- Rulers

LEARNING INDIVIDUALLY

Median time for students to complete MATHia for this topic is ~120 minutes.

MATHia — Workspaces aligned at the lesson level to support benchmarking through self-paced MATHia.

Lesson 1:

- Introduction to Circles
- Exploring the Inscribed Angle Theorem
- Determining Central and Inscribed Angles in Circles

Lesson 2:

- Using Circles to Draw Quadrilaterals
- Angles of an Inscribed Quadrilateral

Skills Practice

For students without access to MATHia.

Problem sets for additional practice of the lesson skills.

Lesson 1:

- Identifying Circle Parts

Lesson 2:

- Using Circles to Construct Quadrilaterals and Triangles
- Making Conjectures About Quadrilaterals

LESSON 3

Into the Ring

Constructing an Inscribed Regular Polygon

TOPIC 1
Composing and Decomposing Shapes
TOPIC 2
Justifying Line and Angle Relationships
TOPIC 3
Using Congruence Theorems
3 Into the Ring

LESSON 3

Into the Ring

Constructing an Inscribed Regular Polygon

KEY TERMS

inscribed polygon

angle bisector

Learning Goals

- Use construction tools to duplicate an angle.
- Construct a regular hexagon inscribed in a circle using a variety of strategies.
- Construct a square inscribed in a circle using patty paper and using a compass and straightedge.
- Use construction tools to bisect an angle.
- Construct an equilateral triangle using a compass and straightedge.
- Construct an equilateral triangle inscribed in a circle.

REVIEW (1–2 minutes)

Rewrite each expression.

1. $x^2 + x^2$
2. $(\sqrt{3})^2$
3. $(\sqrt{3}x)^2$
4. $(\sqrt{3}x)^2 + (\sqrt{3}x)^2$

© Carnegie Learning, Inc.

You have used construction tools to construct figures in a plane.

How can you construct a regular polygon inscribed in a circle?

Lesson 3 > Into the Ring 231

3 Sessions

G.CO.12, G.CO.13

Students construct an equilateral triangle in a circle using radii. They duplicate an angle, construct an angle twice the measure of a given angle, and bisect an angle. They inscribe a regular hexagon, a square, and an equilateral triangle in a circle. Students apply the constructions they learned to construct a 75° angle and a regular octagon.

- Compasses
- Patty paper
- Straightedges

LESSON 4

Tri- Tri- Tri- and Separate Them

Conjectures About Triangles

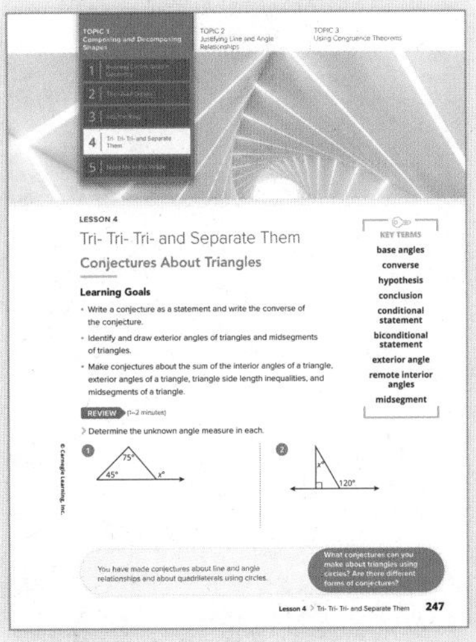
TOPIC 1
Composing and Decomposing Shapes
TOPIC 2
Justifying Line and Angle Relationships
TOPIC 3
Using Congruence Theorems
4 Tri- Tri- Tri- and Separate Them

LESSON 4

Tri- Tri- Tri- and Separate Them

Conjectures About Triangles

KEY TERMS

base angles

converse

hypothesis

conclusion

conditional statement

biconditional statement

exterior angle

remote interior angles

midsegment

Learning Goals

- Write a conjecture as a statement and write the converse of the conjecture.
- Identify and draw exterior angles of triangles and midsegments of triangles.
- Make conjectures about the sum of the interior angles of a triangle, exterior angles of a triangle, triangle side length inequalities, and midsegments of a triangle.

REVIEW (1–2 minutes)

Determine the unknown angle measure in each.

1. 75°, 45°, x°
2. x°, 120°

© Carnegie Learning, Inc.

You have made conjectures about line and angle relationships and about quadrilaterals using circles.

What conjectures can you make about triangles using circles? Are there different forms of conjectures?

Lesson 4 > Tri- Tri- Tri- and Separate Them 247

2 Sessions

G.CO.10†

Students use conjectures about the properties of quadrilaterals to classify quadrilaterals and triangles. They write the converse of conjectures and explore biconditional statements. They use two circles to investigate conjectures about an equilateral triangle, parallel lines, and a perpendicular bisector. Students conjecture about the Triangle Inequality Theorem and midsegments of triangles.

- Compasses
- Protractors
- Rulers

TOPIC 1

For the most up-to-date MATHia alignment, log in to MyCL.

Problem sets for additional practice of the lesson skills.

- Constructing with Angles

- Making Conjectures About Triangles

PLAN FOR
11 class sessions and ~3 MATHia sessions.

Log in to MyCL for **lesson support** including:

- Slides
- Videos

Meet Me in the Middle
Points of Concurrency

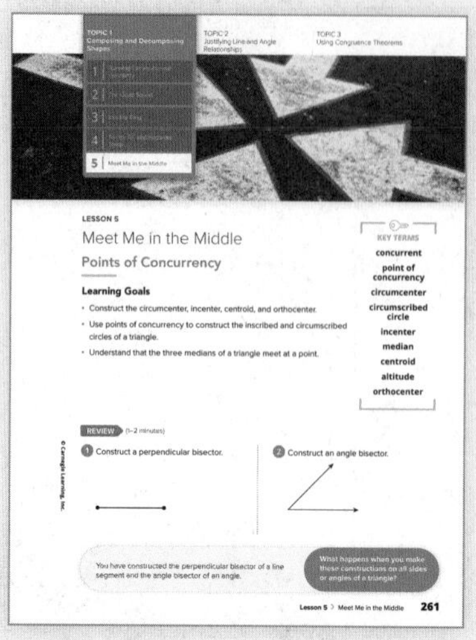

LEARNING TOGETHER — 2 Sessions

STANDARDS: G.CO.10†, G.C.3

MATHbook
Activities sequenced to address standards and meet content goals.

Students construct the incenter, circumcenter, centroid, and orthocenter of triangles. They use constructions to locate each point of concurrency in acute, obtuse, right, and equilateral triangles. Students circumscribe a circle about a triangle using the circumcenter and inscribe a circle in a triangle using the incenter. They use their constructions to make conjectures.

MATERIALS

- Compasses
- Patty paper
- Rulers

LEARNING INDIVIDUALLY — For the most up-to-date MATHia alignment, log in to MyCL.

MATHia
Workspaces aligned at the lesson level to support benchmarking through self-paced MATHia.

- Points on Concurrency

For students without access to MATHia.

Skills Practice

Problem sets for additional practice of the lesson skills.

- Drawing Points of Concurrency

In this topic, students make these conjectures, which they will prove in later topics.

- All circles are similar.
- Vertical angles are congruent.*
- When the measures of two angles *x* and *y* are added, the sum is the measure of another angle, *z*.*
- When the measures of two arcs *x* and *y* are added, the sum is the measure of another arc, *z*.
- When two parallel lines are crossed by a transversal, alternate interior angles are congruent.*
- When two parallel lines are crossed by a transversal, corresponding angles are congruent.*
- When an inscribed angle intercepts the same arc as a central angle, the inscribed angle has half the measure of the central angle.
- Two inscribed angles that intercept the same arc have the same measure.
- When an inscribed angle intercepts a semicircle arc, the inscribed angle measures 90°.
- The angle formed by a tangent line and a radius of a circle is 90°.

* Students explored these conjectures informally in middle school.

Continued on the next page.

In this topic, students make these conjectures, which they will prove in later topics. Continued

- Properties of a parallelogram: opposite sides are parallel; opposite sides are congruent; opposite angles are congruent; and diagonals bisect each other.
- Properties of a rectangle: opposite sides are parallel; opposite sides are congruent; all four angles are congruent; diagonals bisect each other; diagonals are congruent; and all angles are right angles.
- Properties of a rhombus: opposite sides are parallel; all sides are congruent; opposite angles are congruent; diagonals bisect each other; diagonals are perpendicular.
- Properties of a square: opposite sides are parallel; all sides are congruent; opposite angles are congruent; diagonals bisect each other; diagonals are perpendicular; diagonals are congruent; all angles are right angles.
- Properties of an isosceles trapezoid: only 1 pair of opposite sides are parallel; only 1 pair of opposite sides are congruent; diagonals bisect each other; diagonals are congruent.
- Properties of a kite: at least one pair of opposite angles are congruent; diagonals are perpendicular; two pairs of adjacent sides are congruent.
- Opposite angles of cyclic quadrilaterals are supplementary.
- Base angles of an isosceles triangle are congruent.

Connection to Prior Learning

What is the entry point for students?

Since early elementary school, students have been sketching shapes to represent different characteristics. They refined their understanding of shapes, classifying them by side length or angle measure. Precision in drawing shapes became more important to reflect their new understandings. In middle school, students drew geometric shapes with given conditions. They constructed triangles from three measures of angles or sides, noticing when the conditions determined a unique triangle, more than one triangle, or no triangle.

See Math Representations.

Students informally recognized the properties of plane figures and the properties of angle pairs formed when a transversal cuts parallel lines.

MATH REPRESENTATION

You can use construction tools to attempt to construct the triangles.

Construct a triangle given the three segments.

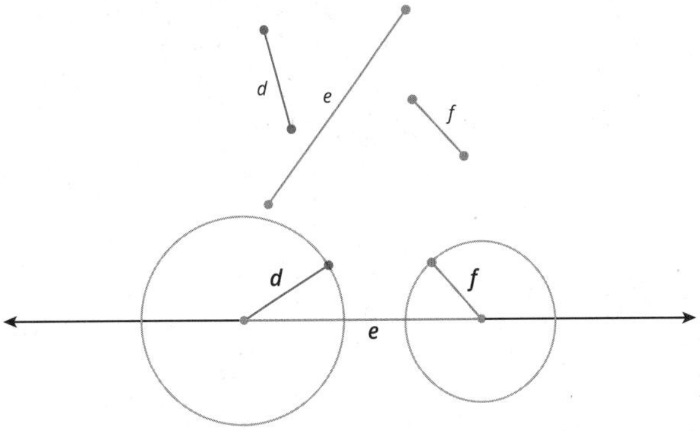

You cannot construct a triangle with these three lengths. The two shorter sides are too short.

Connection to Future Learning

Why is *Composing and Decomposing* Shapes important?

Students' geometric constructions in this topic are an important first step in learning the formal reasoning needed to prove that geometric relationships are true in all cases. Because they need reasons to justify their constructions, they are building their deductive reasoning skills, and this reasoning will serve them well when they write formal proofs in later topics.

MATH REPRESENTATIONS

Consider a conjecture regarding alternate interior angles: if a transversal intersects two parallel lines, then the alternate interior angles are congruent.

Given: $w \parallel x$ and z is a transversal.
Prove: Alternate interior angles are congruent.

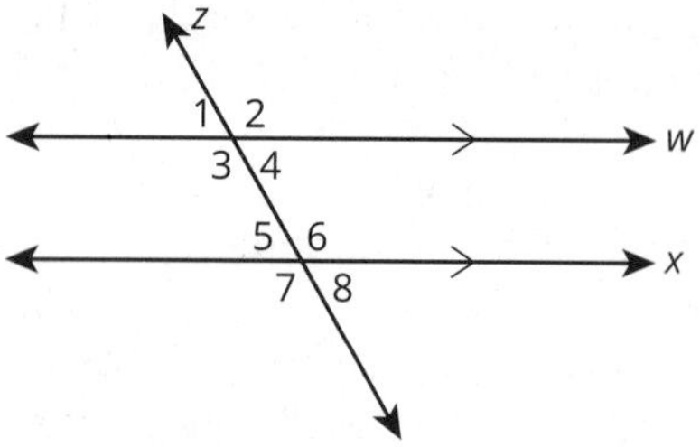

Statements	Reasons
1. $w \parallel x$	**1.** Given
2. $\angle 4$ and $\angle 6$ are supplementary.	**2.** Same Side Interior Angles Theorem
3. $\angle 5$ and $\angle 6$ are supplementary.	**3.** Linear Pair Postulate
4. $m\angle 4 + m\angle 6 = 180°$	**4.** Definition of supplementary angles
5. $m\angle 5 + m\angle 6 = 180$	**5.** Definition of supplementary angles
6. $m\angle 5 = m\angle 4$	**6.** Substitution Property
7. $\angle 5 \cong \angle 4$	**7.** Definition of congruence

Through exploration, construction, and conjecture, students can develop an intuitive understanding of whether a relationship is actually true. Once students believe that it's true, they are better equipped to prove that it is true in all cases.

NOTES

How does a student demonstrate understanding?

Students will demonstrate an understanding of the standards in Composing and Decomposing Shapes when they can:

Log in to MyCL for resources that support **student meta-cognition**.

Conjecture about vertical angles, the angle pairs formed when a transversal intersects parallel lines, and the distance between the points on a perpendicular bisector of a line segment and the endpoints of the line segment.	✓
Conjecture about the sum of the interior angle measures of a triangle, and the base angles of isosceles triangles, and the midsegments of triangles.	✓
Conjecture about the properties of quadrilaterals.	✓
Show that opposite angles in a cyclic quadrilateral are supplementary.	✓
Define the terms *inscribed, circumscribed, angle bisector,* and *perpendicular bisector*.	✓
Use construction tools to bisect an angle.	✓
Define inscribed polygons.	✓
Construct an equilateral triangle inscribed in a circle.	✓
Construct a square inscribed in a circle.	✓
Construct a hexagon inscribed in a circle.	✓
Construct the circumcenter, incenter, centroid, and orthocenter.	✓
Circumscribe a circle about a triangle.	✓
Inscribe a circle within a triangle.	✓
Recognize which point of concurrency is most helpful when solving a given problem.	✓

HABITS OF MIND

How do the activities in *Composing and Decomposing Shapes* promote student expertise in the mathematical practice standards?

All Carnegie Learning topics are written with the goal of creating mathematical thinkers who are active participants in class discourse, so elements of the habits of mind should be evident in all lessons. Students are expected to make sense of problems and work towards solutions, reason using concrete and abstract ideas, and communicate their thinking while providing a critical ear to the thinking of others.

Throughout *Composing and Decomposing Shapes*, students reason about geometric figures to make conjectures about their properties. They use tools of construction to make basic geometric constructions. Once they have had experience with those tools, they can choose the most appropriate tools for each construction. Constructing geometric figures requires students to look for and make use of the structure of the figure and any relationships between lines or angles. As they make each construction, students must attend to precision, as accuracy is necessary to reveal each geometric shape's structure.

Mixed Practice

At the end of each topic, a **Mixed Practice** worksheet provides practice with skills from previous topics and this topic.

Spaced Review
Fluency and problem solving from previous topics

End of Topic Review
Review problems from this topic

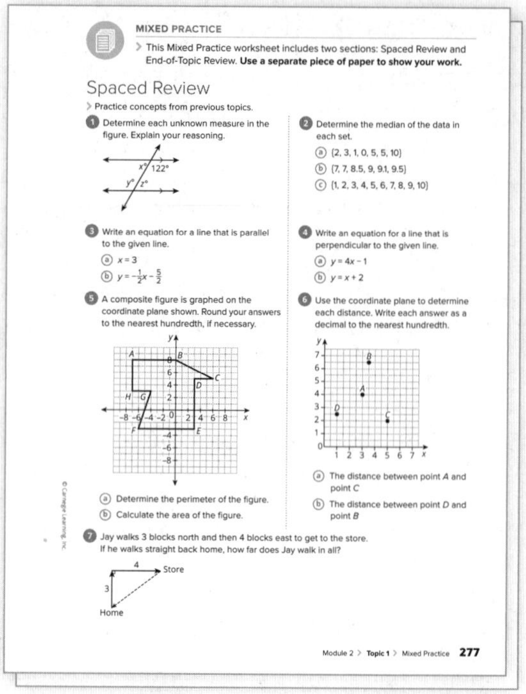
MIXED PRACTICE

This Mixed Practice worksheet includes two sections: Spaced Review and End-of-Topic Review. **Use a separate piece of paper to show your work.**

Spaced Review

Practice concepts from previous topics.

1. Determine each unknown measure in the figure. Explain your reasoning.

2. Determine the median of the data in each set.
   a. {2, 3, 1, 0, 5, 5, 10}
   b. {7, 7, 8.5, 9, 9.1, 9.5}
   c. {1, 2, 3, 4, 5, 6, 7, 8, 9, 10}

3. Write an equation for a line that is parallel to the given line.
   a. $x = 3$
   b. $y = -\frac{1}{2}x - \frac{5}{2}$

4. Write an equation for a line that is perpendicular to the given line.
   a. $y = 4x - 1$
   b. $y = x + 2$

5. A composite figure is graphed on the coordinate plane shown. Round your answers to the nearest hundredth, if necessary.
   a. Determine the perimeter of the figure.
   b. Calculate the area of the figure.

6. Use the coordinate plane to determine each distance. Write each answer as a decimal to the nearest hundredth.
   a. The distance between point A and point C
   b. The distance between point D and point B

7. Jay walks 3 blocks north and then 4 blocks east to get to the store. If he walks straight back home, how far does Jay walk in all?

Module 2 > Topic 1 > Mixed Practice 277

Log in to MyCL for **digital resources**.
A version with **additional space** for students to write their answers.
Downloadable and editable in Word
Editable via Edulastic

Topic Summary

Available online, a **Topic Summary** reviews the main concepts for the topic.

Essential Ideas for each lesson.

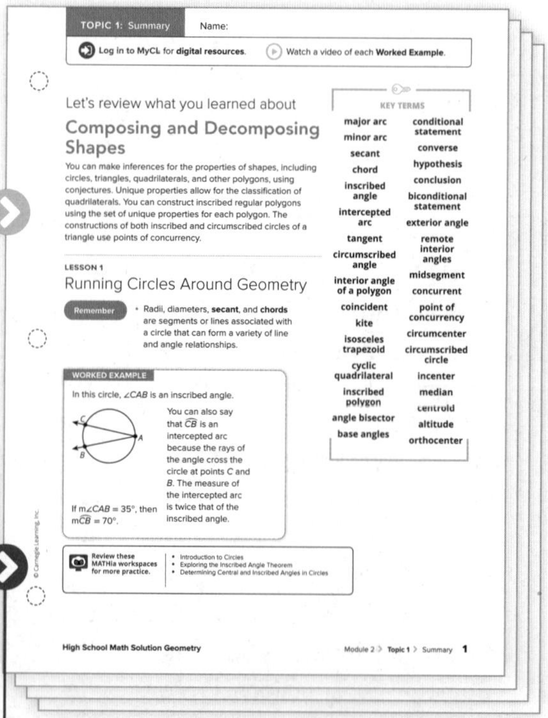
TOPIC 1: Summary Name:

Log in to MyCL for **digital resources**. Watch a video of each **Worked Example**.

Let's review what you learned about

Composing and Decomposing Shapes

You can make inferences for the properties of shapes, including circles, triangles, quadrilaterals, and other polygons, using conjectures. Unique properties allow for the classification of quadrilaterals. You can construct inscribed regular polygons using the set of unique properties for each polygon. The constructions of both inscribed and circumscribed circles of a triangle use points of concurrency.

KEY TERMS: major arc, minor arc, secant, chord, inscribed angle, intercepted arc, tangent, circumscribed angle, interior angle of a polygon, coincident, kite, isosceles trapezoid, cyclic quadrilateral, inscribed polygon, angle bisector, base angles, conditional statement, converse, hypothesis, conclusion, biconditional statement, exterior angle, remote interior angles, midsegment, concurrent, point of concurrency, circumcenter, circumscribed circle, incenter, median, centroid, altitude, orthocenter

LESSON 1

Running Circles Around Geometry

Remember: Radii, diameters, **secant**, and **chords** are segments or lines associated with a circle that can form a variety of line and angle relationships.

WORKED EXAMPLE

In this circle, ∠CAB is an inscribed angle.

You can also say that $\overset{\frown}{CB}$ is an intercepted arc because the rays of the angle cross the circle at points C and B. The measure of the intercepted arc is twice that of the inscribed angle.

If m∠CAB = 35°, then m$\overset{\frown}{CB}$ = 70°.

Review these MATHia workspaces for more practice.
- Introduction to Circles
- Exploring the Inscribed Angle Theorem
- Determining Central and Inscribed Angles in Circles

High School Math Solution Geometry — Module 2 > Topic 1 > Summary 1

Log in to MyCL for **digital resources**.
A printable version available for download.
A video of the **Worked Example** being solved
www.carnegielearning.com/login

MATHia Workspaces are highlighted in select lessons to help you understand the connections and what you might want to review.

TOPIC 1

Assessment

Assessments aligned to this topic:

1. Pre-test
2. Post-test
3. End of Topic Test (Form A)
4. End of Topic Test (Form B)
5. Standardized Test Practice
6. Performance Task with Rubric

An **Assessment Overview** identifies the standard(s) aligned with each item on every test.

Log in to MyCL for digital resources.

- A version with **additional space** for students to write their answers.
- Downloadable and editable in Word
- Editable via Edulastic

End of Topic Test		Standardized Test	
1. G.C.2	11. G.CO.13	1. G.C.2	11. G.CO.12
2. G.C.2	12. G.CO.10	2. G.CO.11	12. G.CO.10
3. G.CO.10	13. G.CO.10	3. G.CO.12	13. G.C.2
4. G.CO.11	14. G.CO.10	4. G.CO.10	14. G.CO.10
5. G.CO.11	15. G.CO.10	5. G.C.2	15. G.CO.11
6. G.C.3	16. G.CO.10	6. G.CO.10	16. G.CO.10
7. G.CO.12	17. G.CO.10	7. G.CO.10	17. G.CO.10
8. G.CO.11	18. G.CO.10	8. G.C.2	18. G.CO.11
9. G.CO.13	19. G.CO.10	9. G.CO.10	19. G.CO.13
10. G.CO.13	20. G.CO.10	10. G.CO.11	20. G.C.2

Family Guide

Teachers, encourage your families to log into the **Home Connection** to access a collection of resources that supports their students as they learn about *Composing and Decomposing Shapes*.

www.carnegielearning.com/home-connection

For families with limited online access, print and send home the **Family Guide**.

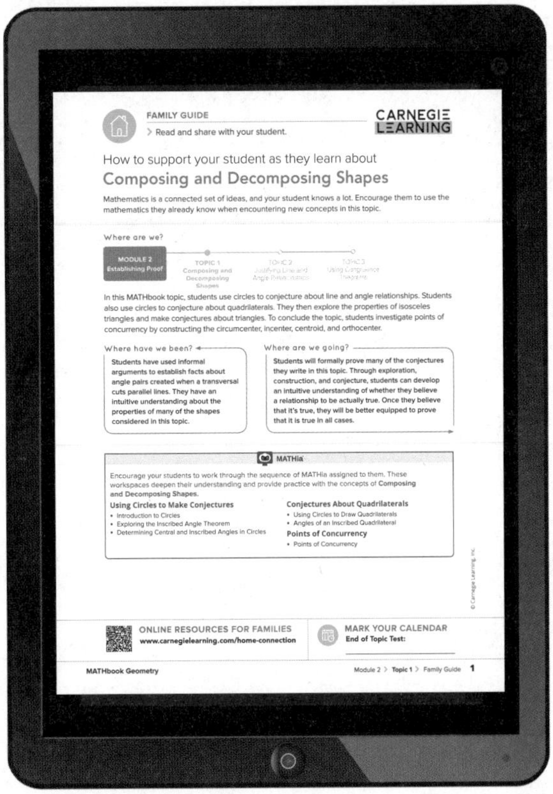
FAMILY GUIDE

> Read and share with your student.

CARNEGIE LEARNING

How to support your student as they learn about

Composing and Decomposing Shapes

Mathematics is a connected set of ideas, and your student knows a lot. Encourage them to use the mathematics they already know when encountering new concepts in this topic.

Where are we?

MODULE 2 Establishing Proof — TOPIC 1 Composing and Decomposing Shapes — TOPIC 2 Justifying Line and Angle Relationships — TOPIC 3 Using Congruence Theorems

In this MATHbook topic, students use circles to conjecture about line and angle relationships. Students also use circles to conjecture about quadrilaterals. They then explore the properties of isosceles triangles and make conjectures about triangles. To conclude the topic, students investigate points of concurrency by constructing the circumcenter, incenter, centroid, and orthocenter.

Where have we been?

Students have used informal arguments to establish facts about angle pairs created when a transversal cuts parallel lines. They have an intuitive understanding about the properties of many of the shapes considered in this topic.

Where are we going?

Students will formally prove many of the conjectures they write in this topic. Through exploration, construction, and conjecture, students can develop an intuitive understanding of whether they believe a relationship to be actually true. Once they believe that it's true, they will be better equipped to prove that it is true in all cases.

MATHia

Encourage your students to work through the sequence of MATHia assigned to them. These workspaces deepen their understanding and provide practice with the concepts of **Composing and Decomposing Shapes.**

Using Circles to Make Conjectures
- Introduction to Circles
- Exploring the Inscribed Angle Theorem
- Determining Central and Inscribed Angles in Circles

Conjectures About Quadrilaterals
- Using Circles to Draw Quadrilaterals
- Angles of an Inscribed Quadrilateral

Points of Concurrency
- Points of Concurrency

© Carnegie Learning, Inc.

ONLINE RESOURCES FOR FAMILIES
www.carnegielearning.com/home-connection

MARK YOUR CALENDAR
End of Topic Test:

MATHbook Geometry — Module 2 > Topic 1 > Family Guide 1

Composing and Decomposing Shapes

Scope out MATHbook and MATHia sessions for this topic, keeping in mind your long term plan.

You can schedule MATHia sessions any time; however, if you are using Skills Practice as the alternative, schedule those sessions after a completed lesson.

1 Session ≈ 45 minutes

Log in to MyCL for:

- Editable templates
- Alternative plans for longer sessions
- Implementations not using MATHia

CORE IMPLEMENTATION PLAN with flexible access to computers/tablets.

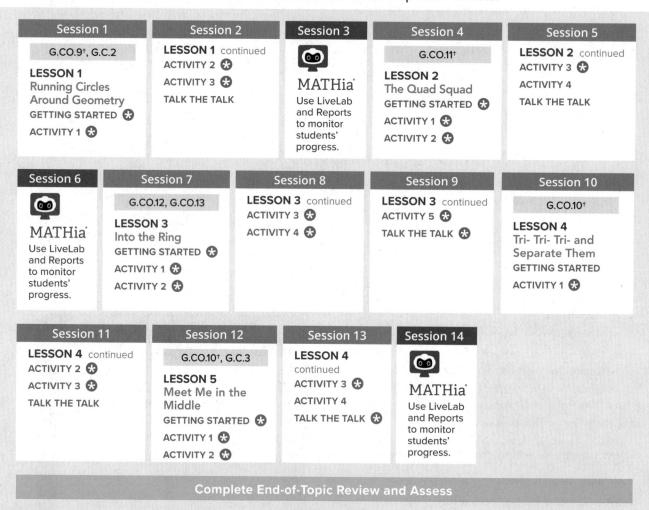

Session 1
G.CO.9†, G.C.2
LESSON 1
Running Circles Around Geometry
GETTING STARTED ✪
ACTIVITY 1 ✪

Session 2
LESSON 1 continued
ACTIVITY 2 ✪
ACTIVITY 3 ✪
TALK THE TALK

Session 3
MATHia
Use LiveLab and Reports to monitor students' progress.

Session 4
G.CO.11†
LESSON 2
The Quad Squad
GETTING STARTED ✪
ACTIVITY 1 ✪
ACTIVITY 2 ✪

Session 5
LESSON 2 continued
ACTIVITY 3 ✪
ACTIVITY 4
TALK THE TALK

Session 6
MATHia
Use LiveLab and Reports to monitor students' progress.

Session 7
G.CO.12, G.CO.13
LESSON 3
Into the Ring
GETTING STARTED ✪
ACTIVITY 1 ✪
ACTIVITY 2 ✪

Session 8
LESSON 3 continued
ACTIVITY 3 ✪
ACTIVITY 4 ✪

Session 9
LESSON 3 continued
ACTIVITY 5 ✪
TALK THE TALK ✪

Session 10
G.CO.10†
LESSON 4
Tri- Tri- Tri- and Separate Them
GETTING STARTED
ACTIVITY 1 ✪

Session 11
LESSON 4 continued
ACTIVITY 2 ✪
ACTIVITY 3 ✪
TALK THE TALK

Session 12
G.CO.10†, G.C.3
LESSON 5
Meet Me in the Middle
GETTING STARTED ✪
ACTIVITY 1 ✪
ACTIVITY 2 ✪

Session 13
LESSON 4 continued
ACTIVITY 3 ✪
ACTIVITY 4
TALK THE TALK ✪

Session 14
MATHia
Use LiveLab and Reports to monitor students' progress.

Complete End-of-Topic Review and Assess

✪ This activity highlights a key term or concept that is essential to the learning goals of the lesson.

Where are we?

TOPIC 1 Composing and Decomposing Shapes	LESSON 1 Running Circles Around Geometry	LESSON 2 The Quad Squad	LESSON 3 Into the Ring	LESSON 4 Tri- Tri- Tri- and Separate Them	LESSON 5 Meet Me in the Middle
Pacing	2 Sessions	2 Sessions	3 Sessions	2 Sessions	2 Sessions

OVERVIEW: LESSON 1

Running Circles Around Geometry

Using Circles to Make Conjectures

ENGAGE

- Students discuss the characteristics of a circle.

DEVELOP

- Students construct a circle, a diameter, a perpendicular bisector of the diameter, and a chord and determine the measures of the resulting angles and arcs.
- They conjecture about vertical angles and the measures of angles formed when a transversal cuts two parallel lines.
- They critique conjectures about inscribed and central angles.

DEMONSTRATE

- Students revisit their conjectures and draw an example of each.

HIGH SCHOOL GEOMETRY

Congruence

Prove geometric theorems.

9. Prove theorems about lines and angles.†

Circles

Understand and apply theorems about circles.

2. Identify and describe relationships among inscribed angles, radii, and chords.

†The full intent of the standard is not met in this lesson. Students make conjectures about these theorems; they will prove them and fully meet the standard in future lessons.

LESSON STRUCTURE AND PACING GUIDE 2 SESSIONS

⊛ This activity highlights a key term or concept that is essential to the learning goals of the lesson.

Session 1		Session 2
INSTRUCTIONAL SEQUENCE		
ENGAGE Connect to prior knowledge	**DEVELOP** Investigation	**DEVELOP** Peer analysis Investigation

GETTING STARTED
Freehand Circle Drawing Championship

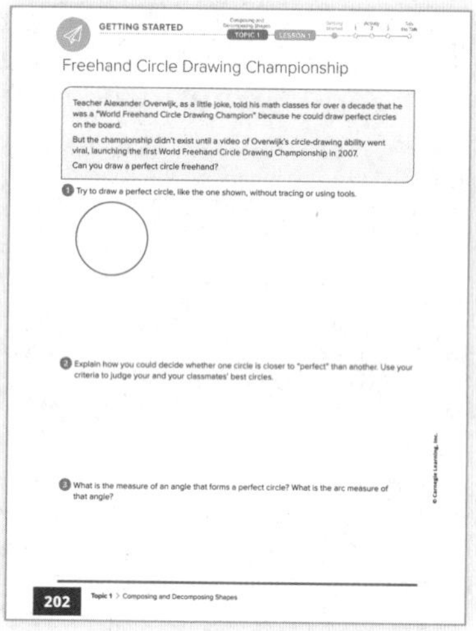

GETTING STARTED
Freehand Circle Drawing Championship
Teacher Alexander Overwijk, as a little joke, told his math classes for over a decade that he was a "World Freehand Circle Drawing Champion" because he could draw perfect circles on the board.
But the championship didn't exist until a video of Overwijk's circle-drawing ability went viral, launching the first World Freehand Circle Drawing Championship in 2007.
Can you draw a perfect circle freehand?
1 Try to draw a perfect circle, like the one shown, without tracing or using tools.
2 Explain how you could decide whether one circle is closer to "perfect" than another. Use your criteria to judge your and your classmates' best circles.
3 What is the measure of an angle that forms a perfect circle? What is the arc measure of that angle?
202
Topic 1 > Composing and Decomposing Shapes

Students discuss criteria they could use to judge the quality of a circle that is drawn freehand.

- They try to draw a "perfect" circle freehand.
- They then compare their circles.

ACTIVITY 1
Circle Parts and Bisectors

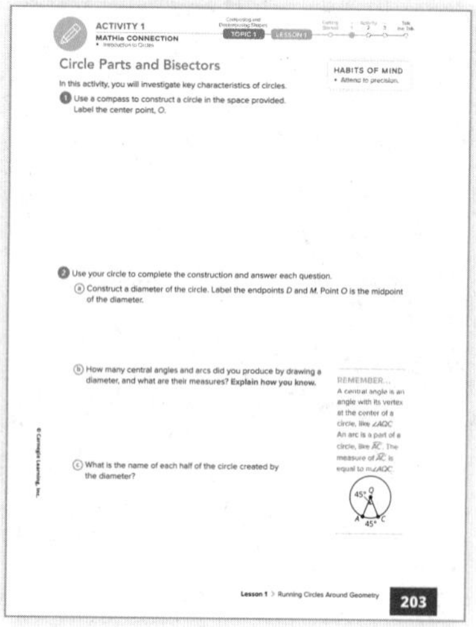

ACTIVITY 1
MATHia CONNECTION
Circle Parts and Bisectors
HABITS OF MIND
In this activity, you will investigate key characteristics of circles.
1 Use a compass to construct a circle in the space provided. Label the center point, O.
2 Use your circle to complete the construction and answer each question.
a Construct a diameter of the circle. Label the endpoints D and M. Point O is the midpoint of the diameter.
b How many central angles and arcs did you produce by drawing a diameter, and what are their measures? Explain how you know.
c What is the name of each half of the circle created by the diameter?
REMEMBER...
45°
Lesson 1 > Running Circles Around Geometry
203

Students construct a circle, a diameter, a perpendicular bisector of the diameter, and a chord.

- They determine the measures of angles and arcs formed.
- They then classify the triangle formed as an isosceles right triangle and conjecture about its side and angle measures.

ACTIVITY 2
Angle and Arc Relationships

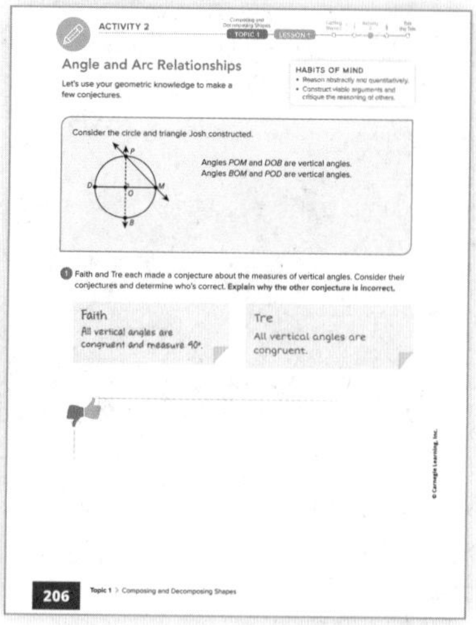

ACTIVITY 2
Angle and Arc Relationships
HABITS OF MIND
Let's use your geometric knowledge to make a few conjectures.
Consider the circle and triangle Josh constructed.
Angles POM and DOB are vertical angles.
Angles BOM and POD are vertical angles.
1 Faith and Tre each made a conjecture about the measures of vertical angles. Consider their conjectures and determine who's correct. Explain why the other conjecture is incorrect.
Faith
All vertical angles are congruent and measure 90°.
Tre
All vertical angles are congruent.
206
Topic 1 > Composing and Decomposing Shapes

Students make conjectures about angle relationships.

- They consider conjectures made about vertical angles.
- They then make conjectures about central angles and their arcs.
- They construct a set of parallel lines cut by a transversal and conjecture about angle measures.

Log in to MyCL for **lesson support** including:

Slides

Videos

www.carnegielearning.com/login

NOTES

TOPIC 1

INSTRUCTIONAL SEQUENCE

DEVELOP	DEMONSTRATE
Investigation Peer analysis	Exit ticket procedures

ACTIVITY 3
Inscribed Angles, Arcs, and Tangents

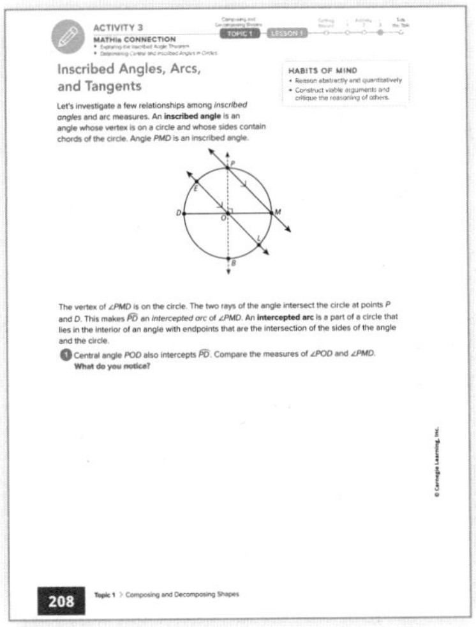

ACTIVITY 3

MATHia CONNECTION

Inscribed Angles, Arcs, and Tangents

HABITS OF MIND
- Reason abstractly and quantitatively
- Construct viable arguments and critique the reasoning of others.

Let's investigate a few relationships among *inscribed angles* and arc measures. An **inscribed angle** is an angle whose vertex is on a circle and whose sides contain chords of the circle. Angle *PMD* is an inscribed angle.

The vertex of $\angle PMD$ is on the circle. The two rays of the angle intersect the circle at points *P* and *D*. This makes $\overset{\frown}{PD}$ an *intercepted arc* of $\angle PMD$. An **intercepted arc** is a part of a circle that lies in the interior of an angle with endpoints that are the intersection of the sides of the angle and the circle.

1 Central angle *POD* also intercepts $\overset{\frown}{PD}$. Compare the measures of $\angle POD$ and $\angle PMD$. **What do you notice?**

© Carnegie Learning, Inc.

208 Topic 1 > Composing and Decomposing Shapes

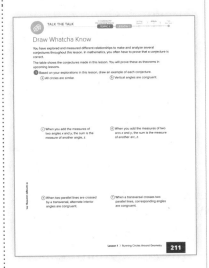

Students critique conjectures about inscribed and central angles.

- They learn the terms *inscribed angle*, *intercepted arc*, *tangent*, and *circumscribed angle*.
- They make conjectures about the angles formed by tangent lines and the radii of a circle.

TALK THE TALK
Draw Whatcha Know

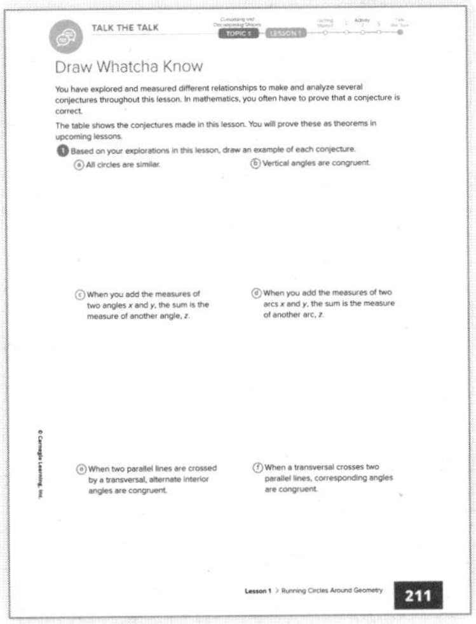

TALK THE TALK

Draw Whatcha Know

You have explored and measured different relationships to make and analyze several conjectures throughout this lesson. In mathematics, you often have to prove that a conjecture is correct.

The table shows the conjectures made in this lesson. You will prove these as theorems in upcoming lessons.

1 Based on your explorations in this lesson, draw an example of each conjecture.

(a) All circles are similar.

(b) Vertical angles are congruent.

(c) When you add the measures of two angles *x* and *y*, the sum is the measure of another angle, *z*.

(d) When you add the measures of two arcs *x* and *y*, the sum is the measure of another arc, *z*.

(e) When two parallel lines are crossed by a transversal, alternate interior angles are congruent.

(f) When a transversal crosses two parallel lines, corresponding angles are congruent.

© Carnegie Learning, Inc.

Lesson 1 > Running Circles Around Geometry 211

Students revisit the conjectures made in this lesson.

- They draw an example of each conjecture.

Log in to MyCL for:
- Editable templates
- Additional planning support

Now that you have read the Module, Topic, and Lesson Overviews, you are ready to plan.

Do the math

> Tear out the lesson planning template (page 201O) and jot down thoughts as you work through this lesson and read the Facilitation Notes.

- Anticipate student responses
- Track your time, so you can estimate how much time to spend on any activity
- Decide which differentiation and collaboration strategies you may use and how that may impact pacing

Connect the learning

MATHbook + MATHia

The table shows a portion of the self-paced MATHia sequence for the *Composing and Decomposing Shapes* Topic.

Median student completion time for the entire topic: ~110–130 minutes

> As you implement this lesson, consider different connections for students who are on pace and those that have not yet completed the workspaces aligned to this lesson.

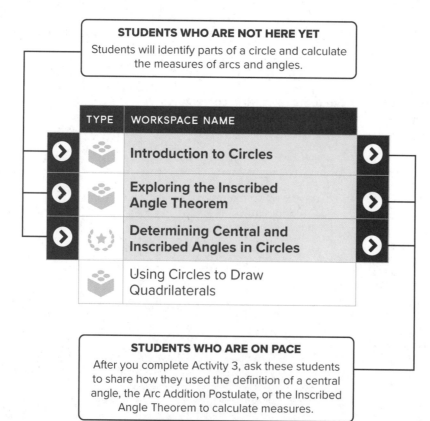

STUDENTS WHO ARE NOT HERE YET
Students will identify parts of a circle and calculate the measures of arcs and angles.

TYPE	WORKSPACE NAME
	Introduction to Circles
	Exploring the Inscribed Angle Theorem
	Determining Central and Inscribed Angles in Circles
	Using Circles to Draw Quadrilaterals

STUDENTS WHO ARE ON PACE
After you complete Activity 3, ask these students to share how they used the definition of a central angle, the Arc Addition Postulate, or the Inscribed Angle Theorem to calculate measures.

Running Circles Around Geometry

Using Circles to Make Conjectures

Session 1

GETTING STARTED Freehand Circle Drawing Championship ✪

Pacing (minutes)	
My Time	Class Time

ACTIVITY 1 Circle Parts and Bisectors ✪

Pacing (minutes)	
My Time	Class Time

KEY TERM
major arc
minor arc
secant
chord

Session 2

ACTIVITY 2 Angle and Arc Relationships ✪

Pacing (minutes)	
My Time	Class Time

ACTIVITY 3 Inscribed Angles, Arcs, and Tangents ✪

Pacing (minutes)	
My Time	Class Time

KEY TERM
inscribed angle
intercepted arc
circumscribed angle
tangent

TALK THE TALK Draw Whatcha Know

Pacing (minutes)	
My Time	Class Time

✪ This activity highlights a key term or concept that is essential to the learning goals of the lesson.

Log in to MyCL for:

- Editable templates
- Additional planning support

Reflect on your lesson

> Consider the effectiveness of your lesson on student learning.

What went well?

What did not go as planned?

> Anticipate how you would change the lesson next time you teach it.

How will you capitalize on the things that went well?

How will you improve things that did not go as planned?

MATERIALS

- Compasses
- Protractors
- Rulers
- Straightedges

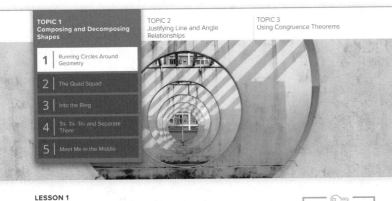

TOPIC 1 Composing and Decomposing Shapes
TOPIC 2 Justifying Line and Angle Relationships
TOPIC 3 Using Congruence Theorems
1 Running Circles Around Geometry
2 The Quad Squad
3 Into the Ring
4 Tri- Tri- Tri- and Separate Them
5 Meet Me in the Middle

LESSON 1

Running Circles Around Geometry

Using Circles to Make Conjectures

Learning Goals

- Identify line segments, lines, and angles associated with the interior and exterior of circles.
- Make conjectures about vertical angles, alternate interior angles, corresponding angles, and points on the perpendicular bisector of a line segment in order to write theorems.
- Make conjectures about inscribed angles on a diameter and the angles formed where tangent lines intersect radii of a circle.

KEY TERMS

- major arc
- minor arc
- secant
- chord
- inscribed angle
- intercepted arc
- circumscribed angle
- tangent

REVIEW (1–2 minutes)

Lines *m* and *n* are parallel, and transversal *t* intersects them. Classify each pair of angles.

1. ∠4 and ∠6
   Alternate interior angles
2. ∠3 and ∠7
   Corresponding angles
3. ∠6 and ∠8
   Vertical angles

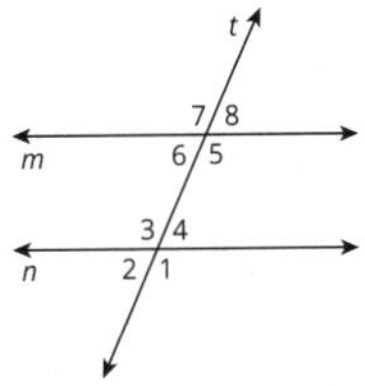

You know a lot about geometry and can reason with geometric objects.

How can you use what you know about circles to make conjectures about line and angle relationships?

Setting the Stage

TOPIC 1

- **Assign Review (optional, 1 – 2 minutes)**
- **Communicate the learning goals and key terms to look out for**
- **Tap into your students' prior learning by reading the narrative statement**
- **Provide a sense of direction by reading the question**

IN THIS REVIEW
Students classify pairs of angles. They will use this skill in **ACTIVITY 2 Angle and Arc Relationships.**

You can use circles to construct geometric figures to make conjectures about line and angle relationships.

Essential Ideas

- Radii, diameters, secants, and chords are segments or lines associated with a circle that can form various line and angle relationships.
- When you conjecture, you use what you know through experience and reasoning to presume that something is true.
- Understanding relationships within a circle can help you make conjectures about line and angle relationships of geometric figures.

SUMMARY **When determining the accuracy of a geometric figure, the use of definitions is often helpful and necessary.**

Chunking the Activity

- **Read and discuss the situation**
- **Have students work individually to complete 1**
- **Check-in and share**
- **Group students to complete 2 and 3**
- **Share and summarize**

LANGUAGE LINK

ELL TIP

Ensure students understand the context by discussing words such as *freehand*, *viral*, and *launching*. As you read through the introduction, encourage students to share their understanding of those words and discuss their meanings in this context.

COMMON MISCONCEPTION

See Page 214A for misconceptions related to 2 and 3.

Student Look-Fors

Different criteria for determining a perfect circle.

- Paper folding
- Using a compass

Freehand Circle Drawing Championship

Teacher Alexander Overwijk, as a little joke, told his math classes for over a decade that he was a "World Freehand Circle Drawing Champion" because he could draw perfect circles on the board.

But the championship didn't exist until a video of Overwijk's circle-drawing ability went viral, launching the first World Freehand Circle Drawing Championship in 2007.

Can you draw a perfect circle freehand?

1. Try to draw a perfect circle, like the one shown, without tracing or using tools.

Answers will vary.

Check students' circles.

2. Explain how you could decide whether one circle is closer to "perfect" than another. Use your criteria to judge your and your classmates' best circles.

Sample answer.

One set of criteria may be that the figure must be closed, and when you divide the circumference by the longest line segment through the center (diameter), the winner is the closest to pi.

3. What is the measure of an angle that forms a perfect circle? What is the arc measure of that angle?

The measures of the angle and the arc are both 360°.

Questions to Support Discourse

		TYPE
2	• Mark the center of your circle. Does the center point of your circle appear to be equidistant from all points on the circle?	Gathering
	• How could you use patty paper to determine which circle is closest to "perfect"?	Probing
	• Did your criteria remain the same as you judged which circle was the best, or did you have to add to your criteria? Why?	Reflecting and justifying
3	• What is the measure of an angle that forms one-fourth of a circle? A semicircle?	Gathering

ACTIVITY 1

SUMMARY You can form various line and angle relationships associated with circles using radii, diameters, secants, and chords.

ACTIVITY 1

MATHia CONNECTION
- Introduction to Circles

Circle Parts and Bisectors

HABITS OF MIND
- Attend to precision.

In this activity, you will investigate key characteristics of circles.

1 Use a compass to construct a circle in the space provided. Label the center point, *O*.

Sample answer.

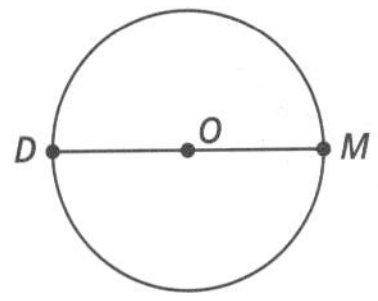

2 Use your circle to complete the construction and answer each question.

(a) Construct a diameter of the circle. Label the endpoints *D* and *M*. Point *O* is the midpoint of the diameter.

See Question 1 for sample answer.

(b) How many central angles and arcs did you produce by drawing a diameter, and what are their measures? **Explain how you know.**

I produced 2 central angles, each measuring 180°.

Two arcs are produced, each measuring 180°.

Each central angle and arc is half of a 360° circle.

(c) What is the name of each half of the circle created by the diameter?

Half of a circle is a semicircle.

REMEMBER...
A central angle is an angle with its vertex at the center of a circle, like $\angle AQC$. An arc is a part of a circle, like $\widehat{AC}$. The measure of $\widehat{AC}$ is equal to $m\angle AQC$.

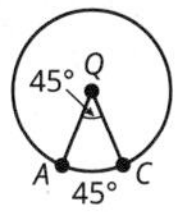

Chunking the Activity

- Group students to complete 1 and 2
- Check-in and share
- Group students to complete 3 - 5
- Check-in and share
- Complete 6 as a class
- Group students to complete 7 and 8
- Share and summarize

DIFFERENTIATION STRATEGY

See Page 214A to assist all students with the vocabulary in the lesson.

COMMON MISCONCEPTION

See Page 214B for a misconception related to 2.

Questions to Support Discourse

		TYPE
1	• How does using a compass to create a circle relate to the definition of a circle?	Seeing structure
2	• What is a midpoint?	Gathering
	• How can you tell whether or not an angle is a central angle?	Probing
	• Do all diameters split a circle into two semicircles? • How can two arcs be different lengths and both have the same measure?	Seeing structure

LANGUAGE LINK

Ensure students understand the meaning of *semicircle* by helping them connect to other uses of the prefix *semi-*. Have students compare this use of *semi-* with other uses such as semi-truck, semi-final, or semi-formal.

NOTES

DIFFERENTIATION STRATEGY

See Page 214B to support students who struggle with 3.

Student Look-Fors

Whether students are demonstrating proficiencies related to this habit of mind.

- Attend to precision

> Use Circle *O* to complete each construction or drawing.

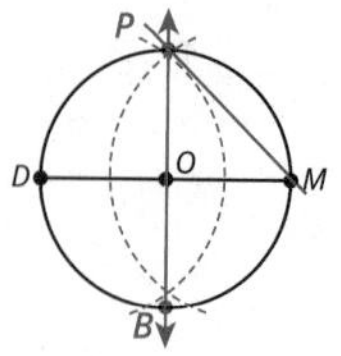

3 Construct a perpendicular bisector of the circle's diameter. Label the points of intersection of the perpendicular bisector and the circle as points *P* and *B*.

See Circle O.

4 Identify all the drawn radii of the circle created by the diameter and its perpendicular bisector.

The 4 drawn radii of the circle are $\overline{OD}$, $\overline{OM}$, $\overline{OP}$, and $\overline{OB}$.

5 What central angles and arcs do the diameter and its perpendicular bisector produce, and what are their measures? **Explain how you know.**

The four central angles are ∠*POM*, ∠*POD*, ∠*DOB*, and ∠*MOB*.

The four arcs are $\overset{\frown}{PM}$, $\overset{\frown}{PD}$, $\overset{\frown}{DB}$, $\overset{\frown}{MB}$.

All central angles and arcs measure 90°, or $\frac{1}{4}$ of a 360° circle.

TAKE NOTE...

Two points on a circle determine a major arc and a minor arc. The arc with the greater measure, $\overset{\frown}{ACB}$, is the **major arc**. The other arc, $\overset{\frown}{AB}$, is the **minor arc**.

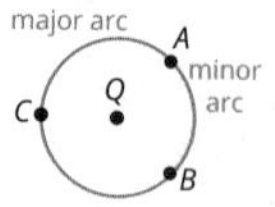

A **secant** of a circle is a line that intersects the circle at two points.
A **chord** is a segment whose endpoints are points on a circle.
In Circle Q, $\overleftrightarrow{CD}$ is a secant and $\overline{CD}$ is a chord.

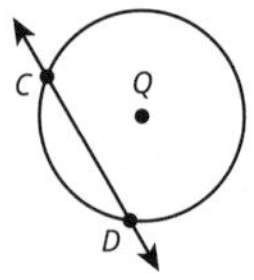

Questions to Support Discourse

		TYPE
3	• Does the perpendicular bisector of the diameter always pass through the center of the circle? Why?	Probing
4	• How many radii are created by the diameter and its perpendicular bisector?	Gathering
	• Do the radii divide the circle into equal pieces? How does that help you determine the measures of the central angles?	Probing
Definitions	• What is the difference between a chord and a secant? • Is a diameter also a chord? Is it also a secant?	Seeing structure

6 Draw a line through two of your labeled points on Circle *O* to form a secant and a chord that is not a diameter. **See Circle O for sample answer.**

(a) Use a protractor to measure the angles of the triangle and a ruler to measure the side lengths.

The angles measure 45°, 45°, and 90°.

The side measures will vary based on the triangle drawn; however, the two legs of each right triangle should be the same length.

(b) Classify the triangle you have created.

The triangle is an isosceles right triangle.

7 Compare your circle diagrams with your classmates' diagrams.

(a) Did everyone create the same triangle? The same type of triangle?

No, some triangles are in a different part of the circle.

Yes, all triangles are isosceles right triangles.

(b) Do you think that all circles are similar? Congruent? **Explain your reasoning.**

All circles are similar. The ratio of the circumference to the diameter of every circle is the constant π.

All circles are not congruent. I can draw circles with radii of different lengths.

THINK ABOUT...
What relationships do you notice among side lengths and angle measures?

Recall that a conjecture in mathematics is often of the form "if *p*, then *q*." Mathematicians write and revise conjectures so that they have clear mathematical statements that they can test and share with others to test.

To make a conjecture in mathematics, you first anticipate that some relationship might exist or some statement might be true (*q*) given one or more assumptions (*p*).

8 What conjecture can you make about this type of triangle?

Sample answer.

If a triangle is isosceles, then the two angles opposite the two congruent sides have the same measure.

NOTES

DIFFERENTIATION STRATEGY

See Page 214B to challenge advanced learners to extend 6.

DIFFERENTIATION STRATEGY

See Page 214B to support students who struggle with 7.

TOPIC 1

Questions to Support Discourse

		TYPE
6	• How would you classify the triangle based on the angle measures? • How would you classify the triangle using the side lengths?	Gathering
7	• Why did everyone's triangle end up being an isosceles triangle?	Probing
	• If the goal is for everyone to construct congruent circles, what directions would the teacher need to provide?	Seeing structure
8	• Do you think there is a relationship between the sides of an isosceles triangle and its angle measures?	Probing

SUMMARY You can use geometric relationships, reasoning, and measurements to make conjectures about angle and arc relationships.

Chunking the Activity

- **Read and discuss the situation**
- **Group students to complete 1 and 2**
- **Check-in and share**
- **Group students to complete 3**
- **Share and summarize**

Student Look-Fors

Whether students make a reasoned judgment after comparing and contrasting the strategies.

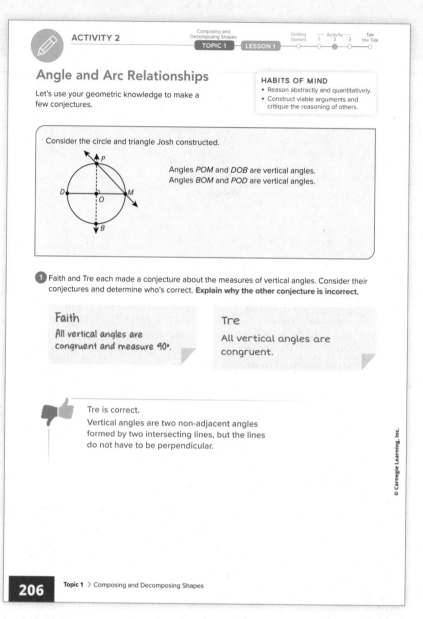

Angle and Arc Relationships

Let's use your geometric knowledge to make a few conjectures.

HABITS OF MIND
- Reason abstractly and quantitatively.
- Construct viable arguments and critique the reasoning of others.

Consider the circle and triangle Josh constructed.

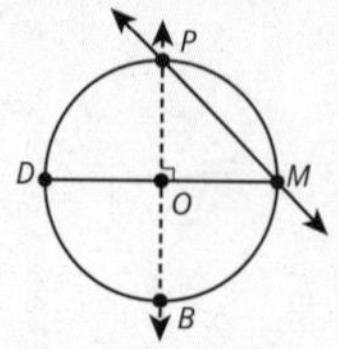

Angles *POM* and *DOB* are vertical angles.
Angles *BOM* and *POD* are vertical angles.

1. Faith and Tre each made a conjecture about the measures of vertical angles. Consider their conjectures and determine who's correct. **Explain why the other conjecture is incorrect.**

Faith
All vertical angles are congruent and measure 90°.

Tre
All vertical angles are congruent.

Tre is correct.
Vertical angles are two non-adjacent angles formed by two intersecting lines, but the lines do not have to be perpendicular.

Questions to Support Discourse

		TYPE
1	• What is the definition of *vertical angles*?	Gathering
	• What conditions need to exist for vertical angles to be congruent and measure 90°?	Probing
2	• Which angles in the figure form linear pairs?	Gathering
	• Why can you consider ∠*MOP* and ∠*POD* a linear pair?	Probing
	• Are angles that form a linear pair always congruent?	Seeing structure

ACTIVITY 2 Continued

2 Consider the central angles ∠MOP and ∠POD and their arcs $\overset{\frown}{MP}$ and $\overset{\frown}{PD}$.

(a) What do you know about the sum m∠MOP + m∠POD?

The measure of the two central angles, 90° + 90°, is equal to the measure of angle ∠DOM, 180°.

(b) What can you conjecture about the sum m$\overset{\frown}{MP}$ + m$\overset{\frown}{PD}$?

The measure of the two arcs, 90° + 90°, is equal to the measure of $\overset{\frown}{MPD}$, 180°.

REMEMBER...

A linear pair of angles are two adjacent angles that have noncommon sides that are opposite rays.

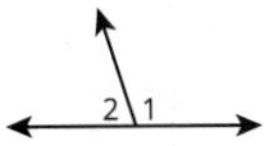

The angles of a linear pair have measures whose sum is 180°.

3 Construct $\overleftrightarrow{EL}$ through the center of the circle parallel to $\overleftrightarrow{PM}$, so that ∠EOP and ∠LOM are both acute angles. Then make conjectures about each angle pair.

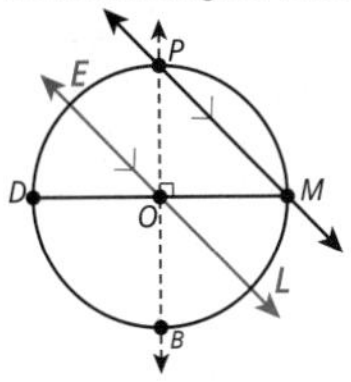

(a) ∠PMO and ∠EOD

Angles *PMO* and *EOD* are congruent corresponding angles.

(b) ∠MPO and ∠POE

Angles *MPO* and *POE* are congruent alternate interior angles.

(c) Make a conjecture about another angle pair that you know something about.

Sample answer.
Angles *MPO* and *POL* are supplementary angles on the interior of the parallel lines and the same side of the transversal.

NOTES

TOPIC 1

DIFFERENTIATION STRATEGY

See Page 214C to support students who struggle with 3.

Questions to Support Discourse

		TYPE
3	• What are the different angle pairs formed when a transversal cuts parallel lines? • What is the relationship between the corresponding angles formed by a transversal intersecting two parallel lines? • What is the relationship between the alternate interior angles formed by a transversal intersecting two parallel lines?	Gathering

SUMMARY **You can use patterns and reasoning about measurements to make conjectures about inscribed angles, arcs, and tangents.**

Chunking the Activity

- **Read and discuss the definitions**
- **Group students to complete 1**
- **Check-in and share**
- **Group students to complete 2 and 3**
- **Check-in and share**
- **Group students to complete 4 and 5**
- **Share and summarize**

DIFFERENTIATION STRATEGY

See Page 214C to assist all students with identifying intercepted arcs.

Student Look-Fors

Utilizing relationship skills by communicating clearly and listening well.

MATHia CONNECTION

- Exploring the Inscribed Angle Theorem
- Determining Central and Inscribed Angles in Circles

Inscribed Angles, Arcs, and Tangents

HABITS OF MIND

- Reason abstractly and quantitatively.
- Construct viable arguments and critique the reasoning of others.

Let's investigate a few relationships among *inscribed angles* and arc measures. An **inscribed angle** is an angle whose vertex is on a circle and whose sides contain chords of the circle. Angle *PMD* is an inscribed angle.

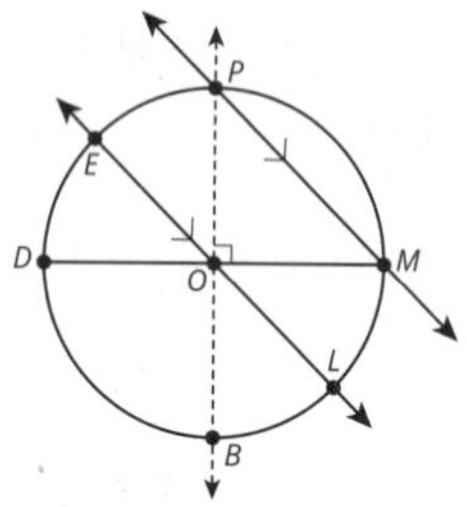

The vertex of $\angle PMD$ is on the circle. The two rays of the angle intersect the circle at points *P* and *D*. This makes $\overset{\frown}{PD}$ an *intercepted arc* of $\angle PMD$. An **intercepted arc** is a part of a circle that lies in the interior of an angle with endpoints that are the intersection of the sides of the angle and the circle.

1. Central angle *POD* also intercepts $\overset{\frown}{PD}$. Compare the measures of $\angle POD$ and $\angle PMD$. **What do you notice?**

   The measure of inscribed $\angle PMD$ is half the measure of central angle $\angle POD$.

Questions to Support Discourse

		TYPE
Diagram	• Which points on the circle are also on more than one segment or line? How does that help you identify inscribed angles?	Seeing structure
1	• How did you determine the measure of $\angle POD$? $\angle PMD$?	Gathering
	• Do all angles that share the same intercepted arc have the same measure? Why or why not?	Probing

ACTIVITY 3 Continued

Within a circle, an interesting relationship exists between the measure of a central angle and the measure of any inscribed angle that intercepts the same arc of the circle.

2. Vicki conjectured that the measure of an inscribed angle is equal to the measure of a central angle when both angles intercept the same arc.

   Do you agree or disagree with Vicki's conjecture? **Use Circle A to draw examples to justify your answer.**

   Sample answer.
   I disagree with Vicki's conjecture.
   m∠*BAC* = 60°
   m∠*BDC* = 30°

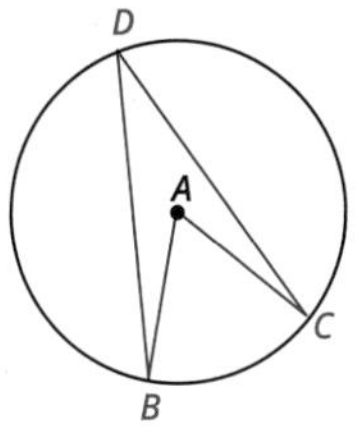

3. Consider the measures of inscribed angles that intercept the same arc. What conjecture can you make about this relationship? **Use points W, X, Y and Z to draw examples to explain your reasoning.**

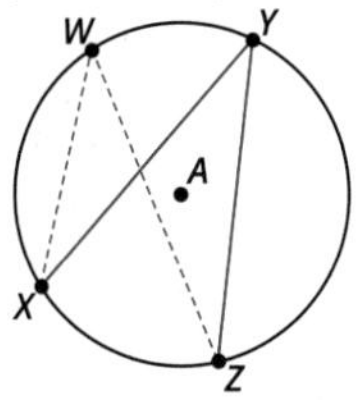

Inscribed angles that intercept the same arc have equal measures.

Sample answer.

m∠*XWZ* = 35°

m∠*XYZ* = 35°

Lesson 1 > Running Circles Around Geometry 209

NOTES

Questions to Support Discourse

		TYPE
2	• What does it mean for an inscribed angle and a central angle to intercept the same arc? • Do you think the relationship changes when the central angle's vertex is outside of the inscribed angle? Why or why not?	Probing
3	• Why could you say that two inscribed angles intercepting the same arc are congruent?	Seeing structure

NOTES

Student Look-Fors

The use of prior knowledge as students analyze Tad's drawing. For example:

- Using relationships between the angles and sides of isosceles right triangles to make new conjectures.
- Looking for angles that are both congruent and supplementary helps to establish perpendicular lines and right angles.

ACTIVITY 3 Continued

4 Ameet measured each of the inscribed angles that intercept a semicircle. He conjectured that the measure of any inscribed angle that intercepts a semicircle arc is equal to 90°.

Do you agree or disagree with Ameet's conjecture? **Use Circle B to draw examples to justify your answer.**

I agree with Ameet's conjecture.

$m\widehat{ADC} = 180°$

$m\angle AXC = 90°$

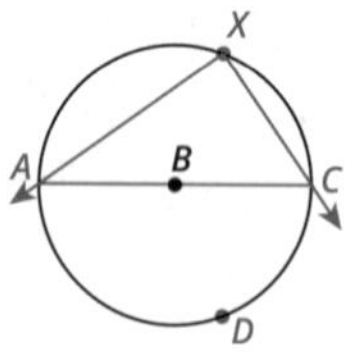

Tad drew two *tangent* lines to the circle, one through point *L* and one through point *G* to form a *circumscribed angle*, ∠*GQL*. A **circumscribed angle** has its two sides tangent to the circle.

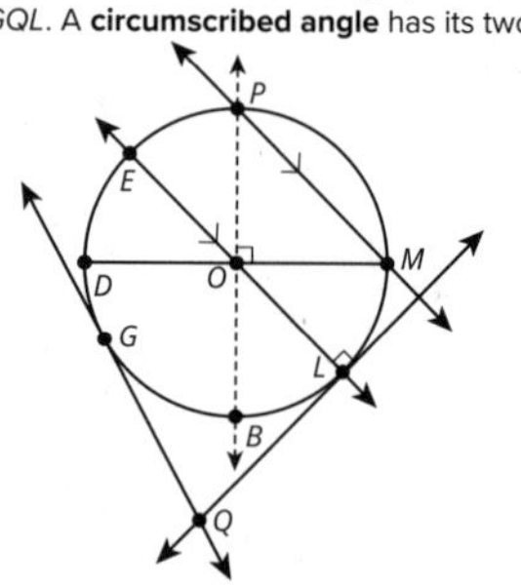

TAKE NOTE...

A **tangent** to a circle is a line that intersects a circle in exactly one point, called the point of tangency.

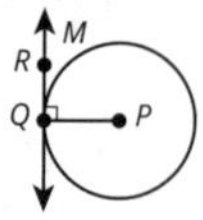

5 What conjecture can you make about the measures of angles formed by tangent lines and the radii of a circle? **Draw examples to explain your reasoning.**

The radius of a circle forms a 90° angle with an intersecting tangent line.

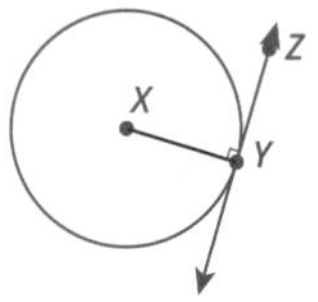

Questions to Support Discourse

		TYPE
5	• What is the arc measure of a semicircle? What does that mean about the measure of an inscribed angle that intercepts that arc?	Seeing structure
Tad's Diagram	• What is the difference between an inscribed angle and a circumscribed angle?	Probing
6	• Which radius of Circle O intercepts $\overleftrightarrow{LQ}$?	Gathering

SUMMARY You can use what you know to make conjectures, but you need to prove conjectures before they become theorems.

Draw Whatcha Know

You have explored and measured different relationships to make and analyze several conjectures throughout this lesson. In mathematics, you often have to prove that a conjecture is correct.

The table shows the conjectures made in this lesson. You will prove these as theorems in upcoming lessons.

1 Based on your explorations in this lesson, draw an example of each conjecture.

(a) All circles are similar.

Sample drawings.
Check students' examples.

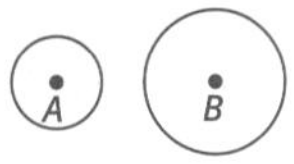

(b) Vertical angles are congruent.

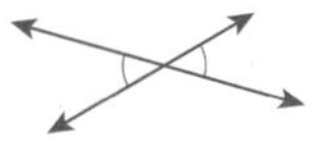

(c) When you add the measures of two angles *x* and *y*, the sum is the measure of another angle, *z*.

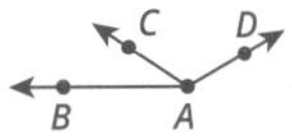

$m\angle BAC + m\angle CAD = m\angle BAD$

(d) When you add the measures of two arcs *x* and *y*, the sum is the measure of another arc, *z*.

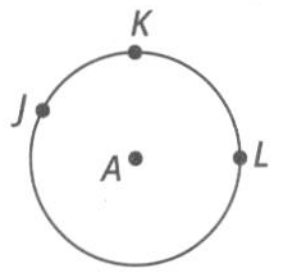

$m\widehat{JK} + m\widehat{KL} = m\widehat{JKL}$

(e) When two parallel lines are crossed by a transversal, alternate interior angles are congruent.

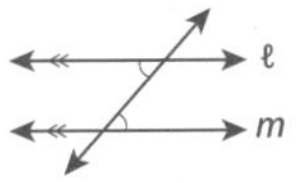

(f) When a transversal crosses two parallel lines, corresponding angles are congruent.

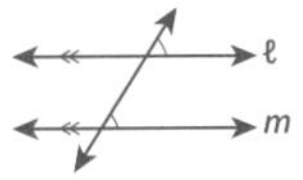

Chunking the Activity

- Read and discuss the directions
- Group students to complete the activity
- Share and summarize

DIFFERENTIATION STRATEGY

See Page 214D to challenge advanced learners to extend the activity.

Questions to Support Discourse

		TYPE
1	• Can all conjectures be proven? Why or why not? • Can you draw other examples that represent the conjecture? Why?	Reflecting and justifying

NOTES

TALK THE TALK Continued

(g) When an inscribed angle intercepts the same arc as a central angle, the inscribed angle has half the central angle measure.

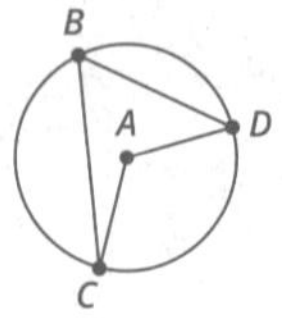

$m\angle CBD = \frac{1}{2} m\angle CAD$

(h) Two inscribed angles that intercept the same arc have the same measure.

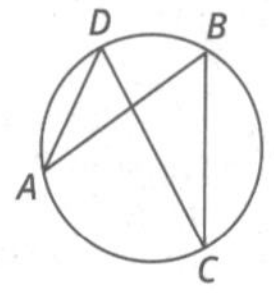

$m\angle ABC = m\angle ADC$

(i) When an inscribed angle intercepts a semicircle arc, the inscribed angle measures 90°.

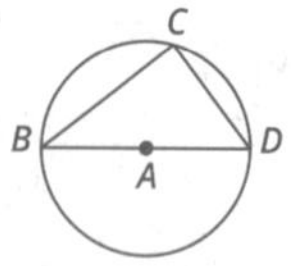

$m\angle BCD = 90°$

(j) The angle formed by a tangent line and a radius of a circle is 90°.

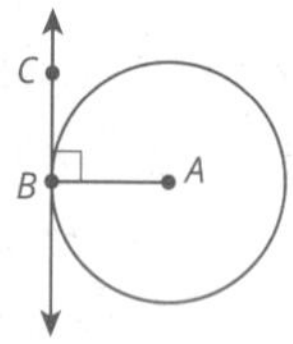

$m\angle ABC = 90°$

212 Topic 1 > Composing and Decomposing Shapes

ASSIGNMENT

LESSON 1 ASSIGNMENT

> Use a separate piece of paper for your Journal entry.

JOURNAL

Match each term with the best description.

REMEMBER

You can use circles to construct geometric figures to make conjectures about line and angle relationships.

1. secant
2. major arc
3. minor arc
4. conjecture
5. inscribed angle
6. intercepted arc
7. tangent
8. circumscribed angle

a. A presumption that something is true or false
b. A line that intersects a circle at exactly one point
c. An angle that has two sides tangent to a circle
d. An angle with a vertex that is on a circle and sides that contain chords of the circle
e. The arc with the greater measure
f. A line that passes through two points on a circle
g. The arc of a circle with endpoints that are intersected by two rays of an angle
h. The arc with the lesser measure

PRACTICE

1. Write a conjecture about each geometric object described. Draw examples to test your conjecture.
   a. Vertical angles

      Vertical angles are congruent.

      Check students' examples.

   b. Points on the perpendicular bisector of a line segment

      Points on the perpendicular bisector of a line segment are equidistant from the endpoints of the segment.

      Check students' examples.

Go to LiveHint.com for help on the PRACTICE questions.

Chunking the Assignment

SESSION 1

- Mixed Practice (page 277) 1 and 2

SESSION 2

- Journal
- Practice 1 and 2
- Stretch (advanced learners)

JOURNAL

1. f
2. e
3. h
4. a
5. d
6. g
7. b
8. c

Encourage students to use LiveHint.com for help with the PRACTICE questions of this assignment.

NOTES

STRETCH

1. See students' constructions.

The perpendicular bisectors of chords in a circle pass through the center of the circle.

(c) Inscribed angles that intercept the same arc of a circle

Inscribed angles that intercept the same arc of a circle are congruent.

Check students' examples.

(d) Tangent

A tangent to a circle and the radius that intersects the point of tangency form a right angle.

Check students' examples.

2. Draw examples of inscribed angles that intercept the diameter of the circle. What conjecture can you make about the measure of the inscribed angle?

Check students' examples.

The measure of an inscribed angle that intercepts the diameter of a circle is 90°.

STRETCH Optional

> Consider the circle with a center at point *P*.

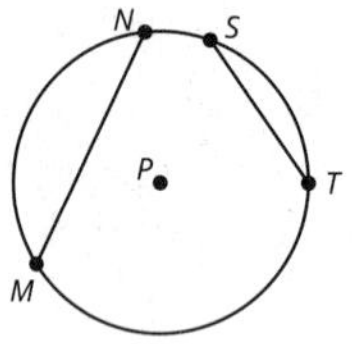

1. Construct the perpendicular bisectors of chord *MN* and chord *ST*. Then make a conjecture about the perpendicular bisectors of chords in a circle.

Running Circles Around Geometry

This resource details additional facilitation notes to fully assist you as you plan each lesson to support all students, students who struggle, and advanced learners. It provides differentiation strategies, common student misconceptions, and suggestions to extend certain activities.

GETTING STARTED

Session 1 of 2

Freehand Circle Drawing Championship

Students try to draw a "perfect" circle freehand. They compare their circles and discuss criteria they could use to judge the quality of a freehand-drawn circle.

CHUNK	AUDIENCE	ADDITIONAL SUPPORTS
As students work on 2	All Students	**COMMON MISCONCEPTION** Some students may think the interior of a circle is part of the circle. Use the definition of a circle to clarify this misunderstanding.
As students work on 3	All Students	**COMMON MISCONCEPTION** Students may be uncertain about which unit of measure you use to describe arc length. Explain that arc measure refers to a degree measure, and arc length refers to a measure of length or distance. If an arc measure is 360°, its arc length is the circumference of the circle. They will formalize their understanding in a later topic.

ACTIVITY 1

Session 1 of 2

Circle Parts and Bisectors

Students construct a circle, a diameter, a perpendicular bisector of the diameter, and a chord. They determine the measures of angles and arcs formed. They then classify the triangle formed as an isosceles right triangle and conjecture regarding its side and angle measures.

CHUNK	AUDIENCE	ADDITIONAL SUPPORTS
As student work on the lesson	All Students	**DIFFERENTIATION STRATEGY** Have students draw three columns on a piece of paper and label the first column with *term*, the second column with *definition*, and the third column with *picture*. As students encounter new terms in the lesson, encourage them to add the term, definition, and a drawing to their table.

CHUNK	AUDIENCE	ADDITIONAL SUPPORTS
As students work on 2	All Students	**COMMON MISCONCEPTION** Students may not think of a straight angle as a central angle. If necessary, discuss the definition of a straight angle. Show students the progression through a visual rotation. First, show an acute angle and how it can increase until it becomes a right angle. Then increase the angle measure again to become an obtuse angle. Finally, increase the angle enough until it becomes a straight angle. The minute or hour hands of a clock are visual references for this idea.
As students work on 3	Students who Struggle	**DIFFERENTIATION STRATEGY** Review what they learned previously about perpendicular bisectors. • Have students define both words to explain what a perpendicular bisector does. • Demonstrate how to construct a perpendicular bisector. • Suggest students label right angles and congruent line segments created by the perpendicular bisector.
To extend 6	Advanced Learners	**DIFFERENTIATION STRATEGY** Have students investigate the ratio between the side lengths of the hypotenuse and a leg of any isosceles right triangle. Students will formally address this special right triangle in trigonometry lessons in a future topic.
As students work on 7	Students who Struggle	**DIFFERENTIATION STRATEGY** Ask students to name other types of triangles based upon the number of congruent sides. Then, have them describe what they know about the side and angle measures of equilateral triangles. Lastly, ask students what relationship they think exists between an isosceles triangle's side lengths and angle measures.

ACTIVITY 2

Session 2 of 2

Angle and Arc Relationships

Students make conjectures about angle relationships. They consider conjectures made about vertical angles. They then make conjectures about central angles and their arcs. They construct a set of two parallel lines cut by a transversal and conjecture about angle measures.

CHUNK	AUDIENCE	ADDITIONAL SUPPORTS
As students work on 3	Students who Struggle	**DIFFERENTIATION STRATEGY** • Provide students with alternate tools, such as patty paper, to create the parallel line. • Help students deal with the complicated diagram by highlighting the parallel lines with the same colored pencil. Suggest they mark angles addressed in the same part of the question with the same color pencil. Give students patty paper to trace the portions of the diagram they are comparing. • Review the names and locations of angle pairs formed by parallel lines cut by a transversal.

ACTIVITY 3

Session 2of 2

Inscribed Angles, Arcs, and Tangents

Students critique conjectures about inscribed and central angles. They learn the terms *inscribed angle*, *intercepted arc*, *tangent*, and *circumscribed angle*. They make conjectures about the angles formed by tangent lines and the radii of a circle.

CHUNK	AUDIENCE	ADDITIONAL SUPPORTS
As students identify intercepted arcs	All Students	**DIFFERENTIATION STRATEGY** Suggest students use a colored pencil to outline the angle associated with the arc and extend its rays beyond the circle.

TALK THE TALK

Session 2 of 2

Draw Whatcha Know

Students revisit the conjectures made in this lesson. They draw an example of each conjecture.

CHUNK	AUDIENCE	ADDITIONAL SUPPORTS
To extend the activity	Advanced Learners	**DIFFERENTIATION STRATEGY** Have students identify any prior knowledge they think will help prove any of the conjectures for all cases. Suggest students ask themselves questions such as: • What information have they already established or can they use? • What definitions do they need to prove this conjecture?

Practice the learning

MATHbook + Skills Practice

The table shows the targeted practice of the skills and mathematical concepts for the *Composing and Decomposing Shapes* Topic. The highlighted Problem Set aligns with **Running Circles Around Geometry**.

PROBLEM SET	
1	**Identifying Circle Parts**
2	Using Circles to Construct Quadrilaterals and Triangles
3	Making Conjectures About Quadrilaterals
4	Constructing with Angles
5	Making Conjectures About Triangles
6	Drawing Points of Concurrency

ANYTIME AFTER ACTIVITY 3

Facilitate students as they work individually on **Problem Set 1**.

ENGAGE + DEVELOP + TEACH

at the **Module** level | at the **Topic** level | Read the facilitation notes and plan learning experiences.

Where are we?

TOPIC 1 Composing and Decomposing Shapes	LESSON 1 Running Circles Around Geometry	**LESSON 2 The Quad Squad**	LESSON 3 Into the Ring	LESSON 4 Tri- Tri- Tri- and Separate Them	LESSON 5 Meet Me in the Middle
Pacing	2 Sessions	**2 Sessions**	3 Sessions	2 Sessions	2 Sessions

OVERVIEW: LESSON 2

The Quad Squad

Conjectures About Quadrilaterals

ENGAGE

- Students conjecture about the diagonals of convex and concave quadrilaterals.

DEVELOP

- Students use diameters to construct and identify quadrilaterals inscribed in a circle.
- They use diameters to construct and identify quadrilaterals constructed in concentric circles.
- They consider side, angle, and diagonal relationships for various types of quadrilaterals.
- Students explore and conjecture about angle relationships in cyclic quadrilaterals.

DEMONSTRATE

- Students apply the definitions of quadrilaterals to complete puzzles.

HIGH SCHOOL GEOMETRY

Congruence

Prove geometric theorems.

11. Prove theorems about parallelograms.†

†The full intent of the standard is not met in this lesson. Students make conjectures about these theorems; they will prove them and fully meet the standard in future lessons.

LESSON STRUCTURE AND PACING GUIDE 2 SESSIONS

✪ This activity highlights a key term or concept that is essential to the learning goals of the lesson.

Session 1

INSTRUCTIONAL SEQUENCE

ENGAGE	DEVELOP	DEVELOP
Establish a situation	Investigation	Investigation Peer analysis

✪ GETTING STARTED
Cattywampus

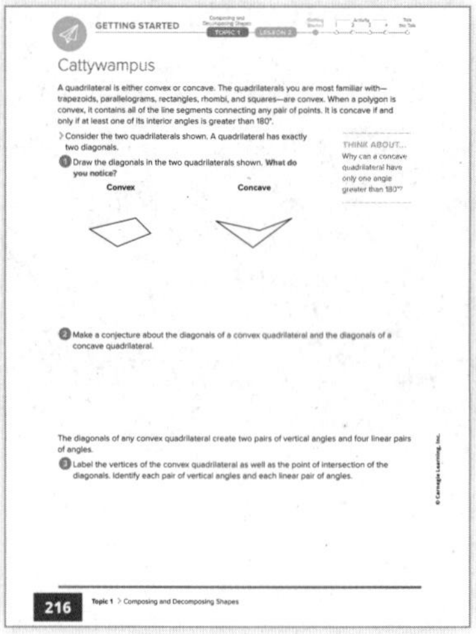

GETTING STARTED

Cattywampus

A quadrilateral is either convex or concave. The quadrilaterals you are most familiar with—trapezoids, parallelograms, rectangles, rhombi, and squares—are convex. When a polygon is convex, it contains all of the line segments connecting any pair of points. It is concave if and only if at least one of its interior angles is greater than 180°.

> Consider the two quadrilaterals shown. A quadrilateral has exactly two diagonals.

1. Draw the diagonals in the two quadrilaterals shown. **What do you notice?**

Convex | Concave

THINK ABOUT... Why can a concave quadrilateral have only one angle greater than 180°?

2. Make a conjecture about the diagonals of a convex quadrilateral and the diagonals of a concave quadrilateral.

The diagonals of any convex quadrilateral create two pairs of vertical angles and four linear pairs of angles.

3. Label the vertices of the convex quadrilateral as well as the point of intersection of the diagonals. Identify each pair of vertical angles and each linear pair of angles.

© Carnegie Learning, Inc.

216 Topic 1 > Composing and Decomposing Shapes

Students make a conjecture about the diagonals of quadrilaterals.

- They review the difference between convex and concave polygons.
- They identify the vertical angles and linear pairs created by the diagonals.

✪ ACTIVITY 1
Quadrilaterals Formed Using a Circle

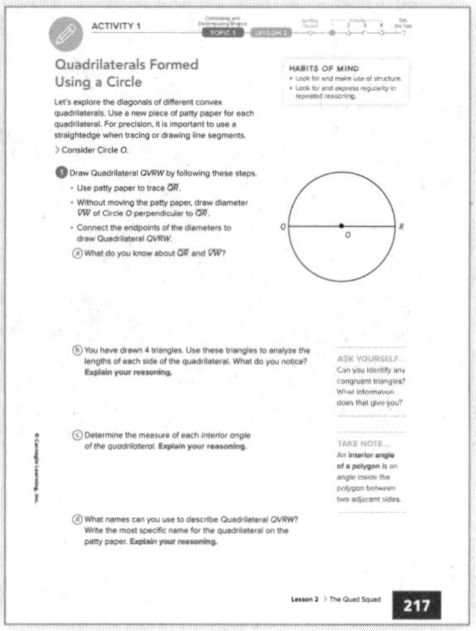

ACTIVITY 1

Quadrilaterals Formed Using a Circle

HABITS OF MIND
- Look for and make use of structure.
- Look for and express regularity in repeated reasoning.

Let's explore the diagonals of different convex quadrilaterals. Use a new piece of patty paper for each quadrilateral. For precision, it is important to use a straightedge when tracing or drawing line segments.

> Consider Circle O.

1. Draw Quadrilateral QVRW by following these steps.
   - Use patty paper to trace $\overline{QR}$.
   - Without moving the patty paper, draw diameter $\overline{VW}$ of Circle O perpendicular to $\overline{QR}$.
   - Connect the endpoints of the diameters to draw Quadrilateral QVRW.

   a. What do you know about $\overline{QR}$ and $\overline{VW}$?

   b. You have drawn 4 triangles. Use these triangles to analyze the lengths of each side of the quadrilateral. What do you notice? **Explain your reasoning.**

   ASK YOURSELF... Can you identify any congruent triangles? What information does that give you?

   c. Determine the measure of each *interior angle of the quadrilateral.* **Explain your reasoning.**

   TAKE NOTE... An **interior angle of a polygon** is an angle inside the polygon between two adjacent sides.

   d. What names can you use to describe Quadrilateral QVRW? Write the most specific name for the quadrilateral on the patty paper. **Explain your reasoning.**

© Carnegie Learning, Inc.

Lesson 2 > The Quad Squad 217

Students construct quadrilaterals inscribed in a circle using perpendicular and non-perpendicular diameters.

- They investigate the angle and side relationships to identify whether the quadrilateral formed is a square or rectangle.

✪ ACTIVITY 2
Quadrilaterals Formed Using Concentric Circles

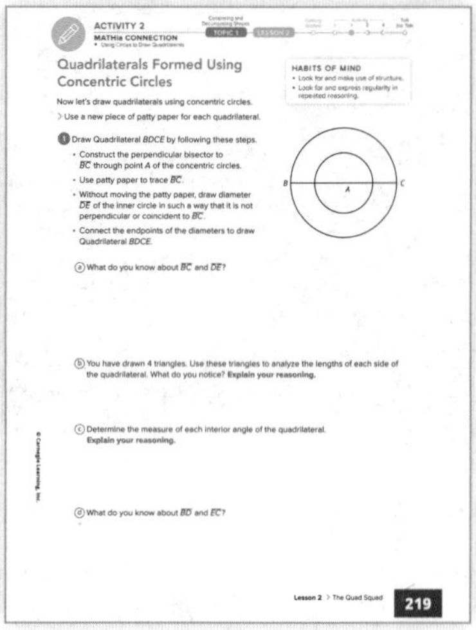

ACTIVITY 2

MATHia CONNECTION

Quadrilaterals Formed Using Concentric Circles

HABITS OF MIND
- Look for and make use of structure.
- Look for and express regularity in repeated reasoning.

Now let's draw quadrilaterals using concentric circles.

> Use a new piece of patty paper for each quadrilateral.

1. Draw Quadrilateral BDCE by following these steps.
   - Construct the perpendicular bisector to $\overline{BC}$ through point A of the concentric circles.
   - Use patty paper to trace $\overline{BC}$.
   - Without moving the patty paper, draw diameter $\overline{DE}$ of the inner circle in such a way that it is not perpendicular or coincident to $\overline{BC}$.
   - Connect the endpoints of the diameters to draw Quadrilateral BDCE.

   a. What do you know about $\overline{BC}$ and $\overline{DE}$?

   b. You have drawn 4 triangles. Use these triangles to analyze the lengths of each side of the quadrilateral. What do you notice? **Explain your reasoning.**

   c. Determine the measure of each interior angle of the quadrilateral. **Explain your reasoning.**

   d. What do you know about $\overline{BD}$ and $\overline{EC}$?

© Carnegie Learning, Inc.

Lesson 2 > The Quad Squad 219

Students construct and identify quadrilaterals constructed using perpendicular and non-perpendicular diameters.

- They investigate angle and side relationships to identify whether the quadrilateral formed is a parallelogram, rhombus, or kite.
- They use the fact that the diagonals of an isosceles trapezoid are congruent to show that its base angles are congruent.

Log in to MyCL for **lesson support** including:

Slides

Videos

www.carnegielearning.com/login

Session 2

INSTRUCTIONAL SEQUENCE

DEVELOP	DEVELOP	DEVELOP
Classification **Peer analysis**	**Investigation**	**Exit ticket application**

TOPIC 1

ACTIVITY 3
Making Conjectures About Quadrilaterals

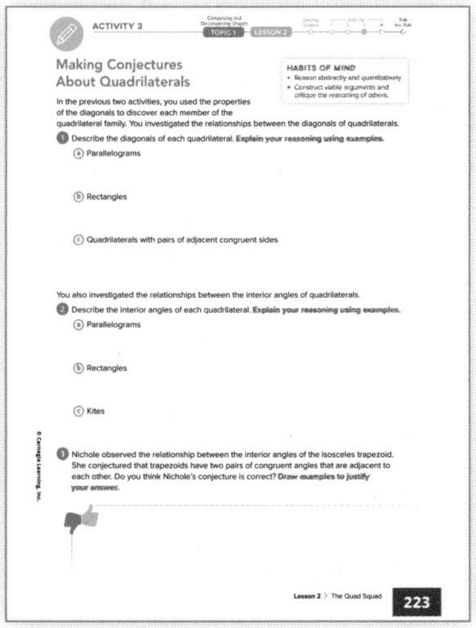
ACTIVITY 3

Making Conjectures About Quadrilaterals

HABITS OF MIND
- Reason abstractly and quantitatively
- Construct viable arguments and critique the reasoning of others.

In the previous two activities, you used the properties of the diagonals to discover each member of the quadrilateral family. You investigated the relationships between the diagonals of quadrilaterals.

1. Describe the diagonals of each quadrilateral. **Explain your reasoning using examples.**
   (a) Parallelograms
   (b) Rectangles
   (c) Quadrilaterals with pairs of adjacent congruent sides

You also investigated the relationships between the interior angles of quadrilaterals.

2. Describe the interior angles of each quadrilateral. **Explain your reasoning using examples.**
   (a) Parallelograms
   (b) Rectangles
   (c) Kites

3. Nichole observed the relationship between the interior angles of the isosceles trapezoid. She conjectured that trapezoids have two pairs of congruent angles that are adjacent to each other. Do you think Nichole's conjecture is correct? **Draw examples to justify your answer.**

© Carnegie Learning, Inc.

Lesson 2 > The Quad Squad 223

Students summarize what they learned about the diagonals, angles, and sides of quadrilaterals.

- They complete a table identifying to which quadrilaterals the properties apply.
- They consider whether the properties they learned about isosceles trapezoids apply to all trapezoids.

ACTIVITY 4
Cyclic Quadrilaterals

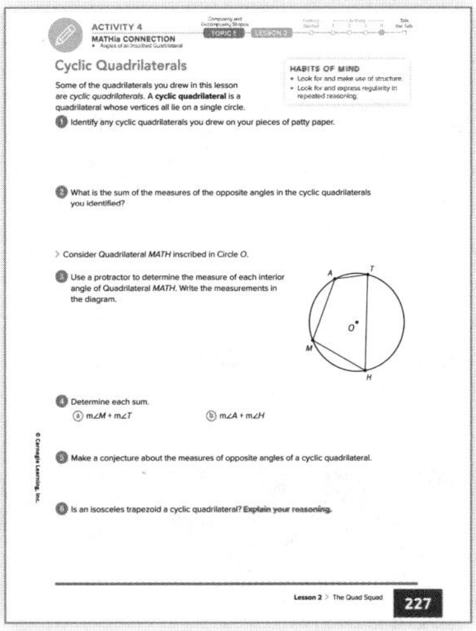
ACTIVITY 4

MATHia CONNECTION
- Angles of an Inscribed Quadrilateral

Cyclic Quadrilaterals

HABITS OF MIND
- Look for and make use of structure.
- Look for and express regularity in repeated reasoning.

Some of the quadrilaterals you drew in this lesson are *cyclic quadrilaterals*. A **cyclic quadrilateral** is a quadrilateral whose vertices all lie on a single circle.

1. Identify any cyclic quadrilaterals you drew on your pieces of patty paper.
2. What is the sum of the measures of the opposite angles in the cyclic quadrilaterals you identified?

> Consider Quadrilateral *MATH* inscribed in Circle *O*.

3. Use a protractor to determine the measure of each interior angle of Quadrilateral *MATH*. Write the measurements in the diagram.
4. Determine each sum.
   (a) $m\angle M + m\angle T$
   (b) $m\angle A + m\angle H$
5. Make a conjecture about the measures of opposite angles of a cyclic quadrilateral.
6. Is an isosceles trapezoid a cyclic quadrilateral? **Explain your reasoning.**

© Carnegie Learning, Inc.

Lesson 2 > The Quad Squad 227

Students explore relationships in cyclic quadrilaterals.

- They identify cyclic quadrilaterals.
- They investigate angle measures in a cyclic quadrilateral and conjecture about the sum of opposite angles.

TALK THE TALK
Zukei, Don't Bother Me

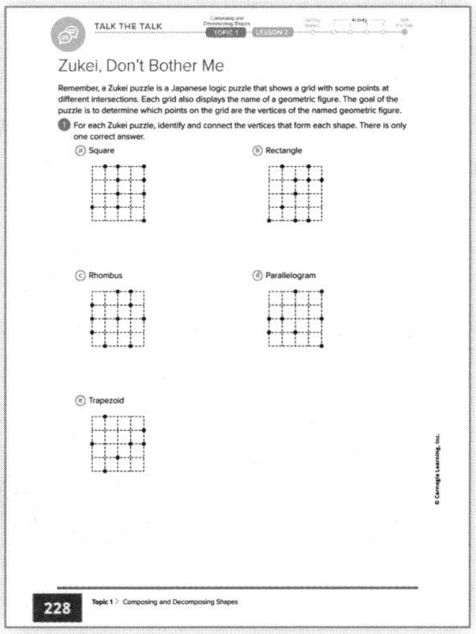
TALK THE TALK

Zukei, Don't Bother Me

Remember, a Zukei puzzle is a Japanese logic puzzle that shows a grid with some points at different intersections. Each grid also displays the name of a geometric figure. The goal of the puzzle is to determine which points on the grid are the vertices of the named geometric figure.

1. For each Zukei puzzle, identify and connect the vertices that form each shape. There is only one correct answer.
   (a) Square
   (b) Rectangle
   (c) Rhombus
   (d) Parallelogram
   (e) Trapezoid

© Carnegie Learning, Inc.

228 Topic 1 > Composing and Decomposing Shapes

Students apply the characteristics of quadrilaterals to puzzles.

- They solve puzzles that require them to identify specific quadrilaterals by their vertices.

Now that you have read the Module, Topic, and Lesson Overviews, you are ready to plan.

Log in to MyCL for:
- Editable templates
- Additional planning support

Do the math

> Tear out the lesson planning template (page 215E) and jot down thoughts as you work through this lesson and read the Facilitation Notes.

Connect the learning

MATHbook + MATHia

The table shows a portion of the self-paced MATHia sequence for *Composing and Decomposing Shapes*.

Median student completion time for the entire topic: ~110–130 minutes

> As you implement this lesson, consider different connections for students who are on pace and those that have not yet completed the workspaces aligned to this lesson.

STUDENTS WHO ARE NOT HERE YET
Students will investigate different quadrilaterals that they can draw using two concentric circles.

TYPE	WORKSPACE NAME
	Exploring the Inscribed Angle Theorem
	Determining Central and Inscribed Angles in Circles
	Using Circles to Draw Quadrilaterals
	Angles of an Inscribed Quadrilateral
	Points of Concurrency

STUDENTS WHO ARE ON PACE
After you complete Activity 4, ask these students to share how they determined the unknown measure of an angle in an inscribed quadrilateral.

The Quad Squad

Conjectures About Quadrilaterals

Session 1

GETTING STARTED Cattywampus ✪

Pacing (minutes)	
My Time	Class Time

ACTIVITY 1 Quadrilaterals Formed Using a Circle ✪

Pacing (minutes)	
My Time	Class Time

KEY TERM
interior angle of a polygon
coincident

ACTIVITY 2 Quadrilaterals Formed Using Concentric Circles ✪

Pacing (minutes)	
My Time	Class Time

KEY TERM
kite
isosceles trapezoid

Session 2

ACTIVITY 3 Making Conjectures About Quadrilaterals ✪

Pacing (minutes)	
My Time	Class Time

ACTIVITY 4 Cyclic Quadrilaterals ✪

Pacing (minutes)	
My Time	Class Time

KEY TERM
cyclic quadrilateral

TALK THE TALK Zukei, Don't Bother Me

Pacing (minutes)	
My Time	Class Time

✪ This activity highlights a key term or concept that is essential to the learning goals of the lesson.

Log in to MyCL for:

- Editable templates
- Additional planning support

Reflect on your lesson

Consider the effectiveness of your lesson on student learning.

What went well?	What did not go as planned?

Anticipate how you would change the lesson next time you teach it.

How will you capitalize on the things that went well?	How will you improve things that did not go as planned?

MATERIALS

- Compasses
- Patty paper
- Protractors
- Rulers

TOPIC 1

TOPIC 1
Composing and Decomposing Shapes

TOPIC 2
Justifying Line and Angle Relationships

TOPIC 3
Using Congruence Theorems

1 Running Circles Around Geometry
2 The Quad Squad
3 Into the Ring
4 Tri- Tri- Tri- and Separate Them
5 Meet Me in the Middle

LESSON 2

The Quad Squad

Conjectures About Quadrilaterals

Learning Goals

- Use diagonals to draw quadrilaterals.
- Make conjectures about the diagonals of special quadrilaterals.
- Make conjectures about the angle relationships of special quadrilaterals.
- Categorize quadrilaterals based upon their properties.
- Understand that the vertices of cyclic quadrilaterals lie on the same circle.

KEY TERMS

interior angle of a polygon
coincident
kite
isosceles trapezoid
cyclic quadrilateral

REVIEW (1–2 minutes)

> Classify each figure using as many names as possible.

1
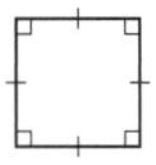
square, rectangle, rhombus, parallelogram, trapezoid (inclusive definition), quadrilateral

2
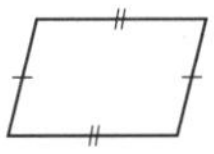
parallelogram, trapezoid, quadrilateral

3
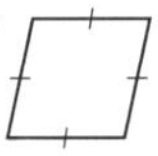
rhombus, parallelogram, trapezoid, quadrilateral

You have classified quadrilaterals by their side measurements and side relationships.

What conjectures can you make about different properties of quadrilaterals?

Setting the Stage

- **Assign Review (optional, 1 - 2 minutes)**
- **Communicate the learning goals and key terms to look out for**
- **Tap into your students prior learning by reading the narrative statement**
- **Provide a sense of direction by reading the question**

IN THIS **REVIEW**
Students classify quadrilaterals. They will use this skill in **ACTIVITY 1 Quadrilaterals Formed Using a Circle.**

The diagonals of a parallelogram bisect each other, and the diagonals of a rectangle are congruent. A square, rhombus, and kite have perpendicular diagonals.

Essential Ideas

- The diagonals of any convex quadrilateral create two pairs of vertical angles and four linear pairs of angles.
- Rectangles, squares, and isosceles trapezoids have congruent diagonals.
- Parallelograms and rhombi have diagonals that are not congruent.
- Circles assist in understanding the characteristics of quadrilaterals.
- You can use the measure and relationship of the diagonals to make conjectures about quadrilaterals.
- A quadrilateral whose vertices all lie on a single circle is a cyclic quadrilateral.

SUMMARY **The diagonals of any convex quadrilateral create two pairs of vertical angles and four linear pairs of angles.**

Chunking the Activity

- **Read and discuss the introduction**
- **Group students to complete the activity**
- **Share and summarize**

DIFFERENTIATION STRATEGY

See Page 230A to assist all students with the introduction.

Student Look-Fors

Working to build relationships within the group to improve teamwork. If groups are struggling to work together effectively, consider facilitating a team-building activity.

Cattywampus

A quadrilateral is either convex or concave. The quadrilaterals you are most familiar with—trapezoids, parallelograms, rectangles, rhombi, and squares—are convex. When a polygon is convex, it contains all of the line segments connecting any pair of points. It is concave if and only if at least one of its interior angles is greater than 180°.

> Consider the two quadrilaterals shown. A quadrilateral has exactly two diagonals.

THINK ABOUT...
Why can a concave quadrilateral have only one angle greater than 180°?

1. Draw the diagonals in the two quadrilaterals shown. **What do you notice?**

Convex

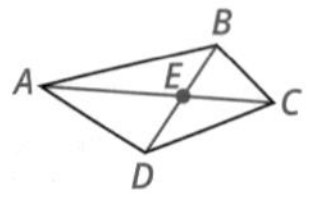

Concave

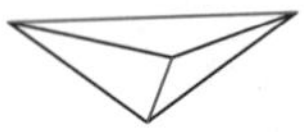

The diagonals of the convex quadrilateral intersect while the diagonals of the concave quadrilateral do not intersect.

2. Make a conjecture about the diagonals of a convex quadrilateral and the diagonals of a concave quadrilateral.

Sample answers.

The diagonals of concave quadrilaterals do not intersect.
The diagonals of convex quadrilaterals intersect.

The diagonals of any convex quadrilateral create two pairs of vertical angles and four linear pairs of angles.

3. Label the vertices of the convex quadrilateral as well as the point of intersection of the diagonals. Identify each pair of vertical angles and each linear pair of angles.

Sample answers.

Vertical angles:	Linear pairs:	
∠AED and ∠BEC	∠AEB and ∠BEC	∠CED and ∠DEA
∠AEB and ∠DEC	∠BEC and ∠CED	∠DEA and ∠AEB

Questions to Support Discourse

		TYPE
Intro	• Can a quadrilateral have two angles greater than 180°? Why or why not?	Probing
1	• Will the diagonals of a quadrilateral always intersect? Why?	Seeing structure
2	• What differences do you notice in the diagonals?	Gathering
	• How could you create a conjecture based on the differences in the figures and their diagonals?	Probing
3	• What do you know about the measures of vertical angles? The measures of linear pairs?	Gathering

ACTIVITY 1

SUMMARY **You can inscribe squares and rectangles in circles. The diagonals of a square are perpendicular, but the diagonals of a rectangle are not.**

Quadrilaterals Formed Using a Circle

HABITS OF MIND
- Look for and make use of structure.
- Look for and express regularity in repeated reasoning.

Let's explore the diagonals of different convex quadrilaterals. Use a new piece of patty paper for each quadrilateral. For precision, it is important to use a straightedge when tracing or drawing line segments.

> Consider Circle *O*.

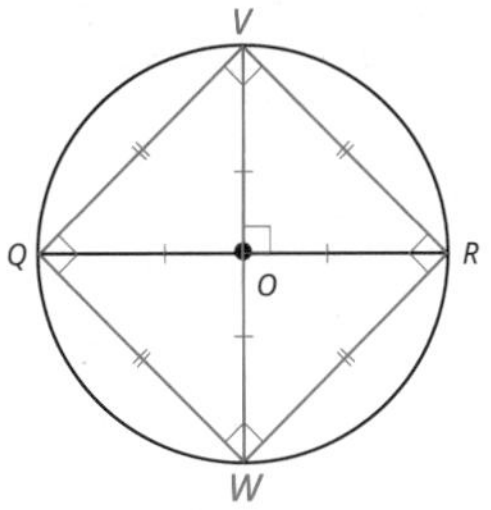

1 Draw Quadrilateral *QVRW* by following these steps.

- Use patty paper to trace $\overline{QR}$.
- Without moving the patty paper, draw diameter $\overline{VW}$ of Circle *O* perpendicular to $\overline{QR}$.
- Connect the endpoints of the diameters to draw Quadrilateral *QVRW*.

(a) What do you know about $\overline{QR}$ and $\overline{VW}$?

Sample answers.

$\overline{QR}$ and $\overline{VW}$ are diagonals of Quadrilateral *QVRW* and are perpendicular. They bisect each other since they intersect at the center of the circle. They are congruent since each is equal to the diameter of the circle.

(b) You have drawn 4 triangles. Use these triangles to analyze the lengths of each side of the quadrilateral. What do you notice? **Explain your reasoning.**

The triangles are all congruent by SAS, so each side of the quadrilateral has the same length.

ASK YOURSELF...
Can you identify any congruent triangles? What information does that give you?

(c) Determine the measure of each *interior angle of the quadrilateral*. **Explain your reasoning.**

Each angle measures 90°.

The two adjacent sides of the square still form an inscribed angle that intercepts a semicircle arc, so the angle measure is 90°.

TAKE NOTE...
An **interior angle of a polygon** is an angle inside the polygon between two adjacent sides.

(d) What names can you use to describe Quadrilateral *QVRW*? Write the most specific name for the quadrilateral on the patty paper. **Explain your reasoning.**

square, rhombus, rectangle, parallelogram, trapezoid

The quadrilateral has four congruent sides and four congruent angles.

Questions to Support Discourse

		TYPE
1	• What is the definition of a square?	Gathering
	• Are diagonals congruent? How do you know? • Do the diagonals bisect each other? How do you know?	Probing
	• How can you use the Perpendicular Bisector Theorem to support your reasoning? • How do you know that each interior angle of the quadrilateral is a right angle?	Seeing structure

Chunking the Activity

- Group students to complete 1
- Check-in and share
- Group students to complete 2
- Share and summarize

DIFFERENTIATION STRATEGY

See Page 230A to assist all students with the lesson.

LANGUAGE LINK

ELL TIP

Discuss the meaning of the term *interior* as it applies to the *interior angle of a polygon*. Help students connect the prefix *in-* to other words or contexts they may know, such as *inside*, the *interior of a car*, or an *interior designer*.

COMMON MISCONCEPTION

See Page 230B for a misconception related to 1 parts (b) and (c).

NOTES

LANGUAGE LINK

ELL TIP

In general, the term *coincident* is an adjective meaning occurring together in time and space. The mathematical definition provided coincides with the general definition.

Students may be familiar with the related term *coincidence* meaning a remarkable concurrence of events or circumstances that have no apparent causal connection with one another.

> Consider Circle *P*.

2 Now draw Quadrilateral *QSRT* by following these steps.

- Construct the perpendicular bisector to $\overline{QR}$ through point *P*.
- Use patty paper to trace $\overline{QR}$.
- Without moving the patty paper, draw diameter $\overline{ST}$ of circle *P* in such a way that it is not perpendicular or *coincident* to $\overline{QR}$.
- Connect the endpoints of the diameters to draw Quadrilateral *QSRT*.

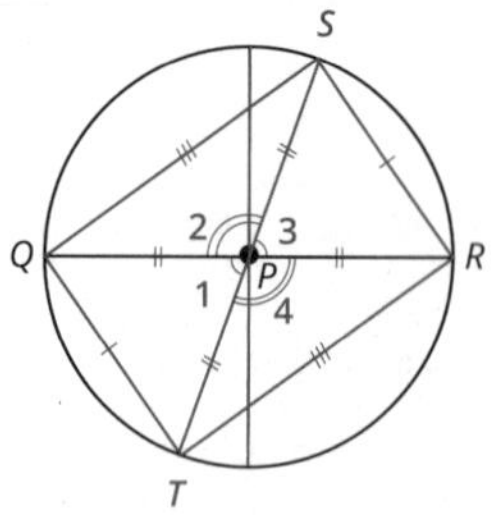

TAKE NOTE...
Two line segments are **coincident** when they lie exactly on top of each other.

(a) What do you know about $\overline{QR}$ and $\overline{ST}$?

Sample answers.

$\overline{QR}$ and $\overline{ST}$ are diagonals of Quadrilateral *QSRT* and are not perpendicular. They bisect each other since they intersect at the center of the circle. They are congruent since each is equal to the diameter of the circle.

(b) You have drawn 4 triangles. Use these triangles to analyze the lengths of each side of the quadrilateral. What do you notice? **Explain your reasoning.**

There are 2 pairs of opposite triangles.
The triangles in each pair are congruent by SAS. So, the quadrilateral has opposite sides congruent.

(c) Determine the measure of each interior angle of the quadrilateral. **Explain your reasoning.**

Each angle measures 90°.
The two adjacent sides of the rectangle form an inscribed angle that intercepts a semicircle arc, so the angle should measure 90°.

(d) What names can you use to describe Quadrilateral *QSRT*? Write the most specific name for the quadrilateral on the patty paper. **Explain your reasoning.**

rectangle, parallelogram, trapezoid

The quadrilateral has opposite sides that are congruent and equal angle measures.

Questions to Support Discourse

		TYPE
2	• How are these directions different from those in Question 1?	Gathering
	• Are diagonals congruent? How do you know? • Do the diagonals bisect each other? How do you know?	Probing
	• How did you use congruent triangles to support your reasoning?	Seeing structure

ACTIVITY 2

SUMMARY You can construct quadrilaterals using concentric circles based on the diagonal length and whether the diagonals are perpendicular or bisect each other.

ACTIVITY 2
MATHia CONNECTION
• Using Circles to Draw Quadrilaterals

Quadrilaterals Formed Using Concentric Circles

HABITS OF MIND
- Look for and make use of structure.
- Look for and express regularity in repeated reasoning.

Now let's draw quadrilaterals using concentric circles.

> Use a new piece of patty paper for each quadrilateral.

1 Draw Quadrilateral *BDCE* by following these steps.

- Construct the perpendicular bisector to $\overline{BC}$ through point *A* of the concentric circles.
- Use patty paper to trace $\overline{BC}$.
- Without moving the patty paper, draw diameter $\overline{DE}$ of the inner circle in such a way that it is not perpendicular or coincident to $\overline{BC}$.
- Connect the endpoints of the diameters to draw Quadrilateral *BDCE*.

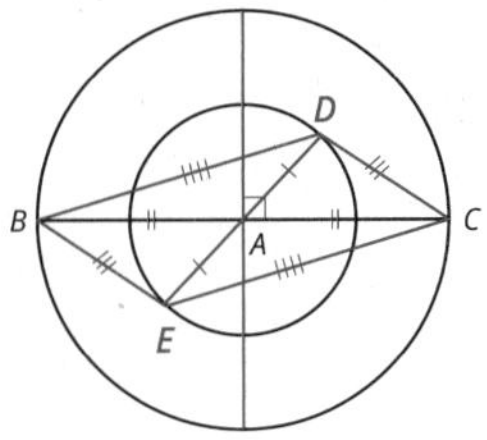

(a) What do you know about $\overline{BC}$ and $\overline{DE}$?

Sample answers.

$\overline{BC}$ and $\overline{DE}$ are diagonals of Quadrilateral *BDCE* and are not perpendicular. They bisect each other since they intersect at the center of the concentric circles. They are not congruent since each is equal to the diameter of a circle that is not congruent to the other.

(b) You have drawn 4 triangles. Use these triangles to analyze the lengths of each side of the quadrilateral. What do you notice? **Explain your reasoning.**

There are 2 pairs of opposite triangles. The triangles in each pair are congruent by SAS. So, the quadrilateral has opposite sides congruent.

(c) Determine the measure of each interior angle of the quadrilateral. **Explain your reasoning.**

The opposite angles of the quadrilateral are congruent.

Triangles *ABD* and *ACE* are congruent by SSS, and Triangles *ABE* and *ACD* are congruent by SSS. So, the opposite angles of the quadrilateral are congruent.

(d) What do you know about $\overline{BD}$ and $\overline{EC}$?

$\overline{BD}$ and $\overline{EC}$ are parallel line segments.

Chunking the Activity

- Read and discuss the introduction
- Group students to complete 1
- Check-in and share
- Group students to complete 2 and 3
- Check-in and share
- Group students to complete 4 – 6
- Share and summarize

NOTE: Remember that this resource uses the inclusive definition of a trapezoid, which is that a trapezoid is a quadrilateral with at least one pair of parallel sides.

Questions to Support Discourse

		TYPE
Intro	• What are concentric circles?	Gathering
1	• What effect does the addition of a second circle have on the diagonals?	Gathering
	• Are diagonals congruent? How do you know? • Do the diagonals bisect each other? How do you know?	Probing
	• Which triangles formed are congruent? How do you know? • Which characteristics must be present to identify the quadrilateral as a parallelogram? • Why can you also classify this figure as a trapezoid?	Seeing structure

NOTES

ACTIVITY 2 Continued

2 Draw Quadrilateral *BFCG* by following these steps.

- Use patty paper to trace $\overline{BC}$.
- Without moving the patty paper, draw diameter $\overline{FG}$ of the inner circle perpendicular to $\overline{BC}$.
- Connect the endpoints of the diameters to draw Quadrilateral *BFCG*.

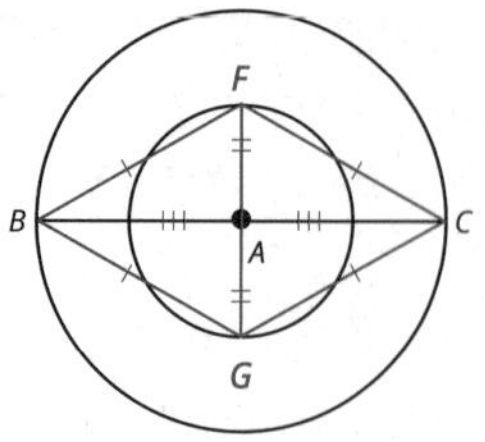

(a) What do you know about $\overline{BC}$ and $\overline{FG}$?

Sample answers.

$\overline{BC}$ and $\overline{FG}$ are diagonals of Quadrilateral *BFCG* and are perpendicular. They bisect each other since they intersect at the center of the concentric circles. They are not congruent since each is equal to the diameter of a circle that is not congruent to the other.

(b) You have drawn 4 triangles. Use these triangles to analyze the lengths of each side of the quadrilateral. What do you notice? **Explain your reasoning.**

The triangles are all congruent by SAS, so each side of the quadrilateral has the same length.

(c) Determine the measure of each interior angle of the quadrilateral. **Explain your reasoning.**

The opposite angles of the quadrilateral are congruent.

Triangles *FCG* and *FBG* are congruent by SSS, and Triangles *BFC* and *BGC* are congruent by SSS. So, the opposite angles of the quadrilateral are congruent.

(d) What names can you use to describe Quadrilateral *BFCG*? Write the name of the quadrilateral on the patty paper. **Explain your reasoning.**

rhombus, parallelogram, and trapezoid

The quadrilateral has congruent side lengths, but it does not have equal angle measures.

Questions to Support Discourse

		TYPE
2	• How do you know that all the triangles formed are congruent? • Which characteristics must be present to identify the quadrilateral as a rhombus?	Seeing structure

ACTIVITY 2 Continued

3 Consider Elijah's statement. What error did Elijah make?

Elijah

In the Quadrilateral BFCG that I drew, ∠BFC and ∠CGB are circumscribed angles.

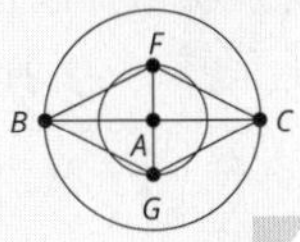

Elijah is confusing the definitions of inscribed angles and circumscribed angles. The vertices of ∠*BFC* and ∠*CGB* are on the small circle, so each angle is an inscribed angle. The sides of ∠*BFC* and ∠*CGB* are not drawn tangent to a circle, so they are not circumscribed angles.

4 Draw Quadrilateral *BHCJ* by following these steps.

- Use patty paper to trace $\overline{BC}$.
- Without moving the patty paper, draw point *H* where the perpendicular bisector intersects the inner circle and point *J* where it intersects the outer circle, such that $\overline{HJ}$ contains point *A*.
- Connect the points to draw $\overline{HJ}$.
- Connect the endpoints of the line segments to create Quadrilateral *BHCJ*.

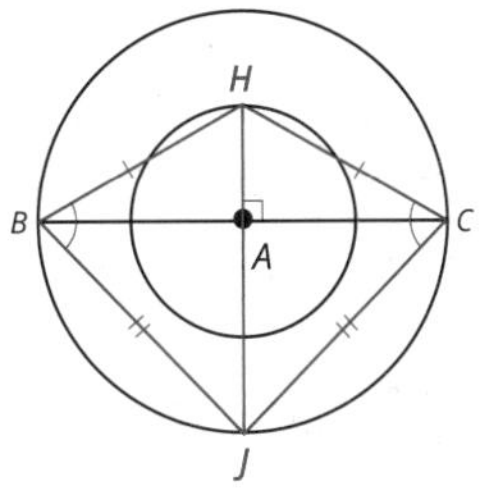

ⓐ What do you know about $\overline{BC}$ and $\overline{HJ}$?

$\overline{BC}$ and $\overline{HJ}$ are diagonals of Quadrilateral *BHCJ* and are perpendicular. Only $\overline{HJ}$ bisects $\overline{BC}$. They are not congruent since one is equal to the outer circle's diameter, and the other is not.

ⓑ Analyze the lengths of each side of the quadrilateral. **What do you notice?**

Because of the Perpendicular Bisector Theorem, $\overline{BH}$ and $\overline{HC}$ will have the same measurement and $\overline{JB}$ and $\overline{JC}$ will have the same measurement.

The adjacent sides of the quadrilateral are congruent.

ⓒ Determine the measure of each interior angle of the quadrilateral. **Explain your reasoning.**

Only one pair of opposite angles are congruent.

Triangles *HBJ* and *HCJ* are congruent by SSS, so angles *B* and *C* are congruent.

Questions to Support Discourse

		TYPE
3	• Draw an example of circumscribed angles to compare to the diagram of inscribed angles.	Gathering
4	• How is this diagram different from the previous two diagrams in this activity?	Gathering
	• How do you know that both pairs of opposite angles are not congruent?	Seeing structure

NOTES

TOPIC 1

Student Look-Fors

Whether students are annotating the strategy. Remind students to ask themselves:

- Where is the error?
- Why is it an error?
- How can I correct it?

DIFFERENTIATION STRATEGY

See Page 230B to challenge advanced learners to extend 4.

NOTES

NOTE: Remember that this resource uses the inclusive definition of a trapezoid, which is that a trapezoid is a quadrilateral with at least one pair of parallel sides. According to this definition, a parallelogram is also a trapezoid.

DIFFERENTIATION STRATEGY

See Page 230B to challenge advanced learners to extend the activity.

The quadrilateral you drew is a *kite*. A **kite** is a quadrilateral with two pairs of equal adjacent sides. When the diagonals of a quadrilateral are perpendicular and only one bisects the other, it is a kite. The diagonals of a kite may or may not be congruent.

THINK ABOUT...
How could you use congruent circles to draw a kite with congruent diagonals?

5. Write the name of the quadrilateral on the patty paper.

   Students should write Kite *BHCJ* on patty paper.

A trapezoid is a quadrilateral with at least one pair of parallel sides, known as the bases. If the other pair of sides are not parallel, they are known as the legs. A special type of trapezoid is an *isosceles trapezoid*. An **isosceles trapezoid** is a trapezoid with congruent legs.

6. Consider the isosceles trapezoid shown.

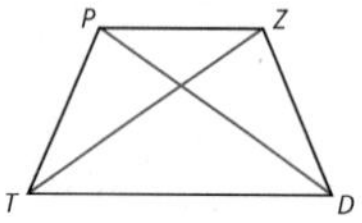

   a. Use a piece of patty paper to trace the trapezoid and draw diagonals $\overline{TZ}$ and $\overline{PD}$.

   b. Determine the measures of $\overline{TZ}$ and $\overline{PD}$. **What do you notice?**

      $\overline{TZ}$ and $\overline{PD}$ are equal in length.

   c. Do $\overline{TZ}$ and $\overline{PD}$ bisect each other? **Explain how you determined your answer.**

      No. I determined the midpoint of each diagonal, and neither diagonal intersects the midpoint of the other.

   d. Determine the measure of each interior angle of the quadrilateral. **What do you notice?**

      The adjacent angles on each base of the trapezoid are congruent.

TAKE NOTE...
Save the quadrilaterals you drew on your pieces of patty paper. You'll need them later.

Questions to Support Discourse

		TYPE
Definition	• What is the difference between a kite and a rhombus?	Probing
5	• What reasoning did you use that prohibits you from using this same process to show the base angles of any trapezoid are congruent?	Probing

ACTIVITY 3

SUMMARY **Various quadrilaterals share specific properties related to their sides, angles, and diagonals.**

Making Conjectures About Quadrilaterals

HABITS OF MIND
- Reason abstractly and quantitatively.
- Construct viable arguments and critique the reasoning of others.

In the previous two activities, you used the properties of the diagonals to discover each member of the quadrilateral family. You investigated the relationships between the diagonals of quadrilaterals.

1. Describe the diagonals of each quadrilateral. **Explain your reasoning using examples.**

   a. Parallelograms

   The diagonals of parallelograms bisect each other.

   b. Rectangles

   The diagonals of rectangles are congruent.

   c. Quadrilaterals with pairs of adjacent congruent sides

   The diagonals of quadrilaterals with pairs of adjacent congruent sides are perpendicular.

You also investigated the relationships between the interior angles of quadrilaterals.

2. Describe the interior angles of each quadrilateral. **Explain your reasoning using examples.**

   a. Parallelograms

   The opposite angles of parallelograms are congruent.

   b. Rectangles

   The angles of a rectangle are congruent.

   c. Kites

   A kite has at least one pair of opposite angles that are congruent.

3. Nichole observed the relationship between the interior angles of the isosceles trapezoid. She conjectured that trapezoids have two pairs of congruent angles that are adjacent to each other. Do you think Nichole's conjecture is correct? **Draw examples to justify your answer.**

   Nichole's conjecture is not correct.
   I can draw any trapezoid that is not isosceles, and the adjacent angles will not be congruent.

Chunking the Activity

- Read and discuss the introduction
- Have students work individually to complete 1 – 3
- Check-in and share
- Group students to complete 4 – 6
- Share and summarize

Questions to Support Discourse

		TYPE
1	• Are the diagonal perpendicular to each other? • Are the diagonals congruent? • Do the diagonals bisect each other? • Is exactly one diagonal bisected?	Gathering
2	• How many pairs of opposite angles are congruent? • Is exactly one pair of opposite angles congruent? • Are opposite angles supplementary? • Are all interior angles congruent? Are they all right angles?	Gathering
3	• How is an isosceles trapezoid different from other trapezoids?	Seeing structure

NOTES

DIFFERENTIATION STRATEGY

See Page 230C to support students who struggle with 4.

Student Look-Fors

Referring to their constructions from previous activities to complete the table.

ACTIVITY 3 Continued

> Use the quadrilaterals you drew on your pieces of patty paper and the observations you made to complete the table.

4 Identify the properties that are always true for the given quadrilateral by placing an X in the appropriate box.

	Property	Parallelogram	Rectangle	Rhombus	Square	Isosceles Trapezoid	Kite
Side Relationships	Opposite sides are parallel.	X	X	X	X		
	Only one pair of opposite sides is parallel.					X	
	Opposite sides are congruent.	X	X	X	X		
	Only one pair of opposite sides is congruent.					X	
	All sides are congruent.			X	X		
	Two pairs of consecutive sides are congruent.			X	X		X
Angle Relationships	Opposite angles are congruent.	X	X	X	X		
	At least one pair of opposite angles is congruent.	X	X	X	X		X
	All angles are right angles.		X		X		
Diagonal Relationships	Diagonals bisect each other.	X	X	X	X		
	Diagonals are perpendicular.			X	X		X
	Diagonals are congruent.		X		X	X	

Questions to Support Discourse

		TYPE
4	• Which properties do squares and rectangles have in common? • Which properties do rectangles and parallelograms have in common? • Which properties do parallelograms and rhombi have in common?	Seeing structure

ACTIVITY 3 Continued

5 Determine whether each statement is true or false. **If it is false, explain why.**

(a) A square is also a rectangle.

True

(b) A rectangle is also a square.

False

If a quadrilateral is a rectangle, that does not imply it has four congruent sides.

(c) A parallelogram is also a trapezoid.

True

(d) The diagonals of a trapezoid are congruent.

False

The diagonals of a trapezoid are congruent only if the trapezoid is isosceles.

(e) A kite is also a parallelogram.

False

Opposite sides of a kite are not always parallel.

(f) The diagonals of a rhombus bisect each other.

True

Lesson 2 > The Quad Squad 225

NOTES

NOTES

DIFFERENTIATION STRATEGY

See Page 230C to support students who struggle with 6.

ACTIVITY 3 Continued

Knowing certain properties of each quadrilateral makes it possible to construct the quadrilateral given only a single diagonal.

6 Describe how you could construct each named quadrilateral with the given diagonal.

(a) Parallelogram *WXYZ* given diagonal $\overline{WY}$

Sample answer

I would begin by duplicating $\overline{WY}$. Then, I would bisect $\overline{WY}$ to locate the midpoint of the diagonal.

Next, I would duplicate $\overline{WY}$ a second time, labeling it $\overline{XZ}$, and locate the midpoint. I would then draw $\overline{XZ}$ intersecting $\overline{WY}$ at both their midpoints.

Finally, I would connect the endpoints of $\overline{WY}$ and $\overline{XZ}$ to form parallelogram WXYZ. This will create a rectangle, which is also a parallelogram.

(b) Rhombus *RHOM* given diagonal $\overline{RO}$

Sample answer.

First, I would begin by duplicating $\overline{RO}$.

Then, I would construct a new line segment on the perpendicular bisector of $\overline{RO}$ such that $\overline{RO}$ also bisects this line segment.

Next, I would label the new $\overline{HM}$. Finally, I would connect the endpoints of $\overline{RO}$ and $\overline{HM}$ to form rhombus *RHOM*.

(c) Kite *KITE* given diagonal $\overline{KT}$

Sample answer.

First, I would begin by duplicating $\overline{KT}$.

Then, I would construct a perpendicular line segment to $\overline{KT}$ such that $\overline{KT}$ bisects the perpendicular line segment. Next, I would label the perpendicular $\overline{IE}$.

Finally, I would connect the endpoints of $\overline{KT}$ and $\overline{IE}$ to form kite *KITE*.

Questions to Support Discourse

		TYPE
6	• How did you use the properties related to diagonals to guide your construction?	Seeing structure

ACTIVITY 4

SUMMARY **A quadrilateral whose vertices all lie on a single circle is a cyclic quadrilateral.**

ACTIVITY 4
MATHia CONNECTION
- Angles of an Inscribed Quadrilateral

Cyclic Quadrilaterals

HABITS OF MIND
- Look for and make use of structure.
- Look for and express regularity in repeated reasoning.

Some of the quadrilaterals you drew in this lesson are *cyclic quadrilaterals*. A **cyclic quadrilateral** is a quadrilateral whose vertices all lie on a single circle.

1 Identify any cyclic quadrilaterals you drew on your pieces of patty paper.

The rectangle and square are cyclic quadrilaterals.

2 What is the sum of the measures of the opposite angles in the cyclic quadrilaterals you identified?

The measures of the opposite angles add up to 180°.

> Consider Quadrilateral *MATH* inscribed in Circle *O*.

3 Use a protractor to determine the measure of each interior angle of Quadrilateral *MATH*. Write the measurements in the diagram.

$m\angle M = 100°$

$m\angle A = 118°$

$m\angle T = 80°$

$m\angle H = 62°$

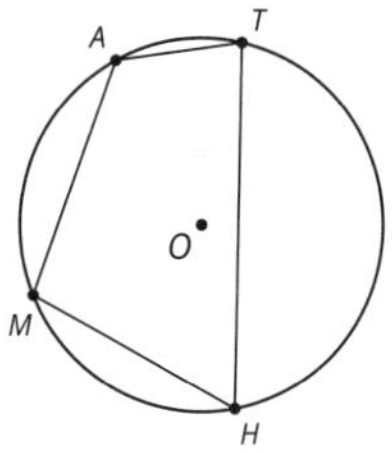

4 Determine each sum.

(a) $m\angle M + m\angle T$

180°

(b) $m\angle A + m\angle H$

180°

5 Make a conjecture about the measures of opposite angles of a cyclic quadrilateral.

The opposite angles of a cyclic quadrilateral are supplementary.

6 Is an isosceles trapezoid a cyclic quadrilateral? **Explain your reasoning.**

Yes. I added the measures of the opposite angles of the isosceles trapezoid from Activity 2, and each pair of opposite angles added up to 180°.

Chunking the Activity

- Read and discuss the definition
- Group students to complete 1 and 2
- Check-in and share
- Group students to complete 3 – 6
- Share and summarize

LANGUAGE LINK

ELL TIP

Suggest students relate the terms *cyclic* and *circle* to make sense of the definition of a cyclic quadrilateral.

Questions to Support Discourse

		TYPE
1	• How are a cyclic quadrilateral and an inscribed quadrilateral related? • Do cyclic quadrilaterals always have right angles? Explain your thinking.	Seeing structure
4	• How do your measurements compare to the cyclic square and cyclic rectangle results in Question 2?	Gathering
5	• Why must your results in Question 4 lead to a conjecture rather than a known fact?	Reflecting and justifying
6	• What is always true about the angles in a cyclic quadrilateral?	Gathering

TALK THE TALK

SUMMARY **You can use what you know about the properties of quadrilaterals to determine the location of their vertices on a grid.**

Chunking the Activity

- **Read and discuss the introduction**
- **Group students to complete the activity**
- **Share and summarize**

LANGUAGE LINK

In Japanese, Zukei is derived from *Zu*, a noun meaning a figure or drawing, and *Katachi*, a noun meaning form, shape, or type.

DIFFERENTIATION STRATEGY

See Page 230C to assist all students with the activity.

Student Look-Fors

Language referencing the definitions or properties of quadrilaterals as they search for their vertices.

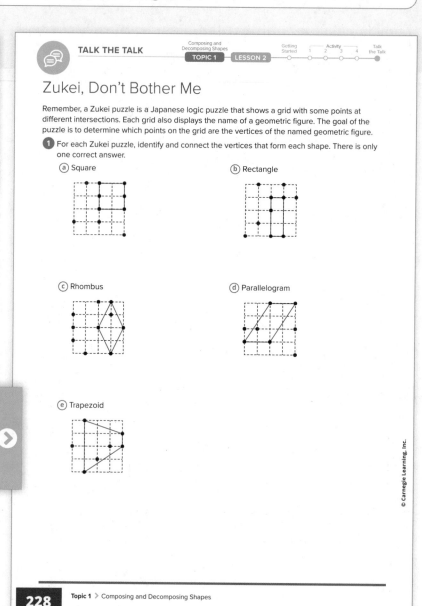

TALK THE TALK | Composing and Decomposing Shapes | TOPIC 1 | LESSON 2 | Getting Started | Activity 1 2 3 4 | Talk the Talk

Zukei, Don't Bother Me

Remember, a Zukei puzzle is a Japanese logic puzzle that shows a grid with some points at different intersections. Each grid also displays the name of a geometric figure. The goal of the puzzle is to determine which points on the grid are the vertices of the named geometric figure.

1. For each Zukei puzzle, identify and connect the vertices that form each shape. There is only one correct answer.

   a. Square

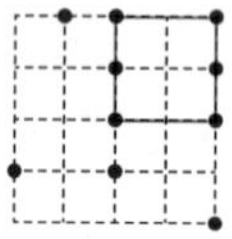

   b. Rectangle

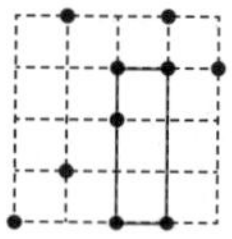

   c. Rhombus

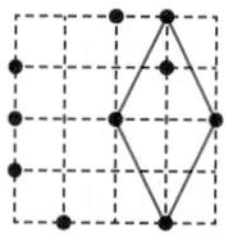

   d. Parallelogram

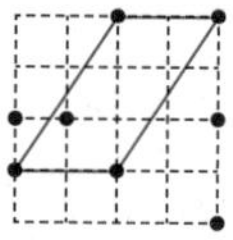

   e. Trapezoid

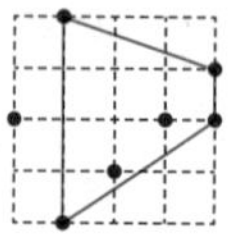

Questions to Support Discourse

		TYPE
1	• Which properties did you use when searching for the vertices of this quadrilateral? • How can slope help to determine parallel line segments in the puzzle?	Probing

ASSIGNMENT

LESSON 2 ASSIGNMENT

> Use a separate piece of paper for your Journal entry.

JOURNAL

Define each term in your own words. Use the words *diagonal* and *interior angle* in your definitions.

1. kite
2. isosceles trapezoid
3. cyclic quadrilateral

REMEMBER

The diagonals of a parallelogram bisect each other, and the diagonals of a rectangle are congruent. A square, rhombus, and kite have perpendicular diagonals.

PRACTICE

1. Determine which quadrilateral each letter in the diagram represents using the list shown.

Kites F | Squares E
Rectangles C | Parallelograms A
Rhombi D | Isosceles Trapezoids B

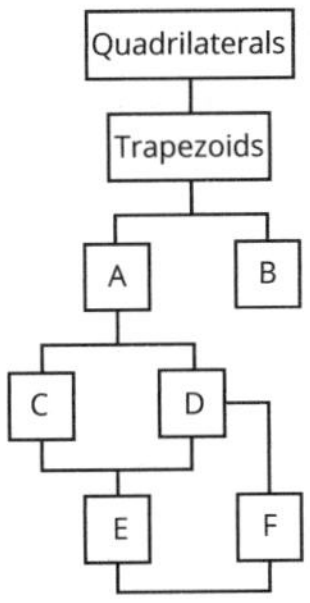

2. State as many properties as you can about each quadrilateral.

ⓐ Rectangle
- opposite sides are parallel
- opposite sides are congruent
- angles are congruent
- diagonals bisect each other and are congruent

ⓑ Isosceles trapezoid
- non-parallel sides are congruent
- pairs of base angles are congruent
- diagonals are congruent

ⓒ Parallelogram
- opposite sides are parallel
- opposite sides are congruent
- opposite angles are congruent
- diagonals bisect each other

ⓓ Rhombus
- opposite sides are parallel
- all sides are congruent
- opposite angles are congruent
- diagonals bisect each other and are perpendicular

Go to LiveHint.com for help on the PRACTICE questions.

Encourage students to use LiveHint.com for help with the PRACTICE questions of this assignment.

Chunking the Assignment

TOPIC 1

SESSION 1

- **Practice 1 and 2**
- **Mixed Practice (page 277) 3**

SESSION 2

- **Journal**
- **Practice 3**
- **Stretch (advanced learners)**

JOURNAL

Sample answers.

1. A kite is a quadrilateral with two pairs of adjacent, congruent sides. It has perpendicular diagonals and one pair of opposite interior angles that are congruent.
2. An isosceles trapezoid is a trapezoid with a pair of non-parallel sides that are congruent. Its diagonals are congruent. The interior angles on the same side of a base are congruent.
3. A cyclic quadrilateral is a quadrilateral whose vertices lie on the same circle. Its diagonals always intersect each other. The opposite interior angles of a cyclic quadrilateral are supplementary.

NOTES

STRETCH

Check students' examples.

(e) Kite

- two pairs of adjacent, congruent sides
- one pair of opposite interior angles are congruent
- diagonals are perpendicular at least one diagonal bisects the other

(f) Square

- opposite sides are parallel
- all sides are congruent
- all angles are congruent
- diagonals are congruent, perpendicular, and bisect each other

3. Describe how to construct each quadrilateral using the given diagonal.

(a) Square *WXYZ* given diagonal *WY*

Sample answer.

First, I would begin by duplicating line segment *WY*. Then, I would construct the perpendicular bisector of *WY*. I would duplicate line segment *WY* a second time on the perpendicular bisector such that the two line segments bisect each other.

Next, I would label the new line segment *XZ*. Finally, I would connect the endpoints of line segment *WY* and line segment *XZ* to form Square *WXYZ*.

(b) Parallelogram *RSTU* that is non-rectangular given diagonal *RT*

Sample answer.

First, I would begin by duplicating line segment *RT*. Then, I would bisect line segment *RT* to locate the midpoint of the diagonal. Then, I would construct another line segment congruent to *RT* through the midpoint such that *RT* bisects the line segment but is not perpendicular to it.

Next, I would label the new line segment *SU*.

Finally, I would connect the endpoints of line segment *RT* and *SU* to form a parallelogram.

STRETCH Optional

> Create a Zukei puzzle for an isosceles trapezoid in which the bases do not lie on the grid lines. Use a minimum of 10 dots. Make sure that your puzzle has only one correct answer.

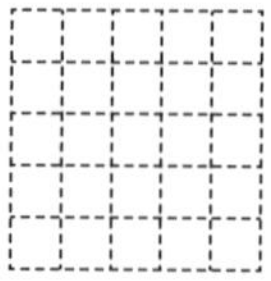

The Quad Squad

This resource details additional facilitation notes to fully assist you as you plan each lesson to support all students, students who struggle, and advanced learners. It provides differentiation strategies, common student misconceptions, and suggestions to extend certain activities.

GETTING STARTED

Session 1 of 2

Cattywampus

Students make a conjecture about the diagonals of a convex quadrilateral and the diagonals of a concave quadrilateral.

CHUNK	AUDIENCE	ADDITIONAL SUPPORTS
As students discuss the introduction	All Students	**DIFFERENTIATION STRATEGY** Provide a method to check whether a quadrilateral is concave. Given any two points in the quadrilateral, when the segment joining the points lies outside the quadrilateral, the quadrilateral is concave.

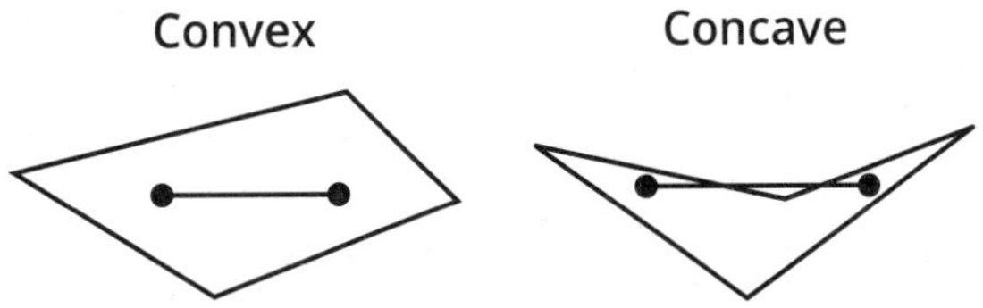

ACTIVITY 1

Session 1 of 2

Quadrilaterals Formed Using a Circle

Students construct and identify quadrilaterals inscribed in a circle using perpendicular and non-perpendicular diameters.

CHUNK	AUDIENCE	ADDITIONAL SUPPORTS
As students work on the lesson	All Students	**DIFFERENTIATION STRATEGY** Have students take notes on the patty paper to assist in summarizing properties of quadrilaterals in Activity 3. They should note when the diagonals are congruent, perpendicular, or bisect one another, the type of quadrilateral, and relationships regarding the sides and angles.

CHUNK	AUDIENCE	ADDITIONAL SUPPORTS
As students work on 1 parts (b) and (c)	All Students	**COMMON MISCONCEPTION** Students may base responses on the assumption that they formed congruent triangles. However, they must use properties and theorems to demonstrate the triangles are congruent.

ACTIVITY 2

Session 1 of 2

Quadrilaterals Formed Using Concentric Circles

Students construct quadrilaterals based on diagonal lengths, perpendicularity, and whether the diagonals bisect each other. They use angle and side relationships to identify the type of quadrilateral formed.

CHUNK	AUDIENCE	ADDITIONAL SUPPORTS
As students complete 4	Advanced Learners	**DIFFERENTIATION STRATEGY** Have students use circles to demonstrate an example of a kite (that is not a square or a rhombus) with congruent diagonals. Have them start by drawing congruent circles with their diameters, each on a separate piece of patty paper, making sure to mark each circle's center. Remind them that the diagonals of a kite are perpendicular, and only one diagonal should bisect the other. Here is an example of kite *VXYZ* drawn using congruent Circles *O* and *A*. 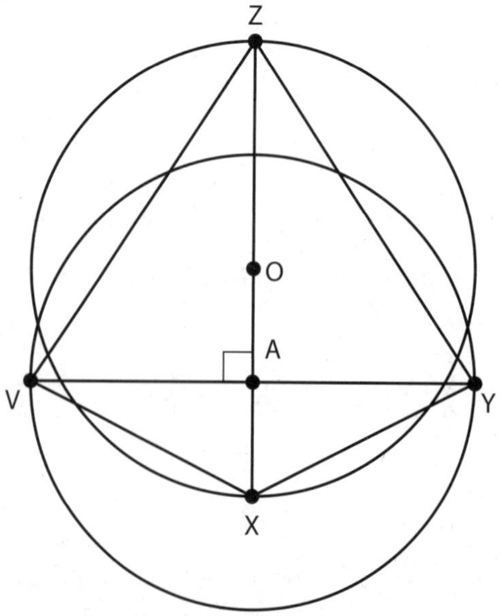
To extend the activity	Advanced Learners	**DIFFERENTIATION STRATEGY** Have students investigate whether the diagonals bisect the vertex angles in each quadrilateral in this activity and the previous one.

Session 2 of 2

ACTIVITY 3
Making Conjectures About Quadrilaterals

Students investigate properties involving diagonals, side measures, and angle measures and complete a table summarizing to which quadrilaterals these properties apply.

CHUNK	AUDIENCE	ADDITIONAL SUPPORTS
As students work on 4	Students who Struggle	**DIFFERENTIATION STRATEGY** Suggest students work vertically to complete the table so that they can focus on each quadrilateral individually. Suggest that they use their patty paper constructions and notes.
As students work on 6	Students who Struggle	**DIFFERENTIATION STRATEGY** Have students construct the parallelogram only. Suggest they refer to the diagonal relationships in the table to guide their construction.

Session 2 of 2

TALK THE TALK
Zukei, Don't Bother Me

Students apply the definitions of quadrilaterals to complete Zukei puzzles.

CHUNK	AUDIENCE	ADDITIONAL SUPPORTS
As students work on the activity	All Students	**DIFFERENTIATION STRATEGY** Provide students patty paper to lay on top of each puzzle to draw attempts without erasing.

Practice the learning

MATHbook + Skills Practice

The table shows the targeted practice of the skills and mathematical concepts for the *Composing and Decomposing Shapes* Topic. The highlighted **Problem Set** aligns with **The Quad Squad**.

PROBLEM SET	
1	Identifying Circle Parts
2	**Using Circles to Construct Quadrilaterals and Triangles**
3	**Making Conjectures About Quadrilaterals**
4	Constructing with Angles
5	Making Conjectures About Triangles
6	Drawing Points of Concurrency

ANYTIME AFTER ACTIVITY 3

Facilitate students as they work individually on **Problem Sets 2** and **3**.

ENGAGE at the **Module** level + DEVELOP at the **Topic** level + TEACH Read the facilitation notes and plan learning experiences.

Where are we?

TOPIC 1 Composing and Decomposing Shapes	LESSON 1 Running Circles Around Geometry	LESSON 2 The Quad Squad	**LESSON 3 Into the Ring**	LESSON 4 Tri- Tri- Tri- and Separate Them	LESSON 5 Meet Me in the Middle
Pacing	2 Sessions	2 Sessions	**3 Sessions**	2 Sessions	2 Sessions

OVERVIEW: LESSON 3

Into the Ring

Constructing an Inscribed Regular Polygon

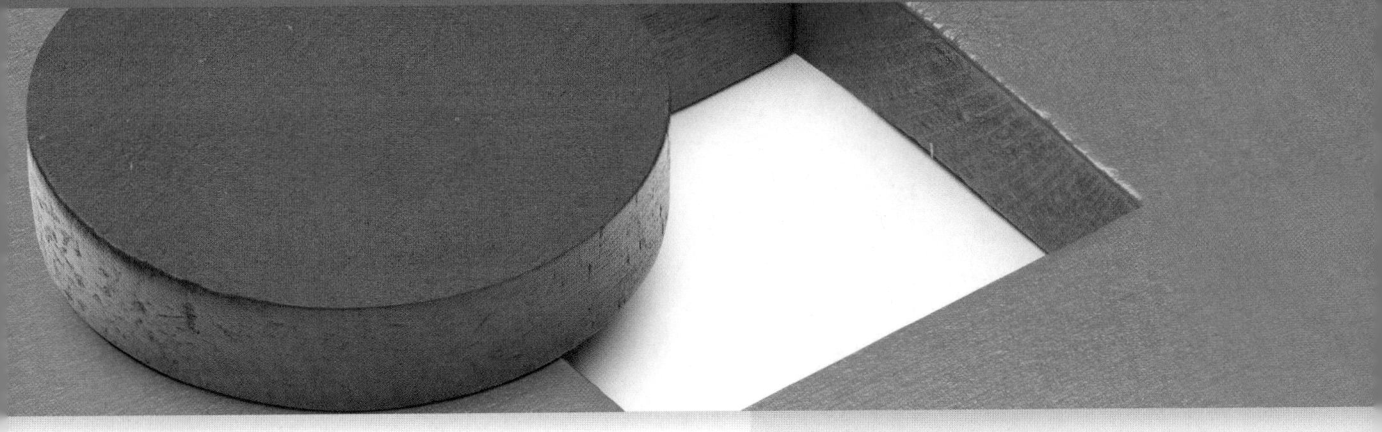

ENGAGE

- Students construct an equilateral triangle in a circle.

DEVELOP

- Students duplicate an angle and construct an angle that is twice the measure of a given angle.
- They construct a regular hexagon inscribed in a circle.
- They construct a square inscribed in a circle.
- They bisect an angle.
- Students inscribe an equilateral triangle in a circle.

DEMONSTRATE

- Students apply the constructions they learned to construct a 75° angle and a regular octagon.

HIGH SCHOOL GEOMETRY

Congruence

Make geometric constructions.

12. Make formal geometric constructions with a variety of tools and methods (compass and straightedge, string, reflective devices, paper folding, dynamic geometric software, etc.).

13. Construct an equilateral triangle, a square, and a regular hexagon inscribed in a circle.

LESSON STRUCTURE AND PACING GUIDE 3 SESSIONS

⊛ This activity highlights a key term or concept that is essential to the learning goals of the lesson.

Session 1

INSTRUCTIONAL SEQUENCE

ENGAGE Establish a situation	DEVELOP Investigation	DEVELOP Investigation
⊛ **GETTING STARTED** **Duped**	⊛ **ACTIVITY 1** **Duplicating an Angle**	⊛ **ACTIVITY 2** **Constructing an Inscribed Hexagon**
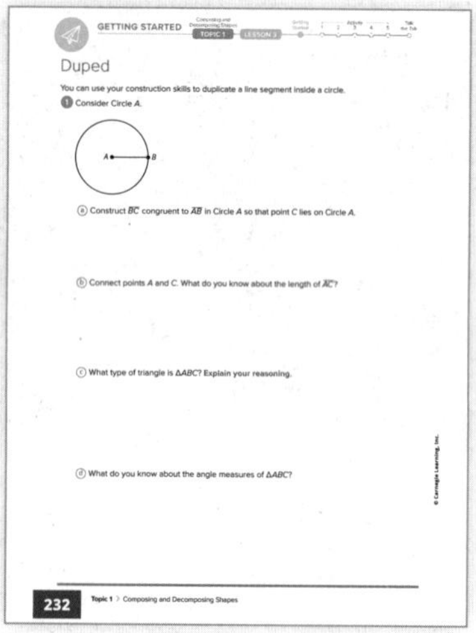	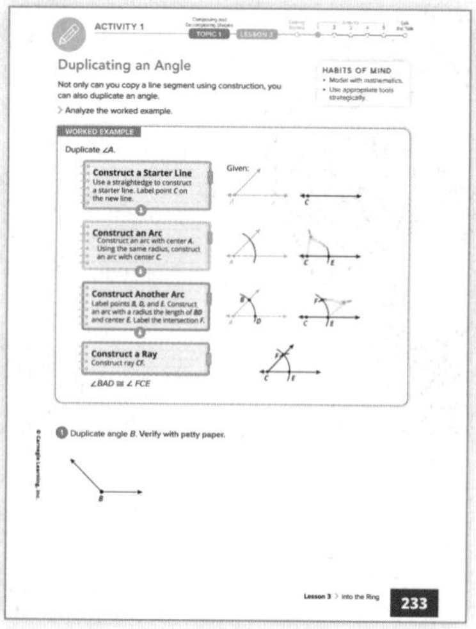	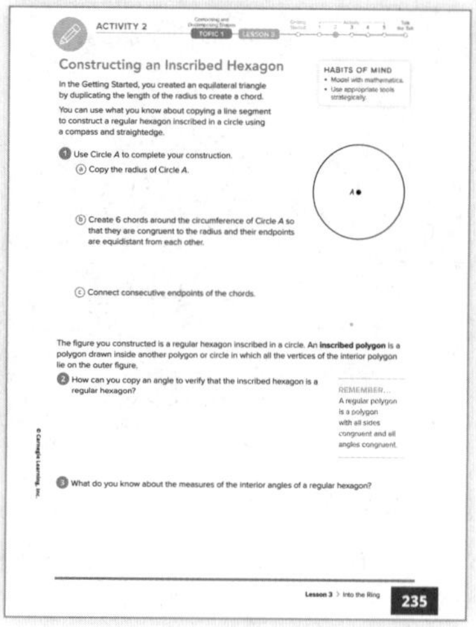
Students construct an equilateral triangle in a circle.	**Students duplicate an angle and construct an angle that is twice the measure of a given angle.**	**Students inscribe a regular hexagon in a circle by constructing six adjacent congruent chords.**
• They duplicate the radius to create the sides of the triangle.	• They compare the processes used to duplicate an angle and duplicate a line segment. • They construct a regular hexagon by duplicating 60° angles.	• They determine the measure of each interior angle of a regular hexagon.

Log in to MyCL for **lesson support** including:

Slides

Videos

www.carnegielearning.com/login

Session 2

Session 3

INSTRUCTIONAL SEQUENCE

DEVELOP	DEVELOP	DEVELOP
Investigation Worked example	Worked example	Peer analysis Mathematical problem solving

ACTIVITY 3
Constructing an Inscribed Square

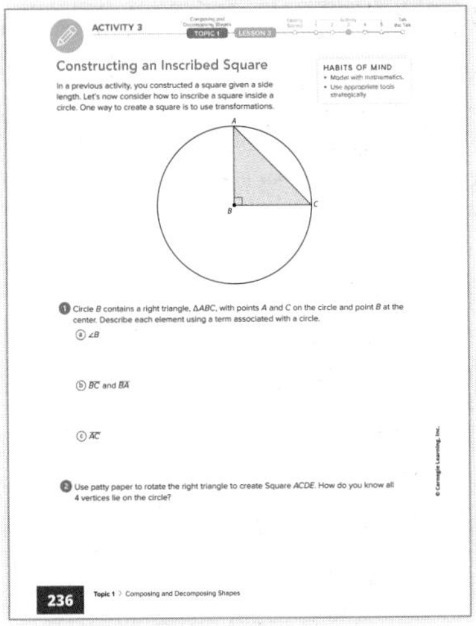

Students inscribe a square in a circle using patty paper and rigid motion transformations.

- They use the Pythagorean Theorem to determine the side lengths of the square based on a radius.
- They use the fact that diagonals of a square are perpendicular to construct a square inscribed in a circle.

ACTIVITY 4
Bisecting an Angle

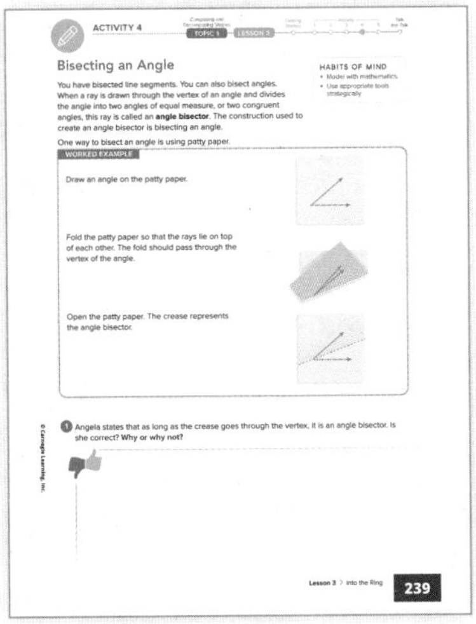

Students analyze worked examples that demonstrate how to bisect an angle.

- The first worked example uses patty paper, and the second uses a compass and straightedge
- They bisect angles and use repeated reasoning to construct angles that are one-fourth and one-eighth the measure of a given angle

ACTIVITY 5
Constructing and Inscribing an Equilateral Triangle

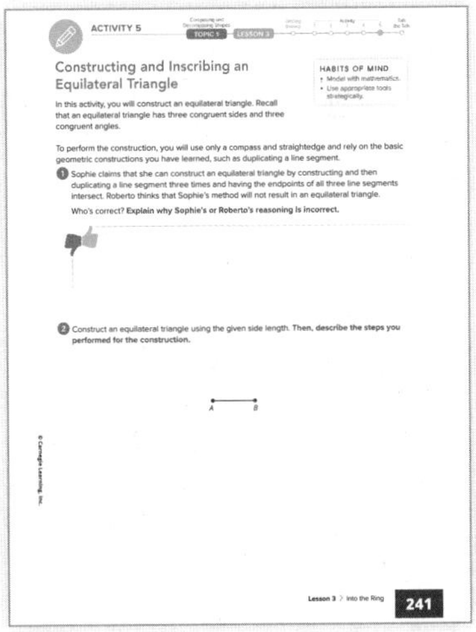

Students inscribe an equilateral triangle in a circle.

- They construct an equilateral triangle.
- They show two different ways to construct an inscribed equilateral triangle in a circle and describe the process they used in each construction.

TOPIC 1

Session 3

INSTRUCTIONAL SEQUENCE

DEMONSTRATE
Exit ticket application

TALK THE TALK
Playing the Angles

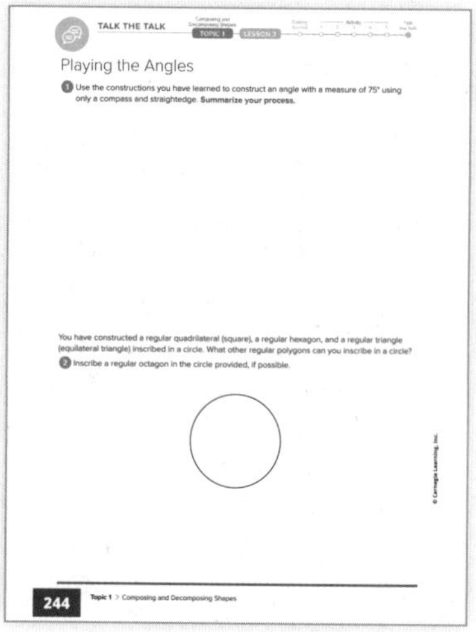
TALK THE TALK
TOPIC 1 LESSON 3

Playing the Angles

1. Use the constructions you have learned to construct an angle with a measure of 75° using only a compass and straightedge. **Summarize your process.**

You have constructed a regular quadrilateral (square), a regular hexagon, and a regular triangle (equilateral triangle) inscribed in a circle. What other regular polygons can you inscribe in a circle?

2. Inscribe a regular octagon in the circle provided, if possible.

© Carnegie Learning, Inc.

244 Topic 1 > Composing and Decomposing Shapes

Students apply the constructions they learned.

- They construct a 75° angle.
- They inscribe a regular octagon in a given circle.

Log in to MyCL for:
- Editable templates
- Additional planning support

Now that you have read the Module, Topic, and Lesson Overviews, you are ready to plan.

Do the math

> Tear out the lesson planning template (page 231E) and jot down thoughts as you work through this lesson and read the Facilitation Notes.

Connect the learning

MATHbook + MATHia®

The table shows a portion of the self-paced MATHia sequence for the *Composing and Decomposing Shapes* Topic.

Median student completion time for the entire topic: ~110 – 130 minutes

> As you implement this lesson, consider different connections for students who are on pace and those that have not yet completed the workspaces aligned to this lesson.

STUDENTS WILL CONTINUE WORKING ON SKILLS RELATED TO THIS TOPIC

TYPE	WORKSPACE NAME
	Using Circles to Draw Quadrilaterals
	Angles of an Inscribed Quadrilateral
	Points of Concurrency

Into the Ring

Constructing an Inscribed Regular Polygon

Session 1

GETTING STARTED Duped ✪

Pacing (minutes)	
My Time	Class Time

ACTIVITY 1 Duplicating an Angle ✪

Pacing (minutes)	
My Time	Class Time

ACTIVITY 2 Constructing an Inscribed Hexagon ✪

Pacing (minutes)	
My Time	Class Time

KEY TERM
inscribed polygon

Session 2

ACTIVITY 3 Constructing an Inscribed Square ✪

Pacing (minutes)	
My Time	Class Time

ACTIVITY 4 Bisecting an Angle ✪

Pacing (minutes)	
My Time	Class Time

KEY TERM
angle bisector

Session 3

ACTIVITY 5 Constructing and Inscribing an Equilateral Triangle ✪

Pacing (minutes)	
My Time	Class Time

TALK THE TALK Playing the Angles ✪

Pacing (minutes)	
My Time	Class Time

✪ This activity highlights a key term or concept that is essential to the learning goals of the lesson.

Log in to MyCL for:
- Editable templates
- Additional planning support

Reflect on your lesson

Consider the effectiveness of your lesson on student learning.

What went well?	What did not go as planned?

Anticipate how you would change the lesson next time you teach it.

How will you capitalize on the things that went well?	How will you improve things that did not go as planned?

MATERIALS

- Compasses
- Patty paper
- Straightedges

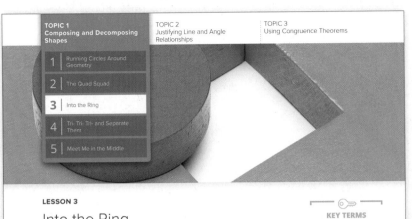

TOPIC 1 Composing and Decomposing Shapes | TOPIC 2 Justifying Line and Angle Relationships | TOPIC 3 Using Congruence Theorems

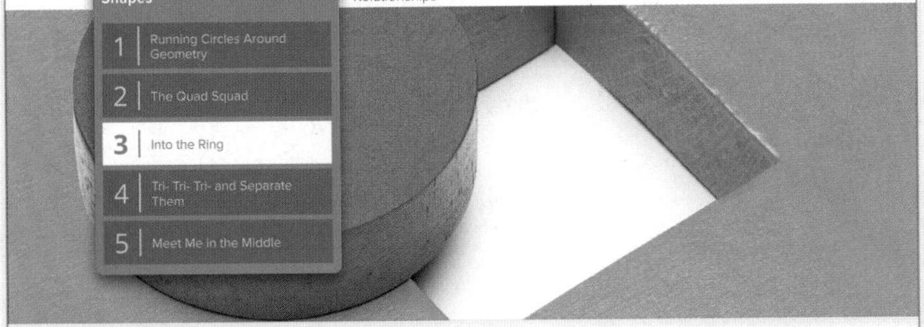

LESSON 3

Into the Ring

Constructing an Inscribed Regular Polygon

KEY TERMS

inscribed polygon

angle bisector

Learning Goals

- Use construction tools to duplicate an angle.
- Construct a regular hexagon inscribed in a circle using a variety of strategies.
- Construct a square inscribed in a circle using patty paper and using a compass and straightedge.
- Use construction tools to bisect an angle.
- Construct an equilateral triangle using a compass and straightedge.
- Construct an equilateral triangle inscribed in a circle.

REVIEW (1–2 minutes)

> Rewrite each expression.

1. $x^2 + x^2$

   $2x^2$

2. $(\sqrt{3})^2$

   3

3. $(\sqrt{3}x)^2$

   $(\sqrt{3})^2 x^2 = 3x^2$

4. $(\sqrt{3}x)^2 + (\sqrt{3}x)^2$

   $3x^2 + 3x^2 = 6x^2$

You have used construction tools to construct figures in a plane.

How can you construct a regular polygon inscribed in a circle?

Setting the Stage

- **Assign Review (optional, 1 – 2 minutes)**
- **Communicate the learning goals and key terms to look out for**
- **Tap into your students' prior learning by reading the narrative statement**
- **Provide a sense of direction by reading the question**

IN THIS REVIEW

Students rewrite expressions with radicals and exponents. They will use this skill in **ACTIVITY 3 Constructing an Inscribed Square.**

You can use constructions, such as duplicating line segments and angles, and bisecting an angle, as well as transformations, to construct a regular polygon inscribed in a circle.

Essential Ideas

- You can use constructions to duplicate a given angle.
- You can duplicate 60° angles to inscribe a regular hexagon in a circle by creating six equilateral triangles sharing the circle's center as a vertex.
- You can inscribe a regular hexagon in a circle by constructing six adjacent congruent chords the same length as the radius of the circle around the circle's circumference.
- The diagonal of a square inscribed in a circle is also the circle's diameter.
- An angle bisector is a line, segment, or ray drawn through the vertex of an angle and divides the angle into two congruent angles.
- You can construct an equilateral triangle inscribed in a circle.

SUMMARY **You can construct a 60° central angle without using measuring tools by creating an equilateral triangle within a circle.**

Chunking the Activity

- **Read and discuss the introduction**
- **Group students to complete the activity**
- **Share and summarize**

DIFFERENTIATION STRATEGY

See Page 246A to assist all students with the activity.

Student Look-Fors

Utilizing relationship skills by communicating clearly and listening well.

Duped

You can use your construction skills to duplicate a line segment inside a circle.

1 Consider Circle *A*.

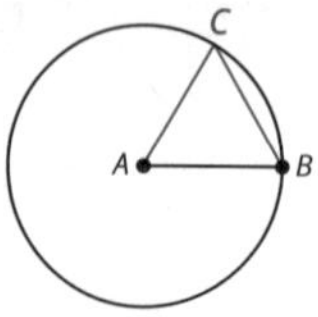

ⓐ Construct $\overline{BC}$ congruent to $\overline{AB}$ in Circle *A* so that point *C* lies on Circle *A*.

ⓑ Connect points *A* and *C*. What do you know about the length of $\overline{AC}$?

The length of $\overline{AC}$ is equal to the radius of circle *A*.

ⓒ What type of triangle is ΔABC? **Explain your reasoning.**

Triangle *ABC* is an equilateral triangle because both $\overline{AB}$ and $\overline{AC}$ are radii, and $\overline{BC}$ is congruent to $\overline{AB}$. All three side lengths are equal.

ⓓ What do you know about the angle measures of ΔABC?

The sum of the angle measures is 180°.

Questions to Support Discourse

		TYPE
1	• What are the possible locations for point *C*? How do you know? • How does $\overline{BC}$ relate to the circle?	Probing
	• If the triangle is equilateral, what do we know about its angles?	Seeing structure

ACTIVITY 1

SUMMARY You can inscribe a regular hexagon in a circle by duplicating 60° angles to create six equilateral triangles sharing the circle's center as a vertex.

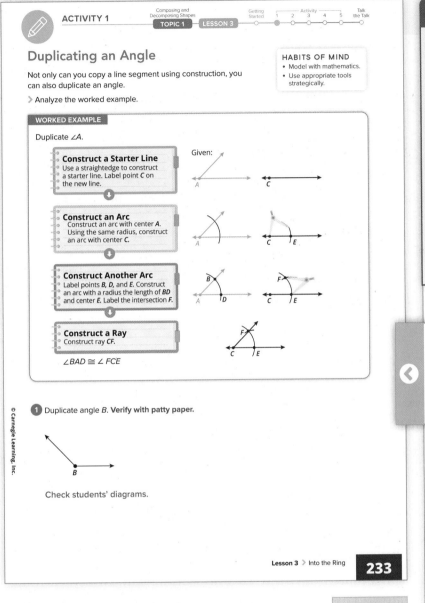

Duplicating an Angle

Not only can you copy a line segment using construction, you can also duplicate an angle.

> Analyze the worked example.

HABITS OF MIND
- Model with mathematics.
- Use appropriate tools strategically.

WORKED EXAMPLE

Duplicate ∠*A*.

Construct a Starter Line
Use a straightedge to construct a starter line. Label point *C* on the new line.

Construct an Arc
Construct an arc with center *A*. Using the same radius, construct an arc with center *C*.

Construct Another Arc
Label points *B*, *D*, and *E*. Construct an arc with a radius the length of *BD* and center *E*. Label the intersection *F*.

Construct a Ray
Construct ray *CF*.

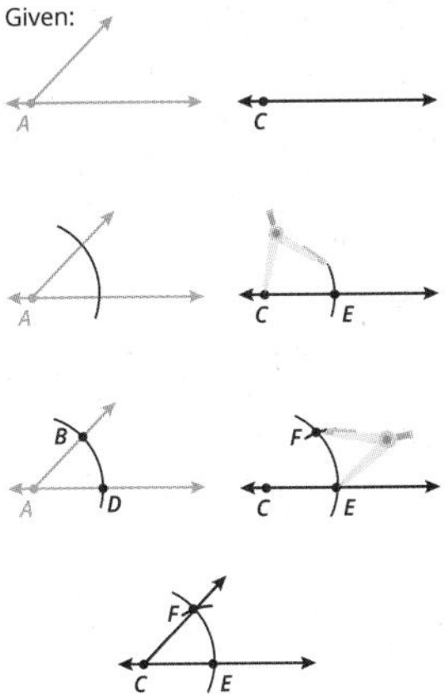

∠*BAD* ≅ ∠ *FCE*

1 Duplicate angle *B*. **Verify with patty paper.**

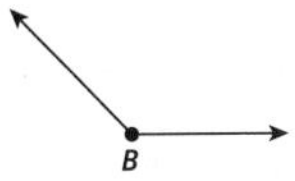

Check students' diagrams.

Questions to Support Discourse

		TYPE
1	• Does the compass setting have to be the same for the arc on the original angle and your construction?	Gathering

Chunking the Activity

- Read and discuss the introduction and worked example
- Complete 1 as a class
- Group students to complete 2 and 3
- Check-in and share
- Group students to complete 4
- Share and summarize

TOPIC 1

DIFFERENTIATION STRATEGY

See Page 246A to assist all students with the activity.

NOTES

DIFFERENTIATION STRATEGY

See Page 246B to assist all students with 2.

ACTIVITY 1 Continued

2 Construct an angle that is twice the measure of ∠A. **Then explain how you performed the construction.**

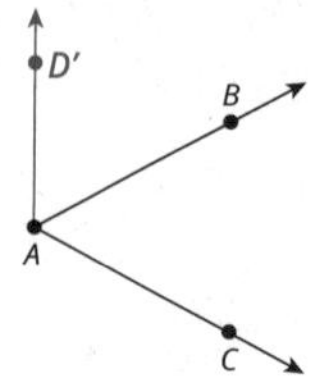

First, I duplicated ∠BAC and labeled it as ∠B′A′C′. Then I used $\overline{A'B'}$ as my starter line, duplicated ∠BAC again, and labeled it as ∠D′A′C′. Angle D′A′C′ is twice the measure of ∠ABC.

3 How is duplicating an angle similar to duplicating a line segment? How is it different?

When duplicating a line segment and an angle, I use the same tools. However, when duplicating a line segment, I have to make only one mark. When duplicating an angle, I must make several marks because I must duplicate both rays of the angle.

4 In the Getting Started, you constructed an Equilateral Triangle *ABC*. Duplicate the 60° angle shown to construct 5 additional equilateral triangles that share the circle's center as a vertex. **What do you notice about the polygon you constructed?**

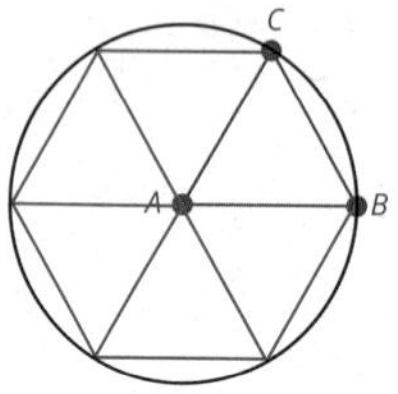

The six triangles compose a regular hexagon.

Questions to Support Discourse

		TYPE
2	• After you duplicated ∠A, which ray did you use as a new starter line? Could you have used the other side of angle *A* as a new starter line?	Gathering
	• What does it mean for an angle to have twice the measure of ∠A? • How would you use patty paper to create an angle twice the measure of ∠A?	Probing
	• Did you change your method because the orientation of the angle was different from in Question 1? If so, what did you do differently?	Seeing structure
4	• What makes this hexagon an inscribed hexagon?	Seeing structure

ACTIVITY 2

SUMMARY **You can inscribe a regular hexagon in a circle by creating six adjacent congruent chords that are the same length as the circle's radius.**

Constructing an Inscribed Hexagon

HABITS OF MIND
- Model with mathematics.
- Use appropriate tools strategically.

In the Getting Started, you created an equilateral triangle by duplicating the length of the radius to create a chord.

You can use what you know about copying a line segment to construct a regular hexagon inscribed in a circle using a compass and straightedge.

1 Use Circle *A* to complete your construction.

(a) Copy the radius of Circle *A*.

Check students' diagrams.

(b) Create 6 chords around the circumference of Circle *A* so that they are congruent to the radius and their endpoints are equidistant from each other.

Check students' diagrams.

(c) Connect consecutive endpoints of the chords.

Check students' diagrams.

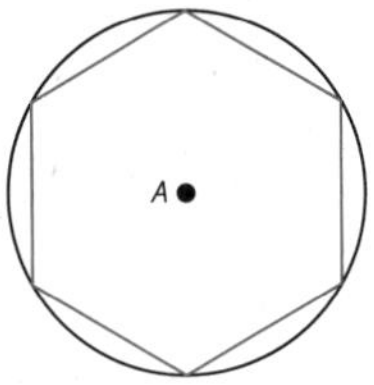

The figure you constructed is a regular hexagon inscribed in a circle. An **inscribed polygon** is a polygon drawn inside another polygon or circle in which all the vertices of the interior polygon lie on the outer figure.

2 How can you copy an angle to verify that the inscribed hexagon is a regular hexagon?

I can use a compass and straightedge to duplicate one angle from my diagram onto patty paper, then use the patty paper to verify that the hexagon angles are congruent.

REMEMBER...
A regular polygon is a polygon with all sides congruent and all angles congruent.

3 What do you know about the measures of the interior angles of a regular hexagon?

The measures of the interior angles of a regular hexagon are 120°.

Chunking the Activity

- Read and discuss the introduction
- Group students to complete 1
- Check-in and share
- Read and discuss the definition
- Group students to complete 2 and 3
- Share and summarize

DIFFERENTIATION STRATEGY

See Page 246B to challenge advanced learners to extend 1.

DIFFERENTIATION STRATEGY

See Page 246B to assist all students to extend the activity.

Questions to Support Discourse

		TYPE
1	• Does it matter where you construct the first chord? Why? • How is this construction of an inscribed hexagon different than the construction you completed in the previous activity? How is it similar?	Probing
	• Do you think the radius of a circle will always map onto the circumference of the circle exactly six times? Do you suppose this happens with any size circle?	Seeing structure
3	• How can the construction from the previous activity help you determine the angle measures?	Probing

ACTIVITY 3

SUMMARY: **You can inscribe a square in a circle by using the fact that a square's diagonals are perpendicular to one another.**

Chunking the Activity

- Read and discuss the introduction
- Complete 1 and 2 as a class
- Group students to complete 3 – 5
- Check-in and share
- Group students to complete 6 and 7
- Share and summarize

Student Look-Fors

Correct placement of the vertices *D* and *E*. Students will reference these points in another question.

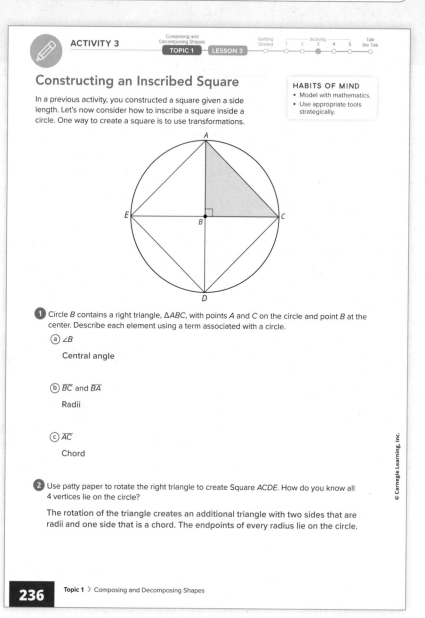

Constructing an Inscribed Square

HABITS OF MIND
- Model with mathematics.
- Use appropriate tools strategically.

In a previous activity, you constructed a square given a side length. Let's now consider how to inscribe a square inside a circle. One way to create a square is to use transformations.

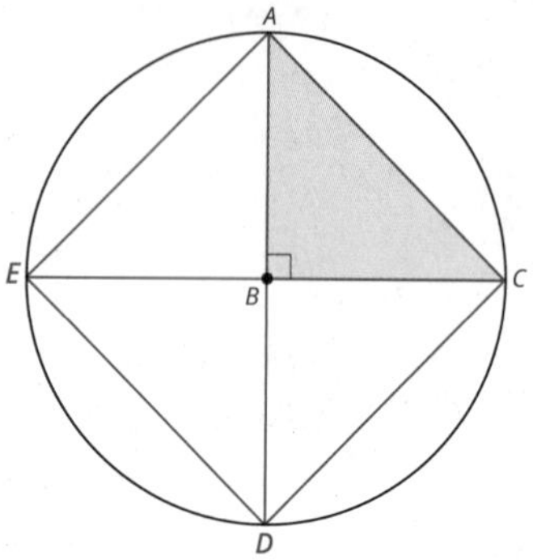

1. Circle *B* contains a right triangle, ΔABC, with points *A* and *C* on the circle and point *B* at the center. Describe each element using a term associated with a circle.

   a. $\angle B$

   Central angle

   b. $\overline{BC}$ and $\overline{BA}$

   Radii

   c. $\overline{AC}$

   Chord

2. Use patty paper to rotate the right triangle to create Square *ACDE*. How do you know all 4 vertices lie on the circle?

   The rotation of the triangle creates an additional triangle with two sides that are radii and one side that is a chord. The endpoints of every radius lie on the circle.

Questions to Support Discourse

		TYPE
1	• Is $\angle B$ a central angle or an inscribed angle? • How do you know that $\overline{BA}$ and $\overline{BC}$ are congruent?	Gathering
2	• Is each central angle created by the rotation of ΔABC also a right angle? How do you know?	Probing
	• What is true about rotations that helps you to know the vertices of ΔABC will lie on the circle when rotated?	Seeing structure

ACTIVITY 3 Continued

You can verify that you created a square inscribed in Circle *B*. To do this, you need to show that all sides lengths of the figure are equal and each interior angle is a right angle.

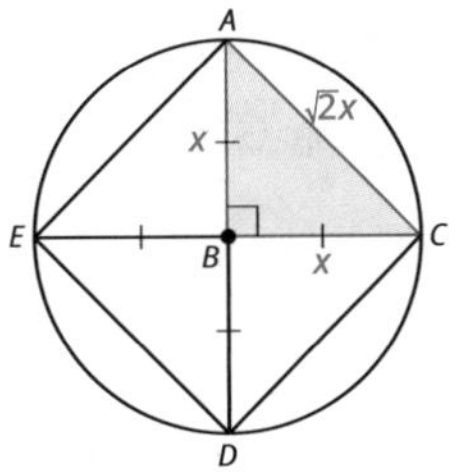

Suppose $BC = x$.

3 Which congruence theorem can you use to verify that all sides of the figure are congruent? **Explain your reasoning.**

I know that all sides of the figure are congruent by SAS.

Each side of the square is the hypotenuse of a right triangle with legs that are radii of the circle.

You can also verify that all sides of the figure have equal measures using the Pythagorean Theorem.

4 Use the Pythagorean Theorem to determine each side length of the figure. **Label each length.**

Each side length of the square is $\sqrt{2}x$.

$x^2 + x^2 = s^2$

$2x^2 = s^2$

$\sqrt{2}x = s$

REMEMBER...
The Pythagorean Theorem says that $a^2 + b^2 = c^2$.

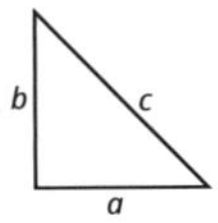

The Converse of the Pythagorean Theorem says that if $a^2 + b^2 = c^2$, then the triangle is a right triangle.

Now that you know each side length of the figure, you can use the Converse of the Pythagorean Theorem to verify that each interior angle is a right angle.

5 Verify that each interior angle measure of the square is a right angle. **Explain your reasoning.**

The diameter of the circle is equal to $2x$. Each side length is $\sqrt{2}x$.

$(\sqrt{2}x)^2 + (\sqrt{2}x)^2 = (2x)^2$

$2x^2 + 2x^2 = 4x^2$

$4x^2 = 4x^2$

The sum of the squares of two side lengths is equal to the diameter squared, so $\angle ACD$ is a right triangle.

NOTES

COMMON MISCONCEPTION

See Page 246C for a misconception related to 3 – 5.

Questions to Support Discourse

		TYPE
4	• How can you use the Pythagorean Theorem to determine the side lengths of the square?	Seeing structure
5	• How can you use the Converse of the Pythagorean Theorem to determine that each angle in the square has a measure of 90°?	Seeing structure

NOTES

6 Consider $\overline{AD}$ and $\overline{CE}$.

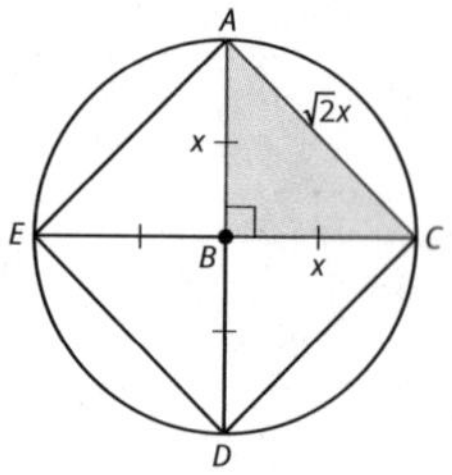

(a) Describe each line segment in terms of the circle and in terms of the square.

Segments *AD* and *CE* are both diameters of the circle and diagonals of the inscribed square.

(b) Describe the relationship between $\overline{AD}$ and $\overline{CE}$.

Segments *AD* and *CE* are perpendicular to each other.

7 Use diagonals to construct a square inscribed in Circle *O*. **Describe your process.**

THINK ABOUT...

Is an inscribed square a cyclic quadrilateral?

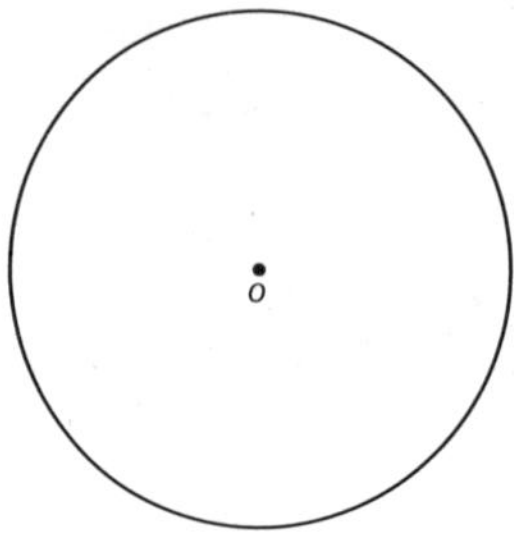

Check students' constructions.

Student Look-Fors

Whether students are demonstrating proficiencies related to these habits of mind.

- Model with mathematics
- Use appropriate tools strategically

ACTIVITY 4

SUMMARY An angle bisector is a line, segment, or ray drawn through the vertex of an angle that divides the angle into two congruent angles.

Bisecting an Angle

HABITS OF MIND
- Model with mathematics.
- Use appropriate tools strategically.

You have bisected line segments. You can also bisect angles. When a ray is drawn through the vertex of an angle and divides the angle into two angles of equal measure, or two congruent angles, this ray is called an **angle bisector**. The construction used to create an angle bisector is bisecting an angle.

One way to bisect an angle is using patty paper.

WORKED EXAMPLE

Draw an angle on the patty paper.

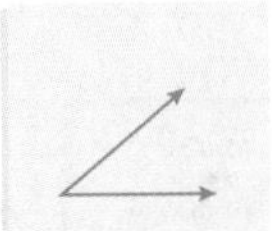

Fold the patty paper so that the rays lie on top of each other. The fold should pass through the vertex of the angle.

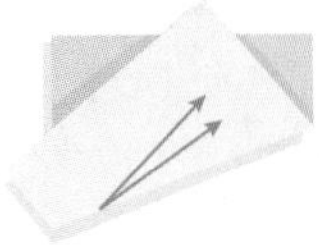

Open the patty paper. The crease represents the angle bisector.

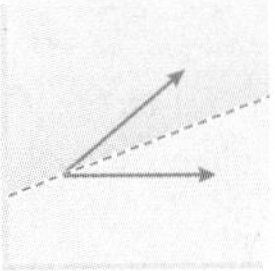

1 Angela states that as long as the crease goes through the vertex, it is an angle bisector. Is she correct? **Why or why not?**

No. Angela is not correct.
Just because the crease goes through the vertex does not mean it bisects the angle. To bisect the angle, the crease must divide the angle into two angles of equal measure.

Chunking the Activity

- Read and discuss the definition and worked example
- Group students to complete 1
- Check-in and share
- Read and discuss the worked example
- Group students to complete 2 – 4
- Share and summarize

LANGUAGE LINK

ELL TIP

Provide students an opportunity to compare perpendicular bisectors with angle bisectors. Help them see that the term *bisector* means to divide into two equal parts.

COMMON MISCONCEPTION

See Page 246D for a misconception related to the patty paper construction.

Questions to Support Discourse

		TYPE
Intro	• How is an angle bisector different than a segment bisector? • What do an angle bisector and a segment bisector have in common? • How is an angle bisector different than a perpendicular bisector?	Probing
1	• How many creases could Angela make through the vertex? • Do all creases through the vertex divide the angle into two congruent angles?	Gathering
	• Would the process change if the angle were obtuse? A right angle?	Probing
	• Can an angle have more than one bisector? Why not?	Seeing structure

NOTES

Student Look-Fors

Whether students are annotating the worked example and making connections.

COMMON MISCONCEPTION

See Page 246D for a misconception related to the compass and straightedge construction.

DIFFERENTIATION STRATEGY

See Page 246D to challenge advanced learners to extend 3.

You can also bisect an angle using a compass and a straightedge.

WORKED EXAMPLE

Bisect ∠*A*.

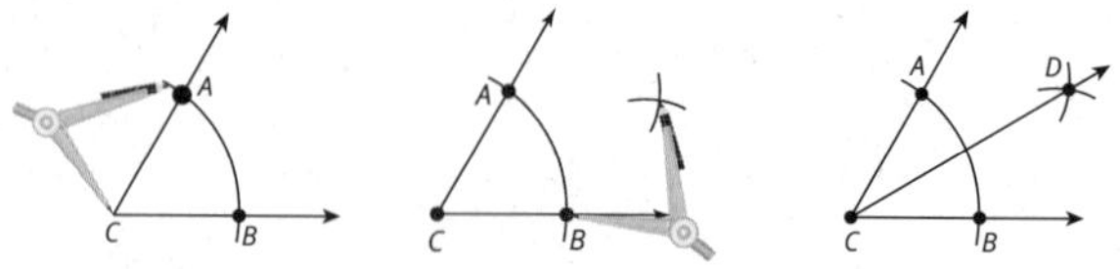

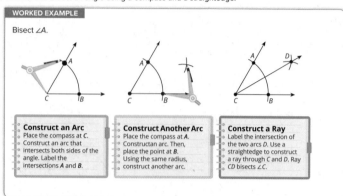

Construct an Arc
Place the compass at *C*. Construct an arc that intersects both sides of the angle. Label the intersections *A* and *B*.

Construct Another Arc
Place the compass at *A*. Constructan arc. Then, place the point at *B*. Using the same radius, construct another arc.

Construct a Ray
Label the intersection of the two arcs *D*. Use a straightedge to construct a ray through *C* and *D*. Ray *CD* bisects ∠*C*.

2 Construct the bisector of ∠*A*. **Use patty paper to verify your construction.**

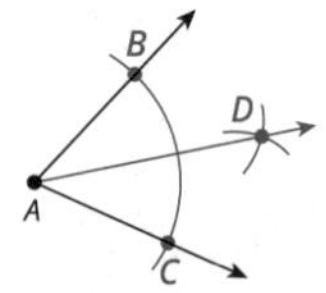

3 Construct an angle that is one-fourth the measure of ∠*H*. **Explain how you performed the construction.**

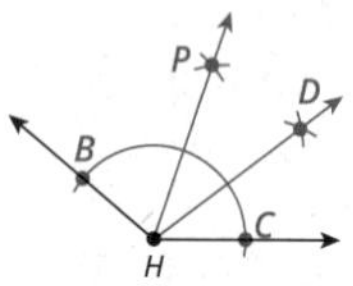

First, bisect ∠*H* to form two angles, ∠*BHP* and ∠*PHC*, each one-half the measure of ∠*H*. Then bisect either ∠*BHP* or ∠*PHC*, to form two angles that are each one-fourth the measure of ∠*BHC*. ∠*PHD* and ∠*DHC* are each one-fourth the measure of ∠*BHC*.

4 Describe how to construct an angle that is one-eighth the measure of ∠*H* from Question 3.

I must bisect one of the angles that are one-fourth the measure of ∠*BHC*. The resulting pair of angles will both be one-eighth the measure of ∠*BHC*.

Questions to Support Discourse

		TYPE
2	• How do you know what setting to use on the compass to create the first arc? • Is it important to maintain the same compass setting from step 1 to step 2?	Gathering
3	• How many times do you need to perform the bisection construction to create an angle that is one-fourth the measure of the given angle?	Seeing structure
4	• How many times do you need to perform bisection construction to create an angle that is one-eighth the measure of the given angle? • What other fractions of an angle can you construct?	Seeing structure

SUMMARY You can construct an equilateral triangle inscribed in a circle by modifying the procedure used for inscribing a hexagon in a circle.

Constructing and Inscribing an Equilateral Triangle

HABITS OF MIND
- Model with mathematics.
- Use appropriate tools strategically.

In this activity, you will construct an equilateral triangle. Recall that an equilateral triangle has three congruent sides and three congruent angles.

To perform the construction, you will use only a compass and straightedge and rely on the basic geometric constructions you have learned, such as duplicating a line segment.

1 Sophie claims that she can construct an equilateral triangle by constructing and then duplicating a line segment three times and having the endpoints of all three line segments intersect. Roberto thinks that Sophie's method will not result in an equilateral triangle.

Who's correct? **Explain why Sophie's or Roberto's reasoning is incorrect.**

Sophie is correct.
Roberto didn't realize that you can always connect three congruent segments at their endpoints to create an equilateral triangle. According to the Triangle Inequality Theorem, if the side lengths are x, x, and x, you can construct a triangle because $2x > x$.

2 Construct an equilateral triangle using the given side length. **Then, describe the steps you performed for the construction.**

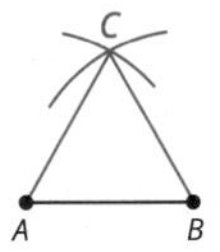

Sample answers.
I set my compass to the length of $\overline{AB}$. I placed my compass point on point A and made an arc, and then on point B and made an arc. I labeled the intersection of the two arcs as point C, and connected point A and point B to point C. All 3 sides of the triangle have the same length.

I used patty paper and traced two additional line segments. I then turned the patty paper so that the endpoints of the line segments connected to make a triangle. I then traced the triangle on a single piece of patty paper.

I repeated the process in the Getting Started. I used the side length as my radius, $\overline{AB}$, and constructed a circle. I created a chord, $\overline{BC}$, the same length as the radius. Then I connected the other endpoint of my chord to create another radius, $\overline{AC}$, and complete the triangle.

Questions to Support Discourse

		TYPE
1	• How is this situation different from when you constructed an equilateral triangle using the radius as a side length? • Do you think you can construct an equilateral triangle without using a circle and its radii to support your construction?	Probing
2	• Did you place the given line segment in a circle to complete your construction? If so, how was that helpful? • How do you know how much to slant the sides so that they connect at their endpoints to make a triangle? • How can you use patty paper to make your constructions?	Probing

Chunking the Activity

- Read and discuss the introduction
- Group students to complete 1 and 2
- Check-in and share
- Group students to complete 3
- Share and summarize

DIFFERENTIATION STRATEGY

See Page 246D to challenge advanced learners to extend 1.

Student Look-Fors

Whether students use patty paper or a compass and straightedge to attempt to construct an equilateral triangle.

NOTES

NOTE: Ensure that students understand at least one strategy to inscribe a triangle. Challenge students to continue to develop a second and third strategy.

An inscribed equilateral triangle is an equilateral triangle inside a circle with all of its vertices touching the circle.

3 Show three different ways to construct an inscribed equilateral triangle using each circle given. **Explain your process for each construction.**

THINK ABOUT...
How can you use the process for constructing an inscribed regular hexagon to inscribe an equilateral triangle?

ⓐ

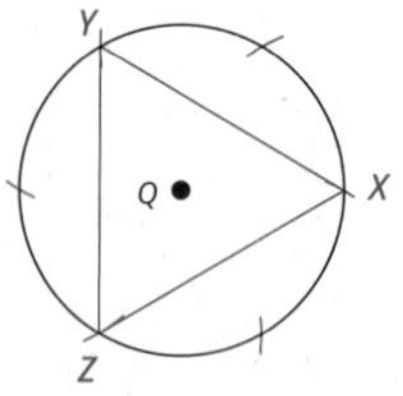

Sample answer.
I used the fact that all sides of an equilateral triangle have equal lengths. I set my compass to the length of the radius and placed 6 points on the circle's circumference as if I was creating a regular hexagon.
Then, I connected every other point to create an equilateral triangle.
Triangle *XYZ* is an equilateral triangle.

ⓑ

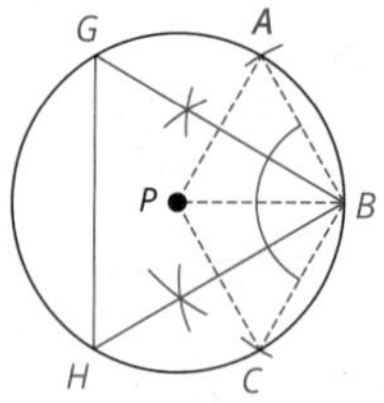

Sample answer.
I used the fact that all angles of an equilateral triangle have a measure of 60°. First, I created two equilateral triangles, Δ*ABP* and Δ*PBC*, that shared a common side, using the radius as the side lengths.

Then, I took the two adjacent 60° angles, ∠*ABP* and ∠*PBC*, and bisected each of them to create a new 60° angle, ∠*GBH* with the center of the circle, point *P*, on the bisector of the angle.

I then connected point *G* and point *H* to create the third side of the triangle. Triangle *BGH* is an inscribed equilateral triangle.

Questions to Support Discourse

		TYPE
3	• How can you use what you know about constructing a hexagon inscribed in a circle to support your thinking? • Is there any way you can use the six equilateral triangles you constructed around the radius of a circle to create a regular hexagon to help in this construction?	Probing

ACTIVITY 5 Continued

(c)

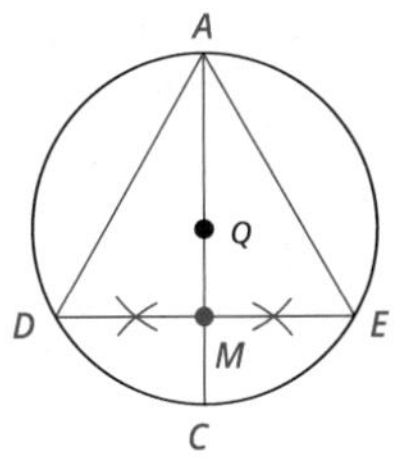

Sample answer.
I constructed diameter *AC*. I determined the midpoint, point *M*, of radius $\overline{QC}$. I then constructed a perpendicular bisector through point *M*, creating chord $\overline{DE}$.

I connected point *D* and point *E* to the endpoint, *A*, of the diameter to create the other two sides of the triangle. Triangle *ADE* is an equilateral triangle.

NOTES

SUMMARY You can use constructions of 90° angles, 60°angles, and angle bisectors to construct angles of other measures.

Chunking the Activity

- **Read and discuss the introduction**
- **Group students to complete the activity**
- **Share and summarize**

DIFFERENTIATION STRATEGY

See Page 246E to group students to complete the activity.

DIFFERENTIATION STRATEGY

See Page 246E to assist all students with 2.

Playing the Angles

1. Use the constructions you have learned to construct an angle with a measure of 75° using only a compass and straightedge. **Summarize your process.**

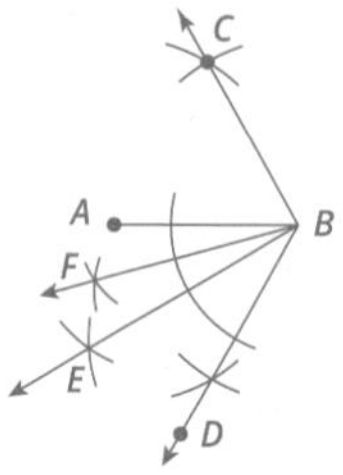

I started with $\overline{AB}$, constructed the vertices for an equilateral triangle, ΔABC, but connected only two sides to create 60° angle, $\angle CBA$. I duplicated the 60° angle to create an adjacent angle, $\angle ABD$. I bisected $\angle ABD$ to create a 30° angle, $\angle ABE$. Then I bisected $\angle ABE$ to create a 15° angle, $\angle ABF$. angle CBF is a 75° angle.

You have constructed a regular quadrilateral (square), a regular hexagon, and a regular triangle (equilateral triangle) inscribed in a circle. What other regular polygons can you inscribe in a circle?

2. Inscribe a regular octagon in the circle provided, if possible.

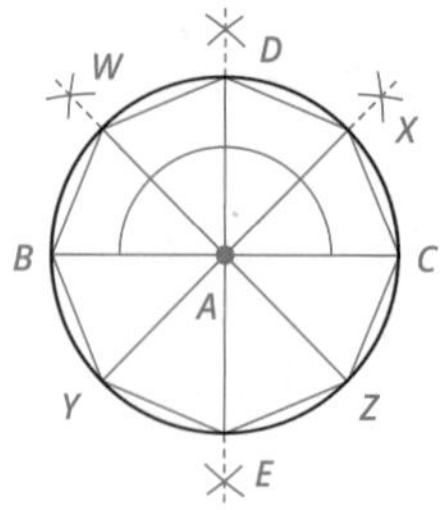

I drew diameter $\overline{BC}$. Then I constructed perpendicular bisector $\overline{DE}$. I bisected $\angle DAC$ and extended the angle bisector to also bisect $\angle BAE$. I then bisected $\angle DAB$ and extended the angle bisector to also bisect $\angle CAE$. I then connected the eight chords on the circumference of the circle to inscribe a regular octagon.

Questions to Support Discourse

		TYPE
1	• Which angles can you construct without the use of a protractor?	Gathering
	• How can a 60° angle be used to determine a 75° angle? • How could bisecting a 60° angle help you construct a 75° angle?	Probing
2	• Which construction can you use to locate the center of the circle? • Which construction divides each of the four right angles into two equivalent angles?	Gathering
	• How can the perpendicular bisectors of two chords be used to locate the center of a circle? • How did you use the fact that you have eight equivalent angles to construct a regular octagon inscribed in a circle?	Probing

ASSIGNMENT

LESSON 3 ASSIGNMENT

> Use a separate piece of paper for your Journal entry.

JOURNAL

Explain how to bisect an angle using patty paper and using a compass and straightedge.

REMEMBER

You can use constructions, such as duplicating line segments and angles, and bisecting an angle, as well as transformations, to construct a regular polygon inscribed in a circle.

PRACTICE

1. Duplicate each angle using construction tools.

(a)

(b)

Check students' constructions against the original angles.

2. Inscribe a hexagon inside a circle. Explain your process.

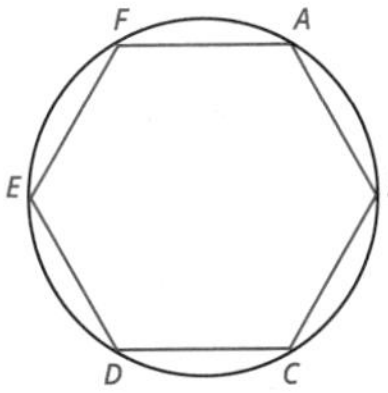

Sample answer.

First, I set my compass to the length of the radius. I then placed the compass point at any location on the circle, and labeled the point *A*. Next, I made an arc that intersected the circle and labeled the intersection point *B*. I continued in the same direction, repeated the process, labeled the intersection points *C*, *D*, *E* , and *F*. Finally, I connected points *A* through *F*.

Go to LiveHint.com for help on the PRACTICE questions.

Encourage students to use LiveHint.com for help with the PRACTICE questions of this assignment.

Chunking the Assignment

SESSION 1

- Practice 1 and 2

SESSION 2

- Journal
- Practice 3 - 5

SESSION 3

- Mixed Practice (page 277) 4
- Stretch (advanced learners)

JOURNAL

Sample answer.

To bisect an angle using patty paper, fold the paper at the vertex so that one ray of the angle lies on top of the other ray. The crease formed is the angle bisector.

To bisect $\angle A$ using a straightedge and a compass, first make an arc joining the two rays of $\angle A$. Label the intersection points as point *X* and point *Y*. From point *X* and point *Y*, make intersecting arcs that have the same radius. Label the point of intersection *Z*. Connect point *A* and point *Z* to construct the angle bisector of $\angle A$.

NOTES

3. Construct a square inscribed in a circle. Then, explain how you know the figure is a square.

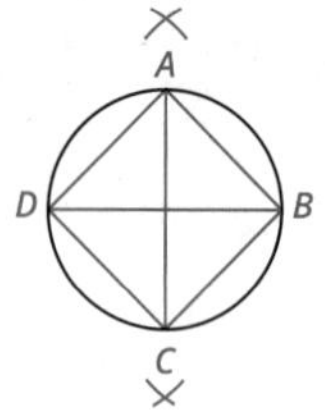

I know the four sides of the square are congruent because each of the square's sides is the hypotenuse of a right triangle with both of its legs being the radii of the same circle.

4. Construct the angle bisector of each given angle.

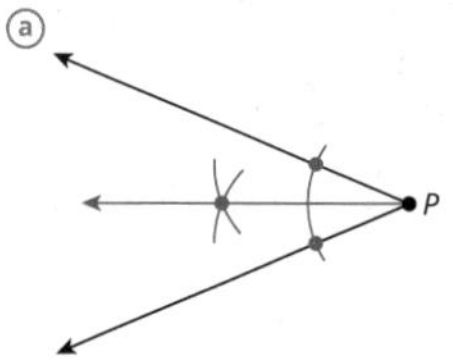

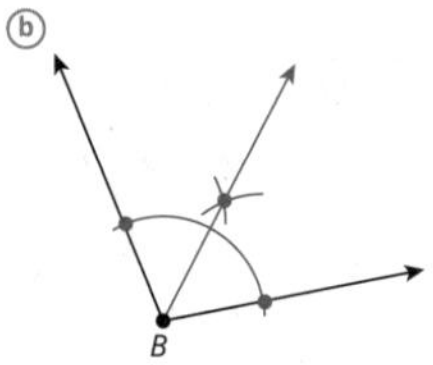

Check students' constructions.

5. Construct a 15° angle using only a compass and straightedge. Summarize your steps.

Check students' constructions.
Construct an equilateral triangle to create a 60° angle.
Bisect the 60° angle to get two 30° angles.
Then, bisect one of the 30° angles to get a 15° angle.

STRETCH Optional

> Determine two different constructions you could use to construct an angle with a measure of 45° using only a compass and straightedge. Summarize the processes and show both constructions.

STRETCH

Check students' constructions. Sample answers.

1. Construct an equilateral triangle. Use one of its interior angles with a measure of 60°. Bisect this angle and then bisect one of the resulting angles to construct two 15° angles. The adjacent 15° angle and 30° angle form a 45° angle.
2. Construct a perpendicular bisector to a line. The two angles formed by the bisector and the line are 90° angles. Bisect one of these 90° angles to create two 45° angles.

Into the Ring

This resource details additional facilitation notes to fully assist you as you plan each lesson to support all students, students who struggle, and advanced learners. It provides differentiation strategies, common student misconceptions, and suggestions to extend certain activities.

GETTING STARTED

Session 1 of 3

Duped

Students construct an equilateral triangle in a circle by duplicating a segment and using the fact that the radii of a circle are congruent.

CHUNK	AUDIENCE	ADDITIONAL SUPPORTS
As students work on the activity	All Students	**DIFFERENTIATION STRATEGY** Highlight the importance of this activity. Have students mark the three sides congruent, label each angle in the triangle with its measure, and make a side note that this is a strategy to construct a 60° angle. Students may need to refer to this strategy to complete other constructions.

ACTIVITY 1

Session 1 of 3

Duplicating an Angle

Students duplicate an angle and construct an angle that is twice the measure of a given angle. They compare the processes used to duplicate an angle and duplicate a line segment. They construct a regular hexagon by duplicating 60° angles.

CHUNK	AUDIENCE	ADDITIONAL SUPPORTS
As students work on the activity	All Students	**DIFFERENTIATION STRATEGY** Allow students to use patty paper or a compass and straightedge to complete constructions unless the question asks them to use specific tools. Provide options for placing patty paper constructions in the textbook. Suggest students either staple their patty paper in the book or transfer the solution from their patty paper to the diagram in the textbook.

CHUNK	AUDIENCE	ADDITIONAL SUPPORTS
As students work on 2	All Students	**DIFFERENTIATION STRATEGY** To help students write concise explanations of how they performed constructions, suggest that they label points of intersection in their diagrams. That way, they can refer to locations by the letter of a point rather than a description of the point's location. You may want to model this practice in the discussion of Question 2. See the answer to Question 2 as an example.

ACTIVITY 2

Session 1 of 3

Constructing an Inscribed Hexagon

Students construct a regular hexagon inscribed in a circle by creating six adjacent congruent chords, each the same length as the circle's radius. They also determine the measure of each interior angle of a regular hexagon.

CHUNK	AUDIENCE	ADDITIONAL SUPPORTS
To extend 1	Advanced Learners	**DIFFERENTIATION STRATEGY** Ask students to draw several circles of different sizes and show that each circle's radius will always map onto the circle's circumference to create exactly six congruent chords.
To extend the activity	All Students	**DIFFERENTIATION STRATEGY** Have students construct other figures by expanding upon their construction of the hexagon. For example: • Connecting every other vertex of the hexagon to the circle's center to create a two-dimensional representation of a cube. • Create a petal pattern by extending the arcs to create the chords inside of the circle. 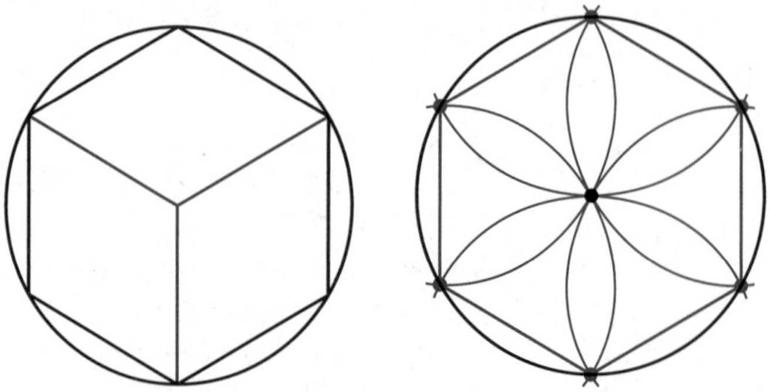

ACTIVITY 3

Session 2 of 3

Constructing an Inscribed Square

Students construct a square inscribed in a circle using patty paper and rigid motion transformations. They use the Pythagorean Theorem to determine the side lengths of the square based on a radius. They use the fact that diagonals of a square are perpendicular to construct a square inscribed in a circle.

CHUNK	AUDIENCE	ADDITIONAL SUPPORTS
As students work on 3 - 5	Students who Struggle	**COMMON MISCONCEPTION** Students sometimes have difficulty recognizing the different relationships that a single segment may have within a complex diagram. For example: • Students may not recognize that the circles' diameters are also diagonals of the square, primarily due to their horizontal and vertical orientation. • When students are verifying that the square's angles are each 90°, they may not recognize that a side of the square is also the hypotenuse of a right triangle. 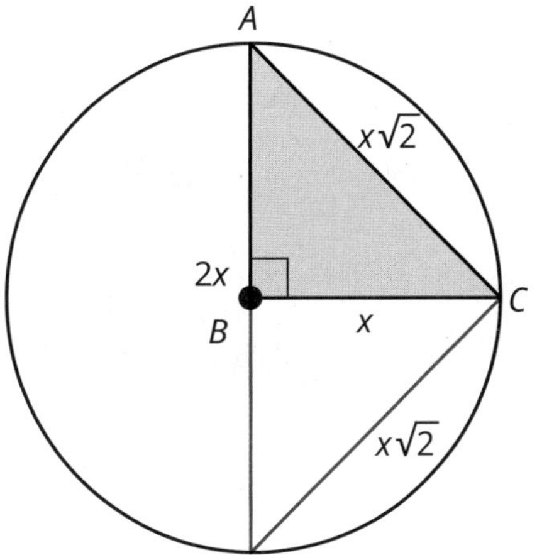

ACTIVITY 4

Session 2 of 3

Bisecting an Angle

Students analyze worked examples that demonstrate how to bisect an angle using patty paper and a compass and straightedge. They then bisect angles and use repeated reasoning to construct angles that are one-fourth and one-eighth the measure of a given angle.

CHUNK	AUDIENCE	ADDITIONAL SUPPORTS
As students analyze the patty paper construction	All Students	**COMMON MISCONCEPTION** Students may associate the size of an angle with the length of the sides forming the angle. Ensure they understand that the size of an angle is a degree measure and determined by the spread between the sides of the angle. The sides' length has no impact on the angle's size. Ask students to generate examples of angles that have the same measure but different side lengths.
As students analyze the compass construction	All Students	**COMMON MISCONCEPTION** Students may assume that the compass must remain in the same position throughout all steps of this construction. The construction will still work if the compass is changed after step 1 to perform step 2, provided the new setting is used twice in step 2 and allows the arcs to intersect. All possible arc intersections will lie on the angle bisector.
To extend 3	Advanced Learners	**DIFFERENTIATION STRATEGY** To extend the activity, have students create an angle $\frac{3}{4}$ the measure of the given angle and an angle that is $\frac{5}{2}$ times the measure of the given angle, then describe the strategy used to create the angles.

ACTIVITY 5

Session 3 of 3

Constructing and Inscribing an Equilateral Triangle

Students use a line segment to construct an equilateral triangle. They then show two different ways to construct an inscribed equilateral triangle in a circle and describe the process they used in each construction.

CHUNK	AUDIENCE	ADDITIONAL SUPPORTS
To extend 1	Advanced Learners	**DIFFERENTIATION STRATEGY** Have students discuss how the Triangle Inequality Theorem could support Sophie's conclusion. The Triangle Inequality Theorem states that the sum of the lengths of any two sides of a triangle is greater than the length of the third side.

TALK THE TALK

Session 3 of 3

Playing the Angles

Students use the constructions they have learned to construct a 75° angle and inscribe a regular octagon in a circle.

CHUNK	AUDIENCE	ADDITIONAL SUPPORTS
As an alternative grouping strategy for the activity	All Students	**DIFFERENTIATION STRATEGY** Pair students and have half the pairs complete Question 1 while the other half completes Question 2. Have pairs that completed Question 1 partner with pairs that completed Question 2 and share their construction strategies.
As students work on 2	All Students	**DIFFERENTIATION STRATEGY** Discuss the relationship between the different strategies to identify the center of the circle. • Using the diameter of a circle and its perpendicular bisector is a special case of using the intersection of the perpendicular bisectors of two chords. This is true because the circle's diameter is a chord that passes through the center of the circle. • Using patty paper to determine the center of the circle relates to constructing a diameter and its perpendicular bisector

Practice the learning

MATHbook + Skills Practice

The table shows the targeted practice of the skills and mathematical concepts for the *Composing and Decomposing Shapes* Topic. The highlighted **Problem Set** aligns with **Into the Ring**.

PROBLEM SET	
1	Identifying Circle Parts
2	Using Circles to Construct Quadrilaterals and Triangles
3	Making Conjectures About Quadrilaterals
4	**Constructing with Angles**
5	Making Conjectures About Triangles
6	Drawing Points of Concurrency

ANYTIME AFTER ACTIVITY 5

Facilitate students as they work individually on **Problem Set 4**.

ENGAGE at the **Module** level + **DEVELOP** at the **Topic** level + **TEACH** Read the facilitation notes and plan learning experiences.

Where are we?

TOPIC 1 Composing and Decomposing Shapes	LESSON 1 Running Circles Around Geometry	LESSON 2 The Quad Squad	LESSON 3 Into the Ring	**LESSON 4 Tri- Tri- Tri- and Separate Them**	LESSON 5 Meet Me in the Middle
Pacing	2 Sessions	2 Sessions	3 Sessions	**2 Sessions**	2 Sessions

OVERVIEW: LESSON 4

Tri- Tri- Tri- and Separate Them

Conjectures About Triangles

ENGAGE

- Students use conjectures they made about the properties of quadrilaterals to classify quadrilaterals and triangles.

DEVELOP

- Students write the converse of conjectures and explore biconditional statements.
- They conjecture about a diagram containing an equilateral triangle, parallel lines, and a perpendicular bisector.
- They make conjectures related to the Triangle Inequality Theorem and midsegments of triangles.

DEMONSTRATE

- Students revisit the conjectures made in this lesson and draw an example of each.

HIGH SCHOOL GEOMETRY

Congruence

Prove geometric theorems.

10. Prove theorems about triangles.†

†The full intent of the standard is not met in this lesson. Students make conjectures about these theorems; they will prove them and fully meet the standard in future lessons.

LESSON STRUCTURE AND PACING GUIDE 2 SESSIONS

⊛ This activity highlights a key term or concept that is essential to the learning goals of the lesson.

Session 1		Session 2
INSTRUCTIONAL SEQUENCE		
ENGAGE Connect to prior knowledge	**DEVELOP** Worked example Peer analysis	**DEVELOP** Investigation

GETTING STARTED
Not an Illusion

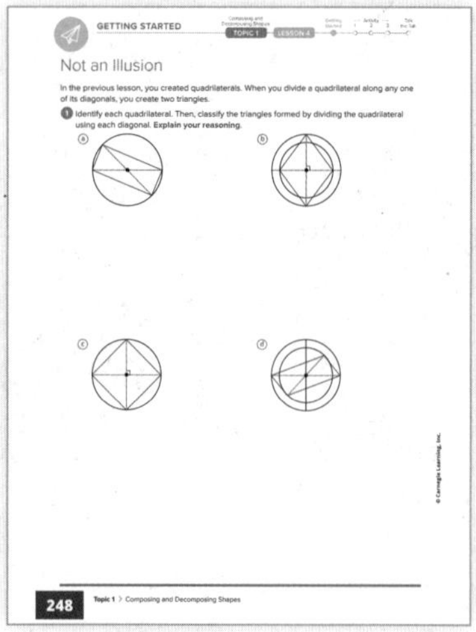

GETTING STARTED

Not an Illusion

In the previous lesson, you created quadrilaterals. When you divide a quadrilateral along any one of its diagonals, you create two triangles.

1 Identify each quadrilateral. Then, classify the triangles formed by dividing the quadrilateral using each diagonal. Explain your reasoning.

248 Topic 1 > Composing and Decomposing Shapes

Students use conjectures about the properties of quadrilaterals to classify quadrilaterals.

- They classify the triangles created by the diagonals

⊛ ACTIVITY 1
Base Angles, Angle Pairs, and Converses

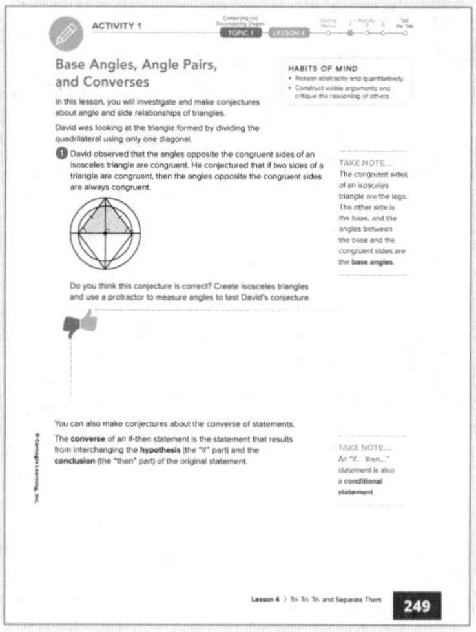

ACTIVITY 1

Base Angles, Angle Pairs, and Converses

In this lesson, you will investigate and make conjectures about angle and side relationships of triangles.

David was looking at the triangle formed by dividing the quadrilateral using only one diagonal.

1 David observed that the angles opposite the congruent sides of an isosceles triangle are congruent. He conjectured that if two sides of a triangle are congruent, then the angles opposite the congruent sides are always congruent.

Do you think this conjecture is correct? Create isosceles triangles and use a protractor to measure angles to test David's conjecture.

You can also make conjectures about the converse of statements.

The **converse** of an if-then statement is the statement that results from interchanging the **hypothesis** (the "if" part) and the **conclusion** (the "then" part) of the original statement.

249

Students write the converse of conjectures and explore biconditional statements.

- They differentiate testing a conjecture from proving a theorem.

⊛ ACTIVITY 2
Triangle Sum, 30°-60°-90°, and Exterior Angles

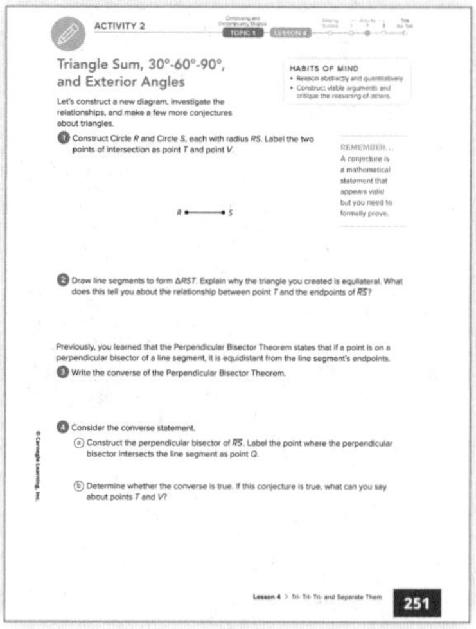

ACTIVITY 2

Triangle Sum, 30°-60°-90°, and Exterior Angles

Let's construct a new diagram, investigate the relationships, and make a few more conjectures about triangles.

1 Construct Circle R and Circle S, each with radius RS. Label the two points of intersection as point T and point V.

2 Draw line segments to form △RST. Explain why the triangle you created is equilateral. What does this tell you about the relationship between point T and the endpoints of RS?

Previously, you learned that the Perpendicular Bisector Theorem states that if a point is on a perpendicular bisector of a line segment, it is equidistant from the line segment's endpoints.

3 Write the converse of the Perpendicular Bisector Theorem.

4 Consider the converse statement.

251

Students use a diagram with two circles to construct an equilateral triangle, parallel lines, and a perpendicular bisector.

- They form a 30°-60°-90° triangle and describe its angle measures and side lengths.
- They identify the relationship between the measure of an exterior angle of a triangle and the measures of the two remote interior angles.

Log in to MyCL for **lesson support** including:

Slides

Videos

www.carnegielearning.com/login

INSTRUCTIONAL SEQUENCE

DEVELOP
Investigation

DEMONSTRATE
Generalization

NOTES

TOPIC 1

ACTIVITY 3
Triangle Inequality and Midsegments

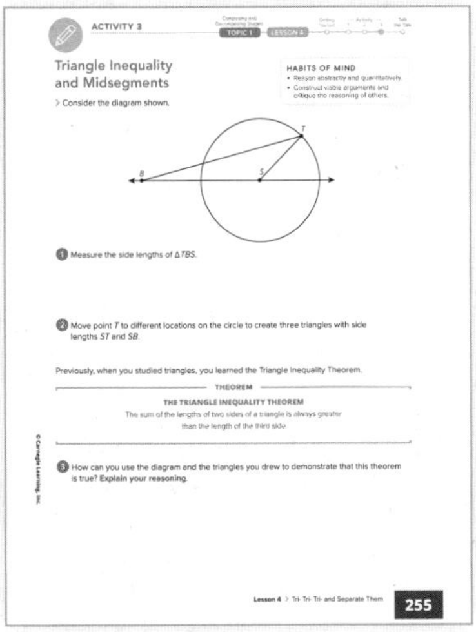
ACTIVITY 3

Triangle Inequality and Midsegments

HABITS OF MIND
- Reason abstractly and quantitatively.
- Construct viable arguments and critique the reasoning of others.

> Consider the diagram shown.

1. Measure the side lengths of ΔTBS.

2. Move point T to different locations on the circle to create three triangles with side lengths ST and SB.

Previously, when you studied triangles, you learned the Triangle Inequality Theorem.

THEOREM
THE TRIANGLE INEQUALITY THEOREM
The sum of the lengths of two sides of a triangle is always greater than the length of the third side.

3. How can you use the diagram and the triangles you drew to demonstrate that this theorem is true? **Explain your reasoning.**

© Carnegie Learning, Inc.

Lesson 4 > Tri- Tri- Tri- and Separate Them 255

Students make conjectures related to the Triangle Inequality Theorem and midsegments of triangles.

- They use a circle diagram to explore the side lengths of a triangle.

TALK THE TALK
You Will Only Come to This Conclusion

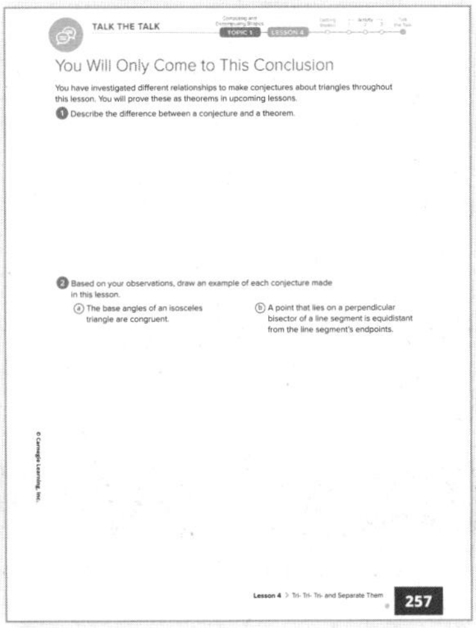
TALK THE TALK

You Will Only Come to This Conclusion

You have investigated different relationships to make conjectures about triangles throughout this lesson. You will prove these as theorems in upcoming lessons.

1. Describe the difference between a conjecture and a theorem.

2. Based on your observations, draw an example of each conjecture made in this lesson.
   (a) The base angles of an isosceles triangle are congruent.
   (b) A point that lies on a perpendicular bisector of a line segment is equidistant from the line segment's endpoints.

© Carnegie Learning, Inc.

Lesson 4 > Tri- Tri- Tri- and Separate Them 257

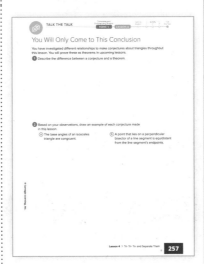

Students revisit the conjectures made in this lesson.

- They draw examples of each conjecture.

Log in to MyCL for:

- Editable templates
- Additional planning support

Now that you have read the Module, Topic, and Lesson Overviews, you are ready to plan.

Do the math

> Tear out the lesson planning template (page 247E) and jot down thoughts as you work through this lesson and read the Facilitation Notes.

Connect the learning

MATHbook + MATHia®

The table shows a portion of the self-paced MATHia sequence for the *Composing and Decomposing Shapes* Topic.

Median student completion time for the entire topic: ~110–130 minutes

> As you implement this lesson, consider different connections for students who are on pace and those that have not yet completed the workspaces aligned to this lesson.

STUDENTS WILL CONTINUE WORKING ON SKILLS RELATED TO THIS TOPIC

TYPE	WORKSPACE NAME
	Using Circles to Draw Quadrilaterals
	Angles of an Inscribed Quadrilateral
	Points of Concurrency

Tri- Tri- Tri- and Separate Them

Conjectures About Triangles

Session 1

GETTING STARTED Not an Illusion

Pacing (minutes)	
My Time	Class Time

ACTIVITY 1 Base Angles, Angle Pairs, and Converses ✪

Pacing (minutes)	
My Time	Class Time

KEY TERM
- base angles
- converse
- hypothesis
- conclusion
- conditional statement
- biconditional statement

Session 2

ACTIVITY 2 Triangle Sum, 30°-60°-90°, and Exterior Angles ✪

Pacing (minutes)	
My Time	Class Time

KEY TERM
- exterior angle
- remote interior angles

ACTIVITY 3 Triangle Inequality and Midsegments ✪

Pacing (minutes)	
My Time	Class Time

KEY TERM
- midsegment

TALK THE TALK You Will Only Come to This Conclusion

Pacing (minutes)	
My Time	Class Time

✪ This activity highlights a key term or concept that is essential to the learning goals of the lesson.

Log in to MyCL for:
- Editable templates
- Additional planning support

Reflect on your lesson

> Consider the effectiveness of your lesson on student learning.

What went well?	What did not go as planned?

> Anticipate how you would change the lesson next time you teach it.

How will you capitalize on the things that went well?	How will you improve things that did not go as planned?

MATERIALS

- Compasses
- Protractors
- Rulers

TOPIC 1 Composing and Decomposing Shapes | TOPIC 2 Justifying Line and Angle Relationships | TOPIC 3 Using Congruence Theorems

1 Running Circles Around Geometry
2 The Quad Squad
3 Into the Ring
4 Tri- Tri- Tri- and Separate Them
5 Meet Me in the Middle

LESSON 4

Tri- Tri- Tri- and Separate Them

Conjectures About Triangles

Learning Goals

- Write a conjecture as a statement and write the converse of the conjecture.
- Identify and draw exterior angles of triangles and midsegments of triangles.
- Make conjectures about the sum of the interior angles of a triangle, exterior angles of a triangle, triangle side length inequalities, and midsegments of a triangle.

KEY TERMS

- base angles
- converse
- hypothesis
- conclusion
- conditional statement
- biconditional statement
- exterior angle
- remote interior angles
- midsegment

REVIEW (1–2 minutes)

> Determine the unknown angle measure in each.

1

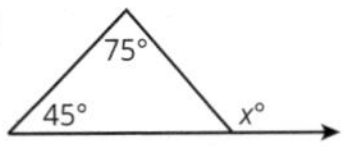

$45 + 75 = x$
$120 = x$, so 120°

2

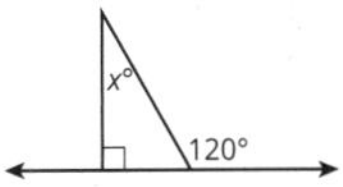

$90 + x = 120$
$x = 30$, so 30°

You have made conjectures about line and angle relationships and about quadrilaterals using circles.

What conjectures can you make about triangles using circles? Are there different forms of conjectures?

Setting the Stage

- **Assign Review (optional, 1 – 2 minutes)**
- **Communicate the learning goals and key terms to look out for**
- **Tap into your students' prior learning by reading the narrative statement**
- **Provide a sense of direction by reading the question**

IN THIS REVIEW

Students determine unknown angle measures in figures involving triangles. They will use this skill in **ACTIVITY 2 Triangle Sum, 30°-60°-90°, and Exterior Angles.**

You write a conditional statement in the form "If...then..." You can form the converse of a conditional statement by interchanging the conditional statement's hypothesis and conclusion. A biconditional statement is one where the conditional and converse are both true.

Essential Ideas

- The converse of a statement is different from the original statement. You form a converse by interchanging the hypothesis and conclusion of the original statement.
- The base angles of an isosceles triangle are congruent.
- A point that lies on a perpendicular bisector of a line segment is equidistant from the endpoints of the line segment.
- The measure of the exterior angle of a triangle is equal to the sum of the measures of the two remote interior angles.
- The length of the third side of a triangle cannot be equal to or greater than the sum of the measures of the other two sides.
- A conjecture is a mathematical statement that appears valid but you need to prove formally. You must prove a conjecture with definitions and theorems for it to be a theorem.

SUMMARY **When you divide a quadrilateral by one diagonal, you form specific triangles based on the quadrilateral's properties.**

Chunking the Activity

- **Read and discuss the directions**
- **Group students to complete the activity**
- **Share and summarize**

DIFFERENTIATION STRATEGY

See Page 260A to support students who struggle with the activity.

Student Look-Fors

Classifications of triangles that they draw from the diagram's visual appearance rather than the use of geometric reasoning.

Not an Illusion

In the previous lesson, you created quadrilaterals. When you divide a quadrilateral along any one of its diagonals, you create two triangles.

1. Identify each quadrilateral. Then, classify the triangles formed by dividing the quadrilateral using each diagonal. **Explain your reasoning.**

(a)

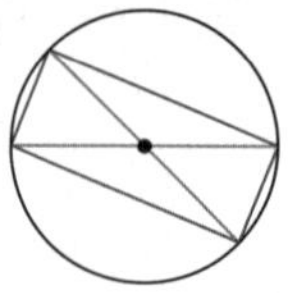

The quadrilateral is a rectangle.

Each triangle is an isosceles triangle. The diameters of the rectangle are congruent. The radii of the circle form two legs of the triangle and are congruent.

(b)

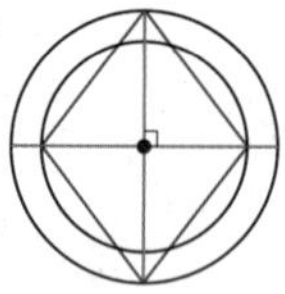

The quadrilateral is a rhombus.

The triangles formed are right scalene triangles. One vertex of each triangle is on the perpendicular bisector of the base of the triangle, so the two sides extending from this vertex to the base's endpoints are congruent.

(c)

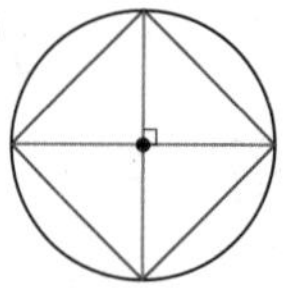

The quadrilateral is a square.

The triangles formed are isosceles right triangles. Inscribed angles intercept diameters to form the right angles. The congruent sides are formed by segments that extend from a point on the perpendicular bisector of the base to the base's endpoints.

(d)

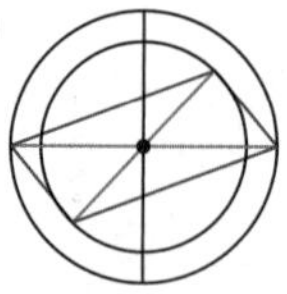

The quadrilateral is a parallelogram.

The triangles formed are scalene. The diagonals of the parallelogram are not congruent.

Questions to Support Discourse

		TYPE
1	• What is the difference between a scalene triangle and an isosceles triangle?	Gathering
	• If the intercepted arc is a semicircle, is the inscribed angle a right angle? Why? • How do you know the quadrilateral in part (a) is a rectangle and not a square? • Are the four chords in part (c) congruent? How do you know? • Why is each triangle formed by one diagonal in part (c) an isosceles right triangle?	Probing

ACTIVITY 1

SUMMARY **The truth value of a conditional statement and its converse are not always the same.**

ACTIVITY 1

Base Angles, Angle Pairs, and Converses

HABITS OF MIND
- Reason abstractly and quantitatively.
- Construct viable arguments and critique the reasoning of others.

In this lesson, you will investigate and make conjectures about angle and side relationships of triangles.

David was looking at the triangle formed by dividing the quadrilateral using only one diagonal.

1 David observed that the angles opposite the congruent sides of an isosceles triangle are congruent. He conjectured that if two sides of a triangle are congruent, then the angles opposite the congruent sides are always congruent.

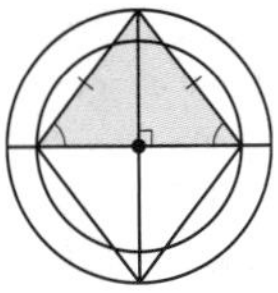

TAKE NOTE...
The congruent sides of an isosceles triangle are the legs. The other side is the base, and the angles between the base and the congruent sides are the **base angles**.

Do you think this conjecture is correct? Create isosceles triangles and use a protractor to measure angles to test David's conjecture.

David's conjecture is correct.
Check students' triangles.

You can also make conjectures about the *converse* of statements.

The **converse** of an if-then statement is the statement that results from interchanging the **hypothesis** (the "if" part) and the **conclusion** (the "then" part) of the original statement.

TAKE NOTE...
An "If... then..." statement is also a **conditional statement**.

Questions to Support Discourse

		TYPE
1	• Thinking about David's conjecture, what conjecture could you make about equilateral triangles?	Seeing structure

Chunking the Activity

- Read and discuss the introduction
- Group students to complete 1
- Check-in and share
- Read and discuss the definitions and worked example
- Complete 2 and 3 as a class
- Share and summarize

DIFFERENTIATION STRATEGY

See Page 260A to challenge advanced learners to extend 1.

Student Look-Fors

Whether students are demonstrating proficiencies related to these habits of mind.

- Reason abstractly and quantitatively
- Construct viable arguments and critique the reasoning of others

NOTES

COMMON MISCONCEPTION

See Page 260A for a misconception related to 2.

COMMON MISCONCEPTION

See Page 260B for a misconception related to 3.

WORKED EXAMPLE

To form the converse of a conditional statement, interchange the hypothesis and conclusion.

Conditional Statement	If **two sides of a triangle are congruent**, then **the base angles opposite the congruent sides are always congruent**.
Converse Statement	If **the base angles opposite the congruent sides are always congruent**, then **two sides of a triangle are congruent.**

2 Do you think the converse of David's conjecture is true? **How could you test the converse conjecture?**

Yes. If I create triangles with the same base angle measurements and then measure the legs, the legs are congruent.

Sample answer.
I could test my conjecture by constructing different isosceles triangles and measuring the base angles.

Testing a conjecture and proving it as a theorem are not the same thing. Remember, a theorem has been proven true in all cases. A proof requires reasoning using definitions and theorems, whereas testing involves making observations, noting counterexamples, and using measuring tools.

When a conditional statement and its converse are both true, this is called a *biconditional statement*. A **biconditional statement** is a statement written in the form "if and only if *p*, then *q*." It is a combination of both a conditional statement and the converse of that conditional statement.

3 Consider the conditional statement:
If Estelle goes out in the rain without an umbrella, she will get wet.

Write the converse and determine whether this is a biconditional statement.

Converse statement:
If you get wet, then you went out in the rain without an umbrella.
The converse is false. Therefore, this is not a biconditional statement.

Questions to Support Discourse

		TYPE
3	• What is a strategy you can use to show that a biconditional statement is not true?	Probing

ACTIVITY 2

SUMMARY **The measure of the exterior angle of a triangle is equal to the sum of the measures of the two remote interior angles.**

Triangle Sum, 30°-60°-90°, and Exterior Angles

Let's construct a new diagram, investigate the relationships, and make a few more conjectures about triangles.

HABITS OF MIND
- Reason abstractly and quantitatively.
- Construct viable arguments and critique the reasoning of others.

1. Construct Circle R and Circle S, each with radius RS. Label the two points of intersection as point T and point V.

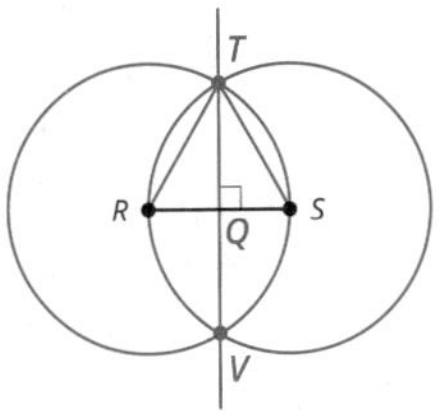

REMEMBER...
A conjecture is a mathematical statement that appears valid but you need to formally prove.

2. Draw line segments to form ΔRST. Explain why the triangle you created is equilateral. What does this tell you about the relationship between point T and the endpoints of $\overline{RS}$?

   The triangle's side lengths are the radii of each circle, which are congruent. Point T is equidistant from endpoints R and S.

Previously, you learned that the Perpendicular Bisector Theorem states that if a point is on a perpendicular bisector of a line segment, it is equidistant from the line segment's endpoints.

3. Write the converse of the Perpendicular Bisector Theorem.

   If a point is equidistant from the endpoints of a line segment, then the point lies on the perpendicular bisector of the line segment.

4. Consider the converse statement.

   a. Construct the perpendicular bisector of $\overline{RS}$. Label the point where the perpendicular bisector intersects the line segment as point Q.

   See diagram in Question 1.

   b. Determine whether the converse is true. If this conjecture is true, what can you say about points T and V?

   The converse is true.

   I can draw a line through points T and V because constructing the two circles with the same line segment is how you construct a perpendicular bisector.

   Points T and V are each equidistant from endpoints R and S because they are on radii of congruent circles. So, both points T and V lie on the perpendicular bisector of line segment RS.

Chunking the Activity

- Read and discuss the introduction
- Group students to complete 1 and 2
- Check-in and share
- Read and discuss the theorem
- Group students to complete 3 and 4
- Check-in and share
- Group students to complete 5 - 8
- Share and summarize

Student Look-Fors

- Whether they are using reasoning or measuring tools to determine the angle measures of ΔQST.
- Common computational errors related to solving for the side lengths.

Questions to Support Discourse

		TYPE
2	• Is Circle R congruent to Circle S? How do you know? • Why is $\overline{RS} \cong \overline{RT}$?	Probing
4	• What is the length of $\overline{QS}$? • What is the relationship between the length of $\overline{QS}$ and the length of $\overline{RS}$?	Gathering
	• Did you have to draw new arcs to construct the perpendicular bisector of $\overline{RS}$? Why?	Seeing structure

NOTES

5 Consider ΔQST. **Justify each measurement.**

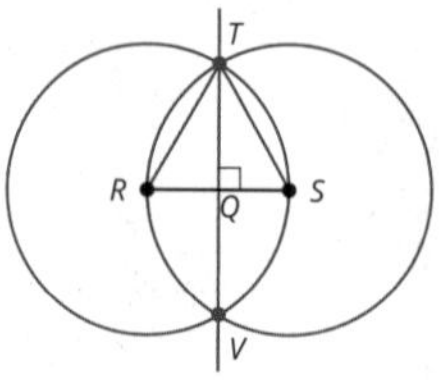

(a) Determine each angle measure.

$\overline{TQ} \perp \overline{QS}$, so $m\angle TQS = 90°$

ΔRST is an equilateral triangle, so $m\angle QST = 60°$.

$180° - 90° - 60° = 30°$, so $m\angle QTS = 30°$.

(b) If $QS = x$, determine the measures of TS and TQ.

$TS = 2x$

$(2x)^2 = x^2 + (TQ)^2$

$3x^2 = (TQ)^2$

$\sqrt{3}x = TQ$

6 Damon translated $\overline{ST}$ to create a parallel line, $\overleftrightarrow{AR}$. He then drew line RS and marked two pairs of congruent angles:

- $\angle ARB \cong \angle TSR$
- $\angle ART \cong \angle RTS$

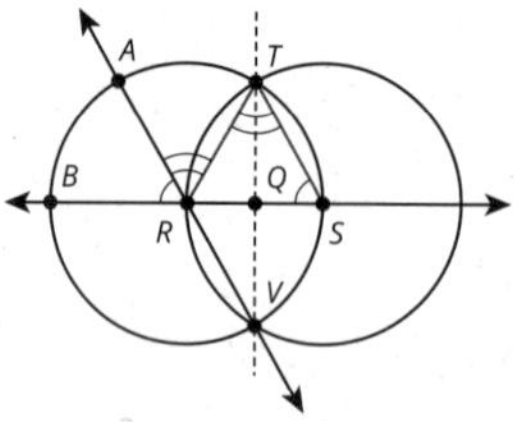

(a) What conjectures did Damon use to mark the congruent angle pairs?

When a transversal cuts two parallel lines, alternate interior angles are congruent, and corresponding angles are congruent.

(b) Consider the central angles $\angle TRS$, $\angle TRA$, and $\angle ARB$ and their intercepted arcs $\overset{\frown}{ST}$, $\overset{\frown}{TA}$, and $\overset{\frown}{AB}$. What is the sum of the measures of these central angles? What is the sum of the measures of the corresponding intercepted arcs?

The sum of the central angle measures is 180°. The sum of the arc measures is 180°.

THINK ABOUT...
What conjectures did you use to describe the angle and arc additions?

DIFFERENTIATION STRATEGY

See Page 260B to support students who struggle with 6 and 7.

Questions to Support Discourse

		TYPE
5	• Which type of angle do you form when constructing a perpendicular bisector?	Gathering
	• How does knowing the angle measures in ΔRST help you determine the angle measures of ΔQST? • How does knowing that $QS = x$ help you determine the length of $\overline{TS}$? • How can you use the Pythagorean Theorem to solve for the length of $\overline{QT}$?	Probing
6	• What are the angle pairs formed when a transversal cuts parallel lines? • Which circle are the three central angles in?	Gathering
	• How can arc $\overset{\frown}{STB}$ help you verify the sum of the three central angles?	Probing

ACTIVITY 2 Continued

ⓒ Using Damon's diagram, what can you conjecture about the sum of the measures of a triangle's interior angles? **Explain your reasoning.**

The sum of the interior angle measures of a triangle is 180°.

A portion of Damon's diagram is shown. Consider ΔRST. Angle *TRB* is an exterior angle, and $\angle RST$ and $\angle STR$ are remote interior angles of ΔRST.

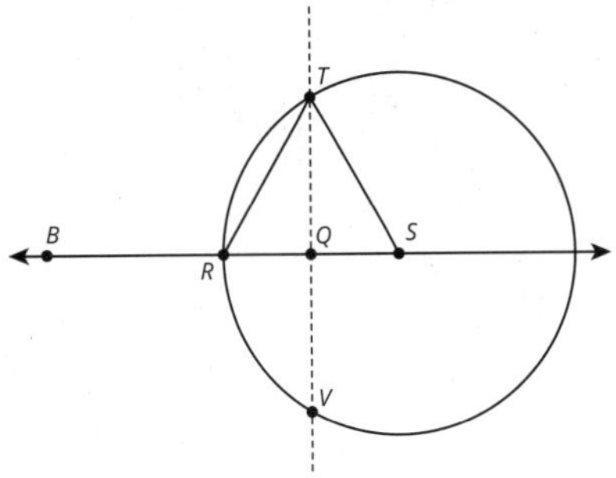

TAKE NOTE...

An **exterior angle** of a polygon is an angle that forms a linear pair with an interior angle of the polygon.

The **remote interior angles** of a triangle are the two angles that are not adjacent to the specified exterior angle.

7 What conjecture can you make about the exterior angle measure, $\angle TRB$, and the two remote interior angles, $\angle RTS$ and $\angle TSR$?

The measure of the exterior angle is equal to the sum of the measures of the two remote interior angles.

Questions to Support Discourse

		TYPE
7	• Which two central angles create $\angle TRB$?	Gathering
	• How does knowing that an exterior angle of a polygon forms a linear pair with an interior angle help you with your conjecture?	Probing

NOTES

TOPIC 1

NOTES

ACTIVITY 2 Continued

8 Each interior angle of a triangle has two corresponding exterior angles. Identify each exterior angle and use a protractor to test your conjecture from Question 7. **What do you notice?**

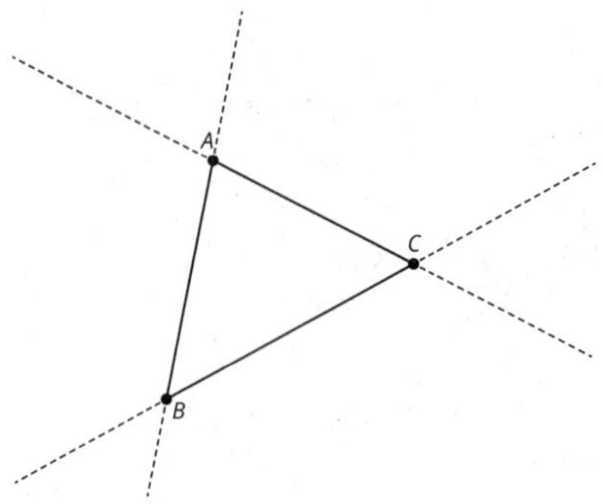

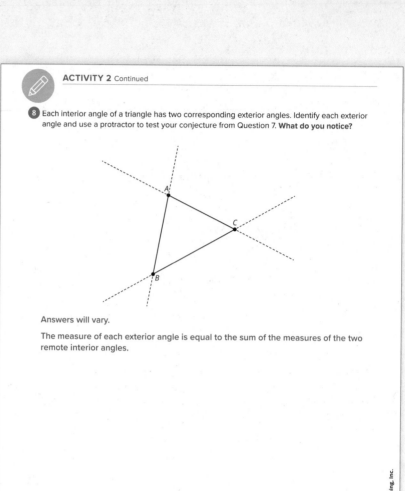

Answers will vary.

The measure of each exterior angle is equal to the sum of the measures of the two remote interior angles.

254 Topic 1 > Composing and Decomposing Shapes

ACTIVITY 3

SUMMARY You can write an inequality to relate the three sides of a triangle. A midsegment of a triangle is one-half the length and parallel to the third side.

Triangle Inequality and Midsegments

HABITS OF MIND
- Reason abstractly and quantitatively.
- Construct viable arguments and critique the reasoning of others.

> Consider the diagram shown.

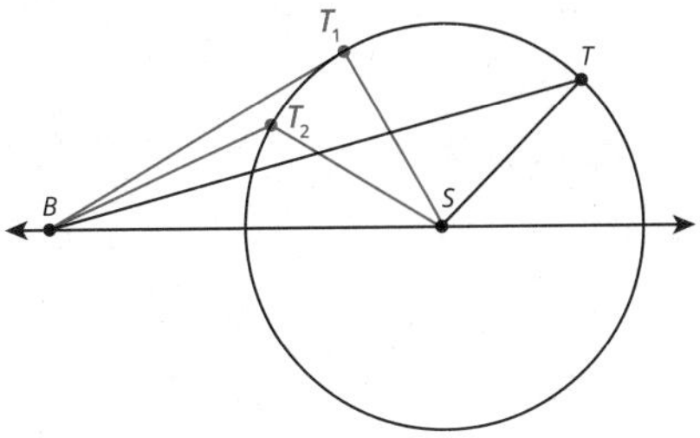

1 Measure the side lengths of ΔTBS.

Check students' measurements.

2 Move point T to different locations on the circle to create three triangles with side lengths ST and SB.

Previously, when you studied triangles, you learned the Triangle Inequality Theorem.

THEOREM

THE TRIANGLE INEQUALITY THEOREM

The sum of the lengths of two sides of a triangle is always greater than the length of the third side.

3 How can you use the diagram and the triangles you drew to demonstrate that this theorem is true? **Explain your reasoning.**

The sum of the measures of $\overline{ST}$ and $\overline{SB}$ stays the same as you draw different sides using the different radii of the circle. The circle diagram shows that the length of the third side cannot be equal to or greater than the sum of the measures of the two fixed sides.

Chunking the Activity

- Read the introduction and discuss the diagram
- Group students to complete 1 - 3
- Check-in and share
- Group students to complete 4
- Share and summarize

DIFFERENTIATION STRATEGY

See Page 260C to assist all students with 2.

DIFFERENTIATION STRATEGY

See Page 260C to support students who struggle with 3.

Questions to Support Discourse

		TYPE
2	• If point T is located anywhere on Circle S, will $\overline{ST}$ remain the same length? Why?	Probing
	• As point T moves, what effect does this have on the measure of central angle TSB? • As point T moves, what effect does this have on the length of side $\overline{SB}$? What effect does it have on the length of side $\overline{BT}$?	Seeing structure
3	• Could the length of side $\overline{BT}$ ever be greater than the sum of the lengths of the sides of $\overline{BS}$ and $\overline{ST}$? Why? • Is the sum of the lengths of sides $\overline{ST}$ and $\overline{SB}$ always greater than the length of side $\overline{BT}$? Why?	Probing

NOTES

DIFFERENTIATION STRATEGY

See Page 260C to challenge advanced learners to extend the activity.

4 Consider the diagram that shows point T at two different locations on the circle that create triangles with side lengths ST and SB.

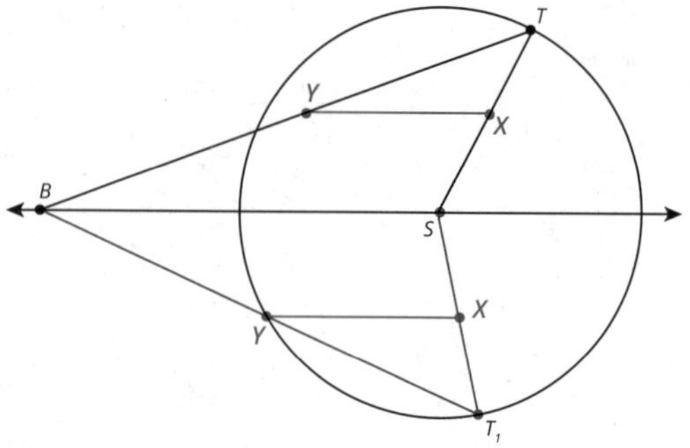

(a) For each triangle, determine and label the midpoint of $\overline{ST}$ as point X and label the midpoint of $\overline{BT}$ as point Y. Connect the midpoints to form a *midsegment*.

TAKE NOTE...

A **midsegment** of a polygon is any line segment that connects two midpoints of the sides of the polygon.

(b) Measure and compare the midsegments with $\overline{SB}$ and the length of SB. Measure and compare the angles formed by the midsegments and the angles formed at each triangle's base. **What do you notice? What conjecture can you make about the midsegment of each triangle?**

Sample answer.

$m\angle TXY = m\angle TSB$ and $m\angle TYX = m\angle TBS$

Each midsegment is parallel to $\overline{SB}$ and congruent to the other midsegment.

The midsegments are each half the length of $\overline{SB}$.

Questions to Support Discourse

		TYPE
4	• How many midsegments does a triangle have?	Gathering
	• Are the midsegments parallel to $\overline{SB}$? How do you know? • Will your conjecture hold true if the location of point T changes?	Seeing structure

TALK THE TALK

SUMMARY **A conjecture is a mathematical statement that appears valid but you need to prove formally.**

TALK THE TALK

You Will Only Come to This Conclusion

You have investigated different relationships to make conjectures about triangles throughout this lesson. You will prove these as theorems in upcoming lessons.

1. Describe the difference between a conjecture and a theorem.

   A conjecture is a statement believed to be true based on observations. You must prove a conjecture with definitions and theorems to be fully accepted. When this happens, it becomes a theorem.

2. Based on your observations, draw an example of each conjecture made in this lesson.

   a. The base angles of an isosceles triangle are congruent.

   Sample answer.

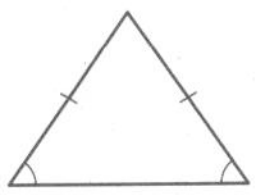

   b. A point that lies on a perpendicular bisector of a line segment is equidistant from the line segment's endpoints.

   Sample answer.

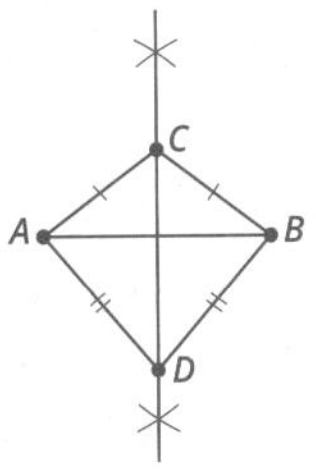

Chunking the Activity

- Read and discuss the directions
- Group students to complete the activity
- Share and summarize

Student Look-Fors

Utilizing relationship skills by communicating clearly and listening well.

Questions to Support Discourse

		TYPE
1	• How are conjectures and theorems similar?	Probing
	• Are conjectures always true?	Reflecting and justifying
2	• Do you think your drawing will match your classmates? Why? • How do the markings on your drawing help to illustrate the conjecture?	Probing

NOTES

TALK THE TALK Continued

ⓒ The measure of the exterior angle of a triangle is equal to the sum of the measures of the two remote interior angles.

Sample answer.

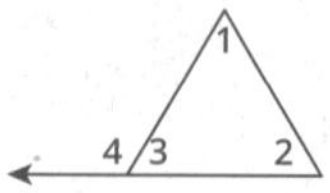

$m\angle 1 + m\angle 2 = m\angle 4$

ⓓ The sum of the measures of the interior angles of a triangle is 180°.

Sample answer.

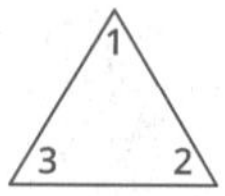

$m\angle 1 + m\angle 2 + m\angle 3 = 180°$

ⓔ The length of the third side of a triangle cannot be equal to or greater than the sum of the measures of the other two sides.

Sample answer.

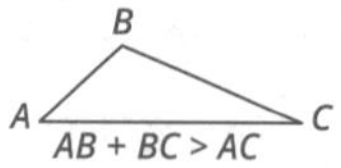

$AB + BC > AC$

ⓕ The midsegment of a triangle is one-half the measure and parallel to the third side.

Sample answer.

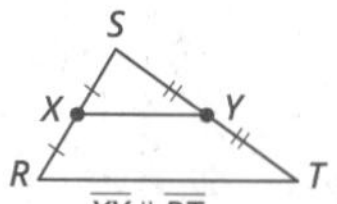

$\overline{XY} \parallel \overline{RT}$

$XY = \frac{1}{2}RT$

ASSIGNMENT

LESSON 4 ASSIGNMENT

> Use a separate piece of paper for your Journal entry.

JOURNAL

When a conditional statement is true, can you assume the converse is also true? Use examples to justify your reasoning.

REMEMBER

You write a conditional statement in the form "If...then..." You can form the converse of a conditional statement by interchanging the conditional statement's hypothesis and conclusion. A biconditional statement is one where the conditional and converse are both true.

PRACTICE

1. Write a conjecture about the geometric objects in each part. Then write the converse of the conjecture. Draw examples to test each conjecture.

   (a) Base angles of an isosceles triangle and their opposite sides

   Conjecture: If a triangle is isosceles, then the sides opposite the triangle's base angles are always congruent.

   Converse: If the sides opposite the base angles in a triangle are congruent, then the triangle is isosceles.

   Check students' drawings.

   (b) The interior angles of a triangle

   Conjecture: If a figure is a triangle, then the sum of the interior angles is 180°.

   Converse: If the sum of the interior angles is 180°, then the figure is a triangle.

   Check students' drawings.

   (c) The side lengths of a triangle

   Conjecture: If a figure is a triangle, then the sum of any two sides' lengths is greater than the length of the third side.

   Converse: If the sum of the lengths of any two sides of a figure is greater than the length of the third side, then the figure is a triangle.

   Check students' drawings.

Go to LiveHint.com for help on the PRACTICE questions.

Chunking the Assignment

TOPIC 1

SESSION 1

- **Journal**
- **Mixed Practice (page 277) 6**

SESSION 2

- **Practice 1 and 2**
- **Stretch (advanced learners)**

JOURNAL

Sample answer.

You cannot assume a converse statement is true if the conditional statement is true.

Conditional statement: If a shape is a square, then it has four sides.

Converse: If a shape has four sides, then it is a square.

In this example, the conditional statement is true, but the converse is not.

Encourage students to use LiveHint.com for help with the PRACTICE questions of this assignment.

NOTES

STRETCH

1.

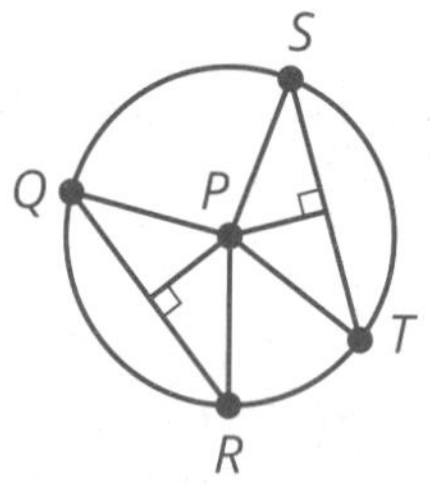

2. Yes, $\Delta QPR \cong \Delta SPT$ by the SSS Congruence Theorem.
3. The altitudes are congruent. $\Delta QPR \cong \Delta SPT$, so the altitudes are congruent.
4. Sample answer.
   Conjecture: If two chords in a circle are congruent, they are equidistant from the center of the circle.
   Converse: If two chords are equidistant from the center of a circle, then they are congruent.

2. Draw examples of triangle midsegments. What conjecture can you make about the midsegment of a triangle?

   Check students' examples.

   The midsegment of a triangle is parallel to the opposite side, and the length of the midsegment is half the length of the opposite side.

STRETCH Optional

> Consider the circle with center *P*. Chords *QR* and *ST* are congruent.

1. Draw ΔQPR and ΔSPT.
2. Is ΔQPR congruent to ΔSPT? Explain your reasoning.
3. Draw the altitude of each triangle. How do the two altitudes compare? Explain your reasoning.
4. Write a conjecture about the distance of congruent chords from the center of the circle. Then write the converse of the conjecture.

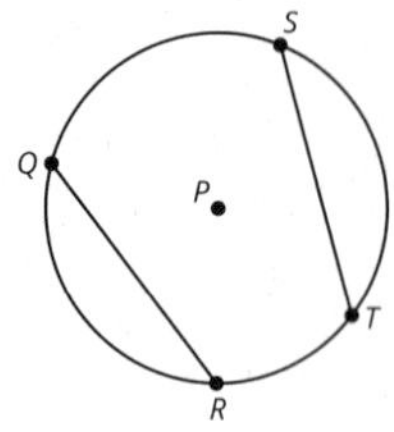

260 Topic 1 > Composing and Decomposing Shapes

Tri- Tri- Tri- and Separate Them

This resource details additional facilitation notes to fully assist you as you plan each lesson to support all students, students who struggle, and advanced learners. It provides differentiation strategies, common student misconceptions, and suggestions to extend certain activities.

GETTING STARTED

Session 1 of 2

Not an Illusion

Students use conjectures about the properties of quadrilaterals to classify quadrilaterals. They classify the triangles created by the diagonals

CHUNK	AUDIENCE	ADDITIONAL SUPPORTS
As students work on the activity	Students who Struggle	**DIFFERENTIATION STRATEGY** Have students mark all congruent side lengths based on the radius of the circle.

ACTIVITY 1

Session 1 of 2

Base Angles, Angle Pairs, and Converses

Students write the converse of conjectures and explore biconditional statements. They differentiate testing a conjecture from proving a theorem.

CHUNK	AUDIENCE	ADDITIONAL SUPPORTS
To extend 1	Advanced Learners	**DIFFERENTIATION STRATEGY** Have students write a conjecture and its converse where the conjecture is not true, but its converse is true. Ask the students to explain which was easier to do: create an example where the conjecture is true and the converse is not true, or vice versa.
As students work on 2	All Students	**COMMON MISCONCEPTION** Students may think *testing* a conjecture and *proving* a conjecture are analogous. Discuss the distinction between these terms as a class. Proof requires the use of definitions and theorems as reasonings, whereas they can test a conjecture by making observations, noting counterexamples, and using measuring tools.

CHUNK	AUDIENCE	ADDITIONAL SUPPORTS
As students work on 3	All Students	**COMMON MISCONCEPTION** Students may think that you can classify a statement that is sometimes true as a true statement. For example, the statement "If school is closed, then today is Sunday" is sometimes true but not always true because school is also closed on days that may not be Sunday. So, this statement's truth value is false.

ACTIVITY 2

Session 2 of 2

Triangle Sum, 30°-60°-90°, and Exterior Angles

Students use a diagram with two circles to construct an equilateral triangle, parallel lines, and a perpendicular bisector. They form a 30°-60°-90° triangle and describe its angle measures and side lengths. They identify the relationship between the measure of an exterior angle of a triangle and the measures of the two remote interior angles.

CHUNK	AUDIENCE	ADDITIONAL SUPPORTS
As students work on 6	Students who Struggle	**DIFFERENTIATION STRATEGY** As students locate the central angles and their intercepted arcs, have them copy Circle *R* and all lines and line segments onto a piece of patty paper. Suggest they use a different color pencil or marker to trace the angles and arcs they are using in this problem. In Question 6, part (c), students use both circles to reason about the sum of the interior angles of a triangle.
As students work on 6 and 7	Students who Struggle	**DIFFERENTIATION STRATEGY** Suggest students use numeric values to see relationships between the angles. For example, before they make a conjecture, let them use a protractor to measure the interior and exterior angles of the triangle. It might be easier to see how the measure of an exterior angle of a triangle is equal to the sum of the measures of the two remote interior angles. Encourage them to draw a few different triangles to see if this same behavior holds true in those situations as well.

ACTIVITY 3

Session 2 of 2

Triangle Inequality and Midsegments

Students use a circle diagram to conjecture about the side lengths of a triangle. They use the same diagram to make conjectures about the midsegments of triangles.

CHUNK	AUDIENCE	ADDITIONAL SUPPORTS
As students work on 2	All Students	**DIFFERENTIATION STRATEGY** Have students use colored pencils to draw each triangle and use congruence markers to identify the congruent segments.
As students work on 3	Students who Struggle	**DIFFERENTIATION STRATEGY** Ask students to draw several different triangles by relocating point *T*. Then have them measure the length of the sides of each triangle. Ask them where point *T* would have to be located to make the length of $\overline{BT}$ equal to the length of $\overline{SB}$ plus the length of $\overline{ST}$.
As students work on 3	Students who Struggle	**DIFFERENTIATION STRATEGY** Create a physical model of this situation where radius *ST* can rotate around Circle *S* like the minute hand of a clock. They can use strips of paper for the line segments and a paper clip or pushpin to hinge the angle at the center of the circle. Moving the radius strip will cause one side to increase in length until it reaches the maximum length and the central angle has opened up into a straight angle, at which point the triangle collapses.
To extend the activity	Advanced Learners	**DIFFERENTIATION STRATEGY** Have students use the diagram to demonstrate the Hinge Theorem. The Hinge Theorem states that two sides of one triangle are congruent to two sides of another triangle, and the included angle of the first pair is larger than the included angle of the second pair, then the third side of the first triangle is longer than the third side of the second triangle.

Practice the learning

MATHbook + Skills Practice

The table shows the targeted practice of the skills and mathematical concepts for the *Composing and Decomposing Shapes* Topic. The highlighted Problem Set aligns with **Tri- Tri- Tri- and Separate Them**.

PROBLEM SET	
1	Identifying Circle Parts
2	Using Circles to Construct Quadrilaterals and Triangles
3	Making Conjectures About Quadrilaterals
4	Constructing with Angles
5	**Making Conjectures About Triangles**
6	Drawing Points of Concurrency

ANYTIME AFTER ACTIVITY 3
Facilitate students as they work individually on **Problem Set 5**.

ENGAGE at the **Module** level + **DEVELOP** at the **Topic** level + **TEACH** Read the facilitation notes and plan learning experiences.

Where are we?

TOPIC 1 Composing and Decomposing Shapes	LESSON 1 Running Circles Around Geometry	LESSON 2 The Quad Squad	LESSON 3 Into the Ring	LESSON 4 Tri- Tri- Tri- and Separate Them	**LESSON 5 Meet Me in the Middle**
Pacing	2 Sessions	2 Sessions	3 Sessions	2 Sessions	**2 Sessions**

OVERVIEW: LESSON 5

Meet Me in the Middle

Points of Concurrency

ENGAGE

- Students inscribe a triangle in a circle and analyze its characteristics.

DEVELOP

- Students construct the perpendicular bisectors of each side of four different triangles, identify the point of concurrency, and make a conjecture.
- They construct the angle bisector of each angle of four different triangles, identify the point of concurrency, and make a conjecture.
- They identify the ratio related to the distance from the centroid to the vertex and the distance from the centroid to the opposite side's midpoint.
- Students construct the altitudes of each side of different triangles, locate the point of concurrency, and make a conjecture.

DEMONSTRATE

- Students generalize each point of concurrency for acute, obtuse, right, and equilateral triangles.

HIGH SCHOOL GEOMETRY

Congruence

Prove geometric theorems.

10. Prove theorems about triangles.†

Circles

Understand and apply theorems about circles.

3. Construct the inscribed and circumscribed circles of a triangle, and prove properties of angles for a quadrilateral inscribed in a circle.

†The full intent of the standard is not met in this lesson. Students make conjectures about these theorems; they will prove them and fully meet the standard in future lessons.

LESSON STRUCTURE AND PACING GUIDE 2 SESSIONS

✪ This activity highlights a key term or concept that is essential to the learning goals of the lesson.

Session 1

INSTRUCTIONAL SEQUENCE

ENGAGE	DEVELOP	DEVELOP
Establish a situation	Investigation Peer analysis	Investigation

✪ GETTING STARTED
It Comes Back Around

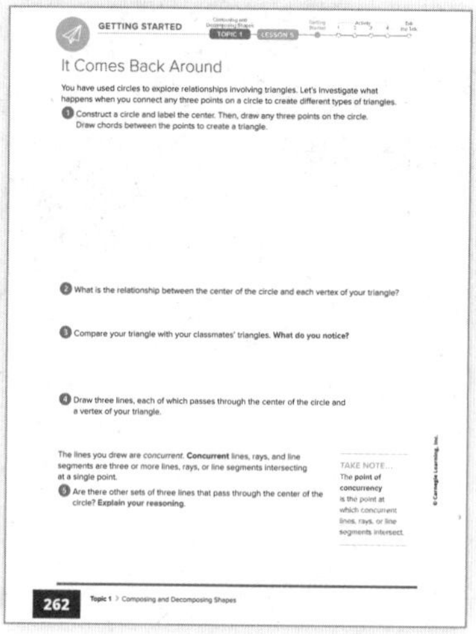

GETTING STARTED

It Comes Back Around

You have used circles to explore relationships involving triangles. Let's investigate what happens when you connect any three points on a circle to create different types of triangles.

1 Construct a circle and label the center. Then, draw any three points on the circle. Draw chords between the points to create a triangle.

2 What is the relationship between the center of the circle and each vertex of your triangle?

3 Compare your triangle with your classmates' triangles. **What do you notice?**

4 Draw three lines, each of which passes through the center of the circle and a vertex of your triangle.

The lines you drew are *concurrent*. **Concurrent** lines, rays, and line segments are three or more lines, rays, or line segments intersecting at a single point.

5 Are there other sets of three lines that pass through the center of the circle? **Explain your reasoning.**

TAKE NOTE... The **point of concurrency** is the point at which concurrent lines, rays, or line segments intersect.

© Carnegie Learning, Inc.

262 Topic 1 > Composing and Decomposing Shapes

Students inscribe a triangle in a circle.

- They note that each vertex of the triangle is equidistant from the circle's center.
- They compare their triangles to see that the center can lie inside, outside, or on the triangle.

✪ ACTIVITY 1
Investigating the Circumcenter

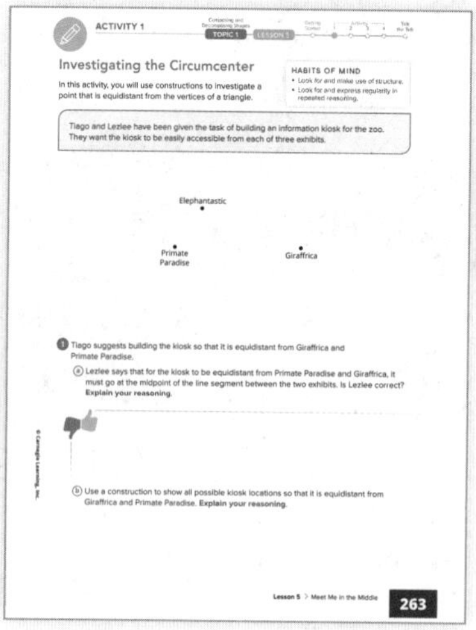

ACTIVITY 1

Investigating the Circumcenter

In this activity, you will use constructions to investigate a point that is equidistant from the vertices of a triangle.

HABITS OF MIND
- Look for and make use of structure.
- Look for and express regularity in repeated reasoning.

Tiago and Lezlee have been given the task of building an information kiosk for the zoo. They want the kiosk to be easily accessible from each of three exhibits.

1 Tiago suggests building the kiosk so that it is equidistant from Giraffrica and Primate Paradise.

(a) Lezlee says that for the kiosk to be equidistant from Primate Paradise and Giraffrica, it must go at the midpoint of the line segment between the two exhibits. Is Lezlee correct? **Explain your reasoning.**

(b) Use a construction to show all possible kiosk locations so that it is equidistant from Giraffrica and Primate Paradise. **Explain your reasoning.**

© Carnegie Learning, Inc.

Lesson 5 > Meet Me in the Middle 263

Students construct the perpendicular bisectors of each side of four different triangles and identify the point of concurrency.

- They consider a situation that requires locating a point that is equidistant from three different points.
- They measure the distance from the circumcenter to each triangle's vertices and sides to understand the relationships necessary to construct a triangle inscribed in a circle.

✪ ACTIVITY 2
Investigating the Incenter

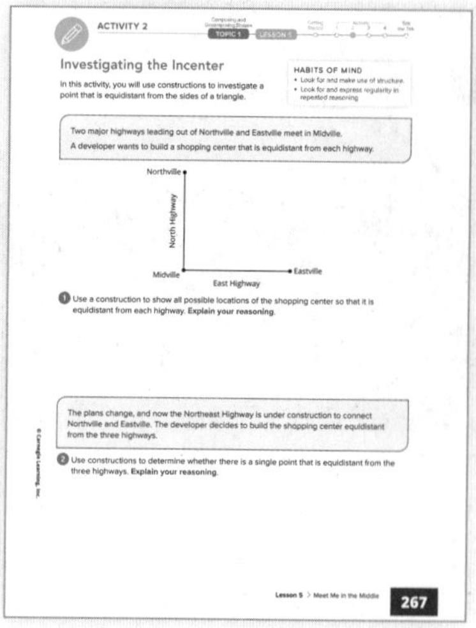

ACTIVITY 2

Investigating the Incenter

In this activity, you will use constructions to investigate a point that is equidistant from the sides of a triangle.

HABITS OF MIND
- Look for and make use of structure.
- Look for and express regularity in repeated reasoning.

Two major highways leading out of Northville and Eastville meet in Midville. A developer wants to build a shopping center that is equidistant from each highway.

1 Use a construction to show all possible locations of the shopping center so that it is equidistant from each highway. **Explain your reasoning.**

The plans change, and now the Northeast Highway is under construction to connect Northville and Eastville. The developer decides to build the shopping center equidistant from the three highways.

2 Use constructions to determine whether there is a single point that is equidistant from the three highways. **Explain your reasoning.**

© Carnegie Learning, Inc.

Lesson 5 > Meet Me in the Middle 267

Students construct the angle bisectors of each angle of four different triangles and identify the point of concurrency.

- They consider a situation that requires locating a point that is equidistant from three different lines.
- They measure the distance from the incenter to each triangle's vertices and sides to understand the relationships necessary to construct a circle inscribed in a triangle.

Log in to MyCL for **lesson support** including:

Slides

Videos

www.carnegielearning.com/login

Session 2

INSTRUCTIONAL SEQUENCE

DEVELOP Investigation	DEVELOP Investigation	DEMONSTRATE Generalization

ACTIVITY 3
Investigating the Centroid

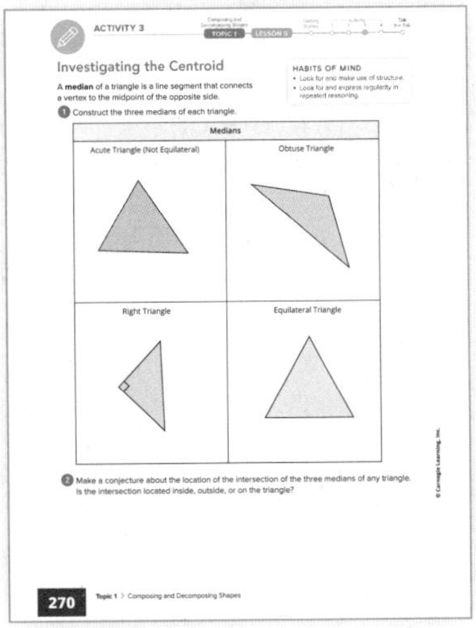
ACTIVITY 3

Investigating the Centroid

A **median** of a triangle is a line segment that connects a vertex to the midpoint of the opposite side.

HABITS OF MIND
- Look for and make use of structure.
- Look for and express regularity in repeated reasoning.

1 Construct the three medians of each triangle.

Medians	
Acute Triangle (Not Equilateral)	Obtuse Triangle
Right Triangle	Equilateral Triangle

2 Make a conjecture about the location of the intersection of the three medians of any triangle. Is the intersection located inside, outside, or on the triangle?

270 Topic 1 > Composing and Decomposing Shapes

Students construct the median of each side of four different triangles and locate the point of concurrency.

- They use their constructions to make a conjecture.
- They identify the ratio related to the distance from the centroid to the vertex and the distance from the centroid to the opposite side's midpoint.

ACTIVITY 4
Investigating the Orthocenter

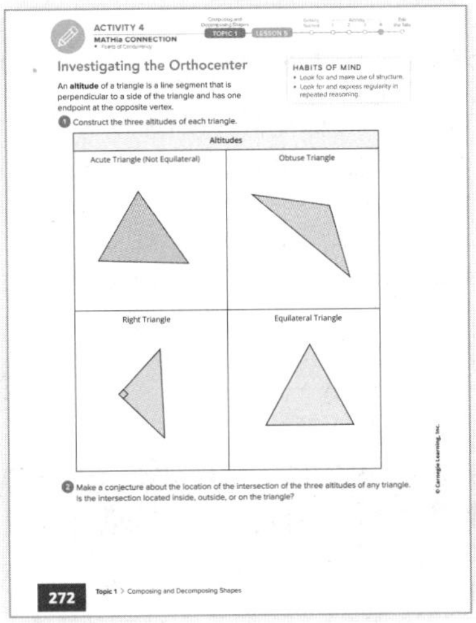
ACTIVITY 4

MATHia CONNECTION

Investigating the Orthocenter

An **altitude** of a triangle is a line segment that is perpendicular to a side of the triangle and has one endpoint at the opposite vertex.

HABITS OF MIND
- Look for and make use of structure.
- Look for and express regularity in repeated reasoning.

1 Construct the three altitudes of each triangle.

Altitudes	
Acute Triangle (Not Equilateral)	Obtuse Triangle
Right Triangle	Equilateral Triangle

2 Make a conjecture about the location of the intersection of the three altitudes of any triangle. Is the intersection located inside, outside, or on the triangle?

272 Topic 1 > Composing and Decomposing Shapes

Students construct the altitudes of each side of different triangles and locate the point of concurrency.

- They use their constructions to make a conjecture.
- They then measure the distance from the orthocenter to the vertices and sides of each triangle.

TALK THE TALK
I Concur

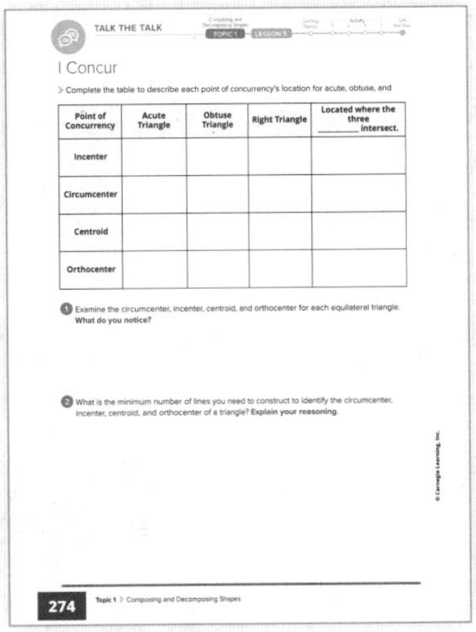
TALK THE TALK

I Concur

> Complete the table to describe each point of concurrency's location for acute, obtuse, and

Point of Concurrency	Acute Triangle	Obtuse Triangle	Right Triangle	Located where the three ___ intersect.
Incenter				
Circumcenter				
Centroid				
Orthocenter				

1 Examine the circumcenter, incenter, centroid, and orthocenter for each equilateral triangle. What do you notice?

2 What is the minimum number of lines you need to construct to identify the circumcenter, incenter, centroid, and orthocenter of a triangle? Explain your reasoning.

274 Topic 1 > Composing and Decomposing Shapes

Students generalize each point of concurrency for acute, obtuse, right, and equilateral triangles.

- They then reason about the minimum number of lines needed to identify a point of concurrency.
- They identify the point of concurrency that is most helpful for a given situation.

TOPIC 1

Log in to MyCL for:

- Editable templates
- Additional planning support

Now that you have read the Module, Topic, and Lesson Overviews, you are ready to plan.

Do the math

> Tear out the lesson planning template (page 261E) and jot down thoughts as you work through this lesson and read the Facilitation Notes.

Connect the learning

MATHbook + MATHia

The table shows a portion of the self-paced MATHia sequence for the *Composing and Decomposing Shapes* Topic.

Median student completion time for the entire topic: ~110–130 minutes

> As you implement this lesson, consider different connections for students who are on pace and those that have not yet completed the workspaces aligned to this lesson.

STUDENTS WHO ARE NOT HERE YET

Students will practice analyzing the points of concurrency for different types of triangles.

TYPE	WORKSPACE NAME
	Using Circles to Draw Quadrilaterals
	Angles of an Inscribed Quadrilateral
	Points of Concurrency

STUDENTS WHO ARE ON PACE

After you complete Activity 4, ask these students to share how the animation depicted the points of concurrency.

Meet Me in the Middle
Points of Concurrency

Session 1

GETTING STARTED It Comes Back Around ✪

Pacing (minutes)	
My Time	Class Time

KEY TERM
concurrent
point of concurrency

ACTIVITY 1 Investigating the Circumcenter ✪

Pacing (minutes)	
My Time	Class Time

KEY TERM
circumcenter
circumscribed circle

ACTIVITY 2 Investigating the Incenter ✪

Pacing (minutes)	
My Time	Class Time

KEY TERM
incenter

Session 2

ACTIVITY 3 Investigating the Centroid ✪

Pacing (minutes)	
My Time	Class Time

KEY TERM
median
centroid

ACTIVITY 4 Investigating the Orthocenter

Pacing (minutes)	
My Time	Class Time

KEY TERM
altitude
orthocenter

TALK THE TALK I Concur ✪

Pacing (minutes)	
My Time	Class Time

✪ This activity highlights a key term or concept that is essential to the learning goals of the lesson.

Log in to MyCL for:
- Editable templates
- Additional planning support

Reflect on your lesson

Consider the effectiveness of your lesson on student learning.

What went well?	What did not go as planned?

Anticipate how you would change the lesson next time you teach it.

How will you capitalize on the things that went well?	How will you improve things that did not go as planned?

MATERIALS

- Compasses
- Patty paper
- Rulers

TOPIC 1
Composing and Decomposing Shapes
TOPIC 2
Justifying Line and Angle Relationships
TOPIC 3
Using Congruence Theorems

1 Running Circles Around Geometry
2 The Quad Squad
3 Into the Ring
4 Tri- Tri- Tri- and Separate Them
5 Meet Me in the Middle

LESSON 5

Meet Me in the Middle

Points of Concurrency

Learning Goals

- Construct the circumcenter, incenter, centroid, and orthocenter.
- Use points of concurrency to construct the inscribed and circumscribed circles of a triangle.
- Understand that the three medians of a triangle meet at a point.

KEY TERMS

- concurrent
- point of concurrency
- circumcenter
- circumscribed circle
- incenter
- median
- centroid
- altitude
- orthocenter

REVIEW (1–2 minutes)

1 Construct a perpendicular bisector.

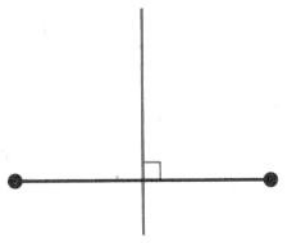

2 Construct an angle bisector.

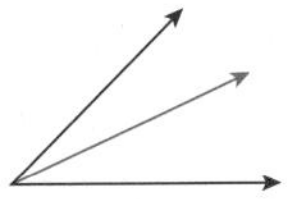

You have constructed the perpendicular bisector of a line segment and the angle bisector of an angle.

What happens when you make these constructions on all sides or angles of a triangle?

Setting the Stage

- **Assign Review (optional, 1 – 2 minutes)**
- **Communicate the learning goals and key terms to look out for**
- **Tap into your students' prior learning by reading the narrative statement**
- **Provide a sense of direction by reading the question**

IN THIS REVIEW

Students construct perpendicular and angle bisectors. They will use these skills throughout the lesson.

For every triangle:

- The circumcenter is the point of concurrency of the perpendicular bisectors of each side.
- The incenter is the point of concurrency of the angle bisectors.
- The centroid is the point of concurrency of the medians.
- The orthocenter is the point of concurrency of the altitudes.

Essential Ideas

- A point of concurrency is a point at which three lines, rays, or line segments intersect.
- The circumcenter is the point of concurrency of the three perpendicular bisectors of the sides of a triangle, and it is equidistant from each vertex of the triangle.
- The incenter is the point at which the three angle bisectors of a triangle are concurrent, and it is equidistant from each side of the triangle.
- The median of a triangle is a line segment formed by connecting a triangle's vertex to the opposite side of the triangle's midpoint.
- The centroid is the point at which the three medians of a triangle are concurrent.
- The orthocenter is the point at which the three altitudes of a triangle are concurrent.

GETTING STARTED

SUMMARY **Three or more lines, rays, or line segments that intersect at a single point are concurrent.**

Chunking the Activity

- Group students to complete 1 and 2
- Check-in and share
- Complete 3 as a class
- Group students to complete 4 and 5
- Share and summarize

Student Look-Fors

Different size circles. Ask students to explain how the circle's size affects the distance each of the vertices is to the center point of the circle.

LANGUAGE LINK

Encourage students to annotate diagrams they have drawn as they encounter the key terms in the lesson.

COMMON MISCONCEPTION

See Page **276A** for a misconception related to *point of concurrency*.

It Comes Back Around

You have used circles to explore relationships involving triangles. Let's investigate what happens when you connect any three points on a circle to create different types of triangles.

1. Construct a circle and label the center. Then, draw any three points on the circle. Draw chords between the points to create a triangle.

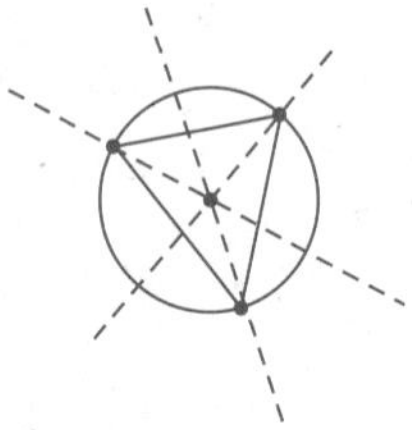

Check students' drawings.

2. What is the relationship between the center of the circle and each vertex of your triangle?

The distance from each vertex to the center of the circle is equal to a circle radius.

3. Compare your triangle with your classmates' triangles. **What do you notice?**

Answers will vary.
The circle's center is sometimes inside the triangle, sometimes outside the triangle, and sometimes it is on the triangle.

4. Draw three lines, each of which passes through the center of the circle and a vertex of your triangle.

Check students' drawings.

The lines you drew are *concurrent*. **Concurrent** lines, rays, and line segments are three or more lines, rays, or line segments intersecting at a single point.

5. Are there other sets of three lines that pass through the center of the circle? **Explain your reasoning.**

Yes. There are an infinite number of lines that can pass through the center of the circle. All these lines are concurrent, and the point of concurrency is the center of the circle.

TAKE NOTE...
The **point of concurrency** is the point at which concurrent lines, rays, or line segments intersect.

Questions to Support Discourse

		TYPE
2	• How do you know that each vertex of the triangle is equidistant from the circle's center?	Reflecting and justifying
3	• Why do you think the center of the circle is sometimes outside or on the triangle?	Probing
5	• Will the circle's center always be the point of concurrency? Explain your thinking. • Explain what would need to happen for the point of concurrency to lie outside of the circle.	Seeing structure

SUMMARY **The circumcenter is the point of concurrency of the three perpendicular bisectors of the sides of a triangle and is equidistant from each triangle's vertex.**

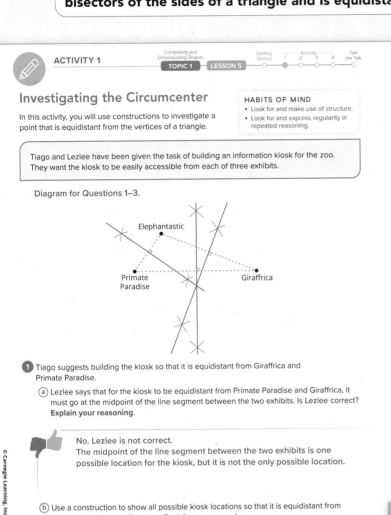

Investigating the Circumcenter

In this activity, you will use constructions to investigate a point that is equidistant from the vertices of a triangle.

HABITS OF MIND
- Look for and make use of structure.
- Look for and express regularity in repeated reasoning.

Tiago and Lezlee have been given the task of building an information kiosk for the zoo. They want the kiosk to be easily accessible from each of three exhibits.

Diagram for Questions 1–3.

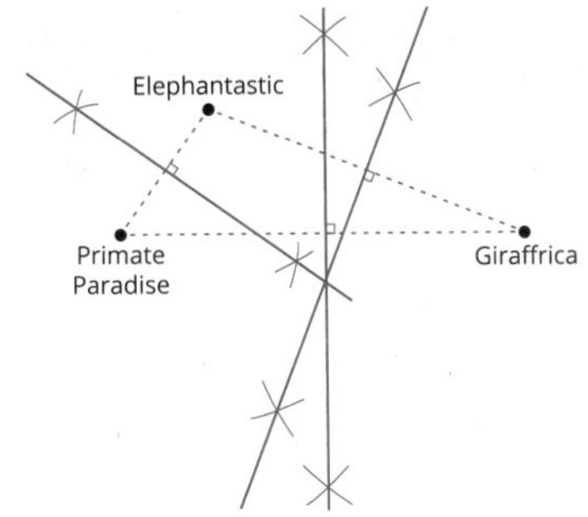

1 Tiago suggests building the kiosk so that it is equidistant from Giraffrica and Primate Paradise.

(a) Lezlee says that for the kiosk to be equidistant from Primate Paradise and Giraffrica, it must go at the midpoint of the line segment between the two exhibits. Is Lezlee correct? **Explain your reasoning.**

No. Lezlee is not correct.
The midpoint of the line segment between the two exhibits is one possible location for the kiosk, but it is not the only possible location.

(b) Use a construction to show all possible kiosk locations so that it is equidistant from Giraffrica and Primate Paradise. **Explain your reasoning.**

The perpendicular bisector of the line segment connecting Giraffrica and Primate Paradise shows all possible kiosk locations that are equidistant from these two exhibits.

Chunking the Activity

- Read and discuss the situation
- Group students to complete 1 - 3
- Check-in and share
- Group students to complete 4 and 5
- Check-in and share
- Group students to complete 6 and 7
- Check-in and share
- Read and discuss the definition
- Group students to complete 8 - 10
- Share and summarize

DIFFERENTIATION STRATEGY

See Page 276A to support students who struggle with the lesson.

Questions to Support Discourse

		TYPE
1	• Is the midpoint the only point equidistant from the endpoints of a line segment? Explain your thinking.	Probing

LANGUAGE LINK

ELL TIP

Ensure students understand the context by discussing the terms *kiosk*, *accessible*, and *exhibits*. Describe other contexts where they might use terms such as a *mall*, *amusement park*, or *aquarium*.

NOTES

Student Look-Fors

Student Look-Fors

Whether students are demonstrating proficiencies related to these habits of mind.

- Look for and make use of structure
- Look for and express regularity in repeated reasoning

ACTIVITY 1 Continued

2 Lezlee suggests building the kiosk so that it is equidistant from Elephantastic and Primate Paradise. Use a construction to show all possible kiosk locations so that it is equidistant from these two exhibits. **Explain your reasoning.**

The perpendicular bisector of the line segment connecting Elephantastic and Primate Paradise shows all possible kiosk locations that are equidistant from these two exhibits.

3 Tiago then wonders where they could build the kiosk so that it is equidistant from Elephantastic and Giraffrica. Use a construction to show all possible kiosk locations so that it is equidistant from these two exhibits. **Explain your reasoning.**

I constructed a perpendicular bisector to the line segment between the two exhibits. Any point along this bisector is a possible location of the kiosk because any point on the perpendicular bisector is equidistant from the segment's endpoints.

4 Describe how to determine a location that is the same distance from all three exhibits. Is there more than one possible location that is equidistant from all three exhibits? **Explain your reasoning.**

Each of the perpendicular bisectors represents possible locations for the kiosk equidistant from a pair of exhibits. So, the intersection of all the perpendicular bisectors represents the location that is equidistant from all three exhibits.

There is only one possible location equidistant from all three exhibits because the three perpendicular bisectors intersect at only one point.

5 Verify that the location you described in Question 4 is equidistant from each exhibit.

I used a ruler to determine the distance from the kiosk to each exhibit. All three distances are equal.

264 Topic 1 > Composing and Decomposing Shapes

Questions to Support Discourse

		TYPE
3	• Does the third perpendicular bisector travel through this point of intersection? Why do you think that is?	Probing
4	• Do you think the perpendicular bisectors of the sides of any triangle will always intersect each other at one location?	Seeing structure

ACTIVITY 1 Continued

You constructed a point of concurrency using the perpendicular bisectors of a triangle.

6 Construct the three perpendicular bisectors of each triangle.

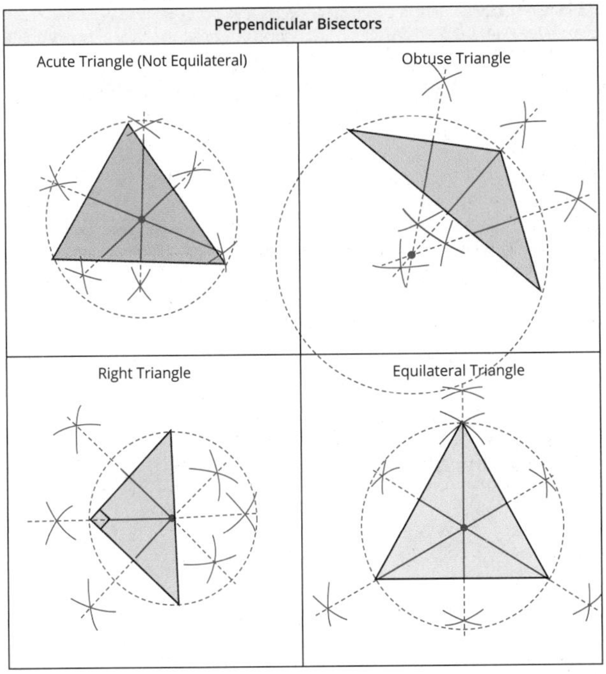

7 Make a conjecture about the location of the intersection of the three perpendicular bisectors of any triangle. Is the intersection located inside, outside, or on the triangle?

The three perpendicular bisectors of any triangle will intersect at a single point.

For an acute triangle, this point will be in the triangle's interior.

For an obtuse triangle, this point will lie on the exterior of the triangle.

For a right triangle, this point will lie on the hypotenuse of the triangle.

NOTES

TOPIC 1

DIFFERENTIATION STRATEGY

See Page 276B to group students to complete 6.

Questions to Support Discourse

		TYPE
7	• Why do you think the points of concurrency are not always inside the triangle?	Probing
	• Which characteristic of the triangle creates a point of concurrency outside of the triangle? Inside the triangle? On the triangle?	Seeing structure

NOTES

The **circumcenter** is the point of concurrency of the three perpendicular bisectors of a triangle.

8 Consider the four triangles and the perpendicular bisectors you constructed.

ⓐ Measure the distance from the circumcenter to each vertex of the triangle. Is the circumcenter always, sometimes, or never equidistant from each vertex of the triangle? **Explain your reasoning.**

The circumcenter is always equidistant from each vertex of the triangle.

ⓑ Measure the distance along each perpendicular from the circumcenter to each side of the triangle. Is the circumcenter always, sometimes, or never equidistant from each side of the triangle? **Explain your reasoning.**

The circumcenter is only equidistant from each side of the triangle if the triangle is equilateral.

9 Revisit the triangles with perpendicular bisectors. Use a compass to construct the circumscribed circle of each triangle.

Check students' drawings.

TAKE NOTE...

A **circumscribed circle** is a circle that passes through all the vertices of a polygon. Circle Q is circumscribed around ΔABC.

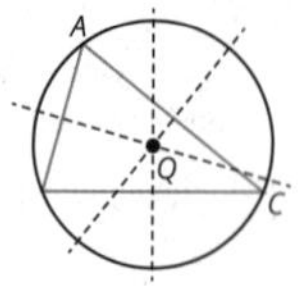

10 What does the circumcenter tell you about the relationship between circles and triangles? **Explain your reasoning.**

You can circumscribe a circle around each triangle using the circumcenter as the center of the circle with a radius equal to the distance of the circumcenter to any vertex.

Questions to Support Discourse

		TYPE
10	• Why do you suppose the name of this point of concurrency the circumcenter? • What significance would the circumcenter have in terms of a real-life example?	Seeing structure

SUMMARY **The incenter is the point of concurrency of the three angle bisectors of a triangle and is equidistant from each side of the triangle.**

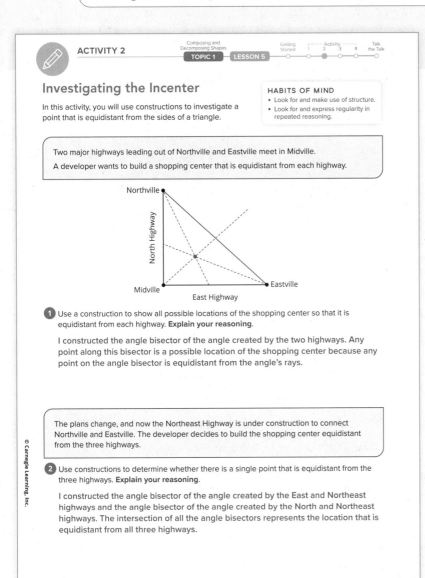

ACTIVITY 2

Investigating the Incenter

In this activity, you will use constructions to investigate a point that is equidistant from the sides of a triangle.

HABITS OF MIND
- Look for and make use of structure.
- Look for and express regularity in repeated reasoning.

Two major highways leading out of Northville and Eastville meet in Midville.
A developer wants to build a shopping center that is equidistant from each highway.

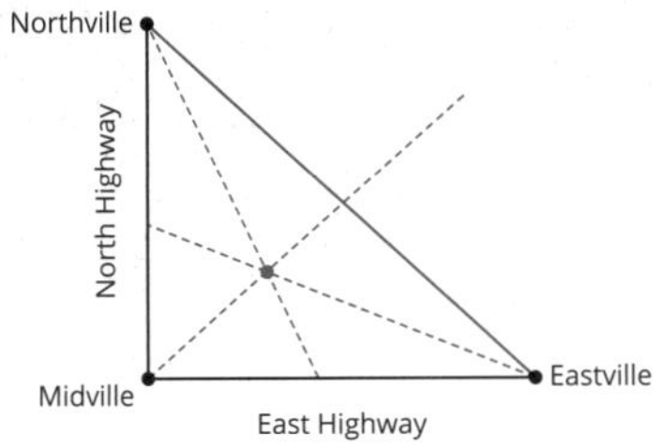

1 Use a construction to show all possible locations of the shopping center so that it is equidistant from each highway. **Explain your reasoning.**

I constructed the angle bisector of the angle created by the two highways. Any point along this bisector is a possible location of the shopping center because any point on the angle bisector is equidistant from the angle's rays.

The plans change, and now the Northeast Highway is under construction to connect Northville and Eastville. The developer decides to build the shopping center equidistant from the three highways.

2 Use constructions to determine whether there is a single point that is equidistant from the three highways. **Explain your reasoning.**

I constructed the angle bisector of the angle created by the East and Northeast highways and the angle bisector of the angle created by the North and Northeast highways. The intersection of all the angle bisectors represents the location that is equidistant from all three highways.

Chunking the Activity

- Read and discuss the situation
- Group students to complete 1
- Check-in and share
- Group students to complete 2
- Check-in and share
- Group students to complete 3 and 4
- Check-in and share
- Read and discuss the definition
- Group students to complete 5 - 7
- Share and summarize

NOTE: All situations provide opportunities for students to learn something new. Consider connecting to students' cultural, social, and geographic backgrounds by encouraging them to share experiences from their lives related to the mathematical content similar to the given real-world situation.

Questions to Support Discourse

	Questions to Support Discourse	TYPE
1	• How many different points are equidistant from the two highways? • How could you use patty paper to determine all of the points equidistant from the two highways?	Gathering
	• Are all points that lie on an angle bisector equidistant from either side of the angle? How do you know?	Probing

NOTES

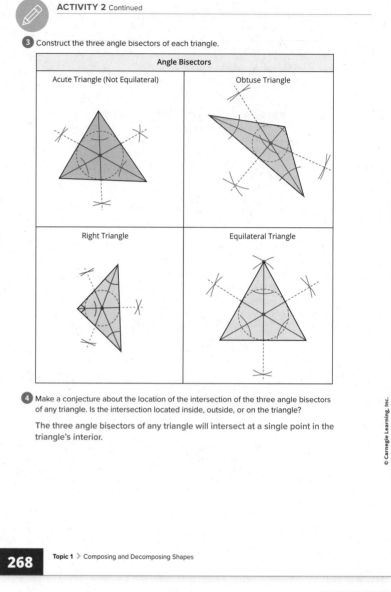

3 Construct the three angle bisectors of each triangle.

Angle Bisectors	
Acute Triangle (Not Equilateral) 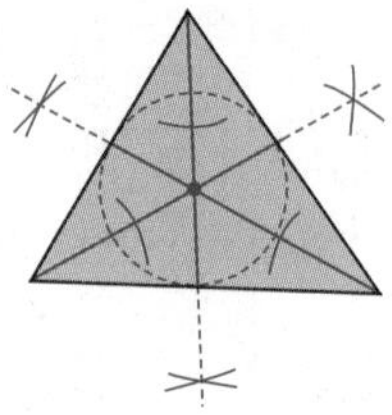	Obtuse Triangle 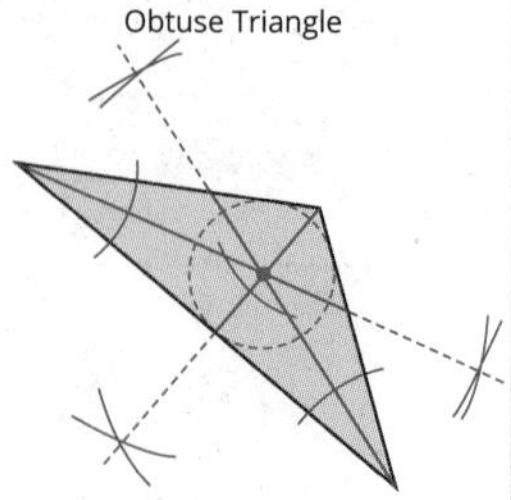
Right Triangle 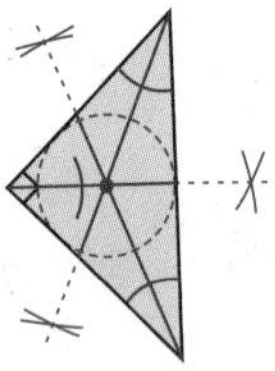	Equilateral Triangle 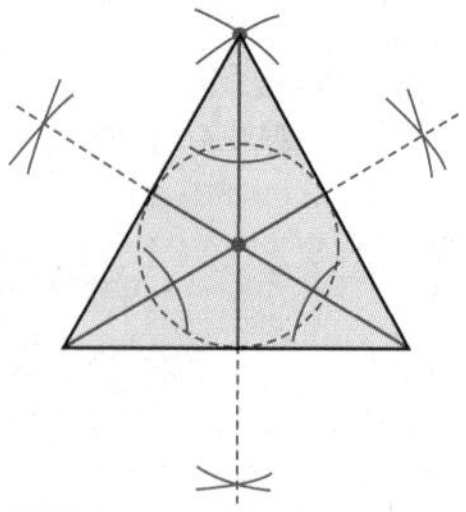

4 Make a conjecture about the location of the intersection of the three angle bisectors of any triangle. Is the intersection located inside, outside, or on the triangle?

The three angle bisectors of any triangle will intersect at a single point in the triangle's interior.

Questions to Support Discourse

		TYPE
3	• Did you construct two or three angle bisectors to determine the point of concurrency? Why? • Which characteristic of the triangle causes the location of the point of concurrency to lie inside of the triangle?	Seeing structure

ACTIVITY 2 Continued

The **incenter** is the point of concurrency of the three angle bisectors of a triangle.

5 Consider the four triangles and the angle bisectors you constructed.

ⓐ Measure the distance from the incenter to each vertex of the triangle. Is the incenter always, sometimes, or never equidistant from each vertex of the triangle? **Explain your reasoning.**

The incenter is equidistant from each vertex of the triangle only if the triangle is equilateral.

ⓑ Measure the perpendicular distance from the incenter to each side of the triangle. Is the incenter always, sometimes, or never equidistant from each side of the triangle? **Explain your reasoning.**

The incenter is always equidistant from each side of the triangle.

6 Revisit the triangles with angle bisectors. Use a compass to construct the inscribed circle of each triangle.

Check students' drawings.

REMEMBER...

An inscribed circle is a circle drawn inside a polygon such that it is tangent to each side.

Circle *Q* is inscribed in ΔABC.

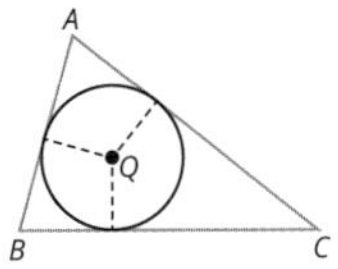

7 What does the incenter tell you about the relationship between circles and triangles? **Explain your reasoning.**

You can inscribe a circle in any triangle using the incenter as the center of the circle where the radius is perpendicular to any side of the triangle.

NOTES

Questions to Support Discourse

		TYPE
5	• How does the incenter compare to the circumcenter?	Seeing structure
7	• Why do you suppose the name of this point of concurrency the incenter? • What significance would the incenter have in terms of a real-life example?	Seeing structure

ACTIVITY 3

Session 2 of 2

SUMMARY **The distance from the centroid to the vertex is twice the distance from the centroid to the midpoint of the opposite side.**

Chunking the Activity

- **Read and discuss the introduction**
- **Group students to complete 1 and 2**
- **Check-in and share**
- **Group students to complete 3 and 4**
- **Share and summarize**

LANGUAGE LINK

ELL TIP

Students may have experience with the key term *median* from when they determined the median of a data set. Help students understand the median of a triangle by connecting the midpoint of the opposite side to the middle of a data set.

ACTIVITY 3

Composing and Decomposing Shapes TOPIC 1 LESSON 5

Getting Started — Activity 1 2 3 4 — Talk the Talk

Investigating the Centroid

HABITS OF MIND
- Look for and make use of structure.
- Look for and express regularity in repeated reasoning.

A **median** of a triangle is a line segment that connects a vertex to the midpoint of the opposite side.

1 Construct the three medians of each triangle.

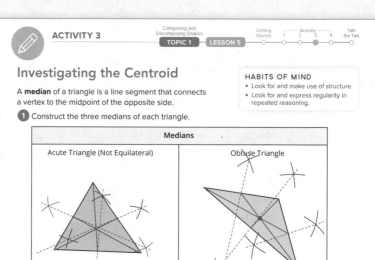

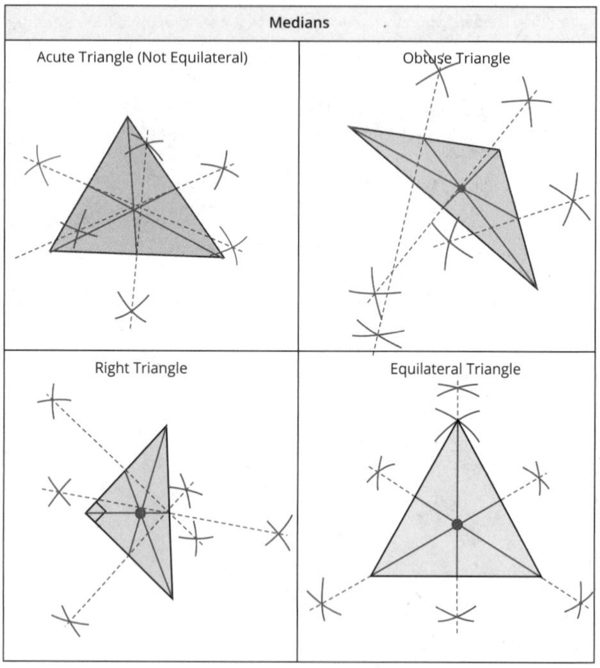

2 Make a conjecture about the location of the intersection of the three medians of any triangle. Is the intersection located inside, outside, or on the triangle?

The three medians of any triangle will intersect at a single point on the interior of the triangle.

Questions to Support Discourse

		TYPE
1	• Which construction did you use to construct the median?	Gathering
	• How does a median compare to a perpendicular bisector?	Seeing structure
2	• Are all of the points that lie on the median of a triangle equidistant from the endpoints of the opposite side containing the midpoint?	Probing

The **centroid** is the point of concurrency of the three medians of a triangle. It is also known as the center of gravity.

3. Consider the four triangles and the medians you constructed.

   a. Measure the distance from the centroid to each vertex of the triangle. Is the centroid always, sometimes, or never equidistant from each vertex of the triangle? **Explain your reasoning.**

      The centroid is equidistant from each vertex of the triangle only if the triangle is equilateral.

   b. Measure the perpendicular distance from the centroid to each side of the triangle. Is the centroid always, sometimes, or never equidistant from each side of the triangle? **Explain your reasoning.**

      The centroid is equidistant from each side of the triangle only if the triangle is equilateral.

The centroid divides each median into two line segments.

4. Compare the distance from the centroid to the vertex and the distance from the centroid to the midpoint of the opposite side in each of the triangles in the graphic organizer. What is the ratio?

   The distance from the centroid to the vertex is twice the distance from the centroid to the midpoint of the opposite side.

NOTES

TOPIC 1

DIFFERENTIATION STRATEGY

See Page 276B to assist all students to extend the activity.

Questions to Support Discourse

		TYPE
3	• Why do you suppose the centroid is the center of balance in the triangle?	Probing
	• How is the centroid different than the incenter and the circumcenter?	Seeing structure

ACTIVITY 4

SUMMARY **The orthocenter is the point of concurrency of the three altitudes of a triangle.**

Chunking the Activity

- **Read and discuss the introduction**
- **Group students to complete 1 and 2**
- **Check-in and share**
- **Read and discuss the definition**
- **Group students to complete 3**
- **Share and summarize**

COMMON MISCONCEPTION

See Page 276B for a misconception related to altitudes.

Investigating the Orthocenter

HABITS OF MIND
- Look for and make use of structure.
- Look for and express regularity in repeated reasoning.

An **altitude** of a triangle is a line segment that is perpendicular to a side of the triangle and has one endpoint at the opposite vertex.

1. Construct the three altitudes of each triangle.

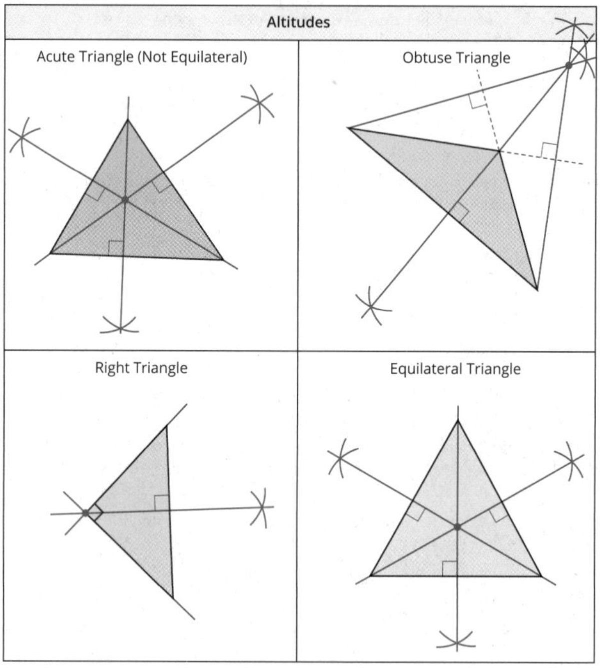

2. Make a conjecture about the location of the intersection of the three altitudes of any triangle. Is the intersection located inside, outside, or on the triangle?

   The three altitudes of any triangle will intersect at a single point.

   For an acute triangle, this point will be in the triangle's interior.

   For an obtuse triangle, this point will be on the exterior of the triangle.

   For a right triangle, this point will be at the vertex of the right angle.

Questions to Support Discourse

	Questions	TYPE
1	• Which construction did you use to construct the altitude?	Gathering
	• How does the point of concurrency in the acute triangle differ from the point of concurrency in the equilateral triangle?	Probing
	• How does an altitude compare to a median? • Could you have determined the point of concurrency by constructing only two altitudes in each triangle?	Seeing structure

ACTIVITY 4 Continued

The **orthocenter** is the point of concurrency of the three altitudes of a triangle.

3 Consider the four triangles and the altitudes you constructed.

(a) Measure the distance from the orthocenter to each vertex of the triangle. Is the orthocenter always, sometimes, or never equidistant from each vertex of the triangle? **Explain your reasoning.**

The orthocenter is equidistant from each vertex of the triangle only if the triangle is equilateral.

(b) Measure the perpendicular distance from the orthocenter to each side of the triangle. Is the orthocenter always, sometimes, or never equidistant from each side of the triangle? **Explain your reasoning.**

The orthocenter is equidistant from each side of the triangle only if the triangle is equilateral.

NOTES

TOPIC 1

Questions to Support Discourse

		TYPE
3	• How is the orthocenter different than the incenter, circumcenter, and centroid? • What does the orthocenter have in common with the incenter, circumcenter, and centroid?	Seeing structure

TALK THE TALK

SUMMARY **In an equilateral triangle, the location of the incenter, circumcenter, centroid, and orthocenter is the same point.**

Chunking the Activity

- **Read and discuss the directions**
- **Group students to complete the table**
- **Check-in and share**
- **Group students to complete 1 and 2**
- **Share and summarize**

NOTE: Encourage responsible decision making by providing an opportunity for students to reflect on their personal behavior and social interactions as they worked with their group to complete tasks.

I Concur

> Complete the table to describe each point of concurrency's location for acute, obtuse, and

Point of Concurrency	Acute Triangle	Obtuse Triangle	Right Triangle	Located where the three ______ intersect.
Incenter	Interior	Interior	Interior	perpendicular bisectors
Circumcenter	Interior	Exterior	On Hypotenuse	angle bisectors
Centroid	Interior	Interior	Interior	medians
Orthocenter	Interior	Exterior	At Vertex of Right Angle	altitudes

1. Examine the circumcenter, incenter, centroid, and orthocenter for each equilateral triangle. **What do you notice?**

   The circumcenter, incenter, centroid, and orthocenter for an equilateral triangle are the same point.

2. What is the minimum number of lines you need to construct to identify the circumcenter, incenter, centroid, and orthocenter of a triangle? **Explain your reasoning.**

   The minimum number of lines you need to construct to identify any point of concurrency is two. The third line will always pass through the point of intersection of the other two lines.

Questions to Support Discourse

		TYPE
2	• What about the triangle causes these points to share the same location?	Probing
	• Is the altitude drawn to each side of an equilateral triangle also a median? Why does this happen?	Seeing structure

ASSIGNMENT

LESSON 5 ASSIGNMENT

Use a separate piece of paper for your Journal entry.

JOURNAL

Describe the similarities and differences between each pair of terms.

1. concurrent and point of concurrency
2. incenter and orthocenter
3. centroid and circumcenter
4. altitude and median

REMEMBER

For every triangle:

- The circumcenter is the point of concurrency of the perpendicular bisectors of each side.
- The incenter is the point of concurrency of the angle bisectors.
- The centroid is the point of concurrency of the medians.
- The orthocenter is the point of concurrency of the altitudes.

PRACTICE

1. Use a compass and straightedge to perform each construction.

ⓐ Construct the incenter of ΔDEF.

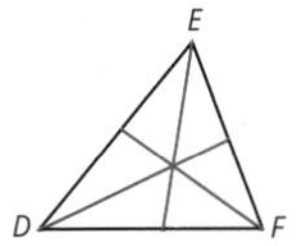

ⓑ Construct the circumcenter of ΔABC.

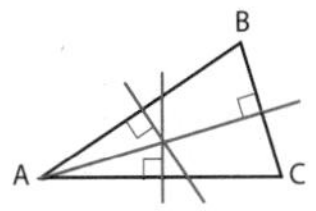

ⓒ Construct the circumcenter of ΔDEF.

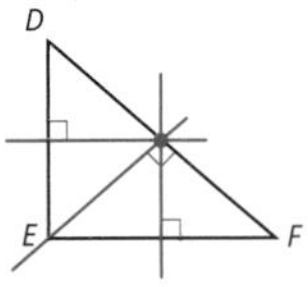

ⓓ Construct the circumcenter of ΔGHI.

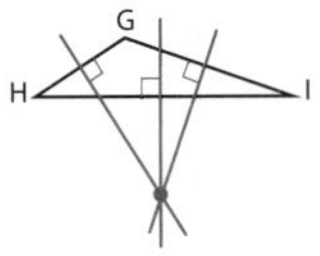

ⓔ Construct the centroid of ΔABC.

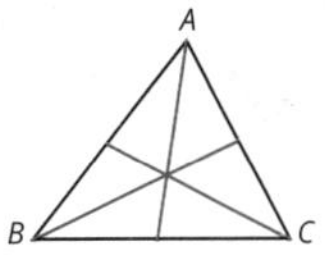

ⓕ Construct the orthocenter of ΔJKL.

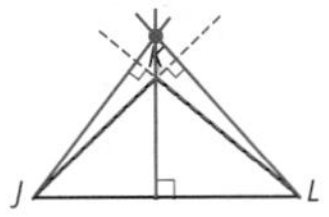

Go to LiveHint.com for help on the PRACTICE questions.

Encourage students to use LiveHint.com for help with the PRACTICE questions of this assignment.

Chunking the Assignment

TOPIC 1

SESSION 1

- **Practice 1 parts (a) – (d)**
- **Mixed Practice (page 277) 7 and 8**

SESSION 2

- **Practice 1 parts (e) and (f), 2 and 3**
- **Journal**
- **Stretch (advanced learners)**

JOURNAL

Sample answers.

1. The term *concurrent* describes three or more lines, rays, or segments that intersect at a single point. The point of concurrency is where the lines, rays, or segments intersect.
2. The incenter is the point at which the three angle bisectors of a triangle intersect, while the orthocenter is the point at which the three altitudes of a triangle intersect.
3. They both involve lines that go through the midpoint of a side. However, the centroid is the point at which the three medians of a triangle intersect, while the circumcenter is the point at which three perpendicular bisectors intersect.
4. The altitude is a line perpendicular to the side that passes through the vertex. The median is a line that passes from the midpoint of a side to the opposite vertex.

NOTES

STRETCH

1a. Sample answer.

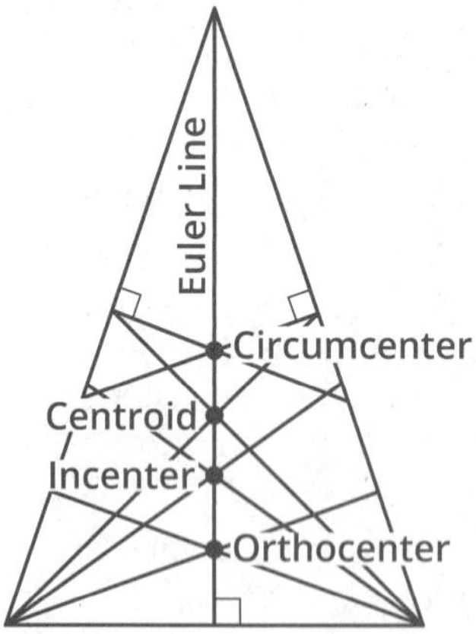

The Euler Line is the line that contains all four points of concurrency.

1b. All four points of concurrency coincide in an equilateral triangle.

2. The centroid is at the point $\left(\frac{2}{3}, 2\right)$.

2 Write the term that best completes each statement.

(a) The incenter of a triangle is the point of concurrency of the **angle bisectors** of a triangle.

(b) The circumcenter of a triangle is the point of concurrency of the **perpendicular bisectors of each side** of a triangle.

(c) The centroid of a triangle is the point of concurrency of the **medians** of a triangle.

(d) The orthocenter of a triangle is the point of concurrency of the **altitudes** of a triangle.

3 Determine which point of concurrency is most appropriate in each situation.

(a) A flea market is on a triangular piece of land. Each entrance is at one of the three vertices of the triangle. Joanie wants to set up her merchandise at a location that is equidistant from all three entrances.

Circumcenter

(b) An artist is building a mobile with several metal triangles of various sizes. The triangles are connected using steel rods, and the rods are welded onto each triangle at a point that would allow the triangle to balance horizontally.

Centroid

(c) Jim's backyard is a triangular plot of land. He is using fencing to build a circular dog pen. He wants the dog pen to be as large as possible and needs to determine the location of the center of the circular dog pen.

Incenter

STRETCH Optional

1 The Euler Line is a line that represents the relationship between the centroid, circumcenter and orthocenter of any triangle.

(a) Construct an isosceles triangle and determine all four points of concurrency. How do the points relate to the Euler Line?

(b) What happens when the triangle is equilateral?

2 Determine the coordinates of the centroid of the triangle on the coordinate grid.

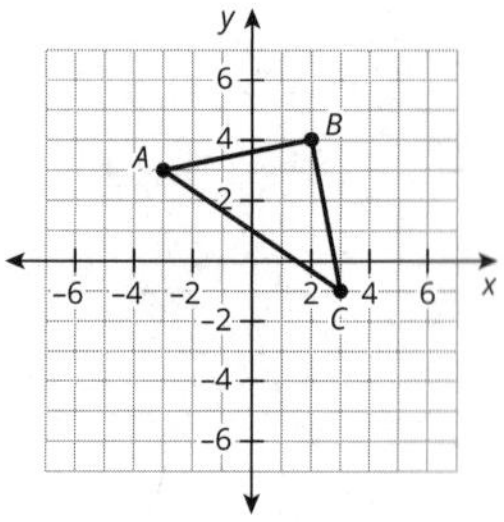

Meet Me in the Middle

This resource details additional facilitation notes to fully assist you as you plan each lesson to support all students, students who struggle, and advanced learners. It provides differentiation strategies, common student misconceptions, and suggestions to extend certain activities.

GETTING STARTED

Session 1 of 2

It Comes Back Around

Students inscribe a triangle in a circle. They note that each vertex of the triangle is equidistant from the circle's center. They compare their triangles to see that the center can lie inside, outside, or on the triangle.

CHUNK	AUDIENCE	ADDITIONAL SUPPORTS
As you discuss the definition of *point of concurrency*	All Students	**COMMON MISCONCEPTION** Students may assume that a circle's center is the only point of concurrency in a circle. Ask students to draw a diagram that contains a circle where the point of concurrency is on the circle. Challenge students to think about points of concurrency that occur in diagrams without circles. Ask students to draw a diagram that contains a point of concurrency that is unrelated to a circle.

ACTIVITY 1

Session 1 of 2

Investigating the Circumcenter

Students construct the perpendicular bisectors of each side of four different triangles and identify the point of concurrency. They measure the distance from the circumcenter to each triangle's vertices and sides to understand the relationships necessary to construct a triangle inscribed in a circle.

CHUNK	AUDIENCE	ADDITIONAL SUPPORTS
As students work on the lesson	Students who Struggle	**DIFFERENTIATION STRATEGY** Provide students with patty paper, instead of a compass and straightedge, to complete the constructions. Have students tape or staple their patty paper in place of the compass construction.

CHUNK	AUDIENCE	ADDITIONAL SUPPORTS
As an alternative grouping strategy for 6	All Students	**DIFFERENTIATION STRATEGY** Have students work in groups of 4. Assign each member of the group one of the constructions to complete. Have students share their constructions within their groups and sketch the construction they did not complete, noting the location of the point of concurrency. Consider using this strategy as students complete similar questions in Activities 2, 3, and 4.

ACTIVITY 3

Session 2 of 2

Investigating the Centroid

Students construct the median of each side of four different triangles and locate the point of concurrency. They identify the ratio related to the distance from the centroid to the vertex and the distance from the centroid to the opposite side's midpoint.

CHUNK	AUDIENCE	ADDITIONAL SUPPORTS
To extend the activity	All Students	**DIFFERENTIATION STRATEGY** Have students draw a triangle on a piece of cardstock. Have them construct the centroid, cut out the triangle, and use the centroid to balance the triangle on their pencil point.

ACTIVITY 4

Session 2 of 2

Investigating the Orthocenter

Students construct the altitudes of each side of different types of triangles and locate the point of concurrency. They then measure the distance from the orthocenter to the vertices and sides of each triangle.

CHUNK	AUDIENCE	ADDITIONAL SUPPORTS
As students construct the altitudes of the triangles	All Students	**COMMON MISCONCEPTION** Students may confuse the altitude of a triangle and the median of a triangle. The median of a triangle is a segment that connects the vertex of a triangle to the midpoint of the opposite side. The altitude of a triangle is a segment that is perpendicular to a side of the triangle and has one endpoint at the opposite vertex.

Practice the learning

MATHbook + Skills Practice

The table shows the targeted practice of the skills and mathematical concepts for the *Composing and Decomposing Shapes* Topic. The highlighted Problem Set aligns with **Meet Me in the Middle**.

PROBLEM SET	
1	Identifying Circle Parts
2	Using Circles to Construct Quadrilaterals and Triangles
3	Making Conjectures About Quadrilaterals
4	Constructing with Angles
5	Making Conjectures About Triangles
6	**Drawing Points of Concurrency**

ANYTIME AFTER ACTIVITY 4

Facilitate students as they work individually on **Problem Set 6**.

NOTES

MIXED PRACTICE

Log in to MyCL to access a downloadable version with **additional space** for students to write their answers.

MIXED PRACTICE

> This Mixed Practice worksheet includes two sections: Spaced Review and End-of-Topic Review. **Use a separate piece of paper to show your work.**

Spaced Review

> Practice concepts from previous topics.

1. Determine each unknown measure in the figure. Explain your reasoning.

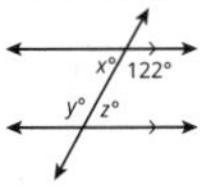

2. Determine the median of the data in each set.
   - ⓐ {2, 3, 1, 0, 5, 5, 10}
   - ⓑ {7, 7, 8.5, 9, 9.1, 9.5}
   - ⓒ {1, 2, 3, 4, 5, 6, 7, 8, 9, 10}

3. Write an equation for a line that is parallel to the given line.
   - ⓐ $x = 3$
   - ⓑ $y = -\frac{1}{2}x - \frac{5}{2}$

4. Write an equation for a line that is perpendicular to the given line.
   - ⓐ $y = 4x - 1$
   - ⓑ $y = x + 2$

5. A composite figure is graphed on the coordinate plane shown. Round your answers to the nearest hundredth, if necessary.

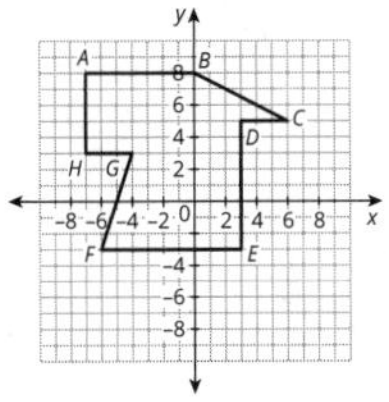

   - ⓐ Determine the perimeter of the figure.
   - ⓑ Calculate the area of the figure.

6. Use the coordinate plane to determine each distance. Write each answer as a decimal to the nearest hundredth.

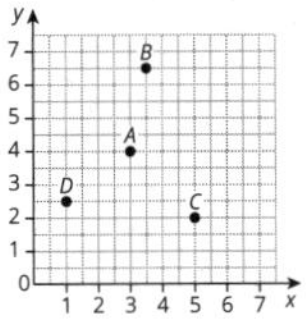

   - ⓐ The distance between point *A* and point *C*
   - ⓑ The distance between point *D* and point *B*

7. Jay walks 3 blocks north and then 4 blocks east to get to the store. If he walks straight back home, how far does Jay walk in all?

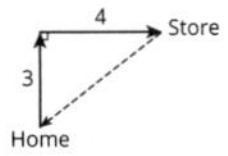

8. Determine the area of each composite figure. Each grid square measures 1 unit by 1 unit.

ⓐ

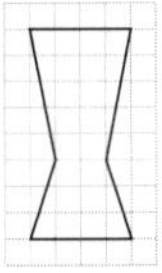

ⓑ

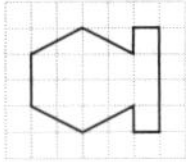

End-of-Topic Review

AVAILABLE ONLINE
1. A **Topic Summary** reviews the main concepts for the topic.
2. A video of the **Worked Example** is provided.

> Practice concepts you learned in **Composing and Decomposing Shapes**.

9. Identify the quadrilaterals that match each description.
   - ⓐ At least one pair of opposite sides is parallel
   - ⓑ At least one pair of opposite angles is congruent

10. State as many properties as you can about a kite.

11. State as many properties as you can about a rectangle.

12. Write a conjecture about alternate interior angles. Draw an example to test your conjecture.

13. Draw examples of inscribed angles that intercept the same arc of a circle. What conjecture can you make about the measures of the inscribed angles?

14. Use a compass and straightedge to construct the incenter of ΔABC.

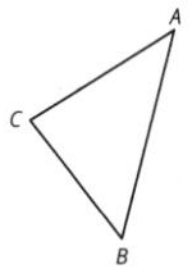

15. Construct the angle bisector of each given angle.

ⓐ

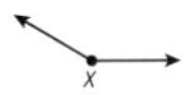

ⓑ

See pages 278–278B for annotated answers.

The **Spaced Review** includes fluency and problem solving from previous topics.

Aligned Standards

1 G.CO.9	2 6.SP.5c
3 G.GPE.5	4 G.GPE.5
5 G.GPE.7	6 8.G.8
7 8.G.7	8 G.GPE.7

Log in to MyCL for more **End-of-Topic** review questions.

Go to **Edulastic**, and search for: G.CO.9, G.CO.12, G.CO.13, G.C.2, G.C.3.

The **End-of-Topic Review** includes questions to practice the key concepts of *Composing and Decomposing Shapes*.

Aligned Standards

9 G.CO.11	10 G.CO.11
11 G.CO.11	12 G.CO.9
13 G.C.2	14 G.CO.12
15 G.CO.12	

Answers included.

MIXED PRACTICE

This Mixed Practice worksheet includes two sections: Spaced Review and End-of-Topic Review.

MODULE 2 Establishing Proof — TOPIC 1 Composing and Decomposing Shapes — TOPIC 2 Justifying Line and Angle Relationships — TOPIC 3 Using Congruence Theorems

Spaced Review

Practice concepts from previous topics.

1 Determine each unknown measure in the figure. Explain your reasoning.

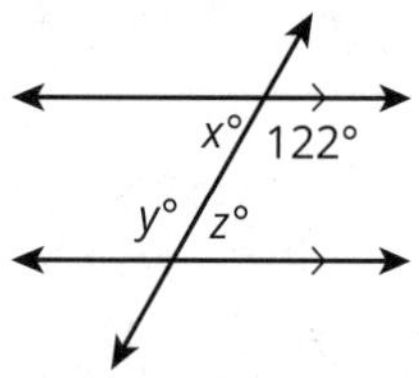

$x = 58°$; $y = 122°$; $z = 58°$

The known angle and x are supplementary.

The known angle and y are alternate interior angles.

The known angle and z are same-side interior angles.

2 Determine the median of the data in each set.

ⓐ {2, 3, 1, 0, 5, 5, 10}

3

ⓑ {7, 7, 8.5, 9, 9.1, 9.5}

$\frac{8.5 + 9}{2} = 8.75$

ⓒ {1, 2, 3, 4, 5, 6, 7, 8, 9, 10}

$\frac{5 + 6}{2} = 5.5$

3 Write an equation for a line that is parallel to the given line.

ⓐ $x = 3$

Sample answer.

$x = 4$

ⓑ $y = -\frac{1}{2}x - \frac{5}{2}$

Sample answer.

$y = -\frac{1}{2}x$

4 Write an equation for a line that is perpendicular to the given line.

ⓐ $y = 4x - 1$

Sample answer.

$y = -\frac{1}{4}x - 1$

ⓑ $y = x + 2$

Sample answer.

$y = -x + 2$

MIXED PRACTICE Continued

5 A composite figure is graphed on the coordinate plane shown. Round your answers to the nearest hundredth, if necessary.

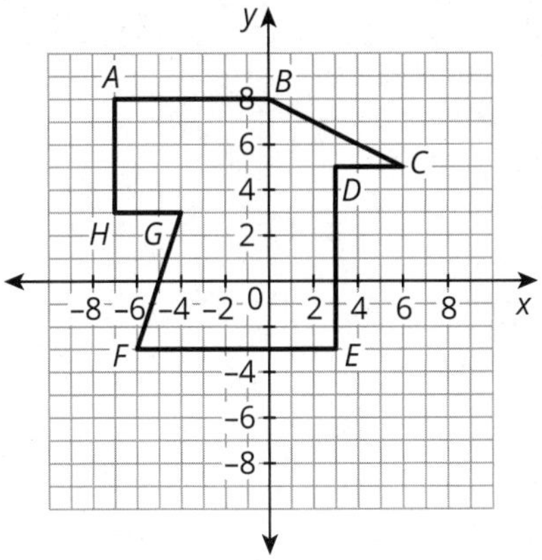

ⓐ Determine the perimeter of the figure.

The perimeter is 48.03 units.

ⓑ Calculate the area of the figure.

The area is 98 square units.

6 Use the coordinate plane to determine each distance. Write each answer as a decimal to the nearest hundredth.

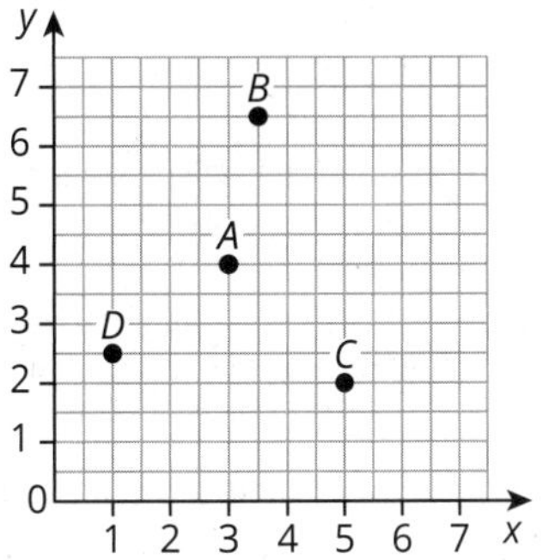

ⓐ The distance between point A and point C

$$\sqrt{(4-2)^2+(3-5)^2} = \sqrt{4+4} = \sqrt{8} \approx 2.83 \text{ units}$$

ⓑ The distance between point D and point B

$$\sqrt{(2.5-6.5)^2+(1-3.5)^2} = \sqrt{16+6.25} = \sqrt{22.25} \approx 4.72 \text{ units}$$

7 Jay walks 3 blocks north and then 4 blocks east to get to the store. If he walks straight back home, how far does Jay walk in all?

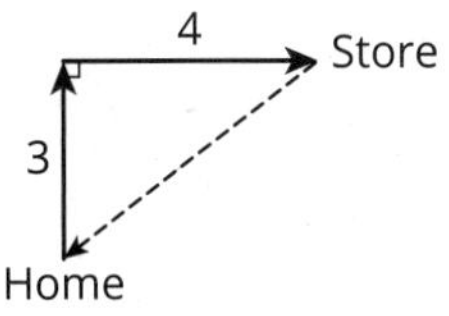

$3^2 + 4^2 = c^2$
$9 + 16 = c^2$
$25 = c^2$
$c = 5$
$3 + 4 + 5 = 12$
12 blocks

8 Determine the area of each composite figure. Each grid square measures 1 unit by 1 unit.

ⓐ

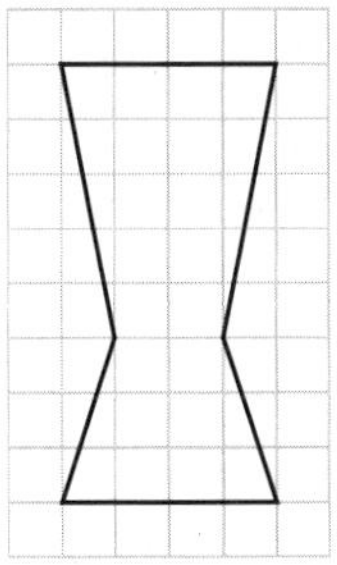

24 square units

ⓑ

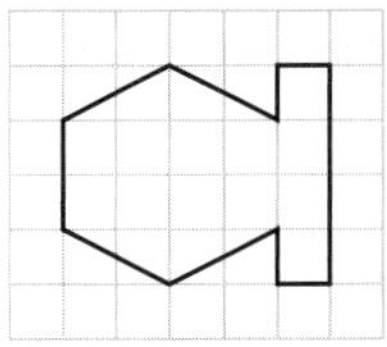

16 square units

Answers included.

MIXED PRACTICE

> This Mixed Practice worksheet includes two sections: Spaced Review and End-of-Topic Review.

End-of-Topic Review

AVAILABLE ONLINE
1. A **Topic Summary** reviews the main concepts for the topic.
2. A video of the **Worked Example** is provided.

> Practice concepts you learned in **Composing and Decomposing Shapes**.

9 Identify the quadrilaterals that match each description.

(a) At least one pair of opposite sides is parallel

Parallelogram, trapezoid, rectangle, rhombus, square

(b) At least one pair of opposite angles is congruent

Kites and all parallelograms

10 State as many properties as you can about a kite.

Two pairs of congruent adjacent sides one pair of congruent opposite angles; only one diagonal bisects the other; the diagonals are perpendicular.

11 State as many properties as you can about a rectangle.

Opposite sides are congruent and parallel; all four angles are right angles; diagonals are congruent and bisect each other.

12 Write a conjecture about alternate interior angles. Draw an example to test your conjecture.

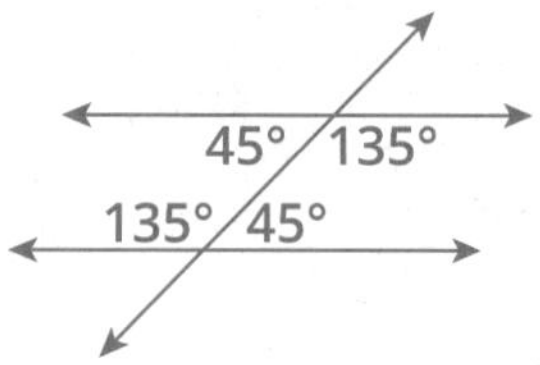

Sample answer.
If two parallel lines are cut by a transversal, alternate interior angles are congruent.

13 Draw examples of inscribed angles that intercept the same arc of a circle. What conjecture can you make about the measures of the inscribed angles?

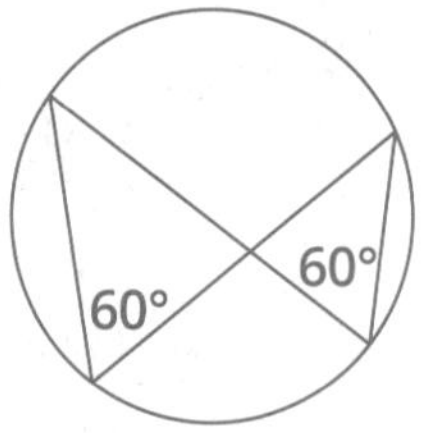

Sample answer.
The measures of inscribed angles that intercept the same arc of a circle are congruent.

14 Use a compass and straightedge to construct the incenter of ΔABC.

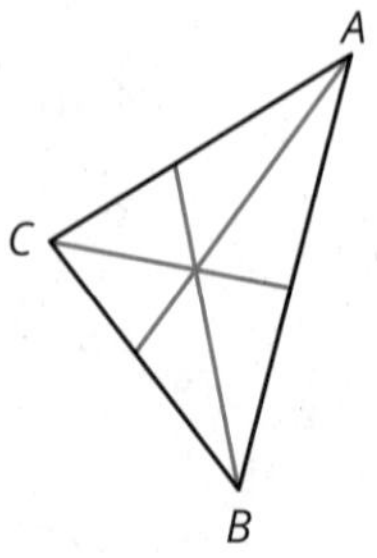

15 Construct the angle bisector of each given angle.

(a)

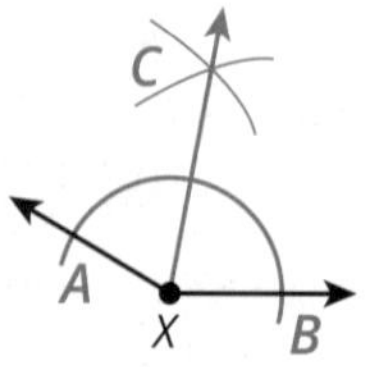

$\overline{XC}$ is the angle bisector of $\angle X$.

(b)

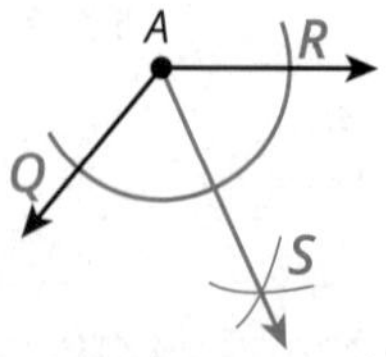

$\overline{AS}$ is the angle bisector of $\angle A$.

OVERVIEW: TOPIC 2

Justifying Line and Angle Relationships

Where are we? **1 Session ≈ 45 minutes**

MODULE 2 Establishing Proof	TOPIC 1 Composing and Decomposing Shapes	**TOPIC 2 Justifying Line and Angle Relationships**	TOPIC 3 Using Congruence Theorems
Pacing	14 Sessions	**24 Sessions**	9 Sessions

How are the key concepts of ***Justifying Line and Angle Relationships*** developed?

The topic begins with an introduction to forms of proof: two-column, flowchart, and paragraph proofs. Students learn they can apply the properties of real numbers to geometric figures and use them in reasoning. They then focus on proving theorems about angle pairs formed when a transversal cuts parallel lines. They develop proof plans before writing formal proofs.

MATH REPRESENTATION

You can use the diagram to prove the Alternate Interior Angles Converse Theorem.

Given: $\angle 3 \cong \angle 6$

Prove: $w \parallel x$

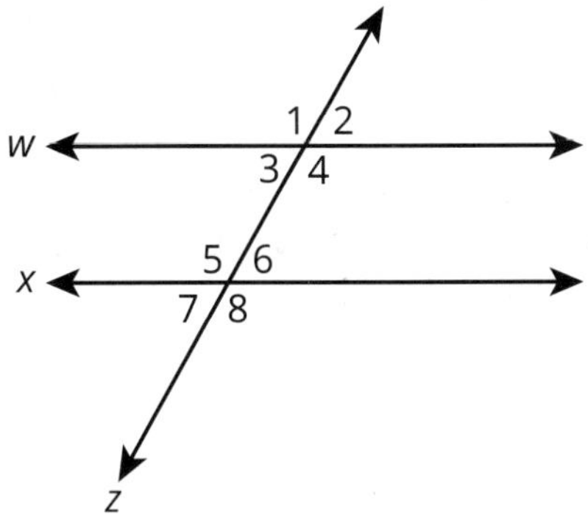

$\angle 3 \cong \angle 6$
Given

$\angle 2 \cong \angle 3$
Vertical angles are congruent.

$\angle 2 \cong \angle 6$
Transitive Property

$w \parallel x$
Corresponding Angle Converse Theorem

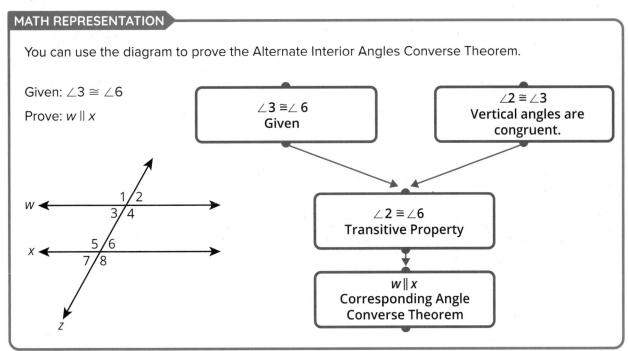

Students then prove theorems about the interior and exterior angles of polygons. They prove the Triangle Sum Theorem and investigate the sum of the interior and exterior angle measures of various polygons.

The focus then shifts to proving theorems about the relationships between angle measures and side measures in triangles. Students use the Perpendicular Bisector Theorem to prove the Isosceles Triangle Base Angles Theorem. They use CPCTC as a reason in proofs and explore the relationship between the sides and angles of special right triangles.

Finally, students explore and prove theorems about angles formed inside and outside the circle by chords, secants, and tangents. They construct a tangent line to a circle from a point outside of the circle.

PLAN FOR 13 class sessions and ~11 MATHia sessions.

Log in to MyCL for **lesson support** including:

- Slides
- Videos

LESSON 1

Proof Positive
Forms of Proof

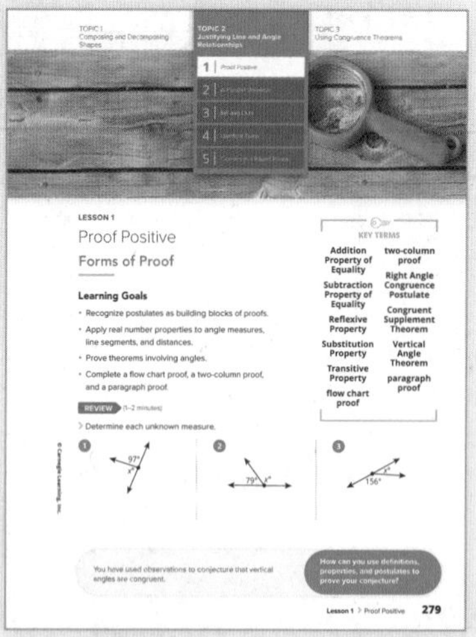
LESSON 1

Proof Positive

Forms of Proof

Learning Goals

- Recognize postulates as building blocks of proofs.
- Apply real number properties to angle measures, line segments, and distances.
- Prove theorems involving angles.
- Complete a flow chart proof, a two-column proof, and a paragraph proof.

KEY TERMS: Addition Property of Equality; Subtraction Property of Equality; Reflexive Property; Substitution Property; Transitive Property; flow chart proof; two-column proof; Right Angle Congruence Postulate; Congruent Supplement Theorem; Vertical Angle Theorem; paragraph proof

REVIEW (1–2 minutes)

Determine each unknown measure.

You have used observations to conjecture that vertical angles are congruent.

How can you use definitions, properties, and postulates to prove your conjecture?

Lesson 1 > Proof Positive 279

LESSON 2

A Parallel Universe
Proving Parallel Line Theorems

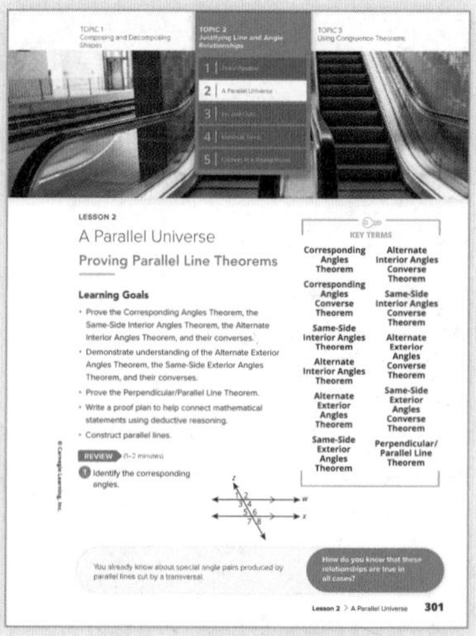
LESSON 2

A Parallel Universe

Proving Parallel Line Theorems

Learning Goals

- Prove the Corresponding Angles Theorem, the Same-Side Interior Angles Theorem, the Alternate Interior Angles Theorem, and their converses.
- Demonstrate understanding of the Alternate Exterior Angles Theorem, the Same-Side Exterior Angles Theorem, and their converses.
- Prove the Perpendicular/Parallel Line Theorem.
- Write a proof plan to help connect mathematical statements using deductive reasoning.
- Construct parallel lines.

KEY TERMS: Corresponding Angles Theorem; Corresponding Angles Converse Theorem; Same-Side Interior Angles Theorem; Alternate Interior Angles Theorem; Alternate Exterior Angles Theorem; Same-Side Exterior Angles Theorem; Alternate Interior Angles Converse Theorem; Same-Side Interior Angles Converse Theorem; Alternate Exterior Angles Converse Theorem; Same-Side Exterior Angles Converse Theorem; Perpendicular/Parallel Line Theorem

REVIEW (1–2 minutes)

1 Identify the corresponding angles.

You already know about special angle pairs produced by parallel lines cut by a transversal.

How do you know that these relationships are true in all cases?

Lesson 2 > A Parallel Universe 301

LEARNING TOGETHER	3 Sessions	2 Sessions
STANDARDS	G.CO.9	G.CO.9
MATHbook Activities sequenced to address standards and meet content goals.	Students apply real number properties to angle measures and segment lengths. Students engage with flow chart and two-column proofs, using them to prove the Right Angle Congruence and Congruent Supplement Theorems. Students analyze a flow chart and write a two-column proof of the Vertical Angle Theorem. They apply theorems to determine unknown measures and learn about paragraph proofs.	Students explore theorems related to parallel lines cut by a transversal, proving special angle pairs are congruent given parallel lines and the converse statements. They prove the theorems in flowcharts and two-column format using definitions, postulates, and already proven theorems. Students build proof plans to help them connect if-then statements using deductive reasoning.
MATERIALS	• Compasses • Glue sticks • Patty paper • Scissors • Straightedges	• Compasses • Glue sticks • Patty paper • Scissors • Straightedges

LEARNING INDIVIDUALLY — Median time for students to complete MATHia for this topic is ~525 minutes.

MATHia Workspaces aligned at the lesson level to support benchmarking through self-paced MATHia.

	Lesson 1	Lesson 2
MATHia	• Introduction to Proofs • Completing Measure Proofs • Connecting Steps in Angle Proofs • Using Angle Theorems	• Classifying Angles Formed by Transversals • Calculating Angle Measures Formed by Transversals • Calculating Angles Formed by Multiple Transversals • Proving Parallel Lines Theorems • Proving the Converses of Parallel Lines Theorems

For students without access to MATHia.

Skills Practice — Problem sets for additional practice of the lesson skills.

	Lesson 1	Lesson 2
Skills Practice	• Properties of Real Numbers	• Angle Relationships Formed from Parallel Lines

LESSON 3

Ins and Outs

Interior and Exterior Angles of Polygons

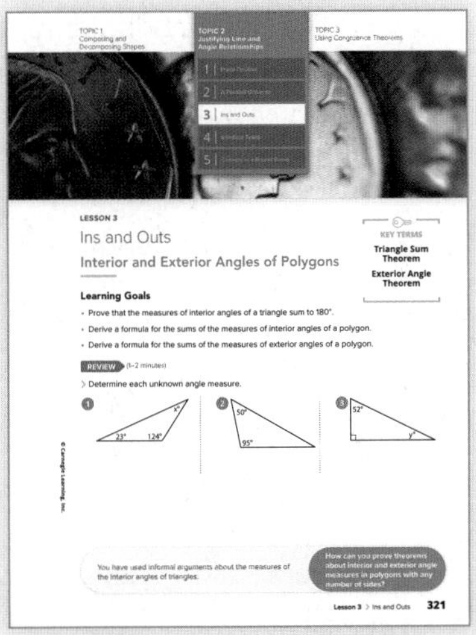
LESSON 3

Ins and Outs

Interior and Exterior Angles of Polygons

KEY TERMS

Triangle Sum Theorem

Exterior Angle Theorem

Learning Goals

- Prove that the measures of interior angles of a triangle sum to 180°.
- Derive a formula for the sums of the measures of interior angles of a polygon.
- Derive a formula for the sums of the measures of exterior angles of a polygon.

REVIEW (1–2 minutes)

> Determine each unknown angle measure.

You have used informal arguments about the measures of the interior angles of triangles.

How can you prove theorems about interior and exterior angle measures in polygons with any number of sides?

© Carnegie Learning, Inc.

Lesson 3 > Ins and Outs 321

2 Sessions

G.CO.10

Students investigate and prove the Triangle Sum Theorem using the parallel line theorems. They use the same diagram to demonstrate the Exterior Angle Theorem. Students generalize to derive a formula to determine the sum of any polygon's interior angle measures and the sum of any polygon's exterior angle measures. Finally, students apply these theorems and formulas to solve mathematical problems.

- Blank paper
- Scissors
- Straightedges

LESSON 4

Identical Twins

Perpendicular Bisector and Isosceles Triangle Theorems

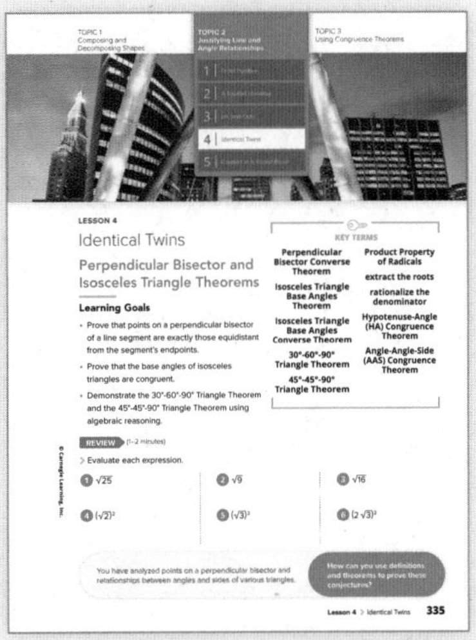
LESSON 4

Identical Twins

Perpendicular Bisector and Isosceles Triangle Theorems

KEY TERMS

Perpendicular Bisector Converse Theorem

Isosceles Triangle Base Angles Theorem

Isosceles Triangle Base Angles Converse Theorem

30°-60°-90° Triangle Theorem

45°-45°-90° Triangle Theorem

Product Property of Radicals

extract the roots

rationalize the denominator

Hypotenuse-Angle (HA) Congruence Theorem

Angle-Angle-Side (AAS) Congruence Theorem

Learning Goals

- Prove that points on a perpendicular bisector of a line segment are exactly those equidistant from the segment's endpoints.
- Prove that the base angles of isosceles triangles are congruent.
- Demonstrate the 30°-60°-90° Triangle Theorem and the 45°-45°-90° Triangle Theorem using algebraic reasoning.

REVIEW (1–2 minutes)

> Evaluate each expression.

1. $\sqrt{25}$
2. $\sqrt{9}$
3. $\sqrt{16}$
4. $(\sqrt{2})^2$
5. $(\sqrt{3})^2$
6. $(2\sqrt{3})^2$

You have analyzed points on a perpendicular bisector and relationships between angles and sides of various triangles.

How can you use definitions and theorems to prove these conjectures?

© Carnegie Learning, Inc.

Lesson 4 > Identical Twins 335

3 Sessions

N.RN.2, G.CO.9, G.CO.10

Students use triangle congruence theorems to explain why pairs of triangles are congruent. Students define CPCTC (corresponding parts of congruent triangles are congruent). They prove the Isosceles Triangle Base Angles Theorem and its converse. They analyze diagrams of triangles to demonstrate the special right triangle theorems algebraically. Students apply theorems to solve problem situations.

- Compasses
- Protractors
- Straightedges

For the most up-to-date MATHia alignment, log in to MyCL.

Lesson 3:

- Proving Triangle Theorems

Lesson 4:

- Proving Triangles Congruent Using SAS and SSS
- Proving Triangles Congruent Using AAS and ASA
- Proving Theorems using Congruent Triangles
- Introduction to Special Right Triangles
- Calculating the Lengths of Sides of Special Right Triangles
- Using Triangle Theorems

Problem sets for additional practice of the lesson skills.

Lesson 3:

- Interior and Exterior Angles of Polygons

Lesson 4:

- Isosceles and Right Triangles

PLAN FOR 13 class sessions and ~11 MATHia sessions.

Log in to MyCL for lesson support including:

- Slides
- Videos

Corners in a Round Room

Angle Relationships Inside and Outside Circles

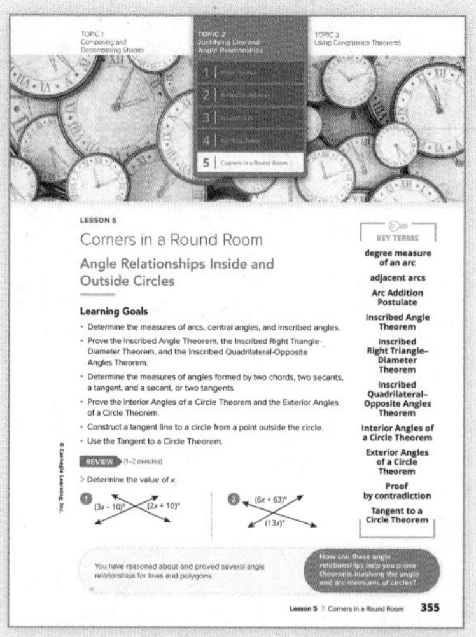
LESSON 5

Corners in a Round Room

Angle Relationships Inside and Outside Circles

Learning Goals

- Determine the measures of arcs, central angles, and inscribed angles.
- Prove the Inscribed Angle Theorem, the Inscribed Right Triangle-Diameter Theorem, and the Inscribed Quadrilateral-Opposite Angles Theorem.
- Determine the measures of angles formed by two chords, two secants, a tangent, and a secant, or two tangents.
- Prove the Interior Angles of a Circle Theorem and the Exterior Angles of a Circle Theorem.
- Construct a tangent line to a circle from a point outside the circle.
- Use the Tangent to a Circle Theorem.

REVIEW (1–2 minutes)

> Determine the value of x.

1. $(3x - 10)°$ $(2x + 10)°$
2. $(6x + 63)°$ $(13x)°$

KEY TERMS: degree measure of an arc; adjacent arcs; Arc Addition Postulate; Inscribed Angle Theorem; Inscribed Right Triangle–Diameter Theorem; Inscribed Quadrilateral–Opposite Angles Theorem; Interior Angles of a Circle Theorem; Exterior Angles of a Circle Theorem; Proof by contradiction; Tangent to a Circle Theorem

You have reasoned about and proved several angle relationships for lines and polygons.

How can these angle relationships help you prove theorems involving the angle and arc measures of circles?

© Carnegie Learning, Inc.

Lesson 5 > Corners in a Round Room 355

LEARNING TOGETHER — 3 Sessions

STANDARDS — G.C.2, G.C.3, G.C.4 (+)

MATHbook
Activities sequenced to address standards and meet content goals.

Students calculate minor arc measures using numbers on a clock. They prove a conjecture relating an inscribed angle's measure to its intercepted arc's measure. They conjecture about the measure of an exterior angle of a circle, and the arc measures intercepted by the angle. Students analyze a proof by contradiction of the Tangent to a Circle Theorem. They apply theorems to solve problems.

MATERIALS

- Compasses
- Protractors
- Straightedges

LEARNING INDIVIDUALLY — For the most up-to-date MATHia alignment, log in to MyCL.

MATHia
Workspaces aligned at the lesson level to support benchmarking through self-paced MATHia.

- Determining Interior and Exterior Angles in Circles

Skills Practice
For students without access to MATHia.

Problem sets for additional practice of the lesson skills.

- Interior and Exterior Angles of a Circle

Theorems proved in *Justifying Line and Angle Relationships:*

- Right Angle Congruence Theorem
- Congruent Supplements Theorem
- Vertical Angle Theorem
- Corresponding Angles Theorem
- Corresponding Angles Converse Theorem
- Alternate Interior Angles Theorem
- Alternate Interior Angles Converse Theorem
- Alternate Exterior Angles Theorem
- Alternate Exterior Angles Converse Theorem
- Same-Side Interior Angles Theorem
- Same-Side Interior Angles Converse Theorem
- Same-Side Exterior Angles Theorem
- Same-Side Exterior Angles Converse Theorem
- Perpendicular/Parallel Lines Theorem
- Triangle Sum Theorem
- Exterior Angles Theorem
- Perpendicular Bisector Theorem
- Perpendicular Bisector Converse Theorem
- Isosceles Triangle Base Angles Theorem
- Isosceles Triangle Base Angles Converse Theorem
- 30°-60°-90° Triangle Theorem
- 45°-45°-90° Triangle Theorem
- Inscribed Angle Theorem
- Inscribed Right Triangle–Diameter Theorem
- Inscribed Quadrilateral–Opposite Angles Theorem
- Interior Angles of a Circle Theorem
- Exterior Angles of a Circle Theorem
- Tangent to a Circle Theorem

Connection to Prior Learning

What is the entry point for students?

Students have used informal arguments to establish facts about the angle sum and exterior angles of triangles, as well as the angles created when a transversal cuts parallel lines.

MATH REPRESENTATION

Trevor organizes a bike race called the Tri-Cities Criterium. Criteriums consist of several laps around a closed circuit. He designs three different triangular circuits.

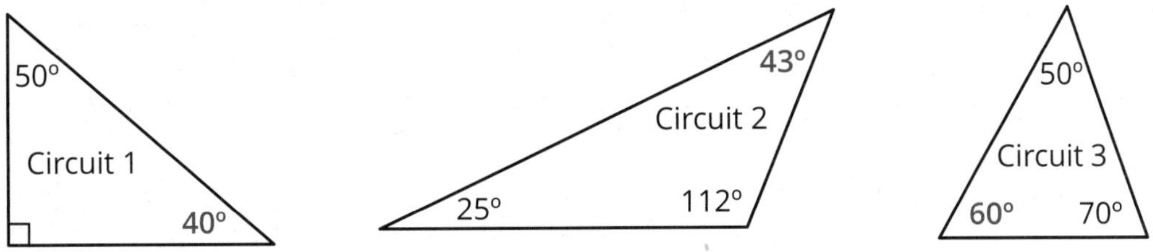

You can use the Triangle Sum Theorem to determine the measure of the third angle in each triangular circuit. Label the triangles with the unknown angle measures.

You can list the angle measures from least to greatest.

Circuit 1: 40°, 50°, 90°

Circuit 2: 25°, 43°, 112°

Circuit 3: 50°, 60°, 70°

You can list the side lengths from shortest to longest.

Circuit 1: 2.7 cm, 3.2 cm, 4.2 cm

Circuit 2: 2.7 cm, 4.4 cm, 6 cm

Circuit 3: 2.6 cm, 2.9 cm, 3.1 cm

In *Composing and Decomposing Shapes,* students explored and conjectured about each of the concepts that they prove in this topic.

Students have used the properties of real numbers to solve equations and reason about equivalencies since middle school. They now apply them with geometric measurements.

Students have explained how the criteria for triangle congruence (ASA, SAS, and SSS) follow from the definition of congruence in terms of rigid motions.

NOTES

Connection to Future Learning

Why is *Justifying Line and Angle Relationships* important?

Throughout this topic, students solidify their understanding of the relationships created between and among angles and sides of geometric shapes. They use the theorems proven in this topic to prove other theorems in future topics, building a system of geometric relationships that prepares them to solve more complicated problems.

MATH REPRESENTATION

You can prove that the base angles of an isosceles trapezoid are congruent.

Given: Isosceles trapezoid *TRAP* with $\overline{TR} \parallel \overline{PA}$, $\overline{TP} \cong \overline{RA}$

Prove: $\angle T \cong \angle R$

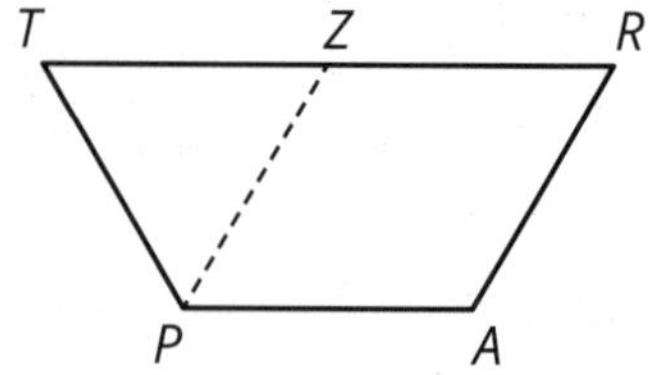

Statements	Reasons
1. Isosceles Trapezoid *TRAP* with $\overline{TR} \parallel \overline{PA}$, $\overline{TP} \cong \overline{RA}$	**1.** Given
2. $\overline{ZP} \parallel \overline{RA}$	**2.** Construction
3. Quadrilateral *ZRAP* is a parallelogram.	**3.** Definition of parallelogram
4. $\overline{ZP} \cong \overline{RA}$	**4.** Opposite sides of a parallelogram are congruent
5. $\overline{TP} \cong \overline{ZP}$	**5.** Transitive Property
6. ΔTPZ is an isosceles triangle.	**6.** Definition of isosceles triangle
7. $\angle T \cong \angle TZP$	**7.** Isosceles Triangle Theorem
8. $\angle TZP \cong \angle R$	**8.** Corresponding Angle Theorem
9. $\angle T \cong \angle R$	**9.** Transitive Property

The algebraic reasoning in this topic is important in integrating the algebra and geometry domains. Students use the Pythagorean Theorem to prove relationships in special right triangles, preparing them for trigonometry.

Throughout this topic, students develop their deductive reasoning skills. These skills prepare students to handle more complex real-world problems.

Log in to MyCL for resources that support **student meta-cognition**.

How does a student demonstrate understanding?

Students will demonstrate an understanding of the standards in *Justifying Line and Angle Relationships* when they can:

Use the properties of congruence and equality in geometric proofs.	✓
Prove that vertical angles, alternate interior angles, and corresponding angles are congruent and that same-side interior angles are supplementary.	✓
Prove that lines are parallel when alternate interior angles and corresponding angles are congruent or when same-side interior angles are supplementary.	✓
Prove that points on a perpendicular bisector of a line segment are equidistant from the segment's endpoints.	✓
Prove that the measures of the interior angles of a triangle sum to 180° and that the measure of an exterior angle of a triangle is equal to the sum of its remote interior angles.	✓
Prove that base angles of an isosceles triangle are congruent.	✓
Prove that the midsegment of a triangle is parallel to and half the length of the base.	✓
Prove that the opposite sides of a parallelogram are parallel and congruent and that the diagonals of a parallelogram bisect each other.	✓
Recognize and prove that an inscribed angle is half the measure of its intercepted arc and the central angle intercepting the same arc.	✓
Prove theorems related to the measure of angles formed at the intersection of chords, secants, and or tangents.	✓
Construct a tangent to a circle from a point outside of the circle.	✓
Prove that the opposite angles of a cyclic quadrilateral are supplementary.	✓

TOPIC 2

HABITS OF MIND

How do the activities in *Justifying Line and Angle Relationships* promote student expertise in the mathematical practice standards?

All Carnegie Learning topics are written with the goal of creating mathematical thinkers who are active participants in class discourse, so elements of the habits of mind should be evident in all lessons. Students are expected to make sense of problems and work towards solutions, reason using concrete and abstract ideas, and communicate their thinking while providing a critical ear to the thinking of others.

Throughout *Justifying Line and Angle Relationships*, students use deductive reasoning to write clear proofs of geometric relationships. They analyze diagrams and conditional statements to understand what they know and what they can and cannot assume in the diagram. Students attend to precision as they write proofs with clear deductive reasoning. They learn three different proof types in this topic—tools they can choose from when writing future proofs. As they build a system of geometric theorems, students see the structure in geometric figures and relationships between parts of figures.

Mixed Practice

At the end of each topic, a **Mixed Practice** worksheet provides practice with skills from previous topics and this topic.

Spaced Review
Fluency and problem solving from previous topics

End of Topic Review
Review problems from this topic

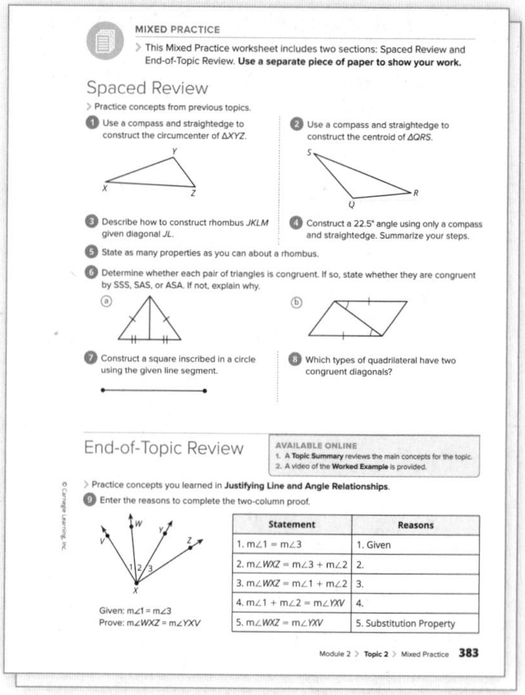
MIXED PRACTICE

> This Mixed Practice worksheet includes two sections: Spaced Review and End-of-Topic Review. **Use a separate piece of paper to show your work.**

Spaced Review

> Practice concepts from previous topics.

1. Use a compass and straightedge to construct the circumcenter of ΔXYZ.
2. Use a compass and straightedge to construct the centroid of ΔQRS.
3. Describe how to construct rhombus *JKLM* given diagonal *JL*.
4. Construct a 22.5° angle using only a compass and straightedge. Summarize your steps.
5. State as many properties as you can about a rhombus.
6. Determine whether each pair of triangles is congruent. If so, state whether they are congruent by SSS, SAS, or ASA. If not, explain why.
7. Construct a square inscribed in a circle using the given line segment.
8. Which types of quadrilateral have two congruent diagonals?

End-of-Topic Review

AVAILABLE ONLINE
1. A **Topic Summary** reviews the main concepts for the topic.
2. A video of the **Worked Example** is provided.

> Practice concepts you learned in **Justifying Line and Angle Relationships**.

9. Enter the reasons to complete the two-column proof.

Given: $m\angle 1 = m\angle 3$
Prove: $m\angle WXZ = m\angle YXV$

Statement	Reasons
1. $m\angle 1 = m\angle 3$	1. Given
2. $m\angle WXZ = m\angle 3 + m\angle 2$	2.
3. $m\angle WXZ = m\angle 1 + m\angle 2$	3.
4. $m\angle 1 + m\angle 2 = m\angle YXV$	4.
5. $m\angle WXZ = m\angle YXV$	5. Substitution Property

Module 2 > Topic 2 > Mixed Practice 383

Log in to MyCL for digital resources.

A version with **additional space** for students to write their answers.

Downloadable and editable in Word

Editable via Edulastic

Topic Summary

Available online, a **Topic Summary** reviews the main concepts for the topic.

Essential Ideas for each lesson.

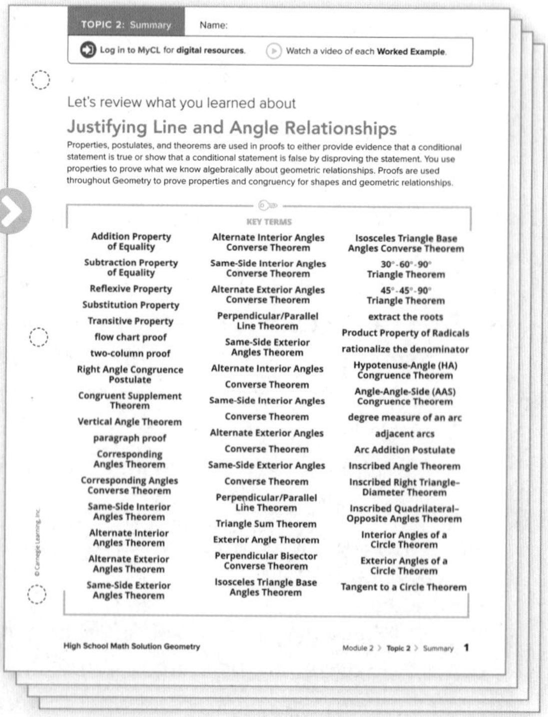
TOPIC 2: Summary Name:

Log in to MyCL for **digital resources**. Watch a video of each **Worked Example**.

Let's review what you learned about

Justifying Line and Angle Relationships

Properties, postulates, and theorems are used in proofs to either provide evidence that a conditional statement is true or show that a conditional statement is false by disproving the statement. You use properties to prove what we know algebraically about geometric relationships. Proofs are used throughout Geometry to prove properties and congruency for shapes and geometric relationships.

KEY TERMS

Addition Property of Equality	Alternate Interior Angles Converse Theorem	Isosceles Triangle Base Angles Converse Theorem
Subtraction Property of Equality	Same-Side Interior Angles Converse Theorem	30°-60°-90° Triangle Theorem
Reflexive Property	Alternate Exterior Angles Converse Theorem	45°-45°-90° Triangle Theorem
Substitution Property	Perpendicular/Parallel Line Theorem	extract the roots
Transitive Property	Same-Side Exterior Angles Theorem	Product Property of Radicals
flow chart proof	Alternate Interior Angles	rationalize the denominator
two-column proof	Converse Theorem	Hypotenuse-Angle (HA) Congruence Theorem
Right Angle Congruence Postulate	Same-Side Interior Angles	Angle-Angle-Side (AAS) Congruence Theorem
Congruent Supplement Theorem	Converse Theorem	degree measure of an arc
Vertical Angle Theorem	Alternate Exterior Angles	adjacent arcs
paragraph proof	Converse Theorem	Arc Addition Postulate
Corresponding Angles Theorem	Same-Side Exterior Angles	Inscribed Angle Theorem
Corresponding Angles Converse Theorem	Converse Theorem	Inscribed Right Triangle-Diameter Theorem
Same-Side Interior Angles Theorem	Perpendicular/Parallel Line Theorem	Inscribed Quadrilateral-Opposite Angles Theorem
Alternate Interior Angles Theorem	Triangle Sum Theorem	Interior Angles of a Circle Theorem
Alternate Exterior Angles Theorem	Exterior Angle Theorem	Exterior Angles of a Circle Theorem
Same-Side Exterior Angles Theorem	Perpendicular Bisector Converse Theorem	Tangent to a Circle Theorem
	Isosceles Triangle Base Angles Theorem	

High School Math Solution Geometry Module 2 > Topic 2 > Summary 1

Log in to MyCL for digital resources.

A printable version available for download.

A video of the **Worked Example** being solved

www.carnegielearning.com/login

MATHia Workspaces are highlighted in select lessons to help you understand the connections and what you might want to review.

Assessment

Assessments aligned to this topic:

1. Pre-test
2. Post-test
3. End of Topic Test (Form A)
4. End of Topic Test (Form B)
5. Standardized Test Practice
6. Performance Task with Rubric

An **Assessment Overview** identifies the standard(s) aligned with each item on every test.

Log in to MyCL for **digital resources**.

- A version with **additional space** for students to write their answers.
- Downloadable and editable in Word
- Editable via Edulastic

TOPIC 2

End of Topic Test		Standardized Test	
1. G.CO.9	11. G.CO.10	1. G.CO.9	11. G.CO.9
2. G.CO.9	12. G.CO.10	2. G.CO.10	12. G.C.2
3. G.CO.9	13. G.CO.10	3. G.CO.10	13. G.CO.9
4. G.CO.9	14. G.CO.10	4. G.CO.9	14. G.C.2
5. G.CO.9	15. G.C.2	5. G.C.3	15. G.CO.10
6. G.CO.9	16. G.C.2	6. G.CO.9	16. G.CO.10
7. G.CO.10	17. G.C.2	7. G.CO.10	17. G.CO.10
8. G.CO.10	18. G.C.2	8. G.CO.10	18. G.CO.10
9. G.CO.10	19. G.C.2	9. G.C.2	19. G.CO.9
10. G.CO.10	20. G.C.3	10. G.CO.10	20. G.C.3

Family Guide

Teachers, encourage your families to log into the **Home Connection** to access a collection of resources that supports their students as they learn about *Justifying Line and Angle Relationships*.

www.carnegielearning.com/home-connection

For families with limited online access, print and send home the **Family Guide**.

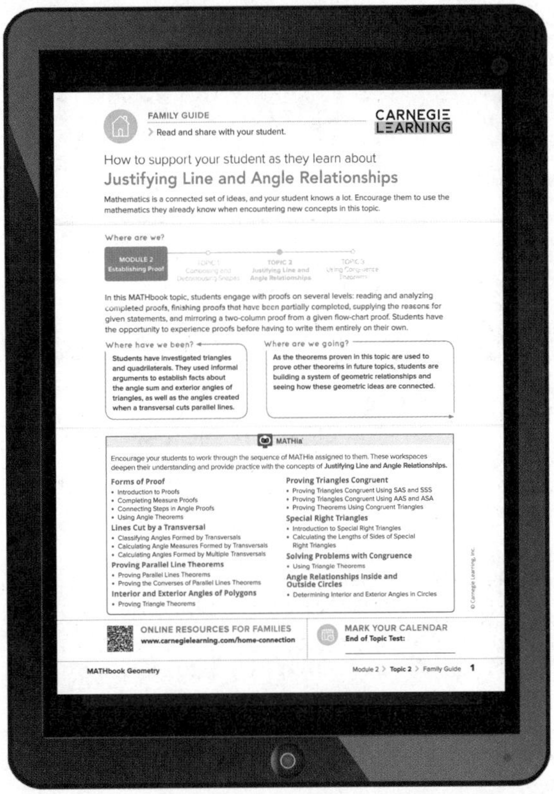

FAMILY GUIDE
> Read and share with your student.

CARNEGIE LEARNING

How to support your student as they learn about
Justifying Line and Angle Relationships

Mathematics is a connected set of ideas, and your student knows a lot. Encourage them to use the mathematics they already know when encountering new concepts in this topic.

Where are we?

MODULE 2 Establishing Proof — TOPIC 1 Composing and Decomposing Shapes — TOPIC 2 Justifying Line and Angle Relationships — TOPIC 3 Using Congruence Theorems

In this MATHbook topic, students engage with proofs on several levels: reading and analyzing completed proofs, finishing proofs that have been partially completed, supplying the reasons for given statements, and mirroring a two-column proof from a given flow-chart proof. Students have the opportunity to experience proofs before having to write them entirely on their own.

Where have we been?
Students have investigated triangles and quadrilaterals. They used informal arguments to establish facts about the angle sum and exterior angles of triangles, as well as the angles created when a transversal cuts parallel lines.

Where are we going?
As the theorems proven in this topic are used to prove other theorems in future topics, students are building a system of geometric relationships and seeing how these geometric ideas are connected.

MATHia

Encourage your students to work through the sequence of MATHia assigned to them. These workspaces deepen their understanding and provide practice with the concepts of **Justifying Line and Angle Relationships.**

Forms of Proof
- Introduction to Proofs
- Completing Measure Proofs
- Connecting Steps in Angle Proofs
- Using Angle Theorems

Lines Cut by a Transversal
- Classifying Angles Formed by Transversals
- Calculating Angle Measures Formed by Transversals
- Calculating Angles Formed by Multiple Transversals

Proving Parallel Line Theorems
- Proving Parallel Lines Theorems
- Proving the Converses of Parallel Lines Theorems

Interior and Exterior Angles of Polygons
- Proving Triangle Theorems

Proving Triangles Congruent
- Proving Triangles Congruent Using SAS and SSS
- Proving Triangles Congruent Using AAS and ASA
- Proving Theorems Using Congruent Triangles

Special Right Triangles
- Introduction to Special Right Triangles
- Calculating the Lengths of Sides of Special Right Triangles

Solving Problems with Congruence
- Using Triangle Theorems

Angle Relationships Inside and Outside Circles
- Determining Interior and Exterior Angles in Circles

ONLINE RESOURCES FOR FAMILIES
www.carnegielearning.com/home-connection

MARK YOUR CALENDAR
End of Topic Test:

MATHbook Geometry — Module 2 > **Topic 2** > Family Guide 1

© Carnegie Learning, Inc.

Justifying Line and Angle Relationships

Scope out MATHbook and MATHia sessions for this topic, keeping in mind your long term plan.

You can schedule MATHia sessions any time; however, if you are using Skills Practice as the alternative, schedule those sessions after a completed lesson.

1 Session ≈ 45 minutes

Log in to MyCL for:

- Editable templates
- Alternative plans for longer sessions
- Implementations not using MATHia

CORE IMPLEMENTATION PLAN with flexible access to computers/tablets.

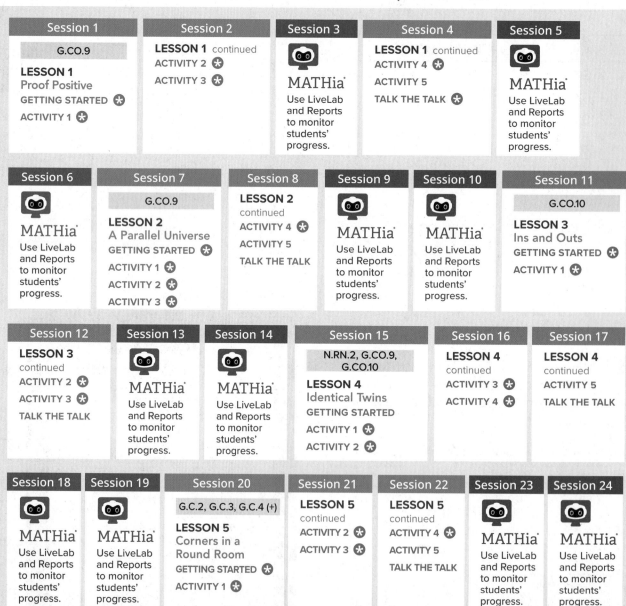

Session 1
G.CO.9
LESSON 1 Proof Positive
GETTING STARTED ✪
ACTIVITY 1 ✪

Session 2
LESSON 1 continued
ACTIVITY 2 ✪
ACTIVITY 3 ✪

Session 3
MATHia
Use LiveLab and Reports to monitor students' progress.

Session 4
LESSON 1 continued
ACTIVITY 4 ✪
ACTIVITY 5
TALK THE TALK ✪

Session 5
MATHia
Use LiveLab and Reports to monitor students' progress.

Session 6
MATHia
Use LiveLab and Reports to monitor students' progress.

Session 7
G.CO.9
LESSON 2 A Parallel Universe
GETTING STARTED ✪
ACTIVITY 1 ✪
ACTIVITY 2 ✪
ACTIVITY 3 ✪

Session 8
LESSON 2 continued
ACTIVITY 4 ✪
ACTIVITY 5
TALK THE TALK

Session 9
MATHia
Use LiveLab and Reports to monitor students' progress.

Session 10
MATHia
Use LiveLab and Reports to monitor students' progress.

Session 11
G.CO.10
LESSON 3 Ins and Outs
GETTING STARTED ✪
ACTIVITY 1 ✪

Session 12
LESSON 3 continued
ACTIVITY 2 ✪
ACTIVITY 3 ✪
TALK THE TALK

Session 13
MATHia
Use LiveLab and Reports to monitor students' progress.

Session 14
MATHia
Use LiveLab and Reports to monitor students' progress.

Session 15
N.RN.2, G.CO.9, G.CO.10
LESSON 4 Identical Twins
GETTING STARTED
ACTIVITY 1 ✪
ACTIVITY 2 ✪

Session 16
LESSON 4 continued
ACTIVITY 3 ✪
ACTIVITY 4 ✪

Session 17
LESSON 4 continued
ACTIVITY 5
TALK THE TALK

Session 18
MATHia
Use LiveLab and Reports to monitor students' progress.

Session 19
MATHia
Use LiveLab and Reports to monitor students' progress.

Session 20
G.C.2, G.C.3, G.C.4 (+)
LESSON 5 Corners in a Round Room
GETTING STARTED ✪
ACTIVITY 1 ✪

Session 21
LESSON 5 continued
ACTIVITY 2 ✪
ACTIVITY 3 ✪

Session 22
LESSON 5 continued
ACTIVITY 4 ✪
ACTIVITY 5
TALK THE TALK

Session 23
MATHia
Use LiveLab and Reports to monitor students' progress.

Session 24
MATHia
Use LiveLab and Reports to monitor students' progress.

Complete End-of-Topic Review and Assess

✪ This activity highlights a key term or concept that is essential to the learning goals of the lesson.

ENGAGE at the **Module** level + **DEVELOP** at the **Topic** level + **TEACH** Read the facilitation notes and plan learning experiences.

Where are we?

TOPIC 2 Justifying Line and Angle Relationships	LESSON 1 Proof Positive	LESSON 2 A Parallel Universe	LESSON 3 Ins and Outs	LESSON 4 Identical Twins	LESSON 5 Corners in a Round Room
Pacing	3 Sessions	2 Sessions	2 Sessions	2 Sessions	2 Sessions

OVERVIEW: LESSON 1

Proof Positive

Forms of Proof

ENGAGE

- Students prove the conjecture that vertical angles are congruent.

DEVELOP

- Students apply properties of real numbers in geometry.
- They rewrite the hypotheses and conclusions of conditional statements as given and prove statements.
- They prove the Congruent Supplement Theorem.
- They prove the Vertical Angle Theorem.
- Students apply theorems to solve for the measures of angles.

DEMONSTRATE

- Students prove that the two arc measures of vertical central angles are congruent.

HIGH SCHOOL GEOMETRY

Congruence

Prove geometric theorems.

9. Prove theorems about lines and angles.

LESSON STRUCTURE AND PACING GUIDE 3 SESSIONS

⊛ This activity highlights a key term or concept that is essential to the learning goals of the lesson.

Session 1		Session 2

INSTRUCTIONAL SEQUENCE

ENGAGE	DEVELOP	DEVELOP
Establish a situation	Mathematical problem solving Worked example	Peer analysis Worked example

GETTING STARTED
Infinite Regression

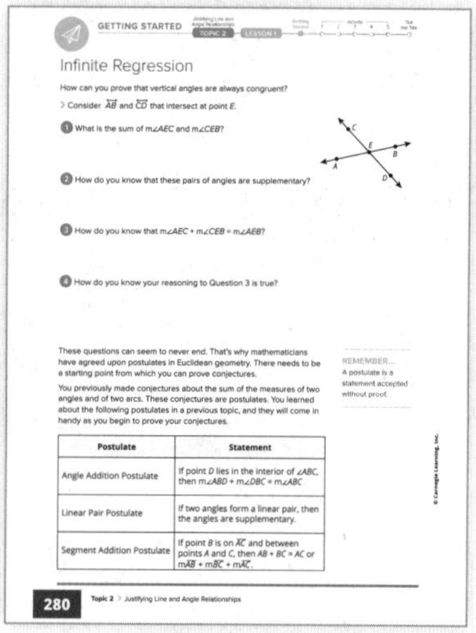

GETTING STARTED

Infinite Regression

How can you prove that vertical angles are always congruent?

> Consider $\overleftrightarrow{AB}$ and $\overleftrightarrow{CD}$ that intersect at point E.

1. What is the sum of $m\angle AEC$ and $m\angle CEB$?
2. How do you know that these pairs of angles are supplementary?
3. How do you know that $m\angle AEC + m\angle CEB = m\angle AEB$?
4. How do you know your reasoning to Question 3 is true?

These questions can seem to never end. That's why mathematicians have agreed upon postulates in Euclidean geometry. There needs to be a starting point from which you can prove conjectures.

You previously made conjectures about the sum of the measures of two angles and of two arcs. These conjectures are postulates. You learned about the following postulates in a previous topic, and they will come in handy as you begin to prove your conjectures.

REMEMBER... A postulate is a statement accepted without proof.

Postulate	Statement
Angle Addition Postulate	If point D lies in the interior of $\angle ABC$, then $m\angle ABD + m\angle DBC = m\angle ABC$
Linear Pair Postulate	If two angles form a linear pair, then the angles are supplementary.
Segment Addition Postulate	If point B is on $\overline{AC}$ and between points A and C, then $AB + BC = AC$ or $m\overline{AB} + m\overline{BC} + m\overline{AC}$.

© Carnegie Learning, Inc.

280 Topic 2 > Justifying Line and Angle Relationships

Students prove the conjecture that vertical angles are congruent.

- They review the Angle Addition Postulate, Linear Pair Postulate, and Segment Addition Postulate.

ACTIVITY 1
Properties of Real Numbers in Geometry

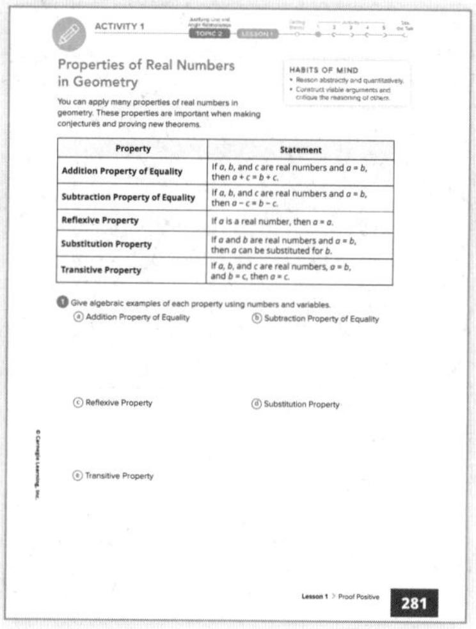

ACTIVITY 1

Properties of Real Numbers in Geometry

HABITS OF MIND
- Reason abstractly and quantitatively.
- Construct viable arguments and critique the reasoning of others.

You can apply many properties of real numbers in geometry. These properties are important when making conjectures and proving new theorems.

Property	Statement
Addition Property of Equality	If a, b, and c are real numbers and $a = b$, then $a + c = b + c$.
Subtraction Property of Equality	If a, b, and c are real numbers and $a = b$, then $a - c = b - c$.
Reflexive Property	If a is a real number, then $a = a$.
Substitution Property	If a and b are real numbers and $a = b$, then a can be substituted for b.
Transitive Property	If a, b, and c are real numbers, $a = b$, and $b = c$, then $a = c$.

1. Give algebraic examples of each property using numbers and variables.
   (a) Addition Property of Equality
   (b) Subtraction Property of Equality
   (c) Reflexive Property
   (d) Substitution Property
   (e) Transitive Property

© Carnegie Learning, Inc.

Lesson 1 > Proof Positive 281

Students apply properties of real numbers in geometry.

- They apply the Addition Property of Equality, the Subtraction Property of Equality, the Reflexive Property, the Substitution Property, and the Transitive Property to angle measures and segment measures.

ACTIVITY 2
Forms of Proof

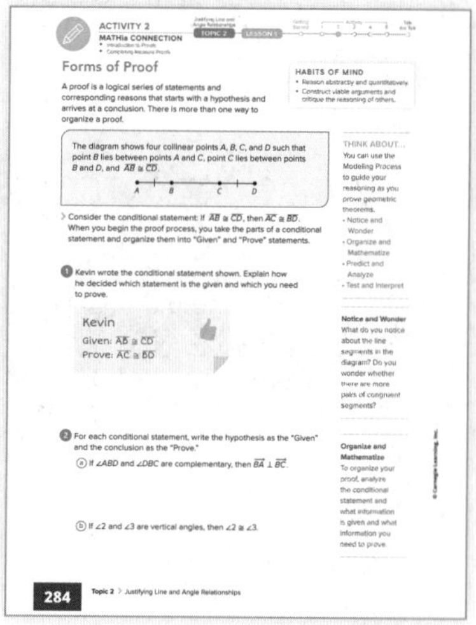

ACTIVITY 2

MATHia CONNECTION

Forms of Proof

HABITS OF MIND
- Reason abstractly and quantitatively.
- Construct viable arguments and critique the reasoning of others.

A proof is a logical series of statements and corresponding reasons that starts with a hypothesis and arrives at a conclusion. There is more than one way to organize a proof.

The diagram shows four collinear points A, B, C, and D such that point B lies between points A and C, point C lies between points B and D, and $\overline{AB} \cong \overline{CD}$.

> Consider the conditional statement: If $\overline{AB} \cong \overline{CD}$, then $\overline{AC} \cong \overline{BD}$. When you begin the proof process, you take the parts of a conditional statement and organize them into "Given" and "Prove" statements.

THINK ABOUT... You can use the Modeling Process to guide your reasoning as you prove geometric theorems.
- Notice and Wonder
- Organize and Mathematize
- Predict and Analyze
- Test and Interpret

1. Kevin wrote the conditional statement shown. Explain how he decided which statement is the given and which you need to prove.

Kevin
Given: $\overline{AB} \cong \overline{CD}$
Prove: $\overline{AC} \cong \overline{BD}$

Notice and Wonder: What do you notice about the line segments in the diagram? Do you wonder whether there are more pairs of congruent segments?

2. For each conditional statement, write the hypothesis as the "Given" and the conclusion as the "Prove."
   (a) If $\angle ABD$ and $\angle DBC$ are complementary, then $\overrightarrow{BA} \perp \overrightarrow{BC}$.
   (b) If $\angle 2$ and $\angle 3$ are vertical angles, then $\angle 2 \cong \angle 3$.

Organize and Mathematize: To organize your proof, analyze the conditional statement and what information is given and what information you need to prove.

© Carnegie Learning, Inc.

284 Topic 2 > Justifying Line and Angle Relationships

Students rewrite the hypotheses and conclusions of conditional statements as given and prove statements.

- They analyze the structure for writing flow chart proofs and two-column proofs.
- They complete a flow chart proof of the Right Angle Congruence Postulate.

Log in to MyCL for **lesson support** including:

Slides

Videos

www.carnegielearning.com/login

Session 3

INSTRUCTIONAL SEQUENCE

DEVELOP	DEVELOP	DEVELOP
Investigation Mathematical problem solving	Worked example	Mathematical problem solving

ACTIVITY 3
Proofs of the Congruent Supplement Theorem

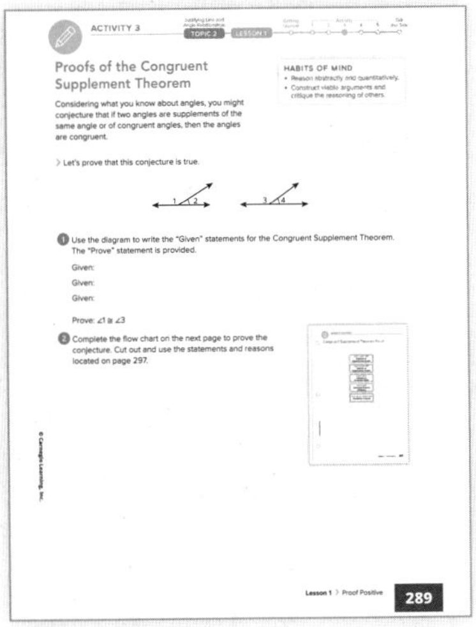
ACTIVITY 3

Proofs of the Congruent Supplement Theorem

HABITS OF MIND
- Reason abstractly and quantitatively.
- Construct viable arguments and critique the reasoning of others.

Considering what you know about angles, you might conjecture that if two angles are supplements of the same angle or of congruent angles, then the angles are congruent.

> Let's prove that this conjecture is true.

1. Use the diagram to write the "Given" statements for the Congruent Supplement Theorem. The "Prove" statement is provided.

Given:

Given:

Given:

Prove: ∠1 ≅ ∠3

2. Complete the flow chart on the next page to prove the conjecture. Cut out and use the statements and reasons located on page 297.

Lesson 1 > Proof Positive 289

Students prove the Congruent Supplement Theorem.

- They cut out preprinted statements with reasons and use them to complete a flow chart proof.
- They use the flow chart proof as a guide to write a two-column proof.

ACTIVITY CUTOUT

ACTIVITY 4
Proofs of the Vertical Angle Theorem

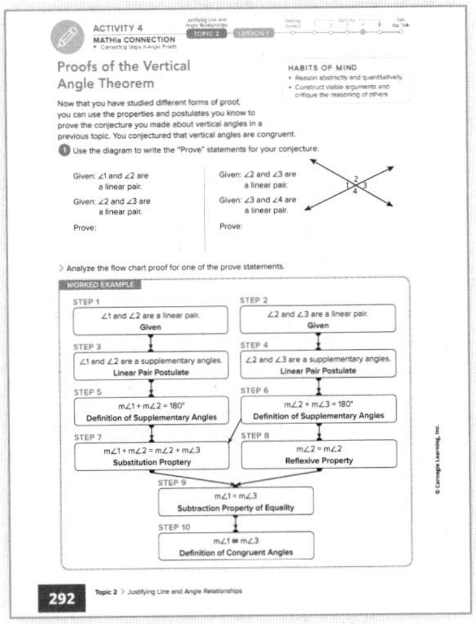
ACTIVITY 4

MATHia CONNECTION

Proofs of the Vertical Angle Theorem

HABITS OF MIND
- Reason abstractly and quantitatively.
- Construct viable arguments and critique the reasoning of others.

Now that you have studied different forms of proof, you can use the properties and postulates you know to prove the conjecture you made about vertical angles in a previous topic. You conjectured that vertical angles are congruent.

1. Use the diagram to write the "Prove" statements for your conjecture.

Given: ∠1 and ∠2 are a linear pair. Given: ∠2 and ∠3 are a linear pair. Prove:

Given: ∠2 and ∠3 are a linear pair. Given: ∠3 and ∠4 are a linear pair. Prove:

> Analyze the flow chart proof for one of the prove statements.

WORKED EXAMPLE

STEP 1: ∠1 and ∠2 are a linear pair. Given

STEP 2: ∠2 and ∠3 are a linear pair. Given

STEP 3: ∠1 and ∠2 are a supplementary angles. Linear Pair Postulate

STEP 4: ∠2 and ∠3 are a supplementary angles. Linear Pair Postulate

STEP 5: m∠1 + m∠2 = 180° Definition of Supplementary Angles

STEP 6: m∠2 + m∠3 = 180° Definition of Supplementary Angles

STEP 7: m∠1 + m∠2 = m∠2 + m∠3 Substitution Property

STEP 8: m∠2 = m∠2 Reflexive Property

STEP 9: m∠1 = m∠3 Subtraction Property of Equality

STEP 10: m∠1 ≅ m∠3 Definition of Congruent Angles

292 Topic 2 > Justifying Line and Angle Relationships

Students prove the Vertical Angle Theorem.

- They analyze the flow chart proving one pair of vertical angles congruent and answer questions about the steps.
- They use the Congruent Supplement Theorem in a two-column proof to prove that the second pair of vertical angles are congruent.

ACTIVITY 5
Using Theorems to Determine Unknown Measures

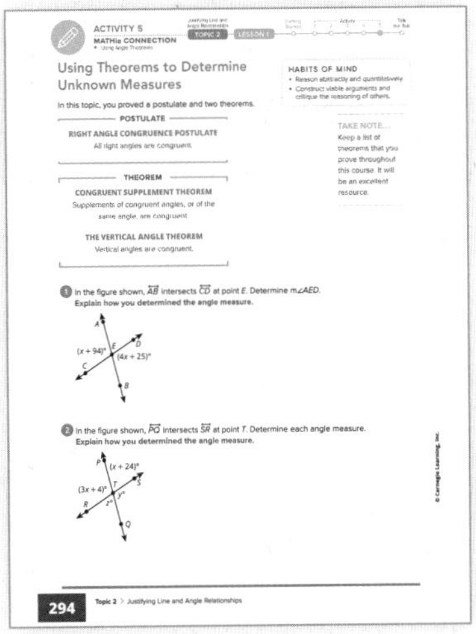
ACTIVITY 5

MATHia CONNECTION

Using Theorems to Determine Unknown Measures

HABITS OF MIND
- Reason abstractly and quantitatively.
- Construct viable arguments and critique the reasoning of others.

In this topic, you proved a postulate and two theorems.

POSTULATE

RIGHT ANGLE CONGRUENCE POSTULATE

All right angles are congruent.

THEOREM

CONGRUENT SUPPLEMENT THEOREM

Supplements of congruent angles, or of the same angle, are congruent.

THE VERTICAL ANGLE THEOREM

Vertical angles are congruent.

TAKE NOTE... Keep a list of theorems that you prove throughout this course. It will be an excellent resource.

1. In the figure shown, $\overline{AB}$ intersects $\overline{CD}$ at point E. Determine m∠AED. Explain how you determined the angle measure.

2. In the figure shown, $\overline{PQ}$ intersects $\overline{SR}$ at point T. Determine each angle measure. Explain how you determined the angle measure.

294 Topic 2 > Justifying Line and Angle Relationships

Students solve for the measures of angles.

- They apply the Congruent Supplement Theorem, Vertical Angle Theorem, or the Linear Pair Postulate

TOPIC 2

Log in to MyCL for:

- Editable templates
- Additional planning support

Session 3

INSTRUCTIONAL SEQUENCE

DEMONSTRATE
Exit ticket procedures

TALK THE TALK
Goof-Proof

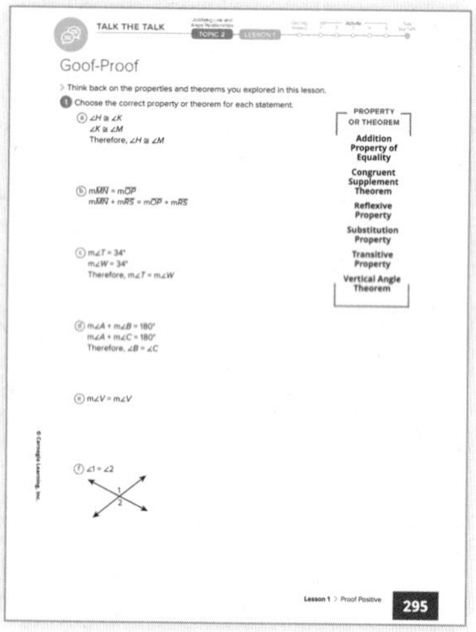
TALK THE TALK

TOPIC 2 LESSON 1

Goof-Proof

> Think back on the properties and theorems you explored in this lesson.

1 Choose the correct property or theorem for each statement.

(a) $\angle H \cong \angle K$
$\angle K \cong \angle M$
Therefore, $\angle H \cong \angle M$

(b) $m\overline{MN} = m\overline{OP}$
$m\overline{MN} + m\overline{RS} = m\overline{OP} + m\overline{RS}$

(c) $m\angle T = 34°$
$m\angle W = 34°$
Therefore, $m\angle T = m\angle W$

(d) $m\angle A + m\angle B = 180°$
$m\angle A + m\angle C = 180°$
Therefore, $\angle B = \angle C$

(e) $m\angle V = m\angle V$

(f) $\angle 1 = \angle 2$

PROPERTY OR THEOREM

Addition Property of Equality
Congruent Supplement Theorem
Reflexive Property
Substitution Property
Transitive Property
Vertical Angle Theorem

© Carnegie Learning, Inc.

Lesson 1 > Proof Positive 295

Students write a paragraph proof to prove that the two arc measures of vertical central angles are congruent.

- They identify the correct property or theorem for given statements.

Now that you have read the Module, Topic, and Lesson Overviews, you are ready to plan.

Do the math

> Tear out the lesson planning template (page 279O) and jot down thoughts as you work through this lesson and read the Facilitation Notes.

Connect the learning

MATHbook + MATHia

The table shows a portion of the self-paced MATHia sequence for the *Justifying Line and Angle Relationships* Topic.

Median student completion time for the entire topic: ~500–530 minutes

> As you implement this lesson, consider different connections for students who are on pace and those that have not yet completed the workspaces aligned to this lesson.

STUDENTS WHO ARE NOT HERE YET
Students will begin completing the steps in scaffolded proofs.

TYPE	WORKSPACE NAME
	Introduction to Proofs
	Completing Measure and Angle Proofs
	Using Angle Theorems

STUDENTS WHO ARE ON PACE
After you complete Activity 5, ask these students to share how they decided how to arrange the steps of the proofs into logical order.

Proof Positive
Forms of Proof

Session 1

GETTING STARTED Infinite Regression ✪

Pacing (minutes)	
My Time	Class Time

ACTIVITY 1 Properties of Real Numbers in Geometry ✪

Pacing (minutes)	
My Time	Class Time

KEY TERM
- Addition Property of Equality
- Subtraction Property of Equality
- Reflexive Property
- Substitution Property
- Transitive Property

Session 2

ACTIVITY 2 Forms of Proof ✪

Pacing (minutes)	
My Time	Class Time

KEY TERM
- flow chart proof
- two-column proof
- Right Angle Congruence Postulate

ACTIVITY CUTOUT

ACTIVITY 3 Proofs of the Congruent Supplement Theorem ✪

Pacing (minutes)	
My Time	Class Time

KEY TERM
- Congruent Supplement Theorem

Session 3

ACTIVITY 4 Proofs of the Vertical Angle Theorem ✪

Pacing (minutes)	
My Time	Class Time

KEY TERM
- Vertical Angle Theorem

ACTIVITY 5 Using Theorems to Determine Unknown Measures

Pacing (minutes)	
My Time	Class Time

TALK THE TALK Goof-Proof ✪

Pacing (minutes)	
My Time	Class Time

KEY TERM
- paragraph proof

✪ This activity highlights a key term or concept that is essential to the learning goals of the lesson.

TOPIC 2

Log in to MyCL for:

- Editable templates
- Additional planning support

Reflect on your lesson

Consider the effectiveness of your lesson on student learning.

What went well?	What did not go as planned?

Anticipate how you would change the lesson next time you teach it.

How will you capitalize on the things that went well?	How will you improve things that did not go as planned?

TOPIC 1
Composing and Decomposing Shapes

TOPIC 2
Justifying Line and Angle Relationships

TOPIC 3
Using Congruence Theorems

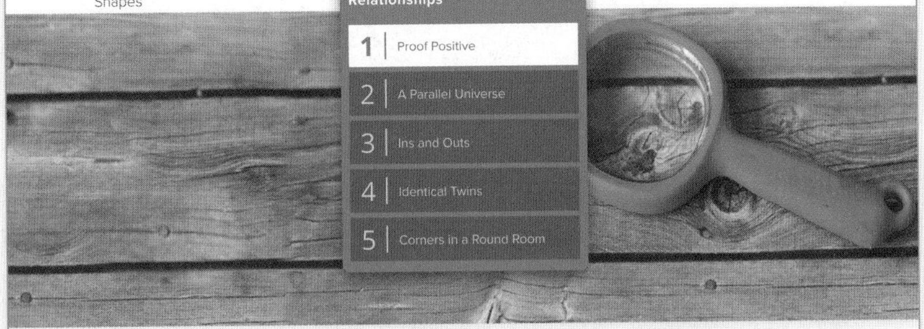

1 | Proof Positive
2 | A Parallel Universe
3 | Ins and Outs
4 | Identical Twins
5 | Corners in a Round Room

LESSON 1

Proof Positive

Forms of Proof

Learning Goals

- Recognize postulates as building blocks of proofs.
- Apply real number properties to angle measures, line segments, and distances.
- Prove theorems involving angles.
- Complete a flow chart proof, a two-column proof, and a paragraph proof.

KEY TERMS

- Addition Property of Equality
- Subtraction Property of Equality
- Reflexive Property
- Substitution Property
- Transitive Property
- flow chart proof
- two-column proof
- Right Angle Congruence Postulate
- Congruent Supplement Theorem
- Vertical Angle Theorem
- paragraph proof

REVIEW (1–2 minutes)

> Determine each unknown measure.

1.
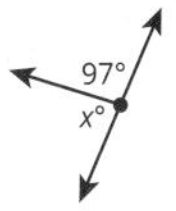

$x = 83°$

2.
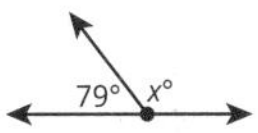

$x = 101°$

3.
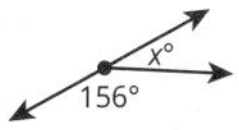

$x = 24°$

You have used observations to conjecture that vertical angles are congruent.

How can you use definitions, properties, and postulates to prove your conjecture?

Lesson 1 > Proof Positive **279**

MATERIALS

- Compasses
- Glue sticks
- Patty paper
- Scissors
- Straightedges

Setting the Stage

- **Assign Review (optional, 1 – 2 minutes)**
- **Communicate the learning goals and key terms to look out for**
- **Tap into your students' prior learning by reading the narrative statement**
- **Provide a sense of direction by reading the question**

TOPIC 2

IN THIS REVIEW
Students calculate angle measure in linear pairs. They will use this skill in **ACTIVITY 1 Properties of Real Numbers in Geometry.**

A proof is a logical series of statements and corresponding reasons that starts with a hypothesis and arrives at a conclusion. There is more than one way to organize a proof.

Essential Ideas

- You can apply the Addition Property of Equality, Subtraction Property of Equality, Reflexive Property, Substitution Property, and Transitive Property to angle measures, segment measures, and distances.
- A construction proof, two-column proof, flow chart proof, and paragraph proof are all acceptable forms of reasoning about geometric relationships.
- The Right Angle Congruence Postulate states that all right angles are congruent.
- The Congruent Supplement Theorem states that if two angles are supplements of the same angle or congruent angles, then the angles are congruent.
- The Vertical Angle Theorem states that vertical angles are congruent.

SUMMARY **Postulates are a building block of Euclidean geometry.**

Chunking the Activity

- **Read and discuss the directions**
- **Group students to complete 1 - 4**
- **Check-in and share**
- **Read and discuss the text and table**

DIFFERENTIATION STRATEGY

See Page 300A to assist all students with the topic.

See Page 300A to support students who struggle with the postulates.

Student Look-Fors

- Use of vocabulary relating lines, linear pairs, and supplementary angles.
- Substitution of measures for the angles to make sense of the questions.

Infinite Regression

How can you prove that vertical angles are always congruent?

> Consider $\overleftrightarrow{AB}$ and $\overleftrightarrow{CD}$ that intersect at point E.

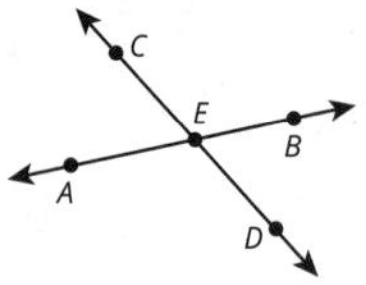

1. What is the sum of m∠AEC and m∠CEB?

   180°

2. How do you know that these pairs of angles are supplementary?

   They form a linear pair.

3. How do you know that m∠AEC + m∠CEB = m∠AEB?

   ∠AEC and ∠CEB share a vertex and side, so they connect to make ∠AEB.

4. How do you know your reasoning to Question 3 is true?

   Sample answer.

   If I remove $\overline{EC}$, the single angle remaining is ∠AEB.

These questions can seem to never end. That's why mathematicians have agreed upon postulates in Euclidean geometry. There needs to be a starting point from which you can prove conjectures.

You previously made conjectures about the sum of the measures of two angles and of two arcs. These conjectures are postulates. You learned about the following postulates in a previous topic, and they will come in handy as you begin to prove your conjectures.

REMEMBER... A postulate is a statement accepted without proof.

Postulate	Statement
Angle Addition Postulate	If point D lies in the interior of ∠ABC, then m∠ABD + m∠DBC = m∠ABC
Linear Pair Postulate	If two angles form a linear pair, then the angles are supplementary.
Segment Addition Postulate	If point B is on $\overline{AC}$ and between points A and C, then $AB + BC = AC$ or $m\overset{\frown}{AB} + m\overset{\frown}{BC} + m\overset{\frown}{AC}$.

Questions to Support Discourse

		TYPE
1	• Which angle has a measure equal to m∠AEC + m∠CEB? • What is the measure of a straight angle?	Gathering
	• Is ∠AEB a straight angle? How do you know?	Probing
Postulates	• Why do you think the Segment Addition Postulate applies to the segment lengths and not the segment itself? • Why do you think you write the Segment Addition Postulate as $AB + BC$ instead of $AB + CB$?	Seeing structure

ACTIVITY 1

SUMMARY **You can apply properties of real numbers to angle and segment measures. You can use them to make conjectures and prove theorems.**

Properties of Real Numbers in Geometry

HABITS OF MIND
- Reason abstractly and quantitatively.
- Construct viable arguments and critique the reasoning of others.

You can apply many properties of real numbers in geometry. These properties are important when making conjectures and proving new theorems.

Property	Statement
Addition Property of Equality	If a, b, and c are real numbers and $a = b$, then $a + c = b + c$.
Subtraction Property of Equality	If a, b, and c are real numbers and $a = b$, then $a - c = b - c$.
Reflexive Property	If a is a real number, then $a = a$.
Substitution Property	If a and b are real numbers and $a = b$, then a can be substituted for b.
Transitive Property	If a, b, and c are real numbers, $a = b$, and $b = c$, then $a = c$.

1. Give algebraic examples of each property using numbers and variables.

(a) Addition Property of Equality

$x = 5$

$x + 2 = 5 + 2$

(b) Subtraction Property of Equality

$x = y$

$x - 3 = y - 3$

(c) Reflexive Property

$6 = 6$

(d) Substitution Property

$x + y = 4$ and $x = 3$, so $3 + y = 4$

(e) Transitive Property

$x = 2$ and $y = 2$, so $x = y$

Chunking the Activity

- Read and discuss the introduction
- Group students to complete 1
- Check-in and share
- Read and discuss the worked example
- Group students to complete 2 and 3
- Share and summarize

TOPIC 2

COMMON MISCONCEPTION

See Page 300B for a misconception related to the properties.

COMMON MISCONCEPTION

See Page 300B for a misconception related to 1.

Questions to Support Discourse

		TYPE
1	• How is the Segment Addition Postulate different from the Addition Property of Equality? • How does your example of the Substitution Property compare with your example of the Transitive Property?	Seeing structure

NOTES

Student Look-Fors

Utilizing relationship skills by communicating clearly and listening well.

You can apply the Addition Property of Equality to angle measures, segment measures, and distances.

WORKED EXAMPLE

Angle measures

If m∠1 = m∠3,
then m∠1 + m∠2 = m∠3 + m∠2.

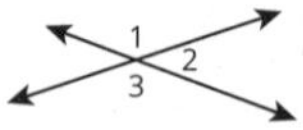

Segment measures

If $m\overline{AB} = m\overline{CD}$,
then $m\overline{AB} + m\overline{BC} = m\overline{BC} + m\overline{CD}$.

Distances

If *AB* = *CD*, then *AB* + *BC* = *BC* + *CD*.

TAKE NOTE...
Notice the symbols used to represent measures of angles and segments. Distance is a numeric measurement that does not require the use of additional symbols.

2 Consider each diagram and write a statement that applies each property to angle measures.

ⓐ Subtraction Property of Equality

If m∠*AEC* = m∠*BED*,
then m∠*AEC* − m∠*BEC* =
m∠*BED* − m∠*BEC*.

So, m∠*AEB* = m∠*CED*.

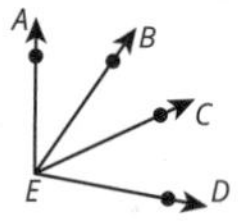

ⓑ Reflexive Property

m∠*A* = m∠*A*

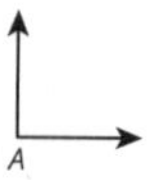

ⓒ Substitution Property

If m∠*A* = 90° and m∠*B* = 90°,
then m∠*A* = m∠*B*.

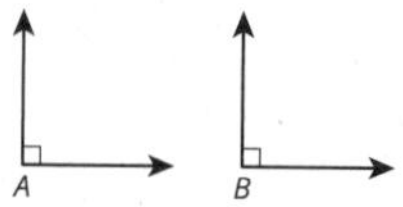

Questions to Support Discourse

		TYPE
Worked Example	• What is the difference between ∠1 and m∠1? • Compare $\overline{AB}$, $m\overline{AB}$, and *AB*.	Seeing structure
2	• Do you think the angles you used need to overlap? Why?	Probing

ⓓ Transitive Property

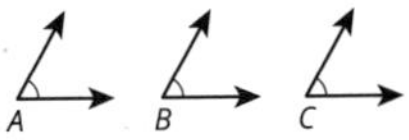

Sample answer.

If m∠A = m∠B and m∠B = m∠C, then m∠A = m∠C.

3 Consider each diagram and write a statement that applies each property to segment measures.

ⓐ Subtraction Property of Equality

If $m\overline{AC} = m\overline{BD}$, then
$m\overline{AC} - m\overline{BC} = m\overline{BD} - m\overline{BC}$.

So, $m\overline{AB} = m\overline{CD}$.

ⓑ Reflexive Property

$m\overline{CD} = m\overline{CD}$

ⓒ Substitution Property

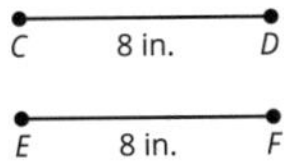

If $m\overline{CD}$ = 8 in. and $m\overline{EF}$ = 8 in., then $m\overline{CD} = m\overline{EF}$.

ⓓ Transitive Property

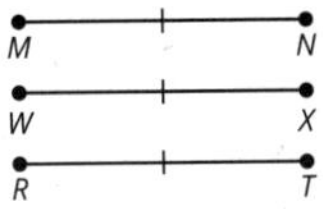

Sample answer.

If $m\overline{MN} = m\overline{WX}$ and $m\overline{WX} = m\overline{RT}$, then $m\overline{MN} = m\overline{RT}$.

NOTES

TOPIC 2

Questions to Support Discourse

		TYPE
3	• How do the statements you wrote for segments differ from the statements you wrote for angles?	Seeing structure

ACTIVITY 2

SUMMARY You can prove conjectures using different methods: flow charts, constructions, and two-column proofs.

Chunking the Activity

- Read and discuss the introduction
- Group students to complete 1 - 4
- Check-in and share
- Read and discuss the definition and worked example
- Group students to complete 5 - 7
- Check-in and share
- Read and discuss the definition and worked example
- Group students to complete 8 and 9
- Check-in and share
- Group students to complete 10 and 11
- Share and summarize

Student Look-Fors

Whether students are annotating the strategy. Remind students to ask themselves:

- Why is this method correct?
- Have I used this method before?

ACTIVITY 2

MATHia CONNECTION
- Introduction to Proofs
- Completing Measure Proofs

Forms of Proof

A proof is a logical series of statements and corresponding reasons that starts with a hypothesis and arrives at a conclusion. There is more than one way to organize a proof.

HABITS OF MIND
- Reason abstractly and quantitatively.
- Construct viable arguments and critique the reasoning of others.

The diagram shows four collinear points *A*, *B*, *C*, and *D* such that point *B* lies between points *A* and *C*, point *C* lies between points *B* and *D*, and $\overline{AB} \cong \overline{CD}$.

Consider the conditional statement: If $\overline{AB} \cong \overline{CD}$, then $\overline{AC} \cong \overline{BD}$. When you begin the proof process, you take the parts of a conditional statement and organize them into "Given" and "Prove" statements.

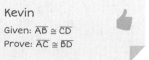

1. Kevin wrote the conditional statement shown. Explain how he decided which statement is the given and which you need to prove.

   Kevin
   Given: $\overline{AB} \cong \overline{CD}$
   Prove: $\overline{AC} \cong \overline{BD}$

   The conditional statement's hypothesis is the "if" statement, so that is the given information the proof builds from. The conclusion is the "then" statement that you need to prove.

2. For each conditional statement, write the hypothesis as the "Given" and the conclusion as the "Prove."

   (a) If $\angle ABD$ and $\angle DBC$ are complementary, then $\overrightarrow{BA} \perp \overrightarrow{BC}$.

   Given: $\angle ABD$ and $\angle DBC$ are complementary.

   Prove: $\overrightarrow{BA} \perp \overrightarrow{BC}$

   (b) If $\angle 2$ and $\angle 3$ are vertical angles, then $\angle 2 \cong \angle 3$.

   Given: $\angle 2$ and $\angle 3$ are vertical angles

   Prove: $\angle 2 \cong \angle 3$

THINK ABOUT...
You can use the Modeling Process to guide your reasoning as you prove geometric theorems.
- Notice and Wonder
- Organize and Mathematize
- Predict and Analyze
- Test and Interpret

Notice and Wonder
What do you notice about the line segments in the diagram? Do you wonder whether there are more pairs of congruent segments?

Organize and Mathematize
To organize your proof, analyze the conditional statement and what information is given and what information you need to prove.

Questions to Support Discourse

		TYPE
1	• Which part of a conditional statement is the hypothesis? Which is the conclusion?	Gathering
2	• Can a conditional statement have more than one given? What is an example?	Seeing structure

ⓒ $m\angle DEG + m\angle GEF = 180°$, if $\angle DEG$ and $\angle GEF$ are a linear pair.

Given: $\angle DEG$ and $\angle GEF$ are a linear pair.

Prove: $m\angle DEG + m\angle GEF = 180°$

You can reason about the proof of conditional statements using constructions.

> Consider the conditional statement from Question 1:
If $\overline{AB} \cong \overline{CD}$, then $\overline{AC} \cong \overline{BD}$.

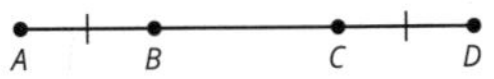

3 Which constructions do you need to prove the conclusion of the conditional statement? **Explain your reasoning.**

You only need to duplicate line segments since you are comparing the lengths of segments.

Predict and Analyze
Think about how you might reason from the given statement to the conclusion. Create or analyze diagrams and consider how you can use them to plan your proof. In geometry, this step of the modeling process can be thought of as Draw and Deduce.

4 Use the diagram and constructions to reason about the validity of the conditional statement.

- I can construct a starter line and duplicate $\overline{AB}$.
- I can then duplicate $\overline{BC}$ starting from point B to construct $\overline{AC}$.
- Next, I can construct a second starter line and duplicate $\overline{CD}$.
- I can then duplicate $\overline{BC}$ starting from point B to construct $\overline{BD}$.
- Finally, I can construct a third starter line and duplicate $\overline{AC}$.
- I can then duplicate $\overline{BD}$ starting at point A to see that point D is the same distance from point B as point A is from point C.

You can also use the postulates and properties you have learned so far to create different forms of proof. A **flow chart proof** is a proof in which the statement and reason for each step are in boxes. Arrows connect the boxes and indicate how each step and reason relates to one or more other steps and reasons.

Questions to Support Discourse

		TYPE
3	• Which tools can you use to show that the lengths of $\overline{AC}$ and $\overline{BD}$ are the same?	Gathering
4	• When $\overline{AB}$ is constructed on a starter ray, why can $\overline{BC}$ be constructed adjacent to $\overline{AB}$ to create $\overline{AC}$? • When you construct $\overline{CD}$ on a starter ray, why can you construct $\overline{BC}$ adjacent to $\overline{CD}$ to create $\overline{BD}$?	Probing
	• How does your construction use a form of the Segment Addition Postulate? How does it use a form of the Addition Property of Equality?	Seeing structure

NOTES

LANGUAGE LINK

ELL TIP

Support students by providing a structure they can use or an alternate way to respond. For example, students could create a list of steps or record a video that describes how they would use the diagram and constructions to verify the conditional statement.

NOTES

COMMON MISCONCEPTION

See Page 300C for a misconception related to the worked example.

WORKED EXAMPLE

You can complete a flow chart proof of the conditional statement: If $\overline{AB} \cong \overline{CD}$, then $\overline{AC} \cong \overline{BD}$.

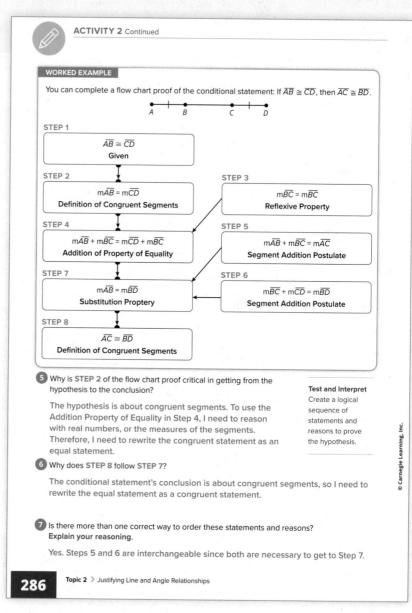

STEP 1
$\overline{AB} \cong \overline{CD}$
Given

STEP 2
$m\overline{AB} = m\overline{CD}$
Definition of Congruent Segments

STEP 3
$m\overline{BC} = m\overline{BC}$
Reflexive Property

STEP 4
$m\overline{AB} + m\overline{BC} = m\overline{CD} + m\overline{BC}$
Addition of Property of Equality

STEP 5
$m\overline{AB} + m\overline{BC} = m\overline{AC}$
Segment Addition Postulate

STEP 6
$m\overline{BC} + m\overline{CD} = m\overline{BD}$
Segment Addition Postulate

STEP 7
$m\overline{AB} = m\overline{BD}$
Substitution Proptery

STEP 8
$\overline{AC} \cong \overline{BD}$
Definition of Congruent Segments

5. Why is **STEP 2** of the flow chart proof critical in getting from the hypothesis to the conclusion?

   The hypothesis is about congruent segments. To use the Addition Property of Equality in Step 4, I need to reason with real numbers, or the measures of the segments. Therefore, I need to rewrite the congruent statement as an equal statement.

Test and Interpret
Create a logical sequence of statements and reasons to prove the hypothesis.

6. Why does **STEP 8** follow **STEP 7**?

   The conditional statement's conclusion is about congruent segments, so I need to rewrite the equal statement as a congruent statement.

7. Is there more than one correct way to order these statements and reasons? **Explain your reasoning.**

   Yes. Steps 5 and 6 are interchangeable since both are necessary to get to Step 7.

Questions to Support Discourse

		TYPE
Worked Example	• Why is it appropriate to use the same reason for Step 2 and Step 8?	Seeing structure
7	• Can you combine Step 5 and Step 6 in a single step since they have the same reason? Why? • Can Step 3 come before Step 2? Why?	Seeing structure

ACTIVITY 2 Continued

A **two-column proof** is a proof in which the steps are in the left column and the corresponding reasons are in the right column.

WORKED EXAMPLE

You can rewrite your flow chart proof in a two-column format.

Statements	Reasons
1. $\overline{AB} \cong \overline{CD}$	1. Given
2. $m\overline{AB} \cong m\overline{CD}$	2. Definition of congruent segments
3. $m\overline{BC} = m\overline{BC}$	3. Reflexive Property
4. $m\overline{AB} + m\overline{BC} = m\overline{CD} + m\overline{BC}$	4. Addition Property of Equality
5. $m\overline{AB} + m\overline{BC} = m\overline{AC}$	5. Segment Addition Postulate
6. $m\overline{BC} + m\overline{CD} = m\overline{BD}$	6. Segment Addition Postulate
7. $m\overline{AC} + m\overline{BD}$	7. Substitution Property
8. $m\overline{AC} \cong m\overline{BD}$	8. Definition of congruent segments

8 How does the two-column proof relate to the flow chart proof?

Each step of the flow chart proof is in the two-column proof in the same order. Each statement from the flow chart is in the left column, and the corresponding reason for the statement is in the right column.

9 Khalil insists the angle in Figure 1 is larger than the angle in Figure 2. Roy disagrees and insists that both angles are the same size.

Figure 1

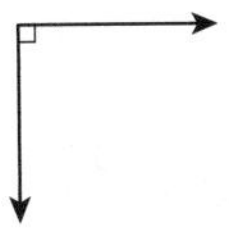

Figure 2

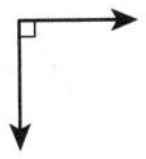

Who is correct? **Justify your reasoning.**

Roy is correct.
Each angle has a measure of 90°, so they are the same size. The size of an angle is not determined by the lengths of its sides.

DID YOU KNOW?

"Q.E.D." is an abbreviation for the Latin phrase *quod erat demonstrandum*, which means *that which was to be demonstrated*. It is a notation often placed at the end of a proof to indicate its completion.

NOTES

DIFFERENTIATION STRATEGY

See Page 300C to assist all students with the worked example.

Questions to Support Discourse

		TYPE
8	• Does each proof have the same number of steps?	Gathering
	• How do the reasons for each of the steps compare in both forms of proof?	Probing
9	• Is there any relationship between the lengths of the sides of an angle and the measure of the angle?	Seeing structure

NOTES

One of Euclid's first five postulates relates to right angles.

POSTULATE

RIGHT ANGLE CONGRUENCE POSTULATE

All right angles are congruent.

While we accept this statement without proof, you can use definitions to prove it.

10 Complete the flow chart of the Right Angle Congruence Postulate by selecting a reason from the word bank for each statement shown and writing it in the correct step.

Given: ∠*ACD* and ∠*BCD* are right angles.
Prove: ∠*ACD* ≅ ∠*BCD*

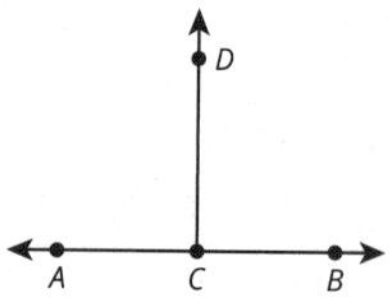

∠*ACD* is a right angle.
Given

↓

m∠*ACD* = 90°
Definition of right angles

∠*BCD* is a right angle.
ⓐ Given

↓

m∠*BCD* = 90°
ⓑ Definition of right angles

↓

m∠*ACD* = m∠*BCD*
ⓒ Transitive Property of Equality

↓

m∠*ACD* ≅ m∠*BCD*
ⓓ Definition of congruent angles

REASONS

Definition of congruent angles

Definition of right angles

Given

Transitive Property of Equality

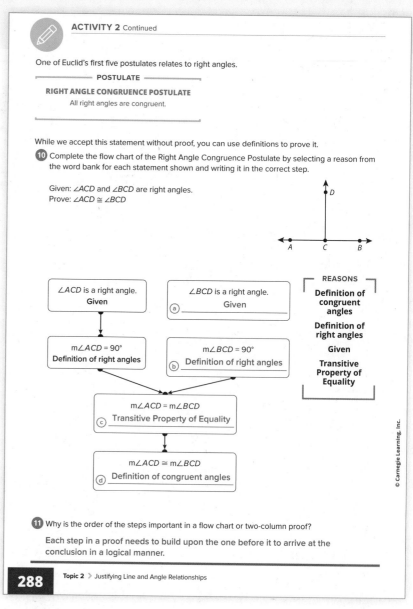

11 Why is the order of the steps important in a flow chart or two-column proof?

Each step in a proof needs to build upon the one before it to arrive at the conclusion in a logical manner.

Questions to Support Discourse

		TYPE
10	• Why do you think the list of reasons includes the Transitive Property instead of the Substitution Property? • Can you use the Substitution Property instead of the Transitive Property?	Probing

ACTIVITY 3

SUMMARY **You can use the Congruent Supplement Theorem to claim two angles supplementary to the same angle are congruent.**

Proofs of the Congruent Supplement Theorem

HABITS OF MIND
- Reason abstractly and quantitatively.
- Construct viable arguments and critique the reasoning of others.

Considering what you know about angles, you might conjecture that if two angles are supplements of the same angle or of congruent angles, then the angles are congruent.

> Let's prove that this conjecture is true.

1. Use the diagram to write the "Given" statements for the Congruent Supplement Theorem. The "Prove" statement is provided.

   Given: $\angle 1$ is supplementary to $\angle 2$.

   Given: $\angle 3$ is supplementary to $\angle 4$.

   Given: $\angle 2 \cong \angle 4$.

   Prove: $\angle 1 \cong \angle 3$

2. Complete the flow chart on the next page to prove the conjecture. Cut out and use the statements and reasons located on page 297.

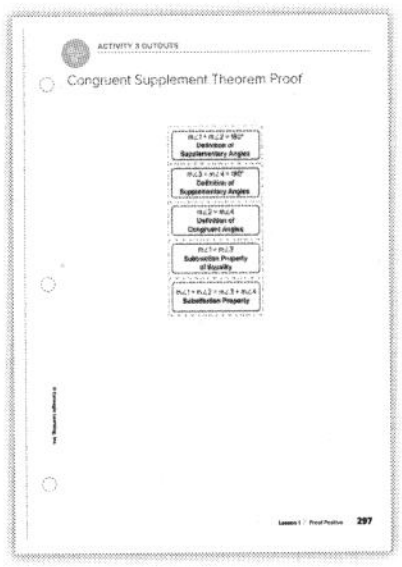

Chunking the Activity

- Read and discuss the introduction
- Group students to complete 1
- Check-in and share
- Group students to complete 2
- Check-in and share
- Group students to complete 3
- Share and summarize

TOPIC 2

DIFFERENTIATION STRATEGY

See Page 300D to support students who struggle with 1.

LANGUAGE LINK

ELL TIP

Ensure students recognize the conditional statement in the introductory text. Have them highlight or underline the conditional statement. This annotation will help them focus on the correct part of the sentence as they complete Question 1.

Questions to Support Discourse

		TYPE
1	• How many given statements do you think you need?	Gathering
	• Why doesn't the order of the given statements make a difference?	Probing

NOTES

DIFFERENTIATION STRATEGY

See Page 300D to support students who struggle with 2.

Student Look-Fors

Using self-motivation and self-discipline to persevere in problem-solving.

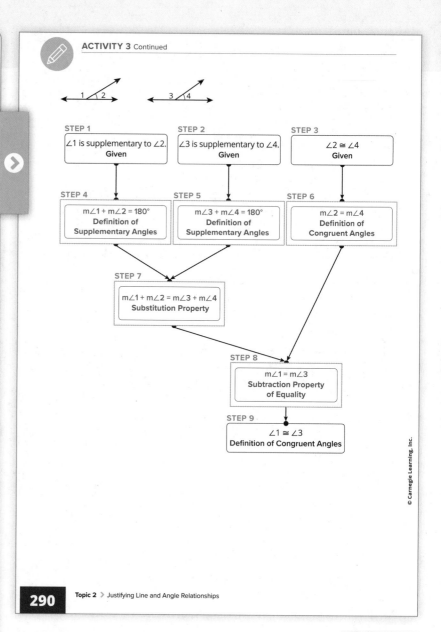

ACTIVITY 3 Continued

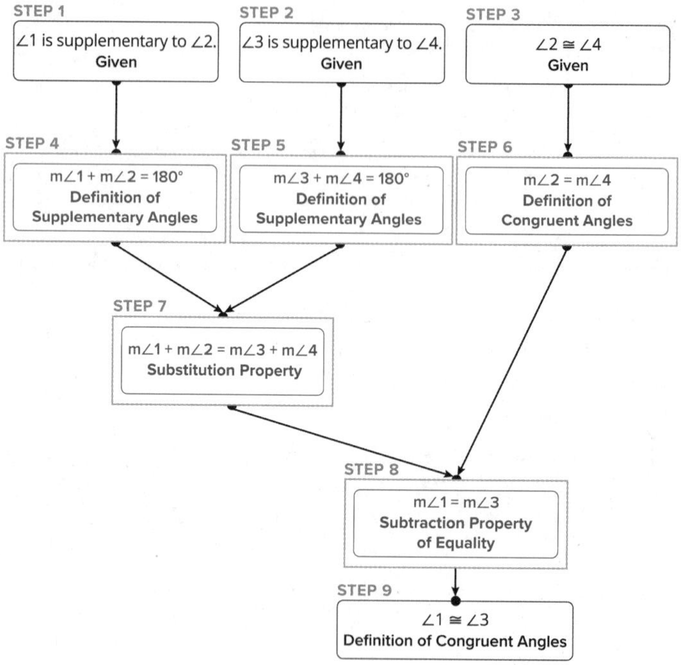

Questions to Support Discourse

		TYPE
2	• What are you subtracting when you apply the Subtraction Property of Equality?	Gathering
	• How are the arrows in the flow chart proof helpful?	Probing

ACTIVITY 3 Continued

3 Create a two-column proof of the conjecture. Each box of the flow chart you completed should appear as a row in the two-column proof.

Statements	Reasons
1. ∠1 is supplementary to ∠2.	1. Given
2. ∠3 is supplementary to ∠4.	2. Given
3. ∠2 ≅ ∠4	3. Given
4. m∠2 = m∠4	4. Definition of congruent angles
5. m∠1 + m∠2 = 180°	5. Definition of supplementary angles
6. m∠3 + m∠4 = 180°	6. Definition of supplementary angles
7. m∠1 + m∠2 = m∠3 + m∠4	7. Substitution Property
8. m∠1 = m∠3	8. Subtraction Property of Equality
9. ∠1 ≅ ∠3	9. Definition of Congruent angles

Because you proved that this conjecture is true, you can now refer to it as a theorem.

THEOREM

CONGRUENT SUPPLEMENT THEOREM

If two angles are supplements of the same angle or of congruent angles, then the angles are congruent.

NOTES

TOPIC 2

Questions to Support Discourse

		TYPE
3	• Are there statements in the two-column proof that are not in the flow chart? Why do you think that is?	Probing
	• Could you put all the given statements together in the same step? Why or why not?	Seeing structure

ACTIVITY 4

SUMMARY **You can state that a pair of vertical angles are congruent because of the Vertical Angle Theorem.**

Chunking the Activity

- **Read and discuss the introduction**
- **Complete 1 as a class**
- **Read and discuss the worked example**
- **Group students to complete 2 – 4**
- **Check-in and share**
- **Group students to complete 5**
- **Share and summarize**

COMMON MISCONCEPTION

See Page 300D for a misconception related to 1.

DIFFERENTIATION STRATEGY

See Page 300E to assist all students with the worked example.

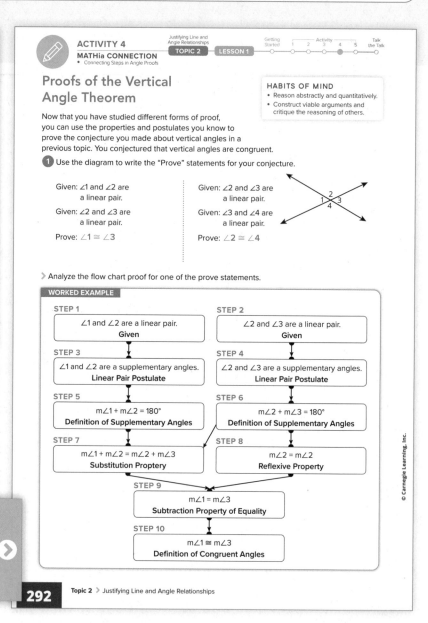

Proofs of the Vertical Angle Theorem

HABITS OF MIND
- Reason abstractly and quantitatively.
- Construct viable arguments and critique the reasoning of others.

Now that you have studied different forms of proof, you can use the properties and postulates you know to prove the conjecture you made about vertical angles in a previous topic. You conjectured that vertical angles are congruent.

1 Use the diagram to write the "Prove" statements for your conjecture.

Given: ∠1 and ∠2 are a linear pair.
Given: ∠2 and ∠3 are a linear pair.
Prove: ∠1 ≅ ∠3

Given: ∠2 and ∠3 are a linear pair.
Given: ∠3 and ∠4 are a linear pair.
Prove: ∠2 ≅ ∠4

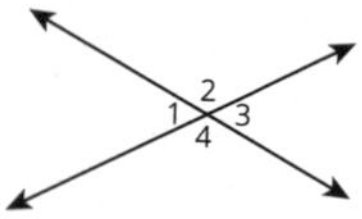

> Analyze the flow chart proof for one of the prove statements.

WORKED EXAMPLE

STEP 1: ∠1 and ∠2 are a linear pair. **Given**

STEP 2: ∠2 and ∠3 are a linear pair. **Given**

STEP 3: ∠1 and ∠2 are a supplementary angles. **Linear Pair Postulate**

STEP 4: ∠2 and ∠3 are a supplementary angles. **Linear Pair Postulate**

STEP 5: m∠1 + m∠2 = 180° **Definition of Supplementary Angles**

STEP 6: m∠2 + m∠3 = 180° **Definition of Supplementary Angles**

STEP 7: m∠1 + m∠2 = m∠2 + m∠3 **Substitution Proptery**

STEP 8: m∠2 = m∠2 **Reflexive Property**

STEP 9: m∠1 = m∠3 **Subtraction Property of Equality**

STEP 10: m∠1 ≅ m∠3 **Definition of Congruent Angles**

Questions to Support Discourse

		TYPE
1	• Why are there two prove statements? • How did you decide which prove statement follows from each set of given statements?	Probing
Worked Example	• What is the Linear Pair Postulate? • When two angles are supplementary, what can you conclude about their measures?	Gathering
	• What information in Step 7 helps you determine which angle to use in Step 8?	Seeing structure

ACTIVITY 4 Continued

2 Could STEP 5 come before STEP 3? Explain your reasoning.

No. You have to assume that the angles are supplementary using the Linear Pair Postulate before you can reason that the sum of the measures = 180°.

3 What is the purpose of STEP 8?

Step 8 states that $m\angle 2$ is equal to itself so that the measure can be subtracted in Step 9 using the Subtraction Property of Equality.

4 What steps would be different in a flow chart proof of the second prove statement of the Vertical Angle Theorem?

All the reasons would be the same, but Steps 2, 4, and 6 would be statements about $\angle 4$ and $\angle 1$, Step 8 would be about $\angle 1$, and Steps 9 and 10 would be about $\angle 4$ and $\angle 2$.

Because the conjecture was proven true, you can now refer to it as a theorem.

THEOREM

VERTICAL ANGLE THEOREM
Vertical angles are congruent.

REMEMBER...
The Congruent Supplement Theorem states: "If two angles are supplements of the same angle, or of congruent angles, then the angles are congruent."

Once you prove a theorem, you can use it as a reason in another proof. This allows you to write shorter proofs.

5 Create a two-column proof for the other prove statement using the Congruent Supplement Theorem.

Statements	Reasons
1. $\angle 2$ and $\angle 3$ are a linear pair.	1. Given
2. $\angle 3$ and $\angle 4$ are a linear pair.	2. Given
3. $\angle 2$ and $\angle 3$ are supplementary angles.	3. Linear Pair Postulate
4. $\angle 3$ and $\angle 4$ are supplementary angles.	4. Linear Pair Postulate
5. $m\angle 2 + m\angle 3 = 180°$	5. Definition of supplementary angles
6. $m\angle 3 + m\angle 4 = 180°$	6. Definition of supplementary angles
7. $\angle 2 \cong \angle 4$	7. Congruent Supplement Theorem

NOTES

Questions to Support Discourse

		TYPE
5	• How does the two-column proof compare to the flow chart proof? • Why is it more efficient to use the Congruent Supplement Theorem?	Seeing structure

ACTIVITY 5

SUMMARY **You can use geometric theorems and postulates to identify angle relationships and determine angle measures.**

Chunking the Activity

- **Read and discuss the introduction**
- **Group students to complete the activity**
- **Share and summarize**

DIFFERENTIATION STRATEGY

See Page 300E to challenge advanced learners to extend 2.

Student Look-Fors

Incomplete work due to solving for *x*, but not calculating the angle measures.

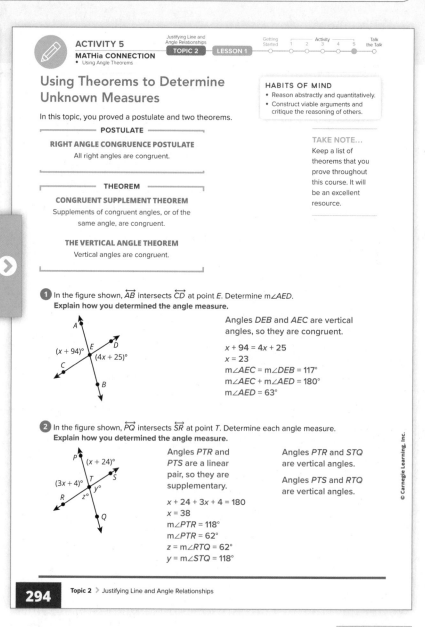

Using Theorems to Determine Unknown Measures

HABITS OF MIND
- Reason abstractly and quantitatively.
- Construct viable arguments and critique the reasoning of others.

In this topic, you proved a postulate and two theorems.

POSTULATE

RIGHT ANGLE CONGRUENCE POSTULATE
All right angles are congruent.

THEOREM

CONGRUENT SUPPLEMENT THEOREM
Supplements of congruent angles, or of the same angle, are congruent.

THE VERTICAL ANGLE THEOREM
Vertical angles are congruent.

TAKE NOTE... Keep a list of theorems that you prove throughout this course. It will be an excellent resource.

1. In the figure shown, $\overleftrightarrow{AB}$ intersects $\overleftrightarrow{CD}$ at point *E*. Determine m∠*AED*. **Explain how you determined the angle measure.**

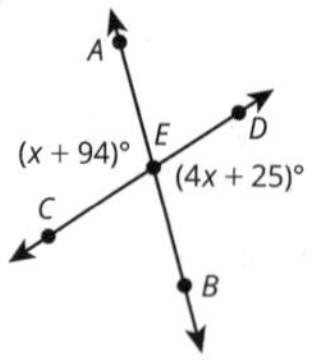

Angles *DEB* and *AEC* are vertical angles, so they are congruent.

$x + 94 = 4x + 25$
$x = 23$
$m\angle AEC = m\angle DEB = 117°$
$m\angle AEC + m\angle AED = 180°$
$m\angle AED = 63°$

2. In the figure shown, $\overleftrightarrow{PQ}$ intersects $\overleftrightarrow{SR}$ at point *T*. Determine each angle measure. **Explain how you determined the angle measure.**

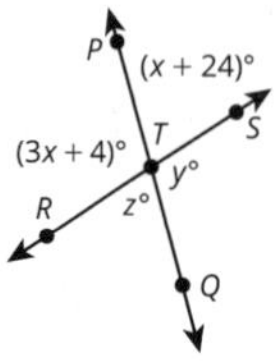

Angles *PTR* and *PTS* are a linear pair, so they are supplementary.

$x + 24 + 3x + 4 = 180$
$x = 38$
$m\angle PTR = 118°$
$m\angle PTR = 62°$
$z = m\angle RTQ = 62°$
$y = m\angle STQ = 118°$

Angles *PTR* and *STQ* are vertical angles.

Angles *PTS* and *RTQ* are vertical angles.

Questions to Support Discourse

	Question	TYPE
1	• What is the relationship between ∠*AEC* and ∠*BED*?	Gathering
	• Why isn't the value of *x* equal to m∠*AEC*?	Probing
2	• What is the relationship between ∠*PTR* and ∠*PTS*?	Gathering
	• Once you have determined ∠*PTR*, which theorems can you use to explain how to determine the remaining angle measures?	Reflecting and justifying

SUMMARY **In a paragraph proof, you write the statements and corresponding reasons in complete sentences.**

Goof-Proof

> Think back on the properties and theorems you explored in this lesson.

1 Choose the correct property or theorem for each statement.

PROPERTY OR THEOREM
Addition Property of Equality
Congruent Supplement Theorem
Reflexive Property
Substitution Property
Transitive Property
Vertical Angle Theorem

(a) $\angle H \cong \angle K$
$\angle K \cong \angle M$
Therefore, $\angle H \cong \angle M$

Transitive Property

(b) $m\overline{MN} = m\overline{OP}$
$m\overline{MN} + m\overline{RS} = m\overline{OP} + m\overline{RS}$

Addition Property of Equality

(c) $m\angle T = 34°$
$m\angle W = 34°$
Therefore, $m\angle T = m\angle W$

Substitution Property

(d) $m\angle A + m\angle B = 180°$
$m\angle A + m\angle C = 180°$
Therefore, $\angle B = \angle C$

Congruent Supplement Theorem

(e) $m\angle V = m\angle V$

Reflexive Property

(f) $\angle 1 = \angle 2$

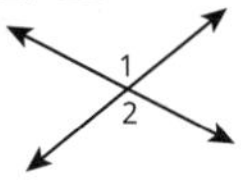

Vertical Angle Theorem

Chunking the Activity

- Read and discuss the directions
- Group students to complete the activity
- Share and summarize

LANGUAGE LINK

ELL TIP

Allow students to create either a flow chart or two-column proof. Ensure they have the opportunity to see the connections between those structures and a paragraph proof.

Questions to Support Discourse

		TYPE
1	• How is the Substitution Property different than the Transitive Property?	Seeing structure

NOTES

TALK THE TALK Continued

> Consider Circle O with diameters $\overline{AC}$ and $\overline{BD}$.

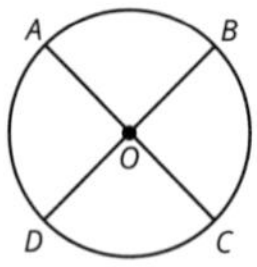

2 What do you know about $\overset{\frown}{AB}$ and $\overset{\frown}{CD}$?

The diameters create vertical central angles, so the arcs are congruent.

You have used reasoning through constructions, flow chart proofs, and two-column proofs to prove theorems. Another type of proof is a **paragraph proof**, in which you write the statements and corresponding reasons in complete sentences.

3 Prove $\overset{\frown}{AB} \cong \overset{\frown}{CD}$ by writing a paragraph proof.

If diameters $\overline{AC}$ and $\overline{BD}$ intersect at the center of Circle O, then $\angle BOA$ and $\angle COD$ are central angles of Circle O by the definition of central angles.

Angle BOA and $\angle COD$ are vertical angles by the definition of vertical angles. By the Vertical Angle Theorem, these angles are congruent.

The measure of $\overset{\frown}{AB}$ is equal to $m\angle AOB$ and the measure of $\overset{\frown}{CD}$ is equal to $m\angle COD$ by the definition of the relationship between arcs and central angles.

By the Substitution Property, $m\overset{\frown}{AB}$ is equal to $m\overset{\frown}{CD}$. Therefore, $\overset{\frown}{AB}$ is congruent to $\overset{\frown}{CD}$ by the definition of congruent arcs.

Questions to Support Discourse

		TYPE
2	• What intercepted arc is associated with $\angle AOB$? $\angle COD$? • What is the relationship between a central angle and the measure of its intercepted arc?	Gathering
	• Are $\angle AOB$ and $\angle COD$ central angles? How do you know?	Probing
3	• How does a paragraph proof compare to a two-column proof? What about a flow chart? • Do you think the order of the statements is important in a paragraph proof? Why?	Seeing structure

ACTIVITY 3 CUTOUTS

Congruent Supplement Theorem Proof

$m\angle 1 + m\angle 2 = 180°$ **Definition of Supplementary Angles**
$m\angle 3 + m\angle 4 = 180°$ **Definition of Supplementary Angles**
$m\angle 2 = m\angle 4$ **Definition of Congruent Angles**
$m\angle 1 = m\angle 3$ **Subtraction Property of Equality**
$m\angle 1 + m\angle 2 = m\angle 3 + m\angle 4$ **Substitution Property**

Lesson 1 > Proof Positive 297

NOTES

NOTES

Why is this page blank?

So you can cut out the statements and reasons on the other side.

LESSON 1 ASSIGNMENT

> Use a separate piece of paper for your Journal entry.

JOURNAL

Describe the differences between a flow chart proof, a two-column proof, and a paragraph proof in your own words.

REMEMBER

A proof is a logical series of statements and corresponding reasons that starts with a hypothesis and arrives at a conclusion. There is more than one way to organize a proof.

PRACTICE

1. Identify the property that justifies each statement.

   (a) If $\overline{AB} \cong \overline{PR}$ and $\overline{PR} \cong \overline{ST}$, then $\overline{AB} \cong \overline{ST}$.

   Transitive Property

   (b) If JK = 6 centimeters and CD = 6 centimeters, then $JK = CD$.

   Substitution Property

   (c) $\angle ABC \cong \angle ABC$

   Reflexive Property

   (d) If $m\angle 3 = m\angle 1$, then $m\angle 3 + m\angle 2 = m\angle 1 + m\angle 2$.

   Addition Property of Equality

2. Enter the reasons to complete the two-column proof.

   Given: $\angle 1 \cong \angle 4$
   Prove: $\angle 2 \cong \angle 3$

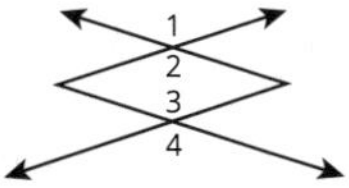

Statements	Reasons
1. $\angle 1 \cong \angle 4$	1. Given
2. $\angle 4 \cong \angle 3$	2. Vertical Angle Theorem
3. $\angle 1 \cong \angle 2$	3. Vertical Angle Theorem
4. $\angle 1 \cong \angle 3$	4. Transitive Property
5. $\angle 2 \cong \angle 3$	5. Transitive Property

Go to LiveHint.com for help on the PRACTICE questions.

Encourage students to use LiveHint.com for help with the PRACTICE questions of this assignment.

Chunking the Assignment

SESSION 1

- Practice 1

SESSION 2

- Mixed Practice (page 383) 1 and 2

SESSION 3

- Journal
- Practice 2 - 4
- Stretch (advanced learners)

TOPIC 2

JOURNAL

Sample answer.

In a flow chart proof, you write the statement and reason for each step in boxes. Arrows connect the boxes and indicate how you generate each step and reason from one or more other steps and reasons.

In a two-column proof, you write the steps in the left column and the corresponding reasons in the right column.

In a paragraph proof, you write the statements and corresponding reasons in complete sentences.

NOTES

STRETCH

Statements	Reasons
1. $\angle A$ and $\angle B$ are complementary	1. Given
2. $\angle A$ and $\angle C$ are congruent and $\angle B$ and $\angle D$ are congruent	2. Defination of complementary angles.
3. $m\angle A + m\angle B = 90°$	3. Vertical Angle Theorem
4. $m\angle A = m\angle C$ and $m\angle B = m\angle D$	4. Defination of congruent angles.
5. $m\angle C + m\angle D = 90°$	5. Substitution Property
6. $\angle C$ and $\angle D$ are complementary	6. Defination of complementary angles.

3 Write a paragraph proof to prove the statement.

Given: $m\angle QRS = 90°$
Given: $\angle RTS \cong \angle QRT$
Prove: $\angle RTS$ and $\angle TRS$ are complementary.

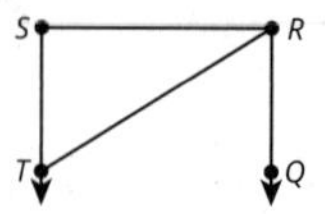

$m\angle QRS = 90°$
By the Angle Addition Postulate, $m\angle TRS + m\angle QRT = m\angle QRS$.
By Substitution, $m\angle TRS + m\angle QRT = 90°$.
$\angle RTS \cong \angle QRT$, so $m\angle RTS = m\angle QRT$ by the definition of congruent angles.
By Substitution, $m\angle TRS + m\angle QRT = 90°$.
So, by the definition of complementary angles, $\angle RTS$ and $\angle TRS$ are complementary.

4 In the figure, $\angle GXF \cong \angle CXD$.

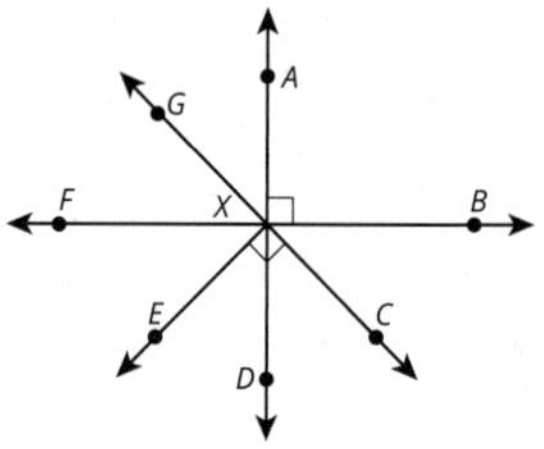

(a) Which theorem tells you that $\angle AXG \cong \angle CXD$?

Vertical Angle Theorem

(b) Which theorem tells you that $\angle EXF \cong \angle EXD$?

Congruent Complement Theorem

(c) Which theorem tells you that $\angle GXD \cong \angle CXF$?

Congruent Supplement Theorem

STRETCH Optional

> Create a two-column proof.

Given: $\angle A$ and $\angle B$ are complementary.
Prove: $\angle C$ and $\angle D$ are complementary.

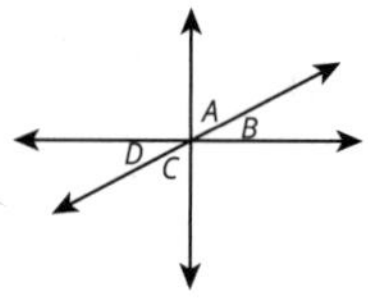

Proof Positive

This resource details additional facilitation notes to fully assist you as you plan each lesson to support all students, students who struggle, and advanced learners. It provides differentiation strategies, common student misconceptions, and suggestions to extend certain activities.

GETTING STARTED

Session 1 of 3

Infinite Regression

Students prove the conjecture that vertical angles are congruent. They review the Angle Addition Postulate, Linear Pair Postulate, and Segment Addition Postulate.

CHUNK	AUDIENCE	ADDITIONAL SUPPORTS
As students work on the topic	All Students	**DIFFERENTIATION STRATEGY** Throughout this topic and the next topic, students will be proving theorems. Have students utilize a strategy such as a loose-leaf ring with hole-punched note cards. As definitions, postulates, properties, theorems, and proof paths are introduced, have students write each one on a separate note card for reference and reinforcement. 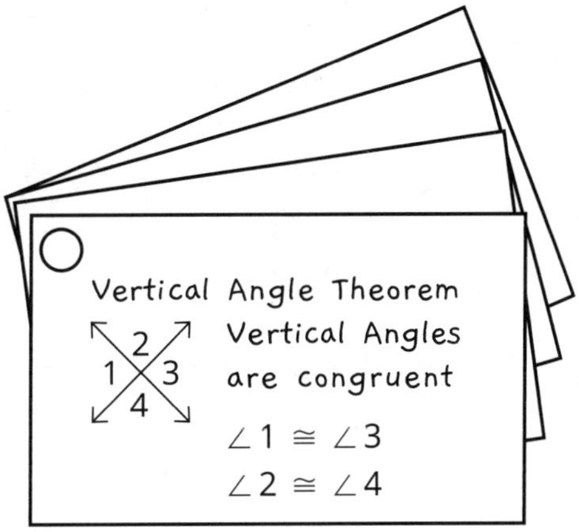
As students discuss the postulates	Students who Struggle	**DIFFERENTIATION STRATEGY** Have students draw a diagram to represent each postulate and statement.

ACTIVITY 1

Session 1 of 3

Properties of Real Numbers in Geometry

Students apply properties of real numbers in geometry. They apply the Addition Property of Equality, the Subtraction Property of Equality, the Reflexive Property, the Substitution Property, and the Transitive Property to angle measures and segment measures.

CHUNK	AUDIENCE	ADDITIONAL SUPPORTS
As students discuss the properties	All Students	**COMMON MISCONCEPTION** Students often believe they can use the Substitution and Transitive Properties interchangeably. Help students understand the difference by providing examples. • If $x = y + 8$ and $y = -3z$, then $x = -3z + 8$. By the Substitution Property, the expression $-3z$ is substituted for y. The Transitive property does not apply in this case because it does not map to "If $a = b$, and $b = c$, then $a = c$." In this case, there is no b-quantity that is the same in both expressions. Transitive Property would apply if the statement were "If $x = y + 8$ and $y + 8 = -3z$, then $x = -3z$."
As students work on 1	Students who Struggle	**COMMON MISCONCEPTION** Students sometimes confuse the Angle and Segment Addition Postulates and the Addition Property of Equality. Ensure students understand that you apply the Angle Addition Postulate when beginning with one measure and the Addition Property of Equality when beginning with two equivalent measures. <u>Angle Addition Postulate</u>: $m\angle A$; $m\angle A + m\angle C$ <u>Addition Property of Equality</u>: $m\angle A = m\angle B$; $m\angle A + m\angle C = m\angle B + m\angle C$

ACTIVITY 2

Session 2 of 3

Forms of Proof

Students rewrite the hypotheses and conclusions of conditional statements as given and prove statements. They analyze the structure for writing flow chart proofs and two-column proofs. They complete a flow chart proof of the Right Angle Congruence Postulate.

CHUNK	AUDIENCE	ADDITIONAL SUPPORTS
As students discuss the first worked example	All Students	**COMMON MISCONCEPTION** Since congruence implies equality, students may not understand why it is essential to go from congruent statements to measurement statements. Ensure they understand that the postulates and properties addressed involve equality statements. Students cannot use these as reasons until they write the statements with equal signs rather than congruent symbols.
As students discuss the second worked example	All Students	**DIFFERENTIATION STRATEGY** Help students make the switch from congruence to equalities then back to congruence when writing a proof by having them note this common proof path on their theorem note cards. 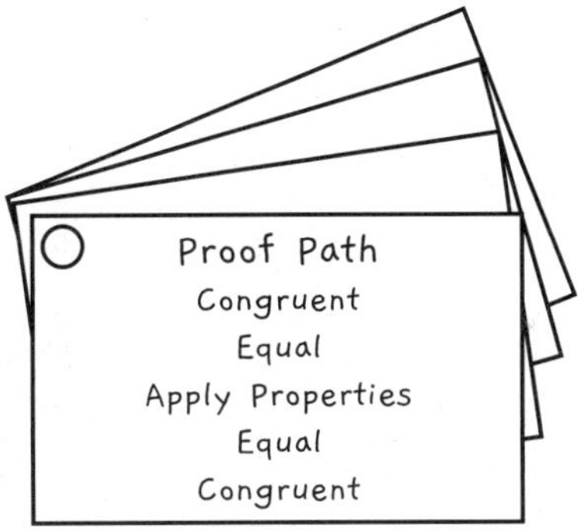

ACTIVITY 3

Session 2 of 3

Proofs of the Congruent Supplement Theorem

Students prove the Congruent Supplement Theorem. They cut out statements with reasons and use them to complete a flow chart proof. They use the flow chart proof as a guide to write a two-column proof.

CHUNK	AUDIENCE	ADDITIONAL SUPPORTS
As students work on 1	Students who Struggle	**DIFFERENTIATION STRATEGY** Help students make sense of the conjecture by substituting 100° and 80° for the angle measures. Throughout the topic, encourage students to make sense of conjectures by thinking about specific examples.
As students work on 2	Students who Struggle	**DIFFERENTIATION STRATEGY** In the flow chart proof, have students write that $m\angle 2$ and $m\angle 4$ are subtracted from their respective sides of the equation when applying the Subtraction Property of Equality. $m\angle 1 + m\angle 2 = m\angle 3 + m\angle 4$ $ - m\angle 2 \qquad - m\angle 4$ $m\angle 1 = m\angle 3$ Be sure students understand that they can apply the Subtraction Property of Equality using two different angles because $m\angle 2$ and $m\angle 4$ represent the same value.

ACTIVITY 4

Session 3 of 3

Proofs of the Vertical Angle Theorem

Students prove the Vertical Angle Theorem. They analyze the flow chart proving one pair of vertical angles congruent and answer questions about the steps. They use the Congruent Supplement Theorem in a two-column proof to prove that the second pair of vertical angles are congruent.

CHUNK	AUDIENCE	ADDITIONAL SUPPORTS
As students work on 1	All Students	**COMMON MISCONCEPTION** Students may claim vertical angles are congruent because of the definition of vertical angles instead of the Vertical Angle Congruence Theorem. Remind students to name vertical angles using the definition of vertical angles and then state they are congruent by the Vertical Angle Congruence Theorem.

CHUNK	AUDIENCE	ADDITIONAL SUPPORTS
As students analyze the worked example	All Students	**DIFFERENTIATION STRATEGY** Have students note this common proof path on their theorem note cards. To state the sum of angle measures in a linear pair is 180°, use the Linear Pair Postulate to justify that the angles are supplementary. Then use the definition of supplementary angles to justify that the sum of the angle measures is 180°.

ACTIVITY 5

Session 3 of 3

Using Theorems to Determine Unknown Measures

Students solve for the measures of angles. They apply the Congruent Supplement Theorem, Vertical Angle Theorem, or the Linear Pair Postulate

CHUNK	AUDIENCE	ADDITIONAL SUPPORTS
To extend 2	Advanced Learners	**DIFFERENTIATION STRATEGY** Have students create a problem like those in this activity. For an extra challenge, require students to provide algebraic expressions for the measures of all four angles.

Practice the learning

MATHbook + Skills Practice

The table shows the targeted practice of the skills and mathematical concepts for the *Justifying Line and Angle Relationships* Topic. The highlighted Problem Set aligns with **Proof Positive**.

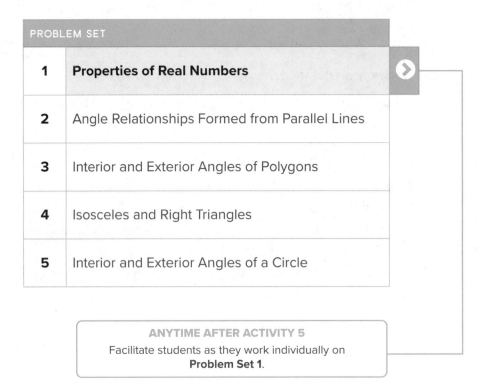

PROBLEM SET	
1	**Properties of Real Numbers**
2	Angle Relationships Formed from Parallel Lines
3	Interior and Exterior Angles of Polygons
4	Isosceles and Right Triangles
5	Interior and Exterior Angles of a Circle

ANYTIME AFTER ACTIVITY 5

Facilitate students as they work individually on **Problem Set 1**.

ENGAGE at the **Module** level + **DEVELOP** at the **Topic** level + **TEACH** Read the facilitation notes and plan learning experiences.

Where are we?

TOPIC 2 Justifying Line and Angle Relationships	LESSON 1 Proof Positive	LESSON 2 A Parallel Universe	LESSON 3 Ins and Outs	LESSON 4 Identical Twins	LESSON 5 Corners in a Round Room
Pacing	3 Sessions	2 Sessions	2 Sessions	2 Sessions	2 Sessions

OVERVIEW: LESSON 2

A Parallel Universe

Proving Parallel Line Theorems

ENGAGE

- Students investigate angle relationships formed when a transversal cuts two parallel lines.

DEVELOP

- Students translate an angle along a transversal to create parallel lines and congruent corresponding angles.
- They use the Corresponding Angles Theorem to prove the Same-Side Interior Angles Theorem.
- They prove the Alternate Interior Angles Theorem, Alternate Exterior Angles Theorem, and Same-Side Exterior Angles Theorem.
- They explore the converse of the theorems they proved in this lesson.
- Students prove the Perpendicular/Parallel Line Theorem.

DEMONSTRATE

- Students justify conditional statements.

HIGH SCHOOL GEOMETRY

Congruence

Prove geometric theorems.

9. Prove theorems about lines and angles.

LESSON STRUCTURE AND PACING GUIDE 2 SESSIONS

✪ This activity highlights a key term or concept that is essential to the learning goals of the lesson.

Session 1

INSTRUCTIONAL SEQUENCE

ENGAGE	DEVELOP	DEVELOP
Connect to prior knowledge	Investigation	Mathematical problem solving

GETTING STARTED
Criss Cross Applesauce

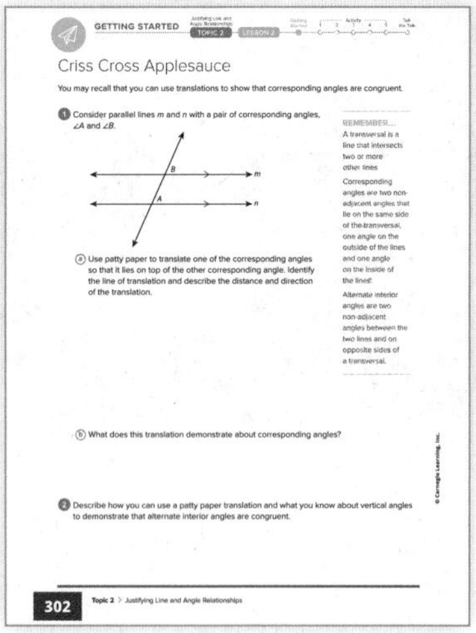
Criss Cross Applesauce

Students use patty paper and rigid motion transformations to investigate angle relationships formed when a transversal cuts two parallel lines.

- They describe how a patty paper translation and congruent vertical angles can show alternate interior angles are congruent.

ACTIVITY 1
Corresponding Angles Theorem

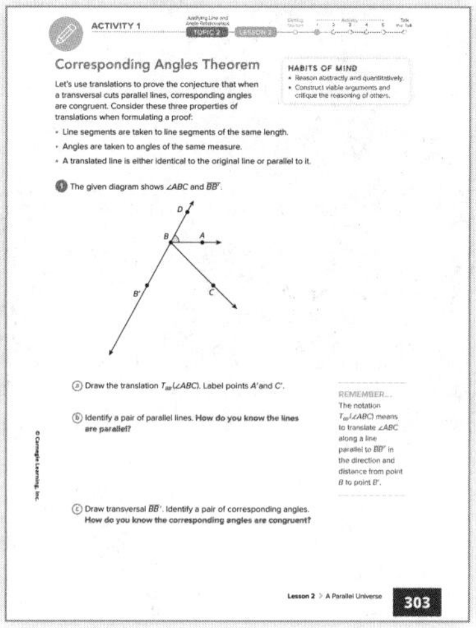
Corresponding Angles Theorem

Students translate an angle along a transversal to create parallel lines and congruent corresponding angles.

- They write a paragraph proof for the Corresponding Angles Theorem.
- They show how to use translations to prove the Corresponding Angles Converse Theorem.

ACTIVITY 2
Same-Side Interior Angles Theorem

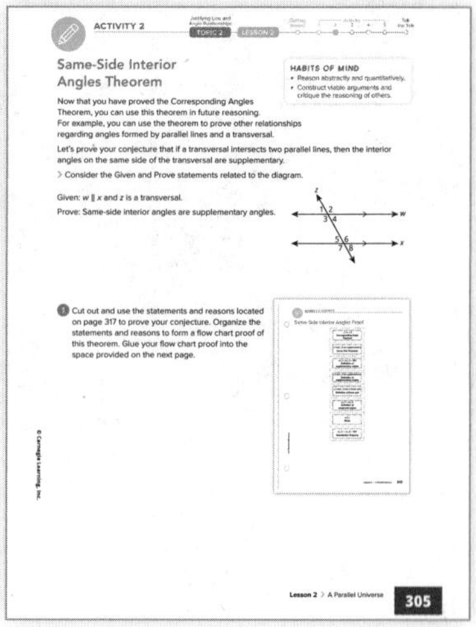
Same-Side Interior Angles Theorem

Students use the Corresponding Angles Theorem to prove the first part of the Same-Side Interior Angles Theorem.

- They assemble statements and reasons into a flow chart proof.

ACTIVITY CUTOUT

Log in to MyCL for **lesson support** including:

Slides

Videos

www.carnegielearning.com/login

Session 2

INSTRUCTIONAL SEQUENCE

ENGAGE	DEVELOP	DEVELOP
Peer analysis **Mathematical problem solving**	**Mathematical problem solving**	**Mathematical problem solving** **Peer analysis**

ACTIVITY 3
Alternate Interior Angles Theorem

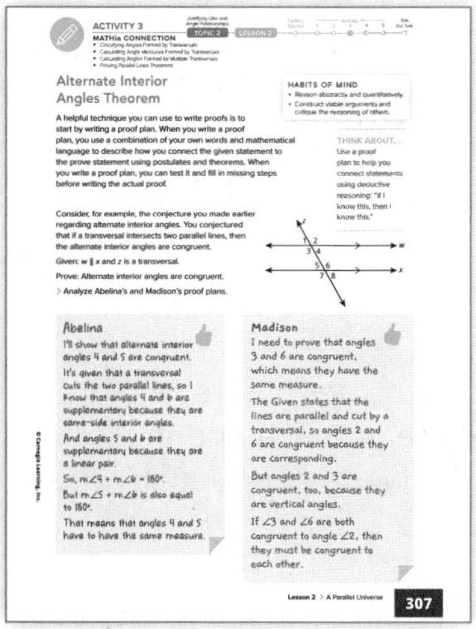

Alternate Interior Angles Theorem

307

Students prove the Alternate Interior Angles Theorem, Alternate Exterior Angles Theorem, and Same-Side Exterior Angles Theorem.

- They list the definitions, postulates, and theorems used in the Alternate Interior Angles Theorem's proof plans.
- They complete a flow chart proof and a two-column proof.

ACTIVITY 4
Parallel Lines Converse Theorems

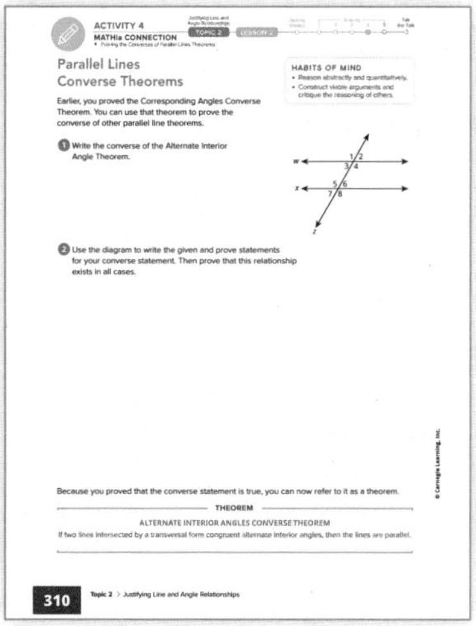

Parallel Lines Converse Theorems

310

Students prove the Alternate Interior Angles Converse Theorem and the Same-Side Interior Angles Converse Theorem

- They draw a diagram and write a proof for the Alternate Exterior Angles Converse Theorem.

ACTIVITY 5
Perpendicular/Parallel Line Theorem

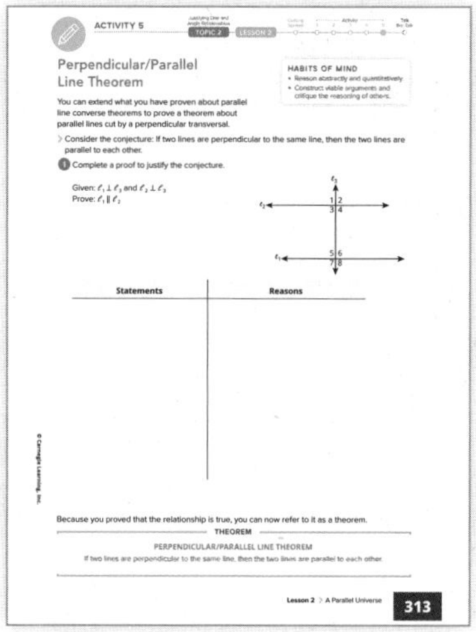

Perpendicular/Parallel Line Theorem

313

Students prove the Perpendicular/Parallel Line Theorem.

- They apply previously proven theorems.

TOPIC 2

Log in to MyCL for:

- Editable templates
- Additional planning support

Session 2

INSTRUCTIONAL SEQUENCE

ENGAGE
Exit ticket procedures

TALK THE TALK
If 'N' Then Again

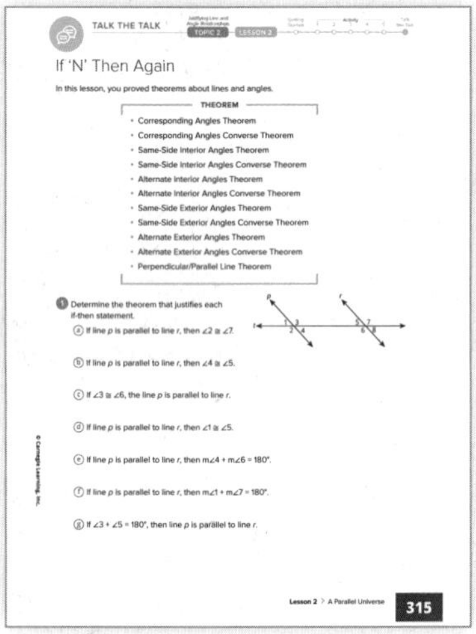
TALK THE TALK

TOPIC 2 LESSON 2

If 'N' Then Again

In this lesson, you proved theorems about lines and angles.

THEOREM

- Corresponding Angles Theorem
- Corresponding Angles Converse Theorem
- Same-Side Interior Angles Theorem
- Same-Side Interior Angles Converse Theorem
- Alternate Interior Angles Theorem
- Alternate Interior Angles Converse Theorem
- Same-Side Exterior Angles Theorem
- Same-Side Exterior Angles Converse Theorem
- Alternate Exterior Angles Theorem
- Alternate Exterior Angles Converse Theorem
- Perpendicular/Parallel Line Theorem

1 Determine the theorem that justifies each if-then statement.

a) If line p is parallel to line r, then $\angle 2 \cong \angle 7$.

b) If line p is parallel to line r, then $\angle 4 \cong \angle 5$.

c) If $\angle 3 \cong \angle 6$, the line p is parallel to line r.

d) If line p is parallel to line r, then $\angle 1 \cong \angle 5$.

e) If line p is parallel to line r, then $m\angle 4 + m\angle 6 = 180°$.

f) If line p is parallel to line r, then $m\angle 1 + m\angle 7 = 180°$.

g) If $\angle 3 + \angle 5 = 180°$, then line p is parallel to line r.

© Carnegie Learning, Inc.

Lesson 2 > A Parallel Universe 315

Students determine the theorem that justifies conditional statements.

- They reason about angle measures formed when a transversal cuts two lines.

Now that you have read the Module, Topic, and Lesson Overviews, you are ready to plan.

Do the math

> Tear out the lesson planning template (page 301E) and jot down thoughts as you work through this lesson and read the Facilitation Notes.

Connect the learning

MATHbook + MATHia

The table shows a portion of the self-paced MATHia sequence for the *Justifying Line and Angle Relationships* Topic.

Median student completion time for entire topic: ~500–530 minutes

> As you implement this lesson, consider different connections for students who are on pace and those that have not yet completed the workspaces aligned to this lesson.

STUDENTS WHO ARE NOT HERE YET
Students practice calculating the measure of angles formed when a transversal cuts parallel lines.

TYPE	WORKSPACE NAME
	Classifying Angles Formed by Transversals
	Calculating Angle Measures Formed by Transversals
	Proving Parallel Lines Theorems and Their Converses

STUDENTS WHO ARE ON PACE
After you complete Activity 2, ask these students to share how they calculated angle measures when there are more than 1 pair of parallel lines.

A Parallel Universe

Proving Parallel Line Theorems

Session 1

GETTING STARTED Criss Cross Applesauce ✪

Pacing (minutes)	
My Time	Class Time

ACTIVITY 1 Corresponding Angles Theorem ✪

Pacing (minutes)	
My Time	Class Time

KEY TERM
Corresponding Angles Theorem
Corresponding Angles Converse Theorem

ACTIVITY 2 Same-Side Interior Angles Theorem ✪

ACTIVITY CUTOUT

Pacing (minutes)	
My Time	Class Time

KEY TERM
Same-Side Interior Angles Theorem

ACTIVITY 3 Alternate Interior Angles Theorem ✪

Pacing (minutes)	
My Time	Class Time

KEY TERM
Alternate Interior Angles Theorem
Alternate Exterior Angles Theorem
Same-Side Exterior Angles Theorem

Session 2

ACTIVITY 4 Parallel Lines Converse Theorems ✪

Pacing (minutes)	
My Time	Class Time

KEY TERM
Alternate Interior Angles Converse Theorem
Same-Side Interior Angles Converse Theorem
Alternate Exterior Angles Converse Theorem
Same-Side Exterior Angles Converse Theorem

ACTIVITY 5 Perpendicular/Parallel Line Theorem

Pacing (minutes)	
My Time	Class Time

KEY TERM
Perpendicular/Parallel Line Theorem

TALK THE TALK If 'N' Then Again

Pacing (minutes)	
My Time	Class Time

✪ This activity highlights a key term or concept that is essential to the learning goals of the lesson.

Log in to MyCL for:

- Editable templates
- Additional planning support

Reflect on your lesson

Consider the effectiveness of your lesson on student learning.

What went well?	What did not go as planned?

Anticipate how you would change the lesson next time you teach it.

How will you capitalize on the things that went well?	How will you improve things that did not go as planned?

MATERIALS

- Compasses
- Glue sticks
- Patty paper
- Scissors
- Straightedges

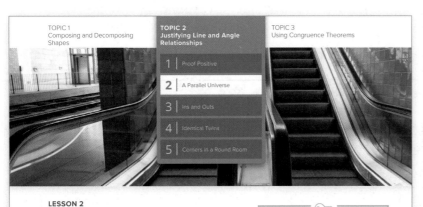

TOPIC 1
Composing and Decomposing Shapes

TOPIC 2
Justifying Line and Angle Relationships

1 | Proof Positive
2 | A Parallel Universe
3 | Ins and Outs
4 | Identical Twins
5 | Corners in a Round Room

TOPIC 3
Using Congruence Theorems

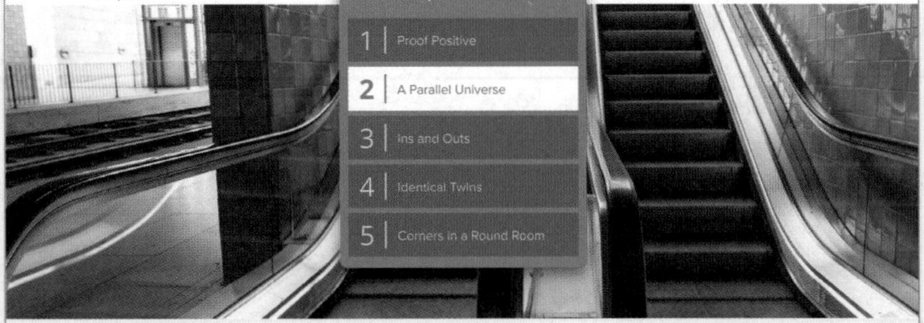

LESSON 2

A Parallel Universe

Proving Parallel Line Theorems

Learning Goals

- Prove the Corresponding Angles Theorem, the Same-Side Interior Angles Theorem, the Alternate Interior Angles Theorem, and their converses.
- Demonstrate understanding of the Alternate Exterior Angles Theorem, the Same-Side Exterior Angles Theorem, and their converses.
- Prove the Perpendicular/Parallel Line Theorem.
- Write a proof plan to help connect mathematical statements using deductive reasoning.
- Construct parallel lines.

KEY TERMS

- Corresponding Angles Theorem
- Corresponding Angles Converse Theorem
- Same-Side Interior Angles Theorem
- Alternate Interior Angles Theorem
- Alternate Exterior Angles Theorem
- Same-Side Exterior Angles Theorem
- Alternate Interior Angles Converse Theorem
- Same-Side Interior Angles Converse Theorem
- Alternate Exterior Angles Converse Theorem
- Same-Side Exterior Angles Converse Theorem
- Perpendicular/Parallel Line Theorem

REVIEW (1–2 minutes)

1 Identify the corresponding angles.

∠1 and ∠5
∠2 and ∠6
∠3 and ∠7
∠4 and ∠8

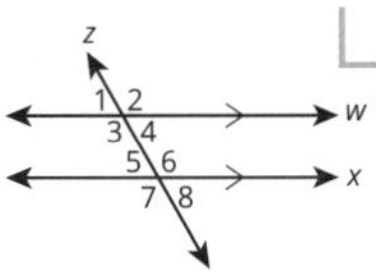

You already know about special angle pairs produced by parallel lines cut by a transversal.

How do you know that these relationships are true in all cases?

Setting the Stage

- **Assign Review (optional, 1 – 2 minutes)**
- **Communicate the learning goals and key terms to look out for**
- **Tap into your students' prior learning by reading the narrative statement**
- **Provide a sense of direction by reading the question**

TOPIC 2

IN THIS REVIEW

Students identify corresponding and alternate interior angles. They will first use this skill in the **GETTING STARTED Criss Cross Applesauce.**

If a transversal intersects two parallel lines, then:

- Corresponding angles are congruent.
- Alternate interior angles are congruent.
- Alternate exterior angles are congruent.
- Same-side interior angles are supplementary.
- Same-side exterior angles are supplementary.

Essential Ideas

- When a transversal cuts parallel lines, corresponding angles are congruent.
- When a transversal cuts parallel lines, the same side interior and same side exterior angles are supplementary.
- When a transversal cuts parallel lines, alternate interior and alternate exterior angles are congruent.
- You can use the converses to theorems about angles formed when a transversal cuts to prove lines are parallel.
- You can use a proof to connect statements using deductive reasoning.

GETTING STARTED

SUMMARY **You can use rigid motions to show that corresponding and alternate interior angles are congruent when a transversal cuts two parallel lines.**

Chunking the Activity

- **Read and discuss the introduction**
- **Group students to complete the activity**
- **Share and summarize**

DIFFERENTIATION STRATEGY

See Page 320A to assist all students with 1.

Student Look-Fors

Whether students are demonstrating self-awareness.

- Showing a sense of confidence and optimism as they approach the problem
- Accurately perceiving their strengths and limitations
- Having a growth mindset

Criss Cross Applesauce

You may recall that you can use translations to show that corresponding angles are congruent.

1 Consider parallel lines *m* and *n* with a pair of corresponding angles, $\angle A$ and $\angle B$.

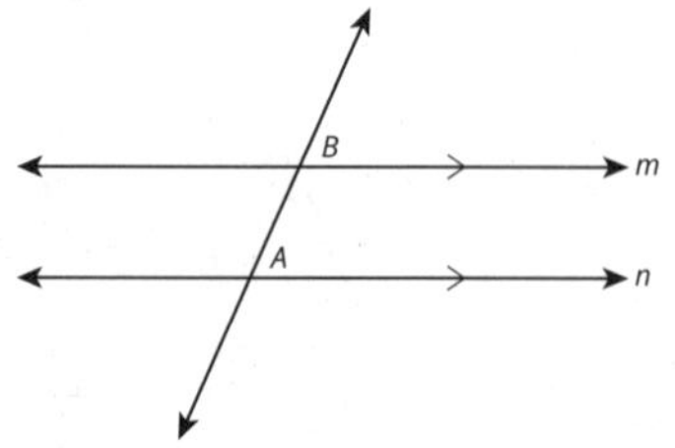

REMEMBER...

A transversal is a line that intersects two or more other lines.

Corresponding angles are two non-adjacent angles that lie on the same side of the transversal, one angle on the outside of the lines and one angle on the inside of the lines.

Alternate interior angles are two non-adjacent angles between the two lines and on opposite sides of a transversal.

ⓐ Use patty paper to translate one of the corresponding angles so that it lies on top of the other corresponding angle. Identify the line of translation and describe the distance and direction of the translation.

Sample answer.
Line *AB* is the line of translation. Angle *A* is translated along line *AB* a distance equal to m$\overline{AB}$ in the direction of ray *AB*.

$T_{AB}(\angle A) = \angle B$

ⓑ What does this translation demonstrate about corresponding angles?

Corresponding angles are congruent.

2 Describe how you can use a patty paper translation and what you know about vertical angles to demonstrate that alternate interior angles are congruent.

Sample answer.
I can label $\angle B$'s vertical angle as $\angle C$. I can reflect $\angle B$ across the vertex to map onto $\angle C$. Since I know that $\angle A$ and $\angle B$ are congruent, I can show that the alternate interior $\angle A$ and $\angle C$ are congruent.

Questions to Support Discourse

		TYPE
1	• Why is $\overleftrightarrow{AB}$ considered the line of translation? • Is $\angle A \cong \angle B$? Why?	Probing
2	• Which angle in the diagram is congruent to $\angle B$? Why?	Probing
	• Since vertical angles are congruent and $\angle A \cong \angle B$, how can you use the Transitive Property to show alternate interior angles are congruent?	Seeing structure

ACTIVITY 1

SUMMARY **When a transversal cuts two lines making congruent corresponding angles, the lines are parallel.**

Corresponding Angles Theorem

Let's use translations to prove the conjecture that when a transversal cuts parallel lines, corresponding angles are congruent. Consider these three properties of translations when formulating a proof:

- Line segments are taken to line segments of the same length.
- Angles are taken to angles of the same measure.
- A translated line is either identical to the original line or parallel to it.

HABITS OF MIND
- Reason abstractly and quantitatively.
- Construct viable arguments and critique the reasoning of others.

1 The given diagram shows $\angle ABC$ and $\overline{BB'}$.

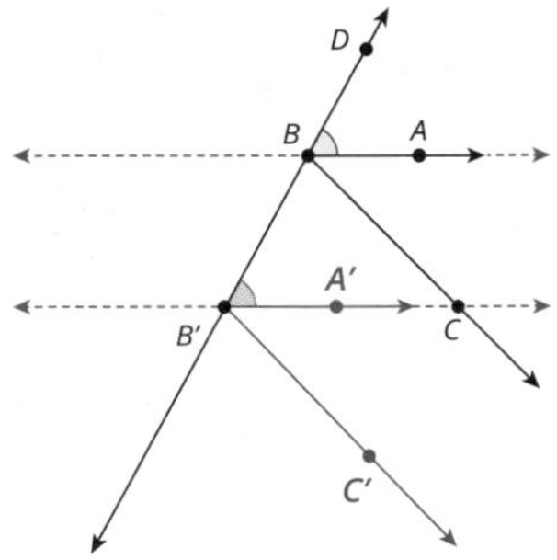

a) Draw the translation $T_{BB'}(\angle ABC)$. Label points A' and C'.

See diagram.

b) Identify a pair of parallel lines. **How do you know the lines are parallel?**

Sample answer.

Lines AB and $A'B'$ are parallel lines because a translated line is either identical to the original line or parallel to it.

REMEMBER...
The notation $T_{BB'}(\angle ABC)$ means to translate $\angle ABC$ along a line parallel to $\overline{BB'}$ in the direction and distance from point B to point B'.

c) Draw transversal $\overline{BB'}$. Identify a pair of corresponding angles. **How do you know the corresponding angles are congruent?**

Sample answer.

Angles ABD and $A'B'B$ are corresponding angles. The angles are congruent because a translation takes angles to angles of the same measure.

Chunking the Activity

- **Read and discuss the introduction**
- **Group students to complete 1 and 2**
- **Check-in and share**
- **Read and discuss the theorem**
- **Group students to complete 3**
- **Read and discuss the theorem**

DIFFERENTIATION STRATEGY

See Page 320A to assist all students with the lesson.

Student Look-Fors

The extension of $\overrightarrow{BA}$ to form $\overleftrightarrow{AB}$, the extension of $\overrightarrow{B'A'}$ to form $\overleftrightarrow{A'B'}$, and extending $\overleftrightarrow{BB'}$ to form $\overleftrightarrow{BB'}$. Students should mark $\angle A'B'B$ congruent to $\angle ABD$.

Questions to Support Discourse

		TYPE
1	• How do you know $\overrightarrow{BA}$ is parallel to $\overrightarrow{B'A'}$? • How do you know $\overrightarrow{BC}$ is parallel to $\overrightarrow{B'C'}$?	Probing
	• Do translations always move lines or rays to a parallel position? • Does the translation of an angle always result in an angle of the same measure?	Reflecting and justifying

NOTES

ACTIVITY 1 Continued

2 Use your work in Question 1 and the properties of translations to write a paragraph proof to demonstrate that two parallel lines intersected by a transversal create corresponding angles that are congruent.

$\angle A'B'C'$ is a translation of $\angle ABC$: $T_{BB'}(\angle ABC)$.
Lines AB and $A'B'$ are parallel lines because translations take lines to parallel lines or identical lines.

$\angle ABD$ and $\angle A'B'D'$ are corresponding angles and are congruent because translations take angles to angles of the same measure.

Because you proved that the relationship is true, you can now refer to it as a theorem.

THEOREM

CORRESPONDING ANGLES THEOREM

If a transversal intersects two parallel lines, then corresponding angles are congruent.

Recall that the converse of a theorem is created by interchanging the hypothesis and conclusion of the original theorem. Let's conjecture that the converse is also true. In other words, if two lines intersected by a transversal form congruent corresponding angles, then the lines are parallel.

3 Show how you can use translations to demonstrate that the converse conjecture is true.

I can demonstrate the Corresponding Angles Converse Theorem by showing that a translation of the angle creates corresponding angles. By definition, a translation involves creating parallel lines.

Because you proved that the conjecture is true, you can now refer to it as a theorem.

THEOREM

CORRESPONDING ANGLES CONVERSE THEOREM

If two lines intersected by a transversal form congruent corresponding angles, then the lines are parallel.

REMEMBER...
When a conditional statement and its converse are both true, this is called a biconditional statement. A biconditional statement is a statement written in the form "if and only if *p*, then *q*."

SUMMARY When a transversal cuts parallel lines, same-side interior angles are supplementary.

Same-Side Interior Angles Theorem

HABITS OF MIND

- Reason abstractly and quantitatively.
- Construct viable arguments and critique the reasoning of others.

Now that you have proved the Corresponding Angles Theorem, you can use this theorem in future reasoning. For example, you can use the theorem to prove other relationships regarding angles formed by parallel lines and a transversal.

Let's prove your conjecture that if a transversal intersects two parallel lines, then the interior angles on the same side of the transversal are supplementary.

> Consider the Given and Prove statements related to the diagram.

Given: $w \parallel x$ and z is a transversal.

Prove: Same-side interior angles are supplementary angles.

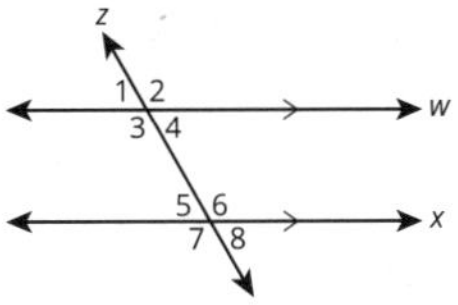

1 Cut out and use the statements and reasons located on page 317 to prove your conjecture. Organize the statements and reasons to form a flow chart proof of this theorem. Glue your flow chart proof into the space provided on the next page.

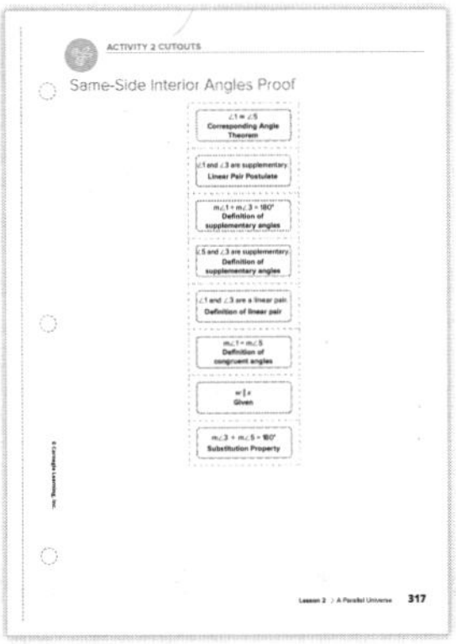

Chunking the Activity

- Read and discuss the introduction
- Group students to complete the activity
- Share and summarize

DIFFERENTIATION STRATEGY

See Page 320B to challenge advanced learners to extend 1.

Student Look-Fors

Different methods students use to sort the order of the statements.

Questions to Support Discourse

		TYPE
1	• Which angles form a linear pair that will help in this proof? • Which statement usually follows the use of the Linear Pair Postulate?	Gathering
	• What can you conclude if m∠1 + m∠3 = 180° and m∠1 = m∠5? Why?	Probing
	• Do we also need to prove ∠6 and ∠4 are supplementary angles to prove this theorem? Why or why not?	Seeing structure

NOTES

Same-Side Interior Angles Proof

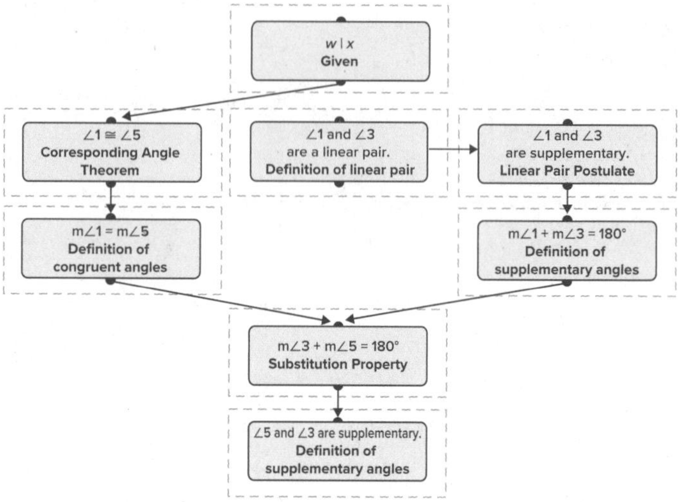

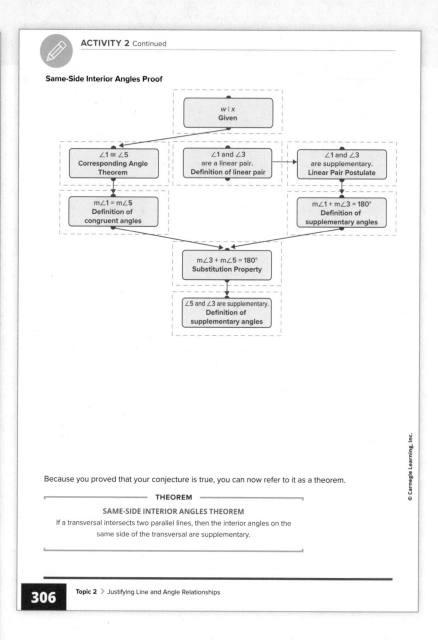

Because you proved that your conjecture is true, you can now refer to it as a theorem.

THEOREM

SAME-SIDE INTERIOR ANGLES THEOREM

If a transversal intersects two parallel lines, then the interior angles on the same side of the transversal are supplementary.

SUMMARY **Use a proof plan to help you connect statements using deductive reasoning.**

MATHia CONNECTION

- Classifying Angles Formed by Transversals
- Calculating Angle Measures Formed by Transversals
- Calculating Angles Formed by Multiple Transversals
- Proving Parallel Lines Theorems

Alternate Interior Angles Theorem

HABITS OF MIND

- Reason abstractly and quantitatively.
- Construct viable arguments and critique the reasoning of others.

A helpful technique you can use to write proofs is to start by writing a proof plan. When you write a proof plan, you use a combination of your own words and mathematical language to describe how you connect the given statement to the prove statement using postulates and theorems. When you write a proof plan, you can test it and fill in missing steps before writing the actual proof.

THINK ABOUT...

Use a proof plan to help you connect statements using deductive reasoning: "If I know this, then I know this."

Consider, for example, the conjecture you made earlier regarding alternate interior angles. You conjectured that if a transversal intersects two parallel lines, then the alternate interior angles are congruent.

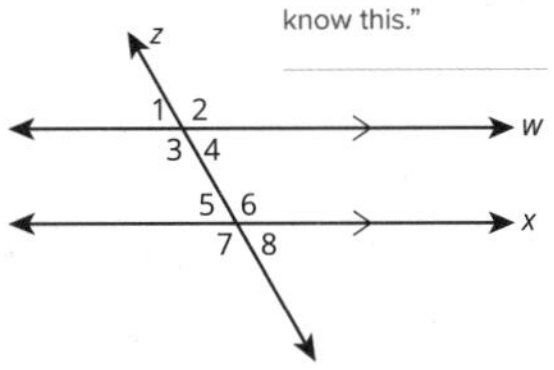

Given: $w \parallel x$ and z is a transversal.

Prove: Alternate interior angles are congruent.

> Analyze Abelina's and Madison's proof plans.

Abelina

I'll show that alternate interior angles 4 and 5 are congruent.

It's given that a transversal cuts the two parallel lines, so I know that angles 4 and 6 are supplementary because they are same-side interior angles.

And angles 5 and 6 are supplementary because they are a linear pair.

So, $m\angle 4 + m\angle 6 = 180°$.

But $m\angle 5 + m\angle 6$ is also equal to $180°$.

That means that angles 4 and 5 have to have the same measure.

Madison

I need to prove that angles 3 and 6 are congruent, which means they have the same measure.

The Given states that the lines are parallel and cut by a transversal, so angles 2 and 6 are congruent because they are corresponding.

But angles 2 and 3 are congruent, too, because they are vertical angles.

If $\angle 3$ and $\angle 6$ are both congruent to angle $\angle 2$, then they must be congruent to each other.

Chunking the Activity

- Read and discuss the introduction and proof plans
- Group students to complete 1 – 3
- Check-in and share
- Read and discuss the theorem
- Group students to complete 4
- Read and discuss the theorem

LANGUAGE LINK

ELL TIP

Chunk Abelina's and Madison's proof plans so students can make sense of their reasoning. Encourage students to annotate the plans, marking different steps and making connections as they go.

NOTES

Student Look-Fors

The correct use of the Transitive Property in Madison's proof and the Substitution Property in Abelina's proof.

ACTIVITY 3 Continued

1 List the definitions, postulates, and theorems Abelina and Madison used in their proof plans. **Explain your reasoning.**

Abelina: Same-Side Interior Angles Theorem, Linear Pair Postulate, definition of supplementary angles, Substitution Property

Madison: Corresponding Angles Theorem, Vertical Angle Theorem, Transitive Property

2 Use Madison's proof plan to complete the flow chart proof of the Alternate Interior Angle Theorem by writing the statement for each reason in the boxes.

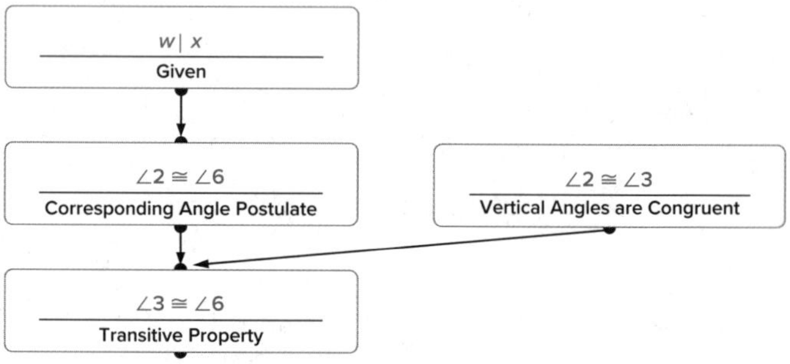

3 Use Abelina's proof plan to create a two-column proof.

Statements	Reasons
1. $w \parallel x$	1. Given
2. ∠4 and ∠6 are supplementary.	2. Same Side Interior Angles Theorem
3. ∠5 and ∠6 are supplementary.	3. Linear Pair Postulate
4. $m\angle 4 + m\angle 6 = 180°$	4. Definition of supplementary angles
5. $m\angle 5 + m\angle 6 = 180$	5. Definition of supplementary angles
6. $m\angle 5 = m\angle 4$	6. Substitution Property
7. $\angle 5 \cong \angle 4$	7. Definition of congruence

Questions to Support Discourse

		TYPE
1	• Do Abelina's and Madison's proof plans use the same definitions, postulates, and theorems?	Gathering
	• How does Abelina's proof plan compare to Madison's proof plan? • Why is it possible for two proof plans to be different but still correct?	Probing

ACTIVITY 3 Continued

Because you proved that your conjecture is true, you can now refer to it as a theorem.

THEOREM

ALTERNATE INTERIOR ANGLES THEOREM

If a transversal intersects two parallel lines, then the alternate interior angles are congruent.

You also conjectured about other relationships regarding angles formed by parallel lines and a transversal.

You conjectured that if a transversal intersects two parallel lines, then the alternate exterior angles are congruent.

You also conjectured that if a transversal intersects two parallel lines, the same-side exterior angles are supplementary.

4 Draw diagrams for these theorems and then write a paragraph proof for each.

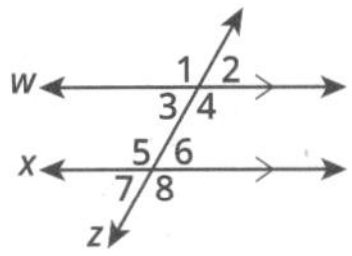

Alternate Exterior Angles Theorem

Since lines *w* and *x* are parallel, angles 1 and 5 are congruent by the Corresponding Angles Theorem. Angles 5 and 8 are congruent by the Vertical Angle Theorem. Therefore, angles 1 and 8 are congruent by the Transitive Property.

Same-Side Exterior Angles Theorem

Since lines *w* and *x* are parallel, angles 3 and 7 are also congruent by the Corresponding Angles Theorem. Angles 1 and 3 are supplementary because they form a linear pair, so $m\angle 1 + m\angle 3 = 180°$ by the definition of supplementary. By substitution, $m\angle 1 + m\angle 7 = 180°$. So $\angle 1$ and $\angle 7$ are supplementary by the definition of supplementary.

Because you proved that your conjecture is true, you can now refer to these as theorems.

THEOREM

ALTERNATE EXTERIOR ANGLES THEOREM

If a transversal intersects two parallel lines, then the alternate exterior angles are congruent.

SAME-SIDE EXTERIOR ANGLES THEOREM

If a transversal intersects two parallel lines, then the same-side exterior angle sare supplementary.

NOTES

Questions to Support Discourse

		TYPE
4	• Can you use the same diagram to prove both theorems? • What is the given information in your proof? What is the prove statement in your proof?	Gathering
	• How do your proofs compare to the proofs of the Alternate Interior Angles Theorem and Same-Side Interior Angles Theorem?	Seeing structure

SUMMARY **You can use the converses of the parallel lines theorems to claim that two lines are parallel.**

Chunking the Activity

- **Read and discuss the introduction**
- **Group students to complete 1 and 2**
- **Check-in and share**
- **Read and discuss the theorem**
- **Group students to complete 3 and 4**
- **Check-in and share**
- **Read and discuss the theorem**
- **Group students to complete 5**
- **Read and discuss the theorems**

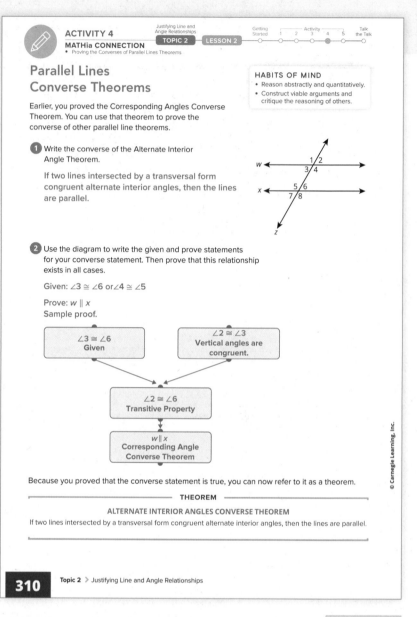

Parallel Lines Converse Theorems

HABITS OF MIND
- Reason abstractly and quantitatively.
- Construct viable arguments and critique the reasoning of others.

Earlier, you proved the Corresponding Angles Converse Theorem. You can use that theorem to prove the converse of other parallel line theorems.

1 Write the converse of the Alternate Interior Angle Theorem.

If two lines intersected by a transversal form congruent alternate interior angles, then the lines are parallel.

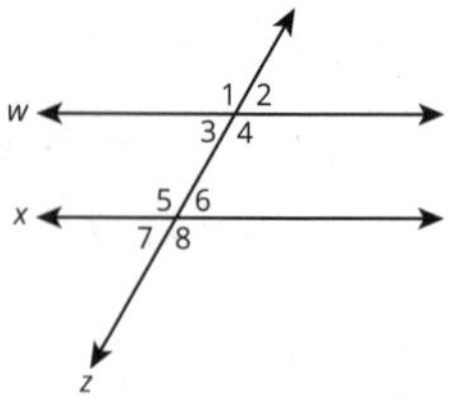

2 Use the diagram to write the given and prove statements for your converse statement. Then prove that this relationship exists in all cases.

Given: ∠3 ≅ ∠6 or∠4 ≅ ∠5

Prove: *w* ∥ *x*

Sample proof.

- ∠3 ≅ ∠6 — Given
- ∠2 ≅ ∠3 — Vertical angles are congruent.
- ∠2 ≅ ∠6 — Transitive Property
- *w* ∥ *x* — Corresponding Angle Converse Theorem

Because you proved that the converse statement is true, you can now refer to it as a theorem.

THEOREM

ALTERNATE INTERIOR ANGLES CONVERSE THEOREM

If two lines intersected by a transversal form congruent alternate interior angles, then the lines are parallel.

Questions to Support Discourse

		TYPE
1	• What is the hypothesis of the Alternate Interior Angle Theorem? What is the conclusion?	Gathering
2	• Which definitions, postulates, and theorems did you use in the proof?	Gathering
	• Do you need one or two given statements to prove this theorem? Explain your reasoning.	Probing

ACTIVITY 4 Continued

3 Write the converse of the Same-Side Interior Angles Theorem.

If two lines intersected by a transversal form supplementary same-side interior angles, then the lines are parallel.

4 Use the diagram to write the given and prove statements for your converse statement. Then prove that this relationship exists in all cases.

Given: $\angle 3$ and $\angle 5$ are supplementary or $\angle 4$ and $\angle 6$ are supplementary.

Prove: $w \parallel x$

Sample proof.

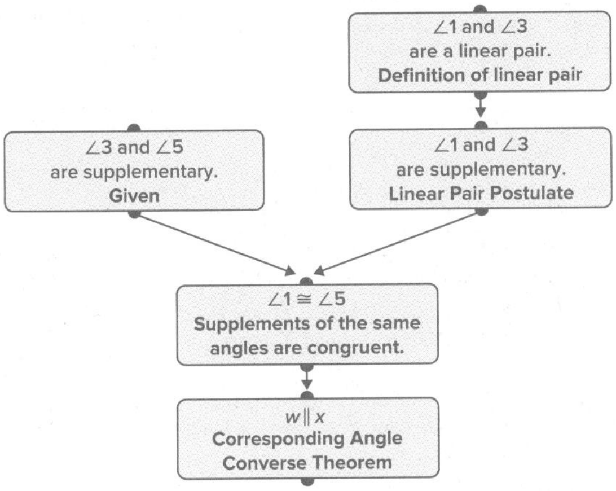

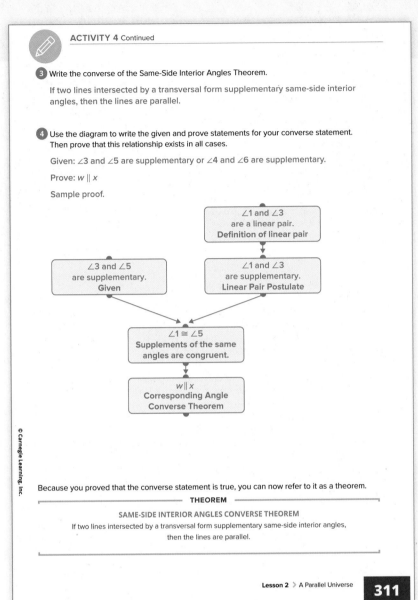

Because you proved that the converse statement is true, you can now refer to it as a theorem.

THEOREM

SAME-SIDE INTERIOR ANGLES CONVERSE THEOREM

If two lines intersected by a transversal form supplementary same-side interior angles, then the lines are parallel.

Questions to Support Discourse

		TYPE
4	• Which of your statements are given, and which can you conclude from definitions?	Gathering

NOTES

NOTES

5 Consider the exterior angles theorems.

(a) Write the converse of the Alternate Exterior Angles Theorem. **Draw a diagram and write a paragraph proof.**

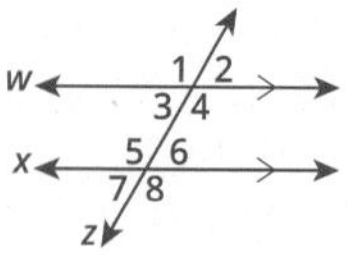

If two lines intersected by a transversal form congruent alternate exterior angles, then the lines are parallel.

It is given that ∠1 and ∠8 are congruent. Angles 1 and 4 are congruent because they are vertical angles. Thus, ∠4 and ∠8 are congruent because of the Transitive Property.

Since ∠4 and ∠8 are congruent corresponding angles, line *w* is parallel to line *x*, because of the Corresponding Angles Converse Theorem.

(b) Write the converse of the Same-Side Exterior Angles Theorem. **Draw a diagram and write a paragraph proof.**

If two lines intersected by a transversal form supplementary same-side exterior angles, then the lines are parallel.

It is given that ∠1 and ∠7 are supplementary. Angles 1 and 2 are supplementary because they are a linear pair. Thus, ∠2 and ∠7 are congruent because they are supplementary to the same angle.

Since ∠2 and ∠7 are congruent alternate exterior angles, line *w* is parallel to line *x*, because of the Alternate Exterior Angles Converse Theorem.

Because you proved that the converse statements are true, you can now refer to them as a theorem. There are other converse theorems that you can show to be true using what you know.

THEOREM

ALTERNATE EXTERIOR ANGLES CONVERSE THEOREM
If two lines intersected by a transversal form congruent alternate exterior angles, then the lines are parallel.

SAME-SIDE EXTERIOR ANGLES CONVERSE THEOREM
If two lines intersected by a transversal form supplementary same-side exterior angles, then the lines are parallel.

Questions to Support Discourse

		TYPE
5	• How do these proofs compare to the proofs of the Alternate Interior Angles Converse Theorem and Same-Side Interior Angles Converse Theorem?	Seeing structure

ACTIVITY 5

SUMMARY **When two lines are perpendicular to the same line, they are parallel.**

ACTIVITY 5

Perpendicular/Parallel Line Theorem

HABITS OF MIND
- Reason abstractly and quantitatively.
- Construct viable arguments and critique the reasoning of others.

You can extend what you have proven about parallel line converse theorems to prove a theorem about parallel lines cut by a perpendicular transversal.

> Consider the conjecture: If two lines are perpendicular to the same line, then the two lines are parallel to each other.

1 Complete a proof to justify the conjecture.

Given: $\ell_1 \perp \ell_3$ and $\ell_2 \perp \ell_3$
Prove: $\ell_1 \parallel \ell_2$

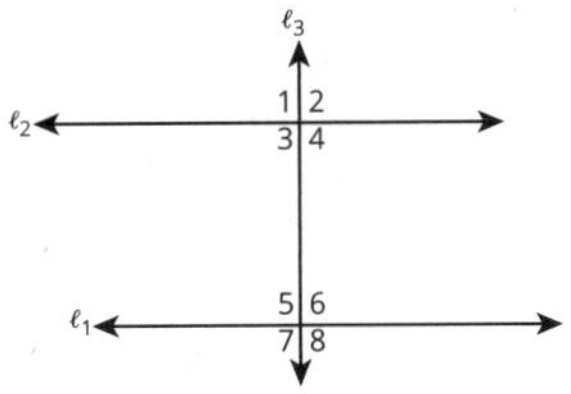

Sample proof.

Statements	Reasons
1. $\ell_1 \perp \ell_2$	1. Given
2. $\ell_2 \perp \ell_3$	2. Given
3. ∠3 and ∠6 are right angles.	3. Definition of perpendicular lines
4. m∠3 = 90°, m∠6 = 90°	4. Definition of a right angle
5. m∠3 = m∠6	5. Substitution
6. ∠3 ≅ ∠6	6. Definition of congruent angles
7. $\ell_1 \parallel \ell_2$	7. Alternate Interior Angle Converse Theorem

Because you proved that the relationship is true, you can now refer to it as a theorem.

THEOREM

PERPENDICULAR/PARALLEL LINE THEOREM

If two lines are perpendicular to the same line, then the two lines are parallel to each other.

Chunking the Activity

- Read and discuss the introduction
- Group students to complete the activity
- Read and discuss the theorem

DIFFERENTIATION STRATEGY

See Page 320B to support students who struggle with 1.

Student Look-Fors

Recognizing the importance of developing critical thinking skills.

Questions to Support Discourse

		TYPE
1	• What is the definition of perpendicular lines? • Are all eight angles right angles?	Gathering
	• Which converse theorems did you use as a reason for stating the lines are parallel? Why isn't that the only theorem you could use?	Probing
	• Are all right angles congruent? Why?	Reflecting and justifying

NOTES

ACTIVITY 5 Continued

2 Use the reasoning in the Perpendicular/Parallel Line Theorem to construct a line parallel to line *m* through point *A*. **Describe your process.**

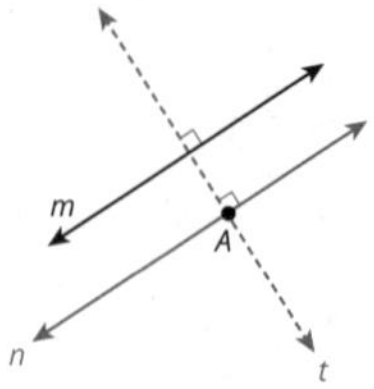

Check students' constructions.
I constructed a line perpendicular to line *m*, labeled line *t*. Then I can translate line *m* along line *t* to point *A* to create line *n*. Line *n* is parallel to line *m*.

3 Explain why Gage is correct.

> Gage
>
> You can duplicate any angle measure, not just right angles, to construct parallel lines.

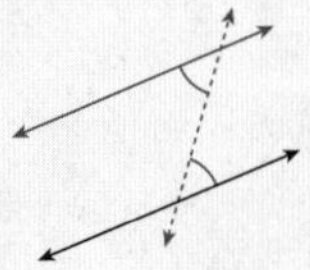

Gage reasoned that if alternate interior angles are congruent when a transversal cuts two lines, then the lines are parallel.

4 Use Gage's reasoning to construct a line parallel to line *q*.

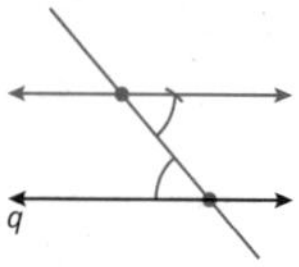

Check students' constructions.

Questions to Support Discourse

		TYPE
2	• Did you use patty paper or a compass and straightedge? Explain your process.	Probing
	• Do you think that when two lines are perpendicular to the same line, they are always parallel to each other? Explain your thinking. • What examples of this do you see in our classroom?	Seeing structure
3	• What is the relationship between the congruent angles that Gage constructed? • According to Gage, what happened first, the parallel lines or the congruent alternate interior angles?	Gathering
4	• What angle relationship did you use to construct parallel lines?	Probing

SUMMARY You can use the parallel line theorems and their converses to determine angle measures and to decide whether two lines are parallel.

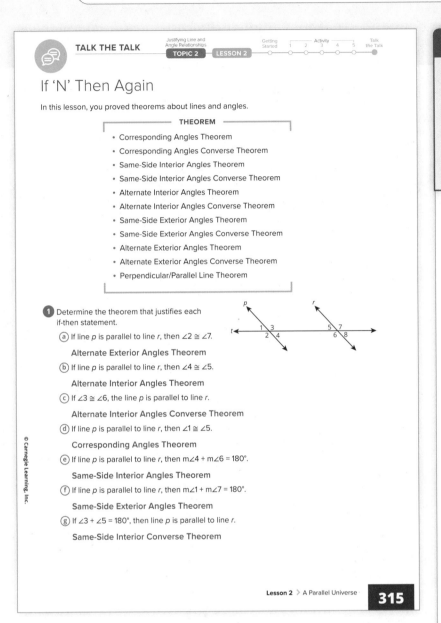

If 'N' Then Again

In this lesson, you proved theorems about lines and angles.

THEOREM

- Corresponding Angles Theorem
- Corresponding Angles Converse Theorem
- Same-Side Interior Angles Theorem
- Same-Side Interior Angles Converse Theorem
- Alternate Interior Angles Theorem
- Alternate Interior Angles Converse Theorem
- Same-Side Exterior Angles Theorem
- Same-Side Exterior Angles Converse Theorem
- Alternate Exterior Angles Theorem
- Alternate Exterior Angles Converse Theorem
- Perpendicular/Parallel Line Theorem

1. Determine the theorem that justifies each if-then statement.

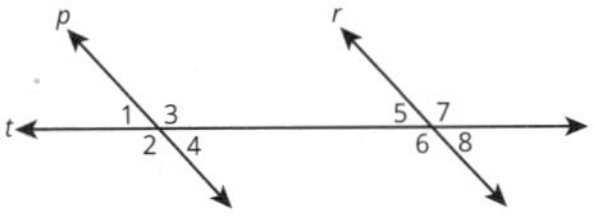

(a) If line *p* is parallel to line *r*, then $\angle 2 \cong \angle 7$.

Alternate Exterior Angles Theorem

(b) If line *p* is parallel to line *r*, then $\angle 4 \cong \angle 5$.

Alternate Interior Angles Theorem

(c) If $\angle 3 \cong \angle 6$, the line *p* is parallel to line *r*.

Alternate Interior Angles Converse Theorem

(d) If line *p* is parallel to line *r*, then $\angle 1 \cong \angle 5$.

Corresponding Angles Theorem

(e) If line *p* is parallel to line *r*, then $m\angle 4 + m\angle 6 = 180°$.

Same-Side Interior Angles Theorem

(f) If line *p* is parallel to line *r*, then $m\angle 1 + m\angle 7 = 180°$.

Same-Side Exterior Angles Theorem

(g) If $\angle 3 + \angle 5 = 180°$, then line *p* is parallel to line *r*.

Same-Side Interior Converse Theorem

Questions to Support Discourse

		TYPE
1	• How did you decide whether to use a theorem or its converse?	Reflecting and justifying

Chunking the Activity

- Read and discuss the introduction
- Group students to complete the activity
- Share and summarize

NOTES

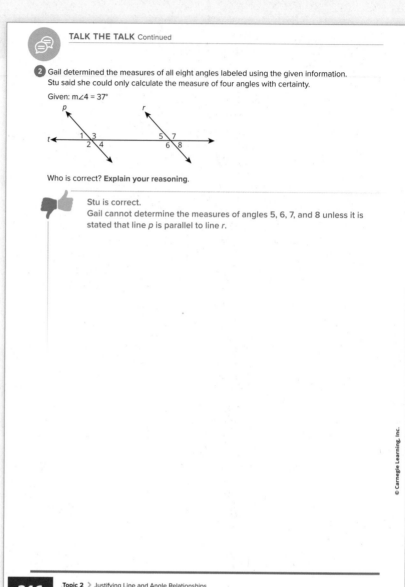

TALK THE TALK Continued

2 Gail determined the measures of all eight angles labeled using the given information. Stu said she could only calculate the measure of four angles with certainty.

Given: $m\angle 4 = 37°$

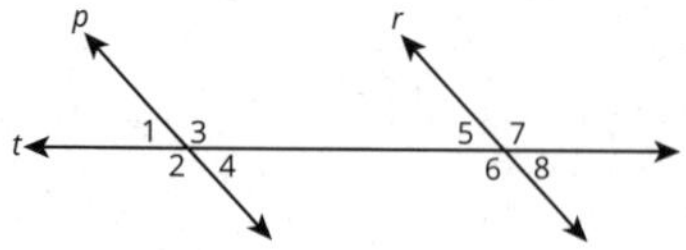

Who is correct? **Explain your reasoning.**

Stu is correct.
Gail cannot determine the measures of angles 5, 6, 7, and 8 unless it is stated that line *p* is parallel to line *r*.

Questions to Support Discourse

		TYPE
2	• What does Gail need to know before she can determine the measures of all eight angles? Why?	Probing

ACTIVITY 2 CUTOUTS

Same-Side Interior Angles Proof

$\angle 1 \cong \angle 5$ **Corresponding Angle Theorem**
$\angle 1$ and $\angle 3$ are supplementary. **Linear Pair Postulate**
$m\angle 1 + m\angle 3 = 180°$ **Definition of supplementary angles**
$\angle 5$ and $\angle 3$ are supplementary. **Definition of supplementary angles**
$\angle 1$ and $\angle 3$ are a linear pair. **Definition of linear pair**
$m\angle 1 = m\angle 5$ **Definition of congruent angles**
$w \parallel x$ **Given**
$m\angle 3 + m\angle 5 = 180°$ **Substitution Property**

Lesson 2 > A Parallel Universe 317

NOTES

TOPIC 2

NOTES

Why is this page blank?

So you can cut out the statements and reasons on the other side.

318 **Topic 2** > Justifying Line and Angle Relationships

ASSIGNMENT

LESSON 2 ASSIGNMENT

> Use a separate piece of paper for your Journal entry.

JOURNAL

Write the converse of each postulate or theorem.

1. Alternate Interior Angle Theorem:
   "If a transversal intersects two parallel lines, then alternate interior angles are congruent."
2. Alternate Exterior Angle Theorem:
   "If a transversal intersects two parallel lines, then alternate exterior angles are congruent."
3. Same-Side Interior Angle Theorem:
   "If a transversal intersects two parallel lines, then same-side interior angles are supplementary."
4. Same-Side Exterior Angle Theorem:
   "If a transversal intersects two parallel lines, then same-side exterior angles are supplementary."

REMEMBER

If a transversal intersects two parallel lines, then:
- Corresponding angles are congruent.
- Alternate interior angles are congruent.
- Alternate exterior angles are congruent.
- Same-side interior angles are supplementary.
- Same-side exterior angles are supplementary.

PRACTICE

1. Consider the diagram shown. Determine which theorem leads to the conclusion that $c \parallel w$ for each statement.

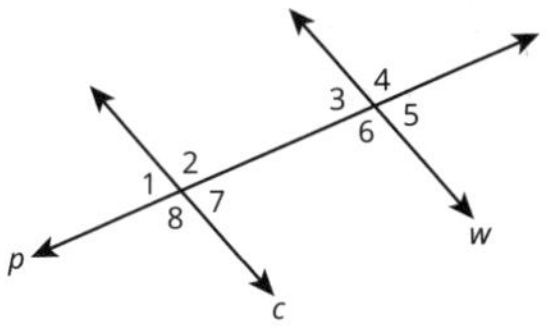

   (a) $\angle 3 \cong \angle 7$

   The Alternate Interior Angle Converse Theorem leads to the conclusion that $c \parallel w$.

   (b) $\angle 5$ and $\angle 8$ are supplementary.

   The Same-Side Exterior Angle Converse Theorem leads to the conclusion that $c \parallel w$.

   (c) $\angle 4 \cong \angle 8$

   The Alternate Exterior Angle Converse Theorem leads to the conclusion that $c \parallel w$.

   (d) $\angle 2$ and $\angle 3$ are supplementary.

   The Same-Side Interior Angle Converse Theorem leads to the conclusion that $c \parallel w$.

Go to LiveHint.com for help on the PRACTICE questions.

Encourage students to use LiveHint.com for help with the PRACTICE questions of this assignment.

Chunking the Assignment

SESSION 1

- **Journal**
- **Stretch (advanced learners)**
- **Mixed Practice (page 383) 3**

SESSION 2

- **Practice 1 and 2**

TOPIC 2

JOURNAL

1. If alternate interior angles formed by two lines and a transversal are congruent, then the two lines are parallel.
2. If alternate exterior angles formed by two lines and a transversal are congruent, then the two lines are parallel.
3. If same-side interior angles formed by two lines and a transversal are supplementary, then the two lines are parallel.
4. If same-side exterior angles formed by two lines and a transversal are supplementary, then the two lines are parallel.

2. Using the diagram in conjunction with postulates and theorems, determine the measure of all unknown angles.
Given: ∠2 ≅ ∠7 ≅ ∠19
m∠2 = 125°

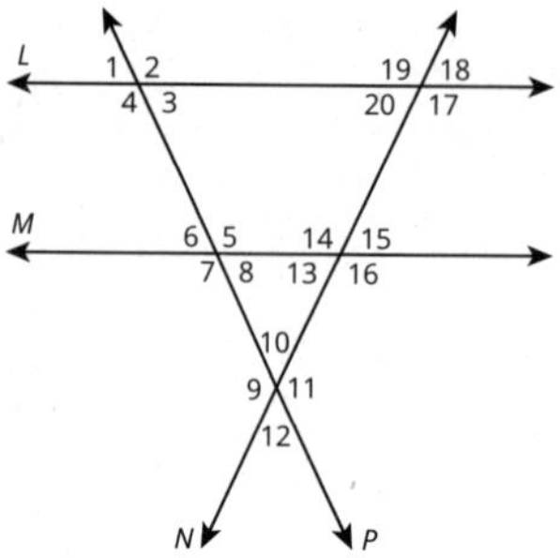

m∠2 = m∠7 = m∠4 = m∠5 = m∠19 = m∠17 = m∠14 = m∠16 = 125°

m∠1 = m∠3 = m∠6 = m∠8 = m∠18 = m∠20 = m∠15 = m∠13 = 55°

m∠10 = m∠12 = 70°

m∠9 = m∠11 = 110°

STRETCH Optional

> Complete a proof using the given information and the related diagram.

Given: ∠*DEG* ≅ ∠*HEF*

Prove: ∠*DEH* ≅ ∠*GEF*

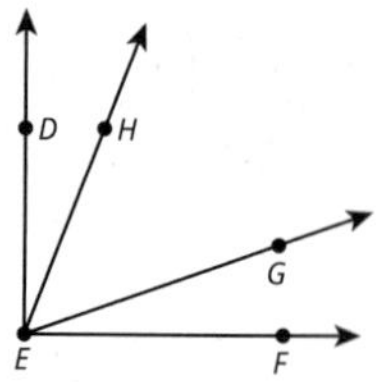

NOTES

STRETCH

Statements	Reasons
1. ∠*DEG* ≅ ∠*HEF*	1. Given
2. m∠*DEG* = m∠*HEF*	2. Definition of congruent angles
3. m∠*DEH* + m∠*HEG* = m∠*DEG*	3. Angle Addition Postulate
4. m∠*GEF* + m∠*HEG* = m∠*HEF*	4. Angle Addition Postulate
5. m∠*HEG* = m∠*HEG*	5. Reflexive Property
6. m∠*DEH* + m∠*HEG* = m∠*GEF* + m∠*HEG*	6. Substitution Property
7. m∠*DEH* = m∠*GEF*	7. Subtraction Property of Equality
8. ∠*DEH* ≅ ∠*GEF*	8. Definition of congruent angles

A Parallel Universe

This resource details additional facilitation notes to fully assist you as you plan each lesson to support all students, students who struggle, and advanced learners. It provides differentiation strategies, common student misconceptions, and suggestions to extend certain activities.

GETTING STARTED

Session 1 of 2

Criss Cross Applesauce

Students use patty paper and rigid motion transformations to investigate angle relationships formed when a transversal cuts two parallel lines. They describe how a patty paper translation and congruent vertical angles can show alternate interior angles are congruent.

CHUNK	AUDIENCE	ADDITIONAL SUPPORTS
As students work on 1	All Students	**DIFFERENTIATION STRATEGY** Review the special angle pairs formed when a transversal cuts two parallel lines.

ACTIVITY 1

Session 1 of 2

Corresponding Angles Theorem

Students translate an angle along a transversal to create parallel lines and congruent corresponding angles. They write a paragraph proof for the Corresponding Angles Theorem. They show how to use translations to prove the Corresponding Angles Converse Theorem.

CHUNK	AUDIENCE	ADDITIONAL SUPPORTS
As students work on the lesson	All Students	**DIFFERENTIATION STRATEGY** Remind students to update their note cards as they encounter new theorems in the lesson.

ACTIVITY 2

Session 1 of 2

Same-Side Interior Angles Theorem

Students use the Corresponding Angles Theorem to prove the first part of the Same-Side Interior Angles Theorem. They assemble statements and reasons into a flow chart proof.

CHUNK	AUDIENCE	ADDITIONAL SUPPORTS
To extend 1	Advanced Learners	**DIFFERENTIATION STRATEGY** Have students write a two-column proof for the other pair of same-side interior angles. Given: $w \parallel x$ and z is the transversal. Prove: $\angle 6$ and $\angle 4$ are supplementary angles

ACTIVITY 5

Session 2 of 2

Perpendicular/Parallel Line Theorem

Students prove the Perpendicular/Parallel Line Theorem. They apply previously proven theorems.

CHUNK	AUDIENCE	ADDITIONAL SUPPORTS
As students work on 1	Students who Struggle	**DIFFERENTIATION STRATEGY** Provide the statements and ask students to write the corresponding reason for each step of the proof.

Practice the learning

MATHbook + Skills Practice

The table shows the targeted practice of the skills and mathematical concepts for the *Justifying Line and Angle Relationships* Topic. The highlighted Problem Set aligns with **A Parallel Universe**.

PROBLEM SET	
1	Identifying Circle Parts
2	**Angle Relationships Formed from Parallel Lines**
3	Interior and Exterior Angles of Polygons
4	Isosceles and Right Triangles
5	Interior and Exterior Angles of a Circle

ANYTIME AFTER ACTIVITY 5

Facilitate students as they work individually on **Problem Set 2**.

NOTES

ENGAGE at the **Module** level + DEVELOP at the **Topic** level + TEACH Read the facilitation notes and plan learning experiences.

Where are we?

TOPIC 2 Justifying Line and Angle Relationships	LESSON 1 Proof Positive	LESSON 2 A Parallel Universe	**LESSON 3 Ins and Outs**	LESSON 4 Identical Twins	LESSON 5 Corners in a Round Room
Pacing	3 Sessions	2 Sessions	**2 Sessions**	2 Sessions	2 Sessions

OVERVIEW: LESSON 3

Ins and Outs

Interior and Exterior Angles of Polygons

ENGAGE

- Students explore the Triangle Sum Theorem by drawing a triangle and rearranging the angles to establish a relationship.

DEVELOP

- Students formally prove the Triangle Sum Theorem and use it to explain the Exterior Angle Theorem.
- They derive a formula to calculate the sum of the measures of a polygon's interior angles, given the number of sides.
- They explore the sum of the measures of the exterior angles of polygons.

DEMONSTRATE

- Students solve problems about the measures of the interior angles and exterior angles of a polygon.

HIGH SCHOOL GEOMETRY

Congruence

Prove geometric theorems.

10. Prove theorems about triangles.

LESSON STRUCTURE AND PACING GUIDE 2 SESSIONS

✪ This activity highlights a key term or concept that is essential to the learning goals of the lesson.

Session 1		Session 2
INSTRUCTIONAL SEQUENCE		
ENGAGE Establish a situation	**DEVELOP** Investigation	**DEVELOP** Investigation Peer Analysis

GETTING STARTED
Rippy Bits

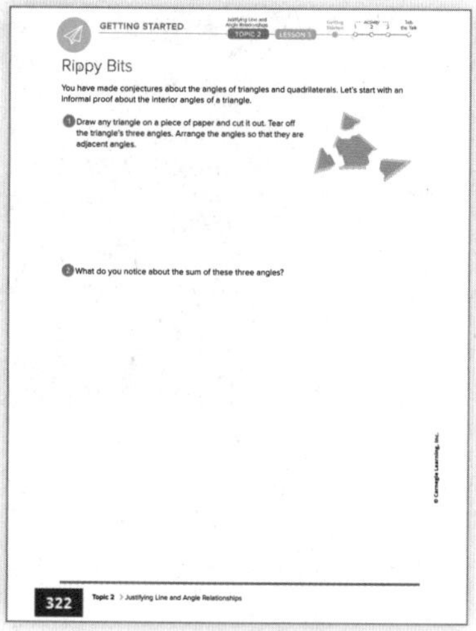
GETTING STARTED

Rippy Bits

You have made conjectures about the angles of triangles and quadrilaterals. Let's start with an informal proof about the interior angles of a triangle.

1 Draw any triangle on a piece of paper and cut it out. Tear off the triangle's three angles. Arrange the angles so that they are adjacent angles.

2 What do you notice about the sum of these three angles?

322 Topic 2 > Justifying Line and Angle Relationships

Students investigate the Triangle Sum Theorem.

- They draw a triangle, cut it out, rip off the three angles and arrange them to investigate the relationship.
- They notice the angles form a straight line, and the sum is 180°.

ACTIVITY 1
Triangle Sum and Exterior Angle Theorems

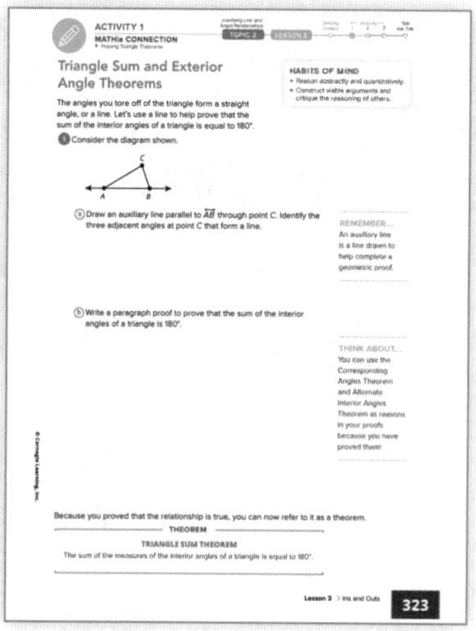
ACTIVITY 1

Triangle Sum and Exterior Angle Theorems

The angles you tore off of the triangle form a straight angle, or a line. Let's use a line to help prove that the sum of the interior angles of a triangle is equal to 180°.

1 Consider the diagram shown.

a Draw an auxiliary line parallel to $\overline{AB}$ through point C. Identify the three adjacent angles at point C that form a line.

b Write a paragraph proof to prove that the sum of the interior angles of a triangle is 180°.

Because you proved that the relationship is true, you can now refer to it as a theorem.

THEOREM

TRIANGLE SUM THEOREM

The sum of the measures of the interior angles of a triangle is equal to 180°.

Lesson 3 > Ins and Outs 323

Students formally prove the Triangle Sum Theorem.

- They use their work to explain the Exterior Angle Theorem.

ACTIVITY 2
The Sum of the Measures of the Interior Angles of a Polygon

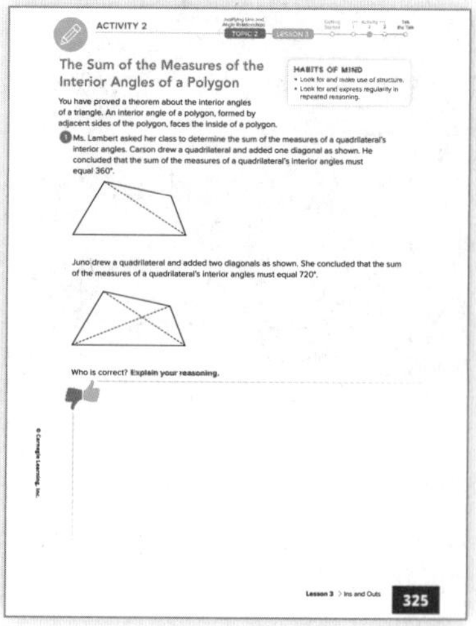
ACTIVITY 2

The Sum of the Measures of the Interior Angles of a Polygon

You have proved a theorem about the interior angles of a triangle. An interior angle of a polygon, formed by adjacent sides of the polygon, faces the inside of a polygon.

1 Ms. Lambert asked her class to determine the sum of the measures of a quadrilateral's interior angles. Carson drew a quadrilateral and added one diagonal as shown. He concluded that the sum of the measures of a quadrilateral's interior angles must equal 360°.

Juno drew a quadrilateral and added two diagonals as shown. She concluded that the sum of the measures of a quadrilateral's interior angles must equal 720°.

Who is correct? Explain your reasoning.

Lesson 3 > Ins and Outs 325

Students derive a formula to calculate the sum a polygon's interior angle measures, given the number of sides.

- They derive a formula to calculate each interior angle measure of a regular polygon, given the number of sides.

Log in to MyCL for **lesson support** including:

Slides

Videos

www.carnegielearning.com/login

INSTRUCTIONAL SEQUENCE

DEVELOP	DEMONSTRATE
Investigation	Exit ticket application

ACTIVITY 3
The Sum of the Measures of the Exterior Angles of a Polygon

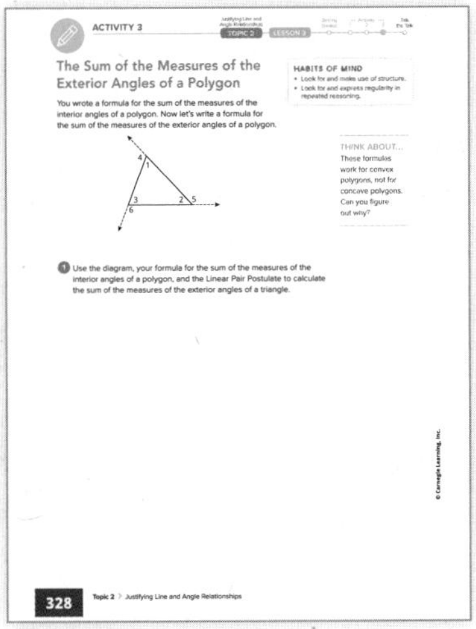
ACTIVITY 3

TOPIC 2 LESSON 3

The Sum of the Measures of the Exterior Angles of a Polygon

HABITS OF MIND
- Look for and make use of structure.
- Look for and express regularity in repeated reasoning.

You wrote a formula for the sum of the measures of the interior angles of a polygon. Now let's write a formula for the sum of the measures of the exterior angles of a polygon.

THINK ABOUT...
These formulas work for convex polygons, not for concave polygons. Can you figure out why?

1. Use the diagram, your formula for the sum of the measures of the interior angles of a polygon, and the Linear Pair Postulate to calculate the sum of the measures of the exterior angles of a triangle.

© Carnegie Learning, Inc.

328 Topic 2 > Justifying Line and Angle Relationships

Students explore the sum of the measures of the exterior angles of polygons.

- They apply the Linear Pair Postulate and the formula for the sum of a polygon's interior angles measures.

TALK THE TALK
Peace Out

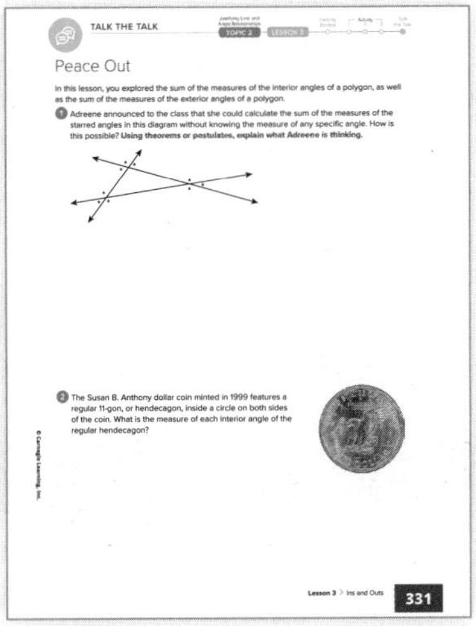
TALK THE TALK

TOPIC 2 LESSON 3

Peace Out

In this lesson, you explored the sum of the measures of the interior angles of a polygon, as well as the sum of the measures of the exterior angles of a polygon.

1. Adreene announced to the class that she could calculate the sum of the measures of the starred angles in this diagram without knowing the measure of any specific angle. How is this possible? **Using theorems or postulates, explain what Adreene is thinking.**

2. The Susan B. Anthony dollar coin minted in 1999 features a regular 11-gon, or hendecagon, inside a circle on both sides of the coin. What is the measure of each interior angle of the regular hendecagon?

© Carnegie Learning, Inc.

Lesson 3 > Ins and Outs 331

Students solve problems about the measures of the interior angles and exterior angles of a polygon.

- They solve both real-world and mathematical problems.

NOTES

TOPIC 2

Log in to MyCL for:

- Editable templates
- Additional planning support

Now that you have read the Module, Topic, and Lesson Overviews, you are ready to plan.

Do the math

> Tear out the lesson planning template (page 321E) and jot down thoughts as you work through this lesson and read the Facilitation Notes.

Connect the learning

MATHbook + MATHia

The table shows a portion of the self-paced MATHia sequence for the *Justifying Line and Angle Relationships* Topic.

Median student completion time for entire topic: ~500–530 minutes

> As you implement this lesson, consider different connections for students who are on pace and those that have not yet completed the workspaces aligned to this lesson.

STUDENTS WHO ARE NOT HERE YET
Students will prove the Triangle Sum and Exterior Angle Theorems.

TYPE	WORKSPACE NAME
★	Proving Parallel Lines Theorems
★	Proving the Converses of Parallel Lines Theorems
★	**Proving Triangle Theorems**
★	Proving Triangles Congruent Using SAS and SSS
★	Proving Triangles Congruent Using AAS and ASA

STUDENTS WHO ARE ON PACE
After you complete Activity 1, ask these students to share how they decided how to connect each step of the proof.

Ins and Outs

Interior and Exterior Angles of Polygons

Session 1

GETTING STARTED Rippy Bits ✪

Pacing (minutes)	
My Time	Class Time

ACTIVITY 1 Triangle Sum and Exterior Angle Theorems ✪

Pacing (minutes)	
My Time	Class Time

KEY TERM
Triangle Sum Theorem
Exterior Angle Theorem

Session 2

ACTIVITY 2 The Sum of the Measures of the Interior Angles of a Polygon ✪

Pacing (minutes)	
My Time	Class Time

ACTIVITY 3 The Sum of the Measures of the Exterior Angles of a Polygon ✪

Pacing (minutes)	
My Time	Class Time

TALK THE TALK Peace Out

Pacing (minutes)	
My Time	Class Time

✪ This activity highlights a key term or concept that is essential to the learning goals of the lesson.

Log in to MyCL for:

- Editable templates
- Additional planning support

Reflect on your lesson

Consider the effectiveness of your lesson on student learning.

What went well?	What did not go as planned?

Anticipate how you would change the lesson next time you teach it.

How will you capitalize on the things that went well?	How will you improve things that did not go as planned?

MATERIALS

- Blank paper
- Scissors
- Straightedges

TOPIC 1 Composing and Decomposing Shapes

TOPIC 2 Justifying Line and Angle Relationships

TOPIC 3 Using Congruence Theorems

1 | Proof Positive
2 | A Parallel Universe
3 | Ins and Outs
4 | Identical Twins
5 | Corners in a Round Room

LESSON 3

Ins and Outs

Interior and Exterior Angles of Polygons

KEY TERMS
- Triangle Sum Theorem
- Exterior Angle Theorem

Learning Goals

- Prove that the measures of interior angles of a triangle sum to 180°.
- Derive a formula for the sums of the measures of interior angles of a polygon.
- Derive a formula for the sums of the measures of exterior angles of a polygon.

REVIEW (1–2 minutes)

Determine each unknown angle measure.

1. 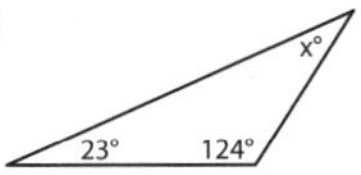

33°

2. 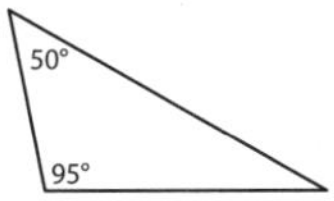

35°

3. 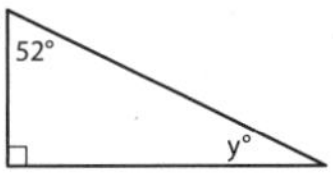

38°

You have used informal arguments about the measures of the interior angles of triangles.

How can you prove theorems about interior and exterior angle measures in polygons with any number of sides?

Setting the Stage

- **Assign Review (optional, 1 – 2 minutes)**
- **Communicate the learning goals and key terms to look out for**
- **Tap into your students' prior learning by reading the narrative statement**
- **Provide a sense of direction by reading the question**

TOPIC 2

IN THIS **REVIEW** Students calculate the unknown angle measure in a triangle. They will use this skill in **ACTIVITY 1 Triangle Sum and Exterior Angle Theorems.**

The sum of the measures of the interior angles of a triangle is 180°, and the sum of the measures of the interior angles of a quadrilateral is 360°.

For a polygon with n sides, the sum of the measures of the interior angles is equal to $180(n - 2)°$, and the sum of the measures of the exterior angles is equal to 360°.

Essential Ideas

- The Triangle Sum Theorem states that the sum of the measures of the interior angles of a triangle is equal to 180°.
- The Exterior Angle Theorem states that the measure of a triangle's exterior angle is equal to the sum of the measures of the two remote interior angles.
- The sum of the measures of the interior angles of a quadrilateral is equal to 360°.
- For a polygon with n sides, the sum of its interior angle measures is equal to $180(n - 2)°$.
- For a regular polygon with n sides, the measure of each interior angle is equal to $\frac{180(n-2)°}{n}$.
- For a polygon with n sides, the sum of the measures of the exterior angles is equal to 360°.

SUMMARY **When you arrange the three interior angles of a triangle adjacent to each other, they form a straight angle or a line.**

Chunking the Activity

- **Read and discuss the introduction**
- **Group students to complete the activity**
- **Share and summarize**

DIFFERENTIATION STRATEGY

See Page 334A for an alternative implementation strategy for 1.

See Page 334A to challenge advanced learners to extend 2.

Student Look-Fors

Different types of triangles.

Rippy Bits

You have made conjectures about the angles of triangles and quadrilaterals. Let's start with an informal proof about the interior angles of a triangle.

1. Draw any triangle on a piece of paper and cut it out. Tear off the triangle's three angles. Arrange the angles so that they are adjacent angles.

   Check students' work.

2. What do you notice about the sum of these three angles?

   The three adjacent angles form a straight angle or line, so the sum of their measures is 180°.

Questions to Support Discourse

		TYPE
1	• What are adjacent angles?	Gathering
	• Do you think the type of triangle you draw will impact what happens when you place the angles adjacent to each other? • Is it possible for three angles to be adjacent? Explain your reasoning.	Probing
2	• Do the three angles form a straight angle?	Gathering
	• How do you know the sum of the measures of the three angles is 180°?	Probing

ACTIVITY 1

SUMMARY **The sum of the interior angle measures of a triangle is 180°. The sum of the measures of the two remote interior angles equals the exterior angle measure.**

Triangle Sum and Exterior Angle Theorems

HABITS OF MIND
- Reason abstractly and quantitatively.
- Construct viable arguments and critique the reasoning of others.

The angles you tore off of the triangle form a straight angle, or a line. Let's use a line to help prove that the sum of the interior angles of a triangle is equal to 180°.

1. Consider the diagram shown.

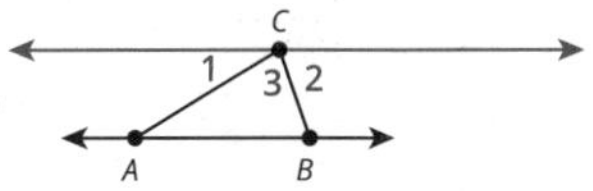

(a) Draw an auxiliary line parallel to $\overleftrightarrow{AB}$ through point *C*. Identify the three adjacent angles at point *C* that form a line.

Sample answer.

Angles 1, 2, and 3 form a straight angle, or a line.

REMEMBER...
An auxiliary line is a line drawn to help complete a geometric proof.

(b) Write a paragraph proof to prove that the sum of the interior angles of a triangle is 180°.

Angles 2 and *CBA* are congruent alternate interior angles.

Angles 1 and *CAB* are congruent alternate interior angles.

$m\angle 1 + m\angle 3 + m\angle 2 = 180°$, so by substitution,
$m\angle CAB + m\angle 3 + m\angle CBA = 180°$.

THINK ABOUT...
You can use the Corresponding Angles Theorem and Alternate Interior Angles Theorem as reasons in your proofs because you have proved them!

Because you proved that the relationship is true, you can now refer to it as a theorem.

THEOREM

TRIANGLE SUM THEOREM

The sum of the measures of the interior angles of a triangle is equal to 180°.

Chunking the Activity

- Read and discuss the introduction
- Group students to complete 1
- Check-in and share
- Group students to complete 2 and 3
- Read and discuss the theorem

DIFFERENTIATION STRATEGY

See Page 334A to assist all students with the lesson.

Student Look-Fors

Utilizing relationship skills by communicating clearly and listening well.

Questions to Support Discourse

		TYPE
1	• How many lines can you draw parallel to a given line through a point not on the line? • What is the given information in this proof? • What is the prove statement?	Gathering
	• How do you know ∠*CAB* and ∠*CBA* are congruent to angles created with the auxiliary line? • How can you use the Substitution Property to determine the prove statement?	Probing

NOTES

DIFFERENTIATION STRATEGY

See Page 334A to support students who struggle with 2.

COMMON MISCONCEPTION

See Page 334B for a misconception related to 2.

DIFFERENTIATION STRATEGY

See Page 334B to challenge advanced learners to extend 3.

ACTIVITY 1 Continued

> Consider another diagram that you can use to prove the Triangle Sum Theorem.

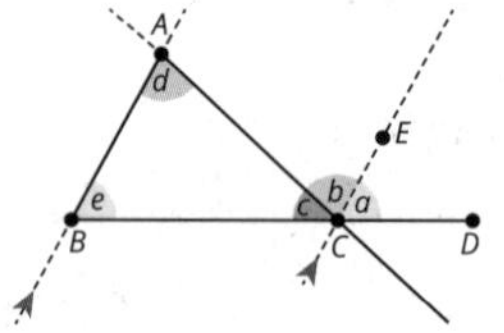

2 Explain how the diagram demonstrates the Triangle Sum Theorem.

Angles *a* and *e* are congruent corresponding angles.

Angles *b* and *d* are congruent alternate interior angles.

$m\angle a + m\angle b + m\angle c = 180°$, so by substitution, $m\angle e + m\angle d + m\angle c = 180°$.

It appears that a relationship exists among the angles of a triangle. The measure of an exterior angle of a triangle is equal to the sum of the measures of the two remote interior angles.

3 Explain how the diagram demonstrates that this relationship exists.

The diagram shows that $\angle a$ and $\angle b$ are congruent to angles $\angle e$ and $\angle d$, respectively.

Thus, the sum of the measures of $\angle a$ and $\angle b$ is equal to the sum of the remote interior angles, $\angle e$ and $\angle d$.

REMEMBER...

The remote interior angles of a triangle are the two angles that are not adjacent to the specified exterior angle.

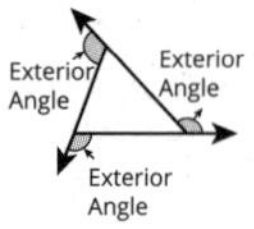

Because you proved that the relationship is true, you can now refer to it as a theorem.

THEOREM

EXTERIOR ANGLE THEOREM

The measure of an exterior angle of a triangle is equal to the sum of the measures of the two remote interior angles.

Questions to Support Discourse

		TYPE
2	• Which letters represent angles? Which represent points on the figure? • Which angle relationship exists between angles *a* and *e*? • Which angle relationship exists between angles *b* and *d*?	Gathering
	• How do you know $\overleftrightarrow{AB} \parallel \overleftrightarrow{EC}$?	Probing
	• Why does $m\angle a + m\angle b + m\angle c = 180°$?	Seeing structure
3	• Which angles in the diagram represent the exterior angle? • Which angles represent the remote interior angles?	Gathering
	• How could you prove the Triangle Sum Theorem using the Exterior Angle Theorem?	Reflecting and justifying

324 Topic 2 > Justifying Line and Angle Relationships

SUMMARY **The sum of the interior angle measures of an *n*-sided polygon is $180(n - 2)°$. Each interior angle measure of an *n*-sided polygon is $\frac{180(n-2)°}{n}$.**

The Sum of the Measures of the Interior Angles of a Polygon

HABITS OF MIND
- Look for and make use of structure.
- Look for and express regularity in repeated reasoning.

You have proved a theorem about the interior angles of a triangle. An interior angle of a polygon, formed by adjacent sides of the polygon, faces the inside of a polygon.

1 Ms. Lambert asked her class to determine the sum of the measures of a quadrilateral's interior angles. Carson drew a quadrilateral and added one diagonal as shown. He concluded that the sum of the measures of a quadrilateral's interior angles must equal 360°.

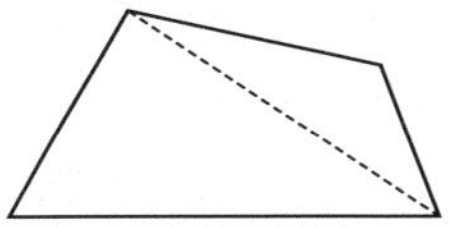

Juno drew a quadrilateral and added two diagonals as shown. She concluded that the sum of the measures of a quadrilateral's interior angles must equal 720°.

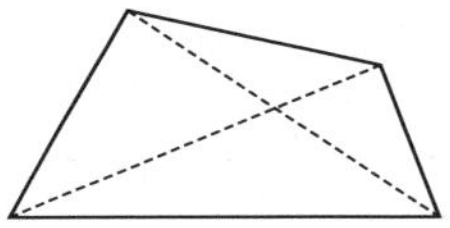

Who is correct? **Explain your reasoning.**

Carson is correct.
Carson concluded the sum of the interior angle measures of a quadrilateral is equal to 360° because the diagonal formed two distinct triangles within the quadrilateral. Thus, the sum of the measures of the interior angles of each triangle is 180°. Therefore, 2(180°) = 360°.

When drawing the two intersecting diagonals, Juno created extra angles that are not considered interior angles of the original quadrilateral. Therefore, her answer has an extra 360° because the additional angles form a circle.

Chunking the Activity

- Read and discuss the introduction
- Group students to complete 1
- Check-in and share
- Group students to complete 2 – 6
- Check-in and share
- Group students to complete 7 – 10
- Check-in and share
- Group students to complete 11 – 14
- Share and summarize

DIFFERENTIATION STRATEGY

See Page 334C to support students who struggle with 1.

Questions to Support Discourse

		TYPE
1	• Which angles do you think Juno included when calculating the sum of the interior angles?	Gathering
	• What is the sum of the additional angles Juno created? How do you know?	Probing
	• Are the additional angles Juno created interior angles of the quadrilateral? Why or why not?	Seeing structure

NOTES

LANGUAGE LINK

ELL TIP

Ensure students recognize different polygons' names by creating a list of polygons and the number of sides they have.

ACTIVITY 2 Continued

You can use the Triangle Sum Theorem to calculate the sum of the measures of the interior angles of other polygons.

2 Draw each polygon. Then calculate the sum of the measures of each polygon's interior angles by drawing all possible diagonals from one vertex of the polygon. Complete the table for 3-, 4-, 5-, and 6-sided polygons.

ⓐ Quadrilateral

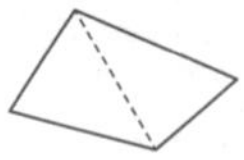

ⓑ Pentagon

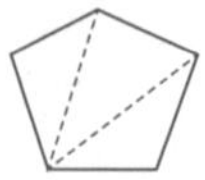

ⓒ Hexagon

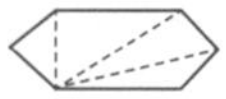

Number of Sides of the Polygon	3	4	5	6	7	8	9	16
Number of Diagonals Drawn	0	1	2	3	4	5	6	13
Number of Triangles Formed	1	2	3	4	5	6	7	14
Sum of the Measures of the Interior Angles	180°	360°	540°	720°	900°	1080°	1260°	2520°

3 What pattern do you notice about the sum of the measures of the interior angles of a polygon as the number of sides of each polygon increases by 1?

As the number of sides increases by 1, the sum of the interior angle measures increases by 180°.

4 Predict the number of possible diagonals drawn from one vertex and the number of triangles formed for 7-, 8-, 9-, and 16-sided polygons. Then, complete the table in Question 2.

5 If a polygon has n sides, how many triangles do you form by drawing all diagonals from one vertex? **Explain your reasoning.**

You form $n - 2$ triangles.
The number of triangles formed is 2 fewer than the number of sides in the polygon.

6 What is the sum of the measures of the interior angles of an n-sided polygon? **Explain your reasoning.**

The sum is $180(n - 2)$ degrees.
The sum of the measures of the interior angles is the number of triangles you form by drawing all diagonals from one vertex multiplied by the sum of the angle measures of a triangle, 180°.

326 Topic 2 > Justifying Line and Angle Relationships

Questions to Support Discourse

		TYPE
2	• How does the number of diagonals drawn from one vertex compare to the number of sides of the polygon? • How does the number of triangles formed compare to the number of sides of the polygon?	Seeing structure
6	• How can you use what you know about the sum of the interior angle measures of a triangle?	Probing
	• What is the relationship between the sum of the interior angle measures of a triangle and the sum of the interior angle measures of any polygon? • Do you think this pattern holds true for all polygons or only regular polygons?	Seeing structure

ACTIVITY 2 Continued

7 Use a formula to calculate the sum of the measures of the interior angles of a polygon with 32 sides.

$180(32 - 2)° = 180(30)° = 5400°$

8 If the sum of the measures of a polygon's interior angles is 9540°, how many sides does the polygon have? **Explain your reasoning.**

$180(n - 2)° = 9540°$

$180n° - 360° = 9540°$

$180n° = 9900°$ and $n = 55$ sides

9 Use the formula you developed to calculate the sum of the measures of the interior angles of a decagon.

$180(10 - 2)° = 180(8) = 1440°$

10 Calculate the measure of each interior angle of a decagon when each interior angle is congruent. **How did you calculate your answer?**

144°
Sample answer.
I divided the sum of the measures of the interior angles of the decagon by the number of vertices in the decagon.

11 Complete the table.

Number of Sides of Regular Polygon	3	4	5	6	7	8
Sum of Measures of Interior Angles	180°	360°	540°	720°	900°	1080°
Measure of Each Interior Angle	60°	90°	108°	120°	128.57°	135°

12 If a regular polygon has n sides, write a formula to calculate the measure of each interior angle.

$\frac{180(n - 2)°}{n}$

13 Use the formula to calculate the measure of each interior angle of a regular 100-sided polygon.

$\frac{180(100 - 2)°}{100} = 176.4°$

14 If the measure of each interior angle of a regular polygon is equal to 150°, determine the number of sides. **How did you calculate your answer?**

$\frac{180(n - 2)°}{n} = 150°$ and $n = 12$

Questions to Support Discourse

		TYPE
11	• What does it mean when a polygon is regular?	Gathering
	• How did you determine the measure of each interior angle?	Probing
12	• How does the number of angles in a polygon relate to the number of sides?	Seeing structure

NOTES

LANGUAGE LINK

ELL TIP

Students may associate the word *regular* with being uniform or common. Ensure students understand the mathematical meaning of *regular polygon*. Connect to their understanding of equilateral triangles, reminding students that all sides and all angles are congruent in a regular polygon.

SUMMARY **The sum of the measures of the exterior angles of any polygon is 360°.**

Chunking the Activity

- **Read and discuss the introduction**
- **Group students to complete 1**
- **Check-in and share**
- **Group students to complete 2 – 4**
- **Check-in and share**
- **Group students to complete 5 – 8**
- **Share and summarize**

DIFFERENTIATION STRATEGY

See Page 334C to support students who struggle with 1.

The Sum of the Measures of the Exterior Angles of a Polygon

HABITS OF MIND
- Look for and make use of structure.
- Look for and express regularity in repeated reasoning.

You wrote a formula for the sum of the measures of the interior angles of a polygon. Now let's write a formula for the sum of the measures of the exterior angles of a polygon.

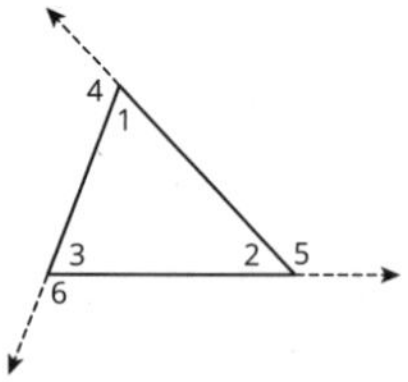

THINK ABOUT...
These formulas work for convex polygons, not for concave polygons. Can you figure out why?

1 Use the diagram, your formula for the sum of the measures of the interior angles of a polygon, and the Linear Pair Postulate to calculate the sum of the measures of the exterior angles of a triangle.

$m\angle 1 + m\angle 4 = 180°$

$m\angle 2 + m\angle 5 = 180°$

$m\angle 3 + m\angle 6 = 180°$

I can add these three equations together:

$m\angle 1 + m\angle 4 + m\angle 2 + m\angle 5 + m\angle 3 + m\angle 6 = 180°+180°+180°$

$(m\angle 1 + m\angle 2 + m\angle 3) + m\angle 4 + m\angle 5 + m\angle 6 = 540°$

$180° + m\angle 4 + m\angle 5 + m\angle 6 = 540°$

$m\angle 4 + m\angle 5 + m\angle 6 = 360°$

The sum of the exterior angle measures is 360°.

Questions to Support Discourse

		TYPE
1	• How many pairs of linear angles are in the diagram?	Gathering
	• How can you use what you know about linear pairs and the Triangle Sum Theorem to determine the sum of the exterior angle measures?	Probing

ACTIVITY 3 Continued

Let's explore the sum of the measures of the exterior angles of other polygons.

2 Draw each polygon. Then calculate the sum of the measures of each polygon's exterior angles by extending each side of the polygon to locate an exterior angle at each vertex. Complete the table for 3-, 4-, 5-, and 6-sided polygons.

(a) Quadrilateral (b) Pentagon (c) Hexagon

Number of Sides of the Polygon	3	4	5	6	7	15
Number of Linear Pairs Formed	3	4	5	6	7	15
Sum of the Measures of the Linear Pairs	540°	720°	900°	1080°	1260°	2700°
Sum of the Measures of the Interior Angles	180°	360°	540°	720°	900°	2340°
Sum of the Measures of the Exterior Angles	360°	360°	360°	360°	360°	360°

3 **What patterns do you notice?**

Sample answer.
The sum of the exterior angles (one exterior angle per vertex) is always 360°.

4 Make predictions about the sum of the measures of the exterior angles of 7- and 15-sided polygons. Complete the table in Question 2.

See the table in Question 2.

5 What is the sum of the measures of the exterior angles of an *n*-sided polygon?

360°

NOTES

TOPIC 2

Questions to Support Discourse

		TYPE
3	• Why is this true for all polygons, even if they are not regular?	Seeing structure
4	• Why is the difference always 360° regardless of the number of sides of the polygon?	Seeing structure

NOTES

6 When the sum of the measures of the exterior angles of a polygon is 360°, how many sides does the polygon have? **Explain your reasoning.**

There is no way to know, because the sum of the exterior angles measures is always 360°, no matter how many sides the polygon has.

7 Calculate the measure of each angle. **Explain your reasoning.**

(a) Each exterior angle of an equilateral triangle

120°
I divided 360° by 3.

(b) Each exterior angle of a square

90°
I divided 360° by 4.

(c) Each exterior angle of a regular pentagon

72°
I divided 360° by 5.

(d) Each exterior angle of a regular hexagon

60°
I divided 360° by 6.

8 When the measure of each exterior angle of a regular polygon is 18°, how many sides does the polygon have? **Explain how you calculated your answer.**

20 sides

$\frac{360}{n} = 18$, and $n = 20$

Questions to Support Discourse

		TYPE
7	• Why can't you calculate the angle measures of a polygon that is not regular?	Seeing structure

SUMMARY **You can use the sum of interior angle measures or the sum of exterior angle measures of a polygon.**

Peace Out

In this lesson, you explored the sum of the measures of the interior angles of a polygon, as well as the sum of the measures of the exterior angles of a polygon.

1. Adreene announced to the class that she could calculate the sum of the measures of the starred angles in this diagram without knowing the measure of any specific angle. How is this possible? **Using theorems or postulates, explain what Adreene is thinking.**

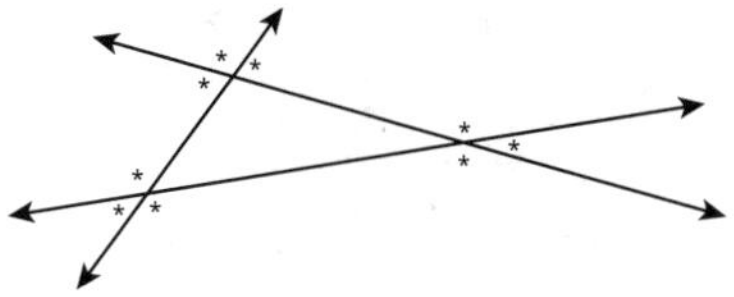

Using the Linear Pair Postulate, Adreene first determined the sum of the measures of all 12 angles formed by the three intersecting lines is 180(6) = 1080°.

She then used the Triangle Sum Theorem to determine that the sum of the triangle's interior angles is 180°.

By subtracting the sum of the measures of the triangle's interior angles from the sum of the 12 angles, 1080°−180°, Adreene determined that the sum of the measures of the starred angles is 900°.

2. The Susan B. Anthony dollar coin minted in 1999 features a regular 11-gon, or hendecagon, inside a circle on both sides of the coin. What is the measure of each interior angle of the regular hendecagon?

180(11 − 2) = 180(9) = 1620

The sum of the measures of the interior angles is 1620°.

$\frac{1620}{11} = 147.\overline{27}$

Each interior angle measure of a regular hendecagon is $147.\overline{27}°$.

Chunking the Activity

- Read and discuss the introduction
- Group students to complete the activity
- Share and summarize

Questions to Support Discourse

		TYPE
1	• What is the sum of the measures of the four angles formed at each vertex of the triangle? • What do the three unstarred angles have in common?	Gathering
	• How can the Linear Pair Postulate help you determine the sum of the measures of all 12 angles in the diagram?	Probing
2	• How do the base angles of the triangle relate to the regular pentagon?	Probing

NOTES

TALK THE TALK Continued

> Solve for x in each diagram.

3 *PENTA* is a regular pentagon.

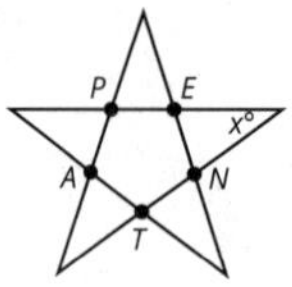

The sum of the measures of the interior angles of Pentagon *PENTA* is 180(3)°, or 540°.

Each angle of Pentagon *PENTA* measures $\frac{540°}{5}$, or 108°.

Each angle that measures 108° in the pentagon forms a linear pair with a base angle of the adjacent triangle, so each base angle of the triangle measures 180° − 108°, or 72°.

By the Triangle Sum Theorem, 72° + 72° + x° = 180°, and x = 36.

4

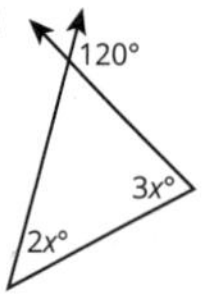

$2x + 3x = 120$

$5x = 120$

$x = 24$

5

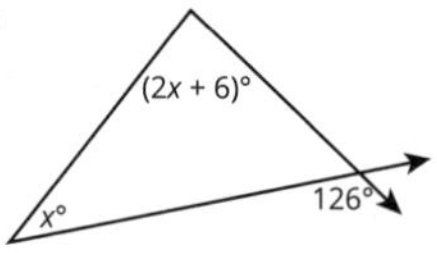

$x + (2x + 6) = 126$

$3x + 6 = 126$

$3x = 120$

$x = 40$

Questions to Support Discourse

		TYPE
3	• How did you determine which theorems, postulates, or properties to use when solving this problem?	Reflecting and justifying

ASSIGNMENT

LESSON 3 ASSIGNMENT

> Use a separate piece of paper for your Journal entry.

JOURNAL

Complete each statement with the correct term.

1. The ________ states that the sum of the measures of a triangle's angles is equal to 180°.
2. The sum of the measures of the ________ of a triangle is equal to the corresponding exterior angle.
3. A(n) ________ is a line drawn to help complete a proof.

REMEMBER

The sum of the measures of the interior angles of a triangle is equal to 180°, and the sum of the measures of the interior angles of a quadrilateral is equal to 360°.

For a polygon with n sides, the sum of the measures of the interior angles is equal to $180(n - 2)°$, and the sum of the measures of the exterior angles is equal to 360°.

PRACTICE

1. Determine the value of x in each diagram.

(a)

$x + 108 = 156$

$x = 48$

$x° = 48°$

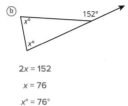

(b)

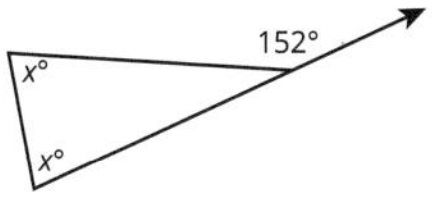

$2x = 152$

$x = 76$

$x° = 76°$

2. Determine the measure of an interior angle of the given regular polygon.

(a) Regular nonagon

$180(9 - 2)° = 180(7)° = 1260°$

$\frac{1260°}{9} = 140°$

(b) Regular 15-gon

$180(15 - 2)° = 180(13)° = 2340°$

$\frac{2340°}{15} = 156°$

(c) Regular decagon

$180(10 - 2)° = 180(8)° = 1440°$

$\frac{1440°}{10} = 144°$

(d) Regular 47-gon

$180(47 - 2)° = 180(45)° = 8100°$

$\frac{8100°}{47} \approx 172.34°$

Go to LiveHint.com for help on the PRACTICE questions.

Encourage students to use LiveHint.com for help with the PRACTICE questions of this assignment.

Chunking the Assignment

SESSION 1

- Journal
- Mixed Practice (page 383) 4 and 5
- Practice 1

SESSION 2

- Practice 2 - 5
- Stretch (advanced learners)

JOURNAL

1. Triangle Sum Theorem
2. remote interior angles
3. auxiliary line

NOTES

STRETCH

1. $x = 25$
2. $\angle A = 100°$
   $\angle B = 75°$
   $\angle C = 265°$
   $\angle D = 85°$
   $\angle E = 260°$
   $\angle F = 55°$
   $\angle G = 30°$
   $\angle H = 280°$
   $\angle I = 110°$

3 Determine the measure of the unknown angle in each figure.

ⓐ 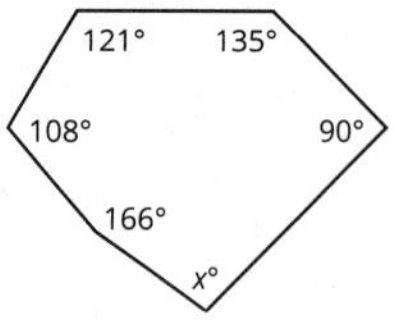

$166° + 108° + 121° + 135° + 90° + x° = 720°$

$620° + x° = 720°$

$x° = 100°$

ⓑ 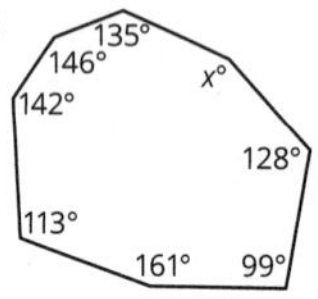

$128° + 99° + 161° + 113° + 142° + 146° + 135° + x° = 1080°$

$924° + x° = 1080°$

$x° = 156°$

4 If a regular polygon has 30 sides, what is the measure of each exterior angle? Explain your reasoning.

The measure of each exterior angle is 12°.

$\frac{360°}{30} = 12°$

5 The degree measure of each exterior angle of a regular octagon is represented by the expression $7x - 4$. Solve for x.

$\frac{360}{8} = 7x - 4$

$45 = 7x - 4$

$49 = 7x$

$7 = x$

STRETCH Optional

> Consider the nonagon shown.

1 Determine the value of x.

2 Determine the value of all the interior angles of the nonagon.

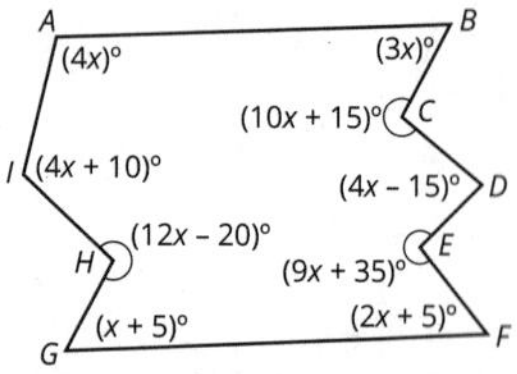

Ins and Outs

This resource details additional facilitation notes to fully assist you as you plan each lesson to support all students, students who struggle, and advanced learners. It provides differentiation strategies, common student misconceptions, and suggestions to extend certain activities.

GETTING STARTED

Session 1 of 2

Rippy Bits

Students informally prove the Triangle Sum Theorem. They draw a triangle, cut it out, rip off the three angles and arrange them to investigate the relationship. They notice the angles form a straight line, and the sum is 180°.

CHUNK	AUDIENCE	ADDITIONAL SUPPORTS
As an alternative implementation strategy 1	All Students	**DIFFERENTIATION STRATEGY** Instead of having students cut out triangles, have them trace each angle on its own piece of patty paper. They can then align the pieces of patty paper to create the straight angle.
To extend 2	Advanced Learners	**DIFFERENTIATION STRATEGY** Have students extend this activity to quadrilaterals. What is the sum of the four interior angles of all quadrilaterals?

ACTIVITY 1

Session 1 of 2

Triangle Sum and Exterior Angle Theorems

Students formally prove the Triangle Sum Theorem. They use their work to explain the Exterior Angle Theorem.

CHUNK	AUDIENCE	ADDITIONAL SUPPORTS
As students work on the lesson	All Students	**DIFFERENTIATION STRATEGY** Remind students to update their note cards as they encounter new theorems in the lesson.
As students work on 2	Students who Struggle	**DIFFERENTIATION STRATEGY** Have students informally prove the Exterior Angles Theorem using a strategy similar to the Getting Started. Have them draw a triangle on paper and cut it out. Then, have them rip off two angles and align them to form the triangle's exterior angle.

<table>
<tr><th>CHUNK</th><th>AUDIENCE</th><th>ADDITIONAL SUPPORTS</th></tr>
<tr><td>As students work on 2</td><td>Students who Struggle</td><td>

COMMON MISCONCEPTION

Students might state the sum of the three adjacent angles at point C is equal to 180° because the sum of the angles on a line is equal to 180°. However, they cannot use that reasoning because that is not a definition or theorem. They must use reasonings based on the postulates or theorems already proven.

</td></tr>
<tr><td>To extend 3</td><td>Advanced Learners</td><td>

Have students prove the Exterior Angle Theorem.

Given: ΔABC with exterior angle $\angle ACD$

Prove: $m\angle A + m\angle B = m\angle ACD$

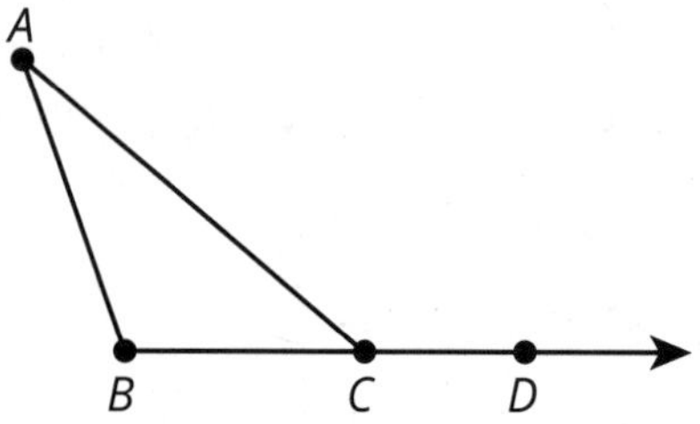

<table>
<tr><th>Statements</th><th>Reasons</th></tr>
<tr><td>1. ΔABC with exterior angle $\angle ACD$</td><td>1. Given</td></tr>
<tr><td>2. $m\angle A + m\angle B + m\angle BCA = 180°$</td><td>2. Triangle Sum Theorem</td></tr>
<tr><td>3. $\angle BCA$ and $\angle ACD$ are a linear pair.</td><td>3. Definition of linear pair</td></tr>
<tr><td>4. $\angle BCA$ and $\angle ACD$ are supplementary</td><td>4. Linear Pair Postulate</td></tr>
<tr><td>5. $m\angle BCA + m\angle ACD = 180°$</td><td>5. Definition of supplementary angles</td></tr>
<tr><td>6. $m\angle A + m\angle B + m\angle BCA = m\angle BCA + m\angle ACD$</td><td>6. Substitution Property using Step 2 and Step 5</td></tr>
<tr><td>7. $m\angle A + m\angle B = m\angle ACD$</td><td>7. Subtraction Property of Equality</td></tr>
</table>

</td></tr>
</table>

ACTIVITY 2

Session 2 of 2

The Sum of the Measures of the Interior Angles of a Polygon

Students derive a formula to calculate the sum a polygon's interior angle measures, given the number of sides. They derive a formula to calculate each interior angle measure of a regular polygon, given the number of sides.

CHUNK	AUDIENCE	ADDITIONAL SUPPORTS
As students work on 1	Students who Struggle	**DIFFERENTIATION STRATEGY** Suggest students use colored pencils to shade the vertex at each interior angle of the quadrilateral. The angles created by the intersecting diagonals will not be included in the shading and become more visual.

ACTIVITY 3

Session 2 of 2

The Sum of the Measures of the Exterior Angles of a Polygon

Students explore the sum of the measures of the exterior angles of polygons. They apply the Linear Pair Postulate and formula for the sum of a polygon's interior angles measures.

CHUNK	AUDIENCE	ADDITIONAL SUPPORTS
As students work on 1	Students who Struggle	**DIFFERENTIATION STRATEGY** Suggest students use a protractor to measure the exterior angles.

Practice the learning

MATHbook + Skills Practice

The table shows the targeted practice of the skills and mathematical concepts for the *Justifying Line and Angle Relationships* Topic. The highlighted **Problem Set** aligns with **Ins and Outs**.

PROBLEM SET	
1	Identifying Circle Parts
2	Angle Relationships Formed from Parallel Lines
3	**Interior and Exterior Angles of Polygons**
4	Isosceles and Right Triangles
5	Interior and Exterior Angles of a Circle

ANYTIME AFTER ACTIVITY 3
Facilitate students as they work individually on **Problem Set 3**.

ENGAGE at the **Module** level + **DEVELOP** at the **Topic** level + **TEACH** Read the facilitation notes and plan learning experiences.

Where are we?

TOPIC 2 Justifying Line and Angle Relationships	LESSON 1 Proof Positive	LESSON 2 A Parallel Universe	LESSON 3 Ins and Outs	LESSON 4 Identical Twins	LESSON 5 Corners in a Round Room
Pacing	3 Sessions	2 Sessions	2 Sessions	3 Sessions	3 Sessions

OVERVIEW: LESSON 4

Identical Twins

Perpendicular Bisector and Isosceles Triangle Theorems

ENGAGE

- Students use triangle congruence theorems to explain why pairs of triangles are congruent.

DEVELOP

- Students define the relationship between corresponding parts of congruent triangles.
- They prove the Isosceles Triangle Base Angles Theorem and the Isosceles Triangle Base Angles Converse Theorem.
- They analyze diagrams of triangles to verify algebraically the special right triangle theorems.
- They demonstrate the validity of the Hypotenuse-Angle and Angle-Angle-Side Congruence Theorems.
- Students apply theorems to solve real-world problems.

DEMONSTRATE

- Students solve problems with special right triangles.

HIGH SCHOOL NUMBER AND QUANTITY

The Real Number System

Extend the properties of exponents to rational numbers.

2. Rewrite expressions involving radicals and rational exponents using the properties of exponents.

HIGH SCHOOL GEOMETRY

Congruence

Prove geometric theorems.

9. Prove theorems about lines and angles.

10. Prove theorems about triangles.

LESSON STRUCTURE AND PACING GUIDE 3 SESSIONS

⊛ This activity highlights a key term or concept that is essential to the learning goals of the lesson.

Session 1

INSTRUCTIONAL SEQUENCE

ENGAGE	DEVELOP	DEVELOP
Connect to prior knowledge	Worked example Mathematical problem solving	Mathematical problem solving

GETTING STARTED
Mappings Matter

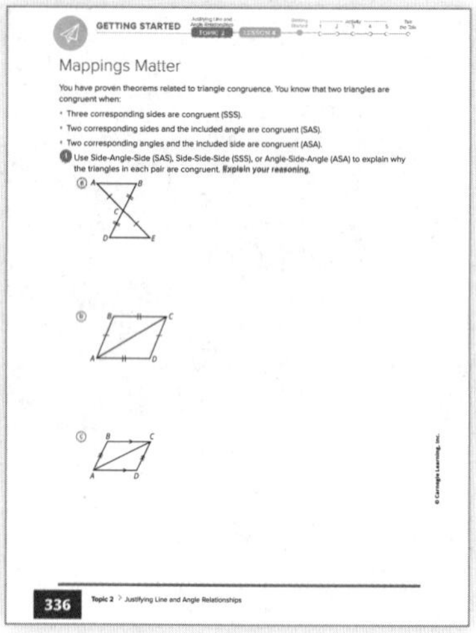

Students use their knowledge of Side-Angle-Side (SAS), Side-Side-Side (SSS), and Angle-Side-Angle (ASA) Congruence Theorems.

- They explain why pairs of triangles are congruent.

ACTIVITY 1 ⊛
The Perpendicular Bisector Theorem

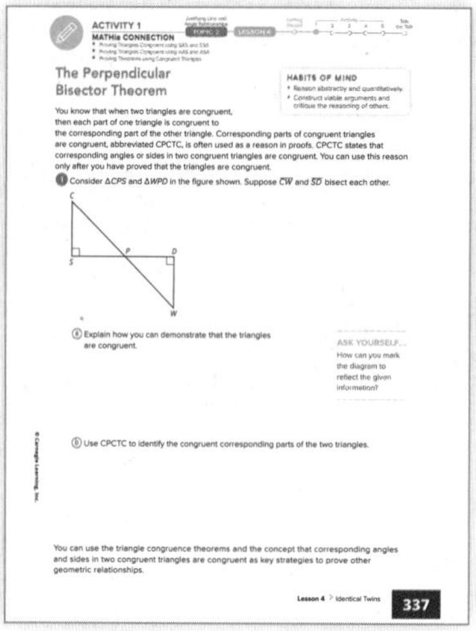

Students explore the relationships between corresponding parts of congruent triangles.

- They define CPCTC.
- They use CPCTC to prove the Perpendicular Bisector Theorem and the Perpendicular Bisector Converse Theorem

ACTIVITY 2 ⊛
Isosceles Triangle Base Angles Theorem

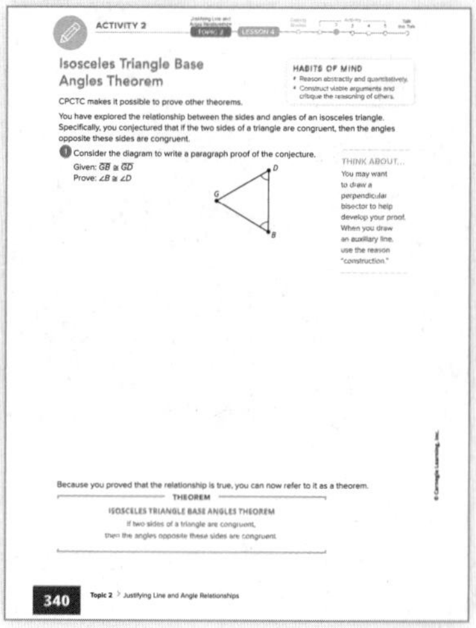

Students prove the Isosceles Triangle Base Angles Theorem and the Isosceles Triangle Base Angles Converse Theorem.

- They use CPCTC and constructions in their proofs.

Log in to MyCL for **lesson support** including:

Slides

Videos

www.carnegielearning.com/login

Session 2

Session 3

INSTRUCTIONAL SEQUENCE

DEVELOP
Worked example
Peer analysis

DEVELOP
Peer analysis

DEVELOP
Real-world problem solving
Mathematical problem solving

ACTIVITY 3
Special Right Triangles

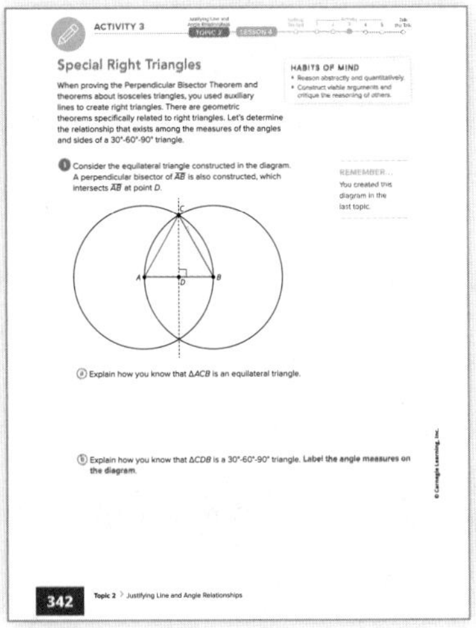

Students analyze diagrams of triangles to demonstrate the special right triangle theorems.

- They verify algebraically the 45°-45°-90° Triangle Theorem and the 30°-60°-90° Triangle Theorem.
- They analyze the procedures for extracting the roots from a radical expression and rationalizing the denominator.

ACTIVITY 4
More Triangle Congruence Theorems

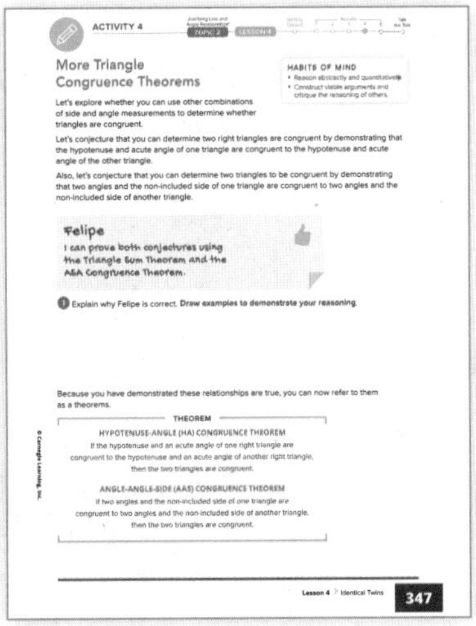

Students demonstrate why the Hypotenuse-Angle (HA) Congruence Theorem is valid.

- They demonstrate why the Angle-Angle-Side (AAS) Congruence Theorem is valid.

ACTIVITY 5
Solving Problems with Congruence

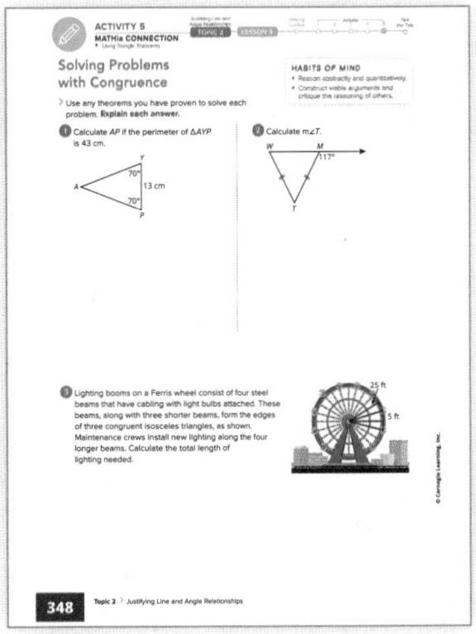

Students apply theorems to solve problem situations.

- They apply theorems such as the Isosceles Triangle Base Angles Theorem, the Pythagorean Theorem, the Exterior Angle Theorem, the Triangle Sum Theorem, triangle congruence theorems, and special right triangle theorems.

TOPIC 2

Log in to MyCL for:
- Editable templates
- Additional planning support

Session 3

INSTRUCTIONAL SEQUENCE

DEMONSTRATE
Exit ticket application

TALK THE TALK
City of Bridges

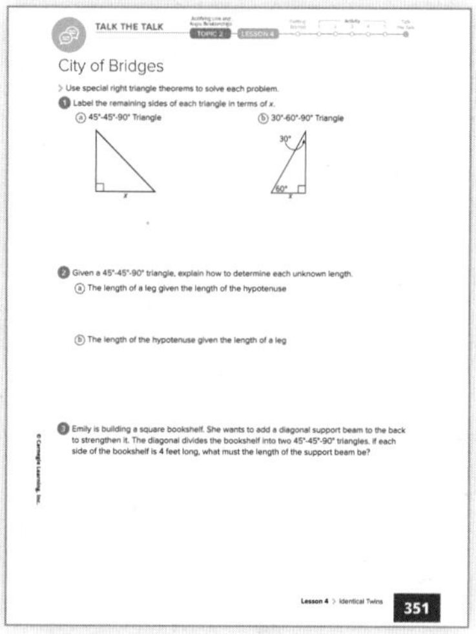
TALK THE TALK

City of Bridges

Use special right triangle theorems to solve each problem.

1 Label the remaining sides of each triangle in terms of x.

a 45°-45°-90° Triangle

b 30°-60°-90° Triangle

2 Given a 45°-45°-90° triangle, explain how to determine each unknown length.

a The length of a leg given the length of the hypotenuse

b The length of the hypotenuse given the length of a leg

3 Emily is building a square bookshelf. She wants to add a diagonal support beam to the back to strengthen it. The diagonal divides the bookshelf into two 45°-45°-90° triangles. If each side of the bookshelf is 4 feet long, what must the length of the support beam be?

Lesson 4 > Identical Twins 351

Students use the 45°-45°-90° Triangle Theorem and the 30°-60°-90° Triangle Theorem to solve problems.

- They solve mathematical and real-world problems.

Now that you have read the Module, Topic, and Lesson Overviews, you are ready to plan.

Connect the learning

MATHbook + MATHia

The table shows a portion of the self-paced MATHia sequence for the *Justifying Line and Angle Relationships* Topic.

Median student completion time for entire topic: ~500–530 minutes

As you implement this lesson, consider different connections for students who are on pace and those that have not yet completed the workspaces aligned to this lesson.

STUDENTS WHO ARE NOT HERE YET
Students will practice completing scaffolded proofs of the Triangle Congruence Theorems.

TYPE	WORKSPACE NAME
	Proving Triangles Congruent Using SAS and SSS
	Proving Triangles Congruent Using AAS and ASA
	Proving Theorems Using Congruent Triangles
	Introduction to Special Right Triangles
	Calculating the Lengths of Sides of Special Right Triangles
	Using Triangle Theorems

STUDENTS WHO ARE ON PACE
After you complete Activity 5, ask these students to share how they applied angle, parallel line, and triangle theorems to prove geometric relationships.

Identical Twins
Perpendicular Bisector and Isosceles Triangle Theorems

Session 1

GETTING STARTED Mappings Matter

Pacing (minutes)	
My Time	Class Time

ACTIVITY 1 The Perpendicular Bisector Theorem ✪

Pacing (minutes)	
My Time	Class Time

KEY TERM
Perpendicular Bisector Converse Theorem

ACTIVITY 2 Isosceles Triangle Base Angles Theorem ✪

Pacing (minutes)	
My Time	Class Time

KEY TERM
Isosceles Triangle Base Angles Theorem
Isosceles Triangle Base Angles Converse Theorem

Session 2

ACTIVITY 3 Special Right Triangles ✪

Pacing (minutes)	
My Time	Class Time

KEY TERM
30°-60°-90° Triangle Theorem
45°-45°-90° Triangle Theorem
Product Property of Radicals
extract the roots
rationalize the denominator

ACTIVITY 4 More Triangle Congruence Theorems ✪

Pacing (minutes)	
My Time	Class Time

KEY TERM
Hypotenuse-Angle (HA) Congruence Theorem
Angle-Angle-Side (AAS) Congruence Theorem

Session 3

ACTIVITY 5 Solving Problems with Congruence

Pacing (minutes)	
My Time	Class Time

TALK THE TALK City of Bridges

Pacing (minutes)	
My Time	Class Time

✪ This activity highlights a key term or concept that is essential to the learning goals of the lesson.

Log in to MyCL for:

- Editable templates
- Additional planning support

Reflect on your lesson

Consider the effectiveness of your lesson on student learning.

What went well?	What did not go as planned?

Anticipate how you would change the lesson next time you teach it.

How will you capitalize on the things that went well?	How will you improve things that did not go as planned?

MATERIALS

- Compasses
- Protractors
- Straightedges

Setting the Stage

- **Assign Review (optional, 1 – 2 minutes)**
- **Communicate the learning goals and key terms to look out for**
- **Tap into your students' prior learning by reading the narrative statement**
- **Provide a sense of direction by reading the question**

TOPIC 2

TOPIC 1 Composing and Decomposing Shapes

TOPIC 2 Justifying Line and Angle Relationships

TOPIC 3 Using Congruence Theorems

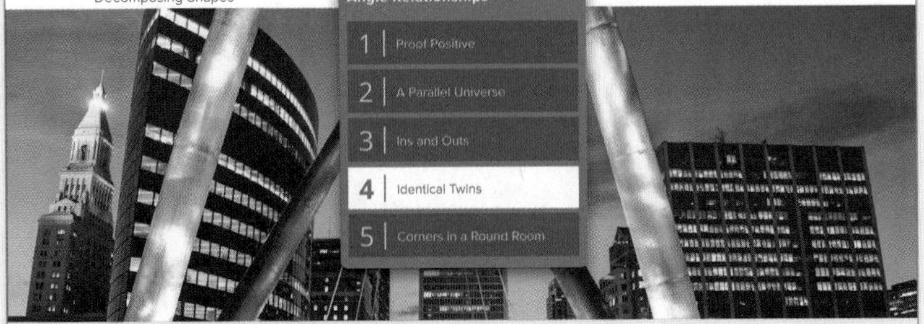

LESSON 4

Identical Twins

Perpendicular Bisector and Isosceles Triangle Theorems

Learning Goals

- Prove that points on a perpendicular bisector of a line segment are exactly those equidistant from the segment's endpoints.
- Prove that the base angles of isosceles triangles are congruent.
- Demonstrate the 30°-60°-90° Triangle Theorem and the 45°-45°-90° Triangle Theorem using algebraic reasoning.

KEY TERMS

- **Perpendicular Bisector Converse Theorem**
- **Isosceles Triangle Base Angles Theorem**
- **Isosceles Triangle Base Angles Converse Theorem**
- **30°-60°-90° Triangle Theorem**
- **45°-45°-90° Triangle Theorem**
- **Product Property of Radicals**
- **extract the roots**
- **rationalize the denominator**
- **Hypotenuse-Angle (HA) Congruence Theorem**
- **Angle-Angle-Side (AAS) Congruence Theorem**

REVIEW (1–2 minutes)

> Evaluate each expression.

1. $\sqrt{25}$
   5
2. $\sqrt{9}$
   3
3. $\sqrt{16}$
   4
4. $(\sqrt{2})^2$
   2
5. $(\sqrt{3})^2$
   3
6. $(2\sqrt{3})^2$
   12

You have analyzed points on a perpendicular bisector and relationships between angles and sides of various triangles.

How can you use definitions and theorems to prove these conjectures?

IN THIS REVIEW

Students evaluate radical expressions. They will use this skill in **ACTIVITY 3 Special Right Triangles.**

The 30°-60°-90° Triangle Theorem states that the length of the hypotenuse in a 30°-60°-90° triangle is 2 times the length of the shorter leg, and the length of the longer leg is $\sqrt{3}$ times the length of the shorter leg.

The 45°-45°-90° Triangle Theorem states that the length of the hypotenuse in a 45°-45°-90° triangle is $\sqrt{2}$ times the length of a leg.

Essential Ideas

- The Perpendicular Bisector Theorem states that the points on a perpendicular bisector of a line segment are equidistant from the segment's endpoints.
- The Isosceles Triangle Base Angles Theorem states that if two sides of a triangle are congruent, then the angles opposite these sides are congruent.
- The 30°-60°-90° Triangle Theorem states that the length of the hypotenuse in a 30°-60°-90° triangle is 2 times the length of the shorter leg, and the length of the longer leg is $\sqrt{3}$ times the length of the shorter leg.
- The 45°-45°-90° Triangle Theorem states that the length of the hypotenuse in a 45°-45°-90° triangle is $\sqrt{2}$ times the length of a leg.

GETTING STARTED

SUMMARY **You can prove two triangles congruent using the Side-Angle-Side (SAS), Side-Side-Side (SSS), and Angle-Side-Angle (ASA) Congruence Theorems.**

Chunking the Activity

- **Read and discuss the introduction**
- **Group students to complete the activity**
- **Share and summarize**

DIFFERENTIATION STRATEGY

See Page 354A to assist all students with 1.

LANGUAGE LINK

ELL TIP

Ensure students understand the term *corresponding* as it relates to the sides and angles of triangles. Have them reference the markings on the figures and make additional markings to make sense of the corresponding parts.

Mappings Matter

You have proven theorems related to triangle congruence. You know that two triangles are congruent when:

- Three corresponding sides are congruent (SSS).
- Two corresponding sides and the included angle are congruent (SAS).
- Two corresponding angles and the included side are congruent (ASA).

1. Use Side-Angle-Side (SAS), Side-Side-Side (SSS), or Angle-Side-Angle (ASA) to explain why the triangles in each pair are congruent. **Explain your reasoning.**

(a)

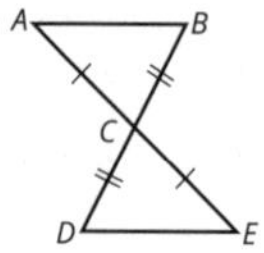

SAS
$\overline{AC} \cong \overline{CE}$, $\overline{BC} \cong \overline{CD}$, and $\angle ACB \cong \angle DCE$ (Vertical Angle Theorem)

(b)

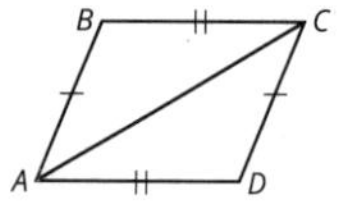

SSS
$\overline{AB} \cong \overline{CD}$, $\overline{BC} \cong \overline{AD}$, and $\overline{AC} \cong \overline{AC}$ (Reflexive Property)

(c)

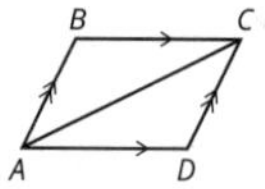

ASA
$\angle BCA \cong \angle DAC$ (Alternate Interior Angles Theorem), $\angle BAC \cong \angle DCA$ (Alternate Interior Angles Theorem), and $\overline{AC} \cong \overline{AC}$ (Reflexive Property)

Questions to Support Discourse

		TYPE
1	• What do the markings on the figures represent?	Gathering
	• Why can't you use the same triangle congruence theorem you used in part (b) for part (c)?	Seeing structure
	• How many pairs of corresponding parts are needed to prove the two triangles congruent?	Reflecting and justifying

ACTIVITY 1

SUMMARY **You can use CPCTC to prove the congruence of corresponding sides and angles in congruent triangles.**

MATHia CONNECTION
- Proving Triangles Congruent using SAS and SSS
- Proving Triangles Congruent using AAS and ASA
- Proving Theorems using Congruent Triangles

The Perpendicular Bisector Theorem

HABITS OF MIND
- Reason abstractly and quantitatively.
- Construct viable arguments and critique the reasoning of others.

You know that when two triangles are congruent, then each part of one triangle is congruent to the corresponding part of the other triangle. Corresponding parts of congruent triangles are congruent, abbreviated CPCTC, is often used as a reason in proofs. CPCTC states that corresponding angles or sides in two congruent triangles are congruent. You can use this reason only after you have proved that the triangles are congruent.

1 Consider ΔCPS and ΔWPD in the figure shown. Suppose $\overline{CW}$ and $\overline{SD}$ bisect each other.

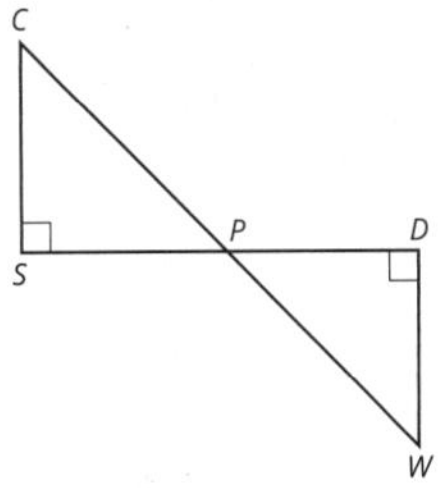

(a) Explain how you can demonstrate that the triangles are congruent.

Sample answer.
$\overline{PC} \cong \overline{PW}$ and $\overline{PS} \cong \overline{PD}$ since $\overline{CW}$ and $\overline{SD}$ bisect each other.
$\angle CPS \cong \angle WPD$ because of the Vertical Angle Theorem.
The triangles are congruent by SAS.

ASK YOURSELF...
How can you mark the diagram to reflect the given information?

(b) Use CPCTC to identify the congruent corresponding parts of the two triangles.

$\overline{CP} \cong \overline{WP}$ $\angle CSP \cong \angle WDP$

$\overline{DP} \cong \overline{SP}$ $\angle CPS \cong \angle WPD$

$\overline{CS} \cong \overline{WD}$ $\angle DWP \cong \angle SCP$

You can use the triangle congruence theorems and the concept that corresponding angles and sides in two congruent triangles are congruent as key strategies to prove other geometric relationships.

Chunking the Activity

- Read and discuss the introduction
- Group students to complete 1
- Check-in and share
- Group students to complete 2
- Check-in and share
- Read and discuss the worked example
- Group students to complete 3
- Share and summarize

DIFFERENTIATION STRATEGY

See Page 354A to assist all students with the lesson.

See Page 354A to support students who struggle with 1.

Questions to Support Discourse

		TYPE
1	• What does it mean for segments to bisect each other?	Gathering
	• What can you conclude about the relationship between $\angle SPC$ and $\angle WPD$? Why? • Why is $\angle S \cong \angle D$?	Probing
	• How many pairs of corresponding parts can you claim are congruent when you know the triangles are congruent?	Seeing structure

NOTES

You have already proved the Perpendicular Bisector Theorem, which states that any point on a perpendicular line segment is equidistant from the segment's endpoints using transformations. You can also prove this relationship using congruent triangles.

2 Consider $\overline{AB}$.

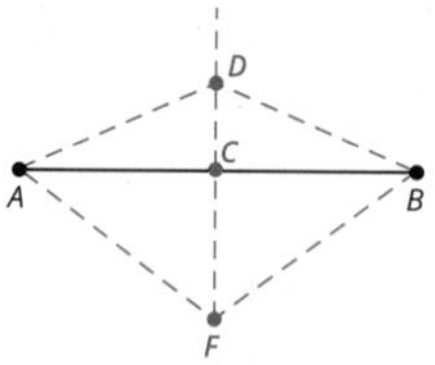

REMEMBER...

The perpendicular bisector of a line segment is the line that divides the line segment into 2 congruent parts and that intersects the line segment at a right angle.

(a) Construct the perpendicular bisector of $\overline{AB}$. Then, draw a line segment from any one point on the bisector to each endpoint of the line segment, *A* and *B*.

See diagram.

(b) Use your construction to identify congruent triangles, and then write a paragraph proof to prove the Perpendicular Bisector Theorem.

Because $\overline{DC}$ is perpendicular to $\overline{AB}$, ΔDCB and ΔDCA are right triangles, with $\angle DCB$ and $\angle DCA$ as right angles, respectively. Because $\overleftrightarrow{DC}$ bisects $\overline{AB}$, $\overline{AC} \cong \overline{BC}$. $\overline{CD}$ is congruent to itself by the Reflexive Property.

Thus, ΔDCB and ΔDCA are congruent by SAS. By CPCTC, $\overline{DB} \cong \overline{DA}$.

Recall that the Perpendicular Bisector Converse Theorem states that if a point is equidistant from a segment's endpoints, then it lies on the perpendicular bisector of the segment.

Questions to Support Discourse

		TYPE
2	• What type of triangles do you have in your figure?	Gathering
	• Which pairs of corresponding sides are congruent? Why? • Which pairs of corresponding angles are congruent? Why?	Probing

ACTIVITY 1 Continued

Analyze the proof of the Perpendicular Bisector Converse Theorem.

WORKED EXAMPLE

Given: Points Q and R are equidistant from point P.

You can draw an auxiliary line segment, $\overline{QR}$, to form an isosceles triangle, ΔRPQ.

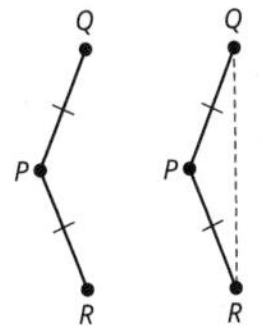

Construct the midpoint of $\overline{QR}$, point M. You can draw another auxiliary line segment, $\overline{PM}$, connecting the midpoint with point P.

The two triangles, ΔPQM and ΔPRM, are congruent triangles by SSS Congruence.

This means that $\angle PMQ$ and $\angle PMR$ are congruent by CPCTC. And since these two angles are congruent and form a linear pair, they are both 90° angles.

Thus, point P lies on the perpendicular bisector of $\overline{QR}$.

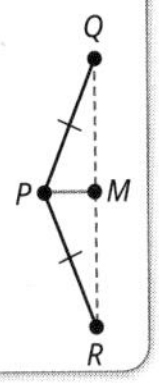

3 Consider the worked example. How would you know that point P lies on the perpendicular bisector of $\overline{QR}$? **Explain your reasoning.**

If point P is equidistant from points Q and R, the point P lies on the perpendicular bisector of $\overline{QR}$.

Because a proof demonstrated that the relationship is true, you can now refer to it as a theorem.

THEOREM

PERPENDICULAR BISECTOR CONVERSE THEOREM

If a point is equidistant from the endpoints of a line segment, then the point lies on the perpendicular bisector of the segment.

This theorem is useful when proving theorems about right triangles.

Lesson 4 > Identical Twins 339

Questions to Support Discourse

		TYPE
Worked Example	• Why is $\overline{RM}$ congruent to $\overline{QM}$?	Probing
3	• Why is the Perpendicular Bisector Theorem a biconditional statement?	Reflecting and justifying

NOTES

TOPIC 2

SUMMARY **You can use the Isosceles Triangle Base Angles Theorem and its converse to solve problems and justify statements in proofs.**

Chunking the Activity

- Read and discuss the introduction
- Group students to complete 1
- Check-in and share
- Group students to complete 2 and 3
- Share and summarize

LANGUAGE LINK

ELL TIP

Provide students with alternate options for completing the proof, such as a flow chart or two-column proof.

Isosceles Triangle Base Angles Theorem

HABITS OF MIND
- Reason abstractly and quantitatively.
- Construct viable arguments and critique the reasoning of others.

CPCTC makes it possible to prove other theorems.

You have explored the relationship between the sides and angles of an isosceles triangle. Specifically, you conjectured that if the two sides of a triangle are congruent, then the angles opposite these sides are congruent.

1 Consider the diagram to write a paragraph proof of the conjecture.

Given: $\overline{GB} \cong \overline{GD}$
Prove: $\angle B \cong \angle D$

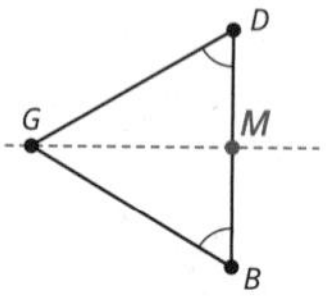

THINK ABOUT...
You may want to draw a perpendicular bisector to help develop your proof. When you draw an auxiliary line, use the reason "construction."

$\overline{GB}$ and $\overline{GD}$ are congruent.

Call the midpoint of $\overline{DB}$ point M because every segment has one midpoint, then draw $\overline{GM}$ by construction.

Using the definition of midpoint and the Reflexive Property, ΔGMD and ΔGMB are congruent by SSS, so corresponding $\angle B$ and $\angle D$ are congruent.

Because you proved that the relationship is true, you can now refer to it as a theorem.

THEOREM

ISOSCELES TRIANGLE BASE ANGLES THEOREM
If two sides of a triangle are congruent, then the angles opposite these sides are congruent.

Questions to Support Discourse

		TYPE
1	• If M is the midpoint of $\overline{BD}$, what is the relationship between $\overline{BM}$ and $\overline{DM}$?	Gathering
	• How can the proof of the Perpendicular Bisector Converse Theorem help with this proof? • Does every line segment have a midpoint?	Seeing structure

ACTIVITY 2 Continued

2 State the converse of the Isosceles Triangle Base Angles Theorem as a conjecture.

If two angles of a triangle are congruent, then the two sides opposite these angles are congruent.

3 Consider the diagram to write a paragraph proof of the conjecture.

Given: $\angle B \cong \angle D$
Prove: $\overline{GB} \cong \overline{GD}$

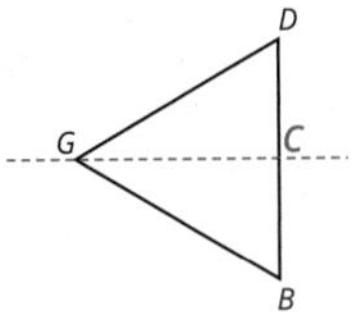

THINK ABOUT...
You can draw an auxiliary line that bisects $\angle G$ and passes through a point somewhere on $\overline{DB}$.

You can form ΔDCG and ΔBCG by constructing a point C on $\overline{DB}$ such that $\overline{GC}$ bisects $\angle DGB$.

Since $\angle DGC$ is congruent to $\angle BGC$ and $\overline{GC}$ is congruent to itself, ΔDCG and ΔBCG are congruent by AAS.

By CPCTC, corresponding sides GD and GB are congruent.

Because you proved this relationship is true, you can now refer to it as a theorem.

THEOREM

ISOSCELES TRIANGLE BASE ANGLES CONVERSE THEOREM

If two angles of a triangle are congruent, then the sides opposite these angles are congruent.

NOTES

DIFFERENTIATION STRATEGY

See Page 354B to challenge advanced learners to extend 2.

Questions to Support Discourse

		TYPE
3	• Why can't you start by constructing a segment from point G to the midpoint of $\overline{DB}$?	Probing
	• What would be the result if you constructed the bisector of $\angle G$ first?	Seeing structure

ACTIVITY 3

SUMMARY **You can use the relationships in special right triangles to determine side lengths and solve problems.**

Chunking the Activity

- **Read and discuss the introduction**
- **Group students to complete 1 - 3**
- **Check-in and share**
- **Group students to complete 4 - 6**
- **Check-in and share**
- **Group students to complete 7**
- **Check-in and share**
- **Read and discuss the worked example**
- **Group students to complete 8**
- **Check-in and share**
- **Read and discuss the worked example**
- **Group students to complete 9**
- **Share and summarize**

Special Right Triangles

HABITS OF MIND
- Reason abstractly and quantitatively.
- Construct viable arguments and critique the reasoning of others.

When proving the Perpendicular Bisector Theorem and theorems about isosceles triangles, you used auxiliary lines to create right triangles. There are geometric theorems specifically related to right triangles. Let's determine the relationship that exists among the measures of the angles and sides of a 30°-60°-90° triangle.

1 Consider the equilateral triangle constructed in the diagram. A perpendicular bisector of $\overline{AB}$ is also constructed, which intersects $\overline{AB}$ at point D.

REMEMBER...
You created this diagram in the last topic.

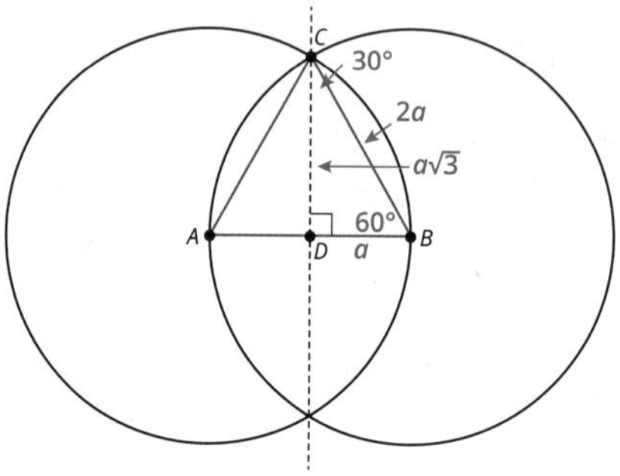

ⓐ Explain how you know that ΔACB is an equilateral triangle.

Circles A and B have the same radius, $\overline{AB}$, so they are congruent. All of the two circles' radii are then congruent. The three sides of the triangle are formed from different radii of the two circles, so all the line segments are congruent. Thus, the triangle is equilateral.

ⓑ Explain how you know that ΔCDB is a 30°-60°-90° triangle. **Label the angle measures on the diagram.**

Sample answer.

I know $\angle CDB$ is a right angle because $\overline{CD}$ is perpendicular to $\overline{DB}$. I know that $\angle B$ measures 60° because each angle in an equilateral triangle measures 60°. Using the Triangle Sum Theorem, I can determine the measure of $\angle BCD$ is 30°.

Questions to Support Discourse

		TYPE
1	• Is point D the midpoint of $\overline{AB}$?	Gathering
	• Is Circle A congruent to circle B? Why?	Probing
	• What is the relationship between $\overline{AB}$ and $\overline{DB}$?	Seeing structure

ACTIVITY 3 Continued

ⓒ Explain how you know that point *C* lies on the perpendicular bisector of $\overline{AB}$.

Because $\overline{CA}$ and $\overline{CB}$ are congruent, point *C* lies on the perpendicular bisector of $\overline{AB}$ because of the converse of the Perpendicular Bisector Theorem.

ⓓ What do you know about the lengths of $\overline{DB}$ and $\overline{CB}$?

$\overline{BC}$ is twice the length of $\overline{DB}$.

2 Use what you know and the Pythagorean Theorem to demonstrate the 30°-60°-90° Triangle Theorem algebraically. Let *a* represent the length of the shorter leg, $\overline{DB}$.

$a^2 + (CD)^2 = (2a)^2$

$a^2 + (CD)^2 = 4a^2$

$(CD)^2 = 3a^2$

$CD = a\sqrt{3}$

shorter leg = a

$CD = a\sqrt{3}$

hypotenuse = $2a$

3 Label the side measures in the diagram.

See diagram in Question 1.

Because you demonstrated that the relationship is true, you can now refer to it as a theorem.

THEOREM

30°-60°-90° TRIANGLE THEOREM

The length of the hypotenuse in a 30°-60°-90° triangle is 2 times the length of the shorter leg, and the length of the longer leg is $\sqrt{3}$ times the length of the shorter leg.

Questions to Support Discourse

		TYPE
2	• If you represent the length of the shorter leg using *a*, what expression represents the length of the hypotenuse? • If you represent the length of the shorter leg using *a*, what expression represents the length of the side opposite the 60° angle?	Gathering

NOTES

TOPIC 2

NOTES

ACTIVITY 3 Continued

Let's determine the relationship that exists among the measures of the angles and sides of a 45°-45°-90° triangle.

4 Consider the isosceles right triangle constructed in the diagram. Line *MP* is a perpendicular bisector of diameter $\overline{QN}$.

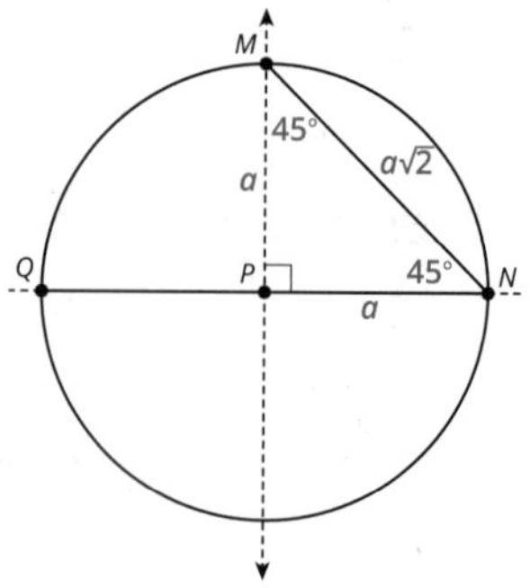

(a) Explain how you know that Δ*MPN* is an isosceles right triangle.

Two of its sides are radii of the circle, which are congruent.

(b) Explain how you know that ∠*PMN* and ∠*PNM* are congruent angles. **Label the angle measures in the diagram.**

The Isosceles Triangle Base Angles Converse Theorem says that the two congruent angles are opposite two congruent sides.

5 Use what you know and the Pythagorean Theorem to demonstrate the 45°-45°-90° Triangle Theorem algebraically. Let *a* represent the length of each congruent leg.

$a^2 + a^2 = (MN)^2$

$2a^2 = (MN)^2$

$\sqrt{2} \cdot a = MN$

6 Label the side measures in the diagram.

See diagram in Question 4.

Because you demonstrated that the relationship is true, you can now refer to it as a theorem.

THEOREM

45°-45°-90° TRIANGLE THEOREM

The length of the hypotenuse in a 45°-45°-90° triangle is $\sqrt{2}$ times the length of a leg.

344 Topic 2 > Justifying Line and Angle Relationships

Questions to Support Discourse

		TYPE
4	• What is true about $\overline{PN}$ and $\overline{PM}$?	Gathering

ACTIVITY 3 Continued

7 Use the 30°-60°-90° and 45°-45°-90° Triangle Theorems to determine the length of sides x and y in each triangle.

(a)

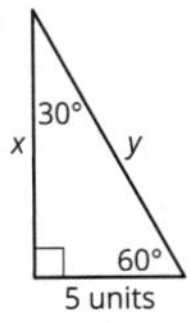

$x = 5\sqrt{3}$ units

$y = 10$ units

(b)

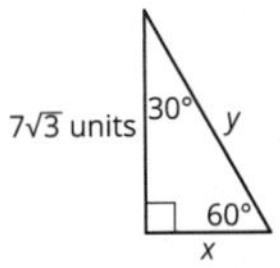

$x = 7$ units

$y = 14$ units

(c)

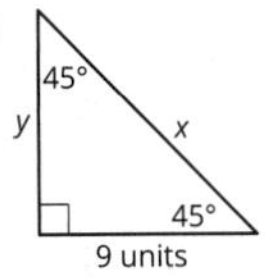

$x = 9\sqrt{2}$ units

$y = 9$ units

(d)

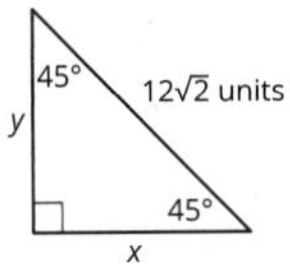

$x = 12$ units

$y = 12$ units

You have practiced identifying the unknown lengths based on the special relationships among the sides of the triangle. Let's consider how to multiply and rewrite radicals.

WORKED EXAMPLE

Determine the unknown side lengths.

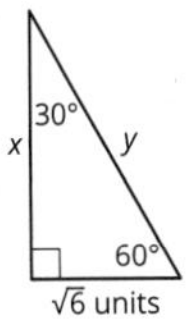

$x = \sqrt{3} \cdot \sqrt{6}$

$= \sqrt{3 \cdot 6}$

$= \sqrt{3 \cdot 3 \cdot 2}$

$= \sqrt{3^2 \cdot 2}$

$= 3\sqrt{2}$ units

$y = 2\sqrt{6}$ units

The **Product Property of Radicals** states that $\sqrt{a} \cdot \sqrt{b} = \sqrt{a \cdot b}$ when a and b are greater than 0.

A standard procedure involving radicals is to **extract the roots**, which is the process of removing all perfect square numbers from under the radical symbol.

NOTES

Questions to Support Discourse

		TYPE
Worked Example	• Why does $y = 2\sqrt{6}$? • In your own words, explain what it means to *extract the roots*?	Probing

NOTES

8 Calculate the length of the legs of the isosceles triangle shown.

Determine who's correct and explain the error in the other student's work.

David

The length of each side is $\sqrt{10}$ units.

$\frac{20}{\sqrt{2}} = \sqrt{\frac{20}{2}} = \sqrt{10}$

Brien

The length of each side is $10\sqrt{2}$ units.

$\frac{20}{\sqrt{2}} \cdot \frac{\sqrt{2}}{\sqrt{2}} = \frac{20\sqrt{2}}{2} = 10\sqrt{2}$

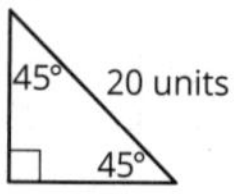

Brien is correct.
The measure of the leg is the measure of the hypotenuse divided by $\sqrt{2}$.

A standard math convention is to **rationalize the denominator**, which is the process of rewriting a fraction with no irrational numbers in the denominator.

To rationalize the denominator of a fraction involving radicals, multiply a fraction by a form of 1 so that the product in the denominator includes a perfect square radicand. Then rewrite, if possible.

WORKED EXAMPLE

Determine the unknown side lengths. Rationalize the denominators.

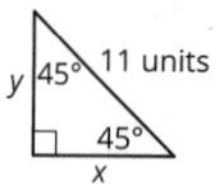

$x = \frac{11}{\sqrt{2}}$

$x = \frac{11}{\sqrt{2}} \cdot \frac{\sqrt{2}}{\sqrt{2}} = \frac{11\sqrt{2}}{2}$ units

$y = \frac{11\sqrt{2}}{2}$ units

9 Label the unknown side lengths of each figure.

ⓐ

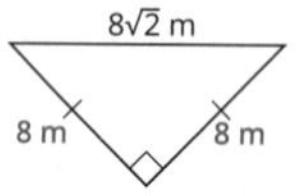

ⓑ

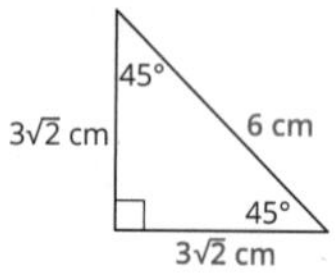

ⓒ

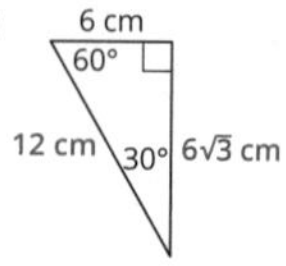

ⓓ

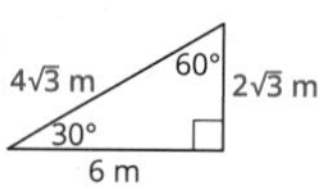

ⓔ

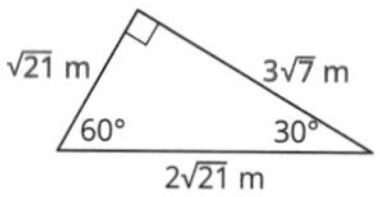

ⓕ

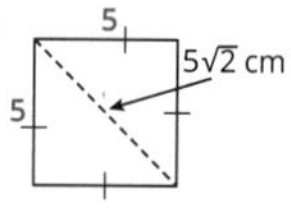

Questions to Support Discourse

		TYPE
8	• Why do you think Brien multiplied by $\frac{\sqrt{2}}{\sqrt{2}}$? • Why does $\sqrt{2} \cdot \sqrt{2} = 2$?	Probing
Worked Example	• What is the form of 1 used to rationalize the denominator? • How is rationalizing a denominator similar to how you have rewritten equivalent fractions in the past?	

SUMMARY You can use the Hypotenuse-Angle (HA) Congruence Theorem and the Angle-Angle-Side (AAS) Congruence Theorem to prove triangles congruent.

More Triangle Congruence Theorems

HABITS OF MIND
- Reason abstractly and quantitatively.
- Construct viable arguments and critique the reasoning of others.

Let's explore whether you can use other combinations of side and angle measurements to determine whether triangles are congruent.

Let's conjecture that you can determine two right triangles are congruent by demonstrating that the hypotenuse and acute angle of one triangle are congruent to the hypotenuse and acute angle of the other triangle.

Also, let's conjecture that you can determine two triangles to be congruent by demonstrating that two angles and the non-included side of one triangle are congruent to two angles and the non-included side of another triangle.

Felipe
I can prove both conjectures using the Triangle Sum Theorem and the ASA Congruence Theorem.

1 Explain why Felipe is correct. **Draw examples to demonstrate your reasoning.**

In each case, the given is that the two triangles have two congruent corresponding angles. Because of the Triangle Sum Theorem, this means that the remaining corresponding angles must be congruent as well. For both the Hypotenuse-Angle Theorem and the Angle-Angle-Side Theorem, then, the triangles are congruent by ASA.

Because you have demonstrated these relationships are true, you can now refer to them as a theorems.

THEOREM

HYPOTENUSE-ANGLE (HA) CONGRUENCE THEOREM
If the hypotenuse and an acute angle of one right triangle are congruent to the hypotenuse and an acute angle of another right triangle, then the two triangles are congruent.

ANGLE-ANGLE-SIDE (AAS) CONGRUENCE THEOREM
If two angles and the non-included side of one triangle are congruent to two angles and the non-included side of another triangle, then the two triangles are congruent.

Chunking the Activity

- Read and discuss the introduction
- Group students to complete the activity
- Share and summarize

DIFFERENTIATION STRATEGY

See Page 354B to challenge advanced learners to extend 1.

Questions to Support Discourse

		TYPE
1	• What is the Triangle Sum Theorem?	Gathering
	• Why can you conclude the third pair of angles in the two triangles are congruent?	Probing

ACTIVITY 5

SUMMARY **You can use geometric reasoning and theorems to solve real-world problems.**

Chunking the Activity

- Read and discuss the introduction
- Group students to complete 1 – 4
- Check-in and share
- Group students to complete 5 – 8
- Share and summarize

DIFFERENTIATION STRATEGY

See Page 354B to group students to complete the activity.

Student Look-Fors

Demonstrating organizational skills by annotating images, sketching congruent shapes, or using other organizational strategies while solving problems.

Solving Problems with Congruence

HABITS OF MIND
- Reason abstractly and quantitatively.
- Construct viable arguments and critique the reasoning of others.

Use any theorems you have proven to solve each problem. **Explain each answer.**

1. Calculate AP if the perimeter of ΔAYP is 43 cm.

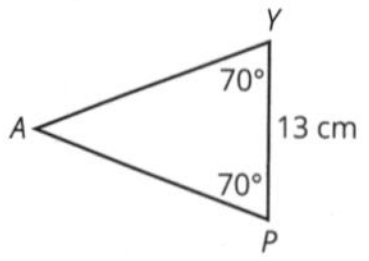

According to the Isosceles Triangle Base Angles Converse Theorem, the sides opposite the 70° are congruent, so $2x + 13 = 43$ and $x = 15$.

$AP = 15$ cm

2. Calculate $m\angle T$.

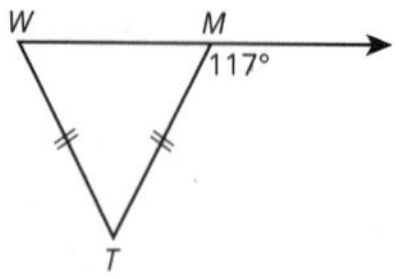

$m\angle WMT + 117° = 180°$, so $m\angle WMT = 63°$

According to the Isosceles Triangle Base Angles Theorem, $\angle WMT \cong \angle MWT$.

$63° + 63° + x° = 180°$, and $x = 54$

$m\angle T = 54°$

3. Lighting booms on a Ferris wheel consist of four steel beams that have cabling with light bulbs attached. These beams, along with three shorter beams, form the edges of three congruent isosceles triangles, as shown. Maintenance crews install new lighting along the four longer beams. Calculate the total length of lighting needed.

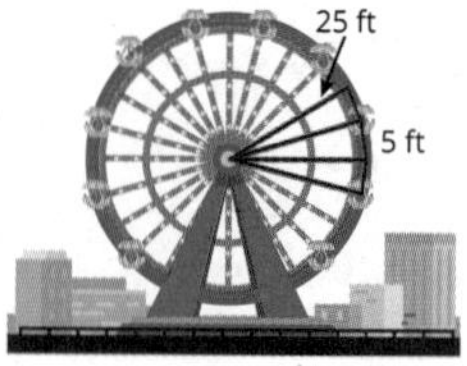

Each of the four longer beams is congruent, so $4(25) = 100$ feet.

Questions to Support Discourse

		TYPE
1	• If the perimeter of $\Delta AYP = 43$ cm, and $m\overline{YP} = 13$ cm, what is $m\overline{AY}$?	Gathering
2	• Which leg has the length of 5 ft? • Is 25 ft the length of the hypotenuse or the length of the longest leg?	Gathering
	• How can you apply the Pythagorean Theorem to this situation?	Probing
3	• How is the Isosceles Triangle Base Angles Theorem helpful in this situation? • How is the Linear Pair Postulate helpful in this situation?	Probing

ACTIVITY 5 Continued

4 Given: $\overline{ST} \cong \overline{SR}$, $\overline{TA} \cong \overline{RA}$. Explain why $\angle T \cong \angle R$.

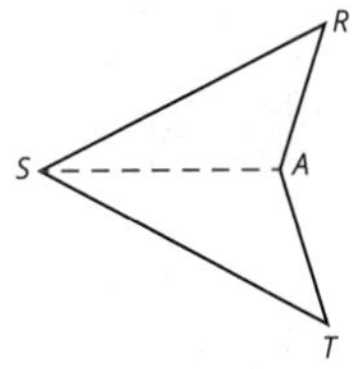

Construct a line from point S to point A to form ΔSAR and ΔSAT. Two pairs of corresponding sides are congruent. Line segment SA is congruent to itself, so, ΔSAR is congruent to ΔSAT by SSS. Therefore, $\angle T$ is congruent to $\angle R$ by CPCTC.

5 A broadcast antenna is on top of a tower. The signal travels from the antenna to your house so you can watch TV. Consider the diagram to calculate the height of the tower and the distance the signal travels.

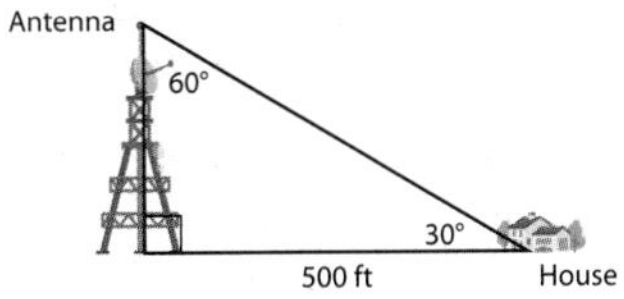

The height of the tower is $\frac{500\sqrt{3}}{3}$ feet, or approximately 288.68 feet.

The distance the signal travels is $\frac{1000\sqrt{3}}{3}$ feet, or approximately 577.36 feet.

6 This stamp is from Mongolia. Suppose the longest side of this stamp is 50 millimeters. Determine the approximate length of the other sides of this stamp. Round your answer to the nearest tenth of a millimeter.

$a = \frac{50}{\sqrt{2}} = \frac{50\sqrt{2}}{2} = 25\sqrt{2}$

The approximate length of the other two sides is 35.4 mm.

NOTES

TOPIC 2

Questions to Support Discourse

		TYPE
4	• Which triangle congruence theorem can you use in this situation?	Gathering
	• How could you use an auxiliary line to solve this problem?	Probing
5	• Which segment of the triangle represents the height of the tower? • What does 500 ft represent in this problem?	Gathering
	• Why can't you use the Pythagorean Theorem to solve this problem?	Seeing structure

NOTES

7 This stamp is from the Netherlands. Suppose the length of each side of the Netherlands stamp is 40 millimeters. Use the 30°-60°-90° Triangle Theorem to determine the height of the stamp.

The height of the Netherlands stamp is $20\sqrt{3}$, or approximately 34.64 mm.

8 In 1929, Uruguay issued a triangular parcel post stamp with sides equal in measure. Suppose the height of the Uruguay stamp is 30 millimeters. Use the 30°-60°-90° Triangle Theorem to determine the length of the three sides of the stamp.

The length of each side of the Uruguayan stamp is $20\sqrt{3}$, or approximately 34.64 mm.

SUMMARY You can use the 45°-45°-90° Triangle Theorem and the 30°-60°-90° Triangle Theorem to solve problems.

City of Bridges

> Use special right triangle theorems to solve each problem.

1. Label the remaining sides of each triangle in terms of x.

(a) 45°-45°-90° Triangle

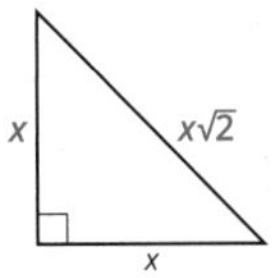

(b) 30°-60°-90° Triangle

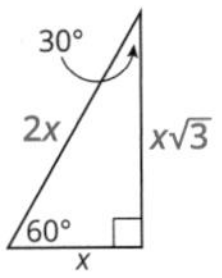

2. Given a 45°-45°-90° triangle, explain how to determine each unknown length.

(a) The length of a leg given the length of the hypotenuse

Divide the length of the hypotenuse by the square root of 2.

(b) The length of the hypotenuse given the length of a leg

Multiply the length of a leg by the square root of 2.

3. Emily is building a square bookshelf. She wants to add a diagonal support beam to the back to strengthen it. The diagonal divides the bookshelf into two 45°-45°-90° triangles. if each side of the bookshelf is 4 feet long, what must the length of the support beam be?

The length of the support beam is 5.7 feet.

Chunking the Activity

- Read and discuss the introduction
- Group students to complete the activity
- Share and summarize

Questions to Support Discourse

		TYPE
3	• How did you determine the length of the support beam?	Probing
	• Why doesn't it matter which diagonal you use to determine the length of the support beam?	Reflecting and justifying

NOTES

4 A cable-stayed bridge has one or more towers erected above piers in the middle of the span. From these towers, cables stretch down diagonally (usually to both sides).

- One cable forms a 60° angle with the bridge deck and is connected to the tower 35 feet above the bridge deck.
- A second cable forms a 45° angle with the bridge deck and connects to the tower 12 feet above the point at which the first cable connects to the tower.

Calculate the length of both cables and the length of the bridge span from each cable to the tower.

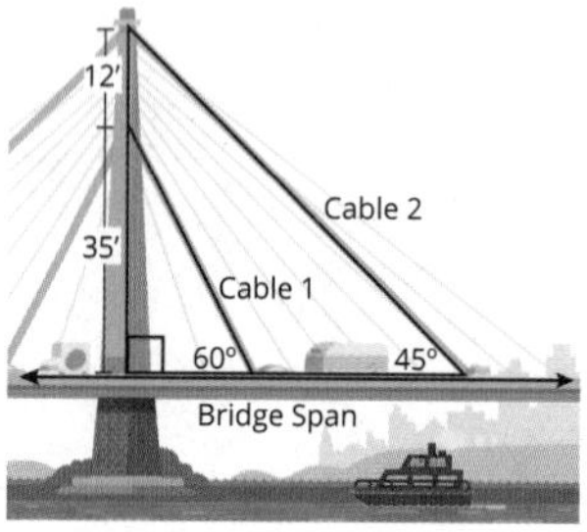

Cable 1 is $\frac{70\sqrt{3}}{3}$, or approximately 40.41, feet long.

Cable 2 is $47\sqrt{2}$, or approximately 66.47, feet long.

Cable 1 bridge span is approximately 20.205 feet long.

Cable 2 bridge span is approximately 47 feet long.

Questions to Support Discourse

		TYPE
4	• Is Cable 1 the hypotenuse of the 45°-45°-90° triangle or the hypotenuse of the 30°-60°-90° triangle? • What is the total height of the tower supporting the cables?	Gathering
	• Did you use the Pythagorean Theorem or the the 45°-45°-90° Triangle Theorem? What is the difference between these two methods?	Seeing structure

LESSON 4 ASSIGNMENT

> Use a separate piece of paper for your Journal entry.

JOURNAL

Provide an example to illustrate each term.

1. Isosceles Triangle Base Angle Theorem
2. Isosceles Triangle Base Angle Converse Theorem
3. Perpendicular Bisector Theorem

REMEMBER

The 30°-60°-90° Triangle Theorem states: "The length of the hypotenuse in a 30°-60°-90° triangle is 2 times the length of the shorter leg, and the length of the longer leg is $\sqrt{3}$ times the length of the shorter leg."

The 45°-45°-90° Triangle Theorem states: "The length of the hypotenuse in a 45°-45°-90° triangle is $\sqrt{2}$ times the length of a leg."

PRACTICE

1. Explain why m∠*NMO* = 20°.

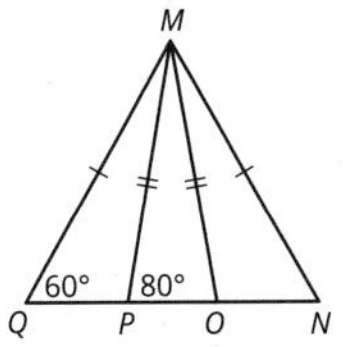

∠*MOP* ≅ ∠*MPO* by the Isosceles Triangle Base Angles Theorem, so m∠*MOP* = 80°.
∠*MOP* and ∠*MON* are a linear pair, so m∠*MON* = 180° − 80° = 100°.
∠*MQN* ≅ ∠*MNQ* by the Isosceles Triangle Base Angles Theorem, so m∠*ONM* = 60°.
The sum of the angles in a triangle is 180°, so for Δ*QMN*, m∠*MON* + m∠*ONM* + m∠*NMO* = 180°.
Using substitution, 100°+60°+m∠*NMO* = 180°, which means m∠*NMO* = 20°.

2. Jill builds a livestock pen in the shape of a triangle. She is using one side of a barn for one of the sides of her pen and has already placed posts in the ground at points *A*, *B*, and *C*, as shown in the diagram. If she places fence posts every 10 feet, how many more posts does she need?

   Note: There will be no other posts placed along the barn wall.

   Jill needs eight more posts.

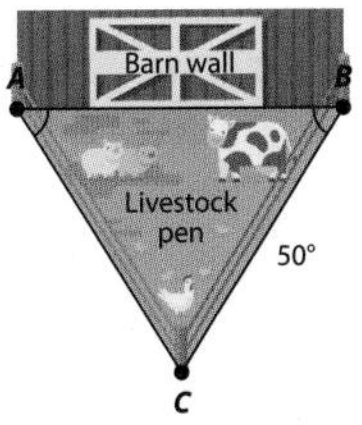

Go to LiveHint.com for help on the PRACTICE questions.

Encourage students to use LiveHint.com for help with the PRACTICE questions of this assignment.

Chunking the Assignment

SESSION 1

- Practice 1 and 2

SESSION 2

- Journal
- Practice 3 and 4
- Stretch (advanced learners)

SESSION 3

- Practice 5
- Mixed Practice (page 383) 6

JOURNAL

Sample answer.

1. 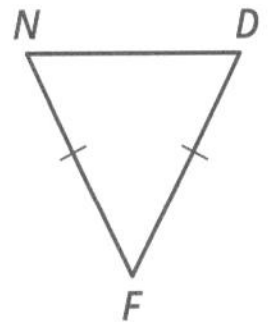

The Isosceles Triangle Base Angles Theorem states that ∠*N* ≅ ∠*D*

2. 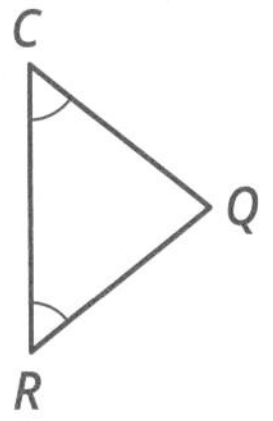

The Isosceles Triangle Base Angles Converse Theorem states that $\overline{QC} \cong \overline{QR}$.

3. 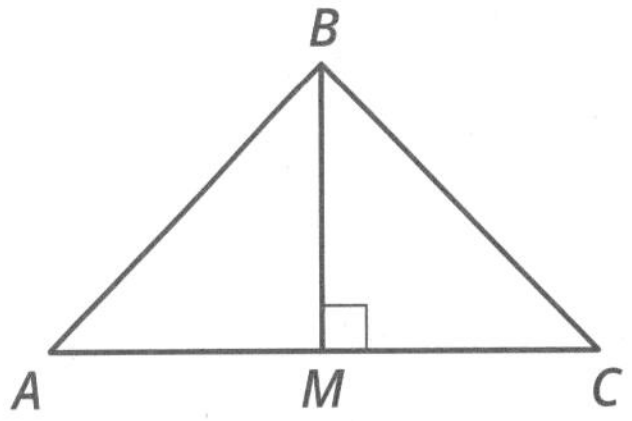

The Perpendicular Bisector Theorem states that $\overline{BA} \cong \overline{BC}$.

NOTES

STRETCH

ΔAXC is an isosceles triangle, so $m\angle AXC = m\angle XAC$. ΔBXC is an isosceles triangle, so $m\angle BCX = m\angle CBX$.

Because it is a right triangle, $m\angle BCA = 90°$. The sum of the measures of the angles in a triangle is 180°.
All this information gives these equations:

$m\angle AXC + m\angle XAC + m\angle ACX = 180°$

$m\angle BCX + m\angle CBX + m\angle BXC = 180°$

$m\angle XAC + m\angle CBX + m\angle BCA = 180°$

$m\angle ACX + m\angle BCX = 90°$

Using substitution and then solving gives $m\angle XAC = 60°$.

3. Label the unknown side lengths.

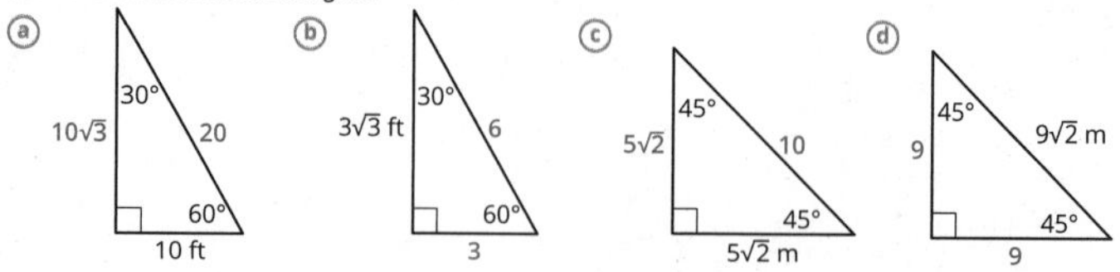

4. The distance between points A and B is 35 feet, the distance between points B and C is 35 feet, and the distance between points C and D is 80 feet. How wide is the canyon? Explain your reasoning.

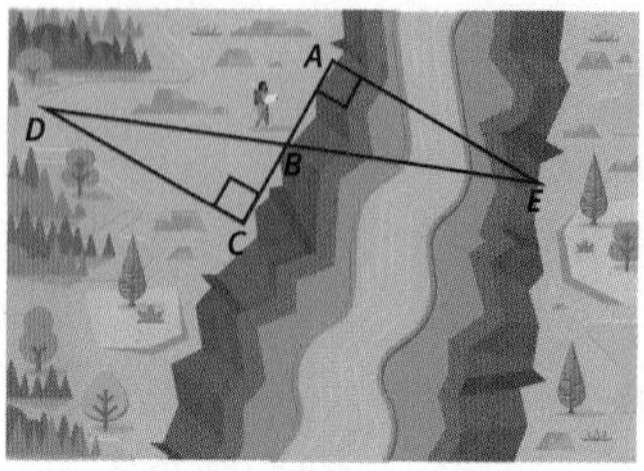

Sample answer.

The canyon is 80 feet wide. The two triangles are congruent by the ASA Congruence Theorem: $\angle A$ and $\angle C$ are both right angles, so they are congruent, and it is given that $\overline{BC}$ is congruent to $\overline{BA}$. $\angle DBC$ and $\angle ABE$ are vertical angles, so they are congruent. Because of CPCTC, $\overline{CD}$ is congruent to $\overline{AE}$, so AE is 80 feet.

5. A mathematical society in India designed this stamp. The pyramidal design is an equilateral triangle. Suppose the height of the pyramidal design on the stamp is 42 millimeters. Determine the area of the pyramidal design on the stamp.

The area of the pyramidal design is $588\sqrt{3}$ mm, or approximately 1,018.45 mm.

STRETCH Optional

> Explain why $m\angle XAC = 60°$.

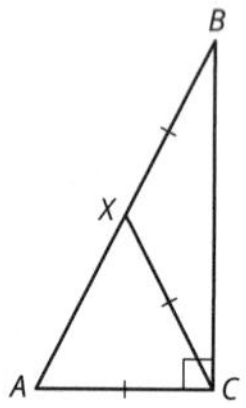

Identical Twins

This resource details additional facilitation notes to fully assist you as you plan each lesson to support all students, students who struggle, and advanced learners. It provides differentiation strategies, common student misconceptions, and suggestions to extend certain activities.

GETTING STARTED

Session 1 of 3

Mappings Matter

Students use their knowledge of Side-Angle-Side (SAS), Side-Side-Side (SSS), and Angle-Side-Angle (ASA) Congruence Theorems. They explain why pairs of triangles are congruent.

CHUNK	AUDIENCE	ADDITIONAL SUPPORTS
As students begin 1	All Students	**DIFFERENTIATION STRATEGY** Have students list theorems they can use to conclude a pair of corresponding sides or angles are congruent.

ACTIVITY 1

Session 1 of 3

The Perpendicular Bisector Theorem

Students define CPCTC and use it to prove the Perpendicular Bisector Theorem and the Perpendicular Bisector Converse Theorem

CHUNK	AUDIENCE	ADDITIONAL SUPPORTS
As students work on the lesson	All Students	**DIFFERENTIATION STRATEGY** Remind students to update their note cards as they encounter new theorems in the lesson.
As students work on 1	Students who Struggle	**DIFFERENTIATION STRATEGY** Have students try one of these strategies to help them visualize the corresponding parts of the triangles. • Trace each triangle on separate pieces of patty paper so that the triangles can be oriented the same way. • Use different colored pencils or markers to highlight the corresponding parts of the triangles.

ACTIVITY 2

Session 1 of 3

Isosceles Triangle Base Angles Theorem

Students prove the Isosceles Triangle Base Angles Theorem and the Isosceles Triangle Base Angles Converse Theorem. They use CPCTC and constructions in their proofs.

CHUNK	AUDIENCE	ADDITIONAL SUPPORTS
To extend 2	Advanced Learners	**DIFFERENTIATION STRATEGY** Have students prove the line drawn through point *G* to the midpoint of $\overline{BD}$ is the perpendicular bisector of $\overline{BD}$.

ACTIVITY 4

Session 2 of 3

More Triangle Congruence Theorems

Students demonstrate why the Hypotenuse-Angle (HA) Congruence Theorem is valid. They demonstrate why the Angle-Angle-Side (AAS) Congruence Theorem is valid.

CHUNK	AUDIENCE	ADDITIONAL SUPPORTS
To extend 1	Advanced Learners	**DIFFERENTIATION STRATEGY** Have students prove the HA Congruence Theorem and the AAS Congruence Theorem.

ACTIVITY 5

Session 3 of 3

Solving Problems with Congruence

Students apply theorems to solve problem situations. They apply theorems such as the Isosceles Triangle Base Angles Theorem, the Pythagorean Theorem, the Exterior Angle Theorem, the Triangle Sum Theorem, triangle congruence theorems, and special right triangle theorems.

CHUNK	AUDIENCE	ADDITIONAL SUPPORTS
As an alternative grouping strategy	All Students	**DIFFERENTIATION STRATEGY** Assign each group a different question to complete. Have students create a poster or presentation to share with the class. Be sure to leave time for students to share their strategies for solving the problem they were assigned.

Practice the learning

MATHbook + Skills Practice

The table shows the targeted practice of the skills and mathematical concepts for the *Justifying Line and Angle Relationships* Topic. The highlighted **Problem Set** aligns with **Identical Twins.**

PROBLEM SET	
1	Identifying Circle Parts
2	Angle Relationships Formed from Parallel Lines
3	Interior and Exterior Angles of Polygons
4	**Isosceles and Right Triangles**
5	Interior and Exterior Angles of a Circle

ANYTIME AFTER ACTIVITY 5

Facilitate students as they work individually on **Problem Set 4.**

NOTES

ENGAGE + DEVELOP + TEACH

at the **Module** level | at the **Topic** level | Read the facilitation notes and plan learning experiences.

Where are we?

TOPIC 2 Justifying Line and Angle Relationships	LESSON 1 Proof Positive	LESSON 2 A Parallel Universe	LESSON 3 Ins and Outs	LESSON 4 Identical Twins	LESSON 5 Corners in a Round Room
Pacing	3 Sessions	2 Sessions	2 Sessions	3 Sessions	3 Sessions

OVERVIEW: LESSON 5

Corners in a Round Room

Angle Relationships Inside and Outside Circles

ENGAGE

- Students calculate minor arc measures on a clock.

DEVELOP

- Students relate the measure of an inscribed angle to the measure of its intercepted arc.
- They explore angles with vertices located inside a circle.
- They conjecture about the measure of an exterior angle of a circle and the arc measures intercepted by the angle.
- They analyze a proof of the Tangent to a Circle Theorem.
- Students apply theorems to solve problems and determine unknown angle measures inside and outside of circles.

DEMONSTRATE

- Students use angle and line relationships along with theorems related to the angles of circles to determine what information they know about given diagrams.

HIGH SCHOOL GEOMETRY

Circles

Understand and apply theorems about circles.

2. Identify and describe relationships among inscribed angles, radii, and chords.

3. Construct the inscribed and circumscribed circles of a triangle, and prove properties of angles for a quadrilateral inscribed in a circle.

4. (+) Construct a tangent line from a point outside a given circle to the circle.

LESSON STRUCTURE AND PACING GUIDE 3 SESSIONS

⊛ This activity highlights a key term or concept that is essential to the learning goals of the lesson.

Session 1 | **Session 2**

INSTRUCTIONAL SEQUENCE

ENGAGE	DEVELOP	DEVELOP
Establish a situation	Worked example Mathematical problem solving	Investigation

GETTING STARTED
Look at the Time

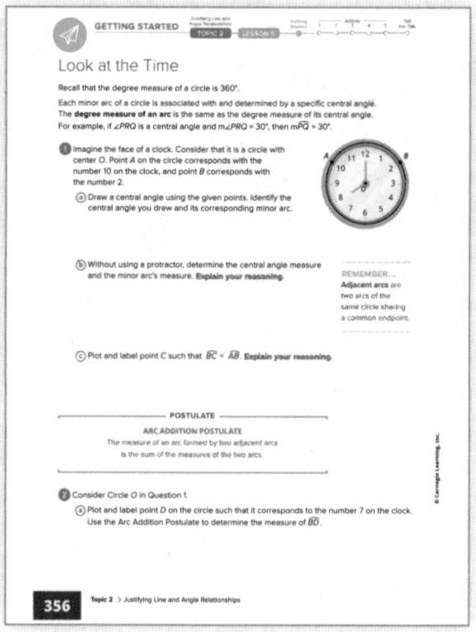

Students calculate minor arc measures using numbers on a clock and their knowledge of a circle's degree measure.

- They conclude that when the measures of two central angles of the same circle (or congruent circles) are equal, their corresponding minor arcs are congruent.

ACTIVITY 1
The Inscribed Angle Theorem

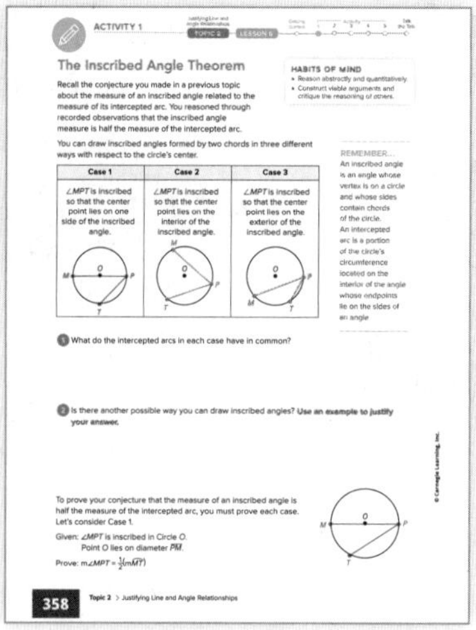

Students prove a conjecture relating the measure of an inscribed angle to the measure of its intercepted arc.

- They look at cases where the center point is on the inscribed angle, inside the inscribed angle, and outside the inscribed angle.
- They use the Inscribed Angle Theorem to prove the Inscribed Right Triangle–Diameter Theorem and the Inscribed Quadrilateral–Opposite Angles Theorem.

ACTIVITY 2
Interior Angles of a Circle Theorem

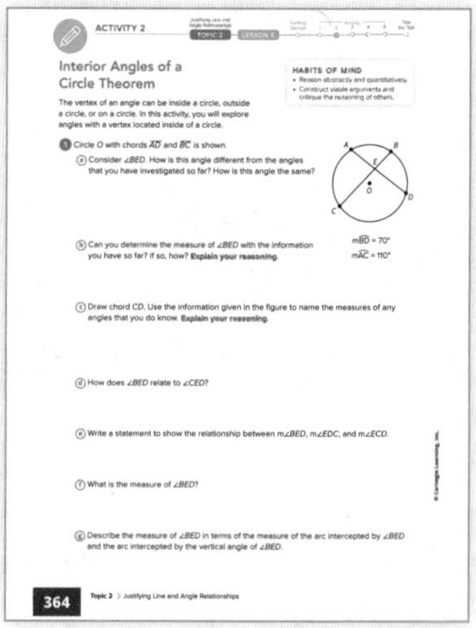

Students explore angles with vertices located inside a circle.

- They draw diagrams, use a protractor to measure angles, look for patterns, and make a conjecture about the measure of an interior angle of a circle related to the sum of the measures of its intercepted arc and its vertical angle's intercepted arc.

Log in to MyCL for **lesson support** including:

Slides

Videos

www.carnegielearning.com/login

Session 3

INSTRUCTIONAL SEQUENCE

DEVELOP	DEVELOP	DEVELOP
Investigation Worked example	Worked example Real-world problem solving	Real-world problem solving Mathematical problem solving

ACTIVITY 3
Exterior Angles of a Circle Theorem

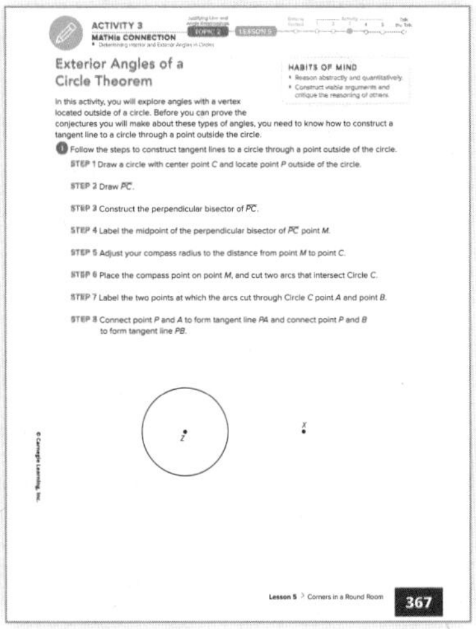

Students make a conjecture about the measure of an exterior angle of a circle and the arc measures intercepted by the angle.

- They analyze a worked example proving the relationship when forming the exterior angle using a secant and a tangent.
- They prove the cases where the exterior angle is formed by two secant lines or by two tangent lines.

ACTIVITY 4
Tangent to a Circle Theorem

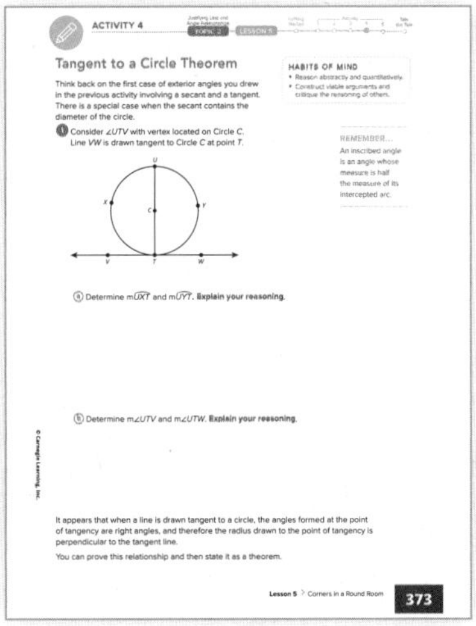

Students analyze a worked example that proves the Tangent to a Circle Theorem by contradiction.

- They apply the theorem to solve problems.

ACTIVITY 5
Determining Measures Inside and Outside Circles

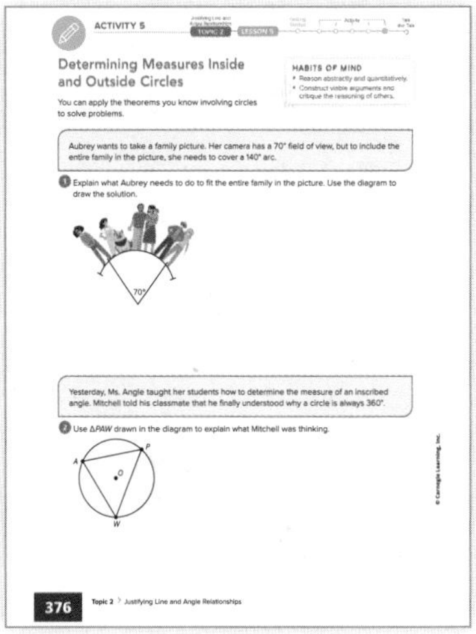

Students apply theorems to solve problems.

- They determine unknown angle measures inside and outside of circles

TOPIC 2

Session 3

INSTRUCTIONAL SEQUENCE

DEMONSTRATE
Exit ticket procedures

TALK THE TALK
Circular Reasoning

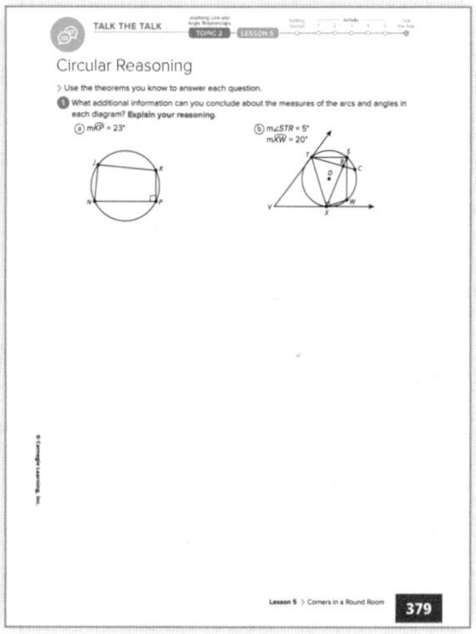

Students use angle and line relationships and theorems related to circles' angles to determine what information they know about given diagrams.

- They investigate mathematical problems.

Log in to MyCL for:

- Editable templates
- Additional planning support

Now that you have read the Module, Topic, and Lesson Overviews, you are ready to plan.

Do the math

Tear out the lesson planning template (page 355E) and jot down thoughts as you work through this lesson and read the Facilitation Notes.

Connect the learning

MATHbook + MATHia

The table shows a portion of the self-paced MATHia sequence for the *Justifying Line and Angle Relationships* Topic.

Median student completion time for entire topic: ~500–530 minutes

As you implement this lesson, consider different connections for students who are on pace and those that have not yet completed the workspaces aligned to this lesson.

STUDENTS WHO ARE NOT HERE YET
Students will practice calculating the measure of arcs and angles using theorems.

TYPE	WORKSPACE NAME
	Proving Theorems using Congruent Triangles
	Calculating the Lengths of Sides of Special Right Triangles
	Using Triangle Theorems
	Determining Interior and Exterior Angles in Circles

STUDENTS WHO ARE ON PACE
After you complete Activity 3, ask these students to share how they represented proportions within this workspace.

Corners in a Round Room

Angle Relationships Inside and Outside Circles

Session 1

GETTING STARTED Look at the Time ✪

Pacing (minutes)	
My Time	Class Time

KEY TERM
degree measure of an arc
adjacent arcs
Arc Addition Postulate

ACTIVITY 1 The Inscribed Angle Theorem ✪

Pacing (minutes)	
My Time	Class Time

KEY TERM
Inscribed Angle Theorem
Inscribed Right Triangle-Diameter Theorem
Inscribed Quadrilateral-Opposite Angles Theorem

Session 2

ACTIVITY 2 Interior Angles of a Circle Theorem ✪

Pacing (minutes)	
My Time	Class Time

KEY TERM
Interior Angles of a Circle Theorem

ACTIVITY 3 Exterior Angles of a Circle Theorem ✪

Pacing (minutes)	
My Time	Class Time

KEY TERM
Exterior Angles of a Circle Theorem

Session 3

ACTIVITY 4 Tangent to a Circle Theorem ✪

Pacing (minutes)	
My Time	Class Time

KEY TERM
proof by contradiction
Tangent to a Circle Theorem

ACTIVITY 5 Determining Measures Inside and Outside Circles

Pacing (minutes)	
My Time	Class Time

TALK THE TALK Circular Reasoning

Pacing (minutes)	
My Time	Class Time

✪ This activity highlights a key term or concept that is essential to the learning goals of the lesson.

Log in to MyCL for:

- Editable templates
- Additional planning support

Reflect on your lesson

Consider the effectiveness of your lesson on student learning.

What went well?	What did not go as planned?

Anticipate how you would change the lesson next time you teach it.

How will you capitalize on the things that went well?	How will you improve things that did not go as planned?

MATERIALS

- Compasses
- Protractors
- Straightedges

TOPIC 1
Composing and Decomposing Shapes

TOPIC 2
Justifying Line and Angle Relationships

1 | Proof Positive
2 | A Parallel Universe
3 | Ins and Outs
4 | Identical Twins
5 | Corners in a Round Room

TOPIC 3
Using Congruence Theorems

LESSON 5

Corners in a Round Room

Angle Relationships Inside and Outside Circles

Learning Goals

- Determine the measures of arcs, central angles, and inscribed angles.
- Prove the Inscribed Angle Theorem, the Inscribed Right Triangle-Diameter Theorem, and the Inscribed Quadrilateral-Opposite Angles Theorem.
- Determine the measures of angles formed by two chords, two secants, a tangent, and a secant, or two tangents.
- Prove the Interior Angles of a Circle Theorem and the Exterior Angles of a Circle Theorem.
- Construct a tangent line to a circle from a point outside the circle.
- Use the Tangent to a Circle Theorem.

KEY TERMS

- degree measure of an arc
- adjacent arcs
- Arc Addition Postulate
- Inscribed Angle Theorem
- Inscribed Right Triangle–Diameter Theorem
- Inscribed Quadrilateral–Opposite Angles Theorem
- Interior Angles of a Circle Theorem
- Exterior Angles of a Circle Theorem
- Proof by contradiction
- Tangent to a Circle Theorem

REVIEW (1–2 minutes)

> Determine the value of x.

1

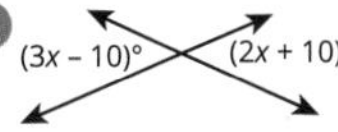

$x = 20$

2

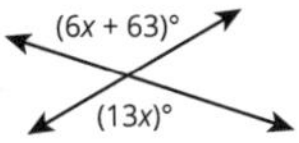

$x = 9$

You have reasoned about and proved several angle relationships for lines and polygons.

How can these angle relationships help you prove theorems involving the angle and arc measures of circles?

Setting the Stage

- **Assign Review (optional, 1 – 2 minutes)**
- **Communicate the learning goals and key terms to look out for**
- **Tap into your students' prior learning by reading the narrative statement**
- **Provide a sense of direction by reading the question**

TOPIC 2

IN THIS REVIEW

Students use vertical angles to calculate missing values. They will use this skill in **ACTIVITY 5 Determining Measures Inside and Outside Circles.**

The measure of an inscribed angle is half the measure of the arc it intercepts.

The measure of an interior angle of a circle is half the sum of the measures of its intercepted arc and its vertical angle's intercepted arc.

The measure of an exterior angle of a circle is half the difference of the measures of its intercepted arcs.

A radius drawn to the point of tangency is perpendicular to the tangent line.

Essential Ideas

- The Inscribed Angle Theorem states that the measure of an inscribed angle is equal to half the measure of its intercepted arc.
- The Inscribed Right Triangle–Diameter Theorem states that when a triangle is inscribed in a circle such that one side of the triangle is a diameter, the triangle is a right triangle.
- The Interior Angles of a Circle Theorem states that if an angle is formed by two intersecting chords or secants of a circle such that the vertex of the angle is in the interior of the circle, then the measure of the angle is half of the sum of the measures of the arcs intercepted by the angle and its vertical angle.
- The Tangent to a Circle Theorem states that a line drawn tangent to a circle is perpendicular to a radius of the circle drawn to the point of tangency.

SUMMARY **When the measures of two minor arcs of the same circle or congruent circles are equal, their corresponding central angles are congruent.**

Chunking the Activity

- Read and discuss the introduction
- Group students to complete 1
- Check-in and share
- Group students to complete 2 - 4
- Check-in and share
- Group students to complete 5
- Share and summarize

Student Look-Fors

Utilizing relationship skills by communicating clearly and listening well.

Look at the Time

Recall that the degree measure of a circle is 360°.

Each minor arc of a circle is associated with and determined by a specific central angle. The **degree measure of an arc** is the same as the degree measure of its central angle. For example, if $\angle PRQ$ is a central angle and $m\angle PRQ = 30°$, then $m\widehat{PQ} = 30°$.

1 Imagine the face of a clock. Consider that it is a circle with center *O*. Point *A* on the circle corresponds with the number 10 on the clock, and point *B* corresponds with the number 2.

(a) Draw a central angle using the given points. Identify the central angle you drew and its corresponding minor arc.

The central angle I drew is $\angle AOB$. Its corresponding minor arc is $\widehat{AB}$.

(b) Without using a protractor, determine the central angle measure and the minor arc's measure. **Explain your reasoning.**

Because a circle has a degree measure of 360°, the measure of an angle between each consecutive pair of clock numbers, such as 12 and 1, is 30°. So, the measure of $\angle AOB$ is $30 \cdot 4 = 120°$. Therefore, the measure of $\widehat{AB}$ is also 120°.

REMEMBER...
Adjacent arcs are two arcs of the same circle sharing a common endpoint.

(c) Plot and label point *C* such that $\widehat{BC} = \widehat{AB}$. **Explain your reasoning.**

The central angle formed by $\angle BOC$ is 120°, so the measure of $\widehat{BC}$ equals 120°. Therefore, $\widehat{AB} \cong \widehat{BC}$.

POSTULATE

ARC ADDITION POSTULATE

The measure of an arc formed by two adjacent arcs is the sum of the measures of the two arcs.

2 Consider Circle *O* in Question 1.

(a) Plot and label point *D* on the circle such that it corresponds to the number 7 on the clock. Use the Arc Addition Postulate to determine the measure of $\widehat{BD}$.

$m\widehat{BD} + m\widehat{CD} = m\widehat{BD}$

$120° + 30° = 150°$

$m\widehat{BD} = 150°$

Questions to Support Discourse

		TYPE
1	• What is the relationship between the measure of the minor arc and the measure of the central angle that determines the minor arc?	Gathering
	• What fraction of the clock does your angle represent? How do you know?	Probing
2	• What do adjacent arcs have in common?	Gathering
	• How is the Arc Addition Postulate like the Angle Addition Postulate?	Seeing structure

ⓑ At which numbers on the clock could you plot point E such that $\overset{\frown}{BD} \cong \overset{\frown}{AE}$? **Explain your reasoning.**

Point E could be plotted on the circle to correspond with either the number 3 or the number 5.
If plotted at the number 3, the central angle measure of $\angle AOE = 150°$ because $m\angle AOB = 120°$ and $m\angle BOE = 30°$. Therefore, $m\overset{\frown}{AB} + m\overset{\frown}{BE} = m\overset{\frown}{AE} = 150°$.
If plotted at the number 5, the central angle measure of $\angle AOE = 150°$ because $m\angle AOC = 120°$ and $m\angle COE = 30°$. Therefore, $m\overset{\frown}{AC} + m\overset{\frown}{CE} = m\overset{\frown}{AE} = 150°$.

3 If the measures of two central angles of the same circle (or congruent circles) are equal, are their corresponding minor arcs congruent? **Explain your reasoning.**

Yes. Because the degree measure of a minor arc is equal to the measure of its central angle, two congruent central angles of the same circle or congruent circles determine arcs of equal measure. When two angles of the same circle are each 46°, the measure of each arc determined by the angles is also 46°.

4 If the measures of two minor arcs of the same circle (or congruent circles) are equal, are their corresponding central angles congruent? **Explain your reasoning.**

Yes. Because the degree measure of a minor arc is equal to the measure of its central angle, two congruent minor arcs of the same circle determine central angles of equal measure. When two arcs of the same circle are each 46°, the measure of each central angle determined by the minor arcs is also 46°.

5 Alicia explains to her classmate that $\overset{\frown}{SC}$ is congruent to $\overset{\frown}{TX}$. How did Alicia arrive at this conclusion? Is Alicia correct? **Explain your reasoning.**

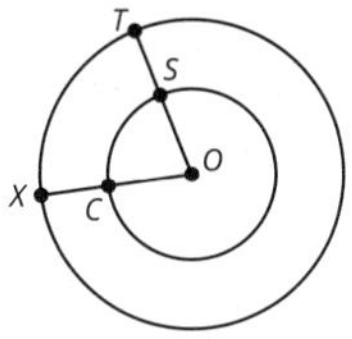

Alicia is not correct. She thinks that because both arcs have the same central angle, and the central angle determines the arc's measure, the arcs must be congruent. But this is only true when the circles are the same circle or congruent circles. That is not the case in this diagram. The radii of each circle are different lengths. The arcs may be the same measure, but that does not imply that the arcs are congruent.

NOTES

TOPIC 2

COMMON MISCONCEPTION

See Page 382A for a misconception related to 5.

Questions to Support Discourse

		TYPE
3	• Why do you think the central angles have to be in the same circle or congruent circles for the minor arcs to be congruent?	Probing
4	• Is it possible that two minor arcs are congruent when they are not on congruent circles? Explain your reasoning.	Probing
5	• When two arcs are the same measure, do they have to be the same length?	Seeing structure

ACTIVITY 1

Session 1 of 2

SUMMARY To prove theorems like the Inscribed Angle Theorem, you need to consider more than one case.

Chunking the Activity

- **Read and discuss the introduction**
- **Group students to complete 1 and 2**
- **Check-in and share**
- **Read and discuss the worked example**
- **Group students to complete 3 – 5**
- **Check-in and share**
- **Group students to complete 6 – 8**
- **Check-in and share**
- **Group students to complete 9 and 10**
- **Read and discuss the theorems**

DIFFERENTIATION STRATEGY

See Page 382A to assist all students with the lesson.

The Inscribed Angle Theorem

HABITS OF MIND
- Reason abstractly and quantitatively.
- Construct viable arguments and critique the reasoning of others.

Recall the conjecture you made in a previous topic about the measure of an inscribed angle related to the measure of its intercepted arc. You reasoned through recorded observations that the inscribed angle measure is half the measure of the intercepted arc.

You can draw inscribed angles formed by two chords in three different ways with respect to the circle's center.

Case 1	Case 2	Case 3
$\angle MPT$ is inscribed so that the center point lies on one side of the inscribed angle.	$\angle MPT$ is inscribed so that the center point lies on the interior of the inscribed angle.	$\angle MPT$ is inscribed so that the center point lies on the exterior of the inscribed angle.
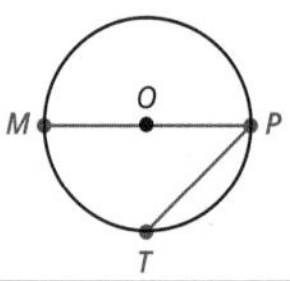	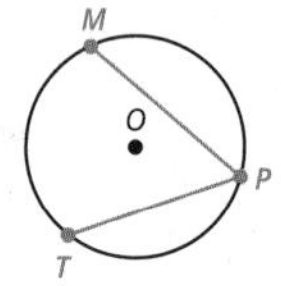	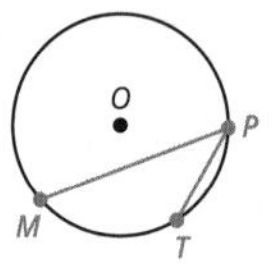

REMEMBER...
An inscribed angle is an angle whose vertex is on a circle and whose sides contain chords of the circle.
An intercepted arc is a portion of the circle's circumference located on the interior of the angle whose endpoints lie on the sides of an angle.

1 What do the intercepted arcs in each case have in common?

They are all minor arcs.

2 Is there another possible way you can draw inscribed angles? **Use an example to justify your answer.**

Yes. You can draw an inscribed angle where the intercepted arc is a major arc.

To prove your conjecture that the measure of an inscribed angle is half the measure of the intercepted arc, you must prove each case. Let's consider Case 1.

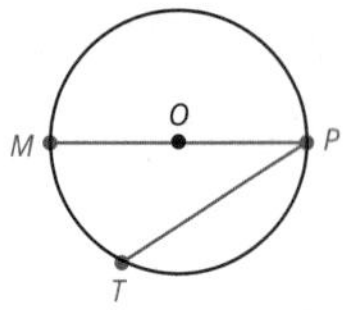

Given: $\angle MPT$ is inscribed in Circle O.
Point O lies on diameter $\overline{PM}$.

Prove: $m\angle MPT = \frac{1}{2}(m\overset{\frown}{MT})$

Questions to Support Discourse

		TYPE
1	• Is $\overset{\frown}{MT}$ in each case a minor arc? How do you know?	Gathering
2	• Is it possible to draw an inscribed angle to intercept a major arc? Explain your reasoning.	Probing
	• Are intercepted arcs always minor arcs? Why?	Reflecting and justifying

You can use construction and algebraic reasoning to create a proof plan.

WORKED EXAMPLE

Let's consider how to prove that $m\angle MPT = \frac{1}{2}(m\widehat{MT})$ for Case 1.

Connect points O and T to form radius $\overline{OT}$.

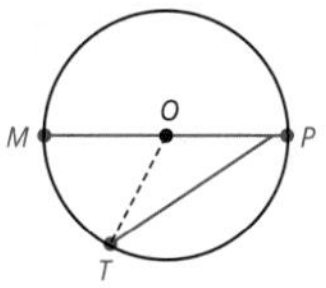

Label $\angle MPT$ as x.

$\angle OTP = x$ because ΔOTP is isosceles.

Then, $\angle MOT = 2x$ and $m\widehat{MT} = 2x$.

Therefore, $m\widehat{MT} = 2(m\angle MPT)$

or $\angle MPT = \frac{1}{2}(m\widehat{MT})$.

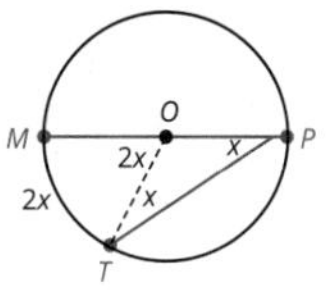

3 Complete a formal proof for Case 1.

Statements	Reasons
1. $\angle MPT$ is inscribed in Circle O. $m\angle MPT = x$ Point O lies on diameter $\overline{PM}$.	1. Given
2. Connect points O and T to form radius $\overline{OT}$.	2. Construction
3. $\overline{OT} \cong \overline{OP}$	3. All radii of the same circle are congruent.
4. $\angle MPT \cong \angle OTP$	4. Isosceles Triangle Base Angles Theorem
5. $m\angle OTP = x$	5. Substitution Property
6. $m\angle MOT = 2x$	6. Exterior Angle Theorem
7. $m\widehat{MT} = 2x$	7. A central angle is equal to the measure of its intercepted arc.
8. $\frac{1}{2}(m\widehat{MT}) = x$	8. Division Property of Equality
9. $\frac{1}{2}(m\widehat{MT}) = m\angle MPT$	9. Substitution Property

THINK ABOUT...

You have used the Addition and Subtraction Properties of Equality as reasons in proofs. You can also use the Multiplication and Division Properties of Equality as reasons in proofs.

Questions to Support Discourse

		TYPE
Worked Example	• Why do you think the proof of this theorem requires the proof of three different cases?	Seeing structure
3	• Which theorems does this proof use?	Gathering
	• How do you know ΔOTP is isosceles? • How does knowing ΔOTP is isosceles help you determine the relationship between $\angle MPT$ and $\angle OTP$?	Probing

NOTES

TOPIC 2

NOTES

ACTIVITY 1 Continued

4 Use algebraic reasoning to demonstrate your conjecture for the other two cases.

(a) Case 2

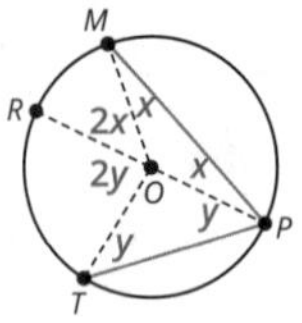

Label ∠*MPO* = *x* and ∠*OPT* = *y*.
∠*MPT* = *x* + *y* ∠*PMO* = *x* and ∠*PTO* = *y* because both Δ*POM* and Δ*POT* are isosceles.
∠*MOR* = 2*x* and ∠*ROT* = 2*y*

Therefore,
$2x + 2y = m\angle MOT = m\widehat{MT}$
$2(x + y) = m\widehat{MT}$ or
$2(m\angle MPT) = m\widehat{MT}$
So, $m\angle MPT = \frac{1}{2}(m\widehat{MT})$

(b) Case 3

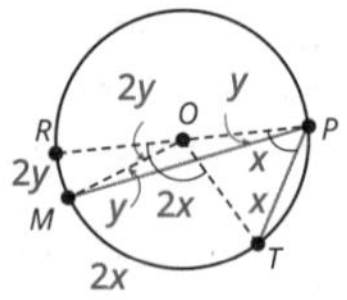

Label ∠*RPT* = *x* and ∠*RPM* = *y*.
∠*MPT* = *x* − *y*, ∠*PTO* = *x*, and ∠*OMP* = *y* because Δ*POM* and Δ*POT* are isosceles.
∠*ROT* = 2*x* and ∠*ROM* = 2*y*

Therefore,
$2x - 2y = m\angle MOT = m\widehat{MT}$
$2(x - y) = m\widehat{MT}$ or
$2(m\angle MPT) = m\widehat{MT}$
So, $m\angle MPT = \frac{1}{2}(m\widehat{MT})$

Because you proved that the relationship is true, you can now refer to it as a theorem.

THEOREM

INSCRIBED ANGLE THEOREM

The measure of an inscribed angle is half the measure of its intercepted arc.

5 State the converse of the Inscribed Angle Theorem. Do you think the converse is true?

An arc on the circle has twice the measure of an inscribed angle that intercepts it. Yes, if you know the measure of an arc, an inscribed angle intercepting it will be half its measure.

360 Topic 2 > Justifying Line and Angle Relationships

Questions to Support Discourse

		TYPE
4	• How does the reasoning for Case 2 and Case 3 compare to Case 1?	Seeing structure

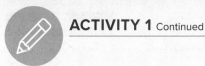

ACTIVITY 1 Continued

There is a special case of the Inscribed Angle Theorem that applies to a specific type of inscribed polygon.

> Consider ΔABC that is inscribed in Circle *P*.

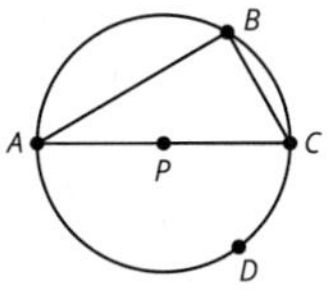

REMEMBER…
An inscribed polygon is a polygon drawn inside a circle such that each vertex of the polygon touches the circle.

6 Which type of triangle is ΔABC? **How do you know?**

Triangle *ABC* is a right triangle. Line segment *AC* is a diameter of Circle *P*, and the measure of $\angle ADC$ is 180° because it is a semicircle. From the Inscribed Angle Theorem, the measure of $\angle ABC$ is 90° because its measure is half the measure of its intercepted arc.

7 Write a conjecture about the type of triangle inscribed in a circle when one side of the triangle is a diameter.

If a triangle is inscribed in a circle such that the triangle's hypotenuse is a diameter of the circle, then the triangle is a right triangle.

8 Write the converse of the conjecture you wrote in Question 2. **Do you think this statement is also true?**

If a right triangle is inscribed in a circle, then the triangle's hypotenuse is a diameter of the circle.
Yes. I think the converse of the conjecture is true.

Lesson 5 > Corners in a Round Room 361

NOTES

TOPIC 2

Questions to Support Discourse

		TYPE
6	• If $\overline{AC}$ is the diameter of Circle *P*, what does this imply about $\widehat{ADC}$ and $\widehat{ABC}$?	Gathering
	• How do you know $\overline{AC}$ the longest chord of Circle *P*? • How can you use the Inscribed Angles Theorem to determine $m\angle ABC$?	Probing
7	• Which part of the triangle is diameter $\overline{AC}$?	Gathering
	• If you move point *B* to a different location on the circle, is ΔABC still a right triangle? How do you know?	Seeing structure
8	• What is the hypothesis of your conjecture? What is the conclusion?	Gathering
	• What do you know about inscribed angles that makes you think the converse of your conjecture is true?	Probing

NOTES

It appears that ΔABC is a right triangle and that $\angle B$ is a right angle. In general, it appears that if a triangle is inscribed in a circle such that one side of the triangle is a diameter of the circle, then the triangle is a right triangle.

9 Create a proof of this conjecture.

Given: ΔHYP is inscribed in Circle O such that $\overline{HP}$ is the diameter of the circle.
Prove: ΔHYP is a right triangle.

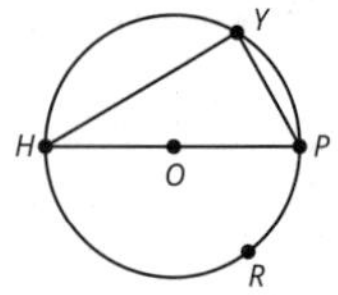

Statements	Reasons
1. ΔHYP is inscribed in Circle O such that $\overline{HP}$ is the diameter of the circle.	1. Given
2. $\overset{\frown}{HRP}$ is a semicircle.	2. The diameter of a circle divides the circle into two semicircles.
3. $m\overset{\frown}{HRP} = 180°$	3. Definition of semicircle
4. $\frac{1}{2}\overset{\frown}{HRP} = 90°$	4. Division Property
5. $m\angle HYP = \frac{1}{2}(m\overset{\frown}{HRP})$	5. Inscribed Angle Theorem
6. $m\angle HYP = 90°$	6. Substitution Property
7. $\angle HYP$ is a right angle.	7. Definition of a right angle
8. ΔHYP is a right triangle.	8. Definition of a right triangle

Because you proved that the relationship is true, you can now refer to it as a theorem.

THEOREM

INSCRIBED RIGHT TRIANGLE–DIAMETER THEOREM

If a triangle is inscribed in a circle such that one side of the triangle is a diameter of the circle, then the triangle is a right triangle.

Questions to Support Discourse

	Questions	TYPE
9	• Which inscribed angle determines $\overset{\frown}{HRP}$?	Gathering
	• How do you know that $\overset{\frown}{HRP}$ is a semicircle? • How can you determine the measure of $\angle HYP$?	Probing

ACTIVITY 1 Continued

In a previous topic, you made a conjecture that the opposite angles of cyclic quadrilaterals, or inscribed quadrilaterals, are supplementary. You can prove this conjecture using the Inscribed Angle Theorem.

10 Create a proof of this conjecture.

Given: Quadrilateral *QUAD* is inscribed in Circle *O*.
Prove: $\angle Q$ and $\angle A$ are supplementary angles.
$\angle U$ and $\angle D$ are supplementary angles.

Statements	Reasons
1. Quadrilateral *QUAD* is inscribed in Circle *O*.	1. Given
2. $m\overset{\frown}{QUA} + m\overset{\frown}{QDA} = 360°$ $m\overset{\frown}{UAD} + m\overset{\frown}{UQD} = 360°$	2. A circle is 360°
3. $m\angle U = \frac{1}{2}(m\overset{\frown}{QDA})$ $m\angle D = \frac{1}{2}(m\overset{\frown}{QUA})$ $m\angle Q = \frac{1}{2}(m\overset{\frown}{UAD})$ $m\angle A = \frac{1}{2}(m\overset{\frown}{UQD})$	3. Inscribed Angle Theorem
4. $m\angle U + m\angle D = \frac{1}{2}(m\overset{\frown}{QUA}) + \frac{1}{2}(m\overset{\frown}{QDA})$ $m\angle Q + m\angle A = \frac{1}{2}(m\overset{\frown}{UAD}) + \frac{1}{2}(m\overset{\frown}{UQD})$	4. Substitution Property
5. $m\angle U + m\angle D = \frac{1}{2}(m\overset{\frown}{QUA} + m\overset{\frown}{QDA})$ $m\angle Q + m\angle A = \frac{1}{2}(m\overset{\frown}{UAD} + m\overset{\frown}{UQD})$	5. Distributive Property
6. $m\angle U + m\angle D = \frac{1}{2}(360°)$ $m\angle Q + m\angle A = \frac{1}{2}(360°)$	6. Substitution Property steps 2 and 5
7. $m\angle U + m\angle D = 180°$ $m\angle Q + m\angle A = 180°$	7. Multiplication
8. $\angle U$ and $\angle D$ are supplementary angles. $\angle Q$ and $\angle A$ are supplementary angles.	8. Definition of supplementary angles.

Because you have proved that this conjecture is true, you can now refer to it as a theorem.

THEOREM

INSCRIBED QUADRILATERAL–OPPOSITE ANGLES THEOREM

If a quadrilateral is inscribed in a circle, then the opposite angles are supplementary.

NOTES

Questions to Support Discourse

		TYPE
10	• What is the sum of the arcs intercepted by $\angle Q$ and $\angle A$? What about $\angle U$ and $\angle D$?	Gathering
	• Do you think there will be multiple cases to this proof? Why or why not? • How can the Inscribed Angles Theorem be applied to this situation?	Probing
	• If $m\angle Q + m\angle A = 180°$, are the angles supplementary? Why?	Seeing structure

TOPIC 2

SUMMARY **You can use the Interior Angles of a Circle Theorem as a reason in proofs and to solve problems.**

Chunking the Activity

- Read and discuss the introduction
- Group students to complete 1
- Check-in and share
- Group students to complete 2 and 3
- Check-in and share
- Group students to complete 4
- Check-in and share
- Group students to complete 5
- Read and discuss the theorem

Interior Angles of a Circle Theorem

HABITS OF MIND
- Reason abstractly and quantitatively.
- Construct viable arguments and critique the reasoning of others.

The vertex of an angle can be inside a circle, outside a circle, or on a circle. In this activity, you will explore angles with a vertex located inside of a circle.

1 Circle *O* with chords $\overline{AD}$ and $\overline{BC}$ is shown.

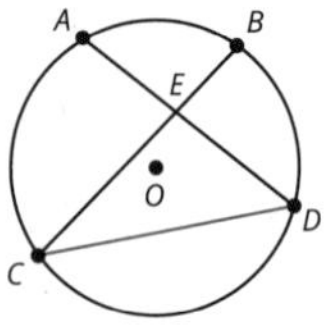

$m\overset{\frown}{BD} = 70°$

$m\overset{\frown}{AC} = 110°$

(a) Consider $\angle BED$. How is this angle different from the angles that you have investigated so far? How is this angle the same?

The angle is different because its vertex is neither at the center of the circle nor on the circle. The angle is the same because its sides intersect the circle.

(b) Can you determine the measure of $\angle BED$ with the information you have so far? If so, how? **Explain your reasoning.**

Answers will vary.

(c) Draw chord *CD*. Use the information given in the figure to name the measures of any angles that you do know. **Explain your reasoning.**

Because the intercepted arc of $\angle BCD$ is $\overset{\frown}{BD}$ and $m\overset{\frown}{BD} = 70°$, $m\angle BCD = 35°$.
Because the intercepted arc of $\angle ADC$ is $\overset{\frown}{AC}$ and $m\overset{\frown}{AC} = 110°$, $m\angle ADC = 55°$.

(d) How does $\angle BED$ relate to $\angle CED$?

Angle *BED* is an exterior angle of the triangle.

(e) Write a statement to show the relationship between $m\angle BED$, $m\angle EDC$, and $m\angle ECD$.

$m\angle EDC + m\angle ECD = m\angle BED$

(f) What is the measure of $\angle BED$?

The measure of $\angle BED$ is $55° + 35° = 90°$.

(g) Describe the measure of $\angle BED$ in terms of the measure of the arc intercepted by $\angle BED$ and the arc intercepted by the vertical angle of $\angle BED$.

The measure of $\angle BED$ is half the sum of the measures of $\overset{\frown}{BD}$ and $\overset{\frown}{AC}$.

Questions to Support Discourse

		TYPE
1	• Which inscribed angles does chord *CD* form? • What is the measure of the arc intercepted by $\angle BCD$? What about $\angle ADC$? • In ΔCED, the measures of exterior $\angle BED$ is the sum of which two remote interior angles?	Gathering
	• Is $\angle BED$ a central angle? Why not? • Is $\angle BED$ an inscribed angle? Why not?	Probing

ACTIVITY 2 Continued

2 Draw a circle with two chords that intersect inside it. Use measuring tools to determine the measure of an angle formed by the intersecting chords and the measures of the arcs that are intercepted by the angle and its vertical angle.

Check students' drawings.

Sample answer. Use the given diagram.

- I drew radii from points *A*, *B*, *C*, and *D* to the center, *O*.
- I measured central angle $\angle AOB$ to calculate the measure of $\overset{\frown}{AB}$.
- I measured central angle $\angle COD$ to calculate the measure of $\overset{\frown}{CD}$.
- I measured $\angle CED$ formed by the chords.
- The measure of $\angle CED$ is half the sum of the measures of $\overset{\frown}{AB}$ and $\overset{\frown}{CD}$.

3 Consider the different measures you determined in the circles from Questions 1 and 2. Look for patterns and make a conjecture about the measure of an interior angle of a circle and the measures of the arcs that are intercepted by the angle and its vertical angle.

It appears that the measure of an interior angle of a circle is equal to half the sum of the measures of the arcs intercepted by the angle and its vertical angle.

Let's first explore your conjecture for a circle where the vertex of the interior angle is at the center of the circle.

4 Consider Circle *O* with diameters *BD* and *PF*. If $\angle BOP$ and $\angle FOD$ form vertical angles, then $m\angle BOP = \frac{1}{2}(m\overset{\frown}{BP} + m\overset{\frown}{FD})$. **Use reasoning to demonstrate why this is true.**

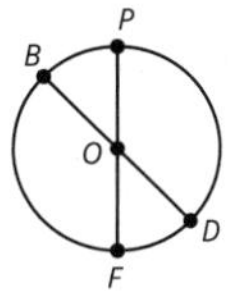

The central angles *BOP* and *FOD* are congruent because they are vertical angles. This means their measures are equal. It also means that the measures of $\overset{\frown}{BP}$ and $\overset{\frown}{FD}$ are equal. If you add the two equal arc measures, $m\angle BOP$ is equal to half the sum, since it is equal to only one of the arc measures.

Questions to Support Discourse

		TYPE
2	• What additional chords or radii did you need to draw to determine the measures of the angles and the arcs?	Probing
3	• Is the measure of an interior angle always equal to half of the sum of the measures of the arcs intercepted by the angle and its vertical angle? How do you know?	Seeing structure
4	• Why is $m\angle BOP = m\angle FOD$? • Why are the measures of $\angle BOP$ and $\angle FOD$ equal to the measures of their intercepted arcs?	Probing
	• Why is $m\angle BOP$ equal to half the sum of $\overset{\frown}{BP}$ and $\overset{\frown}{FD}$?	Seeing structure

NOTES

TOPIC 2

NOTES

You've shown that the conjecture is true for two chords intersecting at the center of the circle. Now let's explore whether the conjecture holds for any two chords that intersect in a circle.

5 Use algebraic reasoning to prove the conjecture.

Given: Chords EK and GH intersect at point F in Circle O.

Prove: $m\angle KFH = \frac{1}{2}(m\widehat{HK} + m\widehat{EG})$

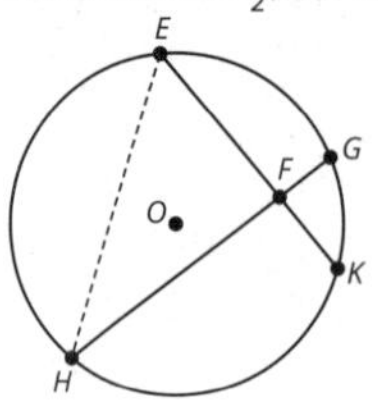

THINK ABOUT...
An auxiliary chord is drawn from point E to point H. How does this chord help you reason about the measure of $\angle KFH$?

The auxiliary chord also creates two inscribed angles, $\angle HEK$ and $\angle EHG$.

I can label the measure of $\widehat{HK}$ as x and the measure of $\widehat{EG}$ as y. This means that $m\angle E = \frac{1}{2}x$ and $m\angle H = \frac{1}{2}y$.

The auxiliary chord also creates ΔEFH. Since $\angle KFH$ is an exterior angle of the triangle, its measure is equal to $\frac{1}{2}x + \frac{1}{2}y$, or $\frac{1}{2}(x + y)$.

Therefore, $m\angle KFH = \frac{1}{2}\left(m\widehat{HK} + m\widehat{EG}\right)$.

Because you proved that this conjecture is true, you can now refer to it as a theorem.

THEOREM

INTERIOR ANGLES OF A CIRCLE THEOREM

If an angle is formed by two intersecting chords or secants of a circle such that the vertex of the angle is in the interior of the circle, then the measure of the angle is half of the sum of the measures of the arcs intercepted by the angle and its vertical angle.

Questions to Support Discourse

		TYPE
5	• Drawing auxiliary chord EH creates which inscribed angles?	Gathering
	• What do you know about the measure of $\widehat{HK}$ and the $m\angle HEK$? • What do you know about the measure of $\widehat{EG}$ and the $m\angle EHG$?	Probing
	• How was the Inscribed Angle Theorem helpful in proving this theorem?	Reflecting and justifying

ACTIVITY 3

SUMMARY **You can use the Exterior Angles of a Circle Theorem to solve problems and as a reason in other proofs.**

Exterior Angles of a Circle Theorem

HABITS OF MIND
- Reason abstractly and quantitatively.
- Construct viable arguments and critique the reasoning of others.

In this activity, you will explore angles with a vertex located outside of a circle. Before you can prove the conjectures you will make about these types of angles, you need to know how to construct a tangent line to a circle through a point outside the circle.

1 Follow the steps to construct tangent lines to a circle through a point outside of the circle.

STEP 1 Draw a circle with center point *C* and locate point *P* outside of the circle.

STEP 2 Draw $\overline{PC}$.

STEP 3 Construct the perpendicular bisector of $\overline{PC}$.

STEP 4 Label the midpoint of the perpendicular bisector of $\overline{PC}$ point *M*.

STEP 5 Adjust your compass radius to the distance from point *M* to point *C*.

STEP 6 Place the compass point on point *M*, and cut two arcs that intersect Circle *C*.

STEP 7 Label the two points at which the arcs cut through Circle *C* point *A* and point *B*.

STEP 8 Connect point *P* and *A* to form tangent line *PA* and connect point *P* and *B* to form tangent line *PB*.

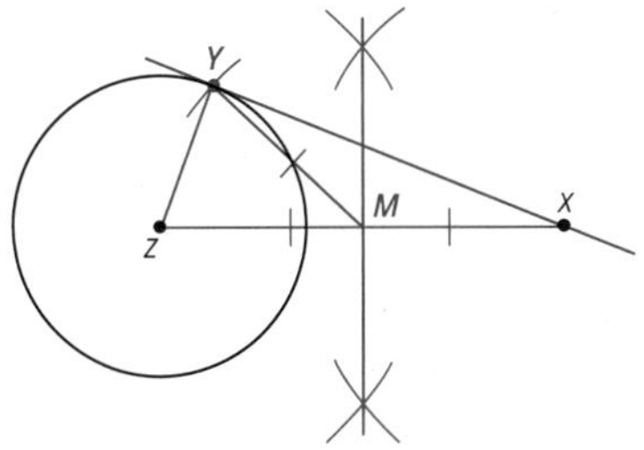

Line *PA* and line *PB* are tangent to Circle *C*.

Check students' constructions.

Chunking the Activity

- Read and discuss the introduction
- Complete 1 as a class
- Group students to complete 2
- Check-in and share
- Group students to complete 3 and 4
- Check-in and share
- Read and discuss the worked example
- Group students to complete 5
- Check-in and share
- Group students to complete 6
- Read and discuss the theorem

NOTES

ACTIVITY 3 Continued

Let's explore how the measure of an angle outside a circle, such as ∠*APB* that you constructed, relates to the measures of the arcs its intercepts.

2 Consider Circle *T* with points *K*, *L*, *M*, and *N*.

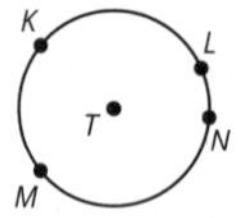

$m\overset{\frown}{KM} = 80°$
$m\overset{\frown}{LN} = 30°$

(a) Draw secants $\overleftrightarrow{KL}$ and $\overleftrightarrow{MN}$. Where do the secants intersect? Label this point as point *P* on the figure.

The secant lines intersect outside the circle.

(b) Draw chord $\overline{KN}$. Can you determine the measure of ∠*KPM* with the information you have so far? If so, how? **Explain your reasoning**.

Answers will vary.

(c) Use the information given in the figure to name the measures of any angles that you do know. **Explain how you determined your answers.**

Because the intercepted arc of ∠*LKN* is $\overset{\frown}{LN}$ and $m\overset{\frown}{LN} = 30°$, m∠*LKN* = 15°.
Because the intercepted arc of ∠*KNM* is $\overset{\frown}{KM}$ and $m\overset{\frown}{KM} = 80°$, m∠*KNM* = 40°.

(d) How does ∠*KPN* relate to Δ*KPN*?

Angle *KPN* is an interior angle of Δ*KPN*.

(e) Write a statement to show the relationship between m∠*KPN*, m∠*NKP*, and m∠*KNM*.

m∠*KPN* + m∠*NKP* = m∠*KNM*.

(f) What is the measure of ∠*KPN*?

The measure of ∠*KPN* is 40° − 15° = 25°.

(g) Describe the measure of ∠*KPM* in terms of the measures of both arcs intercepted by ∠*KPM*.

The measure of ∠*KPM* is half of the difference of the measures of $\overset{\frown}{KM}$ and $\overset{\frown}{LN}$.

368 Topic 2 > Justifying Line and Angle Relationships

Questions to Support Discourse

		TYPE
2	• What shape contains ∠*KPM*? How can that help you determine the measure of ∠*KPM*? • Which inscribed angle determines $\overset{\frown}{KM}$? $\overset{\frown}{LN}$?	Probing

ACTIVITY 3 Continued

You can form an angle with a vertex located in the exterior of a circle using a secant and a tangent, two secants, or two tangents.

3 For each case, draw and label the exterior angle described. Then, determine the measure of the exterior angle and the measures of the arcs that are intercepted by the angle.

(a) Case 1: Exterior angle formed by a secant and a tangent

Sample answer.

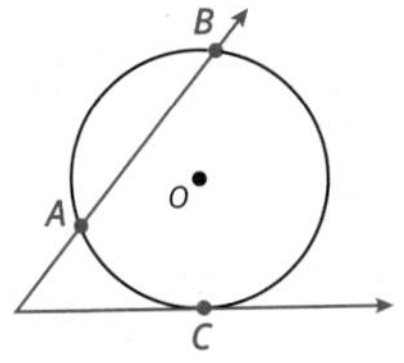

(b) Case 2: Exterior angle formed by two secants

Sample answer.

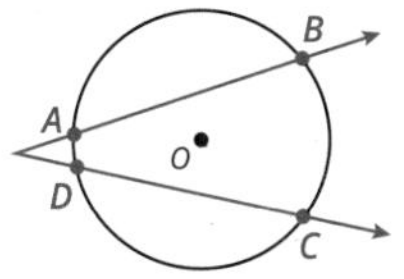

(c) Case 3: Exterior angle

Sample answer.

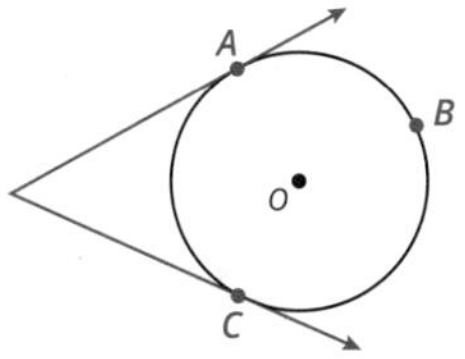

4 Consider the different measures you determined in the circles from Questions 2 and 3. Look for patterns and make a conjecture about the measure of an exterior angle of a circle and the measure of the arcs that are intercepted by the angle.

It appears that the measure of an exterior angle of a circle is equal to half the difference of the measures of the arcs intercepted by the angle.

NOTES

DIFFERENTIATION STRATEGY

See Page 382B to group students to complete 3 and 4.

TOPIC 2

Questions to Support Discourse

		TYPE
3	• Is the intersection of a secant and tangent always outside of the circle? Why or why not? • Is the intersection of two secants always outside of the circle? Why or why not? • Is the intersection of two tangents always outside of the circle? Why or why not?	Probing
4	• Do you think the exterior angle measure is always half the difference of the measures of the arcs intercepted by the angle?	Seeing structure

NOTES

Student Look-Fors

Which triangle students use to apply the Interior Angles Theorem when proving Case 2 and Case 3.

It appears that if an angle is formed by two intersecting chords or secants of a circle such that the vertex of the angle is in the exterior of the circle, then the measure of the angle is half of the difference of the measures of the arcs intercepted by the angle.

To prove this conjecture, you must prove each of the three cases.

> Analyze the proof of Case 1 in the worked example.

WORKED EXAMPLE

Case 1

Given: Secant *ER* and tangent *TJ* intersect at point *J*.

Prove: $m\angle EJT = \frac{1}{2}(m\widehat{ET} - m\widehat{RT})$

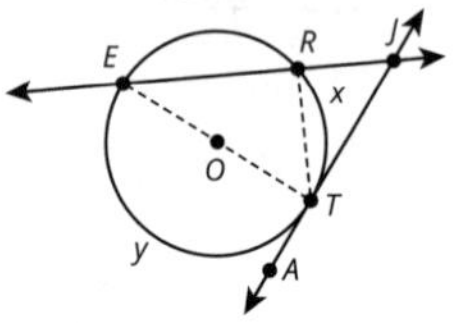

Label the measure of $\widehat{RT}$ as *x* and the measure of $\widehat{ET}$ as *y*.

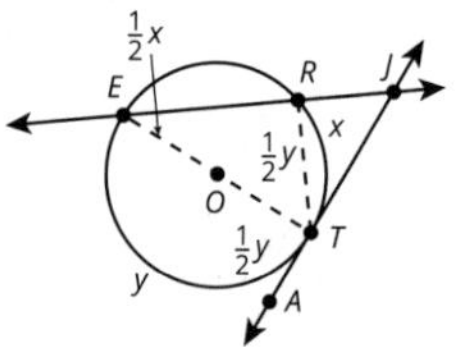

Therefore, $m\angle TER = \frac{1}{2}x$ and $m\angle ETA = \frac{1}{2}y$ since each is an inscribed angle of the intercepted arc.

Angle *ETA* is an exterior angle of ΔTEJ, so $m\angle ETA = m\angle EJT + m\angle TER$.

Using substitution, $\frac{1}{2}y = m\angle EJT + \frac{1}{2}x$.

Therefore, $m\angle EJT = \frac{1}{2}y - \frac{1}{2}x$, or $m\angle EJT = \frac{1}{2}(y - x)$.

Questions to Support Discourse

		TYPE
Worked Example	• In ΔEJT, which two remote interior angles are associated with exterior $\angle ETA$?	Gathering
	• How is the Inscribed Angle Theorem applied in this situation? • How is the Interior Angles Theorem used? Which angles are the remote interior angles?	Seeing structure

ACTIVITY 3 Continued

5 Reason algebraically to prove the remaining cases of the Exterior Angles of a Circle Theorem.

ⓐ Case 2

Given: Secants EJ and RJ intersect at point J.

Prove: $m\angle EJR = \frac{1}{2}(m\widehat{ER} - m\widehat{AT})$

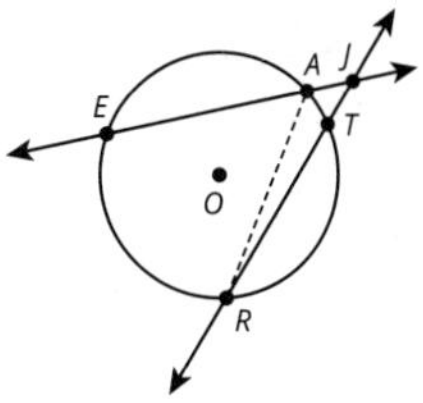

I can label the measure of $\widehat{ER}$ as y and the measure of $\widehat{AT}$ as x. This means $m\angle EAR = \frac{1}{2}y$ and $m\angle ART = \frac{1}{2}x$ since each is an inscribed angle of the intercepted arc.

Angle EAR is an exterior angle of ΔRAJ, so $m\angle EAR = m\angle AJR + m\angle ART$.

Using substitution, $\frac{1}{2}y = m\angle AJR + \frac{1}{2}x$.

Therefore, $m\angle AJR = \frac{1}{2}y - \frac{1}{2}x$, or $m\angle AJR = \frac{1}{2}(y - x)$ and $\angle AJR$ is the same angle as $\angle EJR$.

ⓑ Case 3

Given: Tangents EJ and AJ intersect at point J.

Prove: $m\angle EJT = \frac{1}{2}(m\widehat{ERT} - m\widehat{ET})$

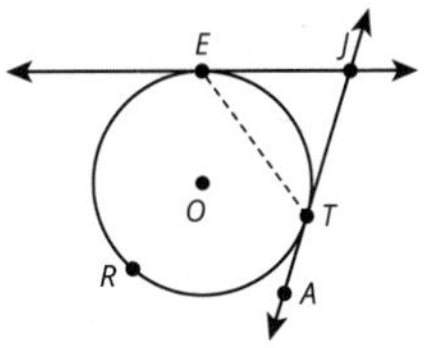

I can label the measure of $\widehat{ERT}$ as y and the measure of $\widehat{ET}$ as x. This means $m\angle ETA = \frac{1}{2}y$ and $m\angle TEJ = \frac{1}{2}x$ since each is an inscribed angle of the intercepted arc.

Angle ETA is an exterior angle of ΔTEJ, so $m\angle ETA = m\angle EJT + m\angle TEJ$.

Using substitution, $\frac{1}{2}y = m\angle EJT + \frac{1}{2}x$.

Therefore, $m\angle EJT = \frac{1}{2}y - \frac{1}{2}x$, or $m\angle EJT = \frac{1}{2}(y - x)$.

Questions to Support Discourse

		TYPE
5	• In Case 3, which two points did you connect to form a triangle?	Gathering
	• How is proving Case 2 similar to proving Case 1? • How is Case 3 similar to Cases 1 and 2?	Seeing structure

NOTES

NOTES

6 Use the diagram shown to determine the measure of each angle or arc.

ⓐ Determine $m\widehat{FI}$.
$m\angle K = 20°$
$m\widehat{GJ} = 80°$

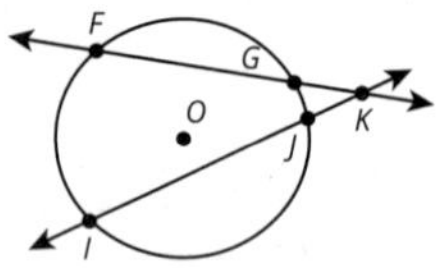

The $m\widehat{FI}$ is 120°.

$m\angle K = \frac{1}{2}(m\widehat{FI} - m\widehat{GJ})$

$20 = \frac{1}{2}(m\widehat{FI} - 80)$

$40 = m\widehat{FI} - 80$

$m\widehat{FI} = 120$

ⓑ Determine $m\angle X$.
$m\widehat{VW} = 40°$
$m\widehat{TU} = 85°$

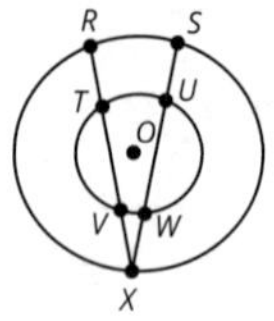

The $m\angle X$ is 22.5°.

$m\angle X = \frac{1}{2}(m\widehat{TU} - m\widehat{VW})$

$= \frac{1}{2}(85 - 40)$

$= \frac{1}{2}(45) = 22.5$

ⓒ Determine $m\angle D$.
$m\widehat{ZXC} = 120°$
$m\widehat{CB} = 30°$

The $m\angle D$ is 90°.

By the Arc Addition Postulate, $m\widehat{ZAB} = 210$.

$m\angle D = \frac{1}{2}(m\widehat{ZAB} - m\widehat{CB})$

$= \frac{1}{2}(210 - 30)$

$= \frac{1}{2}(180) = 90$

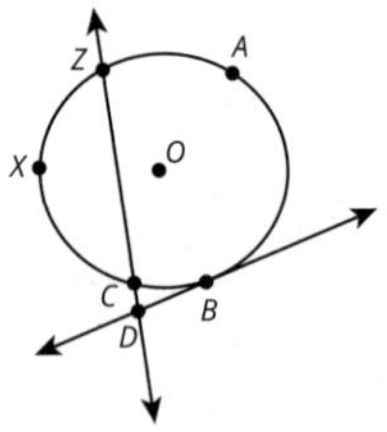

Because you proved that this relationship is true, you can now refer to it as a theorem.

THEOREM

EXTERIOR ANGLES OF A CIRCLE THEOREM

If an angle is formed by two intersecting chords or secants of a circle such that the vertex of the angle is in the exterior of the circle, then the measure of the angle is half of the difference of the measures of the arcs intercepted by the angle.

SUMMARY You can use the Tangent to a Circle Theorem to solve problems and as a reason in proofs.

Tangent to a Circle Theorem

HABITS OF MIND
- Reason abstractly and quantitatively.
- Construct viable arguments and critique the reasoning of others.

Think back on the first case of exterior angles you drew in the previous activity involving a secant and a tangent. There is a special case when the secant contains the diameter of the circle.

REMEMBER... An inscribed angle is an angle whose measure is half the measure of its intercepted arc.

1. Consider $\angle UTV$ with vertex located on Circle C. Line VW is drawn tangent to Circle C at point T.

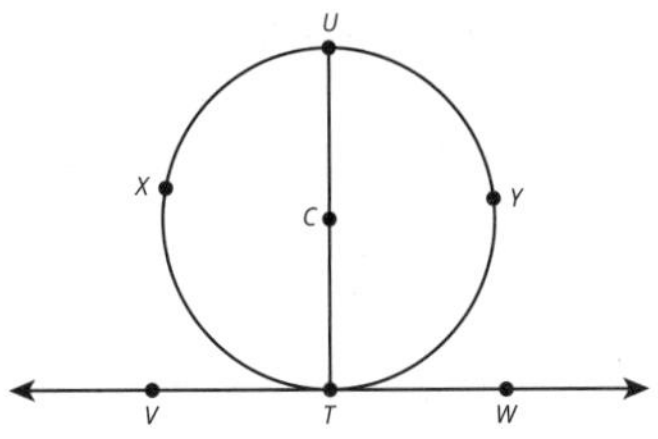

(a) Determine $m\overset{\frown}{UXT}$ and $m\overset{\frown}{UYT}$. **Explain your reasoning.**

$m\overset{\frown}{UXT} = 180°$ and $m\overset{\frown}{UYT} = 180°$ because segment UT is a diameter of Circle C and $\overset{\frown}{UXT}$ and $\overset{\frown}{UYT}$ are semicircles.

(b) Determine $m\angle UTV$ and $m\angle UTW$. **Explain your reasoning.**

$m\angle UTV = 90°$ and $m\angle UTW = 90°$ because the measure of an inscribed angle is equal to half the measure of its intercepted arc.

It appears that when a line is drawn tangent to a circle, the angles formed at the point of tangency are right angles, and therefore the radius drawn to the point of tangency is perpendicular to the tangent line.

You can prove this relationship and then state it as a theorem.

Chunking the Activity

- Read and discuss the introduction
- Group students to complete 1
- Check-in and share
- Read and discuss the worked example
- Group students to complete 2 and 3
- Share and summarize

Questions to Support Discourse

		TYPE
1	• Why are $\angle UTV$ and $\angle UTW$ inscribed angles of Circle C?	Probing

NOTES

COMMON MISCONCEPTION

See Page 382B for a misconception related to the worked example.

LANGUAGE LINK

ELL TIP

Assess students' prior knowledge of the term *contradiction*. If they are unfamiliar, define *contradiction* as a statement or idea that opposes another statement or idea. Discuss how you can use contradictions in debates and discussions which involve proving a statement, theory, or idea. Clarify any misunderstandings students may have about the application of contradiction in the activity.

The proof of this relationship is completed by contradiction. A **proof by contradiction** begins with an assumption that is the opposite of what you would like to prove. Using the assumption and its implications, you arrive at a contradiction. When this happens, the proof is complete.

WORKED EXAMPLE

Line segment *CA* is a radius of Circle *C*. Point *A* is the point at which the radius intersects the tangent line.

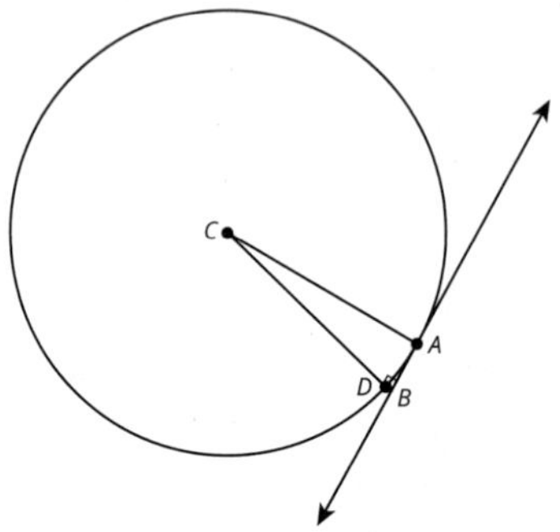

STEP 1 Assumption: The tangent line is not perpendicular to the radius ($\overline{CA}$) of the circle.

STEP 2 Point *B*, another point on the tangent line, is the point at which $\overline{CB}$ is perpendicular to the tangent line.

STEP 3 Consider Right Triangle *CBA* with hypotenuse *CA* and leg *CB*, so *CA* > *CB*.

STEP 4 Impossible!! *CB* > *CA* because *CB* = length of radius (*CD*) + *DB*.

The assumption is incorrect; therefore, the tangent line is perpendicular to the radius ($\overline{CA}$) of the circle.

This completes the proof of the Tangent to a Circle Theorem.

Because the worked example proved that this relationship is true, you can now refer to it as a theorem.

THEOREM

TANGENT TO A CIRCLE THEOREM

A line drawn tangent to a circle is perpendicular to a radius of the circle drawn to the point of tangency.

Questions to Support Discourse

		TYPE
Worked Example	• What is an assumption?	Gathering
	• Why does Step 3 claim *CA* > *CB*?	Probing
	• How is a proof by contradiction different than a direct proof?	Seeing structure

ACTIVITY 4 Continued

You can use the Tangent to a Circle Theorem to solve problems.

2 When you can see past buildings and hills or mountains—when you can look to the horizon—how far is that? You can use the Pythagorean Theorem to help you tell.

Imagine you are standing on the surface of the Earth, and you have a height of h. The distance to the horizon is given by d in the diagram shown, and R is the radius of Earth.

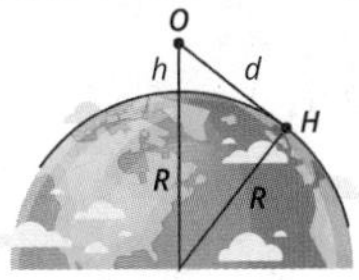

Using your height, create a formula you can use to determine how far away the horizon is.

$$d^2 + R^2 = (R + h)^2$$

$$d^2 + R^2 = R^2 + 2Rh + h^2$$

$$d^2 = h(2R + h)$$

$$d = \sqrt{h(2R + h)}$$

3 Molly is standing at the top of Mount Everest, which has an elevation of 29,029 feet. Her eyes are 5 feet above ground level. The radius of Earth is approximately 3960 miles. How far can Molly see on the horizon?

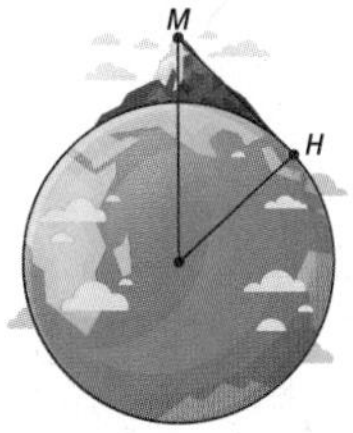

$$29{,}034 \text{ feet} \cdot \frac{1 \text{ mile}}{5280 \text{ feet}} \approx 5.5 \text{ miles}$$

$$HM^2 + HE^2 = ME^2$$

$$HM^2 + (3960)^2 = (3960 + 5.5)^2$$

$$HM^2 + 15{,}681{,}600 = 15{,}725{,}190.25$$

$$HM^2 = 43{,}590.25$$

$$HM = \sqrt{43,590.25} \approx 208.78$$

Molly can see approximately 208.78 miles on the horizon.

NOTES

LANGUAGE LINK

ELL TIP

Help students understand the context by ensuring they know the term *horizon*. Make sure that students know the horizon is the point where the earth seems to meet the sky.

Questions to Support Discourse

		TYPE
2	• Which algebraic expression represents the hypotenuse in this situation?	Gathering
	• How is the value of d determined?	Probing
3	• Which segment represents the distance Molly can see along the horizon?	Gathering
	• How did you use the Pythagorean Theorem to solve this problem?	Probing

SUMMARY **You can use theorems involving circles to solve problems and determine unknown measures inside and outside circles.**

Chunking the Activity

- **Read and discuss the introduction**
- **Group students to complete 1 - 3**
- **Check-in and share**
- **Group students to complete 4**
- **Share and summarize**

Student Look-Fors

A classroom environment where students are mindful of classmates' perspectives, cultures, and experiences.

Determining Measures Inside and Outside Circles

You can apply the theorems you know involving circles to solve problems.

HABITS OF MIND
- Reason abstractly and quantitatively.
- Construct viable arguments and critique the reasoning of others.

Aubrey wants to take a family picture. Her camera has a 70° field of view, but to include the entire family in the picture, she needs to cover a 140° arc.

1. Explain what Aubrey needs to do to fit the entire family in the picture. Use the diagram to draw the solution.

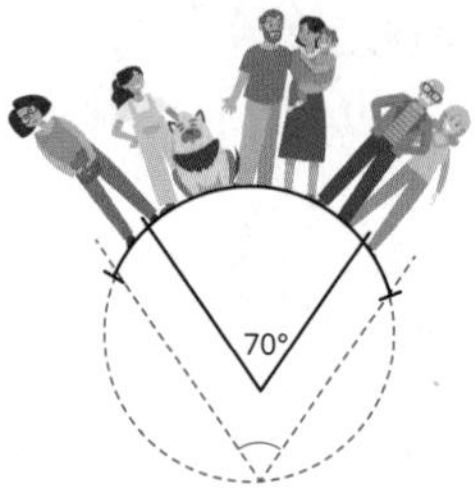

Aubrey can use her location as the center of the circle. The Inscribed Angle Theorem says that the measure of an inscribed angle is half the measure of its intercepted arc. So, if Aubrey moves to a point on the circle, her camera's 70° field of view will be able to capture a 140° arc.

Yesterday, Ms. Angle taught her students how to determine the measure of an inscribed angle. Mitchell told his classmate that he finally understood why a circle is always 360°.

2. Use ΔPAW drawn in the diagram to explain what Mitchell was thinking.

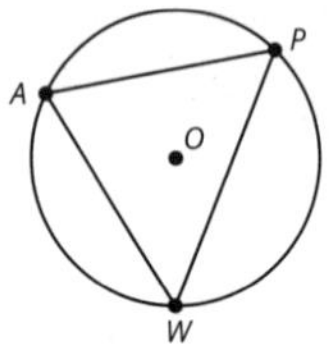

Mitchell learned that the measure of an inscribed angle is equal to half the measure of its intercepted arc. In the diagram, the intercepted arcs of $\angle P$, $\angle A$, and $\angle W$ combined form the entire circle. He knew the sum of the measures of the three angles is equal to 180° using the Triangle Sum Theorem, so he concluded the sum of the measures of the three intercepted arcs must be twice the sum of the measures of the angles.

Questions to Support Discourse

		TYPE
1	• If Aubrey stands at the center of the circle and the measure of the central angle is 70°, what will be the measure of the field of view?	Gathering
	• Why does Aubrey need to move to a point on the circle?	Probing
2	• How is the Triangle Sum Theorem applicable to this situation?	Probing
	• How does each interior angle of the triangle relate to the circle?	Seeing structure

ACTIVITY 5 Continued

3 Safiye says that using only the given information in the diagram, she can determine all the unknown measures of the circle. Is she correct? **Justify your reasoning.**

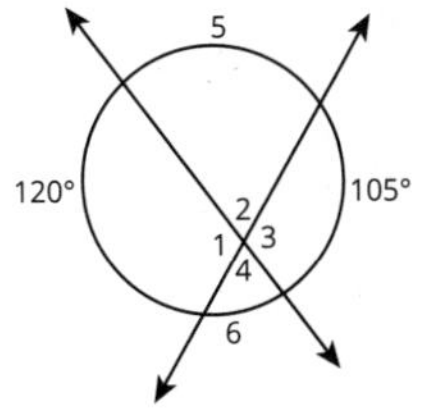

Safiye is not correct.

She can use the Interior Angles of a Circle Theorem to determine m∠1:

$m\angle 1 = \frac{1}{2}(120° + 105°) = 112.5°$.

Angles 1 and 3 are vertical angles, so m∠3 = 112.5°.

Angles 1 and-are a linear pair, so m∠2 = 180°−112.5° = 67.5°.

Angles 2 and 4 are vertical angles, so m∠4 = 67.5°. However, she cannot determine the individual measures of the intercepted arcs associated with angles 2 and 4. She can only determine that the sum of the arcs is equal to 360°−120°−105° = 135°.

NOTES

Questions to Support Discourse

		TYPE
3	• Which angle measures can Safiye solve for first?	Gathering
	• If Safiye knows the sum of the measures of arcs 5 and 6, is that enough information to determine the measures of arcs 5 and 6? Why or why not?	Seeing structure

NOTES

ACTIVITY 5 Continued

4 Apply the theorems you know to determine each measure.

(a) Determine $m\overset{\frown}{RT}$.
$m\overset{\frown}{FG} = 86°$
$m\overset{\frown}{HP} = 21°$

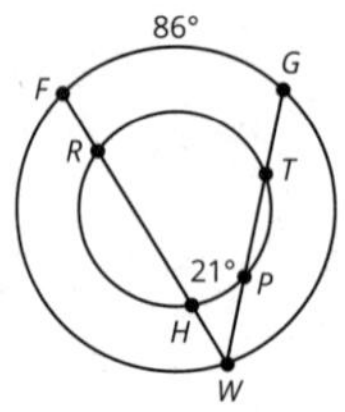

$m\angle FWG = 43°$

$\frac{1}{2}(m\overset{\frown}{RT} - 21°) = 43°$

$m\overset{\frown}{RT} - 21° = 86°$

$m\overset{\frown}{RT} = 107°$

(b) Determine $m\overset{\frown}{CD}$.
$m\overset{\frown}{AB} = 88°$
$m\angle AED = 80°$

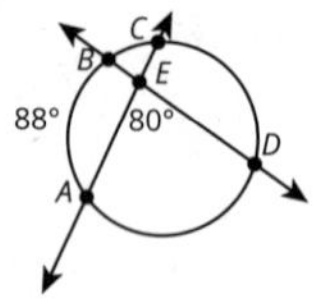

$m\angle AEB = 100°$

$\frac{1}{2}(88° + m\overset{\frown}{CD}) = 100°$

$88° + m\overset{\frown}{CD} = 200°$

$m\overset{\frown}{CD} = 112°$

(c) Determine $m\angle TCX$.
$m\angle TSX = 17°$
$m\angle STW = 50°$

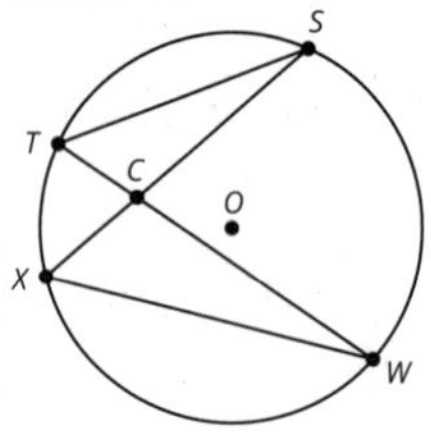

$m\overset{\frown}{TX} = 34°$ and $m\overset{\frown}{SW} = 100°$

$\frac{1}{2}(34° + 100°) = m\angle TCX$

$\frac{1}{2}(134°) = m\angle TCX$

$m\angle TCX = 67°$

(d) Determine $m\angle EXT$.
$m\angle RET = 40°$

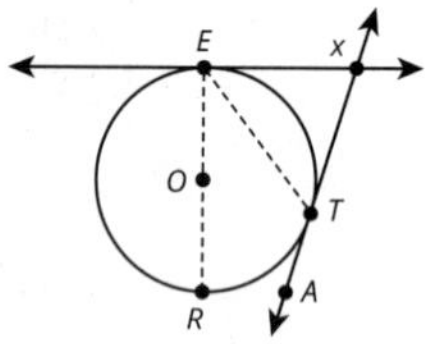

$m\overset{\frown}{RT} = 80°$

$m\angle ERT = 260°$ and $m\overset{\frown}{ET} = 100°$

$m\angle EXT = \frac{1}{2}(260° - 100°)$

$m\angle EXT = \frac{1}{2}(160°)$

$m\angle EXT = 80°$

378 Topic 2 > Justifying Line and Angle Relationships

SUMMARY Sometimes, you only need a few given measurements of a circle to determine many other measurements of the circle.

Circular Reasoning

> Use the theorems you know to answer each question.

1 What additional information can you conclude about the measures of the arcs and angles in each diagram? **Explain your reasoning.**

(a) $m\overset{\frown}{KP} = 23°$

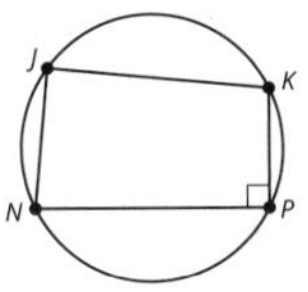

(b) $m\angle STR = 5°$
$m\overset{\frown}{XW} = 20°$

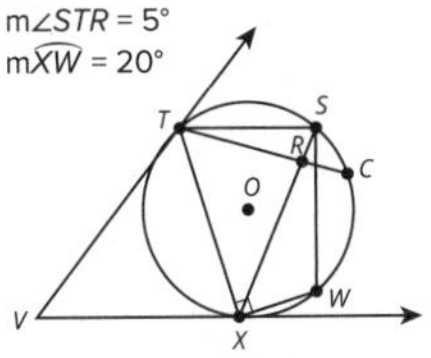

- $m\overset{\frown}{NJK} = 180°$; the inscribed angle determining this angle is a right angle, and an inscribed angle is half the measure of its intercepted arc.
- $m\overset{\frown}{NPK} = 180°$; a circle is 360° and this arc and the measure of $\overset{\frown}{NJK}$ determine the entire circle.
- $m\overset{\frown}{NP} = 157°$; $m\overset{\frown}{NP} + m\overset{\frown}{PK} = m\overset{\frown}{NPK}$ using the Arc Addition Postulate.
- $m\angle J = 90°$; an inscribed angle is half the measure of its intercepted arc.
- $m\overset{\frown}{TSW} = 180°$; the measure of the inscribed angle with this intercepted arc is a right angle, and the measure of an inscribed angle is equal to half the measure of its intercepted arc.
- $m\overset{\frown}{TWX} = 200°$, using the Arc Addition Postulate.
- $m\overset{\frown}{TX} = 160°$; $360° - 200° = 160°$.
- $m\angle TCX = 80°$; an exterior angle is half the difference of the measure of its intercepted arcs.
- $m\overset{\frown}{SC} = 10°$; the measure of the inscribed angle with this intercepted arc is 5° and the measure of an inscribed angle is equal to half the measure of its intercepted arc.
- $m\angle TRX = 85°$; the measure of an interior angle is half the sum of the measure of its intercepted arc and its vertical angles intercepted arc.
- $m\angle SRC = 85°$; vertical angles are congruent.
- $m\angle TRS = 95°$; it forms a linear pair with $\angle SRC$
- $m\angle XRC = 95°$; it forms a linear pair with $\angle SRC$.
- $m\angle XSW = 10°$; the measure of the inscribed angle intercepted arc is 20°, and the measure of an inscribed angle is equal to half the measure of its intercepted arc.
- $m\angle TSW = 90°$; it is supplementary to $\angle TXW$.
- $m\angle TSR = 80°$; the sum of the measures of the interior angles of a triangle equal 180°.

Questions to Support Discourse

		TYPE
1	• Why is the measure of $\overset{\frown}{NJK}$ equal to 180? • Why is the measure of $\overset{\frown}{NP}$ equal to 157°? • Why is $m\angle J = 90°$? • Which theorem did you use to determine $m\angle TCX$ in part (b)? • How is the Arc Addition Postulate used to determine the measure of $\overset{\frown}{TWX}$? • Why is the measure of $\overset{\frown}{SC}$ equal to 10°?	Probing

Chunking the Activity

- Read and discuss the introduction
- Group students to complete the activity
- Share and summarize

LANGUAGE LINK

ELL TIP

Suggest students use bullet points or some other structure as they explain their reasoning.

NOTE: Encourage responsible decision-making by providing an opportunity for students to reflect on their personal behavior and social interactions as they worked with their group to complete tasks.

NOTES

TALK THE TALK Continued

2 Karl raises his hand and informs Ms. Rhombi that he has discovered another property related to the angles of an inscribed quadrilateral. Karl shows his teacher the diagram shown.

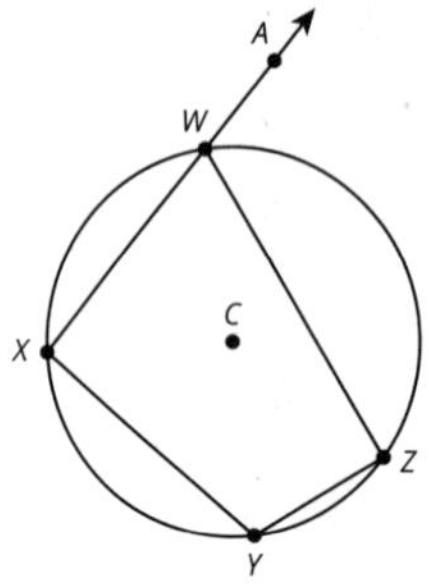

He claims that the measure of any exterior angle of the quadrilateral is equal to the measure of the opposite interior angle in the quadrilateral. In other words, $m\angle AWZ = m\angle Y$.
Explain Karl's reasoning.

Karl used the Inscribed Quadrilateral–Opposite Angles Theorem to conclude that $m\angle XWZ + m\angle Y = 180°$. Next, he used the definition of a linear pair of angles to conclude that $m\angle XWZ + m\angle AWZ = 180°$.

Using substitution and subtraction, Karl was able to conclude that $m\angle Y = m\angle AWZ$.

380 Topic 2 > Justifying Line and Angle Relationships

Questions to Support Discourse

		TYPE
2	• What is the Inscribed Quadrilateral–Opposite Angles Theorem? • Which definitions, postulates, and theorems did you need to explain Karl's reasoning?	Gathering
	• Do you think Karl's claim holds true for the exterior angles of any quadrilateral or only for quadrilaterals inscribed in circles? Why?	Reflecting and justifying

ASSIGNMENT

LESSON 5 ASSIGNMENT

> Use a separate piece of paper for your Journal entry.

JOURNAL

Define each theorem in your own words.

1. Inscribed Angle Theorem
2. Inscribed Right Triangle-Diameter Theorem
3. Inscribed Quadrilateral-Opposite Angles Theorem
4. Interior Angles of a Circle Theorem
5. Exterior Angles of a Circle Theorem
6. Tangent to a Circle Theorem

REMEMBER

- The measure of an inscribed angle is half the measure of the arc it intercepts.
- The measure of an interior angle of a circle is half the sum of the measures of its intercepted arc and its vertical angle's intercepted arc.
- The measure of an exterior angle of a circle is half the difference of the measures of its intercepted arcs.
- A radius drawn to the point of tangency is perpendicular to the tangent line.

PRACTICE

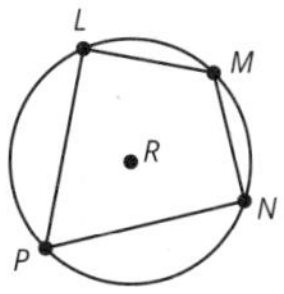

1. In the figure shown, Quadrilateral *LMNP* is inscribed in Circle *R*, $m\angle P = 57°$, and $m\angle L = m\angle N$. What are $m\angle M$, $m\angle L$, and $m\angle N$? Explain your reasoning.

   By the Inscribed Quadrilateral–Opposite Angles Theorem, $\angle P$ and $\angle M$ are supplementary.
   $m\angle M + m\angle P = 180°$, $m\angle M + 57° = 180°$, $m\angle M = 123°$
   By the Inscribed Quadrilateral–Opposite Angles Theorem, $\angle L$ and $\angle N$ are supplementary, and you know that the measures of angles L and N are equal. If two angles are both equal and supplementary, then the measure of each angle is 90. So, $m\angle L = m\angle N = 90°$.
   The measure of $\angle M$ is 123°, the measure of $\angle L$ is 90°, and the measure of $\angle N$ is 90°.

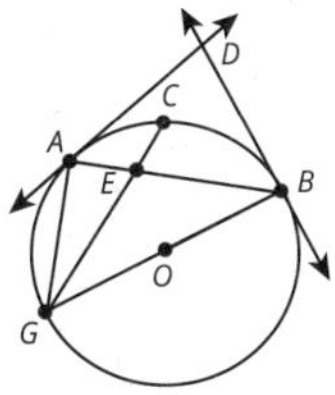

2. Consider Circle *O* with diameter *GB*. Line *AD* is tangent to Circle *O* at point *A* and $\overleftrightarrow{DB}$ is tangent to Circle *O* at point *B*. The measure of $\angle GBA$ is 38°. Chord *GC* bisects $\angle G$. Determine each measure.

   (a) $m\angle A$

   90°

   (b) $m\angle G$

   52°

   (c) $m\widehat{AG}$

   76°

   (d) $m\widehat{AB}$

   104°

   (e) $m\angle ADB$

   76°

   (f) $m\widehat{AC}$

   52°

Go to LiveHint.com for help on the PRACTICE questions.

Encourage students to use LiveHint.com for help with the PRACTICE questions of this assignment.

Chunking the Assignment

SESSION 1

- Practice 1
- Mixed Practice (page 383) 7 and 8

SESSION 2

- Journal
- Practice 2 - 4

JOURNAL

Sample answers.

1. The measure of an angle formed from two chords with a common endpoint on the circle is half the measure of the arc that the two chords intersect.
2. If a triangle has vertices that are three different points on a circle and one of the triangle's sides is the circle's diameter, then the angle opposite that side of the triangle is a right angle.
3. A quadrilateral can only be drawn inside a circle with all four vertices on the circle if the measures of the opposite angles of the quadrilateral add up to 180°.
4. If two chords intersect on the inside of a circle, each angle's measure equals one-half the sum of the measures of the arcs intercepted by the angle and its vertical angle.
5. If two chords or secants intersect so that they form an angle with a vertex outside of a circle, then the measure of that angle is one-half of the difference between the measures of the arcs formed by both chords or secants.
6. The angle formed by the radius of a circle and a line drawn tangent to a circle is a right angle.

NOTES

STRETCH

1. Sample answer.
   You can inscribe a right triangle inside a circle so that the triangle's hypotenuse is the circle's diameter. You can then draw a segment from the vertex of the triangle at the right angle of the triangle to the halfway point of the hypotenuse, or the center of the circle. The segment drawn represents the radius of the circle. The length of the radius is half the length of the diameter, which in this case is the hypotenuse. So the segment drawn is always half the length of the hypotenuse.

3 Explain how knowing m∠*ERT* can help you determine m∠*EXT*.

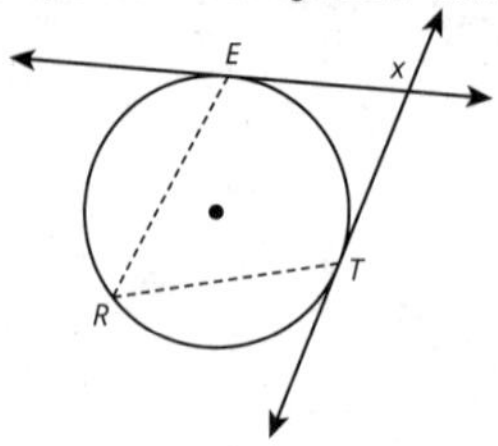

If I know the measure of inscribed ∠*ERT*, that will give me the measure of $\overset{\frown}{ET}$ because the measure of an inscribed angle is one-half the measure of its intercepted arc. Then, knowing the measure of $\overset{\frown}{ET}$, I can subtract that measure from 360° to get the measure of $\overset{\frown}{ERT}$. Finally, I can use the measures of $\overset{\frown}{ERT}$ and $\overset{\frown}{ET}$ to calculate the measure of ∠*EXT*.

4 Construct a tangent line to Circle *Z* through point *X*. Label the point of tangency as point *Y*. Then determine the measure of ∠*ZYX*. Explain your reasoning.

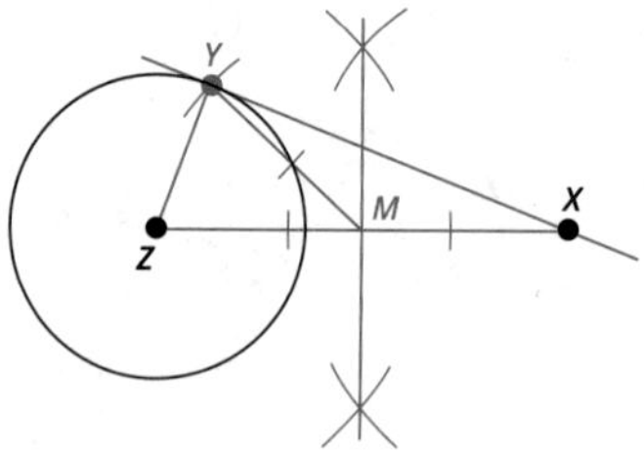

The measure of ∠*ZYX* is 90° by the Tangent to a Circle Theorem, which states that a line drawn tangent to a circle is perpendicular to a radius of the circle drawn to the point of tangency.

STRETCH Optional

Ruben says that, in a right triangle, when you draw a line segment from the right angle's vertex to the center of the hypotenuse, the segment that you draw is always half the length of the hypotenuse.

1 How can you show that Ruben's conjecture is correct?

Corners in a Round Room

This resource details additional facilitation notes to fully assist you as you plan each lesson to support all students, students who struggle, and advanced learners. It provides differentiation strategies, common student misconceptions, and suggestions to extend certain activities.

GETTING STARTED

Session 1 of 2

Look at the Time

Students calculate minor arc measures using numbers on a clock and their knowledge of a circle's degree measure. They conclude that when the measures of two central angles of the same circle (or congruent circles) are equal, their corresponding minor arcs are congruent.

CHUNK	AUDIENCE	ADDITIONAL SUPPORTS
As students work on 5	All Students	**COMMON MISCONCEPTION** Students may confuse the degree measure of an arc with the length of an arc. Ask students to describe arcs of equal measure, arcs of equal length, and congruent arcs. • If the length of two arcs is the same, or the measure of two arcs is the same, are the two arcs are congruent. • If two arcs are congruent, are the two arcs the same length or the same measure or both?

ACTIVITY 1

Session 1 of 2

The Inscribed Angle Theorem

Students prove a conjecture relating the measure of an inscribed angle to the measure of its intercepted arc. They look at cases where the center point is on the inscribed angle, inside the inscribed angle, and outside the inscribed angle. They use the Inscribed Angle Theorem to prove the Inscribed Right Triangle–Diameter Theorem and the Inscribed Quadrilateral–Opposite Angles Theorem.

CHUNK	AUDIENCE	ADDITIONAL SUPPORTS
As students work on the lesson	All Students	**DIFFERENTIATION STRATEGY** Remind students to update their note cards as they encounter new theorems in the lesson.

ACTIVITY 3

Session 2 of 2

Exterior Angles of a Circle Theorem

Students make a conjecture about the measure of an exterior angle of a circle and the arc measures intercepted by the angle. They analyze a worked example proving the relationship when forming the exterior angle using a secant and a tangent. They prove the cases where two secant lines or two tangent lines form an exterior angle.

CHUNK	AUDIENCE	ADDITIONAL SUPPORTS
As an alternative grouping strategy for 3 and 4	All Students	**DIFFERENTIATION STRATEGY** Use the jigsaw method to complete Questions 3 and 4. Assign different groups of students Case 1, 2, or 3 to investigate for both questions. Reorganize the class into new groups of three students, ensuring each student in the group investigated a different case. Have group members explain their work to one another.

ACTIVITY 4

Session 2 of 2

Tangent to a Circle Theorem

Students analyze a worked example that proves the Tangent to a Circle Theorem by contradiction. They apply the theorem to solve problems.

CHUNK	AUDIENCE	ADDITIONAL SUPPORTS
As students analyze the worked example	All Students	**COMMON MISCONCEPTION** Students have only experienced direct proof and likely think all forms of proof start with the given information. Proof by contradiction is an indirect proof. It begins with an assumption that is usually the negation of the conclusion of the theorem.

Practice the learning

MATHbook + Skills Practice

The table shows the targeted practice of the skills and mathematical concepts for the *Justifying Line and Angle Relationships* Topic. The highlighted Problem Set aligns with **Corners in a Round Room**.

PROBLEM SET	
1	Identifying Circle Parts
2	Angle Relationships Formed from Parallel Lines
3	Interior and Exterior Angles of Polygons
4	Isosceles and Right Triangles
5	**Interior and Exterior Angles of a Circle**

ANYTIME AFTER ACTIVITY 5

Facilitate students as they work individually on **Problem Set 5.**

NOTES

MIXED PRACTICE

Log in to MyCL to access a downloadable version with **additional space** for students to write their answers.

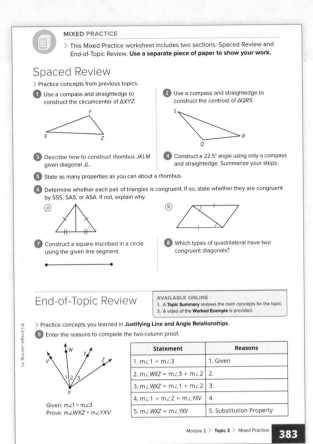

MIXED PRACTICE

> This Mixed Practice worksheet includes two sections: Spaced Review and End-of-Topic Review. **Use a separate piece of paper to show your work.**

Spaced Review

> Practice concepts from previous topics.

1. Use a compass and straightedge to construct the circumcenter of ΔXYZ.

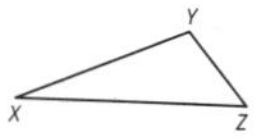

2. Use a compass and straightedge to construct the centroid of ΔQRS.

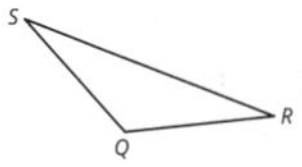

3. Describe how to construct rhombus *JKLM* given diagonal *JL*.

4. Construct a 22.5° angle using only a compass and straightedge. Summarize your steps.

5. State as many properties as you can about a rhombus.

6. Determine whether each pair of triangles is congruent. If so, state whether they are congruent by SSS, SAS, or ASA. If not, explain why.

ⓐ

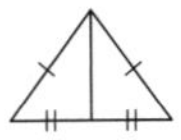

ⓑ

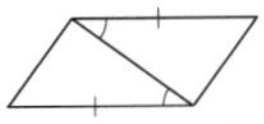

7. Construct a square inscribed in a circle using the given line segment.

8. Which types of quadrilateral have two congruent diagonals?

End-of-Topic Review

AVAILABLE ONLINE
1. A **Topic Summary** reviews the main concepts for the topic.
2. A video of the **Worked Example** is provided.

> Practice concepts you learned in **Justifying Line and Angle Relationships**.

9. Enter the reasons to complete the two-column proof.

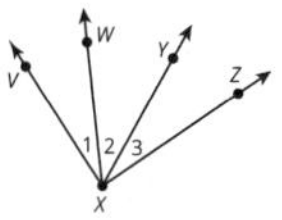

Given: $m\angle 1 = m\angle 3$
Prove: $m\angle WXZ = m\angle YXV$

Statement	Reasons
1. $m\angle 1 = m\angle 3$	1. Given
2. $m\angle WXZ = m\angle 3 + m\angle 2$	2.
3. $m\angle WXZ = m\angle 1 + m\angle 2$	3.
4. $m\angle 1 + m\angle 2 = m\angle YXV$	4.
5. $m\angle WXZ = m\angle YXV$	5. Substitution Property

MIXED PRACTICE Continued

10. Given: $\angle 12 \cong \angle 7$, $m\angle 12 = 65°$, $m\angle 8 = 50°$

Using the diagram in conjunction with postulates and theorems, determine the measures of the unknown angles.

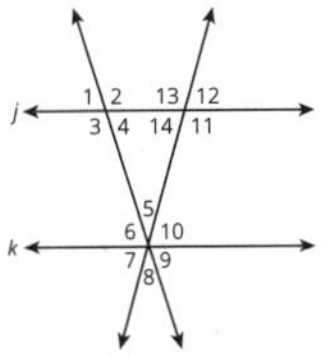

11. If ∠1 and ∠4 are supplementary, which theorem leads to the conclusion that $q \parallel s$?

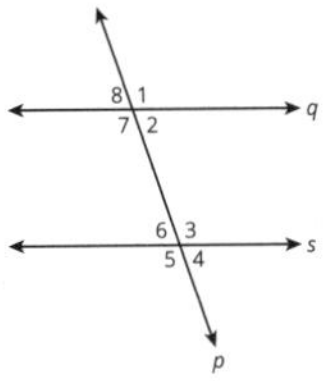

12. A hazard sign is placed near a steep stair well. The sign is an equilateral triangle. Suppose the height of the sign is 15 inches. Determine the area of the sign.

13. Determine the measure of an interior angle of a regular 18-gon.

14. When a regular polygon has 15 sides, what is the measure of each exterior angle?

15. In the figure shown, Quadrilateral *ABCD* is inscribed in Circle *P*, $m\widehat{BC} = 55°$, $m\widehat{CD} = 109°$, and $m\widehat{DA} = 91°$. What are $m\angle A$, $m\angle B$, $m\angle C$, and $m\angle D$? Explain your reasoning.

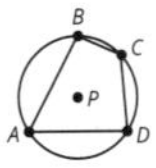

16. Consider Circle *O*. The measure of $\angle EOD$ is 155°. The measure of $\angle A$ is 40°. Determine $m\widehat{BC}$.

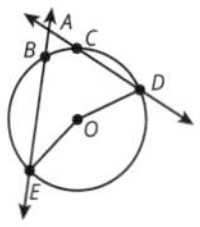

See pages 383–384C for annotated answers.

The **Spaced Review** includes fluency and problem solving from previous topics.

Aligned Standards

1 G.CO.12	2 G.CO.12
3 G.CO.12	4 G.CO.12
5 G.CO.11	6 G.CO.8
7 G.C.3	8 G.CO.11

TOPIC 2

Log in to MyCL for more **End-of-Topic** review questions.

Go to **Edulastic**, and search for: N.RN.2, G.CO.9, G.CO.10, G.C.2, G.C.3, G.C.4 (+)

The **End-of-Topic Review** includes questions to practice the key concepts of *Justifying Line and Angle Relationships*.

Aligned Standards

9 G.CO.9	10 G.CO.9
11 G.CO.9	12 G.CO.10
13 G.C.3	14 G.C.3
15 G.C.3	16 G.C.2

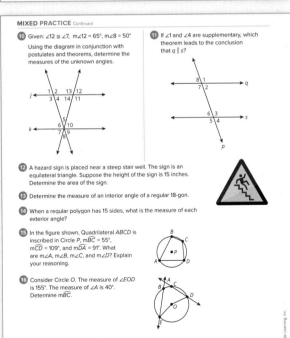

Answers included.

MIXED PRACTICE

> This Mixed Practice worksheet includes two sections: Spaced Review and End-of-Topic Review.

MODULE 2
Establishing Proof

TOPIC 1
Composing and Decomposing Shapes

TOPIC 2
Justifying Line and Angle Relationships

TOPIC 3
Using Congruence Theorems

Spaced Review

> Practice concepts from previous topics.

1. Use a compass and straightedge to construct the circumcenter of ΔXYZ.

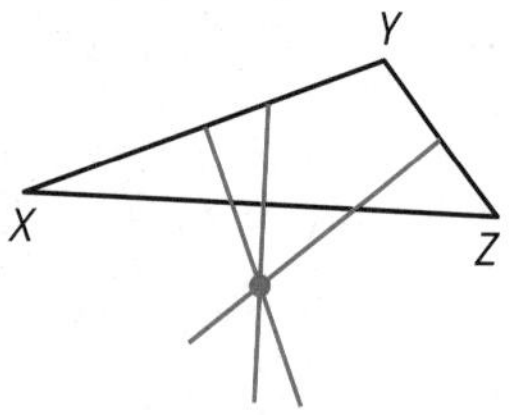

2. Use a compass and straightedge to construct the centroid of ΔQRS.

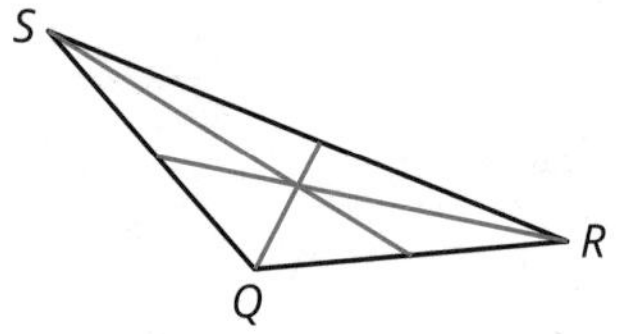

3. Describe how to construct rhombus *JKLM* given diagonal *JL*.

   Sample answer.

   First, I would begin by duplicating line segment *JL*. Then, I would construct the perpendicular bisector through *JL* and label the point of intersection *P*. I would then use a compass to place two points on the perpendicular bisector so that the points are equidistant from *P*. I would label one of the points *K* and the other point *M*. Finally, I would connect points *J*, *K*, *L*, and *M* to form Rhombus *JKLM*.

4. Construct a 22.5° angle using only a compass and straightedge. Summarize your steps.

   Sample answer.

   First draw line segment *AB*. Then find the perpendicular bisector through point *M*.

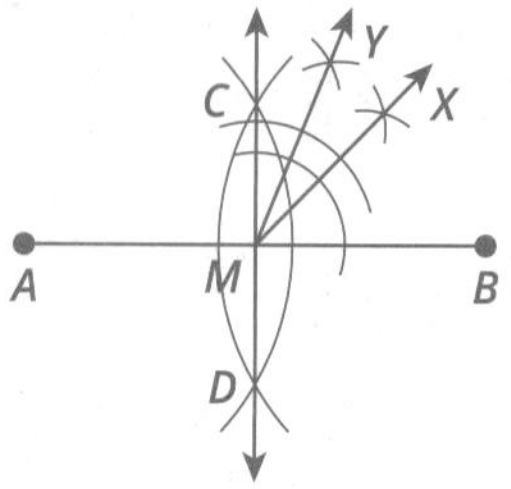

   This forms right angle *CMB*. Bisect angle *CMB* to get angle *CMX*, which is half of 90°, or 45°. Then bisect angle *CMX* to get angle *CMY*, which is half of 45°, or 22.5°.

5. State as many properties as you can about a rhombus.

   Sample answer.

   opposite sides are parallel, opposite angles are congruent, all sides are congruent, the diagonals bisect the angles, the diagonals are perpendicular bisectors of each other

Answers included.

MIXED PRACTICE Continued

6 Determine whether each pair of triangles is congruent. If so, state whether they are congruent by SSS, SAS, or ASA. If not, explain why.

ⓐ

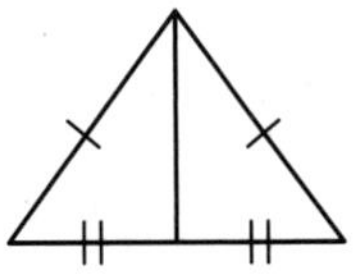

They are congruent by SSS.

ⓑ

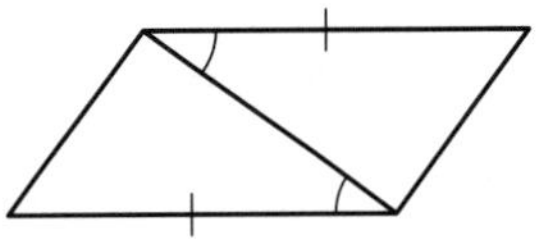

They are congruent by SAS.

7 Construct a square inscribed in a circle using the given line segment.

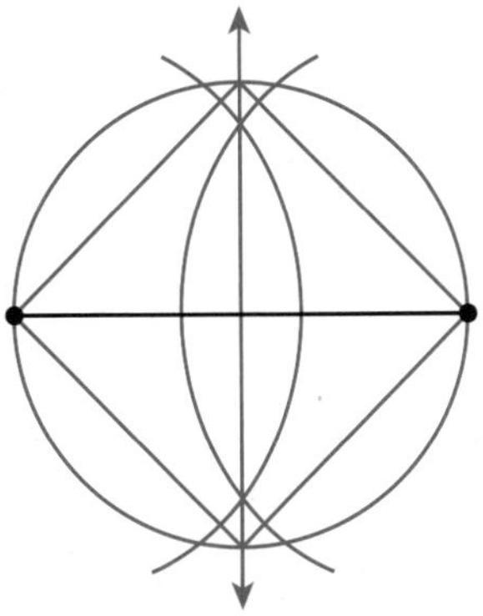

8 Which types of quadrilateral have two congruent diagonals?

Square, rectangle, isosceles trapezoid

End-of-Topic Review

AVAILABLE ONLINE

1. A **Topic Summary** reviews the main concepts for the topic.
2. A video of the **Worked Example** is provided.

› Practice concepts you learned in **Justifying Line and Angle Relationships**.

9 Enter the reasons to complete the two-column proof.

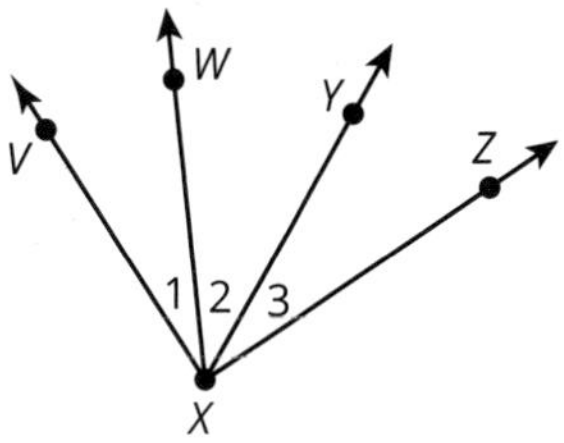

Given: $m\angle 1 = m\angle 3$
Prove: $m\angle WXZ = m\angle YXV$

Statement	Reasons
1. $m\angle 1 = m\angle 3$	1. Given
2. $m\angle WXZ = m\angle 3 + m\angle 2$	2. Angle Addition Postulate
3. $m\angle WXZ = m\angle 1 + m\angle 2$	3. Substitution Property
4. $m\angle 1 + m\angle 2 = m\angle YXV$	4. Angle Addition Postulate
5. $m\angle WXZ = m\angle YXV$	5. Substitution Property

Answers included.

MIXED PRACTICE

> This Mixed Practice worksheet includes two sections: Spaced Review and End-of-Topic Review.

10 Given: $\angle 12 \cong \angle 7$, $m\angle 12 = 65°$, $m\angle 8 = 50°$

Using the diagram in conjunction with postulates and theorems, determine the measures of the unknown angles.

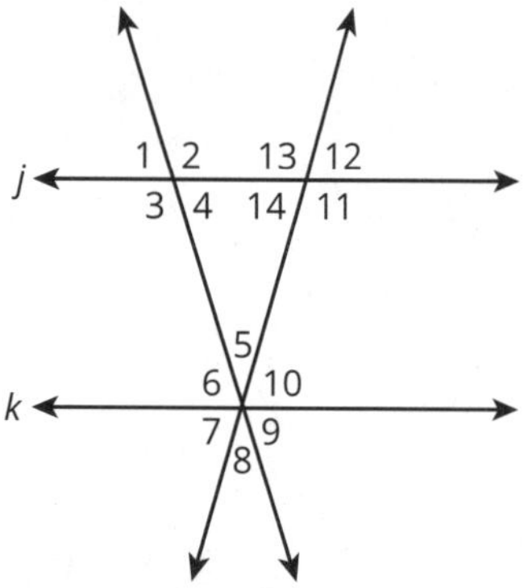

$m\angle 1 = m\angle 4 = m\angle 6 = m\angle 7 = m\angle 9 = 65°$

$m\angle 10 = m\angle 14 = 65°$

$m\angle 2 = m\angle 3 = m\angle 11 = m\angle 13 = 115°$

$m\angle 5 = 50°$

11 If $\angle 1$ and $\angle 4$ are supplementary, which theorem leads to the conclusion that $q \parallel s$?

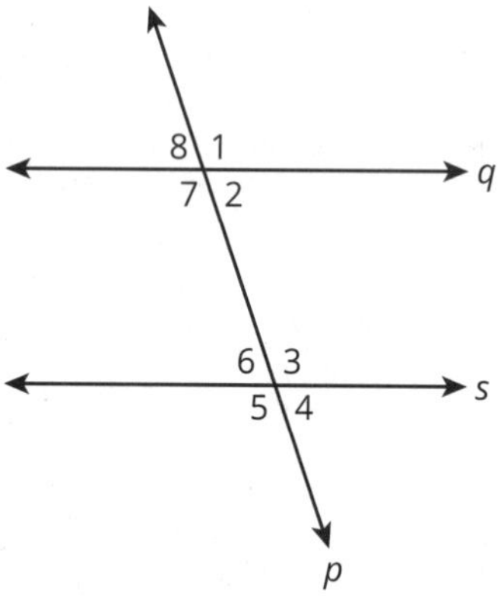

The Same-Side Exterior Angle Converse Theorem leads to the conclusion that $q \parallel s$.

12 A hazard sign is placed near a steep stair well. The sign is an equilateral triangle. Suppose the height of the sign is 15 inches. Determine the area of the sign.

The height of the triangle divides it into two 30°-60°-90° triangles.

$a\sqrt{3} = 15$

$a = \frac{15}{\sqrt{3}} = 5\sqrt{3}$

$2a = 10\sqrt{3}$

Area $= \frac{1}{2}(10\sqrt{3})(15) = 75\sqrt{3}$

The area of the sign is $75\sqrt{3}$ mm, or approximately 129.9 inches.

Answers included.

MIXED PRACTICE Continued

13 Determine the measure of an interior angle of a regular 18-gon.

$$\frac{(18-2)\cdot 180^\circ}{18} = 160^\circ$$

14 If a regular polygon has 15 sides, what is the measure of each exterior angle?

$$\frac{360^\circ}{15} = 24^\circ$$

15 In the figure shown, Quadrilateral *ABCD* is inscribed in Circle *P*, $m\widehat{BC} = 55^\circ$, $m\widehat{CD} = 109^\circ$, and $m\widehat{DA} = 91^\circ$. What are $m\angle A$, $m\angle B$, $m\angle C$, and $m\angle D$? Explain your reasoning.

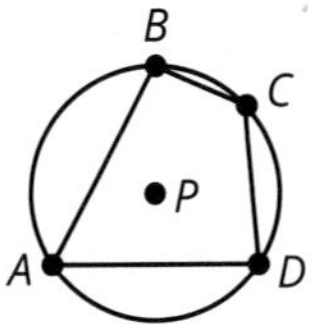

$m\angle A = \frac{55^\circ + 109^\circ}{2} = 82^\circ$

$m\angle C = 180 - m\angle A = 98^\circ$

$m\angle B = \frac{91^\circ + 109^\circ}{2} = 100^\circ$

$m\angle D = 180 - m\angle B = 80^\circ$

16 Consider Circle *O*. The measure of $\angle EOD$ is 155°. The measure of $\angle A$ is 40°. Determine $m\widehat{BC}$.

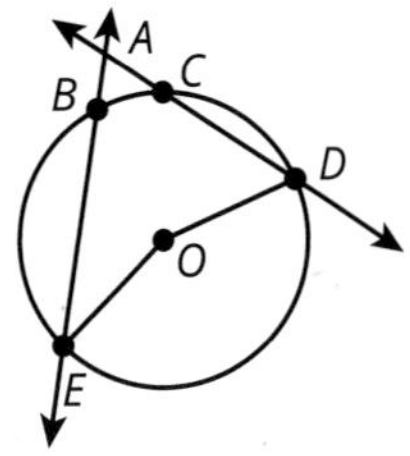

$40^\circ = \frac{1}{2}(155^\circ - m\widehat{BC})$

$80^\circ = 155^\circ - m\widehat{BC}$

$m\widehat{BC} = 75^\circ$

NOTES

ENGAGE at the **Module** level + **DEVELOP** Read the **Topic Overview** and do the math to experience the content development. + **TEACH** at the **Lesson** level

OVERVIEW: TOPIC 3

Using Congruence Theorems

Where are we?

1 Session ≈ 45 minutes

Pacing	TOPIC 1 Composing and Decomposing Shapes	TOPIC 2 Justifying Line and Angle Relationships	TOPIC 3 Using Congruence Theorems
MODULE 2 Establishing Proof	14 Sessions	24 Sessions	9 Sessions

How are the key concepts of *Using Congruence Theorems* developed?

Students use the four triangle congruence theorems that apply to all triangles to prove three additional right triangle congruence theorems. They then solve problems using those theorems. Finally, they investigate tangent segments before proving the Tangent Segment Theorem and using it to solve problems.

Students then use triangle congruence theorems to verify the properties of parallelograms. They prove that the base angles and the diagonals of isosceles trapezoids are congruent. Students use what they know about midpoints, parallel lines, and triangle midsegments to prove the Trapezoid Midsegment Theorem. They demonstrate their understanding by considering the minimum criteria required to classify a quadrilateral.

Students next use the congruence theorems they have proven to prove theorems related to the chords of circles. They learn that the perpendicular bisectors of chords go through the center; a diameter that is perpendicular to a chord also bisects the chord and the arc determined by the chord; congruent chords are equidistant from the center of a circle; and chords equidistant from the center are congruent. They then prove that two chords are congruent if and only if their corresponding arcs are congruent.

TOPIC 3

MATH REPRESENTATION

Farrah's cat knocked a cookie plate onto the floor, shattering it into many pieces! One large chunk has remained intact. Unfortunately, cookie plates come in various sizes, and Farrah needs to know the broken plate's exact diameter to fix it. Her sister, Sarah, tells Farrah that she learned how to determine the plate's diameter in geometry class. What do you think Sarah did?

- First, Sarah places the broken plate on a piece of paper. Using the marker and a straightedge, she draws two chords on the broken chunk of plate.
- Then, she constructs the perpendicular bisector of each chord. The point at which the two perpendicular bisectors intersect is the center of the plate.
- Now that Sarah knows where the center is, she uses the ruler to measure the distance from the point of intersection to any point on the plate's edge to determine its radius.
- Finally, she doubles the radius to determine the diameter of the plate.

PLAN FOR 6 class sessions and ~3 MATHia sessions.

Log in to MyCL for **lesson support** including:
- Slides
- Videos

LESSON 1

SSS, SAS, AAS, ...S.O.S.!

Using Triangle Congruence to Determine Relationships Between Segments

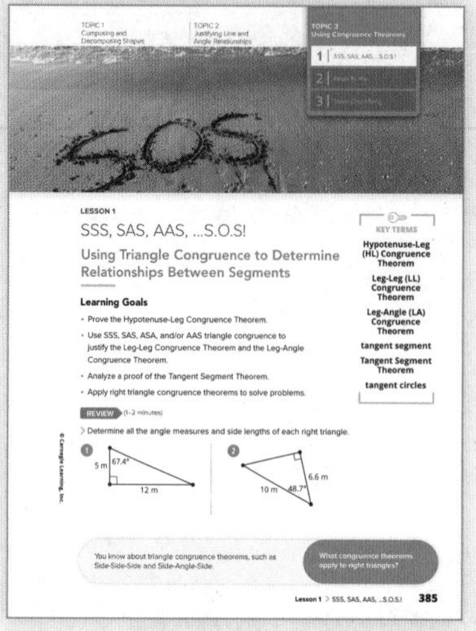
LESSON 1

SSS, SAS, AAS, ...S.O.S!

Using Triangle Congruence to Determine Relationships Between Segments

Learning Goals
- Prove the Hypotenuse-Leg Congruence Theorem.
- Use SSS, SAS, ASA, and/or AAS triangle congruence to justify the Leg-Leg Congruence Theorem and the Leg-Angle Congruence Theorem.
- Analyze a proof of the Tangent Segment Theorem.
- Apply right triangle congruence theorems to solve problems.

KEY TERMS: Hypotenuse-Leg (HL) Congruence Theorem; Leg-Leg (LL) Congruence Theorem; Leg-Angle (LA) Congruence Theorem; tangent segment; Tangent Segment Theorem; tangent circles

REVIEW (1–2 minutes)

Determine all the angle measures and side lengths of each right triangle.

You know about triangle congruence theorems, such as Side-Side-Side and Side-Angle-Side.

What congruence theorems apply to right triangles?

Lesson 1 > SSS, SAS, AAS, ...S.O.S! 385

LESSON 2

Props To You

Properties of Quadrilaterals

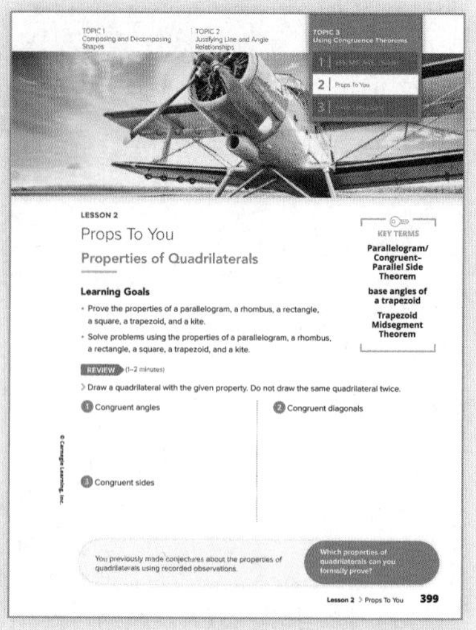
LESSON 2

Props To You

Properties of Quadrilaterals

Learning Goals
- Prove the properties of a parallelogram, a rhombus, a rectangle, a square, a trapezoid, and a kite.
- Solve problems using the properties of a parallelogram, a rhombus, a rectangle, a square, a trapezoid, and a kite.

KEY TERMS: Parallelogram/Congruent-Parallel Side Theorem; base angles of a trapezoid; Trapezoid Midsegment Theorem

REVIEW (1–2 minutes)

Draw a quadrilateral with the given property. Do not draw the same quadrilateral twice.

1 Congruent angles

2 Congruent diagonals

3 Congruent sides

You previously made conjectures about the properties of quadrilaterals using recorded observations.

Which properties of quadrilaterals can you formally prove?

Lesson 2 > Props To You 399

LEARNING TOGETHER

	Lesson 1	Lesson 2
	2 Sessions	3 Sessions
STANDARDS	G.CO.10	G.CO.11
MATHbook Activities sequenced to address standards and meet content goals.	Students construct a right triangle in a circle given a leg and hypotenuse length. They use formal proofs and algebraic reasoning to prove the Hypotenuse-Leg Congruence Theorem. Using triangle congruence theorems, students demonstrate the Leg-Leg and Leg-Angle Congruence Theorems must be true. They then apply these congruence theorems and the Tangent Segment Theorem to solve problems.	Students verify the properties of a parallelogram, a rhombus, a rectangle, a square, a trapezoid, and a kite using formal two-column or paragraph formats, as well as informal reasoning. They apply the theorems to arrive at solutions to problem situations.
MATERIALS	• Compasses • Protractors • Straightedges	• Glue sticks • Scissors

LEARNING INDIVIDUALLY

Median time for students to complete MATHia for this topic is ~120 minutes.

	Lesson 1	Lesson 2
MATHia Workspaces aligned at the lesson level to support benchmarking through self-paced MATHia.	• Proving Triangles Congruent Using HL and HA	• Understanding Parallelograms • Determining Parts of Quadrilaterals and Parallelograms • Proofs About Parallelograms

For students without access to MATHia.

Problem sets for additional practice of the lesson skills.

	Lesson 1	Lesson 2
Skills Practice	• Right Triangle Congruence and Tangent Segments	• Properties of Quadrilaterals

Three-Chord Song
Relationships Between Chords

TOPIC 1
Composing and Decomposing Shapes
TOPIC 2
Justifying Line and Angle Relationships
TOPIC 3
Using Congruence Theorems
3 | Three-Chord Song

LESSON 3
Three-Chord Song
Relationships Between Chords

Learning Goals
- Prove the Diameter–Chord Theorem.
- Prove the Equidistant Chord Theorem and its converse.
- Prove the Congruent Chord–Congruent Arc Theorem and its converse.

KEY TERMS
Diameter-Chord Theorem
Equidistant Chord Theorem
Equidistant Chord Converse Theorem
Congruent Chord–Congruent Arc Theorem
Congruent Chord–Congruent Arc Converse Theorem

REVIEW (1–2 minutes)
1 Write everything you know about this diagram.

© Carnegie Learning, Inc.

You have analyzed relationships among angles and chords.
What relationships exist between chord lengths and other parts of a circle?

Lesson 3 > Three-Chord Song 425

1 Session

G.C.2

Students explore a situation that asks them to determine the circular plate's diameter given only a broken piece. They conjecture about methods to determine the diameter. Students then prove the Diameter-Chord, Equidistant Chord Theorem, and Congruent Chord–Congruent Arc Theorem. Finally, they revisit and solve the broken-plate problem from the Getting Started.

- Compasses
- Straightedges

For the most up-to-date MATHia alignment, log in to MyCL.

Problem sets for additional practice of the lesson skills.

- Chord Relationships

Theorems proved in *Using Congruence Theorems:*

- Hypotenuse-Leg Congruence Theorem
- Leg-Leg Congruence Theorem
- Leg-Angle Congruence Theorem
- Tangent Segment Theorem
- Parallelogram/Congruent-Parallel Side Theorem
- Trapezoid Midsegment Theorem
- Diameter-Chord Theorem
- Equidistant Chord Theorem
- Equidistant Chord Converse Theorem
- Congruent Chord–Congruent Arc Theorem
- Congruent Chord–Congruent Arc Converse Theorem

TOPIC 3

Connection to Prior Learning

What is the entry point for students?

Previously, students explained how the triangle congruence theorems follow from the definition of congruence in terms of rigid motion. They proved the AAS Congruence Theorem and the HA Congruence Theorem for right triangles.

In elementary school, students classified quadrilaterals. In middle school, they composed and decomposed figures to derive the area formulas for shapes.

They also conjectured about relationships among angles and chords and constructed the points of concurrency, including the circumcenter.

MATH REPRESENTATION

Aubrey wants to take a family picture. Her camera has a 70° field of view, but to include the entire family in the picture, she needs to cover a 140° arc.

The Inscribed Angle Theorem says that the measure of an inscribed angle is half the measure of its intercepted arc. So, if Aubrey moves to a point on the circle, her camera's 70° field of view can capture a 140° arc.

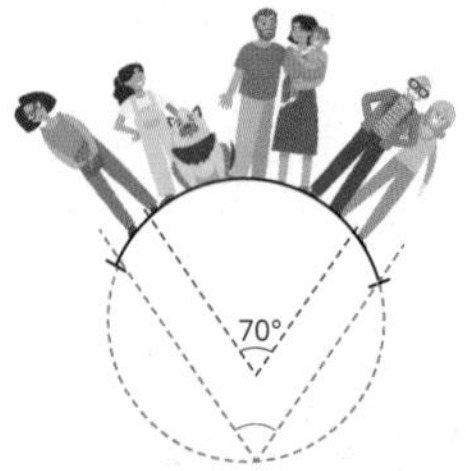

Connection to Future Learning

Why is *Using Congruence Theorems* important?

By writing logical proofs of geometric properties, students learn each shape's structure and its corresponding sides and angles. This allows students to move beyond the specificity of one shape to recognize properties that exist across shapes. When writing valid proofs, students demonstrate that they understand a specific concept and how it fits into other concepts they know and have proven true in all cases. Students will use this logical reasoning, not just in geometry but as they progress through advanced mathematics.

MATH REPRESENTATION

You can prove that if a line parallel to one side of a triangle intersects the other two sides, it divides the two sides proportionally.

Given: $\overline{BC} \parallel \overline{DE}$ Prove: $\frac{BD}{DA} = \frac{CE}{EA}$

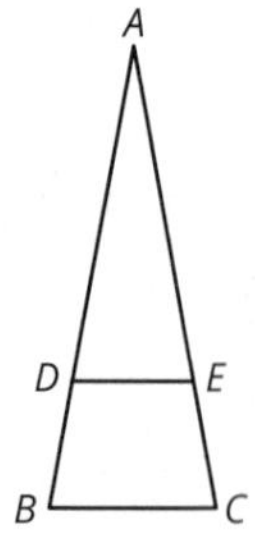

Statements	Reasons
1. $\overline{BC} \parallel \overline{DE}$	**1.** Given
2. $\angle ADE = \angle B$	**2.** Corresponding Angle Postulate
3. $\angle AED = \angle C$	**3.** Corresponding Angle Postulate
4. $\triangle ADE \sim \triangle ABC$	**4.** AA Similarity Theorem
5. $\frac{BA}{DA} = \frac{CA}{EA}$	**5.** Corresponding sides of similar triangles are proportional
6. $BA = BD + DA$ and $CA = CE + EA$	**6.** Segment Addition Postulate
7. $\frac{BD + DA}{DA} = \frac{CE + EA}{EA}$	**7.** Substitution Property
8. $\frac{BD}{DA} = \frac{CE}{EA}$	**8.** Distributive Property over Division and Subtraction Property of Equality

How does a student demonstrate understanding?

Students will demonstrate an understanding of the standards in *Using Congruence Theorems* when they can:

Log in to MyCL for resources that support **student meta-cognition**.

Prove the Hypotenuse-Leg Congruence Theorem.	✓
Use triangle congruence theorems to justify the Leg-Leg and Leg-Angle Congruence Theorems.	✓
Apply right triangle congruence theorems to solve problems.	✓
Understand a proof of the Tangent Segment Theorem.	✓
Use the Tangent Segment Theorem to solve problems.	✓
Classify types of quadrilaterals.	✓
Prove properties about sides, diagonals, and angles of parallelograms, rhombi, rectangles, squares, trapezoids, and kites.	✓
Use properties of special quadrilaterals in proofs.	✓
Prove that the segment joining midpoints of two sides of a trapezoid with only one pair of parallel sides is parallel to the bases and one half the sum of their lengths.	✓
Apply the properties of parallelograms to solve real-world problems.	✓
Prove the Diameter-Chord Theorem, the Equidistant Chord Theorem and its converse, and the Congruent Chord–Congruent Arc Theorem and its converse.	✓
Solve real-world problems using relationships among chords in a circle.	✓
Conjecture about the midsegments of triangles.	✓

HABITS OF MIND

How do the activities in *Using Congruence Theorems* promote student expertise in the mathematical practice standards?

All Carnegie Learning topics are written with the goal of creating mathematical thinkers who are active participants in class discourse, so elements of the habits of mind should be evident in all lessons. Students are expected to make sense of problems and work towards solutions, reason using concrete and abstract ideas, and communicate their thinking while providing a critical ear to the thinking of others.

Throughout *Using Congruence Theorems*, students are reasoning as they write proofs of given theorems. They have to make sense of diagrams and the relationships between constituent parts. Students are taking the conjectures they have made previously and building a logical progression of statements to explore the truth of the conjectures, justifying their conclusions at each step. They use modeling as they apply the mathematics they know to solve problems from the real world. When examining diagrams, students look for and make use of structure—recognizing the significance of an existing line or angle and drawing auxiliary lines as appropriate.

Mixed Practice

At the end of each topic, a **Mixed Practice** worksheet provides practice with skills from previous topics and this topic.

Spaced Review
Fluency and problem solving from previous topics

End of Topic Review
Review problems from this topic

Log in to MyCL for digital resources.

- A version with **additional space** for students to write their answers.
- Downloadable and editable in Word
- Editable via Edulastic

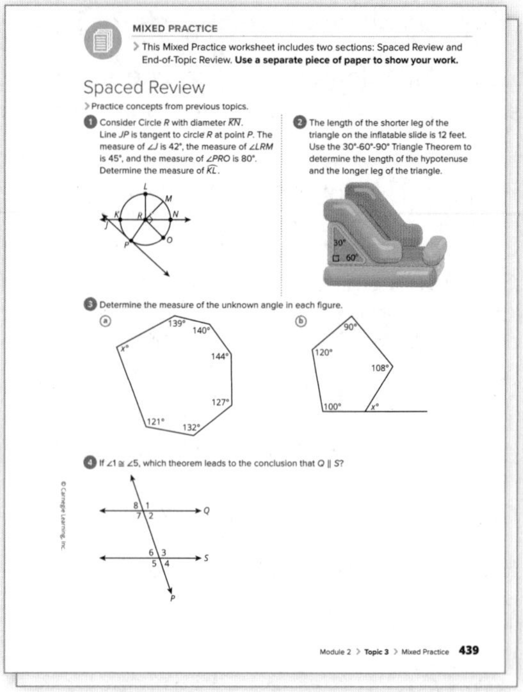

Topic Summary

Available online, a **Topic Summary** reviews the main concepts for the topic.

Essential Ideas for each lesson.

Log in to MyCL for digital resources.

- A printable version available for download.
- A video of the **Worked Example** being solved

www.carnegielearning.com/login

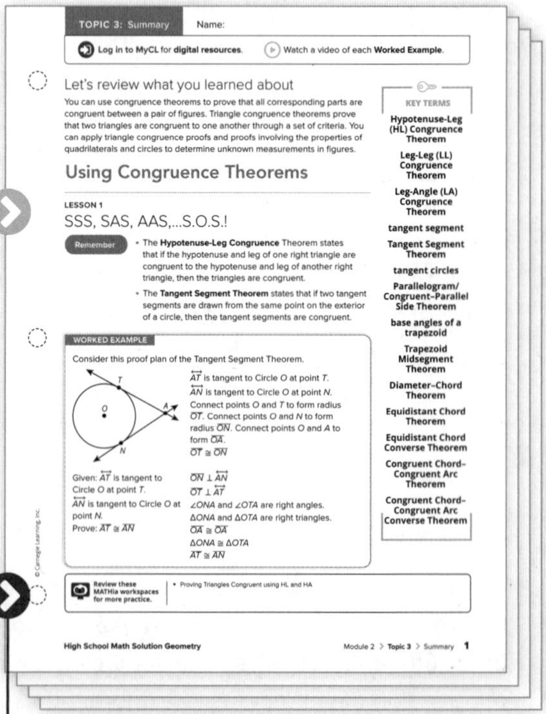

MATHia Workspaces are highlighted in select lessons to help you understand the connections and what you might want to review.

Assessment

Assessments aligned to this topic:

1. Pre-test
2. Post-test
3. End of Topic Test (Form A)
4. End of Topic Test (Form B)
5. Standardized Test Practice
6. Performance Task with Rubric

An **Assessment Overview** identifies the standard(s) aligned with each item on every test.

Log in to MyCL for digital resources.

- A version with **additional space** for students to write their answers.
- Downloadable and editable in Word
- Editable via Edulastic

End of Topic Test		Standardized Test	
1. G.CO.10	11. G.CO.11	1. G.CO.10	11. G.CO.10
2. G.CO.10	12. G.CO.11	2. G.CO.11	12. G.CO.10
3. G.CO.10	13. G.C.2	3. G.C.2	13. G.C.2
4. G.CO.10	14. G.C.2	4. G.CO.10	14. G.CO.11
5. G.CO.10	15. G.C.2	5. G.CO.11	15. G.C.2
6. G.C.2		6. G.C.2	16. G.CO.10
7. G.CO.11		7. G.CO.10	17. G.CO.11
8. G.CO.11		8. G.CO.11	18. G.C.2
9. G.CO.11		9. G.C.2	19. G.CO.10
10. G.CO.11		10. G.CO.10	20. G.CO.11

TOPIC 3

Family Guide

Teachers, encourage your families to log into the **Home Connection** to access a collection of resources that supports their students as they learn about *Using Congruence Theorems*.

www.carnegielearning.com/home-connection

For families with limited online access, print and send home the **Family Guide**.

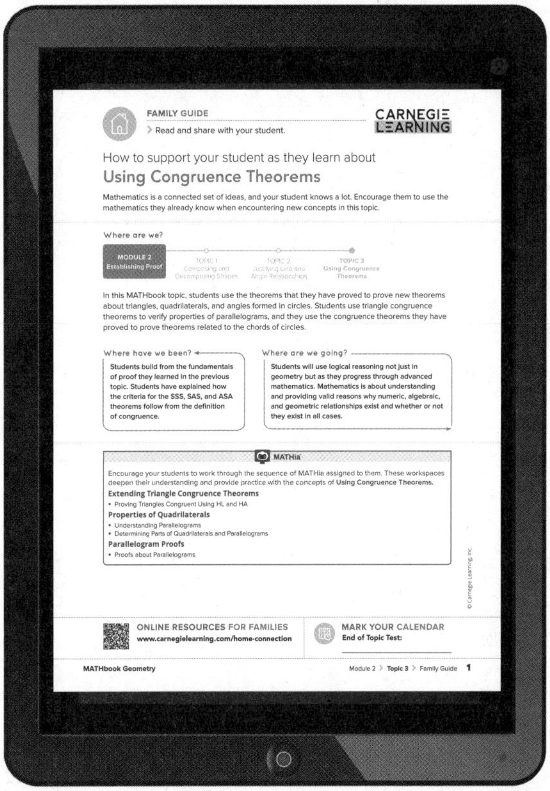
FAMILY GUIDE

> Read and share with your student.

CARNEGIE LEARNING

How to support your student as they learn about

Using Congruence Theorems

Mathematics is a connected set of ideas, and your student knows a lot. Encourage them to use the mathematics they already know when encountering new concepts in this topic.

Where are we?

MODULE 2 Establishing Proof — TOPIC 1 Composing and Decomposing Shapes — TOPIC 2 Justifying Line and Angle Relationships — TOPIC 3 Using Congruence Theorems

In this MATHbook topic, students use the theorems that they have proved to prove new theorems about triangles, quadrilaterals, and angles formed in circles. Students use triangle congruence theorems to verify properties of parallelograms, and they use the congruence theorems they have proved to prove theorems related to the chords of circles.

Where have we been?

Students build from the fundamentals of proof they learned in the previous topic. Students have explained how the criteria for the SSS, SAS, and ASA theorems follow from the definition of congruence.

Where are we going?

Students will use logical reasoning not just in geometry but as they progress through advanced mathematics. Mathematics is about understanding and providing valid reasons why numeric, algebraic, and geometric relationships exist and whether or not they exist in all cases.

MATHia

Encourage your students to work through the sequence of MATHia assigned to them. These workspaces deepen their understanding and provide practice with the concepts of **Using Congruence Theorems.**

Extending Triangle Congruence Theorems
- Proving Triangles Congruent Using HL and HA

Properties of Quadrilaterals
- Understanding Parallelograms
- Determining Parts of Quadrilaterals and Parallelograms

Parallelogram Proofs
- Proofs about Parallelograms

© Carnegie Learning, Inc.

ONLINE RESOURCES FOR FAMILIES
www.carnegielearning.com/home-connection

MARK YOUR CALENDAR
End of Topic Test:

MATHbook Geometry — Module 2 > Topic 3 > Family Guide 1

Using Congruence Theorems

Scope out MATHbook and MATHia sessions for this topic, keeping in mind your long term plan.

You can schedule MATHia sessions any time; however, if you are using Skills Practice as the alternative, schedule those sessions after a completed lesson.

1 Session ≈ 45 minutes

Log in to MyCL for:

- Editable templates
- Alternative plans for longer sessions
- Implementations not using MATHia

CORE IMPLEMENTATION PLAN with flexible access to computers/tablets.

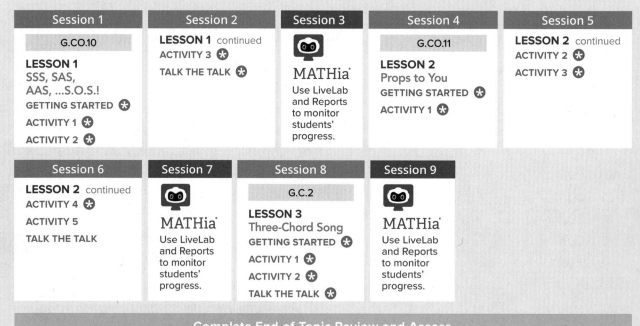

Session 1	Session 2	Session 3	Session 4	Session 5
G.CO.10 **LESSON 1** SSS, SAS, AAS, ...S.O.S.! GETTING STARTED ✪ ACTIVITY 1 ✪ ACTIVITY 2 ✪	**LESSON 1** continued ACTIVITY 3 ✪ TALK THE TALK ✪	MATHia Use LiveLab and Reports to monitor students' progress.	G.CO.11 **LESSON 2** Props to You GETTING STARTED ✪ ACTIVITY 1 ✪	**LESSON 2** continued ACTIVITY 2 ✪ ACTIVITY 3 ✪

Session 6	Session 7	Session 8	Session 9
LESSON 2 continued ACTIVITY 4 ✪ ACTIVITY 5 TALK THE TALK	MATHia Use LiveLab and Reports to monitor students' progress.	G.C.2 **LESSON 3** Three-Chord Song GETTING STARTED ✪ ACTIVITY 1 ✪ ACTIVITY 2 ✪ TALK THE TALK ✪	MATHia Use LiveLab and Reports to monitor students' progress.

Complete End-of-Topic Review and Assess

✪ This activity highlights a key term or concept that is essential to the learning goals of the lesson.

ENGAGE + DEVELOP + TEACH

ENGAGE at the **Module** level

DEVELOP at the **Topic** level

TEACH Read the facilitation notes and plan learning experiences.

Where are we?

TOPIC 3 Using Congruence Theorems	LESSON 1 SSS, SAS, AAS, ...S.O.S.!	LESSON 2 Props To You	LESSON 3 Three-Chord Song
Pacing	2 Sessions	3 Sessions	1 Session

OVERVIEW: LESSON 1

SSS, SAS, AAS, ...S.O.S!

Using Triangle Congruence to Determine Relationships Between Segments

ENGAGE

- Students construct a right triangle given line segments representing the lengths of a leg and the hypotenuse.

DEVELOP

- Students prove the Hypotenuse-Leg Congruence Theorem.
- They explain the connections between the SAS, ASA, and AAS Congruence Theorems and the Leg-Leg Congruence Theorem and Leg-Angle Congruence Theorem.
- They analyze a proof plan of the Tangent Segment Theorem.

DEMONSTRATE

- Students describe the relationships between the right triangle congruence theorems and the general triangle congruence theorems.

HIGH SCHOOL GEOMETRY

Congruence

Prove geometric theorems.

10. Prove theorems about triangles.

LESSON STRUCTURE AND PACING GUIDE 2 SESSIONS

⊛ This activity highlights a key term or concept that is essential to the learning goals of the lesson.

Session 1

INSTRUCTIONAL SEQUENCE

ENGAGE	DEVELOP	DEVELOP
Connect to prior knowledge	Mathematical problem solving Peer analysis	Mathematical problem solving Real-world problem solving

⊛ GETTING STARTED
Pulling Your Leg

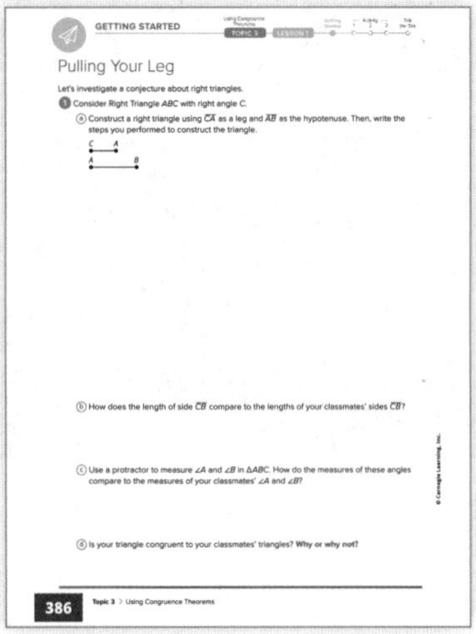
GETTING STARTED

Pulling Your Leg

Let's investigate a conjecture about right triangles.

1 Consider Right Triangle ABC with right angle C.

a. Construct a right triangle using $\overline{CA}$ as a leg and $\overline{AB}$ as the hypotenuse. Then, write the steps you performed to construct the triangle.

b. How does the length of side $\overline{CB}$ compare to the lengths of your classmates' sides $\overline{CB}$?

c. Use a protractor to measure $\angle A$ and $\angle B$ in $\triangle ABC$. How do the measures of these angles compare to the measures of your classmates' $\angle A$ and $\angle B$?

d. Is your triangle congruent to your classmates' triangles? Why or why not?

386 Topic 3 > Using Congruence Theorems

Students construct a right triangle given line segments representing the lengths of a leg and the hypotenuse.

- They use measuring tools to determine the measure of each angle and side
- They conclude that the given information determine a unique triangle.

⊛ ACTIVITY 1
Hypotenuse-Leg Congruence Theorem

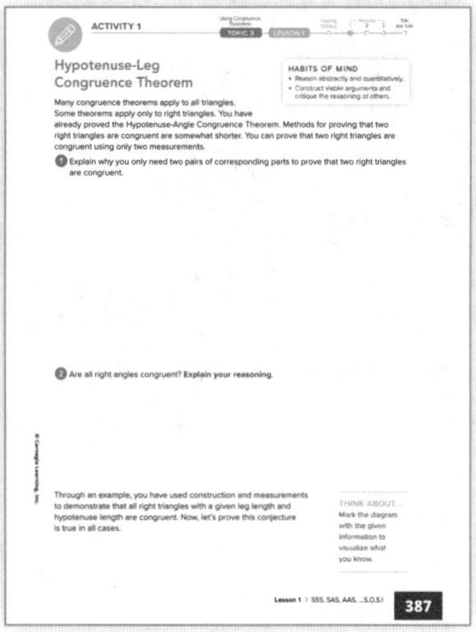
ACTIVITY 1

Hypotenuse-Leg Congruence Theorem

HABITS OF MIND
- Reason abstractly and quantitatively.
- Construct viable arguments and critique the reasoning of others.

Many congruence theorems apply to all triangles. Some theorems apply only to right triangles. You have already proved the Hypotenuse-Angle Congruence Theorem. Methods for proving that two right triangles are congruent are somewhat shorter. You can prove that two right triangles are congruent using only two measurements.

1 Explain why you only need two pairs of corresponding parts to prove that two right triangles are congruent.

2 Are all right angles congruent? Explain your reasoning.

Through an example, you have used construction and measurements to demonstrate that all right triangles with a given leg length and hypotenuse length are congruent. Now, let's prove this conjecture is true in all cases.

THINK ABOUT... Mark the diagram with the given information to visualize what you know.

Lesson 1 > SSS, SAS, AAS, ...S.O.S! 387

Students prove the Hypotenuse-Leg Congruence Theorem.

- They explain the algebraic reasoning used to justify this theorem.

⊛ ACTIVITY 2
Applying Triangle Congruence Theorems

ACTIVITY 2

MATHia CONNECTION

Applying Triangle Congruence Theorems

HABITS OF MIND
- Reason abstractly and quantitatively.
- Construct viable arguments and critique the reasoning of others.

You have learned about the Hypotenuse-Angle Congruence Theorem and the Hypotenuse-Leg Congruence Theorem. There are two other right angle theorems you can prove with similar reasoning.

THEOREM

LEG-LEG (LL) CONGRUENCE THEOREM
If the two corresponding shorter legs of two right triangles are congruent, then the two triangles are congruent.

LEG-ANGLE (LA) CONGRUENCE THEOREM
If the leg and an acute angle of one right triangle are congruent to the corresponding leg and acute angle of another right triangle, then the triangles are congruent.

1 Explain how the LL Congruence Theorem and the LA Congruence Theorem are each equivalent to another triangle congruence theorem that you know.

390 Topic 3 > Using Congruence Theorems

Students explain the connections between the SAS, ASA, and AAS Congruence Theorems and the Leg-Leg and Leg-Angle Congruence Theorems.

- They solve problems using these theorems.

Log in to MyCL for **lesson support** including:

Slides

Videos

www.carnegielearning.com/login

Session 2

INSTRUCTIONAL SEQUENCE

DEVELOP	DEMONSTRATE
Investigation **Worked example**	**Generalization**

ACTIVITY 3
Tangent Segments

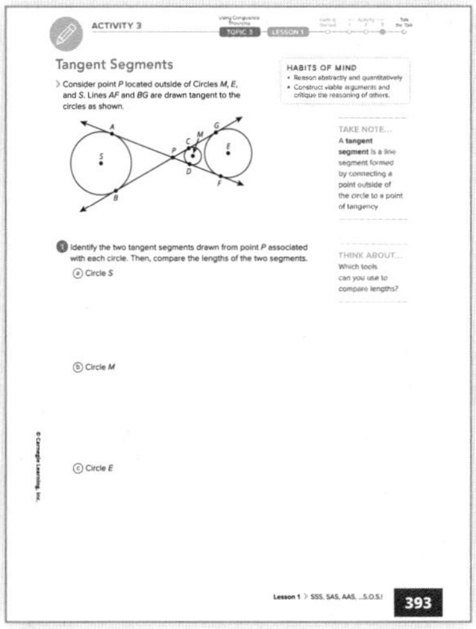
ACTIVITY 3

Tangent Segments

> Consider point P located outside of Circles M, E, and S. Lines AF and BG are drawn tangent to the circles as shown.

HABITS OF MIND
- Reason abstractly and quantitatively
- Construct viable arguments and critique the reasoning of others.

TAKE NOTE... A **tangent segment** is a line segment formed by connecting a point outside of the circle to a point of tangency.

1. Identify the two tangent segments drawn from point P associated with each circle. Then, compare the lengths of the two segments.
   (a) Circle S
   (b) Circle M
   (c) Circle E

THINK ABOUT... Which tools can you use to compare lengths?

Lesson 1 > SSS, SAS, AAS, ...S.O.S.! 393

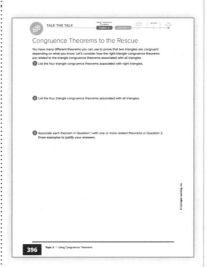

Students analyze a proof plan of the Tangent Segment Theorem.

- They compare the lengths of tangent segments drawn from the same point on the exterior of a circle.
- They solve problems using the Tangent Segment Theorem.

TALK THE TALK
Congruence Theorems to the Rescue

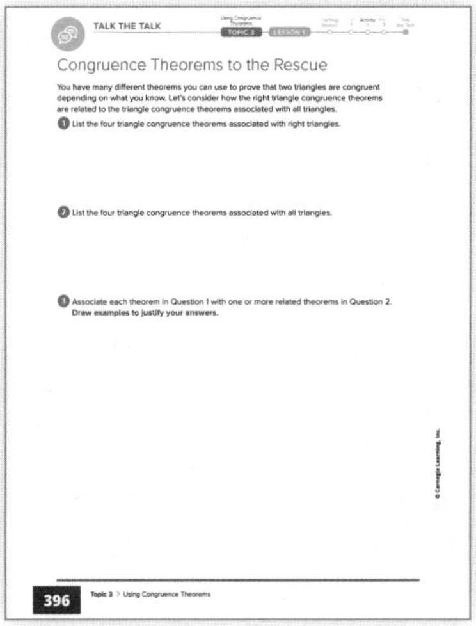
TALK THE TALK

Congruence Theorems to the Rescue

You have many different theorems you can use to prove that two triangles are congruent depending on what you know. Let's consider how the right triangle congruence theorems are related to the triangle congruence theorems associated with all triangles.

1. List the four triangle congruence theorems associated with right triangles.
2. List the four triangle congruence theorems associated with all triangles.
3. Associate each theorem in Question 1 with one or more related theorems in Question 2. Draw examples to justify your answers.

396 Topic 3 > Using Congruence Theorems

Students describe the relationships between the right triangle congruence theorems and the general triangle congruence theorems.

- They draw examples to demonstrate the connections.

NOTES

TOPIC 3

Now that you have read the Module, Topic, and Lesson Overviews, you are ready to plan.

Log in to MyCL for:
- Editable templates
- Additional planning support

Do the math

Tear out the lesson planning template (page 385M) and jot down thoughts as you work through this lesson and read the Facilitation Notes.

- Anticipate student responses
- Track your time, so you can estimate how much time to spend on any activity
- Decide which differentiation and collaboration strategies you may use and how that may impact pacing

Connect the learning

MATHbook + MATHia

The table shows the self-paced MATHia sequence for the *Using Congruence Theorems* Topic.

Median student completion time: ~100–125 minutes

As you implement this lesson, consider different connections for students who are on pace and those that have not yet completed the workspaces aligned to this lesson.

STUDENTS WHO ARE NOT HERE YET
Students will practice proving triangles congruent using the HL and HA Congruence Theorems.

TYPE	WORKSPACE NAME
	Proving Triangles Congruent Using HL and HA
	Understanding Parallelograms
	Determining Parts of Quadrilaterals and Parallelograms
	Proofs about Parallelograms

STUDENTS WHO ARE ON PACE
After you complete Activity 2, ask these students to share how they determined how to connect each step in the proofs.

SSS, SAS, AAS, ...S.O.S!

Using Triangle Congruence to Determine Relationships Between Segments

Session 1

GETTING STARTED Pulling Your Leg ✪

Pacing (minutes)	
My Time	Class Time

ACTIVITY 1 Hypotenuse-Leg Congruence Theorem ✪

Pacing (minutes)	
My Time	Class Time

KEY TERM

Hypotenuse-Leg (HL) Congruence Theorem

ACTIVITY 2 Applying Triangle Congruence Theorems ✪

Pacing (minutes)	
My Time	Class Time

KEY TERM

Leg-Leg (LL) Congruence Theorem

Leg-Angle (LA) Congruence Theorem

Session 2

ACTIVITY 3 Tangent Segments ✪

Pacing (minutes)	
My Time	Class Time

KEY TERM

tangent segment

Tangent Segment Theorem

tangent circles

TALK THE TALK Congruence Theorems to the Rescue ✪

Pacing (minutes)	
My Time	Class Time

✪ This activity highlights a key term or concept that is essential to the learning goals of the lesson.

Reflect on your lesson

Log in to MyCL for:
- Editable templates
- Additional planning support

› Consider the effectiveness of your lesson on student learning.

What went well?	**What did not go as planned?**

› Anticipate how you would change the lesson next time you teach it.

How will you capitalize on the things that went well?	**How will you improve things that did not go as planned?**

MATERIALS

- Compasses
- Protractors
- Straightedges

TOPIC 1 Composing and Decomposing Shapes
TOPIC 2 Justifying Line and Angle Relationships
TOPIC 3 Using Congruence Theorems
1 | SSS, SAS, AAS, ...S.O.S.!
2 | Props To You
3 | Three-Chord Song

LESSON 1

SSS, SAS, AAS, ...S.O.S!

Using Triangle Congruence to Determine Relationships Between Segments

Learning Goals

- Prove the Hypotenuse-Leg Congruence Theorem.
- Use SSS, SAS, ASA, and/or AAS triangle congruence to justify the Leg-Leg Congruence Theorem and the Leg-Angle Congruence Theorem.
- Analyze a proof of the Tangent Segment Theorem.
- Apply right triangle congruence theorems to solve problems.

KEY TERMS

- **Hypotenuse-Leg (HL) Congruence Theorem**
- **Leg-Leg (LL) Congruence Theorem**
- **Leg-Angle (LA) Congruence Theorem**
- **tangent segment**
- **Tangent Segment Theorem**
- **tangent circles**

REVIEW (1–2 minutes)

> Determine all the angle measures and side lengths of each right triangle.

1

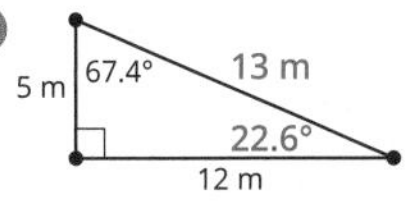

2

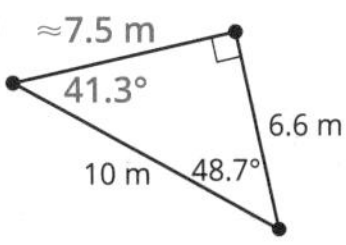

You know about triangle congruence theorems, such as Side-Side-Side and Side-Angle-Side.

What congruence theorems apply to right triangles?

Setting the Stage

- **Assign Review (optional, 1 - 2 minutes)**
- **Communicate the learning goals and key terms to look out for**
- **Tap into your students' prior learning by reading the narrative statement**
- **Provide a sense of direction by reading the question**

IN THIS REVIEW

Students calculate angle measures and side lengths. They will use this skill in **ACTIVITY 3 Tangent Segments.**

The Hypotenuse-Leg Congruence Theorem states that if the hypotenuse and leg of one right triangle are congruent to the hypotenuse and leg of another right triangle, then the triangles are congruent.

The Tangent Segment Theorem states that if two tangent segments are drawn from the same point on the exterior of a circle, then the tangent segments are congruent.

TOPIC 3

Essential Ideas

- The Hypotenuse-Leg Congruence Theorem states that if the hypotenuse and leg of one right triangle are congruent to the hypotenuse and leg of another right triangle, then the triangles are congruent.
- The Leg-Leg Congruence Theorem states that if the two corresponding shorter legs of two right triangles are congruent, then the triangles are congruent.
- The Leg-Angle Congruence Theorem states that if the leg and an acute angle of one right triangle are congruent to the corresponding leg and acute angle of another triangle, then the triangles are congruent.
- The Tangent Segment Theorem states that if two tangent segments are drawn from the same point on the exterior of a circle, then the tangent segments are congruent.

SUMMARY **You can determine one unique right triangle from a given hypotenuse length and a given leg length.**

Chunking the Activity

- **Read and discuss the directions**
- **Group students to complete the activity**
- **Share and summarize**

COMMON MISCONCEPTION

See Page 398A for a misconception related to 1 part (d).

Pulling Your Leg

Let's investigate a conjecture about right triangles.

1 Consider Right Triangle ABC with right angle C.

(a) Construct a right triangle using $\overline{CA}$ as a leg and $\overline{AB}$ as the hypotenuse. Then, write the steps you performed to construct the triangle.

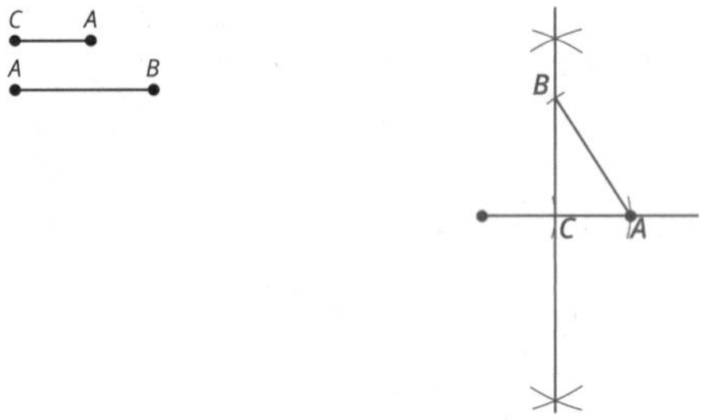

I drew a starter segment. I constructed a segment twice the length of $\overline{CA}$, then used its endpoints to construct a perpendicular bisector to create right angle C.

Next, I used half of the line segment as a leg of the triangle.

Lastly, I opened my compass to the length of $\overline{AB}$, placed my compass point on point A and marked the point B on the perpendicular bisector to create hypotenuse $\overline{AB}$.

(b) How does the length of side $\overline{CB}$ compare to the lengths of your classmates' sides $\overline{CB}$?

All of the lengths of $\overline{CB}$ were equal, at approximately 3 cm.

(c) Use a protractor to measure $\angle A$ and $\angle B$ in ΔABC. How do the measures of these angles compare to the measures of your classmates' $\angle A$ and $\angle B$?

All the measures of $\angle A$ were equal, at approximately 56°.
All the measures of $\angle B$ were equal, at approximately 34°.

(d) Is your triangle congruent to your classmates' triangles? **Why or why not?**

The triangles are congruent. The measures of all the angles and sides were equal.

Questions to Support Discourse

		TYPE
1	• How did you construct the right angle?	Gathering
	• How did you determine the location of point C? What about points A and B?	Probing
	• Do you think that knowing the length of the hypotenuse and a leg of a right triangle is enough to know that you have a unique triangle?	Seeing structure

ACTIVITY 1

SUMMARY **You can use the Hypotenuse-Leg (HL) Congruence Theorem to prove right triangles congruent.**

ACTIVITY 1

Hypotenuse-Leg Congruence Theorem

HABITS OF MIND
- Reason abstractly and quantitatively.
- Construct viable arguments and critique the reasoning of others.

Many congruence theorems apply to all triangles. Some theorems apply only to right triangles. You have already proved the Hypotenuse-Angle Congruence Theorem. Methods for proving that two right triangles are congruent are somewhat shorter. You can prove that two right triangles are congruent using only two measurements.

1. Explain why you only need two pairs of corresponding parts to prove that two right triangles are congruent.

   If you know any two side lengths of two right triangles, then you can determine the other side length of each triangle using the Pythagorean Theorem. If you know the measure of an acute angle of a right triangle, then you can determine the other acute angle using the Triangle Sum Theorem.

2. Are all right angles congruent? **Explain your reasoning.**

   Yes. All right angles are congruent according to the Right Angle Congruence Postulate.

Through an example, you have used construction and measurements to demonstrate that all right triangles with a given leg length and hypotenuse length are congruent. Now, let's prove this conjecture is true in all cases.

THINK ABOUT...
Mark the diagram with the given information to visualize what you know.

Chunking the Activity

- Read and discuss the introduction
- Group students to complete 1 and 2
- Check-in and share
- Group students to complete 3
- Check-in and share
- Group students to complete 4
- Read and discuss the theorem

Questions to Support Discourse

	Question	TYPE
1	• Which pairs of corresponding parts would lead you to conclude the triangles are congruent?	Gathering
	• If given two pairs of congruent corresponding acute angles in two right triangles, could you prove the right triangles congruent? Why or why not?	Seeing structure

NOTES

DIFFERENTIATION STRATEGY

See Page 398A to challenge advanced learners to extend ❸.

LANGUAGE LINK

ELL TIP

Support students by providing them with a bank of theorems and properties that they can use to complete the proof.

ACTIVITY 1 Continued

❸ Complete the two-column proof of this conjecture.

Given:
Right triangle *ABC* with right angle *C*.
Right triangle *DEF* with right angle *F*.
$\overline{AC} \cong \overline{DF}$
$\overline{AB} \cong \overline{DE}$

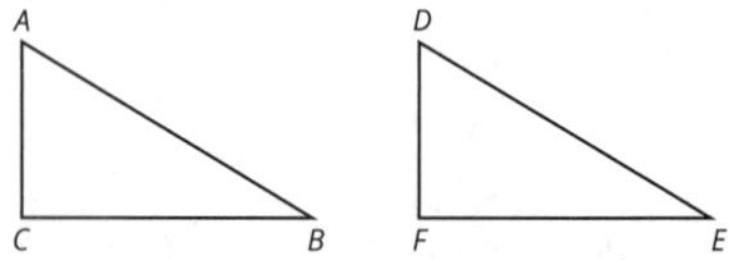

Prove: $\Delta ABC \cong \Delta DEF$

Statements	Reasons
1. Right triangle *ABC* with right angle *C*. Right triangle *DEF* with right angle *F*.	1. Given
2. $\angle C \cong \angle F$	2. Right Angle Congruence Postulate
3. $\overline{AC} \cong \overline{DF}$ and $\overline{AB} \cong \overline{DE}$	3. Given
4. $AC = DF$ and $AB = DE$	4. Definition of congruent segments
5. $(AC)^2 = (DF)^2$ and $(AB)^2 = (DE)^2$	5. Squaring both sides of an equation maintains equality
6. $(AC)^2 + (CB)^2 = (AB)^2$ and $(DF)^2 + (FE)^2 = (DE)^2$	6. Pythagorean Theorem
7. $(AC)^2 + (CB)^2 = (DF)^2 + (FE)^2$	7. Transitive Property or Substitution Property
8. $(CB)^2 = (FE)^2$	8. Subtraction Property of Equality
9. $CB = FE$	9. Taking the square root of both sides of an equation maintains equality since $CB > 0$ and $FE > 0$
10. $\overline{CB} \cong \overline{FE}$	10. Definition of congruent segments
11. $\Delta ABC \cong \Delta DEF$	11. SAS or SSS Congruence Theorem

Questions to Support Discourse

		TYPE
❸	• Why do you have to rewrite the given statements $\overline{AC} \cong \overline{DF}$ and $\overline{AB} \cong \overline{DE}$ as $AC = DF$ and $AB = DE$?	Gathering

ACTIVITY 1 Continued

4 Sam used algebra to reason about the conjecture. **Explain why Sam's reasoning is correct. Show your work.**

Sam

$a^2 + x^2 = y^2$ and $b^2 + x^2 = y^2$

So $a = b$, and the triangles are congruent by SSS or SAS.

Sam used x to represent the length of each congruent leg, $\overline{AC}$ and $\overline{DF}$, and y to represent the length of each congruent hypotenuse, $\overline{AB}$ and $\overline{DE}$. The variables a and b represent the unknown lengths of the remaining corresponding legs. When you set up the equations, you get that $a^2 + x^2 = b^2 + x^2$, or $a^2 = b^2$, therefore $a = b$.

The two remaining corresponding side lengths are the same length, which means all corresponding side lengths of the triangles are congruent.

So, the triangles are congruent because the three pairs of corresponding sides are congruent (SSS) or because two pairs of corresponding sides and their corresponding included right angles are congruent (SAS).

Because you proved that the conjecture is true, you can now refer to it as a theorem.

THEOREM

HYPOTENUSE-LEG (HL) CONGRUENCE THEOREM

If the hypotenuse and leg of one right triangle are congruent to the hypotenuse and leg of another right triangle, then the triangles are congruent.

Lesson 1 > SSS, SAS, AAS, ...S.O.S.! 389

Questions to Support Discourse

		TYPE
4	• Where does the two-column proof in Question 3 use Sam's reasoning?	Seeing structure

NOTES

TOPIC 3

SUMMARY **You can use the Leg-Leg Congruence Theorem and the Leg-Angle Congruence Theorem to prove right triangles congruent and solve problems.**

Chunking the Activity

- **Read and discuss the introduction**
- **Group students to complete 1**
- **Check-in and share**
- **Group students to complete 2 – 5**
- **Share and summarize**

DIFFERENTIATION STRATEGY

See Page 398B to challenge advanced learners to extend 1.

Student Look-Fors

The use of the HA Congruence Theorem versus the Vertical Angle Theorem and the AAS Congruence Theorem.

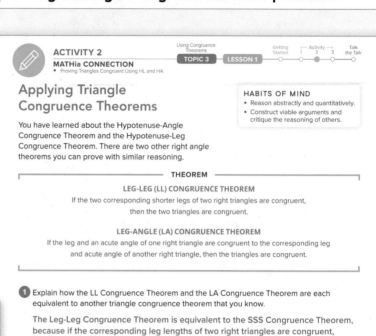

Applying Triangle Congruence Theorems

HABITS OF MIND
- Reason abstractly and quantitatively.
- Construct viable arguments and critique the reasoning of others.

You have learned about the Hypotenuse-Angle Congruence Theorem and the Hypotenuse-Leg Congruence Theorem. There are two other right angle theorems you can prove with similar reasoning.

THEOREM

LEG-LEG (LL) CONGRUENCE THEOREM

If the two corresponding shorter legs of two right triangles are congruent, then the two triangles are congruent.

LEG-ANGLE (LA) CONGRUENCE THEOREM

If the leg and an acute angle of one right triangle are congruent to the corresponding leg and acute angle of another right triangle, then the triangles are congruent.

1 Explain how the LL Congruence Theorem and the LA Congruence Theorem are each equivalent to another triangle congruence theorem that you know.

The Leg-Leg Congruence Theorem is equivalent to the SSS Congruence Theorem, because if the corresponding leg lengths of two right triangles are congruent, then the Pythagorean Theorem says that the remaining side, the hypotenuse, is also congruent.

It is also equivalent to the SAS Congruence Theorem because the right angle is the included side.

The Leg-Angle Congruence Theorem is equivalent to either ASA or AAS, depending on how the congruent corresponding parts are oriented in the right triangles.

LA triangles are congruent by ASA.

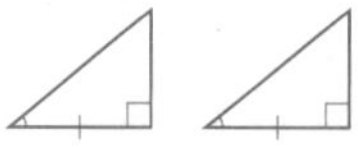

LA triangles are congruent by AAS.

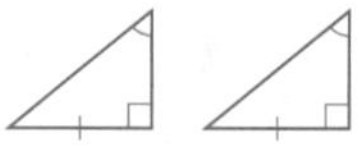

Questions to Support Discourse

		TYPE
1	• Which congruence theorems require 1 pair of congruent corresponding sides and 2 pairs of congruent corresponding angles?	Gathering
	• How is the Leg-Leg Congruence Theorem equivalent to the SSS Congruence Theorem?	Seeing structure

390 Topic 3 > Using Congruence Theorems

> Determine whether there is enough information to prove that the two triangles are congruent. If so, name the congruence theorem used.

2 If $\overline{CS} \perp \overline{SD}$, $\overline{WD} \perp \overline{SD}$, and P is the midpoint of $\overline{CW}$, is $\Delta CSP \cong \Delta WDP$?

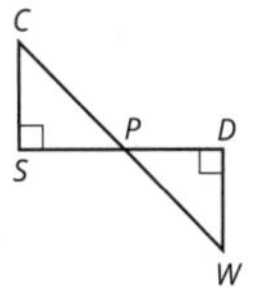

Yes. The triangles are congruent by HA.

3 Pat always trips on the third step, and she thinks that step may be a different size. The contractor told her that all the treads and risers are perpendicular to each other. Is that enough information to state that the steps are the same size? In other words, if $\overline{WN} \perp \overline{NZ}$ and $\overline{ZH} \perp \overline{HK}$, is $\Delta WNZ \cong \Delta ZHK$?

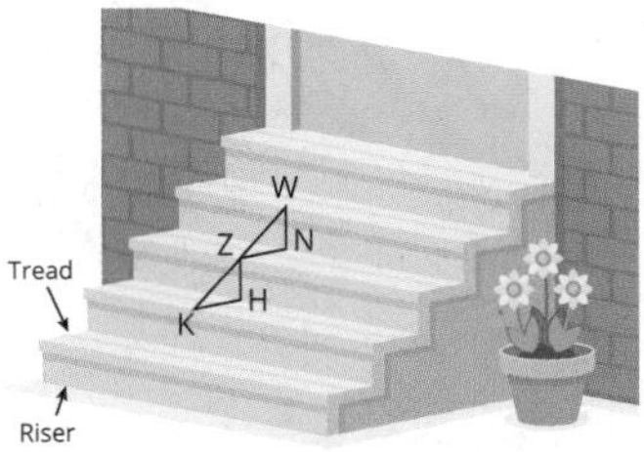

No. There is not enough information.

I only know that the treads and risers are perpendicular. I don't know any other measurements.

NOTES

COMMON MISCONCEPTION

See Page 398B for a misconception related to **2**.

LANGUAGE LINK

ELL TIP

Ensure students understand the terms *treads* and *risers*. Refer to the diagram of the stairs and note that the *treads* of a staircase are the horizontal parts of the staircase on which people walk. The *risers* are the vertical parts of the staircase that form the space between one step and the next.

Student Look-Fors

Making sense of problems by annotating the figures based on the given information.

Questions to Support Discourse

		TYPE
2	• What information would you need to prove the triangles congruent by HA?	Gathering
	• Since P is the midpoint of $\overline{CW}$, what is true about $\overline{CP}$ and $\overline{PW}$?	Seeing structure
	• Can the HA Congruence Theorem and the AAS Congruence Theorem both apply? Why?	Reflecting and justifying
3	• Is it possible for steps to have different sizes?	Gathering

NOTES

COMMON MISCONCEPTION

See Page 398B for a misconception related to 4.

4 If $\overline{JA} \perp \overline{MY}$ and $\overline{JY} \cong \overline{AY}$, is $\Delta JYM \cong \Delta AYM$?

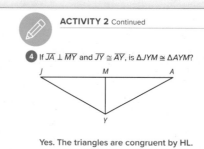

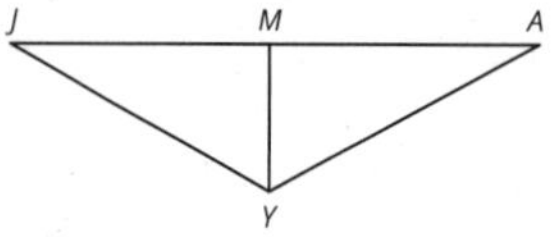

Yes. The triangles are congruent by HL.

5 If $\overline{ST} \perp \overline{SR}$, $\overline{AT} \perp \overline{AR}$, and $\angle STR \cong \angle ATR$, is $\Delta STR \cong \Delta ATR$?

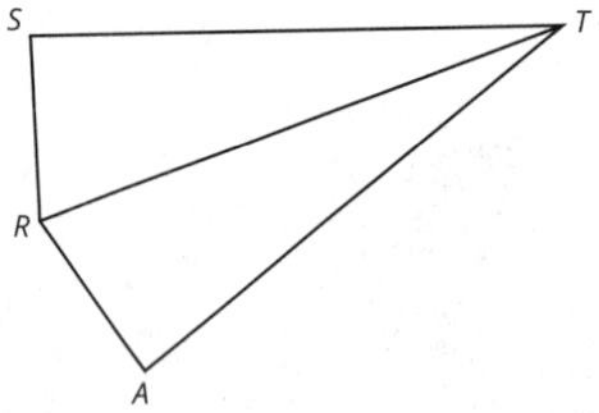

Yes. The triangles are congruent by HA.

392 Topic 3 > Using Congruence Theorems

Questions to Support Discourse

		TYPE
4	• How do you know ΔJYM and ΔAYM are right triangles? • How does knowing ΔJYM shares a side with ΔAYM help you prove the triangles congruent?	Probing

ACTIVITY 3

SUMMARY **You can use theorems about tangent segments to solve problems.**

Tangent Segments

Consider point P located outside of Circles M, E, and S. Lines AF and BG are drawn tangent to the circles as shown.

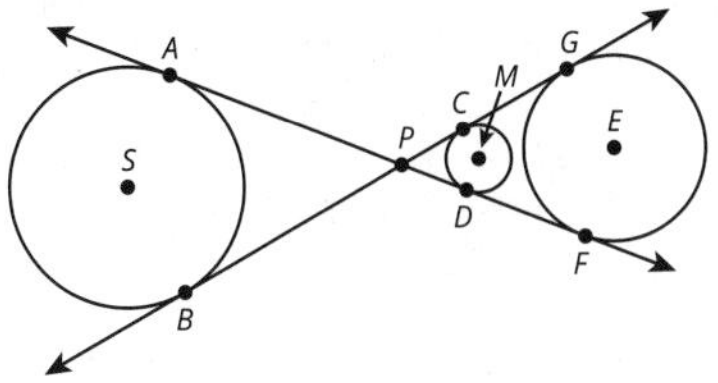

HABITS OF MIND
- Reason abstractly and quantitatively.
- Construct viable arguments and critique the reasoning of others.

TAKE NOTE...
A **tangent segment** is a line segment formed by connecting a point outside of the circle to a point of tangency.

THINK ABOUT...
Which tools can you use to compare lengths?

1 Identify the two tangent segments drawn from point P associated with each circle. Then, compare the lengths of the two segments.

(a) Circle S

The tangent segments associated with Circle S are $\overline{PA}$ and $\overline{PB}$.
The two tangent segments are congruent.

(b) Circle M

The tangent segments associated with Circle M are $\overline{PC}$ and $\overline{PD}$.
The two tangent segments are congruent.

(c) Circle E

The tangent segments associated with Circle E are $\overline{PG}$ and $\overline{PF}$.
The two tangent segments are congruent.

Questions to Support Discourse

		TYPE
1	• How many tangent segments can you draw to a circle from a single point on the exterior of a circle?	Gathering
	• How does the location of the exterior point affect the length of the tangent segment? • What do you notice about the major and minor arcs determined by a pair of tangent segments?	Probing

Chunking the Activity

- Read and discuss the introduction
- Group students to complete 1
- Check-in and share
- Read and discuss the worked example
- Group students to complete 2 and 3
- Check-in and share
- Group students to complete 4 - 6
- Share and summarize

COMMON MISCONCEPTION
See Page 398B for a misconception related to 1.

LANGUAGE LINK

ELL TIP

Provide students with sentence frames, mirroring the sample answers, to assist them as they answer the questions.

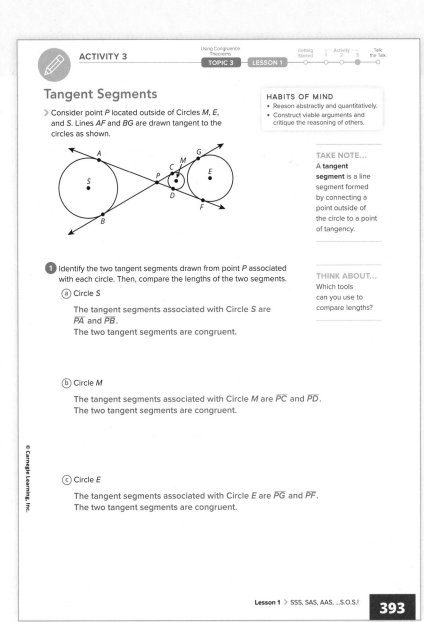

NOTES

DIFFERENTIATION STRATEGY

See Page 398B to challenge advanced learners before analyzing the worked example.

Student Look-Fors

Making sense of the worked example by:

- Drawing in the radii and $\overline{OA}$
- Marking the diagram to show congruent parts

It appears that tangent segments drawn from the same point on the exterior of a circle are congruent.

WORKED EXAMPLE

Consider this proof of the Tangent Segment Theorem.

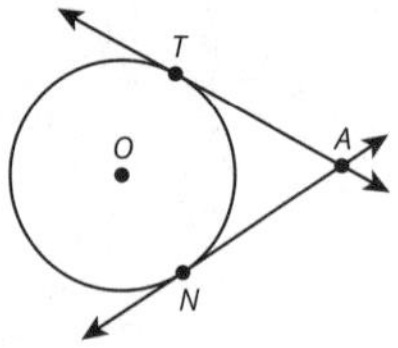

$\overleftrightarrow{AT}$ is tangent to Circle O at point T.
$\overleftrightarrow{AN}$ is tangent to Circle O at point N.
Connect points O and T to form radius $\overline{OT}$.
Connect points O and N to form radius $\overline{ON}$.
Connect points O and A to form $\overline{OA}$.
$\overline{OT} \cong \overline{ON}$

Given: $\overleftrightarrow{AT}$ is tangent to Circle O at point T.
$\overleftrightarrow{AN}$ is tangent to Circle O at point N.
Prove: $\overline{AT} \cong \overline{AN}$

$\overline{ON} \perp \overleftrightarrow{AN}$
$\overline{OT} \perp \overleftrightarrow{AT}$
$\angle ONA$ and $\angle OTA$ are right angles.
ΔONA and ΔOTA are right triangles.
$\overline{OA} \cong \overline{OA}$
$\Delta ONA \cong \Delta OTA$
$\overline{AT} \cong \overline{AN}$

2 How do you know that $OT = ON$?

Both segments are radii of the same circle.

3 How do you know that $\Delta ONA \cong \Delta OTA$?

The triangles are congruent by HL.

Because you proved that the relationship is true, you can now refer to it as a theorem.

THEOREM

TANGENT SEGMENT THEOREM

If two tangent segments are drawn from the same point on the exterior of a circle, then the tangent segments are congruent.

Questions to Support Discourse

		TYPE
Worked Example	• What is the hypothesis of the Tangent Segment Theorem? What is the conclusion? • What theorem justifies $\overline{OT} \perp \overline{AT}$ and $\overline{ON} \perp \overline{AN}$?	Gathering
2	• What is the relationship between $\overline{OT}$ and $\overline{ON}$ and Circle O?	Gathering
3	• Do the two triangles share a common angle or a common side? Explain your reasoning.	Probing

ACTIVITY 3 Continued

4. In the figure, $\overleftrightarrow{KP}$ and $\overleftrightarrow{KS}$ are tangent to Circle W and $m\angle PKS = 46°$. Calculate $m\angle KPS$.
Explain your reasoning.

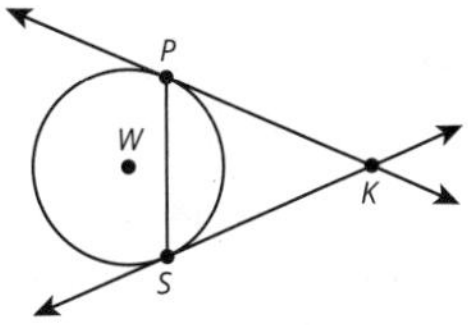

Line segments $\overleftrightarrow{PK}$ and $\overleftrightarrow{SK}$ are congruent according to the Tangent Segment Theorem, so ΔPKS is an isosceles triangle.
According to the Isosceles Triangle Base Angles Theorem, $m\angle KPS = m\angle KSP$.

By the Triangle Sum Theorem,
$2(m\angle KPS) + 46° = 180°$.

$2(m\angle KPS) = 134°$

$m\angle KPS = 67°$

5. In the figure, $\overleftrightarrow{PS}$ is tangent to Circle M and $m\angle SMO = 119°$. Calculate $m\angle MPS$. **Explain your reasoning.**

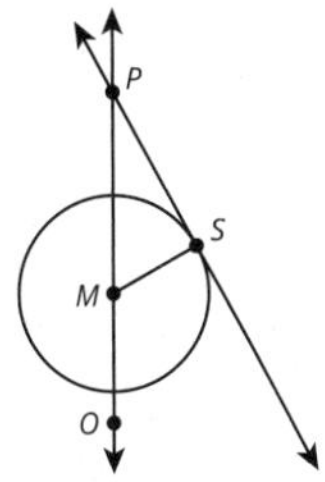

According to the Tanget to a Circle Theorem, $m\angle PSM = 90°$.

$\angle PMS$ and $\angle SMO$ are a linear pair, so the $m\angle PMS = 180° - 119° = 61°$.

By the Triangle Sum Theorem,
$m\angle MPS + 90° + 61° = 180°$.

$m\angle MPS = 29°$

6. Consider the figure.

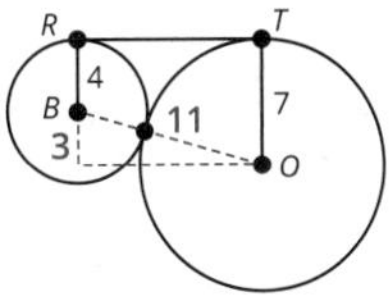

- Circle B and Circle O are tangent circles.
- The length of radius BR is 4.
- The length of radius OT is 7.
- Segment RT is a common tangent.

Calculate the length of segment RT.

$11^2 = 3^2 + (m\overline{RT})^2$

$112 = (m\overline{RT})^2$

$m\overline{RT} = \sqrt{112} = 4\sqrt{7}$

$m\overline{RT} \approx 10.58$

TAKE NOTE...
Tangent circles are circles that lie in the same plane and intersect at exactly one point.

Lesson 1 > SSS, SAS, AAS, ...S.O.S.! 395

Questions to Support Discourse

		TYPE
4	• What does the Tangent Segment Theorem tell you about $\overline{KP}$ and $\overline{KS}$?	Gathering
	• How is the Isosceles Triangle Base Angles Theorem helpful?	Probing
5	• What is the relationship between $\angle SMP$ and $\angle SMO$?	Gathering
	• How does knowing $\overleftrightarrow{PS}$ is tangent to Circle M impact your strategy to calculate $m\angle MPS$?	Probing
6	• What does it mean for circles to be tangent to each other?	Gathering
	• What happens if you draw a rectangle using the vertices R, T, and O? How does it support calculating the length of $\overline{RT}$?	Probing
	• Are points B, O, and the point at which the two circles are tangent to each other collinear? Why do you think that is?	Seeing structure

NOTES

TOPIC 3

SUMMARY **The right triangle congruence theorems, HA, HL, LL, and LA, are special cases of the SSS, SAS, ASA, and AAS Congruence Theorems.**

Chunking the Activity

- **Read and discuss the introduction**
- **Group students to complete the activity**
- **Share and summarize**

Student Look-Fors

Utilizing relationship skills by communicating clearly and listening well.

Congruence Theorems to the Rescue

You have many different theorems you can use to prove that two triangles are congruent depending on what you know. Let's consider how the right triangle congruence theorems are related to the triangle congruence theorems associated with all triangles.

1. List the four triangle congruence theorems associated with right triangles.

   HL, HA, LL, LA

2. List the four triangle congruence theorems associated with all triangles.

   SAS, SSS, ASA, AAS

3. Associate each theorem in Question 1 with one or more related theorems in Question 2. **Draw examples to justify your answers.**

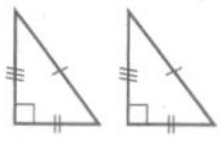

HL: SSS or SAS

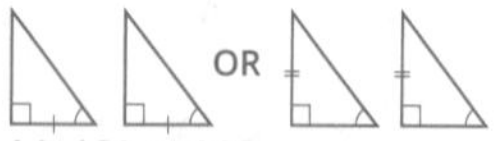

LA: ASA or AAS

HA: AAS

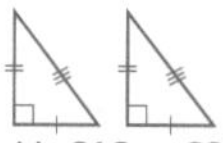

LL: SAS or SSS

Questions to Support Discourse

		TYPE
3	• Which congruence theorems use two pairs of corresponding angles? Two pairs of corresponding sides?	Gathering
	• How many unique examples can you draw for LA? Why?	Probing
	• Why is AAS the only triangle congruence theorem that relates to HA?	Seeing structure

ASSIGNMENT

LESSON 1 ASSIGNMENT

> Use a separate piece of paper for your Journal entry.

JOURNAL

Determine what information you need to show that the triangles are congruent by the indicated theorem.

1. Hypotenuse-Leg (HL) Congruence Theorem
2. Leg-Leg (LL) Congruence Theorem
3. Leg-Angle (LA) Congruence Theorem

REMEMBER

The Hypotenuse-Leg Congruence Theorem states that if the hypotenuse and leg of one right triangle are congruent to the hypotenuse and leg of another right triangle, then the triangles are congruent.

The Tangent Segment Theorem states that if two tangent segments extend from the same point on the exterior of a circle, then the tangent segments are congruent.

PRACTICE

1. Determine the information you need to show that the triangles are congruent by the indicated theorem.

ⓐ $\Delta RQW \cong \Delta RPW$ by HL

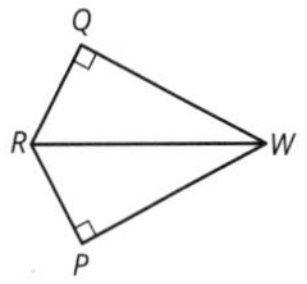

$\overline{RQ} \cong \overline{RP}$ or $\overline{QW} \cong \overline{PW}$

ⓑ $\Delta JNZ \cong \Delta HNC$ by LA

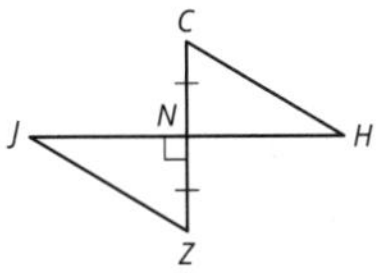

$\angle J \cong \angle H$ or $\angle Z \cong \angle C$

Go to LiveHint.com for help on the PRACTICE questions.

Encourage students to use LiveHint.com for help with the PRACTICE questions of this assignment.

Chunking the Assignment

SESSION 1

- Journal
- Practice 1

SESSION 2

- Practice 2
- Mixed Practice (page 437) 1 and 2
- Stretch (advanced learners)

JOURNAL

Sample answer.

1. Given the hypotenuse and a leg, I can determine the length of the other leg. So, I can use SSS.
2. Given two legs, I can determine the length of the hypotenuse. So, I can use SSS.
3. Given a leg and an acute angle measure, I can use either ASA or AAS.

NOTES

STRETCH

1. $\overline{HJ} \cong \overline{HF}$ and $\overline{PJ} \cong \overline{PG}$
   $m\overline{EF} = m\overline{EG} = 10$

   Since $\overline{HJ} \cong \overline{HF}$,
   $EH + HJ = EH + EF$.

   So, $EH + HJ = 10$.

   Similarly,
   $EP + PJ = EP + PG = 10$.

   So, the perimeter of ΔEHP is 20 units.

2. Calculate the measure of each angle. Explain your reasoning.

ⓐ If $\overline{RS}$ is a tangent segment and $\overline{OS}$ is a radius, what is the measure of $\angle ROS$?

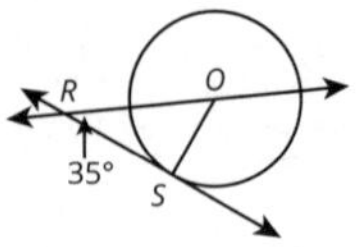

The measure of angle *ROS* is 55°.

$m\angle SRO + m\angle OSR + m\angle ROS = 180$

$35 + 90 + m\angle ROS = 180$

$125 + m\angle ROS = 180$

$m\angle ROS = 55°$

ⓑ If $\overline{UT}$ is a tangent segment and $\overline{OU}$ is a radius, what is the measure of $\angle TOU$?

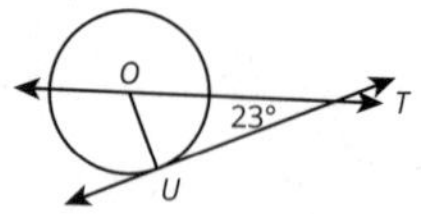

The measure of angle *TOU* is 67°.

$m\angle UTO + m\angle OUT + m\angle TOU = 180$

$23 + 90 + m\angle TOU = 180$

$113 + m\angle TOU = 180$

$m\angle TOU = 67°$

ⓒ If $\overline{VW}$ is a tangent segment and $\overline{OV}$ is a radius, what is the measure of $\angle VWO$?

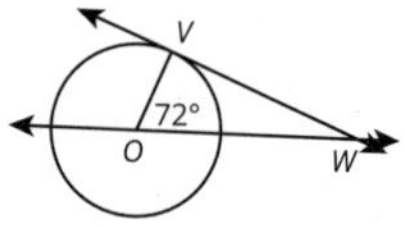

The measure of angle *VWO* is 18°.

To determine the measure of angle *VWO*, I used the fact that the interior angles of a triangle sum to 180° and that the measure of angle *OVW* is 90°.

$m\angle WOV + m\angle OVW + m\angle VWO = 180$

$72 + 90 + m\angle VWO = 180$

$162 + m\angle VWO = 180$

$m\angle VWO = 18°$

STRETCH Optional

In the figure shown, $\overline{EF}$ is tangent to the circle at *F*, and $\overline{EG}$ is tangent to the circle at *G*. Line segments *HF*, *PG*, *HJ*, and *PJ* are also tangent segments.

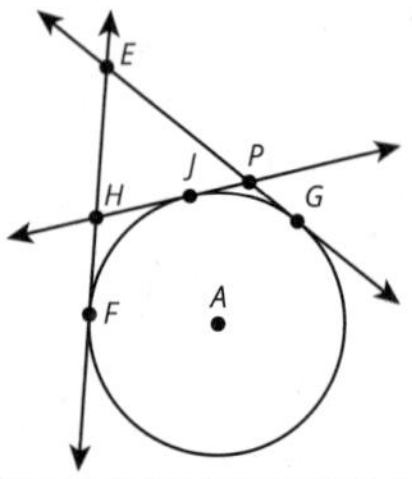

1. When $m\overline{EF} = 10$ units, what is the perimeter of ΔEHP? Explain your reasoning.

SSS, SAS, AAS, ...S.O.S!

This resource details additional facilitation notes to fully assist you as you plan each lesson to support all students, students who struggle, and advanced learners. It provides differentiation strategies, common student misconceptions, and suggestions to extend certain activities.

GETTING STARTED

Session 1 of 2

Pulling Your Leg

Students construct a right triangle given line segments representing the lengths of a leg and the hypotenuse. They use measuring tools to determine the measure of each angle and side. They conclude that the given information determined a unique triangle.

CHUNK	AUDIENCE	ADDITIONAL SUPPORTS
As students discuss 1 part (d)	All Students	**COMMON MISCONCEPTION** Students may assume this is not enough information to conclude that the triangles are congruent because it is a Side-Side-Angle relationship. Take the opportunity to explain this lesson involves the special case of right triangles, and students will investigate connections to the triangle congruence theorems they know and love.

ACTIVITY 1

Session 1 of 2

Hypotenuse-Leg Congruence Theorem

Students prove the Hypotenuse-Leg Congruence Theorem. They explain the algebraic reasoning used to justify this theorem.

CHUNK	AUDIENCE	ADDITIONAL SUPPORTS
As alternative directions for 3	Advanced Learners	**DIFFERENTIATION STRATEGY** Ask students to prove the theorem themselves without using the template in Question 3.

ACTIVITY 2

Session 1 of 2

Applying Triangle Congruence Theorems

Students explain the connections between the SAS, ASA, or AAS Congruence Theorems and the Leg-Leg Congruence Theorem and Leg-Angle Congruence Theorem. They solve problem situations using these theorems.

CHUNK	AUDIENCE	ADDITIONAL SUPPORTS
To extend 1	Advanced Learners	**DIFFERENTIATION STRATEGY** Have students write a formal proof for the LL Congruence Theorem and the LA Congruence Theorem.
As students work on 2	Students who Struggle	**COMMON MISCONCEPTION** Students may assume point *P* is the midpoint of $\overline{SD}$ because it is the midpoint of $\overline{CW}$. Have students mark given information on the diagram. Remind them they can only use given information or statements that they can prove.
As students work on 4	Students who Struggle	**COMMON MISCONCEPTION** Students may assume that because $JA \perp MY$, *MY* also bisects *JA*. This assumption is not given but may prove to be true. Remind students of the difference between perpendicular and perpendicular bisectors.

ACTIVITY 3

Session 2 of 2

Tangent Segments

Students analyze a proof plan of the Tangent Segment Theorem. They use measuring tools to compare the lengths of tangent segments drawn from the same point on the exterior of a circle. They solve problems using the Tangent Segment Theorem.

CHUNK	AUDIENCE	ADDITIONAL SUPPORTS
As students work on 1	All Students	**COMMON MISCONCEPTION** Students know they can draw an infinite number of tangents to a circle. They may also believe that they can draw more than two tangents to a circle through a single exterior point. Allow students to attempt drawing additional tangent points through point *P* to either circle to help ensure that students understand they can draw only two tangents from a single exterior point.
Before analyzing the worked example	Advanced Learners	**DIFFERENTIATION STRATEGY** Have the students prove the Tangent Segment Theorem before analyzing the proof plan in the worked example.

Practice the learning

MATHbook + Skills Practice

The table shows the targeted practice of the skills and mathematical concepts for the *Using Congruence Theorems* Topic. The highlighted Problem Set aligns with **SSS, SAS, AAS, ...S.O.S!**.

PROBLEM SET	
1	**Right Triangle Congruence and Tangent Segments**
2	Properties of Quadrilaterals
3	Chord Relationships

ANYTIME AFTER ACTIVITY 3

Facilitate students as they work individually on **Problem Set 1**.

NOTES

ENGAGE at the **Module** level + **DEVELOP** at the **Topic** level + **TEACH** Read the facilitation notes and plan learning experiences.

Where are we?

TOPIC 3 Using Congruence Theorems	LESSON 1 SSS, SAS, AAS, ...S.O.S.!	**LESSON 2 Props To You**	LESSON 3 Three-Chord Song
Pacing	2 Sessions	**3 Sessions**	1 Session

OVERVIEW: LESSON 2

Props To You

Properties of Quadrilaterals

ENGAGE

- Students create a flow chart relating quadrilaterals and the properties that apply to them.

DEVELOP

- Students prove the properties of a parallelogram, rhombus, and rectangle.
- They draw midsegments that connect the midpoints of adjacent sides of a quadrilateral and describe the figure formed.
- They prove that the base angles and the diagonals of an isosceles trapezoid are congruent.
- They prove that one pair of opposite angles of a kite are congruent and the diagonals of a kite are perpendicular.
- Students apply the properties of quadrilaterals to solve problems.

DEMONSTRATE

- Students create a list of yes-no questions to identify an unknown quadrilateral.

HIGH SCHOOL GEOMETRY

Congruence

Prove geometric theorems.

11. Prove theorems about parallelograms.

LESSON STRUCTURE AND PACING GUIDE 3 SESSIONS

⊛ This activity highlights a key term or concept that is essential to the learning goals of the lesson.

Session 1 | **Session 2**

INSTRUCTIONAL SEQUENCE

ENGAGE
Connect to prior knowledge

GETTING STARTED
Making Connections

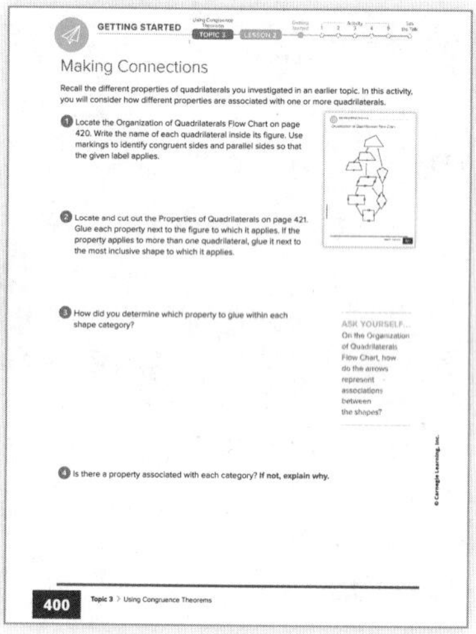
GETTING STARTED — TOPIC 3 — LESSON 2

Making Connections

Recall the different properties of quadrilaterals you investigated in an earlier topic. In this activity, you will consider how different properties are associated with one or more quadrilaterals.

1. Locate the Organization of Quadrilaterals Flow Chart on page 420. Write the name of each quadrilateral inside its figure. Use markings to identify congruent sides and parallel sides so that the given label applies.
2. Locate and cut out the Properties of Quadrilaterals on page 421. Glue each property next to the figure to which it applies. If the property applies to more than one quadrilateral, glue it next to the most inclusive shape to which it applies.
3. How did you determine which property to glue within each shape category?

ASK YOURSELF... On the Organization of Quadrilaterals Flow Chart, how do the arrows represent associations between the shapes?

4. Is there a property associated with each category? If not, explain why.

© Carnegie Learning, Inc.

400 Topic 3 > Using Congruence Theorems

Students create a flow chart relating quadrilaterals and the properties that apply to them.

- They explain their reasoning and conclude that squares are a subset of other quadrilateral categories.

ACTIVITY CUTOUT

DEVELOP
Mathematical problem solving
Peer analysis

ACTIVITY 1
Properties of Quadrilaterals

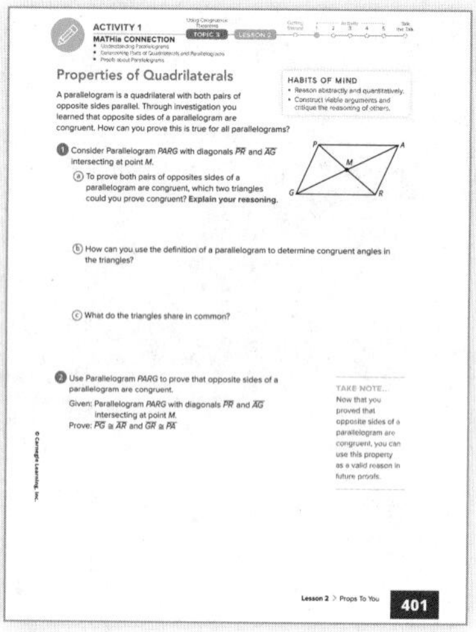
ACTIVITY 1 — TOPIC 3 — LESSON 2

MATHia CONNECTION

Properties of Quadrilaterals

HABITS OF MIND
- Reason abstractly and quantitatively.
- Construct viable arguments and critique the reasoning of others.

A parallelogram is a quadrilateral with both pairs of opposite sides parallel. Through investigation you learned that opposite sides of a parallelogram are congruent. How can you prove this is true for all parallelograms?

1. Consider Parallelogram *PARG* with diagonals $\overline{PR}$ and $\overline{AG}$ intersecting at point *M*.
   a. To prove both pairs of opposites sides of a parallelogram are congruent, which two triangles could you prove congruent? **Explain your reasoning.**
   b. How can you use the definition of a parallelogram to determine congruent angles in the triangles?
   c. What do the triangles share in common?
2. Use Parallelogram *PARG* to prove that opposite sides of a parallelogram are congruent.
   Given: Parallelogram *PARG* with diagonals $\overline{PR}$ and $\overline{AG}$ intersecting at point *M*.
   Prove: $\overline{PG} \cong \overline{AR}$ and $\overline{GR} \cong \overline{PA}$

TAKE NOTE... Now that you proved that opposite sides of a parallelogram are congruent, you can use this property as a valid reason in future proofs.

© Carnegie Learning, Inc.

Lesson 2 > Props To You 401

Students prove the properties of a parallelogram, rhombus, and rectangle.

- They conclude that a square inherits the properties of both a rectangle and a rhombus.

DEVELOP
Investigation

ACTIVITY 2
Midsegments of Quadrilaterals

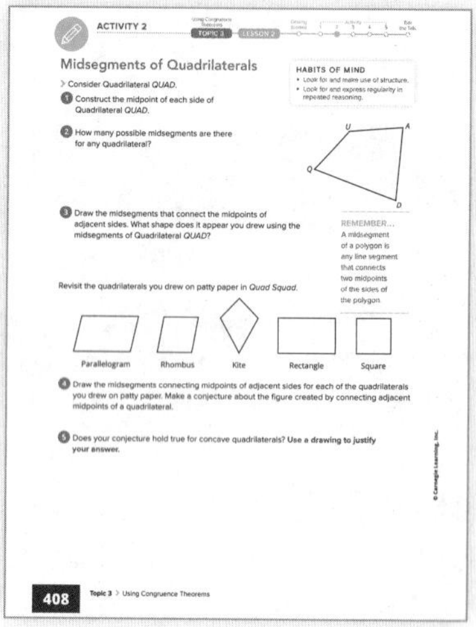
ACTIVITY 2 — TOPIC 3 — LESSON 2

Midsegments of Quadrilaterals

HABITS OF MIND
- Look for and make use of structure.
- Look for and express regularity in repeated reasoning.

> Consider Quadrilateral *QUAD*.

1. Construct the midpoint of each side of Quadrilateral *QUAD*.
2. How many possible midsegments are there for any quadrilateral?
3. Draw the midsegments that connect the midpoints of adjacent sides. What shape does it appear you drew using the midsegments of Quadrilateral *QUAD*?

REMEMBER... A midsegment of a polygon is any line segment that connects two midpoints of the sides of the polygon.

Revisit the quadrilaterals you drew on patty paper in *Quad Squad*.

Parallelogram — Rhombus — Kite — Rectangle — Square

4. Draw the midsegments connecting midpoints of adjacent sides for each of the quadrilaterals you drew on patty paper. Make a conjecture about the figure created by connecting adjacent midpoints of a quadrilateral.
5. Does your conjecture hold true for concave quadrilaterals? **Use a drawing to justify your answer.**

© Carnegie Learning, Inc.

408 Topic 3 > Using Congruence Theorems

Students draw midsegments connecting the midpoints of adjacent sides of a quadrilateral and describe the figure formed.

- They investigate the midsegments of a trapezoid and conjecture about the length of the midsegments.

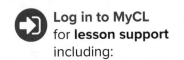

Log in to MyCL for **lesson support** including:

Slides

Videos

www.carnegielearning.com/login

Session 2

Session 3

INSTRUCTIONAL SEQUENCE

DEVELOP
Worked example
Peer analysis

ACTIVITY 3

Properties of Trapezoids with One Pair of Parallel Sides

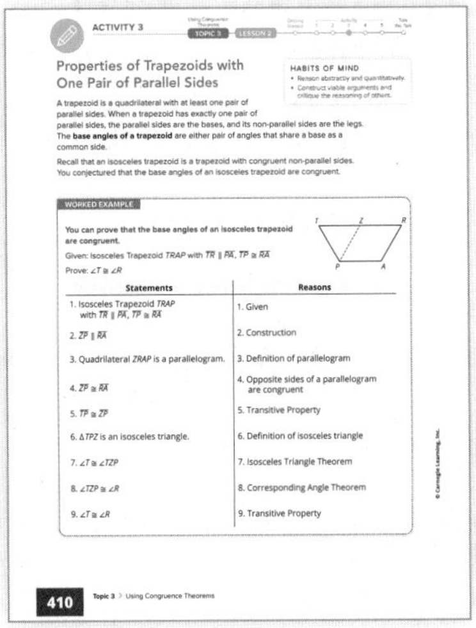

Students prove that the base angles and the diagonals of an isosceles trapezoid are congruent.

- They plan a proof of the Trapezoid Midsegment Theorem using the Triangle Midsegment Theorem.

DEVELOP
Mathematical problem solving

ACTIVITY 4

Properties of Kites

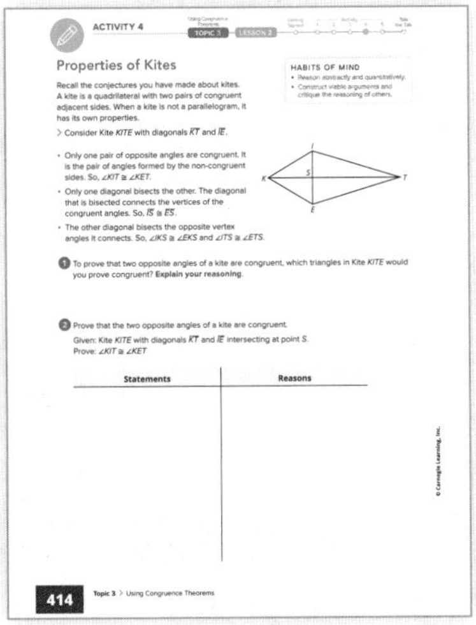

Students prove one pair of opposite angles of a kite are congruent.

- They prove the diagonals of a kite are perpendicular to each other.

DEVELOP
Mathematical problem solving

ACTIVITY 5

Using Properties to Solve Problems

Students apply the properties of quadrilaterals to solve problems.

- They make sense of problems and justify their reasoning.

TOPIC 3

Log in to MyCL for:
- Editable templates
- Additional planning support

Session 3

INSTRUCTIONAL SEQUENCE

DEMONSTRATE
Writing task

TALK THE TALK
Name That Shape

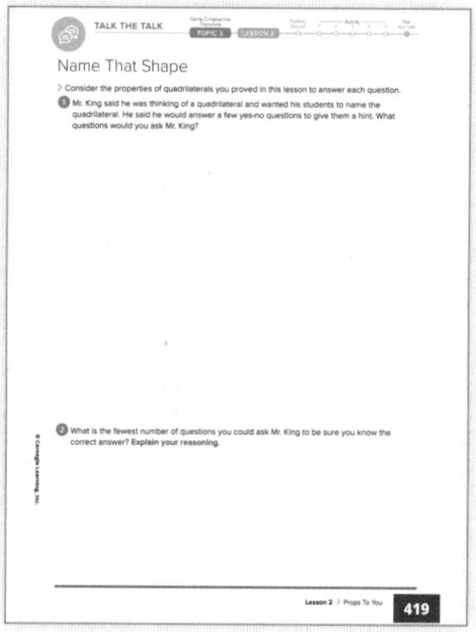
TALK THE TALK

Name That Shape

> Consider the properties of quadrilaterals you proved in this lesson to answer each question.

1 Mr. King said he was thinking of a quadrilateral and wanted his students to name the quadrilateral. He said he would answer a few yes-no questions to give them a hint. What questions would you ask Mr. King?

2 What is the fewest number of questions you could ask Mr. King to be sure you know the correct answer? Explain your reasoning.

Lesson 2 > Props To You 419

Students create a list of yes-no questions to identify an unknown quadrilateral.

- They reason about the least number of questions needed to identify the quadrilateral.

Now that you have read the Module, Topic, and Lesson Overviews, you are ready to plan.

Do the math

> Tear out the lesson planning template (page 399E) and jot down thoughts as you work through this lesson and read the Facilitation Notes.

Connect the learning

MATHbook + MATHia

The table shows the self-paced MATHia sequence for the *Using Congruence Theorems* Topic.

Median student completion time: ~100–125 minutes

> As you implement this lesson, consider different connections for students who are on pace and those that have not yet completed the workspaces aligned to this lesson.

STUDENTS WHO ARE NOT HERE YET
Students will practice applying the properties of quadrilaterals to determine unknown measures.

TYPE	WORKSPACE NAME
	Proving Triangles Congruent using HL and HA
	Understanding Parallelograms
	Determining Parts of Quadrilaterals and Parallelograms
	Proofs About Parallelograms

STUDENTS WHO ARE ON PACE
After you complete Activity 1, ask these students to share how they applied their knowledge of congruent triangles and parallel lines to prove theorems about parallelograms.

Props To You

Properties of Quadrilaterals

ACTIVITY CUTOUT

Session 1

GETTING STARTED Making Connections ✪

Pacing (minutes)	
My Time	Class Time

ACTIVITY 1 Properties of Quadrilaterals ✪

Pacing (minutes)	
My Time	Class Time

KEY TERM
Parallelogram/Congruent-Parallel Side Theorem

Session 2

ACTIVITY 2 Midsegments of Quadrilaterals ✪

Pacing (minutes)	
My Time	Class Time

ACTIVITY 3 Properties of Trapezoids with One Pair of Parallel Sides ✪

Pacing (minutes)	
My Time	Class Time

KEY TERM
base angles of a trapezoid
Trapezoid Midsegment Theorem

Session 3

ACTIVITY 4 Properties of Kites ✪

Pacing (minutes)	
My Time	Class Time

ACTIVITY 5 Using Properties to Solve Problems

Pacing (minutes)	
My Time	Class Time

TALK THE TALK Name That Shape

Pacing (minutes)	
My Time	Class Time

✪ This activity highlights a key term or concept that is essential to the learning goals of the lesson.

Reflect on your lesson

Log in to MyCL for:
- Editable templates
- Additional planning support

Consider the effectiveness of your lesson on student learning.

What went well?	What did not go as planned?

Anticipate how you would change the lesson next time you teach it.

How will you capitalize on the things that went well?	How will you improve things that did not go as planned?

MATERIALS

- Glue sticks
- Scissors

TOPIC 1
Composing and Decomposing Shapes

TOPIC 2
Justifying Line and Angle Relationships

TOPIC 3
Using Congruence Theorems

1 | SSS, SAS, AAS, ...S.O.S.!

2 | Props To You

3 | Three-Chord Song

LESSON 2

Props To You

Properties of Quadrilaterals

Learning Goals

- Prove the properties of a parallelogram, a rhombus, a rectangle, a square, a trapezoid, and a kite.
- Solve problems using the properties of a parallelogram, a rhombus, a rectangle, a square, a trapezoid, and a kite.

KEY TERMS

Parallelogram/Congruent–Parallel Side Theorem

base angles of a trapezoid

Trapezoid Midsegment Theorem

REVIEW (1–2 minutes)

> Draw a quadrilateral with the given property. Do not draw the same quadrilateral twice.

1. Congruent angles

   Students could draw a rectangle or a square.

2. Congruent diagonals

   Students could draw a rectangle, square, isosceles trapezoid, or a kite.

3. Congruent sides

   Students could draw a rhombus or a square.

You previously made conjectures about the properties of quadrilaterals using recorded observations.

Which properties of quadrilaterals can you formally prove?

Setting the Stage

- **Assign Review (optional, 1 – 2 minutes)**
- **Communicate the learning goals and key terms to look out for**
- **Tap into your students' prior learning by reading the narrative statement**
- **Provide a sense of direction by reading the question**

IN THIS REVIEW

Students draw quadrilaterals with given properties. They will use this skill throughout the lesson.

Properties of a parallelogram: opposite sides are parallel and congruent; opposite angles are congruent; diagonals bisect each other.

Properties of a rhombus: all sides are congruent; diagonals are perpendicular and bisect the vertex angles.

Properties of a rectangle: angles and diagonals are congruent.

Essential Ideas

- You can prove the properties of quadrilaterals by proving triangles formed by the diagonals are congruent.
- A square has all of the properties of the rectangle and rhombus.
- A quadrilateral's midsegment is a line segment connecting the midpoints of two sides of the rectangle.
- The Trapezoid Midsegment Theorem states that the midsegment of a trapezoid is parallel to each of the bases, and its length is one-half the sum of the lengths of the bases.
- You can use the properties of quadrilaterals to solve problems.

GETTING STARTED

SUMMARY **A quadrilateral has the properties of every set to which it belongs.**

Chunking the Activity

- **Read and discuss the introduction**
- **Group students to complete the activity**
- **Share and summarize**

DIFFERENTIATION STRATEGY

See Page 424A to support students who struggle with 2.

LANGUAGE LINK

Ensure students understand what is meant by the *most inclusive shape* as they work on Question 2. Give students an example, such as both pairs of opposites sides are parallel, and discuss why parallelograms would be considered the most inclusive.

Making Connections

Recall the different properties of quadrilaterals you investigated in an earlier topic. In this activity, you will consider how different properties are associated with one or more quadrilaterals.

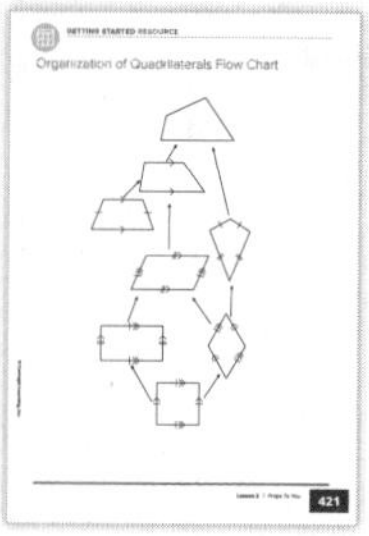

1. Locate the Organization of Quadrilaterals Flow Chart on page 420. Write the name of each quadrilateral inside its figure. Use markings to identify congruent sides and parallel sides so that the given label applies.

   See flow chart located on page 420.

2. Locate and cut out the Properties of Quadrilaterals on page 421. Glue each property next to the figure to which it applies. If the property applies to more than one quadrilateral, glue it next to the most inclusive shape to which it applies.

   See Question 1.

3. How did you determine which property to glue within each shape category?

   Sample answer.

   I referred to the diagrams for properties related to sides and angles. I drew the diagonals in each quadrilateral for properties related to the diagonals.

ASK YOURSELF...
On the Organization of Quadrilaterals Flow Chart, how do the arrows represent associations between the shapes?

4. Is there a property associated with each category? **If not, explain why.**

   Squares are a subset of other quadrilateral categories. There is not an individual property that a square has that isn't shared with one of the more inclusive quadrilateral categories.

Questions to Support Discourse

		TYPE
1	• Which markings did you use to identify parallel sides? • How did you mark the diagram to differentiate between pairs of congruent sides?	Gathering
	• Why is the square at the bottom of the chart? • What is true about a square that relates to a kite? • Why are all squares rectangles, but not all rectangles are squares?	Seeing structure
2	• Which figures have congruent diagonals? Perpendicular diagonals?	Gathering
4	• What does the flow chart suggest about the properties of a square?	Probing

ACTIVITY 1

SUMMARY **You can prove the properties of quadrilaterals by proving that triangles formed by the diagonals are congruent.**

ACTIVITY 1

MATHia CONNECTION
- Understanding Parallelograms
- Determining Parts of Quadrilaterals and Parallelograms
- Proofs about Parallelograms

Properties of Quadrilaterals

HABITS OF MIND
- Reason abstractly and quantitatively.
- Construct viable arguments and critique the reasoning of others.

A parallelogram is a quadrilateral with both pairs of opposite sides parallel. Through investigation you learned that opposite sides of a parallelogram are congruent. How can you prove this is true for all parallelograms?

1 Consider Parallelogram *PARG* with diagonals $\overline{PR}$ and $\overline{AG}$ intersecting at point *M*.

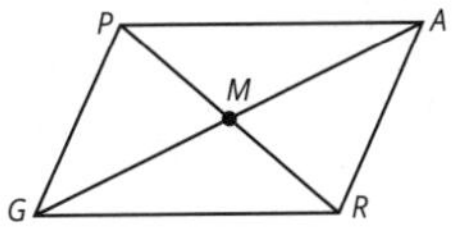

(a) To prove both pairs of opposites sides of a parallelogram are congruent, which two triangles could you prove congruent? **Explain your reasoning.**

I can prove either $\Delta PGR \cong \Delta RAP$ or $\Delta APG \cong \Delta GRA$.

(b) How can you use the definition of a parallelogram to determine congruent angles in the triangles?

Since opposite sides are parallel, the diagonals are transversals. I can use the Alternate Interior Angle Theorem to determine congruent angles in the triangles.

(c) What do the triangles share in common?

The triangles share a side in common, which is one of the diagonals of the parallelogram.

2 Use Parallelogram *PARG* to prove that opposite sides of a parallelogram are congruent.

Given: Parallelogram *PARG* with diagonals $\overline{PR}$ and $\overline{AG}$ intersecting at point *M*.

Prove: $\overline{PG} \cong \overline{AR}$ and $\overline{GR} \cong \overline{PA}$

Sample paragraph proof using ΔPGR and ΔRAP.

From the given information, I know that $\overline{PG} \parallel \overline{AR}$ and $\overline{GR} \parallel \overline{PA}$ because of the definition of a parallelogram.

By the Alternate Interior Angle Theorem, $\angle GPR \cong \angle ARP$ and $\angle APR \cong \angle GRP$.

Also, $\overline{PR} \cong \overline{PR}$ by the Reflexive Property, so $\Delta PGR \cong \Delta RAP$ by ASA.

Therefore, $\overline{PG} \cong \overline{RA}$ and $\overline{GR} \cong \overline{AP}$ by CPCTC.

TAKE NOTE...
Now that you proved that opposite sides of a parallelogram are congruent, you can use this property as a valid reason in future proofs.

Chunking the Activity

- Read and discuss the introduction
- Group students to complete 1 and 2
- Check-in and share
- Group students to complete 3 - 6
- Check-in and share
- Group students to complete 7 and 8
- Check-in and share
- Group students to complete 9 and 10
- Check-in and share
- Group students to complete 11 - 13
- Share and summarize

DIFFERENTIATION STRATEGY

See Page 424A to support students who struggle with 2.

Questions to Support Discourse

		TYPE
1	• What is the definition of a parallelogram?	Gathering
	• How can you use the idea of two parallel lines cut by a transversal to help identify additional congruent parts of a parallelogram?	Probing
	• Why can't you use ΔPMG, ΔRMA, ΔPMA, or ΔRMG to prove both pairs of opposite sides congruent?	Seeing structure

COMMON MISCONCEPTION

See Page 424A for a misconception related to 2.

NOTES

Now let's consider how to prove that pairs of opposite angles of a parallelogram are congruent. There is not enough information from your previous proof to conclude that both pairs of opposite angles are congruent.

3. Which additional angles would you need to show congruent to prove that opposite angles of a parallelogram are congruent?

   I would also need to show $\angle GPA \cong \angle ARG$. I can prove these angles congruent by CPCTC if I can prove $\Delta APG \cong \Delta GRA$.

4. Use Parallelogram *PARG* to prove that opposite angles of a parallelogram are congruent.

   Given: Parallelogram *PARG* with diagonals $\overline{PR}$ and $\overline{AG}$ intersecting at point *M*.
   Prove: $\angle GPA \cong \angle ARG$

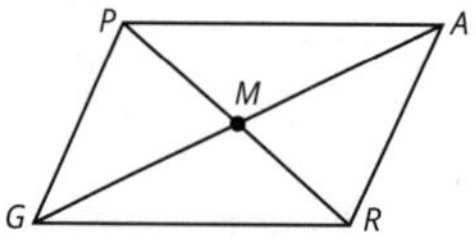

Sample answer using ΔAPG and ΔGRA.

Statements	Reasons
1. Parallelogram *PARG* with diagonals $\overline{PR}$ and $\overline{AG}$ intersect at point *M*	1. Given
2. $\overline{PG} \parallel \overline{AR}$ and $\overline{GR} \parallel \overline{PA}$	2. Definition of a parallelogram
3. $\angle PAG \cong \angle RGA$ and $\angle PGA \cong \angle RAG$	3. Alternate Interior Angle Theorem
4. $\overline{PR} \cong \overline{PR}$	4. Reflexive Property
5. $\Delta APG \cong \Delta GRA$	5. ASA Congruence Theorem
6. $\angle GPA \cong \angle ARG$	6. CPCTC

Questions to Support Discourse

		TYPE
3	• How could you use CPCTC to show a pair of opposite angles are congruent?	Probing
	• Would you have to prove two different angles congruent to prove the second pair of opposite angles congruent? Or could you use CPCTC and the Angle Addition Postulate?	Seeing structure

ACTIVITY 1 Continued

5 Prove that the diagonals of a parallelogram bisect each other using what you have already proved about the angles and sides of the parallelogram.

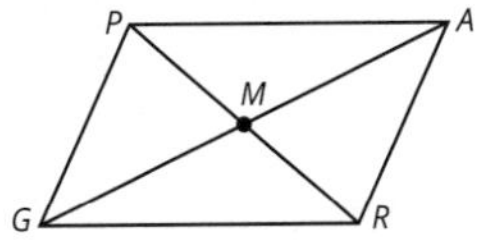

I can prove $\Delta PMA \cong \Delta RMG$ by the AAS Congruence Theorem, so $\overline{PM} \cong \overline{RM}$ and $\overline{GM} \cong \overline{AM}$ by CPCTC, proving the diagonals of a parallelogram bisect each other.

ASK YOURSELF...
Which segments in parallelogram *PARG* do you need to prove congruent? Which triangles can help you prove their congruency?

6 Ray told his math teacher that he thinks a quadrilateral is a parallelogram if only one pair of opposite sides is known to be both congruent and parallel.

Is Ray correct? **Use the diagram from Question 1 to either prove or disprove his conjecture.**

Ray is correct.
He can prove $\Delta PAR \cong \Delta RGP$ by the ASA Congruence Theorem, so $\overline{PG} \cong \overline{AR}$ and $\angle PRA \cong \angle RPG$ by CPCTC.

Then, he can use the Alternate Interior Angle Converse Theorem to show $\overline{PG} \parallel \overline{AR}$, proving Quadrilateral *PARG* is a parallelogram.

ASK YOURSELF...
How can you prove that a pair of lines are parallel?

Which triangle congruence theorem can you use in your reasoning?

NOTES

Questions to Support Discourse

		TYPE
5	• What does it mean for two segments to bisect each other?	Gathering
	• How do the Ask Yourself questions help you plan your strategy? • Do you need to prove both diagonals are bisected to prove the diagonals bisect each other? Explain your reasoning.	Probing
6	• Which triangles do you think Ray used to prove this statement?	Gathering
	• Why can you use either pair of sides to prove Ray's statement? • Is the Alternate Interior Angle Theorem or the Alternate Interior Angle Converse Theorem used in this proof? Why?	Probing

NOTES

LANGUAGE LINK

ELL TIP

Encourage students to record their proof in whichever format is most comfortable for them. Have the names of the theorems listed on the board, along with other key terms. Suggest students reference the other proofs from this activity to support the structure of their arguments.

Because you proved that the relationship is true, you can now refer to it as a theorem.

THEOREM

PARALLELOGRAM/CONGRUENT-PARALLEL SIDE THEOREM

If one pair of opposite sides of a quadrilateral is both congruent and parallel, then the quadrilateral is a parallelogram.

A rhombus is a parallelogram with all sides congruent. Can you prove this classification?

7 Prove that Rhombus *RHOM* is a parallelogram.

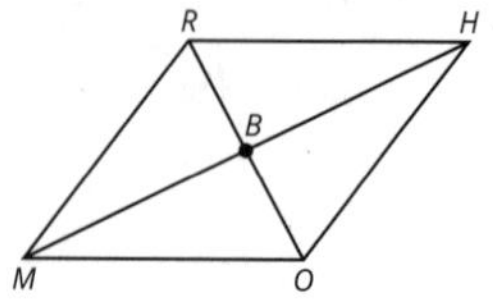

I can prove $\Delta ROM \cong \Delta ORH$ by SSS by using the definition of a rhombus and the Reflexive Property of congruence to show $\angle HRO \cong \angle MOR$ by CPCTC. This gives us $\overline{RH} \parallel \overline{OM}$ by the Alternate Interior Angle Converse Theorem.

Similarly, $\angle HOR \cong \angle MRO$ by CPCTC, which shows $\overline{MR} \parallel \overline{OH}$ by the Alternate Interior Angle Converse Theorem.

8 Since a rhombus is a parallelogram, which properties hold true for all rhombi?

Opposite angles are congruent, opposite sides are congruent, and diagonals bisect each other.

Questions to Support Discourse

		TYPE
7	• What is the given information for this proof? • Which pair of triangles can you prove congruent using the SSS Triangle Congruence Theorem?	Gathering
	• Why do you need to prove angles congruent to show the opposite sides of the rhombus are parallel?	Probing

ACTIVITY 1 Continued

9 Prove that the diagonals of a rhombus are perpendicular. Use Rhombus *RHOM*.

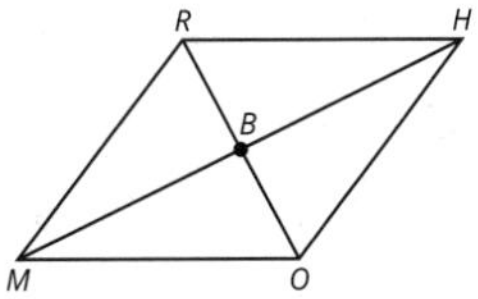

I can prove $\Delta RBH \cong \Delta RBM$ by SSS by using the definition of a rhombus as a parallelogram whose diagonals bisect each other and the Reflexive Property of congruence to show $\angle RBH \cong \angle RBM$ by CPCTC.

These angles also form a linear pair using the Linear Pair Postulate.
The angles are supplementary using the definition of a linear pair, and two angles that are both congruent and supplementary are right angles.

If they are right angles, then the line segments forming the angles must be perpendicular.

10 Prove that the diagonals of a rhombus bisect the vertex angles. Use Rhombus *RHOM*.

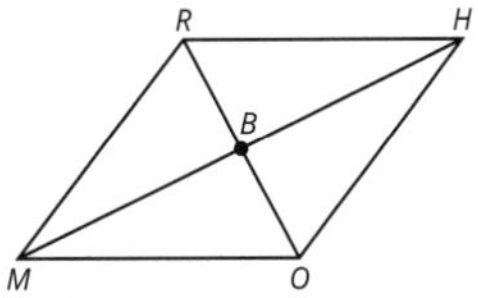

I can prove $\Delta RBH \cong \Delta RBM$ by SSS by using the definition of a rhombus as a parallelogram whose diagonals bisect each other and the Reflexive Property of congruence to show $\angle HRB \cong \angle MRB$ by CPCTC.

Then $\overline{OR}$ must bisect $\angle HRM$ by the definition of bisect.

This can be done with each angle of the rhombus using the two different triangles for each vertex angle of the rhombus.

Questions to Support Discourse

		TYPE
9	• Are $\angle RBH$ and $\angle RBM$ a linear pair? What else do you need to know to prove they are both right angles? • Besides $\angle RBH$ and $\angle RBM$, which other angle pairs could you use to show $\overline{OR} \perp \overline{MH}$?	Gathering
10	• What does it mean for the diagonals to bisect the vertex angle? • When the diagonals of a rhombus bisect the vertex angles of the rhombus, which angle pairs are congruent?	Gathering
	• Why do you have to start by proving two adjacent triangles congruent?	Seeing structure

NOTES

NOTES

A rectangle is a parallelogram with all angles congruent. Can you prove that this is true for all rectangles?

11 Consider Rectangle *ABCD*.

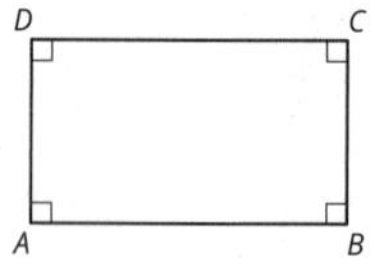

(a) What is the measure of each angle? **Explain your reasoning.**

Each angle measures 90°.

The sum of the measures of the interior angles of a quadrilateral is 360°, and by the definition of a rectangle, each angle is congruent, so 360° ÷ 4 = 90°.

(b) What do the angle measures tell you about the relationships between adjacent sides?

Since each angle measures 90°, the adjacent sides of the rectangle form perpendicular line segments.

(c) Which theorem can you use to prove $\overline{DA} \parallel \overline{CB}$ and $\overline{DC} \parallel \overline{AB}$? Is this enough information to conclude Rectangle *ABCD* is a parallelogram? **Explain your reasoning.**

The Perpendicular/Parallel Line Theorem; since $\overline{AD}$ and $\overline{BC}$ are perpendicular to $\overline{DC}$, they are parallel to each other, and since $\overline{DC}$ and $\overline{AB}$ are perpendicular to $\overline{DA}$, they are parallel to each other.

Yes. I have just proven that opposite sides of a rectangle are parallel.

(d) Based on your reasoning, which properties hold true for all rectangles?

Opposite sides are congruent, opposite angles are congruent, and diagonals bisect each other.

Questions to Support Discourse

		TYPE
11	• If the sum of the four interior angles is 360° and the four angles are the same measure, what can you conclude? • Do you think all of the properties that hold true for parallelograms also hold true for rectangles? Why?	Probing
	• If two lines are perpendicular to the same line, what is their relationship to each other?	Reflecting and justifying

ACTIVITY 1 Continued

12 Prove that the diagonals of a rectangle are congruent.

Given: Rectangle *RECT* with diagonals $\overline{RC}$ and $\overline{ET}$ intersecting at point *A*.

Prove: $\overline{RC} \cong \overline{TE}$

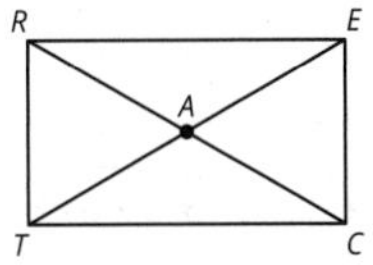

Sample answer.

Statements	Reasons
1. Rectangle *RECT* with diagonals $\overline{RC}$ and $\overline{ET}$ intersecting at point *A*	1. Given
2. Quadrilateral *RECT* is a parallelogram. $\angle TRE \cong \angle REC \cong \angle ECT \cong \angle CTR$	2. Definition of a rectangle
3. $\overline{RT} \parallel \overline{EC}$	3. Definition of parallelogram
4. $\overline{RT} \cong \overline{EC}$	4. Opposite sides of a parallelogram are congruent.
5. $\overline{RE} \cong \overline{RE}$	5. Reflexive Property
6. $\triangle REC \cong \triangle ERT$	6. SAS
7. $\overline{RC} \cong \overline{TE}$	7. CPCTC

A square is a parallelogram with all angles and all sides congruent.

13 Margot says you have to prove that the diagonals of a square are perpendicular and congruent, and they bisect the vertex angles. Vanessa says you don't have to prove these properties of a square. Who is correct? **Explain your reasoning.**

Vanessa is correct.
A square has all sides congruent, which means it is a rhombus by definition. Since all sides are congruent, the opposite sides are congruent. A square has all angles congruent and opposite sides congruent, which means it is a rectangle by definition. Since you have already proven these properties for a rhombus and a rectangle, you do not have to prove them for a square.

Lesson 2 > Props To You 407

Questions to Support Discourse

		TYPE
12	• Which triangles do you need to prove congruent to prove the diagonals are congruent?	Gathering
	• How does the definition of a rectangle help you show the triangles are congruent?	Probing
13	• Which other names of quadrilaterals also apply to a square?	Gathering
	• How does knowing that a square is both a rectangle and a rhombus help you decide whether Margot or Vanessa is correct?	Probing

NOTES

TOPIC 3

ACTIVITY 2

SUMMARY **The midsegment of a quadrilateral is any line segment connecting two midpoints of the sides of the quadrilateral.**

Chunking the Activity

- **Read and discuss the introduction**
- **Group students to complete 1 – 3**
- **Check-in and share**
- **Group students to complete 4 and 5**
- **Check-in and share**
- **Group students to complete 6**
- **Share and summarize**

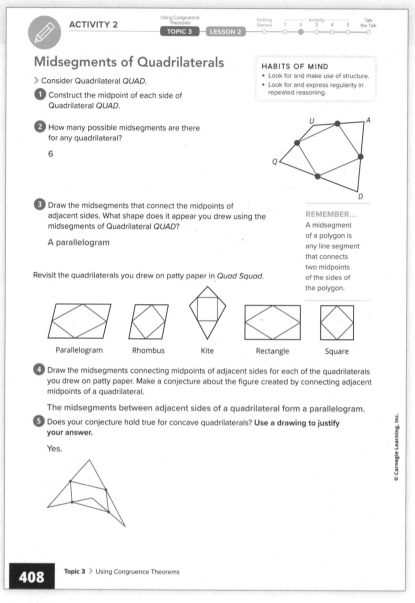

Midsegments of Quadrilaterals

HABITS OF MIND
- Look for and make use of structure.
- Look for and express regularity in repeated reasoning.

> Consider Quadrilateral *QUAD*.

1. Construct the midpoint of each side of Quadrilateral *QUAD*.

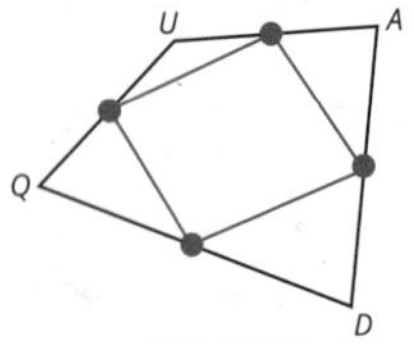

2. How many possible midsegments are there for any quadrilateral?

   6

3. Draw the midsegments that connect the midpoints of adjacent sides. What shape does it appear you drew using the midsegments of Quadrilateral *QUAD*?

   A parallelogram

REMEMBER...
A midsegment of a polygon is any line segment that connects two midpoints of the sides of the polygon.

Revisit the quadrilaterals you drew on patty paper in *Quad Squad*.

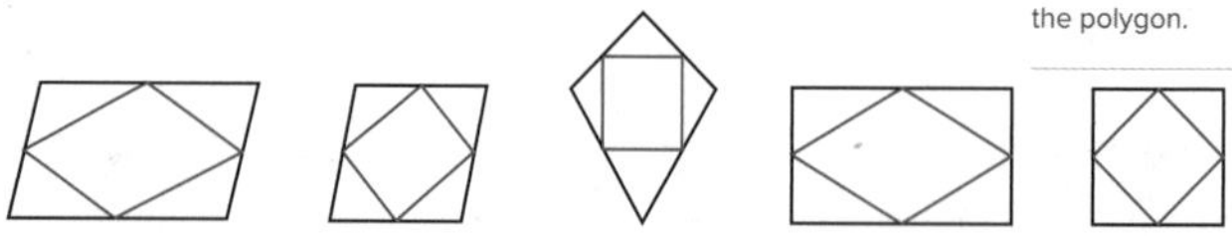

Parallelogram Rhombus Kite Rectangle Square

4. Draw the midsegments connecting midpoints of adjacent sides for each of the quadrilaterals you drew on patty paper. Make a conjecture about the figure created by connecting adjacent midpoints of a quadrilateral.

   The midsegments between adjacent sides of a quadrilateral form a parallelogram.

5. Does your conjecture hold true for concave quadrilaterals? **Use a drawing to justify your answer.**

   Yes.

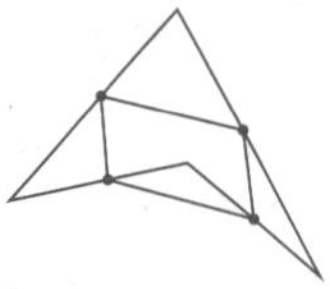

Questions to Support Discourse

		TYPE
1	• How did you locate the midpoint of $\overline{QU}$?	Gathering
2	• Are there more than 4 ways to connect the midpoints?	Gathering
3	• Does the newly formed quadrilateral appear to be a parallelogram? Explain your reasoning.	Probing
	• Why must the figure formed by connecting the midpoints of the adjacent sides be another quadrilateral?	Seeing structure
4	• Why do you suppose the quadrilateral formed by connecting the midpoints of adjacent sides is a parallelogram? • Do you think the midsegments between adjacent sides will always form a parallelogram? Why?	Probing
5	• Why do you suppose the results are the same when the quadrilateral is concave?	Probing

ACTIVITY 2 Continued

Let's explore one of the midsegments of a trapezoid.

6 Use the given parallel line segments and a straightedge to complete this question.

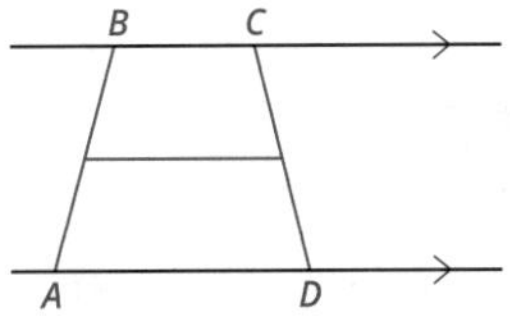

(a) Draw any trapezoid with only one pair of parallel sides. Label the vertices.

Check students' drawings. Sample trapezoid provided.

(b) Construct the midsegment of your trapezoid that connects the non-parallel sides. Label the endpoints.

Check students' constructions.

The midsegment appears to be parallel to each base of the trapezoid.

(c) Use your ruler to determine the length of each base and the length of the midsegment.

Measurements will vary.

(d) Determine the average of the lengths of the bases. **What do you notice?**

The average of the length of the bases is equal to the length of the midsegment.

(e) Compare your answer to part (d) with those of your classmates. Make a conjecture about the midsegment of a trapezoid that connects non-parallel sides.

The midsegment of a trapezoid that connects non-parallel sides is parallel to each base and equal to the average of the lengths of the bases of the trapezoid.

Questions to Support Discourse

		TYPE
6	• How do you determine the average of two lengths?	Gathering
	• How does your midsegment relate to the bases of your trapezoid?	Seeing structure

NOTES

SUMMARY An isosceles trapezoid has congruent base angles and congruent diagonals.

Chunking the Activity

- Read and discuss the introduction and worked example
- Complete 1 as a class
- Group students to complete 2 and 3
- Check-in and share
- Group students to complete 4 and 5
- Share and summarize

DIFFERENTIATION STRATEGY

See Page 424B to support students who struggle with the worked example.

Properties of Trapezoids with One Pair of Parallel Sides

HABITS OF MIND
- Reason abstractly and quantitatively.
- Construct viable arguments and critique the reasoning of others.

A trapezoid is a quadrilateral with at least one pair of parallel sides. When a trapezoid has exactly one pair of parallel sides, the parallel sides are the bases, and its non-parallel sides are the legs. The **base angles of a trapezoid** are either pair of angles that share a base as a common side.

Recall that an isosceles trapezoid is a trapezoid with congruent non-parallel sides. You conjectured that the base angles of an isosceles trapezoid are congruent.

WORKED EXAMPLE

You can prove that the base angles of an isosceles trapezoid are congruent.

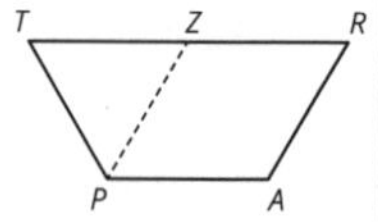

Given: Isosceles Trapezoid *TRAP* with $\overline{TR} \parallel \overline{PA}$, $\overline{TP} \cong \overline{RA}$

Prove: $\angle T \cong \angle R$

Statements	Reasons
1. Isosceles Trapezoid *TRAP* with $\overline{TR} \parallel \overline{PA}$, $\overline{TP} \cong \overline{RA}$	1. Given
2. $\overline{ZP} \parallel \overline{RA}$	2. Construction
3. Quadrilateral *ZRAP* is a parallelogram.	3. Definition of parallelogram
4. $\overline{ZP} \cong \overline{RA}$	4. Opposite sides of a parallelogram are congruent
5. $\overline{TP} \cong \overline{ZP}$	5. Transitive Property
6. ΔTPZ is an isosceles triangle.	6. Definition of isosceles triangle
7. $\angle T \cong \angle TZP$	7. Isosceles Triangle Theorem
8. $\angle TZP \cong \angle R$	8. Corresponding Angle Theorem
9. $\angle T \cong \angle R$	9. Transitive Property

Questions to Support Discourse

		TYPE
Worked Example	• Is proving $\angle T \cong \angle R$ enough to prove that the base angles of an isosceles trapezoid are congruent? Why or why not?	Probing

ACTIVITY 3 Continued

1 Analyze the worked example.

(a) How does constructing $\overline{ZP}$ parallel to $\overline{RA}$ help lead to the conclusion?

Constructing $\overline{ZP}$ parallel to $\overline{RA}$ helps create a parallelogram to reason that $\overline{ZP} \cong \overline{RA}$. This helps define ΔTPZ as an isosceles triangle to reason that $\angle T$ is congruent to $\angle TZP$.

(b) Why is Statement 8 important?

Once you reason that $\angle T$ is congruent to $\angle TZP$ because of the Isosceles Triangle Theorem, you need Statement 8 to reason that $\angle TZP$ is congruent to $\angle R$ in order to reason that $\angle T$ is congruent to $\angle R$ by the Transitive Property.

2 You must also prove $\angle A \cong \angle TPA$. Show $\angle A \cong \angle TPA$.

Angle T and P as well as R and A are pairs of supplementary angles using the Same Side Interior Angle Theorem.

Since $\angle T \cong \angle R$, then $\angle P \cong \angle A$ by supplements of congruent angles are congruent.

3 Kala insists that if a trapezoid with one pair of parallel sides has one pair of congruent base angles, then the trapezoid must be isosceles. She thinks proving two pairs of base angles are congruent is not necessary. Is Kala correct? **Use reasoning and the trapezoid from the worked example to justify your answer.**

Kala is correct.
According to the Same-Side Interior Angle Theorem, $\angle T$ and $\angle P$ are supplementary and $\angle R$ and $\angle A$ are supplementary.

If you know that $\angle T \cong \angle R$, you know that $\angle P \cong \angle A$ because supplements of congruent angles are congruent.

Questions to Support Discourse

		TYPE
1	• How do you know that ΔTPZ is an isosceles triangle?	Probing
2	• How is proving $\angle TPA \cong \angle A$ different than proving $\angle T \cong \angle R$?	Seeing structure
3	• What is the hypothesis of Kala's conjecture? • If ΔTZP is isosceles, what two segments are congruent?	Gathering
	• How can you work backward to support Kala's reasoning?	Probing

NOTES

Student Look-Fors

Whether students are modeling appropriate social awareness.

- Listening to the perspectives of others
- Empathizing with others' experiences
- Respecting others

NOTES

Student Look-Fors

Using patty paper to trace and separate the overlapping triangles.

DIFFERENTIATION STRATEGY

See Page 424B to challenge advanced learners to extend 4.

4 Prove that the diagonals of an isosceles trapezoid are congruent.

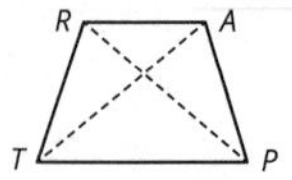

Given: Isosceles Trapezoid *TRAP* with $\overline{TP} \parallel \overline{RA}$, $\overline{TR} \cong \overline{PA}$, and diagonals $\overline{TA}$ and $\overline{PR}$.

Prove: $\overline{TA} \cong \overline{PR}$

Statements	Reasons
1. Isosceles Trapezoid *TRAP* with $\overline{TP} \parallel \overline{RA}$, $\overline{TR} \cong \overline{PA}$	1. Given
2. $\angle RTP \cong \angle APT$	2. Base angles of an isosceles trapezoid are congruent.
3. $\overline{TP} \cong \overline{TP}$	3. Reflexive Property
4. $\Delta RTP \cong \Delta APT$	4. SAS Congruence Theorem
5. $\overline{TA} \cong \overline{PR}$	5. CPCTC

You also conjectured that the length of the midsegment connecting the legs of a trapezoid is half the sum of its base lengths and that the midsegment is parallel to each base.

To prove this conjecture regarding the midsegment of a trapezoid, it is necessary to connect points *M* and *E* of Trapezoid *MDSG* to form $\overline{ME}$, and then extend $\overline{ME}$ until it intersects the extension of $\overline{DS}$ at point *T*.

5 Complete the Prove statement and answer each question to plan to prove the Trapezoid Midsegment Theorem.

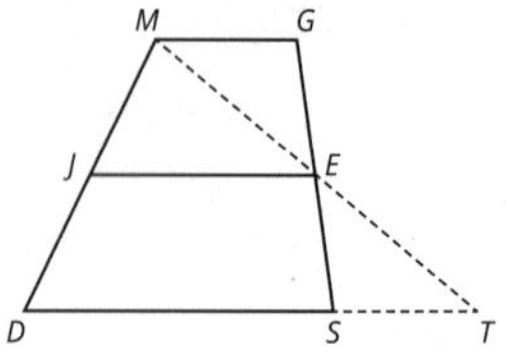

ⓐ Given: *MDSG* is a trapezoid with bases $\overline{MG}$ and $\overline{DS}$.
J is the midpoint of $\overline{MD}$.
E is the midpoint of $\overline{GS}$.

Prove: $\overline{JE} \parallel \overline{MG}$

$\overline{JE} \parallel \overline{DS}$

$JE = \frac{1}{2}(MG + DS)$

Questions to Support Discourse

		TYPE
4	• Which triangles do you need to prove congruent to prove $\overline{TP} \cong \overline{PR}$? • What would the triangles look like if they were not overlapping?	Gathering
5	• What is the Triangle Midsegment Theorem?	Gathering
	• Which segments are parallel? How do you know? • If two lines are parallel to the same line, what is the relationship between the two lines?	Probing

ACTIVITY 3 Continued

(b) Is $\angle MGE$ is congruent to $\angle TSE$? **Explain your reasoning.**

Yes. Because I know $\overline{MG} \parallel \overline{DT}$ because of the definition of a trapezoid, the angles are congruent by the Alternate Interior Angle Theorem, where $\overline{GS}$ acts as a transversal.

(c) Is ΔMGE congruent to ΔTSE? **Explain your reasoning.**

Yes; because $\angle GEM$ and $\angle TES$ are vertical angles, they are congruent, and because point E is the midpoint of $\overline{GS}$, $\overline{GE} \cong \overline{ES}$.
Therefore, $\Delta MGE \cong \Delta TSE$ by the ASA Congruence Theorem.

(d) How does $\overline{JE}$ relate to ΔMDT? **Explain your reasoning.**

$\overline{JE}$ is a midsegment of ΔMDT.
I know this because $\overline{ME} \cong \overline{TE}$ by CPCTC, which makes point E the midpoint of $\overline{MT}$.

(e) Use the Midsegment of a Triangle Theorem and reasoning to prove that $\overline{JE} \parallel \overline{MG}$ and $\overline{JE} \parallel \overline{DS}$.

I know that $\overline{JE}$ is parallel to $\overline{DT}$ by the Midsegment of a Triangle Theorem, so it is also parallel to $\overline{DS}$. Therefore, $\overline{JE} \parallel \overline{MG}$ because two lines parallel to the same line are parallel to each other.

(f) Use the Midsegment of a Triangle Theorem and reasoning to prove that $JE = \frac{1}{2}(MG + DS)$.

I know that $JE = \frac{1}{2}DT$ by the Midsegment of a Triangle Theorem. The length of DT is equal to $DS + ST$ by the segment addition postulate. $ST \cong MG$ by CPCTC and the definition of congruent segments. Therefore, through substitution, $JE = \frac{1}{2}(DS + MG)$.

Because you proved that your conjecture is true, you can now refer to it as a theorem.

THEOREM

TRAPEZOID MIDSEGMENT THEOREM

The midsegment that connects the legs of a trapezoid is parallel to each of the bases and its length is one-half the sum of the lengths of the bases.

NOTES

SUMMARY **One diagonal of a kite bisects a pair of opposite angles. One diagonal of a kite is the perpendicular bisector of the other diagonal.**

Chunking the Activity

- Read and discuss the introduction
- Complete 1 as a class
- Group students to complete 2
- Check-in and share
- Group students to complete 3 - 7
- Share and summarize

Properties of Kites

HABITS OF MIND
- Reason abstractly and quantitatively.
- Construct viable arguments and critique the reasoning of others.

Recall the conjectures you have made about kites. A kite is a quadrilateral with two pairs of congruent adjacent sides. When a kite is not a parallelogram, it has its own properties.

> Consider Kite *KITE* with diagonals $\overline{KT}$ and $\overline{IE}$.

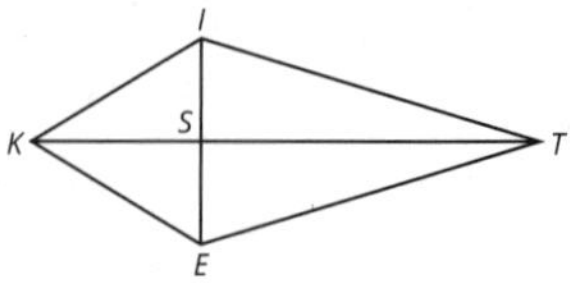

- Only one pair of opposite angles are congruent. It is the pair of angles formed by the non-congruent sides. So, $\angle KIT \cong \angle KET$.
- Only one diagonal bisects the other. The diagonal that is bisected connects the vertices of the congruent angles. So, $\overline{IS} \cong \overline{ES}$.
- The other diagonal bisects the opposite vertex angles it connects. So, $\angle IKS \cong \angle EKS$ and $\angle ITS \cong \angle ETS$.

1 To prove that two opposite angles of a kite are congruent, which triangles in Kite *KITE* would you prove congruent? **Explain your reasoning.**

I can prove $\Delta KIT \cong \Delta KET$ to show $\angle KIT \cong \angle KET$ by CPCTC.

2 Prove that the two opposite angles of a kite are congruent.

Given: Kite *KITE* with diagonals $\overline{KT}$ and $\overline{IE}$ intersecting at point *S*.
Prove: $\angle KIT \cong \angle KET$ **Sample proof.**

Statements	Reasons
1. Kite *KITE* with diagonals $\overline{KT}$ and $\overline{IE}$ intersecting at point *S*	1. Given
2. $\overline{KI} \cong \overline{KE}$, $\overline{TI} \cong \overline{TE}$	2. Definition of kite
3. $\overline{KT} \cong \overline{KT}$	3. Reflexive Property
4. $\Delta KIT \cong \Delta KET$	4. SSS Congruence Theorem
5. $\angle KIT \cong \angle KET$	5. CPCTC

Questions to Support Discourse

		TYPE
1	• Which triangles contain $\angle KIT$ and $\angle KET$?	Gathering
2	• What information does the definition of a kite give you? • Do the triangles share a common angle or a common side?	Gathering
	• How can you use the SSS Congruence Theorem in your proof?	Probing

ACTIVITY 4 Continued

3 Do you have enough information to conclude $\overline{KT}$ bisects $\angle IKE$ and $\angle ITE$? **Explain your reasoning.**

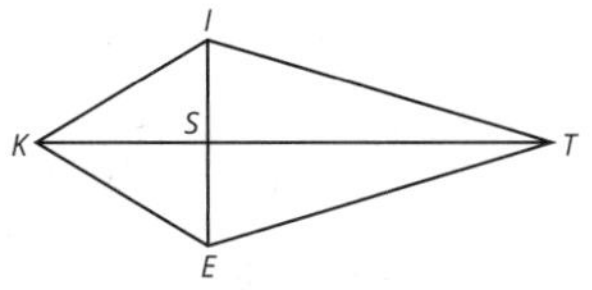

Yes. There is enough information to make this conclusion because $\angle IKT \cong \angle EKT$ and $\angle ITK \cong \angle ETK$ by CPCTC.

4 What two triangles could you use to prove $\overline{IS} \cong \overline{ES}$?

I can first prove $\Delta KIS \cong \Delta KES$, or $\Delta ITS \cong \Delta ETS$, by the SAS Congruence Theorem, and then $\overline{IS} \cong \overline{ES}$ by CPCTC.

5 If $\overline{IS} \cong \overline{ES}$, is that enough information to determine that one diagonal of a kite bisects the other diagonal? **Explain your reasoning.**

Yes. If $\overline{IS} \cong \overline{ES}$, then by the definition of bisect, diagonal $\overline{KT}$ bisects diagonal $\overline{IE}$.

6 Prove that the diagonals of a kite are perpendicular to each other.

I can first prove $\Delta KIS \cong \Delta KES$ by the SAS Congruence Theorem, and then $\angle KSI \cong \angle KSE$ by CPCTC. These angles also form a linear pair by the Linear Pair Postulate. The angles are supplementary by the definition of a linear pair, and two angles that are both congruent and supplementary are right angles. If they are right angles, then the lines forming the angles must be perpendicular.

7 What does your proof tell you about the classification of a rhombus?

A rhombus is also a kite because I previously proved that the diagonals of a rhombus are perpendicular and now proved that the diagonals of kites are perpendicular.

Lesson 2 > Props To You 415

Questions to Support Discourse

		TYPE
3	• What does it mean for a segment to bisect an angle? • Which angles would be congruent if $\overline{KT}$ bisects $\angle IKE$ and $\angle ITE$?	Gathering
	• How can you use your proof in Question 2 to prove $\angle IKT \cong \angle EKT$?	Probing
5	• What does it mean for one segment to bisect another?	Gathering
6	• Which two triangles would you prove congruent? Which congruence theorem would you use?	Probing
7	• Are all rhombi also kites? Explain your reasoning. • Are all kites also rhombi? Why do you think that?	Seeing structure

NOTES

ACTIVITY 5

SUMMARY **You can use the properties of quadrilaterals to solve problems.**

Chunking the Activity

- **Read and discuss the introduction**
- **Group students to complete the activity**
- **Share and summarize**

DIFFERENTIATION STRATEGY

See Page 424B to group students to complete the activity.

LANGUAGE LINK

ELL TIP

Throughout the activity, ensure students are familiar with terms related to each context. Use the images in the activity or have students locate additional images to support their understanding of each context.

ACTIVITY 5 — Using Congruence Theorems TOPIC 3 LESSON 2 — Getting Started, Activity 1 2 3 4 5, Talk the Talk

Using Properties to Solve Problems

HABITS OF MIND
- Reason abstractly and quantitatively.
- Construct viable arguments and critique the reasoning of others.

> Use what you know about the properties of quadrilaterals to solve each problem.

1. Ofelia is making a square mat for a picture frame. How can she make sure the mat is a square using only a ruler?

   Ofelia can measure the four sides and measure the diagonals. If the four sides are congruent and the diagonals are congruent, then it must be a square.

2. Gretchen is putting together a bookcase. It came with diagonal support bars that she will screw into the top and bottom on the back of the bookcase. Unfortunately, the instructions were lost, and Gretchen does not have the directions or a measuring tool. She has a screwdriver, a marker, and a piece of string.

   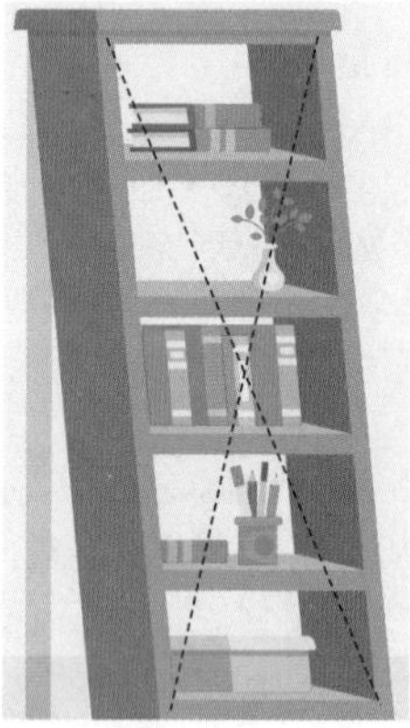

   How can Gretchen attach the supports to make certain the bookcase will be a rectangle, and the shelves are parallel to the ground?

   Gretchen can use the string to locate the middle of both support bars before attaching them by spanning the length of a bar with the string and folding the string in half.

   Next, she can mark the middle point on both support bars. Then, she can connect the first support to the bookcase, and position the second support such that the support bars cross each other at the middle point of each bar.

   If the diagonals of a quadrilateral are congruent and bisect each other, the quadrilateral is a rectangle. She can also use the strings to make sure the shelves are equidistant, and therefore parallel to the ground.

Questions to Support Discourse

		TYPE
1	• How can Ofelia guarantee the mat is a square and not a rhombus? • If Ofelia only measures the diagonals, is that enough information to conclude that the mat is square? Why or why not?	Probing
2	• Which are the properties of the diagonals of a rectangle?	Gathering
	• How can Gretchen determine the midpoint of each support bar using a string? • Besides making sure the support bars cross at the midpoint, what else does Gretchen need to check so that the bookcase forms a rectangle? • How can you use the string to ensure the shelves are parallel?	Probing

NOTES

ACTIVITY 5 Continued

3 Ms. Baker told her geometry students that anyone bringing in a picture of a flag with a parallelogram would get extra credit.

(a) Albert brought in a picture of the United States flag. The teacher handed Albert a ruler and told him to prove the quadrilateral that contains the stars is a parallelogram. What are two ways Albert could prove the specified quadrilateral is a parallelogram?

Albert could measure the opposite sides and show they are congruent, or he could measure the diagonals and show they bisect each other.

(b) Ms. Baker told Albert he needed to prove that if a quadrilateral has opposite sides congruent, then the quadrilateral is a parallelogram. Use the diagram to help Albert prove the statement.

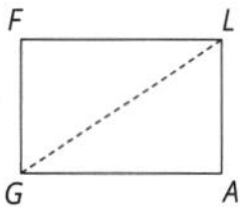

Given: Quadrilateral *FLAG* with diagonal $\overline{GL}$, $\overline{FL} \cong \overline{GA}$, $\overline{LA} \cong \overline{GF}$

Prove: Quadrilateral *FLAG* is a parallelogram.

Statements	Reasons
1. Quadrilateral *FLAG* with diagonal $\overline{GL}$, $\overline{FL} \cong \overline{GA}$, $\overline{LA} \cong \overline{GF}$	1. Given
2. $\overline{GL} \cong \overline{GL}$	2. Reflexive Property
3. $\Delta FLG \cong \Delta AGL$	3. SSS Congruence Theorem
4. $\angle FGL \cong \angle ALG$ and $\angle FLG \cong \angle AGL$	4. CPCTC
5. $\overline{FL} \parallel \overline{AG}$ and $\overline{FG} \parallel \overline{AL}$	5. Alternate Interior Angle Converse Theorem
6. *FLAG* is a parallelogram	6. Definition of parallelogram

Lesson 2 > Props To You 417

TOPIC 3

Questions to Support Discourse

		TYPE
3	• How would Albert use the diagonals' lengths to show the quadrilateral is a parallelogram? • Does Albert need to know the angle measures to prove it is a parallelogram? Why? • How can Albert use the Alternate Interior Angle Converse Theorem to help prove Quadrilateral *FLAG* is a parallelogram?	Probing

NOTES

ACTIVITY 5 Continued

4 Ms. Baker held up two different lengths of rope shown and a piece of chalk. She asked her students whether they could use this rope and chalk to construct a rhombus on the blackboard. Rena raised her hand and said she could construct a rhombus with the materials. Ms. Baker handed Rena the chalk and rope. What did Rena do?

First Rope

Second Rope

Rena folded each piece of rope in half to locate the middle and marked it.

Then, she crossed the two ropes such that the middle points overlapped and created a perpendicular bisector.
Next, she used the chalk to connect the ends of the ropes to form the rhombus.
To be sure the ropes were perpendicular, after drawing the rhombus, she removed one rope and used it to compare the length of each side to verify all four sides were the same length.

5 Could Quadrilaterals 1, 2, and 3 on the kite shown be squares if the kite is not a parallelogram? **Explain your reasoning.**

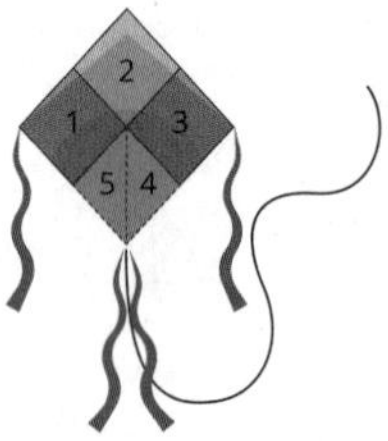

No. Quadrilaterals 1, 2, and 3 could not be squares. If they were squares, Triangles 4 and 5 would be congruent right triangles, with each triangle half the area of one square as shown. The entire kite would be a square, which is a parallelogram.

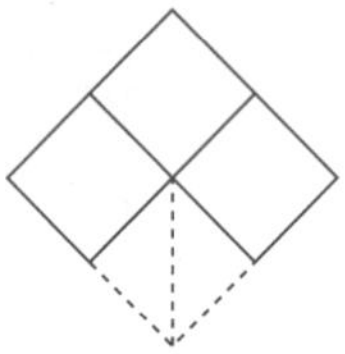

418 Topic 3 > Using Congruence Theorems

Questions to Support Discourse

		TYPE
4	• What are the properties of the diagonals of a rhombus?	Gathering
	• How would folding each piece of rope in half be helpful? • How did Rena verify that all four sides were congruent?	Probing
5	• What makes a kite different from all of the other quadrilaterals?	Probing

TALK THE TALK

SUMMARY **You can identify quadrilaterals by their properties.**

Name That Shape

> Consider the properties of quadrilaterals you proved in this lesson to answer each question.

1. Mr. King said he was thinking of a quadrilateral and wanted his students to name the quadrilateral. He said he would answer a few yes-no questions to give them a hint. What questions would you ask Mr. King?

Sample answers.

Does the quadrilateral contain 4 right angles?
(Tells you it is a rectangle or square if it has 4 right angles)

Are there 2 pairs of parallel sides in the quadrilateral?
(Tells you it is a parallelogram if it has 2 pairs of parallel sides)

Is there exactly 1 pair of parallel sides in the quadrilateral?
(Tells you it is a trapezoid if it has 1 pair of parallel sides)

Are all 4 sides congruent in the quadrilateral?
(Tells you it is a rhombus or square if it has 4 congruent sides)

Are the 2 diagonals congruent to each other?
(Tells you it is not a square, rectangle, or isosceles trapezoid if it does not have congruent diagonals)

Are the 2 diagonals perpendicular to each other?
(Tells you it is a kite, rhombus, or square if it has perpendicular diagonals)

Is exactly 1 pair of opposite angles congruent in the quadrilateral?
(Tells you it is a kite if exactly 1 pair of opposite angles are congruent)

2. What is the fewest number of questions you could ask Mr. King to be sure you know the correct answer? **Explain your reasoning.**

The fewest number of questions would depend on Mr. King's answers. If he says it has 4 right angles, then I know it is a square or a rectangle, and I would only have to ask if the diagonals are perpendicular to each other to know the correct answer. In this case, I would only have to ask 2 questions.

Chunking the Activity

- Read and discuss the introduction
- Group students to complete the activity
- Share and summarize

DIFFERENTIATION STRATEGY

See Page 424C to assist all students in extending the activity.

Questions to Support Discourse

		TYPE
1	• Which question would eliminate the possibility of a square or rhombus? Why? • Which question would narrow it down to a square or rectangle? Why? • Which question would eliminate an isosceles trapezoid? Explain your reasoning.	Probing
	• Is more information revealed when the shape has the property or does not have the property? Why?	Reflecting and justifying

NOTES

GETTING STARTED RESOURCE

Organization of Quadrilaterals Flow Chart

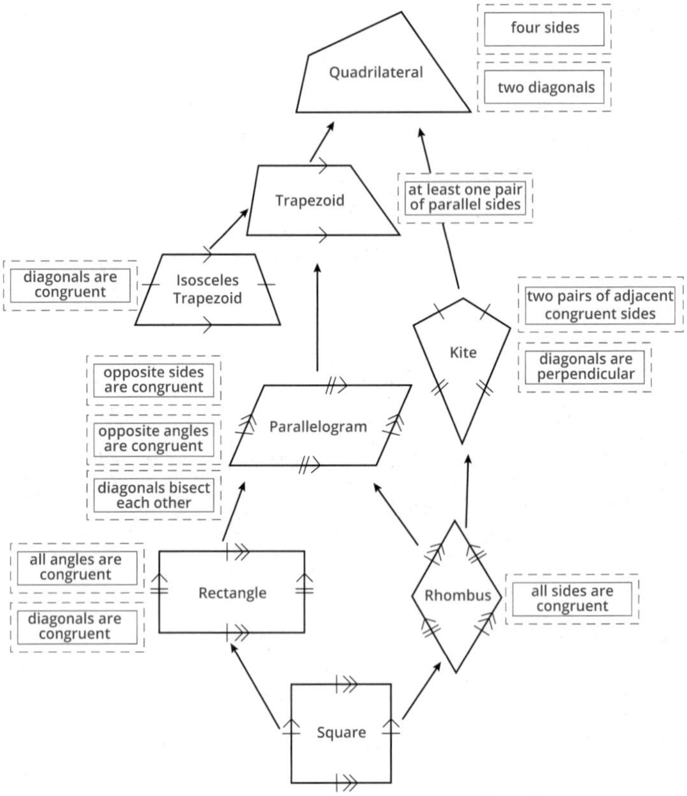

420 Topic 3 > Using Congruence Theorems

GETTING STARTED CUTOUTS

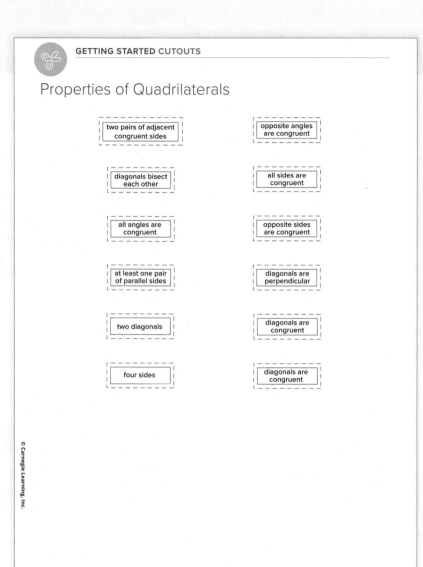

Properties of Quadrilaterals

two pairs of adjacent congruent sides	opposite angles are congruent
diagonals bisect each other	all sides are congruent
all angles are congruent	opposite sides are congruent
at least one pair of parallel sides	diagonals are perpendicular
two diagonals	diagonals are congruent
four sides	diagonals are congruent

NOTES

NOTES

Why is this page blank?

So you can cut out the properties on the other side.

ASSIGNMENT

LESSON 2 ASSIGNMENT

Use a separate piece of paper for your Journal entry.

JOURNAL

Define each term in your own words.

1. Parallelogram/Congruent–Parallel Side Theorem
2. base angles of a trapezoid
3. Trapezoid Midsegment Theorem

REMEMBER

- Properties of a parallelogram: opposite sides are parallel and congruent; opposite angles are congruent; diagonals bisect each other.
- Properties of a rhombus: all sides are congruent; diagonals are perpendicular and bisect the vertex angles.
- Properties of a rectangle: angles and diagonals are congruent.

PRACTICE

1. The neighbors in a rural community get together for a barn-raising. The first step is to build the rectangular base of the barn. One neighbor explains to everyone how they can use the diagonals to verify the base is rectangular. What could the neighbor have said?

   He told them the diagonals of a rectangle were congruent and bisected each other. All they had to do was check to make sure this was true, and that would verify the base was rectangular.

2. Jim tells you he is thinking of a quadrilateral that is either a square or a rhombus, but not both. He wants you to guess which quadrilateral he is thinking of and allows you to ask one question about the quadrilateral. Which question should you ask?

   You don't need to ask Jim any questions to determine the identity of the quadrilateral. If it is a square, then it is also considered a rhombus. Since Jim said that it couldn't be a rhombus and a square, then it must be a rhombus that is not a square.

Go to LiveHint.com for help on the PRACTICE questions.

Encourage students to use LiveHint.com for help with the PRACTICE questions of this assignment.

Chunking the Assignment

SESSION 1

- Practice 1 and 2

SESSION 2

- Journal
- Practice 3

SESSION 3

- Mixed Practice (page 437) 3 and 4
- Stretch (advanced learners)

JOURNAL

Sample answer.

1. The Parallelogram/Congruent–Parallel Side Theorem states that if one pair of opposite sides of a quadrilateral are both congruent and parallel, then the quadrilateral is a parallelogram.
2. The base angles of a trapezoid are a pair of angles formed by the same base of the trapezoid and the sides of the trapezoid.
3. The Trapezoid Midsegment Theorem states that the trapezoid's midsegment is parallel to both bases of the trapezoid. The length of the midsegment of a trapezoid is equal to half of the sum of the lengths of both bases.

NOTES

3 Consider the Ace of Diamonds playing card shown. The large diamond in the center of the playing card is a quadrilateral. Classify the quadrilateral based only on each piece of given information.

(a) The diagonals of the quadrilateral bisect each other.

The quadrilateral is a parallelogram if the diagonals bisect each other.

(b) The four sides of the quadrilateral are congruent.

The quadrilateral is a rhombus if the four sides are congruent.

(c) The four angles and the four sides of the quadrilateral are congruent.

The quadrilateral is a square if the four angles and the four sides are congruent.

(d) The diagonals of the quadrilateral bisect the vertex angles.

The quadrilateral is a rhombus if the diagonals bisect the vertex angles.

(e) The four angles of the quadrilateral are congruent.

The quadrilateral is a rectangle if the four angles are congruent.

(f) The opposite sides of the quadrilateral are both congruent and parallel.

The quadrilateral is a parallelogram if the opposite sides are both congruent and parallel.

(g) The opposite angles of the quadrilateral are congruent.

The quadrilateral is a parallelogram if the opposite angles are congruent.

STRETCH Optional

> Consider the circle shown. Diameter *MI* is perpendicular to chord *DA*.

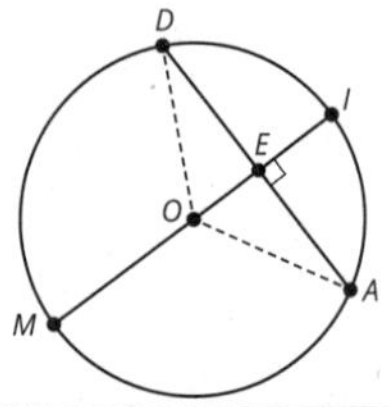

1 Write a conjecture about the relationship between a diameter and a chord when they are perpendicular. Prove that your conjecture is true in all cases.

STRETCH

1. Sample answer.
   The diameter of a circle that intersects a chord at a right angle bisects the chord.
   I can reason this because the triangles are congruent, so by CPCTC, $ED \cong EA$, which means the diameter bisects $\overline{DA}$.

Props To You

This resource details additional facilitation notes to fully assist you as you plan each lesson to support all students, students who struggle, and advanced learners. It provides differentiation strategies, common student misconceptions, and suggestions to extend certain activities.

GETTING STARTED

Session 1 of 3

Making Connections

Students create a flow chart relating quadrilaterals and the properties that apply to them. They explain their reasoning and conclude that squares are a subset of other quadrilateral categories.

CHUNK	AUDIENCE	ADDITIONAL SUPPORTS
As students work on 2	Students who Struggle	**DIFFERENTIATION STRATEGY** Suggest students draw the diagonals in each figure to visualize the properties regarding diagonals.

ACTIVITY 1

Session 1 of 3

Properties of Quadrilaterals

Students prove the properties of a parallelogram, rhombus, and rectangle. They conclude that a square inherits the properties of both a rectangle and a rhombus.

CHUNK	AUDIENCE	ADDITIONAL SUPPORTS
As students work on 2	Students who Struggle	**DIFFERENTIATION STRATEGY** Help students identify angle pairs associated with parallel lines by suggesting they use a colored pencil to outline and extend parallel lines and a different color for the transversal.
As students work on 2	All Students	**COMMON MISCONCEPTION** Students may confuse the use of the Alternate Interior Angle Theorem with the Alternate Interior Angle Converse Theorem. Discuss what information they need to apply each theorem.

ACTIVITY 3

Session 2 of 3

Properties of Trapezoids with One Pair of Parallel Sides

Students prove the base angles and the diagonals of an isosceles trapezoid are congruent. They plan a proof of the Trapezoid Midsegment Theorem using the Triangle Midsegment Theorem.

CHUNK	AUDIENCE	ADDITIONAL SUPPORTS
As students analyze the worked example	Students who Struggle	**DIFFERENTIATION STRATEGY** Guide students through the proof step-by-step. Have them annotate the figure at each step and justify each reason.
To extend 4	Advanced Learners	**DIFFERENTIATION STRATEGY** Have students prove the converse of the statement that the diagonals of an isosceles trapezoid are congruent. Then have students write the statement as a biconditional statement using double arrows or "if and only if."

ACTIVITY 5

Session 3 of 3

Using Properties to Solve Problems

Students apply the properties of quadrilaterals to solve problem situations. They make sense of problems and justify their reasoning.

CHUNK	AUDIENCE	ADDITIONAL SUPPORTS
As an alternative grouping strategy for the activity	All Students	**DIFFERENTIATION STRATEGY** Assign each group a different problem to complete. Tell groups to be ready to present their work. Save time for groups to present to the class.

TALK THE TALK

Session 3 of 3

Name That Shape

Students create a list of yes-no questions to identify an unknown quadrilateral. They reason about the least number of questions needed to identify the quadrilateral.

CHUNK	AUDIENCE	ADDITIONAL SUPPORTS
As students work on the activity	All Students	**DIFFERENTIATION STRATEGY** Have students work with a partner or in small groups to continue playing the game, "Can You Guess My Quadrilateral?' One student writes the name of a quadrilateral on a slip of paper and reveals it only when another student correctly guesses its name. The student guessing should pose the yes-no question carefully and use as few clues as possible.

Practice the learning

MATHbook + Skills Practice

The table shows the targeted practice of the skills and mathematical concepts for the *Using Congruence Theorems* Topic. The highlighted Problem Set aligns with **Props to You**.

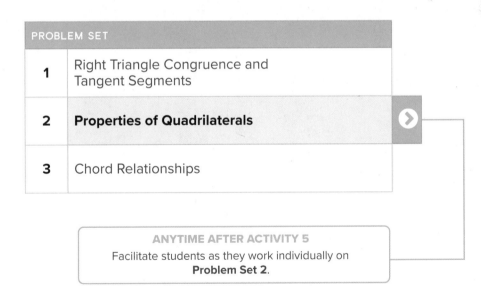

PROBLEM SET	
1	Right Triangle Congruence and Tangent Segments
2	**Properties of Quadrilaterals**
3	Chord Relationships

ANYTIME AFTER ACTIVITY 5

Facilitate students as they work individually on **Problem Set 2**.

NOTES

ENGAGE + DEVELOP + TEACH

at the **Module** level | at the **Topic** level | Read the facilitation notes and plan learning experiences.

Where are we?

TOPIC 3 Using Congruence Theorems	LESSON 1 SSS, SAS, AAS, ...S.O.S.!	LESSON 2 Props To You	LESSON 3 Three-Chord Song
Pacing	2 Sessions	3 Sessions	1 Session

OVERVIEW: LESSON 3

Three-Chord Song

Relationships Between Chords

ENGAGE

- Students think of a method they can use to determine the diameter of a broken plate.

DEVELOP

- They investigate perpendicular bisectors of chords of the same circle and conclude they pass through the center point of the circle.
- They prove the Congruent Chord–Congruent Arc Theorem and its converse.

DEMONSTRATE

- Students apply their knowledge of chords to solve problems.

HIGH SCHOOL GEOMETRY

Circles

Understand and apply theorems about circles.

2. Identify and describe relationships among inscribed angles, radii, and chords.

LESSON STRUCTURE AND PACING GUIDE 1 SESSION

⊛ This activity highlights a key term or concept that is essential to the learning goals of the lesson.

Session 1

INSTRUCTIONAL SEQUENCE

ENGAGE	DEVELOP	DEVELOP
Establish a situation	Investigation Mathematical problem solving	Investigation Mathematical problem solving

⊛ GETTING STARTED
That Darn Kitty!

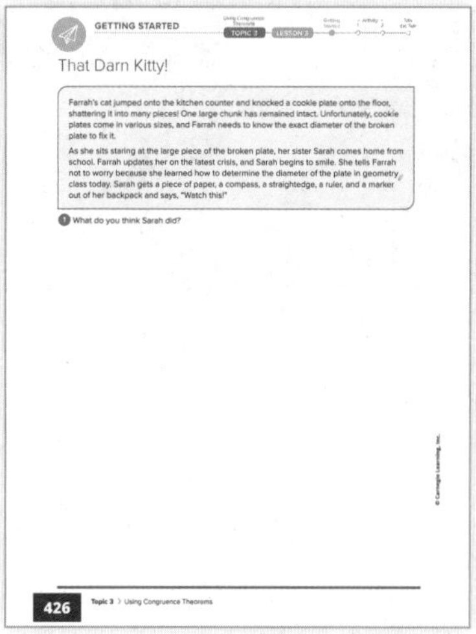

GETTING STARTED

That Darn Kitty!

Farrah's cat jumped onto the kitchen counter and knocked a cookie plate onto the floor, shattering it into many pieces! One large chunk has remained intact. Unfortunately, cookie plates come in various sizes, and Farrah needs to know the exact diameter of the broken plate to fix it.

As she sits staring at the large piece of the broken plate, her sister Sarah comes home from school. Farrah updates her on the latest crisis, and Sarah begins to smile. She tells Farrah not to worry because she learned how to determine the diameter of the plate in geometry class today. Sarah gets a piece of paper, a compass, a straightedge, a ruler, and a marker out of her backpack and says, "Watch this!"

1. What do you think Sarah did?

© Carnegie Learning, Inc.

426 Topic 3 > Using Congruence Theorems

Students think of a method they can use to determine the diameter of a broken plate.

- They investigate a piece of broken plate and try to determine the diameter.

⊛ ACTIVITY 1
Chord Theorems

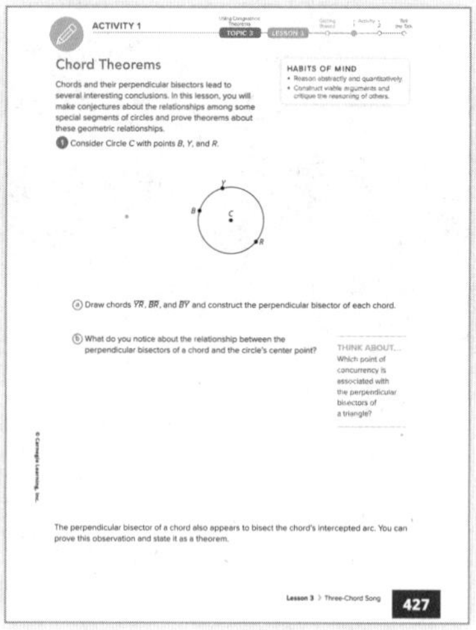

ACTIVITY 1

Chord Theorems

Chords and their perpendicular bisectors lead to several interesting conclusions. In this lesson, you will make conjectures about the relationships among some special segments of circles and prove theorems about these geometric relationships.

HABITS OF MIND
- Reason abstractly and quantitatively.
- Construct viable arguments and critique the reasoning of others.

1. Consider Circle C with points B, Y, and R.

a. Draw chords $\overline{YR}$, $\overline{BR}$, and $\overline{BY}$ and construct the perpendicular bisector of each chord.

b. What do you notice about the relationship between the perpendicular bisectors of a chord and the circle's center point?

THINK ABOUT... Which point of concurrency is associated with the perpendicular bisectors of a triangle?

The perpendicular bisector of a chord also appears to bisect the chord's intercepted arc. You can prove this observation and state it as a theorem.

© Carnegie Learning, Inc.

Lesson 3 > Three-Chord Song 427

Students investigate perpendicular bisectors of chords of the same circle and conclude they pass through the center point of the circle.

- They prove the Diameter–Chord Theorem, Equidistant Chord Theorem, and Equidistant Chord Converse Theorem.

⊛ ACTIVITY 2
Chords and Arcs

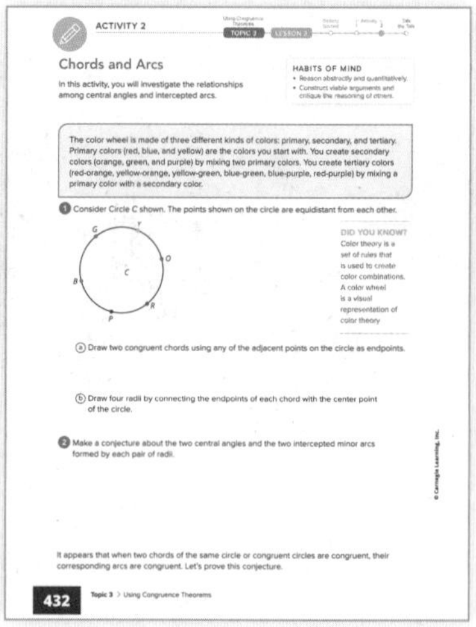

ACTIVITY 2

Chords and Arcs

In this activity, you will investigate the relationships among central angles and intercepted arcs.

HABITS OF MIND
- Reason abstractly and quantitatively.
- Construct viable arguments and critique the reasoning of others.

The color wheel is made of three different kinds of colors: primary, secondary, and tertiary. Primary colors (red, blue, and yellow) are the colors you start with. You create secondary colors (orange, green, and purple) by mixing two primary colors. You create tertiary colors (red-orange, yellow-orange, yellow-green, blue-green, blue-purple, red-purple) by mixing a primary color with a secondary color.

1. Consider Circle C shown. The points shown on the circle are equidistant from each other.

DID YOU KNOW? Color theory is a set of rules that is used to create color combinations. A color wheel is a visual representation of color theory.

a. Draw two congruent chords using any of the adjacent points on the circle as endpoints.

b. Draw four radii by connecting the endpoints of each chord with the center point of the circle.

2. Make a conjecture about the two central angles and the two intercepted minor arcs formed by each pair of radii.

It appears that when two chords of the same circle or congruent circles are congruent, their corresponding arcs are congruent. Let's prove this conjecture.

© Carnegie Learning, Inc.

432 Topic 3 > Using Congruence Theorems

Students prove the Congruent Chord–Congruent Arc Theorem and its converse.

- They draw two congruent chords and connect the endpoints of each chord with the center point forming four radii.
- They then make a conjecture about the two central angles and the two intercepted minor arcs formed by each pair of radii.

Log in to MyCL for **lesson support** including:

Slides

Videos

www.carnegielearning.com/login

INSTRUCTIONAL SEQUENCE

DEMONSTRATE
Exit ticket application

TALK THE TALK
Broken Plate

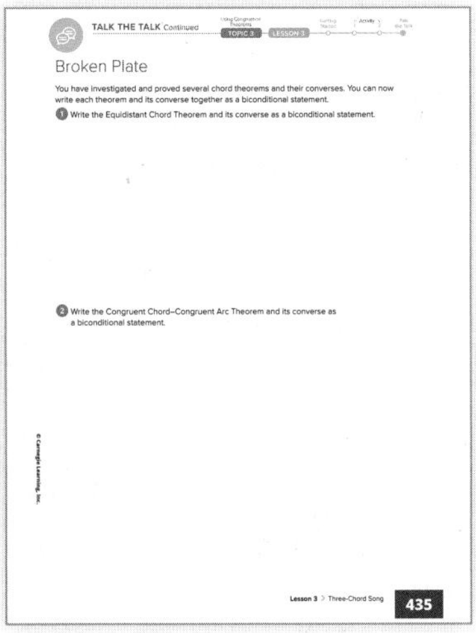
TALK THE TALK Continued

TOPIC 3 LESSON 3

Broken Plate

You have investigated and proved several chord theorems and their converses. You can now write each theorem and its converse together as a biconditional statement.

1 Write the Equidistant Chord Theorem and its converse as a biconditional statement.

2 Write the Congruent Chord–Congruent Arc Theorem and its converse as a biconditional statement.

© Carnegie Learning, Inc.

Lesson 3 > Three-Chord Song 435

Students apply their knowledge of chords to solve problems.

- They write biconditional statements for the theorems and corresponding converses they proved in this lesson.
- They explain how to locate the center of a circle using two chords and their perpendicular bisectors.

NOTES

TOPIC 3

Log in to MyCL for:

- Editable templates
- Additional planning support

Now that you have read the Module, Topic, and Lesson Overviews, you are ready to plan.

Do the math

> Tear out the lesson planning template (page 425E) and jot down thoughts as you work through this lesson and read the Facilitation Notes.

Connect the learning

MATHbook + MATHia®

The table shows the self-paced MATHia sequence for the *Using Congruence Theorems* Topic.

Median student completion time: ~100–125 minutes

> As you implement this lesson, consider different connections for students who are on pace and those that have not yet completed the workspaces aligned to this lesson.

STUDENTS WILL CONTINUE WORKING ON SKILLS RELATED TO THIS TOPIC

TYPE	WORKSPACE NAME
★	Proving Triangles Congruent using HL and HA
▣	Understanding Parallelograms
★	Determining Parts of Quadrilaterals and Parallelograms
★	Proofs about Parallelograms

Three-Chord Song
Relationships Between Chords

Session 1

GETTING STARTED That Darn Kitty! ✪

Pacing (minutes)	
My Time	Class Time

ACTIVITY 1 Chord Theorems ✪

Pacing (minutes)	
My Time	Class Time

KEY TERM

Diameter-Chord Theorem

Equidistant Chord Theorem

Equidistant Chord Converse Theorem

ACTIVITY 2 Chords and Arcs ✪

Pacing (minutes)	
My Time	Class Time

KEY TERM

Congruent Chord–Congruent Arc Theorem

Congruent Chord–Congruent Arc Converse Theorem

TALK THE TALK Broken Plate ✪

Pacing (minutes)	
My Time	Class Time

✪ This activity highlights a key term or concept that is essential to the learning goals of the lesson.

Log in to MyCL for:

- Editable templates
- Additional planning support

Reflect on your lesson

Consider the effectiveness of your lesson on student learning.

What went well?	What did not go as planned?

Anticipate how you would change the lesson next time you teach it.

How will you capitalize on the things that went well?	How will you improve things that did not go as planned?

MATERIALS

- Compasses
- Straightedges

TOPIC 1
Composing and Decomposing Shapes

TOPIC 2
Justifying Line and Angle Relationships

TOPIC 3
Using Congruence Theorems

1 | SSS, SAS, AAS, ...S.O.S.!

2 | Props To You

3 | Three-Chord Song

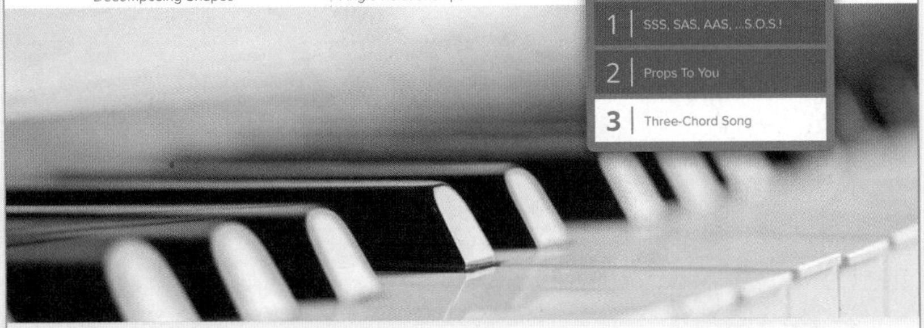

LESSON 3

Three-Chord Song

Relationships Between Chords

Learning Goals

- Prove the Diameter–Chord Theorem.
- Prove the Equidistant Chord Theorem and its converse.
- Prove the Congruent Chord–Congruent Arc Theorem and its converse.

KEY TERMS

- Diameter-Chord Theorem
- Equidistant Chord Theorem
- Equidistant Chord Converse Theorem
- Congruent Chord–Congruent Arc Theorem
- Congruent Chord–Congruent Arc Converse Theorem

REVIEW (1–2 minutes)

1 Write everything you know about this diagram.

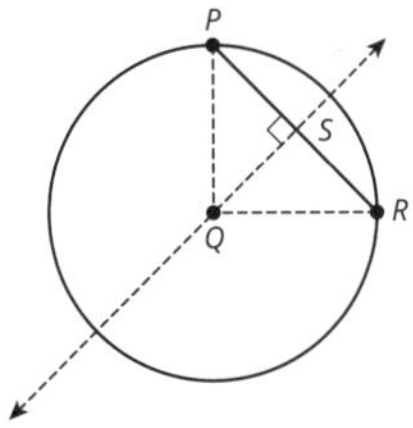

Sample answers.

$\overline{PQ}$ and $\overline{QR}$ are radii of Circle Q.

Triangle PQR is an isosceles triangle.

Line SQ is a perpendicular bisector of chord PR and contains a diameter of the circle.

Angles QPR and QRP are congruent.

$\Delta PSQ \cong \Delta RSQ$ (by SAS).

You have analyzed relationships among angles and chords.

What relationships exist between chord lengths and other parts of a circle?

Setting the Stage

- **Assign Review (optional, 1 – 2 minutes)**
- **Communicate the learning goals and key terms to look out for**
- **Tap into your students' prior learning by reading the narrative statement**
- **Provide a sense of direction by reading the question**

IN THIS REVIEW

Students describe relationships they observe in a circle diagram. They will use this skill throughout the lesson.

The perpendicular bisector of a chord is the diameter of the circle containing the chord.

Congruent chords are equidistant from the center of the circle.

When two chords are congruent, their corresponding arcs are congruent.

Essential Ideas

- The Diameter–Chord Theorem states that if a circle's diameter is perpendicular to a chord, then the diameter bisects the chord and bisects the arc determined by the chord.
- The Equidistant Chord Theorem states that if two chords of the same circle or congruent circles are congruent, then they are equidistant from the center of the circle.
- The Equidistant Chord Converse Theorem states that if two chords of the same circle or congruent circles are equidistant from the center of the circle, then the chords are congruent.
- The Congruent Chord–Congruent Arc Theorem states that if two chords of the same circle or congruent circles are congruent, then their corresponding arcs are congruent.
- The Congruent Chord–Congruent Arc Converse Theorem states that if two arcs of the same circle or congruent circles are congruent, then their corresponding chords are congruent.

SUMMARY **You can use various strategies to construct a specific circle.**

Chunking the Activity

- **Read and discuss the introduction**
- **Group students to complete the activity**
- **Share and summarize**

NOTE: In this activity, students do not need to do the task. Instead, they are developing a strategy to complete the task. A picture of the broken piece of plate is not provided for this reason.

That Darn Kitty!

Farrah's cat jumped onto the kitchen counter and knocked a cookie plate onto the floor, shattering it into many pieces! One large chunk has remained intact. Unfortunately, cookie plates come in various sizes, and Farrah needs to know the exact diameter of the broken plate to fix it.

As she sits staring at the large piece of the broken plate, her sister Sarah comes home from school. Farrah updates her on the latest crisis, and Sarah begins to smile. She tells Farrah not to worry because she learned how to determine the diameter of the plate in geometry class today. Sarah gets a piece of paper, a compass, a straightedge, a ruler, and a marker out of her backpack and says, "Watch this!"

1 What do you think Sarah did?

Sample answer.

I think Sarah tried to recreate the circle by using the one large piece of the plate.

Questions to Support Discourse

	Question	TYPE
1	• Which constructions did you include in your strategy?	Gathering
	• What do you think Sarah did with each of the different tools? • Does your strategy include using central angles of the circle? Inscribed angles of the circle? Why? • Does your strategy include perpendicular lines? Explain your reasoning.	Probing

ACTIVITY 1

SUMMARY **The perpendicular bisector of a chord passes through the center of a circle, and two congruent chords are equidistant from the center of the circle.**

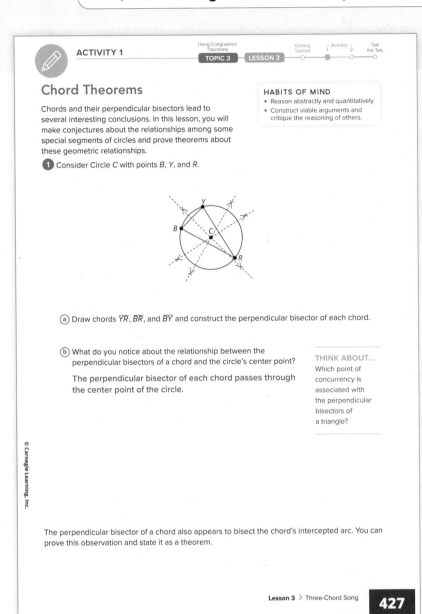

Chord Theorems

Chords and their perpendicular bisectors lead to several interesting conclusions. In this lesson, you will make conjectures about the relationships among some special segments of circles and prove theorems about these geometric relationships.

HABITS OF MIND
- Reason abstractly and quantitatively.
- Construct viable arguments and critique the reasoning of others.

1 Consider Circle C with points B, Y, and R.

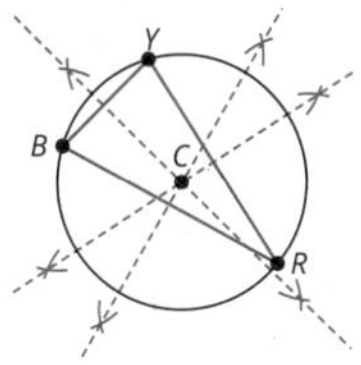

a) Draw chords $\overline{YR}$, $\overline{BR}$, and $\overline{BY}$ and construct the perpendicular bisector of each chord.

b) What do you notice about the relationship between the perpendicular bisectors of a chord and the circle's center point?

The perpendicular bisector of each chord passes through the center point of the circle.

THINK ABOUT...
Which point of concurrency is associated with the perpendicular bisectors of a triangle?

The perpendicular bisector of a chord also appears to bisect the chord's intercepted arc. You can prove this observation and state it as a theorem.

Chunking the Activity

- Read and discuss the introduction
- Group students to complete 1
- Check-in and share
- Group students to complete 2
- Check-in and share
- Group students to complete 3
- Check-in and share
- Group students to complete 4 and 5
- Share and summarize

Student Look-Fors

Connections made between the perpendicular bisectors of the chords and the diameters of the circle.

Questions to Support Discourse

		TYPE
1	• What is the point of concurrency of the three perpendicular bisectors?	Gathering
	• Do you think the perpendicular bisector of all chords will pass through the center of the circle? Why?	Probing
	• Are the perpendicular bisectors of each chord diameters of the circle? Explain your reasoning.	Seeing structure

NOTES

DIFFERENTIATION STRATEGY

See Page 436A to challenge advanced learners to extend 2.

2 Prove this relationship between a diameter and a chord.

Given: $\overline{MI}$ is a diameter of Circle O.
$\overline{MI} \perp \overline{DA}$

Prove: $\overline{MI}$ bisects $\overline{DA}$.
$\overline{MI}$ bisects $\overset{\frown}{DA}$.

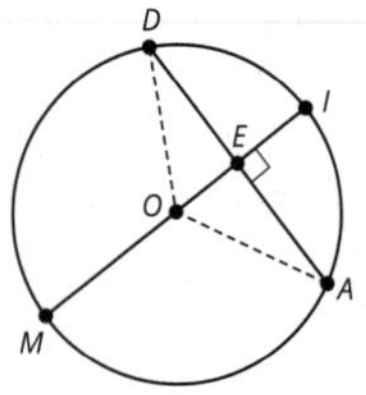

Statements	Reasons
1. $\overline{MI}$ is a diameter of Circle O. $\overline{MI} \perp \overline{DA}$	1. Given
2. Connect points O and D to form radius $\overline{OD}$. Connect points O and A to form radius $\overline{OA}$.	2. Construction
3. $\angle OED$ and $\angle OEA$ are right angles.	3. Definition of perpendicular lines.
4. ΔOED and ΔOEA are right triangles.	4. Definition of right triangles.
5. $\overline{OD} \cong \overline{OA}$	5. All radii of the same circle or congruent circles are congruent.
6. $\overline{OE} \cong \overline{OE}$	6. Reflexive Property
7. $\Delta OED \cong \Delta OEA$	7. HL Congruence Theorem
8. $\overline{ED} \cong \overline{EA}$	8. CPCTC
9. $\overline{MI}$ bisects $\overline{DA}$	9. Definition of bisection
10. $\angle DOE \cong \angle AOE$	10. CPCTC
11. $\overset{\frown}{ID} \cong \overset{\frown}{IA}$	11. Congruent central angles determine congruent corresponding arcs.
12. $\overline{MI}$ bisects $\overset{\frown}{DA}$	12. Definition of bisection

THEOREM

DIAMETER-CHORD THEOREM

If a circle's diameter is perpendicular to a chord, then the diameter bisects the chord and bisects the arc determined by the chord.

Questions to Support Discourse

		TYPE
2	• Which right triangle congruence theorem can you use to prove that $\Delta ODE \cong \Delta OAE$?	Gathering
	• What type of triangles are ΔODE and ΔOAE? How do you know?	Probing
	• To show that $\overline{MI}$ bisects $\overline{DA}$, what must you prove?	Seeing structure

ACTIVITY 1 Continued

3 Use Circle *T* to draw two congruent chords that are not parallel to each other and do not pass through the center point of the circle.

Sample answer.

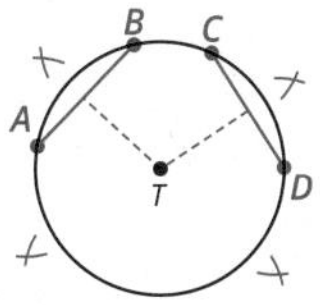

(a) Construct the perpendicular bisector of each chord.

(b) Choose a construction tool and compare the distance each chord is from the center point of the circle.

Each chord is the same distance from the center.

Congruent chords appear to be equidistant from the center point of the circle. You can prove this observation and state it as a theorem.

Questions to Support Discourse

		TYPE
3	• How did you ensure the chords are congruent? • How can you compare distances without a measuring tool? • How do you know which distance to use when comparing the distances from the chords to the center of the circle?	Probing

NOTES

COMMON MISCONCEPTION

See Page 436A for a misconception related to 3.

NOTES

DIFFERENTIATION STRATEGY

See Page 436A to group students to complete 4 and 5.

4 Prove this relationship regarding chords. (Here's a hint. You need to show $OE = OI$.)

Given: $\overline{CH} \cong \overline{DR}$
$\overline{OE} \perp \overline{CH}$
$\overline{OI} \perp \overline{DR}$

Prove: $\overline{CH}$ and $\overline{DR}$ are equidistant from center O.

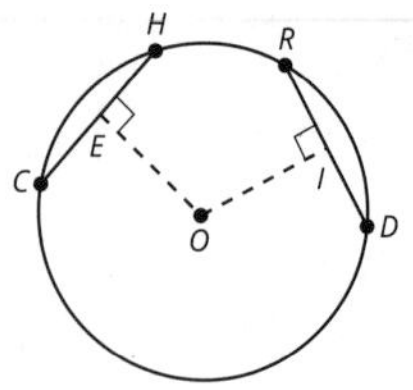

Statements	Reasons
1. $\overline{CH} \cong \overline{DR}$; $\overline{OE} \perp \overline{CH}$; $\overline{OI} \perp \overline{DR}$	1. Given
2. Connect points O and H, O and C, O and D, and O and R to form radii $\overline{OH}$, $\overline{OC}$, $\overline{OD}$, and $\overline{OR}$, respectively.	2. Construction
3. $\overline{OH} \cong \overline{OC} \cong \overline{OD} \cong \overline{OR}$	3. All radii of the same circle are congruent.
4. $\Delta COH \cong \Delta DOR$	4. SSS congruence Theorem
5. $\angle RDO \cong \angle HCO$	5. CPCTC
6. $\angle OEH$ and $\angle OID$ are right angles.	6. Definition of perpendicular lines
7. $\angle OEH \cong \angle OID$	7. All right angles are congruent.
8. $\Delta OEH \cong \Delta OID$	8. AAS Congruence Theorem
9. $\overline{OE} \cong \overline{OI}$	9. CPCTC
10. $OE = OI$	10. Definition of congruent segments
11. $\overline{CH}$ and $\overline{DR}$ are equidistant from the center point.	11. Definition of equidistance

THEOREM

EQUIDISTANT CHORD THEOREM

If two chords of the same circle or congruent circles are congruent, then they are equidistant from the center of the circle.

Let's conjecture that the converse of this theorem is also true. If two chords of the same circle or congruent circles are equidistant from the center of the circle, then the chords are congruent.

Questions to Support Discourse

		TYPE
4	• Which segments do you need to prove congruent to show $\overline{CH}$ and $\overline{DR}$ are equidistant from center O? • What is true about all radii of a circle? • Which triangles contain sides labeled $\overline{CH}$ and $\overline{DR}$?	Gathering
	• Why is ΔCOH congruent to ΔDOR?	Probing

ACTIVITY 1 Continued

5 Prove this converse statement is true in all cases.

Given: $OE = OI$

($\overline{CH}$ and $\overline{DR}$ are equidistant from the center point.)

$\overline{OE} \perp \overline{CH}$

$\overline{OI} \perp \overline{DR}$

Prove: $\overline{CH} \cong \overline{DR}$

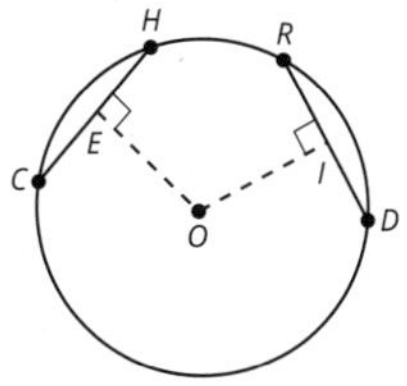

Statements	Reasons
1. $OE = OI$; $\overline{OE} \perp \overline{CH}$; $\overline{OI} \perp \overline{DR}$	1. Given
2. Connect points O and H, O and C, O and D, and O and R to form radii $\overline{OH}$, $\overline{OC}$, $\overline{OD}$, and $\overline{OR}$, respectively.	2. Construction
3. $\overline{OE} \cong \overline{OI}$	3. Definition of congruent segments
4. $\overline{OH} \cong \overline{OC} \cong \overline{OD} \cong \overline{OR}$	4. All radii of the same circle are congruent
5. $\angle OEH$, $\angle OEC$, $\angle OID$, and $\angle OIR$ are right angles.	5. Definition of perpendicular lines
6. ΔOHE, ΔOCE, ΔODI, and ΔORI are right triangles.	6. Definition of right triangles
7. $\Delta OHE \cong \Delta OCE \cong \Delta ODI \cong \Delta ORI$	7. HL Congruence Theorem
8. $\overline{HE} \cong \overline{EC} \cong \overline{DI} \cong \overline{IR}$	8. CPCTC
9. $HE = EC = DI = IR$	9. Definition of congruent segments
10. $HE + EC = CH$ and $DI + IR = DR$	10. Segments Addition Postulate
11. $CH = DR$	11. Substitution Property steps 10 and 11
12. $\overline{CH} \cong \overline{DR}$	12. Definition of congruent segments

THEOREM

EQUIDISTANT CHORD CONVERSE THEOREM

If two chords of the same circle or congruent circles are equidistant from the center of the circle, then the chords are congruent.

NOTES

Questions to Support Discourse

		TYPE
5	• What is the Segment Addition Postulate?	Gathering
	• How would you show $\Delta OHE \cong \Delta OCE$? • Why are ΔOHE and ΔOCE congruent to ΔODI? Are they all also congruent to ΔORI?	Probing
	• Why do you think you are given that $OE = OI$ instead of $\overline{OE} \cong \overline{OI}$?	Seeing structure

TOPIC 3

ACTIVITY 2

SUMMARY **When two chords are congruent, you know that their corresponding arcs are also congruent.**

Chunking the Activity

- **Read and discuss the situation**
- **Group students to complete 1 and 2**
- **Check-in and share**
- **Group students to complete 3 and 4**
- **Share and summarize**

Student Look-Fors

Utilizing relationship skills by communicating clearly and listening well.

LANGUAGE LINK

ELL TIP

Ensure that students understand the meaning of *tertiary* as the third in order, importance, or value.

Chords and Arcs

In this activity, you will investigate the relationships among central angles and intercepted arcs.

HABITS OF MIND
- Reason abstractly and quantitatively.
- Construct viable arguments and critique the reasoning of others.

The color wheel is made of three different kinds of colors: primary, secondary, and tertiary. Primary colors (red, blue, and yellow) are the colors you start with. You create secondary colors (orange, green, and purple) by mixing two primary colors. You create tertiary colors (red-orange, yellow-orange, yellow-green, blue-green, blue-purple, red-purple) by mixing a primary color with a secondary color.

1. Consider Circle C shown. The points shown on the circle are equidistant from each other.

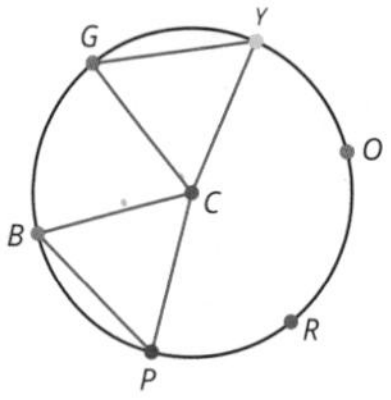

DID YOU KNOW?
Color theory is a set of rules that is used to create color combinations. A color wheel is a visual representation of color theory.

   a. Draw two congruent chords using any of the adjacent points on the circle as endpoints.

   Sample answer provided.

   b. Draw four radii by connecting the endpoints of each chord with the center point of the circle.

2. Make a conjecture about the two central angles and the two intercepted minor arcs formed by each pair of radii.

   The two central angles formed by each pair of radii appear to be congruent. Therefore, the minor arcs associated with each central angle are also congruent.

It appears that when two chords of the same circle or congruent circles are congruent, their corresponding arcs are congruent. Let's prove this conjecture.

Questions to Support Discourse

		TYPE
1	• How do you know the chords are congruent?	Probing
2	• What are the names of the central angles associated with each chord? • What are the names of the arcs intercepted by each chord?	Gathering
	• In this situation, did the chords determine the arcs, or did the arcs determine the chords? Why do you think that is?	Probing

3 Prove this conjecture relating chords and their corresponding arcs.

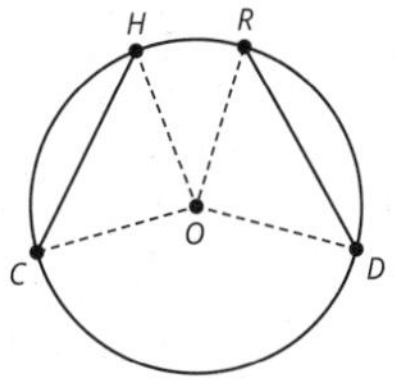

Given: $\overline{CH} \cong \overline{DR}$
Prove: $\widehat{CH} \cong \widehat{DR}$

Sample paragraph proof.

I can construct the radii $\overline{OH}$, $\overline{OC}$, $\overline{OD}$, and $\overline{OR}$ which are all congruent. Using this and the given information, I know that $\Delta COH \cong \Delta DOR$ by SSS, so $\angle COH \cong \angle DOR$ by CPCTC. Therefore, $\widehat{CH} \cong \widehat{DR}$ because congruent central angles of the same circle or congruent circles determine congruent arcs.

Because you proved that this relationship is true, you can now refer to it as a theorem.

THEOREM

CONGRUENT CHORD–CONGRUENT ARC THEOREM

If two chords of the same circle or congruent circles are congruent, then their corresponding arcs are congruent.

NOTES

TOPIC 3

Questions to Support Discourse

		TYPE
3	• What congruence theorem can you use to show $\Delta COH \cong \Delta DOR$?	Gathering
	• How can you use central angles to show that $\widehat{CH} \cong \widehat{DR}$?	Probing

NOTES

4 Prove the Congruent Chord–Congruent Arc Converse Theorem.

Given: $\overset{\frown}{CH} \cong \overset{\frown}{DR}$
Prove: $\overline{CH} \cong \overline{DR}$

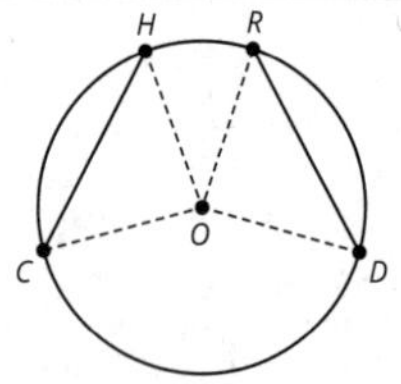

Sample paragraph proof.

I can construct the radii $\overline{OH}$, $\overline{OC}$, $\overline{OD}$, $\overline{OR}$ which are all congruent. Using the given information, I know that $\angle COH \cong \angle DOR$ because congruent minor arcs of the same circle determine congruent central angles. Therefore, $\Delta COH \cong \Delta DOR$ by the SAS Congruence Theorem and $\overline{CH} \cong \overline{DR}$ by CPCTC.

Because you proved that this relationship is true, you can now refer to it as a theorem.

THEOREM

CONGRUENT CHORD–CONGRUENT ARC CONVERSE THEOREM

If arcs of the same circle or congruent circles are congruent, then their corresponding chords are congruent.

Questions to Support Discourse

		TYPE
4	• When you know that two arcs are congruent, what does this imply about their central angles?	Probing

TALK THE TALK

SUMMARY **You can use chords of a circle and theorems about chords to solve problems.**

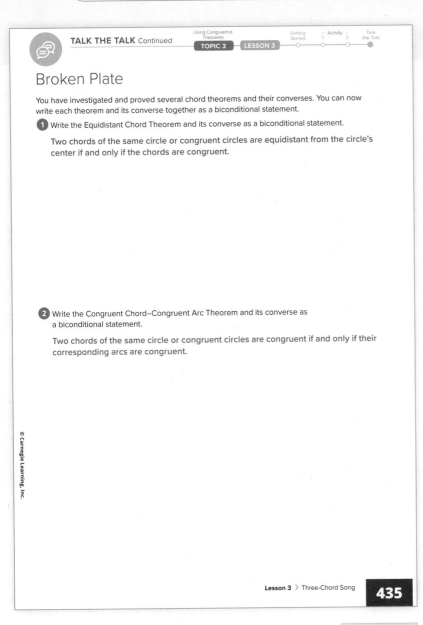

Broken Plate

You have investigated and proved several chord theorems and their converses. You can now write each theorem and its converse together as a biconditional statement.

1. Write the Equidistant Chord Theorem and its converse as a biconditional statement.

   Two chords of the same circle or congruent circles are equidistant from the circle's center if and only if the chords are congruent.

2. Write the Congruent Chord–Congruent Arc Theorem and its converse as a biconditional statement.

   Two chords of the same circle or congruent circles are congruent if and only if their corresponding arcs are congruent.

Chunking the Activity

- Read and discuss the introduction
- Group students to complete the activity
- Share and summarize

NOTE: Before beginning the next module, take a moment to build students' capacity for self-management by having them review and reflect on their goals set during **A Meeting of the Minds**.

Questions to Support Discourse

		TYPE
1	• Why can you write the Equidistant Chord Theorem as a biconditional statement?	Probing
2	• Why can you write the Congruent Chord–Congruent Arc Theorem as a biconditional statement?	Probing

TALK THE TALK

SUMMARY **You can use chords of a circle and theorems about chords to solve problems.**

NOTES

TALK THE TALK Continued

> Consider the problem from the Getting Started.

3 Describe how Sarah can determine the diameter of the plate with the broken piece. Then, show your work on the broken plate shown.

First, Sarah places the broken plate on a piece of paper. Using the marker and a straightedge, she draws two chords on the broken chunk of plate.

Then, she constructs the perpendicular bisector of each chord. The point at which the two perpendicular bisectors intersect is the center of the plate.

Now that Sarah knows where the center is, she uses the ruler to measure the distance from the point of intersection (*P*) to any point on the plate's edge (*R*) to determine the radius of the plate.

Finally, she doubles the radius to determine the diameter of the plate.

Questions to Support Discourse

	Questions	TYPE
3	• How can Sarah use the length of the radius to determine the length of the diameter?	Gathering
	• Is it possible for Sarah to draw two chords on the piece of broken plate? • If Sarah locates the center of the circular plate, how can she determine the length of the radius of the plate?	Probing
	• How can you use two chords to determine the location of the center point of a circle?	Reflecting and justifying

ASSIGNMENT

LESSON 3 ASSIGNMENT

> Use a separate piece of paper for your Journal entry.

JOURNAL

> Match each definition with its corresponding term.

REMEMBER

The perpendicular bisector of a chord is the diameter of the circle containing the chord. Congruent chords are equidistant from the center of the circle. When two chords are congruent, their corresponding arcs are congruent.

1. Diameter–Chord Theorem
2. Equidistant Chord Theorem
3. Congruent Chord–Congruent Arc Theorem

(a) If two chords of the same circle or congruent circles are congruent, their corresponding arcs are congruent.

(b) If two chords of the same circle or congruent circles are congruent, then they are equidistant from the center of the circle.

(c) If a circle's diameter is perpendicular to a chord, then the diameter bisects the chord and bisects the arc determined by the chord.

PRACTICE

1. Use Circle *T* to complete parts (a) through (e).

(a) Draw an inscribed right angle in Circle *T*. Label each point where the angle intersects the circle. What is the name of the right angle?

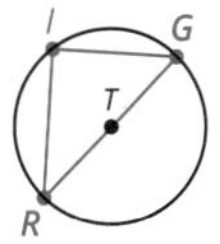

Sample answer.

$\angle RIG$

(b) Draw the chord determined by the inscribed right angle. What is the name of the chord?

$\overline{RG}$

(c) Draw a second inscribed right angle in Circle *T*. Label each point where the angle intersects the circle. What is the name of the second right angle?

Sample answer.

$\angle ENA$

(d) Draw the chord determined by the second inscribed right angle. What is the name of the chord?

$\overline{AE}$

(e) Describe the relationship between the arcs that correspond to the chords you named in parts (b) and (d). Explain your reasoning.

Arcs *RIG* and *ENA* are congruent by the Congruent Chords–Congruent Arc Theorem.

Go to LiveHint.com for help on the PRACTICE questions.

Chunking the Assignment

- Journal
- Practice 1 and 2
- Stretch (advanced learners)
- Mixed Practice (page 437) 5 and 6

JOURNAL

1. c
2. b
3. a

TOPIC 3

Encourage students to use LiveHint.com for help with the PRACTICE questions of this assignment.

NOTES

STRETCH

1. The length of *CU* is 12 cm. I used the Pythagorean Theorem. *CV* is the radius of the circle, which is half the diameter, so the radius is 20 cm.

$$CU^2 + UV^2 = CV^2$$
$$CU^2 + 16^2 = 20^2$$
$$CU^2 = 144$$
$$CU = 12$$

2. The length of *QS* is 32 cm. *QS* is congruent to *TV* by the Equidistant Chord Converse Theorem. The length of *TV* is 32 cm by the Diameter–Chord Theorem.

2. In Circle *G* shown below, *MG* = 1.84 centimeters, *GL* = 1.98 centimeters, m∠*GLH* = 90°, and m∠*GMK* = 90°. Determine whether $\overline{IH} \cong \overline{JK}$. Explain your reasoning.

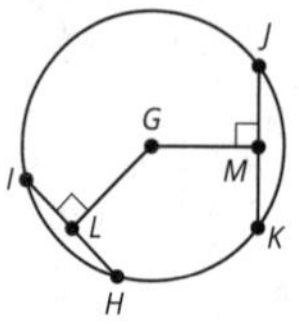

$\overline{IH}$ is not congruent to $\overline{JK}$ because $\overline{MG}$ is not congruent to $\overline{GL}$.

STRETCH Optional

> The circle shown has a diameter of 40 centimeters. The length of *RC* is 12 centimeters, and the length of *UV* is 16 centimeters.

1. Determine the length of *CU*. Explain your reasoning.
2. Determine the length of *QS*. Explain your reasoning.

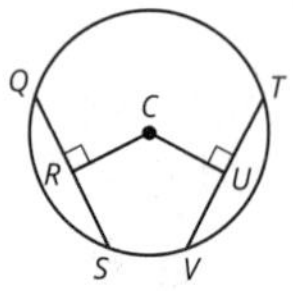

Three-Chord Song

This resource details additional facilitation notes to fully assist you as you plan each lesson to support all students, students who struggle, and advanced learners. It provides differentiation strategies, common student misconceptions, and suggestions to extend certain activities.

ACTIVITY 1

Session 1 of 1

Chord Theorems

Students construct perpendicular bisectors of three chords of the same circle and conclude that the perpendicular bisector of a chord passes through the center point of the circle. Students use a two-column proof to prove the Diameter–Chord Theorem, the Equidistant Chord Theorem, and the Equidistant Chord Converse Theorem.

CHUNK	AUDIENCE	ADDITIONAL SUPPORTS
To extend 2	Advanced Learners	**DIFFERENTIATION STRATEGY** Have students prove the Diameter–Chord Converse Theorem and then write the theorem and its converse as a biconditional statement.
As students work on 3	All Students	**COMMON MISCONCEPTION** Students may think that they must know specific distances to compare them. They can compare distances with a compass. They do not need to know a measurement to compare distances.
As an alternative grouping strategy for 4 and 5	All Students	**DIFFERENTIATION STRATEGY** Have half the groups complete the proof for Question 4 and the other half complete the proof for Question 5. Leave time for groups to share their proofs.

TOPIC 3

Practice the learning

MATHbook + Skills Practice

The table shows the targeted practice of the skills and mathematical concepts for the *Using Congruence Theorems* Topic. The highlighted Problem Set aligns with **Three-Chord Song.**

PROBLEM SET	
1	Right Triangle Congruence and Tangent Segments
2	Properties of Quadrilaterals
3	**Chord Relationships**

ANYTIME AFTER ACTIVITY 2

Facilitate students as they work individually on **Problem Set 3.**

MIXED PRACTICE

Log in to MyCL to access a downloadable version with **additional space** for students to write their answers.

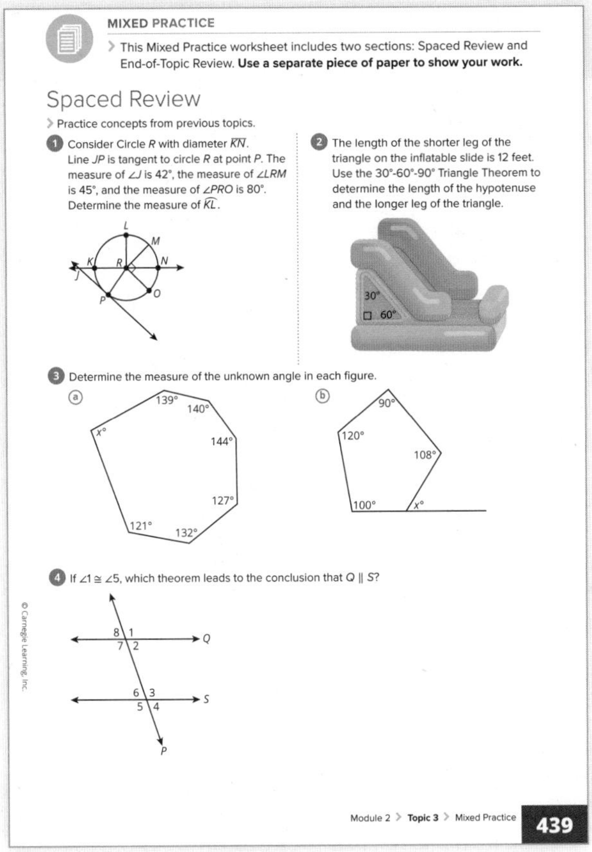

MIXED PRACTICE

> This Mixed Practice worksheet includes two sections: Spaced Review and End-of-Topic Review. **Use a separate piece of paper to show your work.**

Spaced Review

> Practice concepts from previous topics.

1. Consider Circle *R* with diameter $\overline{KN}$. Line *JP* is tangent to circle *R* at point *P*. The measure of ∠*J* is 42°, the measure of ∠*LRM* is 45°, and the measure of ∠*PRO* is 80°. Determine the measure of $\overset{\frown}{KL}$.

2. The length of the shorter leg of the triangle on the inflatable slide is 12 feet. Use the 30°-60°-90° Triangle Theorem to determine the length of the hypotenuse and the longer leg of the triangle.

3. Determine the measure of the unknown angle in each figure.
   (a) (b)

4. If ∠1 ≅ ∠5, which theorem leads to the conclusion that *Q* ∥ *S*?

© Carnegie Learning, Inc.

Module 2 > **Topic 3** > Mixed Practice **439**

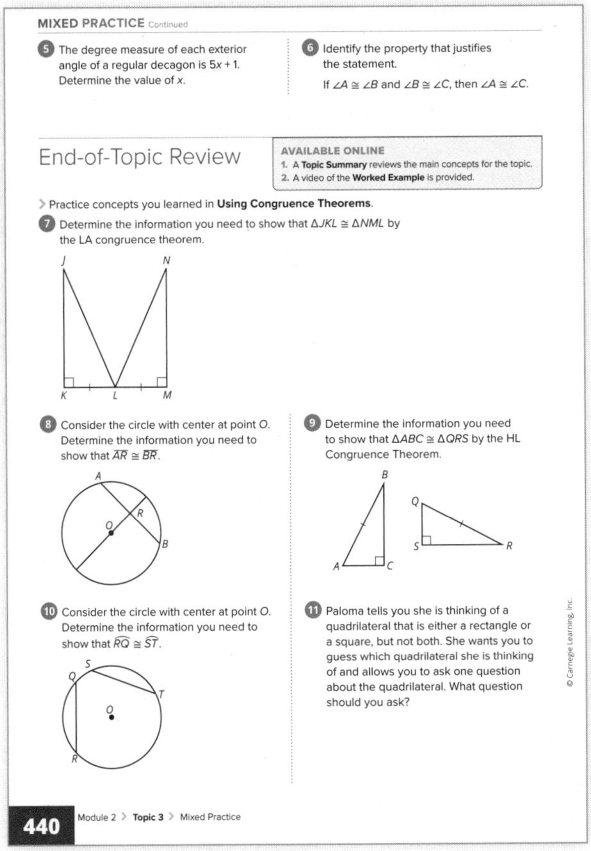

MIXED PRACTICE Continued

5. The degree measure of each exterior angle of a regular decagon is 5*x* + 1. Determine the value of *x*.

6. Identify the property that justifies the statement.
   If ∠*A* ≅ ∠*B* and ∠*B* ≅ ∠*C*, then ∠*A* ≅ ∠*C*.

End-of-Topic Review

AVAILABLE ONLINE
1. A **Topic Summary** reviews the main concepts for the topic.
2. A video of the **Worked Example** is provided.

> Practice concepts you learned in **Using Congruence Theorems**.

7. Determine the information you need to show that Δ*JKL* ≅ Δ*NML* by the LA congruence theorem.

8. Consider the circle with center at point *O*. Determine the information you need to show that $\overline{AR} \cong \overline{BR}$.

9. Determine the information you need to show that Δ*ABC* ≅ Δ*QRS* by the HL Congruence Theorem.

10. Consider the circle with center at point *O*. Determine the information you need to show that $\overline{RQ} \cong \overline{ST}$.

11. Paloma tells you she is thinking of a quadrilateral that is either a rectangle or a square, but not both. She wants you to guess which quadrilateral she is thinking of and allows you to ask one question about the quadrilateral. What question should you ask?

© Carnegie Learning, Inc.

440 Module 2 > **Topic 3** > Mixed Practice

See pages 440–440B for annotated answers.

The **Spaced Review** includes fluency and problem solving from previous topics.

Aligned Standards

1 G.C.2	2 G.CO.10
3 G.CO.10	4 G.CO.9
5 G.CO.10	6 G.CO.9

Log in to MyCL for more **End-of-Topic** review questions.

Go to **Edulastic**, and search for: G.CO.10, G.CO.11, G.C.2.

The **End-of-Topic Review** includes questions to practice the key concepts of *Using Congruence Theorems*.

Aligned Standards

7 G.CO.10	8 G.C.2
9 G.CO.10	10 G.C.2
11 G.CO.11	

Answers included.

MIXED PRACTICE

> This Mixed Practice worksheet includes two sections: Spaced Review and End-of-Topic Review.

MODULE 2 Establishing Proof | TOPIC 1 Composing and Decomposing Shapes | TOPIC 2 Justifying Line and Angle Relationships | **TOPIC 3 Using Congruence Theorems**

Spaced Review

> Practice concepts from previous topics.

1 Consider Circle R with diameter $\overline{KN}$. Line JP is tangent to circle R at point P. The measure of $\angle J$ is 42°, the measure of $\angle LRM$ is 45°, and the measure of $\angle PRO$ is 80°. Determine the measure of $\widehat{KL}$.

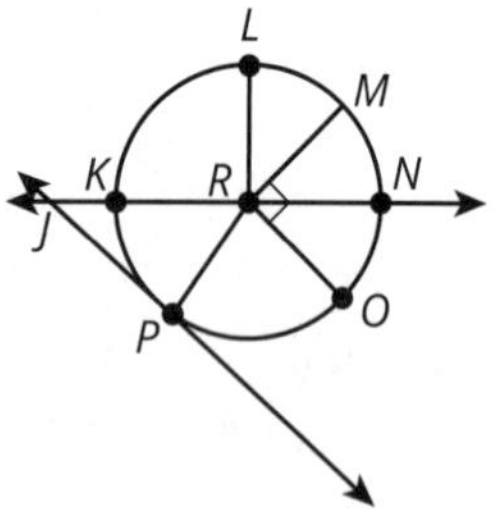

The measure of $\widehat{KL}$ is 97°.

2 The length of the shorter leg of the triangle on the inflatable slide is 12 feet. Use the 30°-60°-90° Triangle Theorem to determine the length of the hypotenuse and the longer leg of the triangle.

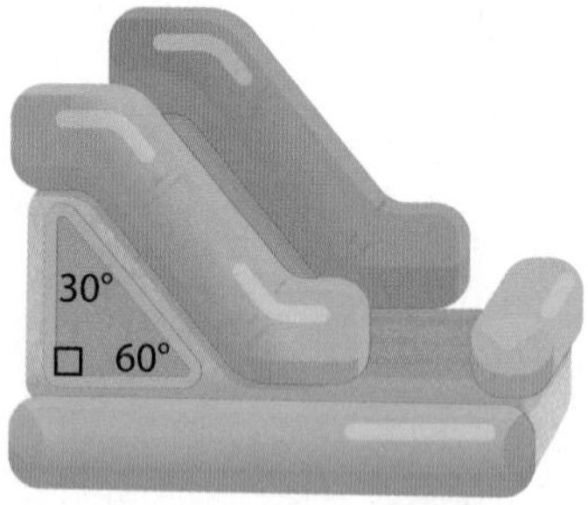

The length of the hypotenuse is 24 feet. The length of the longer leg of the triangle is $12\sqrt{3}$ feet.

3 Determine the measure of the unknown angle in each figure.

ⓐ

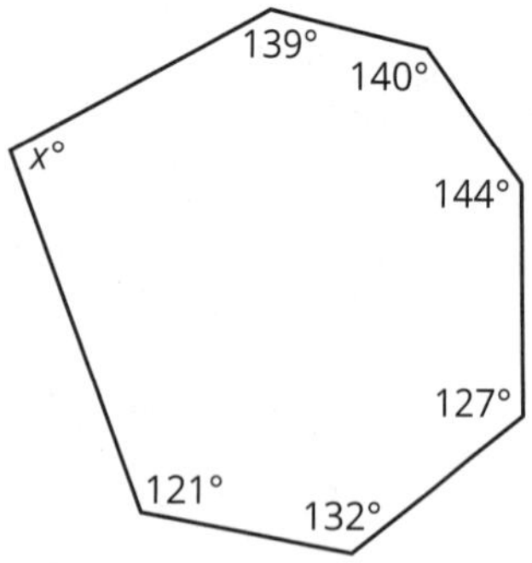

The sum of the measures of the interior angles is 180°(5) = 900°.

$x° + 803° = 900°$

$x° = 97°$

ⓑ

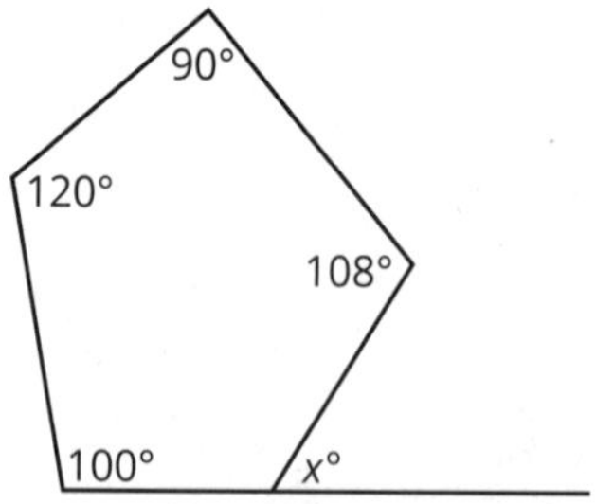

The sum of the measures of the interior angles is 180°(3) = 540°.

The unknown angle inside the figure has a measure of 540° − 418° = 122°.

$180° - 122° = x°$

$x° = 58°$

Answers included.

MIXED PRACTICE Continued

4 If $\angle 1 \cong \angle 5$, which theorem leads to the conclusion that $Q \parallel S$?

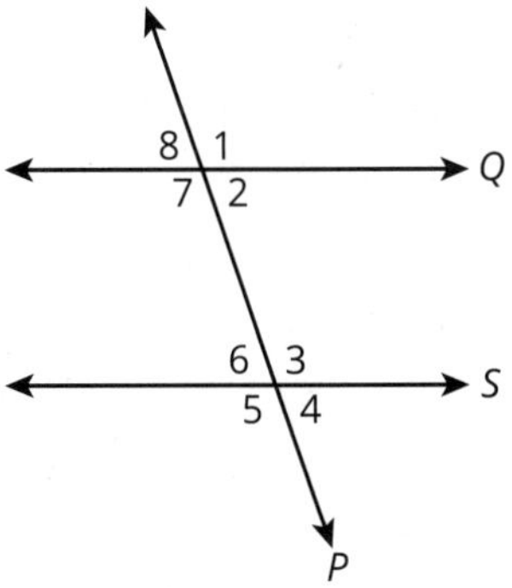

The Alternate Exterior Angle Converse Theorem leads to the conclusion that $Q \parallel S$.

5 The degree measure of each exterior angle of a regular decagon is $5x + 1$. Determine the value of x.

$\frac{360}{10} = 5x + 1$

$36 = 5x + 1$

$35 = 5x$

$x = 7$

6 Identify the property that justifies the statement.

If $\angle A \cong \angle B$ and $\angle B \cong \angle C$, then $\angle A \cong \angle C$.

Transitive Property

End-of-Topic Review

AVAILABLE ONLINE

1. A **Topic Summary** reviews the main concepts for the topic.
2. A video of the **Worked Example** is provided.

> Practice concepts you learned in **Using Congruence Theorems**.

7 Determine the information you need to show that $\Delta JKL \cong \Delta NML$ by the LA congruence theorem.

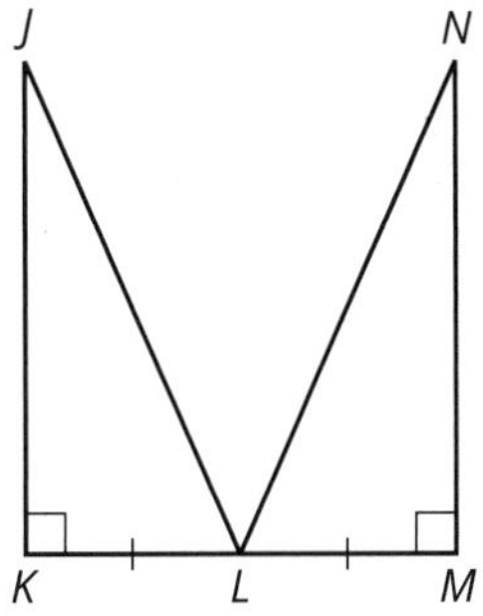

$\angle J \cong \angle N$ or $\angle JLK \cong \angle NLM$

TOPIC 3

Answers included.

MIXED PRACTICE

> This Mixed Practice worksheet includes two sections: Spaced Review and End-of-Topic Review.

8 Consider the circle with center at point *O*. Determine the information you need to show that $\overline{AR} \cong \overline{BR}$.

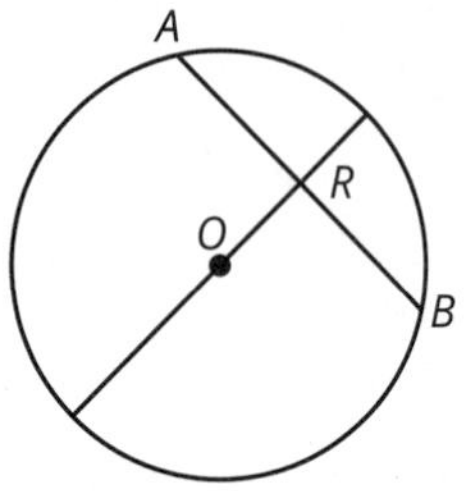

The diameter of the circle through point *R*; diameter through *O* must be perpendicular to chord *AB*.

9 Determine the information you need to show that $\Delta ABC \cong \Delta QRS$ by the HL Congruence Theorem.

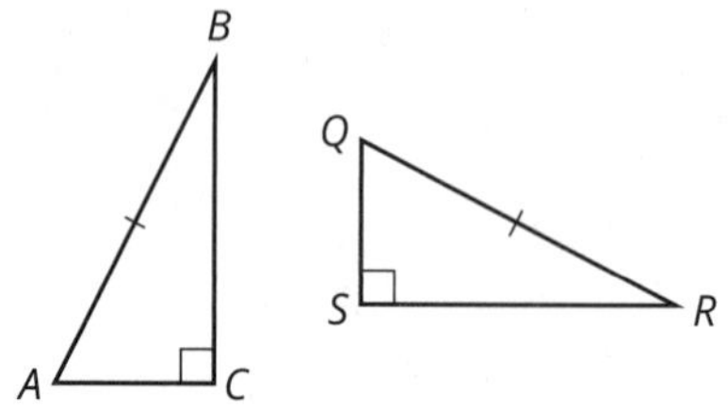

$\overline{BC} \cong \overline{RS}$ or $\overline{AC} \cong \overline{QS}$

10 Consider the circle with center at point *O*. Determine the information you need to show that $\overset{\frown}{RQ} \cong \overset{\frown}{ST}$.

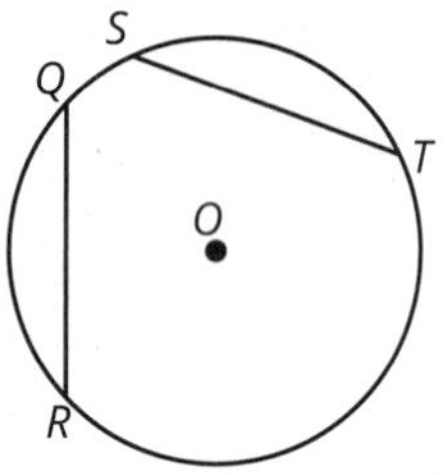

$RQ \cong ST$

11 Paloma tells you she is thinking of a quadrilateral that is either a rectangle or a square, but not both. She wants you to guess which quadrilateral she is thinking of and allows you to ask one question about the quadrilateral. What question should you ask?

You don't need to ask Paloma any questions to determine the identity of the quadrilateral. If it is a square, then it is also considered a rectangle. Since Paloma said that it can't be rectangle and a square, then it must be a rectangle, which is not a square.

Appendix

Getting Ready for Module 1

Reasoning with Shapes

Review Answers

1. $P = 4(13) = 52$ cm

   $A = 13\ 2 = 169$ cm 2

2. $P = 2(14) + 2(8.5) = 45$ in.

   $A = 7(14) = 98$ in.

Getting Ready for Module 2

Establishing Proof

Review Answers

$w = 180° - (80° + 65°) = 35°$

$x = 180° - (20° + 25°) = 135°$

$y = 80° + 65° = 145°$

$z = 180° - 20° = 160°$

Getting Ready for Module 3

Investigating Proportionality

Review Answers

1. $x = -8.3$
2. $x = 12$
3. $x = 2$
4. $x = 4.08$

Getting Ready for Module 4

Connecting Geometric and Algebraic Descriptions

Review Answers

1. $C = 2\pi r$

   $C = 2(5)\pi = 10\pi$ cm

   $A = \pi r^2$

   $A = \pi(5^2) = 25\pi$ cm^2

2. $C = d\pi$

   $C = 7\pi$ cm

   $A = \pi r^2$

   $A = \pi(3.5^2) = 12.25\pi$ cm^2

Getting Ready for Module 5

Making Informed Decisions

Review Answers

1. $P(B) = \frac{11}{18}$

2. $P(A) = \frac{3}{18} = \frac{1}{6}$

3. $P(\text{not } A) = P(B) + P(C)$

   $\frac{11}{18} + \frac{4}{18} = \frac{15}{18}$

4. $P(\text{not } C) = P(A) + P(B)$

   $\frac{3}{18} + \frac{11}{18} = \frac{14}{18} = \frac{7}{9}$

Glossary

A

Addition Property of Equality

The addition property of equality states: "If $a = b$, then $a + c = b + c$."

EXAMPLE

If $x = 2$, then $x + 5 = 2 + 5$, or $x + 5 = 7$ is an example of the Addition Property of Equality.

Addition Rule for Probability

The Addition Rule for Probability states: "The probability that Event *A* occurs or Event *B* occurs is the probability that Event *A* occurs plus the probability that Event *B* occurs minus the probability that both *A* and *B* occur."

$$P(A \text{ or } B) = P(A) + P(B) = P(A \text{ and } B)$$

EXAMPLE

You flip a coin two times. Calculate the probability of flipping heads on the first flip or flipping heads on the second flip.

Let *A* represent the event of flipping heads on the first flip. Let *B* represent the event of flipping heads on the second flip.

$P(A \text{ or } B) = P(A) + P(B) - P(A \text{ and } B)$

$P(A \text{ or } B) = \frac{1}{2} + \frac{1}{2} - \frac{1}{4}$

$P(A \text{ or } B) = \frac{3}{4}$

So, the probability of flipping heads on the first flip or flipping heads on the second flip is $\frac{3}{4}$.

adjacent arcs

Adjacent arcs are two arcs of the same circle sharing a common endpoint.

EXAMPLE

Arcs *ZA* and *AB* are adjacent arcs.

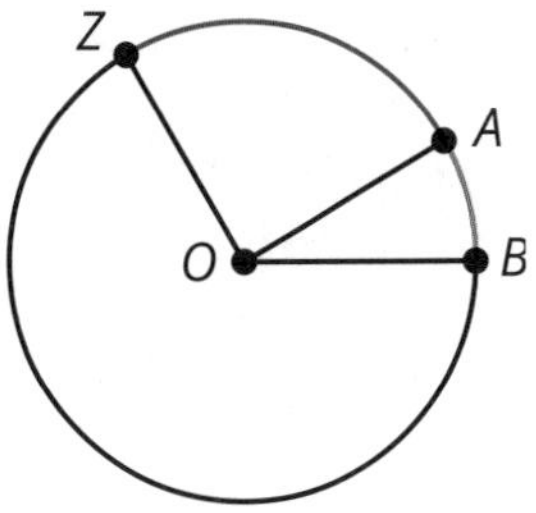

---

adjacent side

The adjacent side of a triangle is the side adjacent to the reference angle that is not the hypotenuse.

EXAMPLE

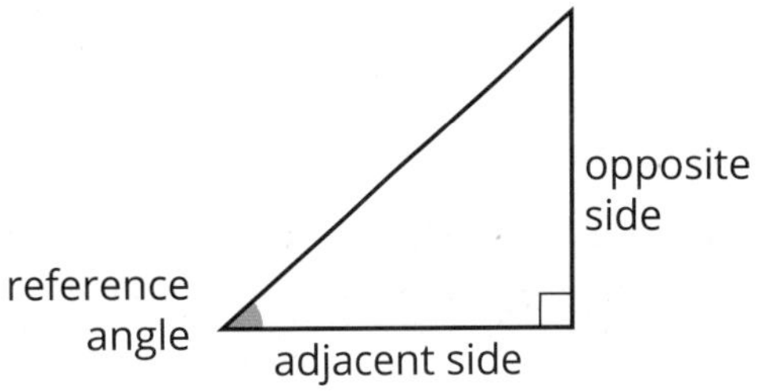

---

altitude

An altitude is a line segment perpendicular to the line containing the opposite side and has one endpoint at the opposite vertex.

EXAMPLE

Segment *EG* is an altitude of ΔFED.

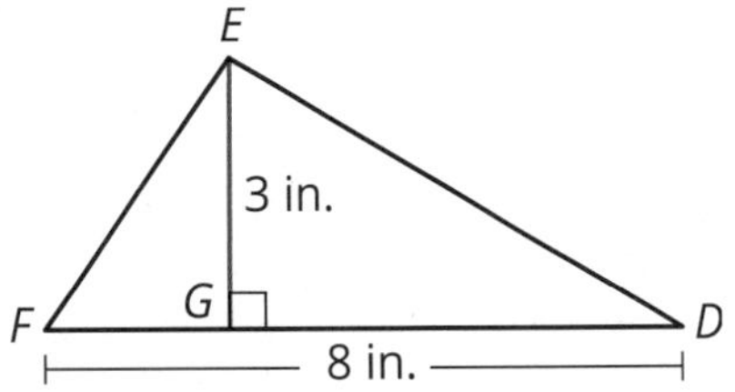

Glossary Continued

angle

An angle is a set of points consisting of a vertex point and two rays extending from the vertex point.

angle bisector

An angle bisector is a ray drawn through the vertex of an angle that divides the angle into two angles of equal measure, or two congruent angles.

EXAMPLE

Ray *BY* is an angle bisector.

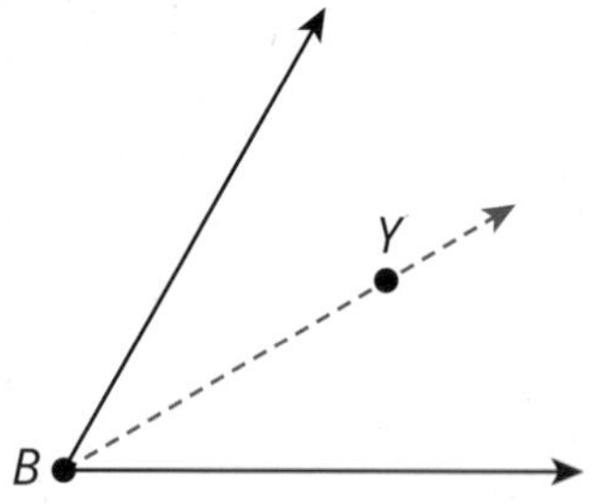

angle of incidence

The angle of incidence is the angle formed by the incidence ray and a line perpendicular to the surface of a mirror.

EXAMPLE

The angle of incidence measures 40°.

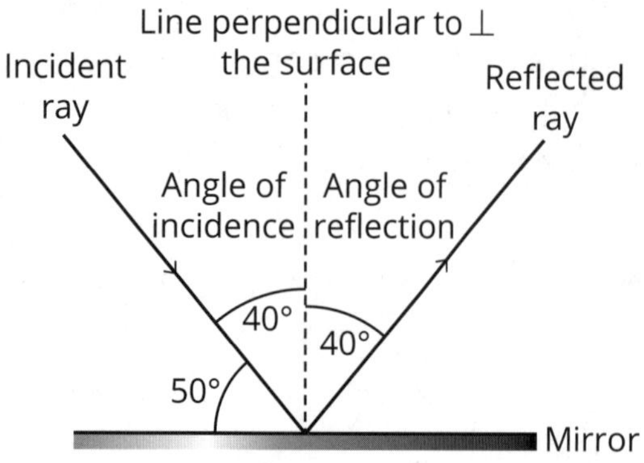

angle of reflection

The angle of reflection is the angle formed by the reflected ray and a line perpendicular to the surface of a mirror.

EXAMPLE

The angle of reflection measures 40°.

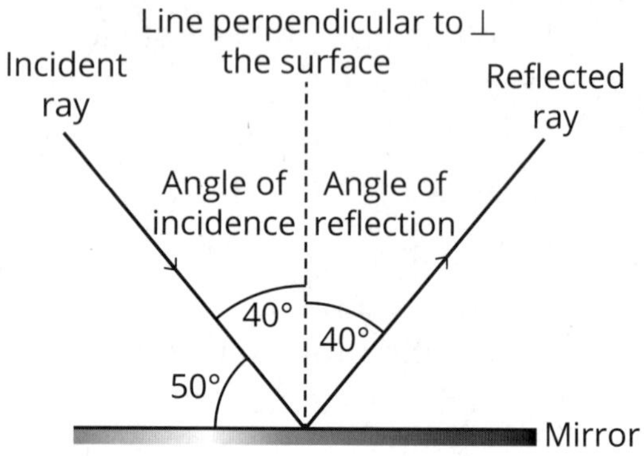

angular velocity

Angular velocity is a type of circular velocity described as an amount of angle movement in radians over a specified amount of time. You an express angular velocity as $\omega = \frac{\theta}{t}$, where ω = angular velocity, θ = angular measurement in radians, and t = time.

arc

An arc is a part of the circumference of a circle and is the curve between two points on the circle. You label an arc using its two endpoints.

EXAMPLE

Arc *CD* is an arc of Circle *O*. The symbol used to describe arc *CD* is $\overset{\frown}{CD}$.

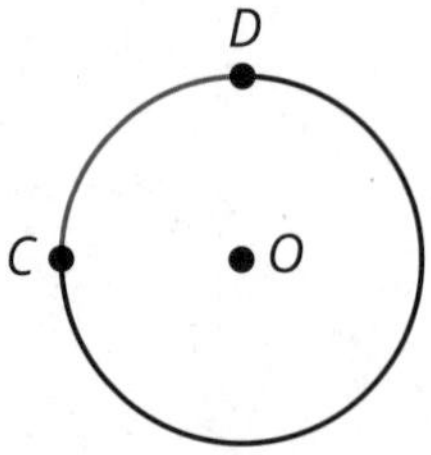

arc length

An arc length is a portion of the circumference of a circle. You can calculate the length of an arc of a circle by multiplying the circumference of the circle by the ratio of the measure of the arc to 360°.

arc length $= 2\pi r \cdot \frac{x°}{360°}$

EXAMPLE

The length of $\overset{\frown}{BC}$ is approximately 4.35 centimeters.

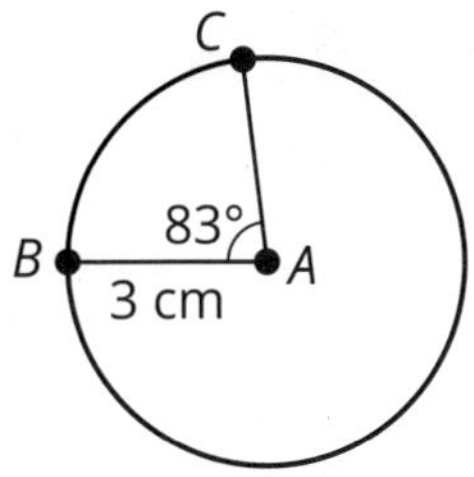

$$(2\pi r)\left(\frac{m\overset{\frown}{BC}}{360°}\right) = 2\pi(3)\left(\frac{83°}{360°}\right)$$
$$\approx 4.35$$

---

area

The number of square units needed to cover a two-dimensional shape or the surface of an object is the area.

EXAMPLE

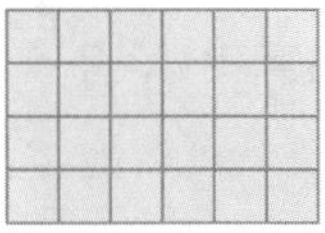

The rectangle has an area of 24 square units.

auxiliary line

An auxiliary line is a line or line segment added to a diagram to help in solving or proving a concept.

EXAMPLE

An auxiliary line is drawn parallel to $\overleftrightarrow{AB}$ through point C.

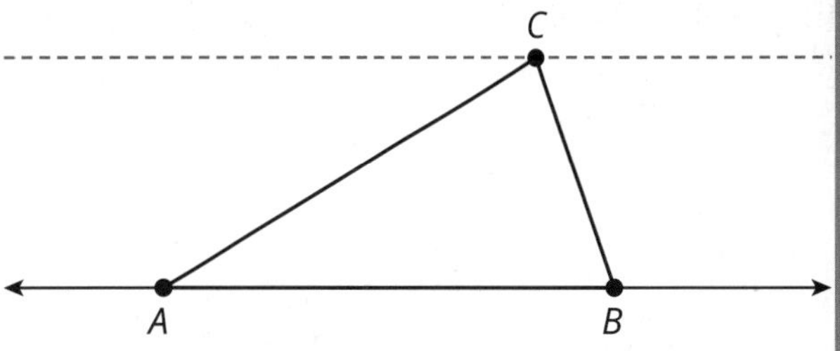

B

base angles of an isosceles triangle

The base angles of an isosceles triangle are the angles between the base and the congruent sides of the triangle.

EXAMPLE

Angles A and C are the base angles of isosceles triangle ABC.

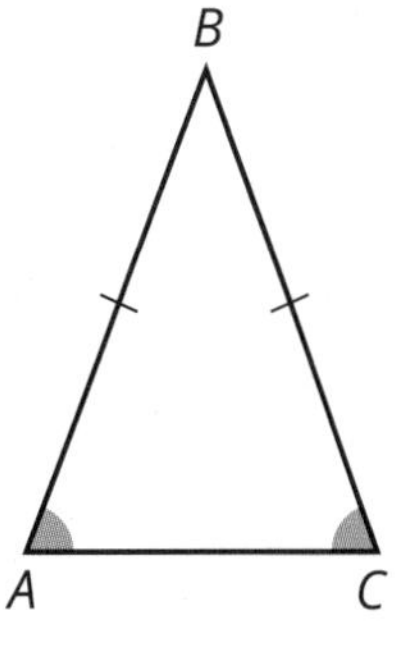

base angles of a trapezoid

The base angles of a trapezoid are either pair of angles that share a base as a common side.

EXAMPLE

Angle *T* and angle *R* are one pair of base angles of trapezoid *PART*. Angle *P* and angle *A* are another pair of base angles.

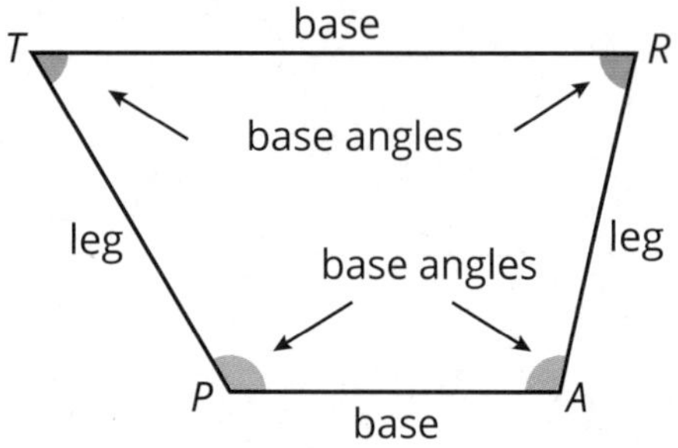

biconditional statement

A biconditional statement is a statement in the form "if and only if *p*, then *q*." It is a combination of both a conditional statement and the converse of that conditional statement. A biconditional statement is true only when the conditional statement and the converse of the statement are both true.

EXAMPLE

Consider the statement: "If a trapezoid is isosceles, then the diagonals are congruent." The converse of this statement is true: "If the diagonals of a trapezoid are congruent, then the trapezoid is an isosceles trapezoid." So, you can write this property as a biconditional statement: "A trapezoid is isosceles if and only if its diagonals are congruent."

C

categorical data (qualitative data)

Categorical data are data that fit into exactly one of several different groups, or categories. Categorical data are also called "qualitative data."

EXAMPLE

Animals: lions, tigers, bears, etc.
U.S. Cities: Los Angeles, Atlanta, New York City, Dodge City, etc.

The set of animals and the set of U.S. cities are two examples of categorical data sets.

Cavalieri's Principle

Cavalieri's Principle states that if all one-dimensional slices of two-dimensional figures have the same lengths, then the two-dimensional figures have the same area. The principle also states that given two solid figures included between parallel planes, if every plane cross section parallel to the given planes has the same area in both solids, then the volumes of the solids are equal.

center of dilation

The fixed point from which you generate a dilation is the center of dilation.

EXAMPLE

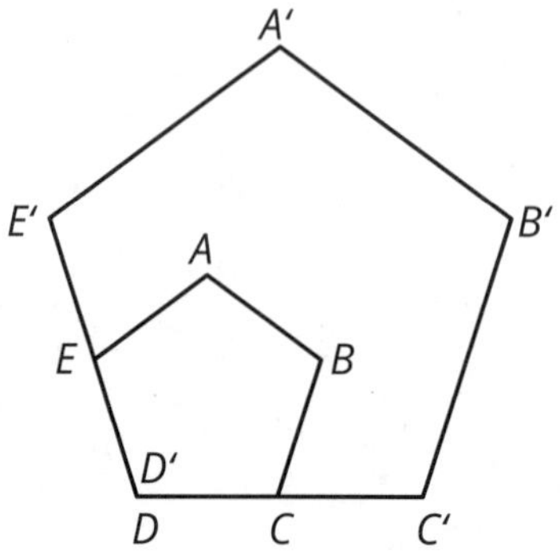

The center of dilation is point *D*.

central angle

A central angle is an angle with its vertex at the center of a circle. The measure of a central angle is equal to the measure of its intercepted arc.

EXAMPLE

In Circle *O*, $\angle AOC$ is a central angle and $\widehat{AC}$ is its intercepted arc.

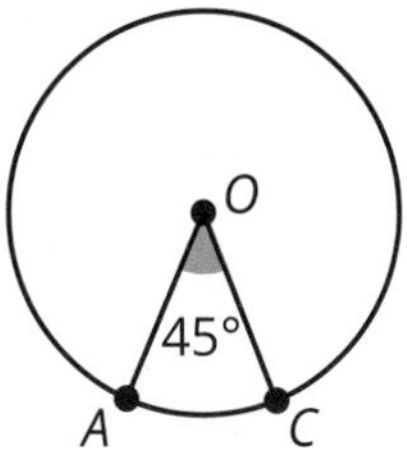

centroid

The centroid of a triangle is the point at which the medians of the triangle intersect.

EXAMPLE

Point *X* is the centroid of triangle ΔABC.

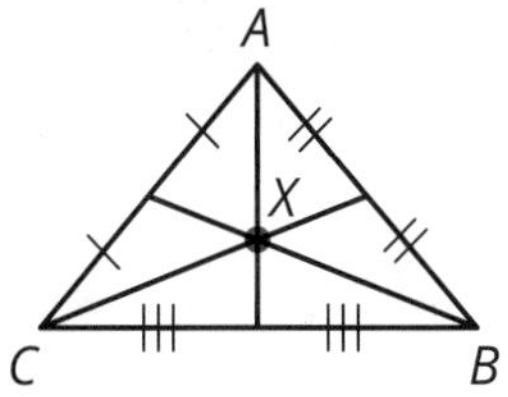

chord

A chord is a line segment whose endpoints are points on a circle.

EXAMPLE

Segment *CD* is a chord of Circle *O*.

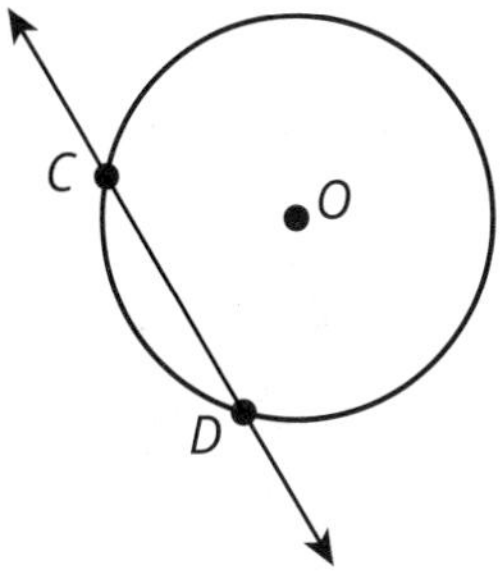

circle

A circle is a collection of points on the same plane equidistant from the same point. The center of a circle is the point from which all points on the circle are equidistant. You name circles by their center point.

EXAMPLE

The circle shown is Circle *O*.

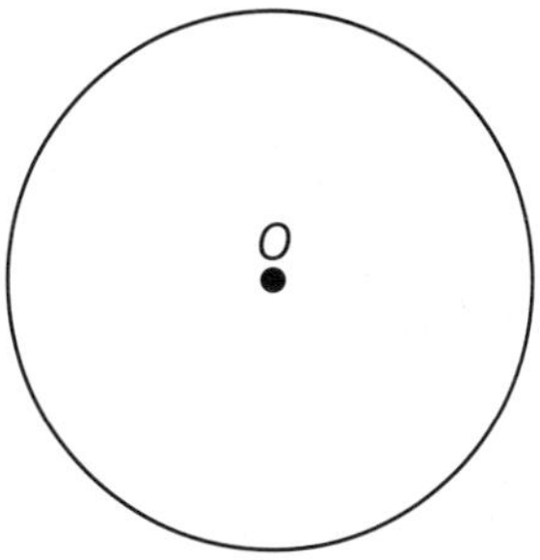

circular permutation

A circular permutation is a permutation in which there is no starting point and no ending point. The circular permutation of *n* objects is $(n - 1)!$.

EXAMPLE

A club consists of four officers: a president (P), a vice-president (VP), a secretary (S), and a treasurer (T). There are $(4 - 1)!$, or 6 ways for the officers to sit around a round table.

circumcenter

The circumcenter of a triangle is the point at which the perpendicular bisectors of the triangle intersect.

EXAMPLE

Point *X* is the circumcenter of ΔABC.

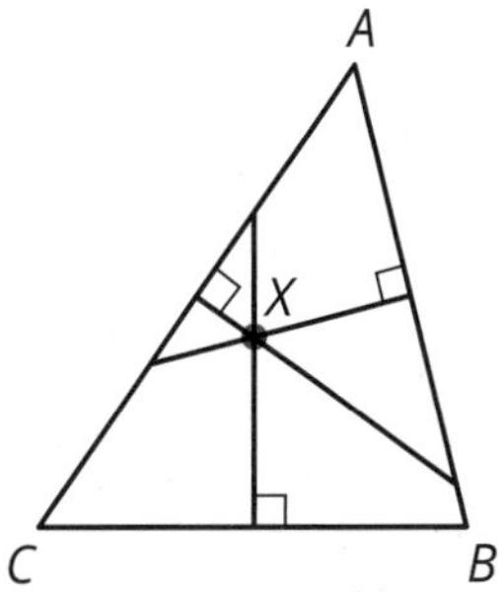

circumference

You call the distance around a circle the circumference of the circle. The circumference is calculated by the formula: $C = \pi(d)$.

EXAMPLE

The diameter of Circle *O* is 12 centimeters. The circumference of Circle *O* is 12π.

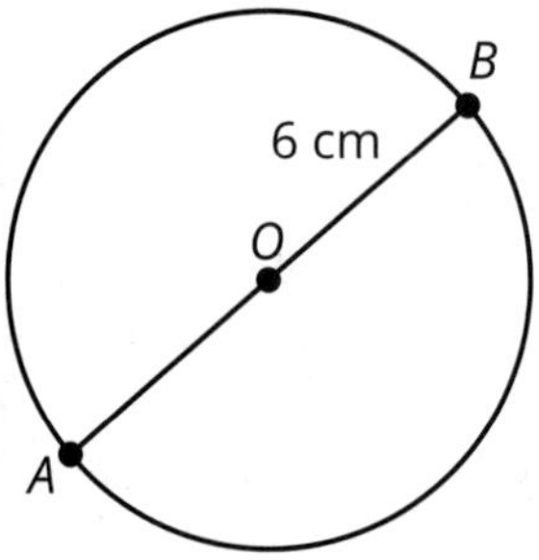

circumscribed angle

A circumscribed angle has its two sides tangent to a circle.

EXAMPLE

Angle *ABC* is circumscribed in Circle *O*.

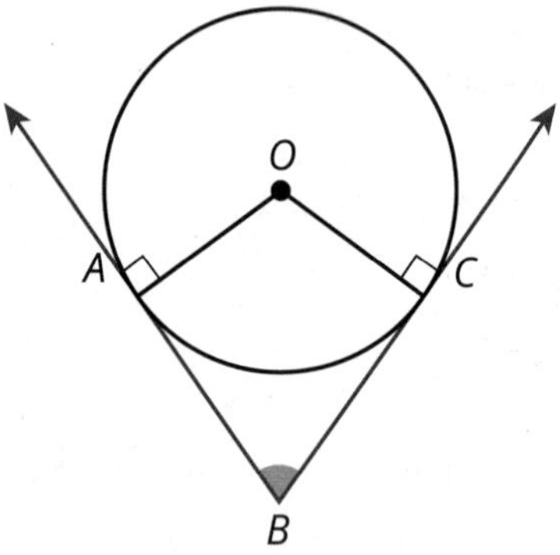

circumscribed circle

A circumscribed circle is a circle that passes through all the vertices of a polygon.

EXAMPLE

Circle *Q* is circumscribed around ΔABC.

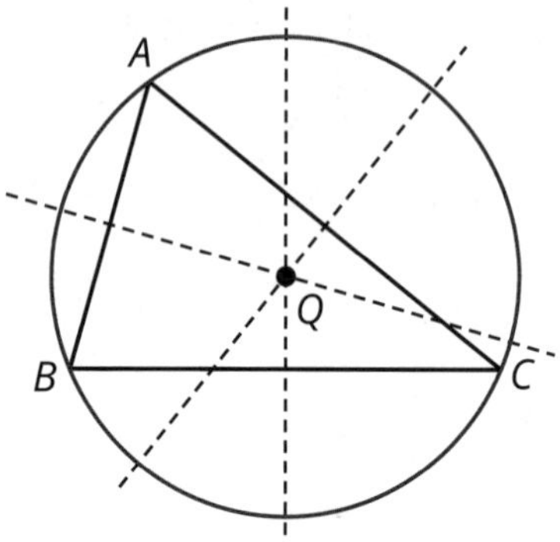

coincident

Two line segments are coincident when they lie exactly on top of each other.

collinear points

Collinear points are points that lie along the same line.

EXAMPLE

Points *A*, *B*, and *C* are collinear.

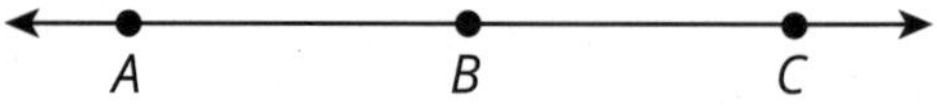

combination

A combination is an unordered collection of items. One notation for the combination of *r* elements taken from a collection of *n* elements is:

$${}_nC_r = C(n, r) = C_r^n$$

EXAMPLE

The two-letter combinations of the letters *A*, *B*, and *C* are: *AB*, *AC*, *BC*.

compass

A compass is a tool used to create arcs and circles.

EXAMPLE

complement of an event

The complement of an event is an event that contains all the outcomes in the sample space that are not outcomes in the event. In mathematical notation, if E is an event, then the complement of E is often denoted as $\overline{E}$ or E^c.

EXAMPLE

A number cube contains the numbers 1 though 6. Let E represent the event of rolling an even number. The complement of Event E is rolling an odd number.

complementary angles

Two angles are complementary angles when the sum of their angle measures is equal to 90°.

EXAMPLE

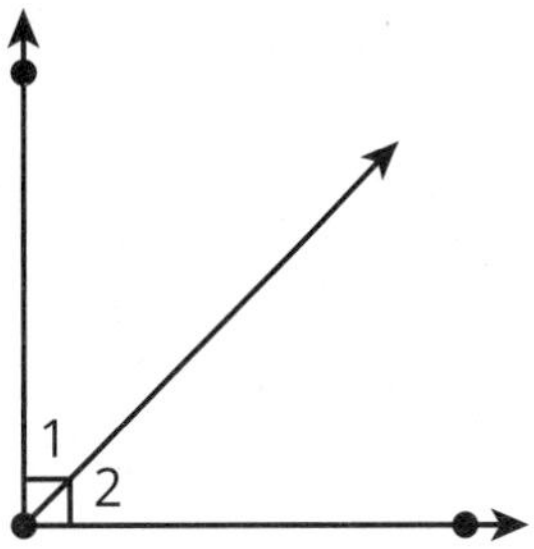

Angles 1 and 2 are complementary angles.

composite figure

A composite figure is a figure formed by combining different shapes.

compound event

A compound event combines two or more events, using the word *and* or the word *or*.

EXAMPLE

You roll a number cube twice. Rolling a six on the first roll and rolling an odd number on the second roll are compound events.

concavity

The concavity of a parabola describes the orientation of the curvature of the parabola.

EXAMPLE

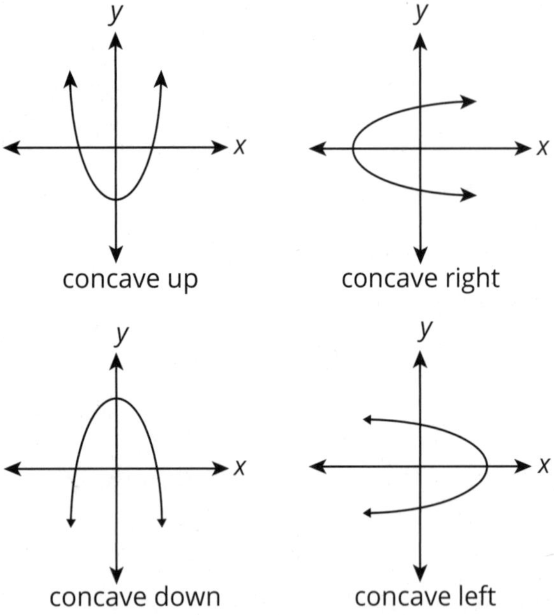

conclusion

A conclusion is the "then" part of an "if-then" statement.

EXAMPLE

In the statement "If two positive numbers are added, then the sum is positive," the conclusion is "the sum is positive."

concurrent

Concurrent lines, rays, or line segments are three or more lines, rays, or line segments intersecting at a single point.

EXAMPLE

Lines *r*, *m*, and *n* are concurrent lines.

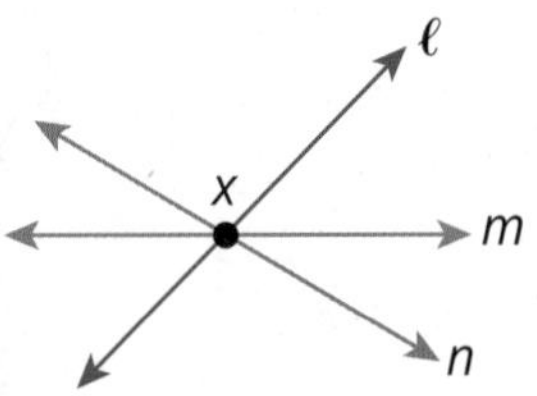

conditional statement

A conditional statement is a statement written in the form "If *p*, then *q*."

conditional probability

A conditional probability is the probability of event *B*, given that event *A* has already occurred. The notation for conditional probability is $P(B|A)$, which reads, "the probability of event *B*, given event *A*."

EXAMPLE

The probability of rolling a 4 or less on the second roll of a number cube, given that a 5 is rolled first, is an example of a conditional probability.

conic section

A conic section forms when a plane intersects a double-napped cone.

EXAMPLE

A parabola is a conic section that results from the intersection of a plane with one nappe of a double-napped cone, parallel to the edge of the cone.

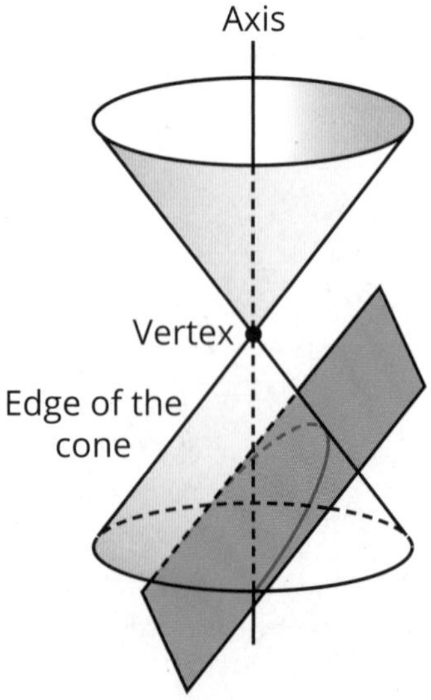

GLOSSARY

conjecture

A conjecture is a mathematical statement that appears valid but you need to formally prove.

conjugate axis

The conjugate axis is the line through the center of a hyperbola and perpendicular to the transverse axis.

construct

When you construct geometric figures, you create exact figures without measurements, using paper folding or a compass and a straightedge—and geometric reasoning.

converse

To state the converse of a conditional statement, interchange the hypothesis and the conclusion.

Conditional Statement: If p, then q.
Converse: If q, then p.

EXAMPLE

Conditional Statement: If $a = 0$ or $b = 0$, then $ab = 0$.

Converse: If $ab = 0$, then $a = 0$ or $b = 0$.

corresponding parts

Corresponding parts are sides or angles that have the same relative positions in geometric figures.

corresponding parts of congruent triangles are congruent (CPCTC)

CPCTC states that if two triangles are congruent, then each part of one triangle is congruent to the corresponding part of the other triangle.

EXAMPLE

$\Delta XYZ \cong \Delta LMN$

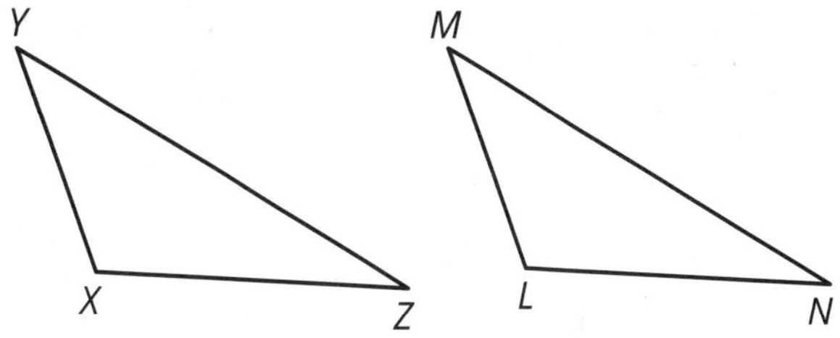

Because corresponding parts of congruent triangles are congruent (CPCTC), the following corresponding parts are congruent.

- $\angle X \cong \angle L$
- $\angle Y \cong \angle M$
- $\angle Z \cong \angle N$
- $\overline{XY} \cong \overline{LM}$
- $\overline{YZ} \cong \overline{MN}$
- $\overline{XZ} \cong \overline{LN}$

cosecant (csc)

The cosecant (csc) of an acute angle in a right triangle is the ratio of the length of the hypotenuse to the length of the side opposite the angle.

EXAMPLE

$$\csc A = \frac{\text{length of hypotenuse}}{\text{length of side opposite } \angle A} = \frac{AB}{BC}$$

The expression "csc A" means "the cosecant of angle A."

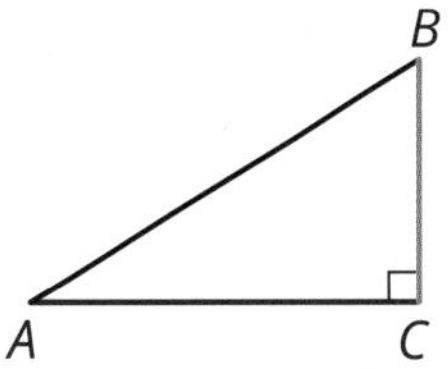

cosine (cos)

The cosine (cos) of an acute angle in a right triangle is the ratio of the length of the side adjacent to the angle to the length of the hypotenuse.

EXAMPLE

$$\cos A = \frac{\text{length of side adjacent to } \angle A}{\text{length of hypotenuse}} = \frac{AC}{AB}$$

The expression "cos A" means "the cosine of angle A."

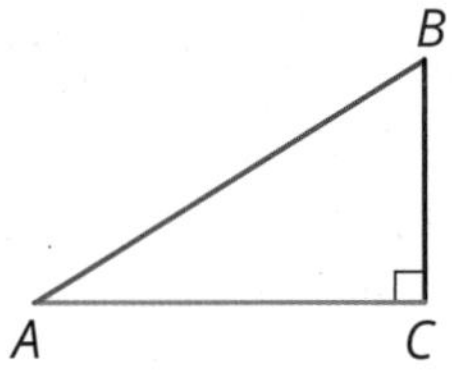

cotangent (cot)

The cotangent (cot) of an acute angle in a right triangle is the ratio of the length of the side adjacent to the angle to the length of the side opposite the angle.

EXAMPLE

$$\cot A = \frac{\text{length of side adjacent to } \angle A}{\text{length of side opposite } \angle A} = \frac{AC}{BC}$$

The expression "cot A" means "the cotangent of angle A."

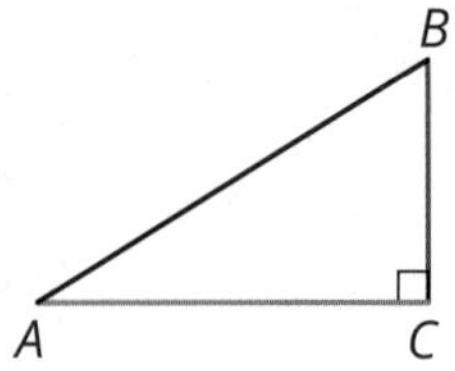

Counting Principle

The Counting Principle states that if action A can occur in m ways and for each of these m ways action B can occur in n ways, then actions A and B can occur in $m \cdot n$ ways.

EXAMPLE

In the school cafeteria, there are 3 different main entrées and 4 different sides. So, there are $3 \cdot 4$, or 12 different lunches that you can create.

co-vertices

The endpoints of the minor axis of an ellipse are the co-vertices.

cross-section

A cross-section of a solid is the two-dimensional figure formed by the intersection of a plane and a solid when a plane passes through the solid.

EXAMPLE

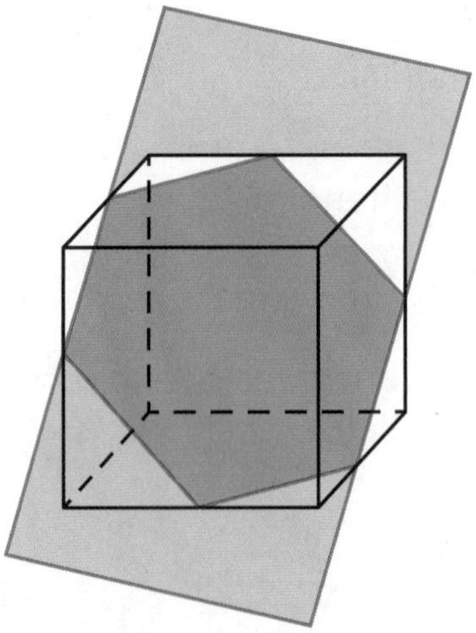

When a plane intersects a cube through all six faces, the cross-section is a hexagon.

cyclic quadrilateral

A cyclic quadrilateral is a quadrilateral whose vertices all lie on a single circle.

EXAMPLE

Quadrilateral *MATH* is a cyclic quadrilateral whose vertices all lie on Circle *O*.

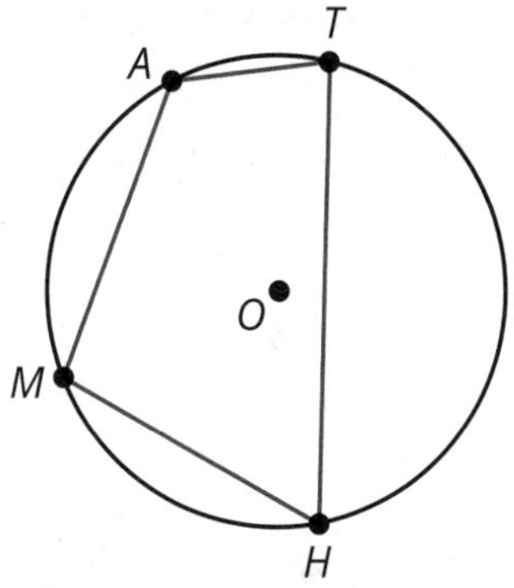

D

degenerate conics

The intersections of a plane and a double-napped cone that form a point, a line, or intersecting lines are degenerate conics.

degree measure of an arc

The degree measure of a minor arc is equal to the degree measure of its central angle. You determine the degree measure of a major arc by subtracting the degree measure of the minor arc from 360°.

EXAMPLE

The measure of minor arc *AB* is 30°. The measure of major arc *BZA* is $360° - 30° = 330°$.

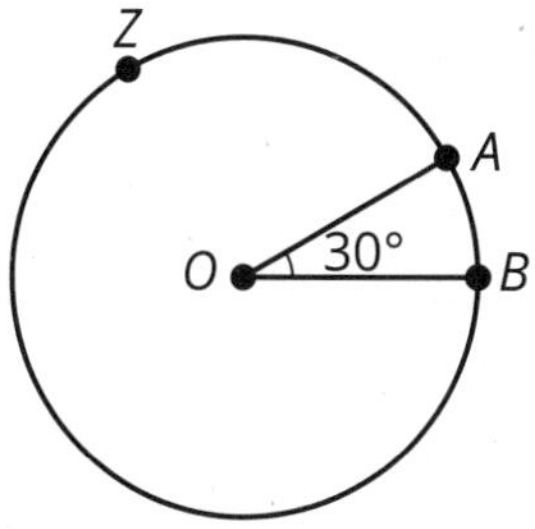

dependent events

Dependent events are events for which the occurrence of one event has an impact on the occurrence of subsequent events.

EXAMPLE

A jar contains 1 blue marble, 1 green marble, and 2 yellow marbles. You randomly choose a yellow marble without replacing the marble in the jar, and then randomly choose a yellow marble again. The events of randomly choosing a yellow marble first and randomly choosing a yellow marble second are dependent events because the 1st yellow marble was not replaced in the jar.

diagonal

A diagonal is a line segment joining two non-consecutive vertices of the polygon.

diameter of a sphere

The diameter of a sphere is a line segment with each endpoint on the sphere that passes through the center of the sphere.

EXAMPLE

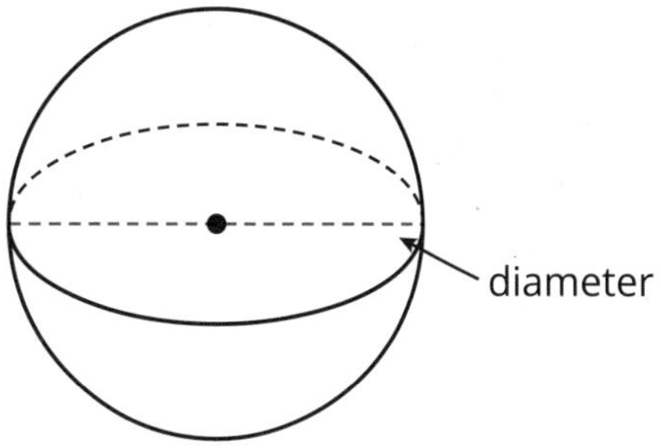

dilation

A dilation is a transformation of the figure in which the figure stretches or shrinks with respect to a fixed point, or center of dilation.

EXAMPLE

Triangle *DEF* is a dilation of ΔABC. The center of dilation is point *Y*.

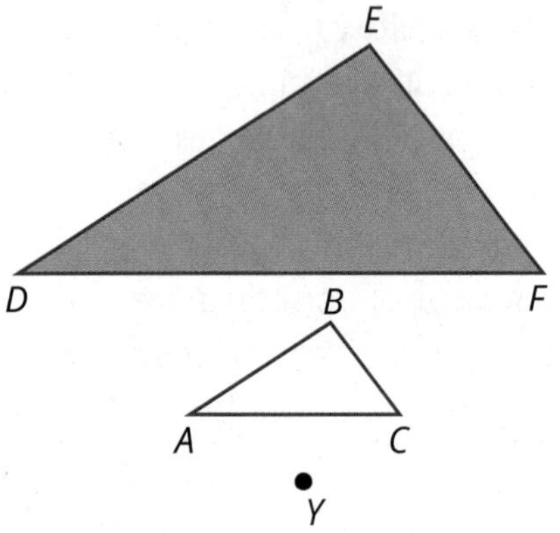

directed line segment

A directed line segment is assigned a direction from one endpoint to the other.

EXAMPLE

Directed line segment *AB* is mathematically different from directed line segment *BA*.

directrix

The directrix of a parabola is a line such that all points on the parabola are equidistant from the focus and the directrix.

EXAMPLE

The focus of the parabola shown is the point (0, 2). The directrix of the parabola shown is the line $y = -2$. All points on the parabola are equidistant from the focus and the directrix.

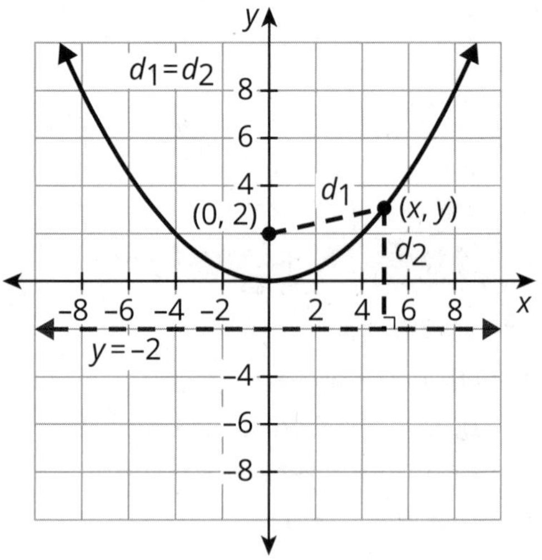

disc

A disc is the set of all points on a circle and in the interior of a circle.

disjoint sets

Two or more sets are disjoint sets if they do not have any common elements.

EXAMPLE

Let *N* represent the set of 9th grade students. Let *T* represent the set of 10th grade students. The sets *N* and *T* are disjoint sets because the two sets do not have any common elements. Any student can be in one grade only.

Distance Formula

The Distance Formula states that when (x_1, y_1) and (x_2, y_2) are two points on the coordinate plane, you calculate the distance d between (x_1, y_1) and (x_2, y_2) using the formula $d = \sqrt{(x_2 - x_1)^2 + (y_2 - y_1)^2}$.

EXAMPLE

To find the distance between the points $(-1, 4)$ and $(2, -5)$, substitute the coordinates into the Distance Formula.

$d = \sqrt{(x_2 - x_1)^2 + (y_2 - y_1)^2}$

$d = \sqrt{(2 + 1)^2 + (-5 - 4)^2}$

$d = \sqrt{3^2 + (-9)^2}$

$d = \sqrt{9 + 81}$

$d = \sqrt{90}$

$d \approx 9.49$

So, the distance between the points $(-1, 4)$ and $(2, -5)$ is approximately 9.49 units.

draw

To draw is to create a geometric figure using tools such as a ruler, straightedge, compass, or protractor. A drawing is more accurate than a sketch.

duplicate

To duplicate a geometric figure, you use construction tools to create an exact copy.

E

eccentricity

Eccentricity, e, is a parameter associated with every conic section. It is a measure of how much the conic section deviates from being a circle. When $e = 0$, the conic section is a circle.

element

A member of a set is an element of that set.

EXAMPLE

Set B contains the elements a, b, and c.

$B = \{a, b, c\}$

ellipse

When a plane intersects a single nappe not perpendicular to the axis, but at an angle that is less than the central angle of the nappe, the curve that results is an ellipse. An ellipse is the locus of all points in a plane for which the sum of whose distances from two given points is a constant.

EXAMPLE

The sum of the distances from each focus to any point, P, on the curve of the ellipse is constant.

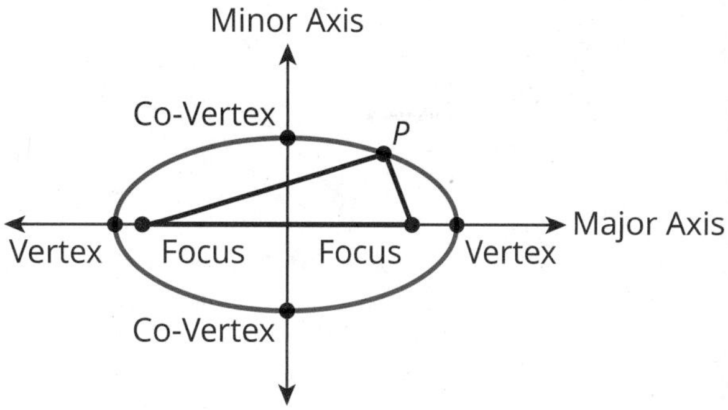

Euclidean geometry

Euclidean geometry is a geometry of straight lines and flat planes based on postulates developed by the ancient Greek mathematician Euclid. There are other types of geometry, such as spherical geometry and hyperbolic geometry, which are used to study curved space.

event

An event is an outcome or a set of outcomes in a sample space.

EXAMPLE

A number cube contains the numbers 1 through 6. Rolling a 6 is one event. Rolling an even number is another event.

expected value

The expected value is the average value when the number of trials in a probability experiment is large.

exterior angle of a polygon

An exterior angle of a polygon is an angle that forms a linear pair with an interior angle of the polygon.

EXAMPLE

Angle *JHI* is an exterior angle of Quadrilateral *FGHI*. Angle *EDA* is an exterior angle of Quadrilateral *ABCD*.

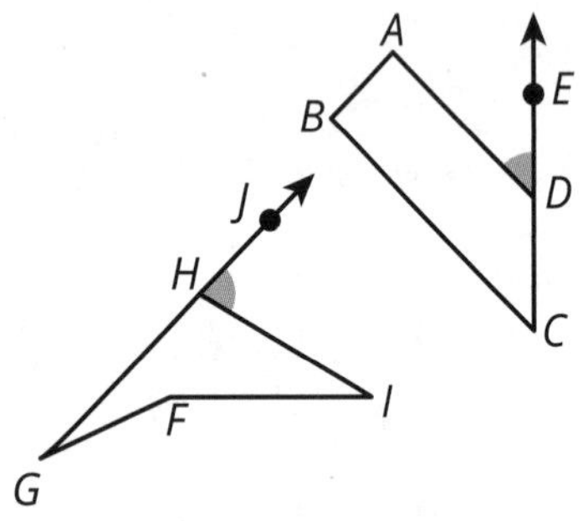

extract the roots

To extract a root is the process of removing all perfect square numbers from under the radical symbol.

EXAMPLE

To extract the root for $\sqrt{18}$, remove all perfect square numbers that are factors of 18.

$$\begin{aligned}\sqrt{18} &= \sqrt{9 \cdot 2}\\ &= \sqrt{3^2 \cdot 2}\\ &= 3\sqrt{2}\end{aligned}$$

F

factorial

The factorial of *n*, written as *n*!, is the product of all non-negative integers less than or equal to *n*.

EXAMPLE

$3! = 3 \times 2 \times 1 = 6$

flow chart proof

A flow chart proof is a proof in which the steps and corresponding reasons are in boxes. Arrows connect the boxes and indicate how each step and reason generates from one or more other steps and reasons.

EXAMPLE

A flow chart proof is shown for the conditional statement: If $\overline{AB} \cong \overline{CD}$, then $\overline{AC} \cong \overline{BD}$.

Given: $\overline{AB} \cong \overline{CD}$

Prove: $\overline{AC} \cong \overline{BD}$

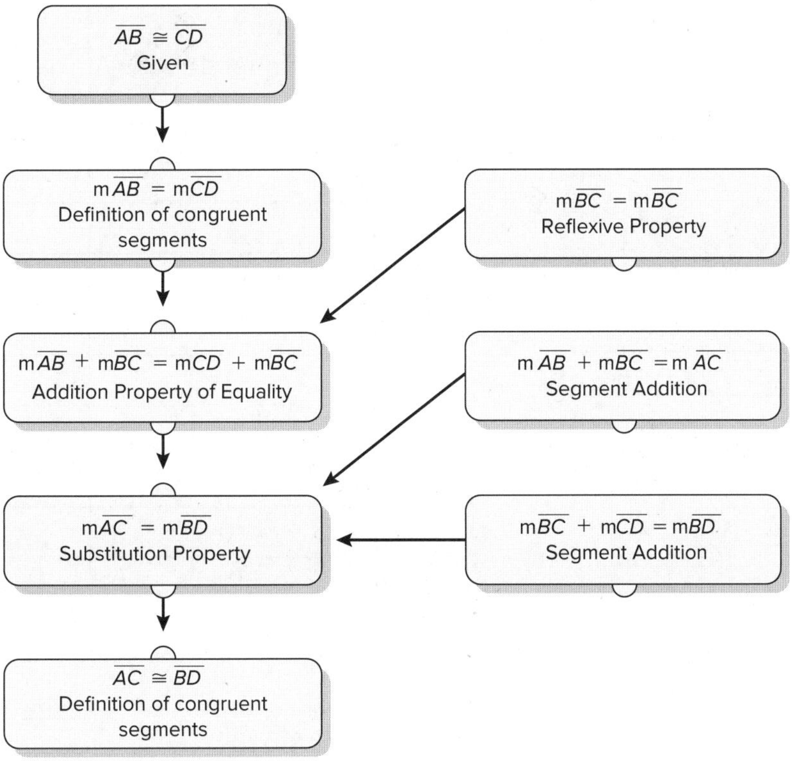

focus

The focus of a parabola is a point such that all points on the parabola are equidistant from the focus and the directrix.

EXAMPLE

The focus of the parabola shown is the point (0, 2). The directrix of the parabola shown is the line $y = -2$. All points on the parabola are equidistant from the focus and the directrix.

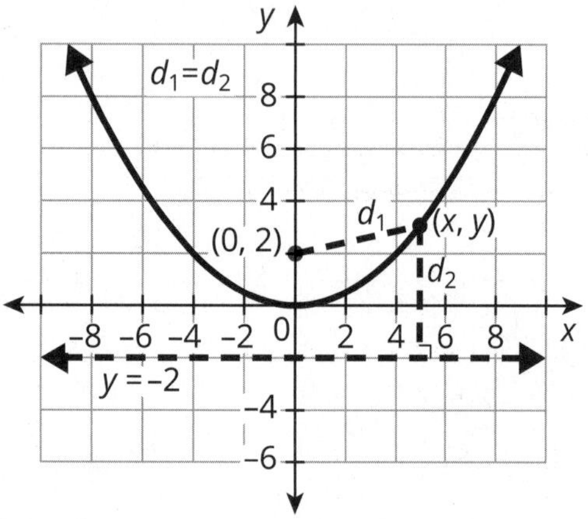

foci (focus)

For two given points, the foci, an ellipse is the locus of points such that the sum of the distance to each focus is constant, and a hyperbola is the locus of points such that the difference of the distances from each focus is constant.

frequency table

A frequency table shows the frequency of an item, number, or event appearing in a sample space.

EXAMPLE

The frequency table shows the number of times a sum of two number cubes occurred.

Sum of Two Number Cubes	Frequency
2	1
3	2
4	3
5	4
6	5
7	6
8	5
9	4
10	3
11	2
12	1

function

A function takes points, distances, and angles as inputs and outputs a new set of points after applying a transformation.

G

general form of a parabola

The general form of a parabola centered at the origin is an equation of the form $Ax^2 + Dy = 0$ or $By^2 + Cx = 0$.

EXAMPLE

You can write the equation for the parabola shown in general form as $x^2 - 2y = 0$.

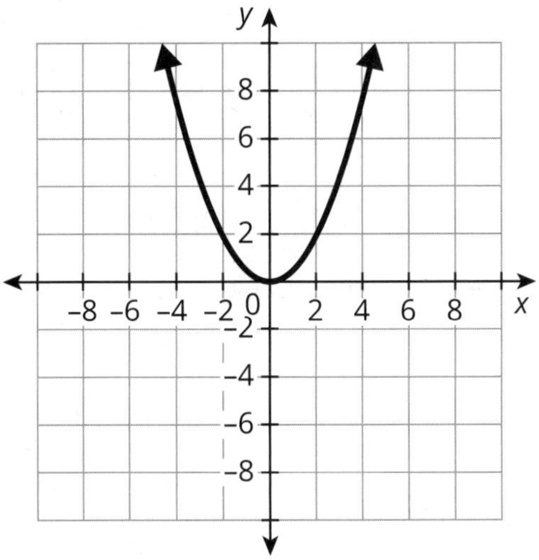

geometric mean

The geometric mean of two positive numbers a and b is the positive number x such that $\frac{a}{x} = \frac{x}{b}$.

EXAMPLE

The geometric mean of 3 and 12 is 6.

$\frac{3}{x} = \frac{x}{12}$

$x^2 = 36$

$x = 6$

geometric probability

Geometric probability is probability that involves a geometric measure, such as length, area, volume, and so on.

EXAMPLE

A dartboard has the size and shape shown. The shaded area represents a scoring section of the dartboard.
The probability that a dart that lands on a random part of the target lands in a scoring section is 68%.

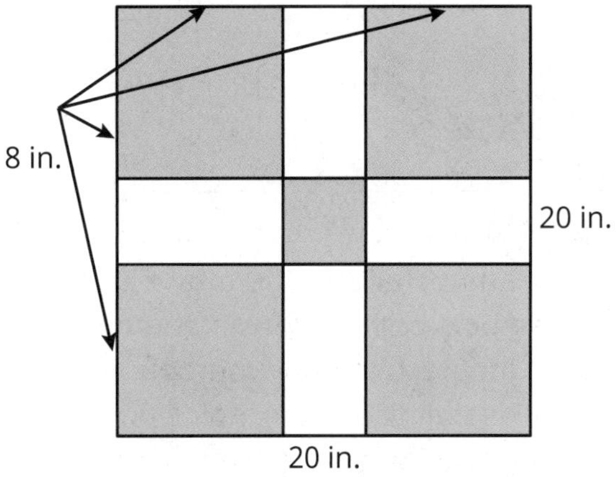

Area of dartboard: $20(20) = 400$ in.^{2}

Area of scoring sections:
$4(8)(8) + 4(4) = 272$ in.^{2}

$\frac{272}{400} = 0.68 = 68\%$.

great circle of a sphere

The great circle of a sphere is a cross-section of a sphere when a plane passes through the center of the sphere.

EXAMPLE

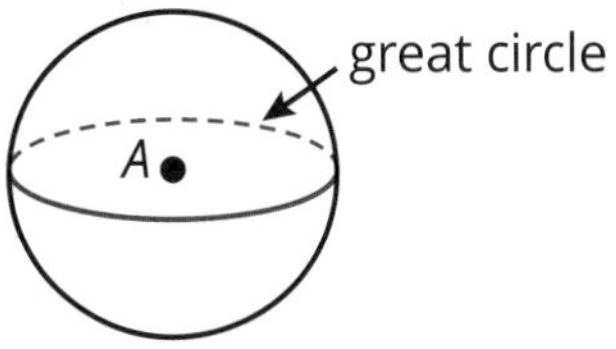

H

hemisphere

A hemisphere is half of a sphere bounded by a great circle.

EXAMPLE

A hemisphere is shown.

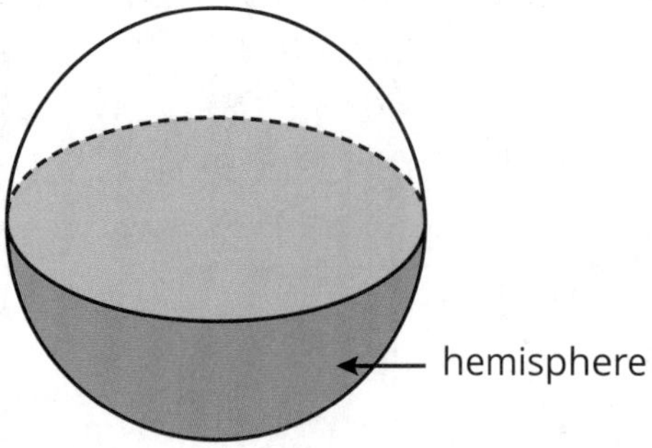

hyperbola

When a plane parallel to the axis of the cone intersects both nappes of the cone, the curve that results is a hyperbola. A hyperbola is the locus of all points in a plane for which the difference of whose distances from two given points is a constant.

EXAMPLE

The difference of the distances from each focus to any point, P, on the curves of a hyperbola is constant.

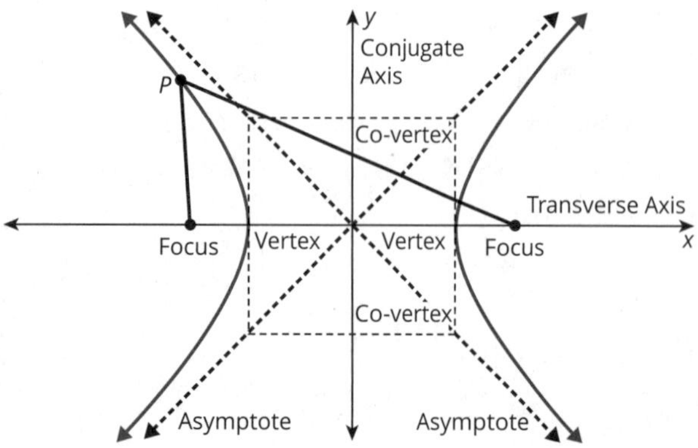

hypothesis

A hypothesis is the "if" part of an "if-then" statement.

EXAMPLE

In the statement, "If the last digit of a number is a 5, then the number is divisible by 5," the hypothesis is "If the last digit of a number is a 5."

I

incenter

The incenter of a triangle is the point at which the angle bisectors of the triangle intersect.

EXAMPLE

Point X is the incenter of ΔABC.

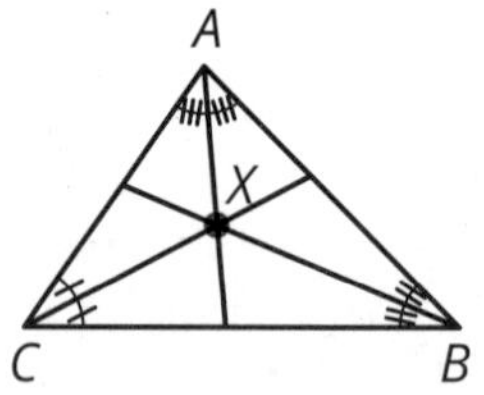

included angle

An included angle is an angle formed by two consecutive sides of a figure.

EXAMPLE

In ΔABC, $\angle A$ is the included angle formed by consecutive sides $\overline{AB}$ and $\overline{AC}$.

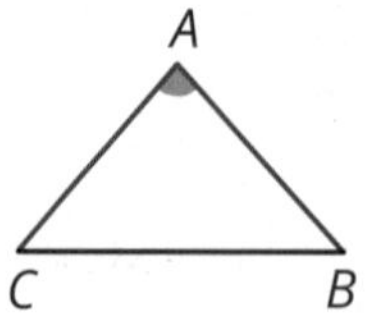

included side

An included side is a line segment between two consecutive angles of a figure.

EXAMPLE

In ΔABC, $\overline{AB}$ is the included side formed by consecutive angles A and B.

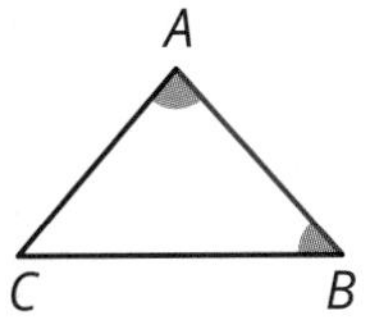

independent events

Independent events are events for which the occurrence of one event has no impact on the occurrence of the other event.

EXAMPLE

You randomly choose a yellow marble, replace the marble in the jar, and then randomly choose a yellow marble again. The events of randomly choosing a yellow marble first and randomly choosing a yellow marble second are independent events because the 1st yellow marble was replaced in the jar.

indirect measurement

Indirect measurement is a technique that uses proportions to determine a measurement when direct measurement is not possible.

inscribed angle

An inscribed angle is an angle whose vertex is on a circle and whose sides contain chords of the circle.

EXAMPLE

Angle BAC is an inscribed angle. The vertex of angle BAC is on the circle and the sides of angle BAC contain the chords $\overline{AB}$ and $\overline{AC}$.

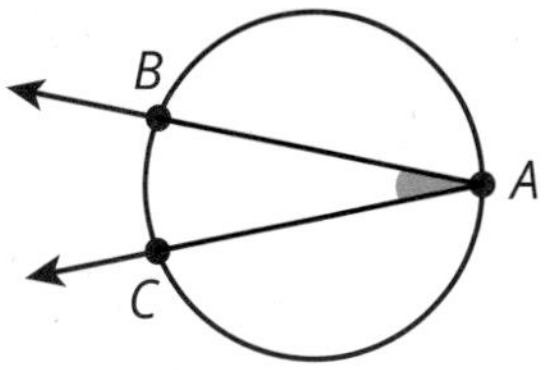

inscribed polygon

An inscribed polygon is a polygon drawn inside another polygon or circle in which all the vertices of the interior polygon lie on the outer figure.

EXAMPLE

Quadrilateral $KLMN$ is inscribed in Circle J.

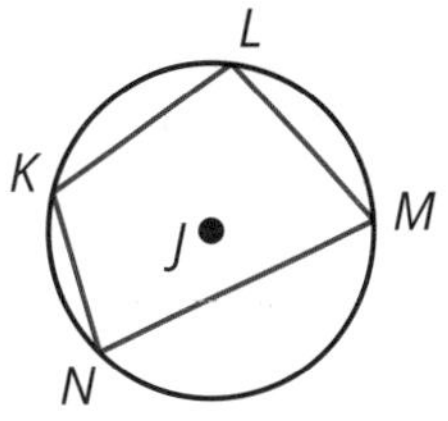

intercepted arc

An intercepted arc is a part of a circle that lies in the interior of an angle with endpoints that are the intersection of the sides of the angle and the circle.

EXAMPLE

$\overset{\frown}{PR}$ is an intercepted arc of inscribed angle PSR.

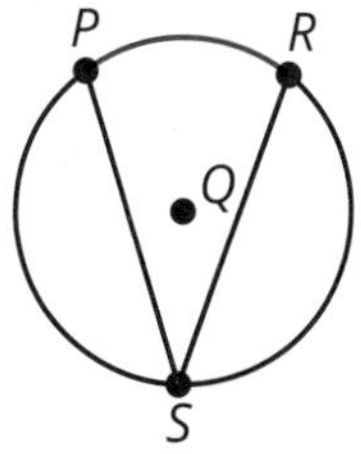

interior angle of a polygon

An interior angle of a polygon is an angle inside the polygon between two adjacent sides.

EXAMPLE

The interior angles of ΔABC are $\angle ABC$, $\angle BCA$, and $\angle CAB$.

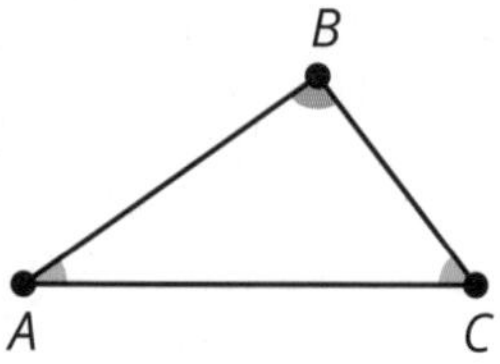

intersecting sets

Two or more sets are intersecting sets when they have common elements.

EXAMPLE

Let V represent the set of students who are on the volleyball team. Let M represent the set of students who are in the math club. Julia is on the volleyball team and belongs to the math club. The sets V and M are intersecting sets because the two sets have at least one common element, Julia.

inverse cosine

The inverse cosine, or arccosine, of x is the measure of an acute angle whose cosine is x.

EXAMPLE

In Right Triangle ABC, when $\cos A = x$, $\cos^{-1} x = m\angle A$.

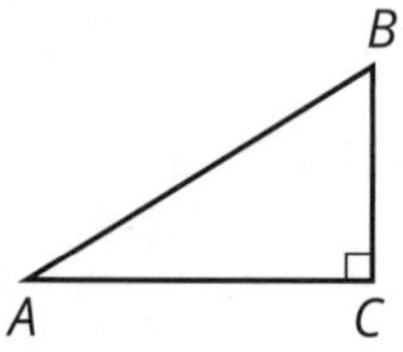

inverse sine

The inverse sine, or arcsine, of x is the measure of an acute angle whose sine is x.

EXAMPLE

In Right Triangle ABC, when $\sin A = x$, $\sin^{-1} x = m\angle A$.

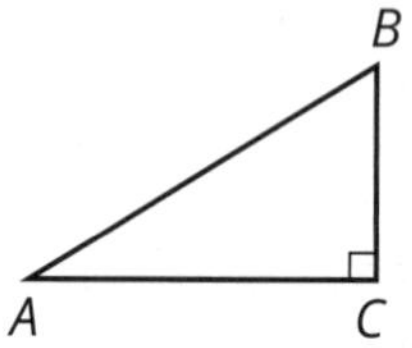

inverse tangent

The inverse tangent (or arctangent) of x is the measure of an acute angle whose tangent is x.

EXAMPLE

In Right Triangle ABC, when $\tan A = x$, $\tan^{-1} x = m\angle A$.

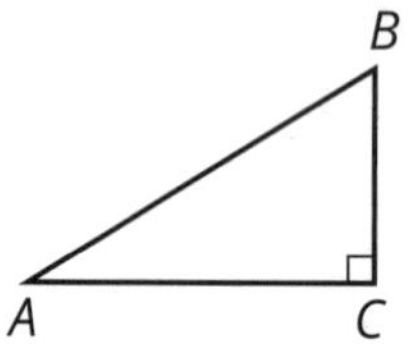

isometric paper

You can use isometric paper, or dot paper, to create three-dimensional views of objects in two dimensions.

EXAMPLE

The rectangular prism is shown on isometric paper.

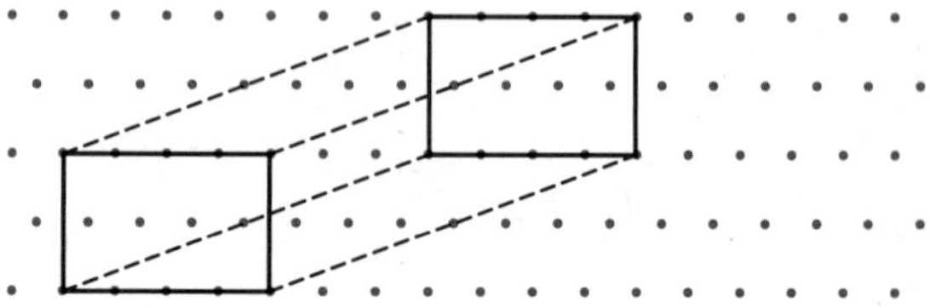

isometry

An isometry is a rigid motion transformation that preserves size and shape.

isosceles trapezoid

An isosceles trapezoid is a trapezoid with nonparallel sides congruent.

EXAMPLE

In Trapezoid *JKLM*, side $\overline{KL}$ is parallel to side $\overline{JM}$, and the length of side $\overline{JK}$ is equal to the length of side $\overline{LM}$, so Trapezoid *JKLM* is an isosceles trapezoid.

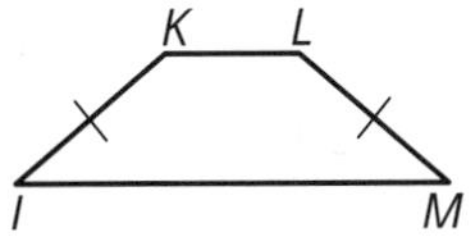

K

kite

A kite is a quadrilateral with two pairs of equal adjacent sides. When the diagonals of a quadrilateral are perpendicular, and only one bisects the other, you can only classify it as a kite.

EXAMPLE

Quadrilateral *ABCD* is a kite.

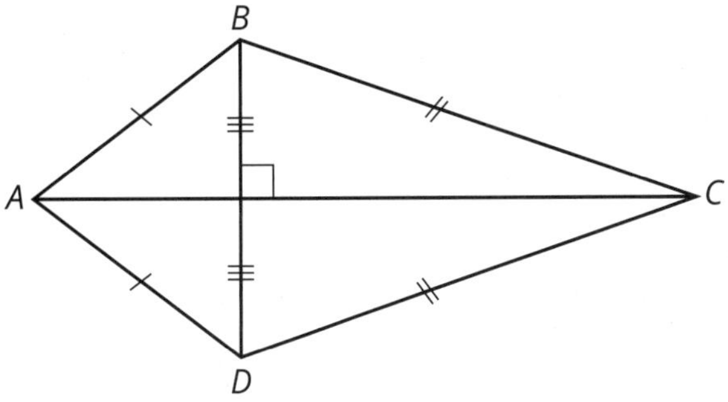

L

lateral face

A lateral face of a three-dimensional object is a face that is not a base.

EXAMPLE

Each lateral face of a right triangular prism is a rectangle.

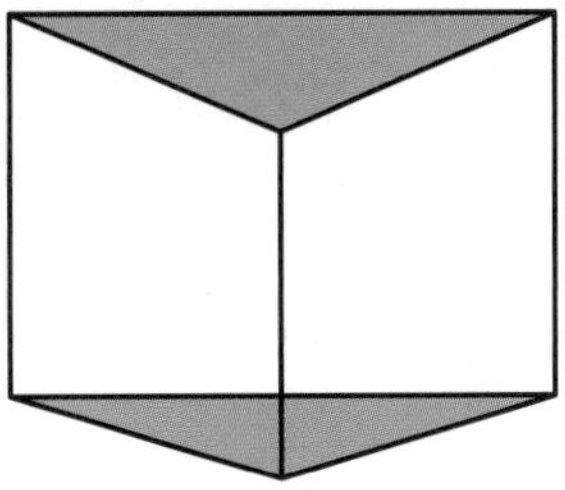

lateral surface area

The lateral surface area of a three-dimensional figure is the sum of the areas of its lateral faces.

EXAMPLE

The lateral surface area of the right triangular prism is 108 square centimeters.

$$\begin{aligned}\text{Lateral surface area} &= (5 \cdot 6) + (5 \cdot 6) + (8 \cdot 6)\\ &= 30 + 30 + 48\\ &= 108\end{aligned}$$

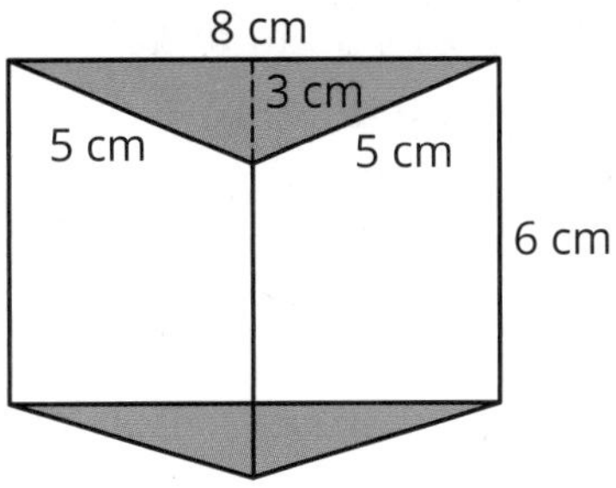

Law of Cosines

You can use the Law of Cosines, or

$a^2 = c^2 + b^2 - 2bc \cdot \cos A$

$b^2 = a^2 + c^2 - 2ac \cdot \cos B$

$c^2 = a^2 + b^2 - 2ab \cdot \cos C$

to determine the unknown lengths of sides or the unknown measures of angles in any triangle.

EXAMPLE

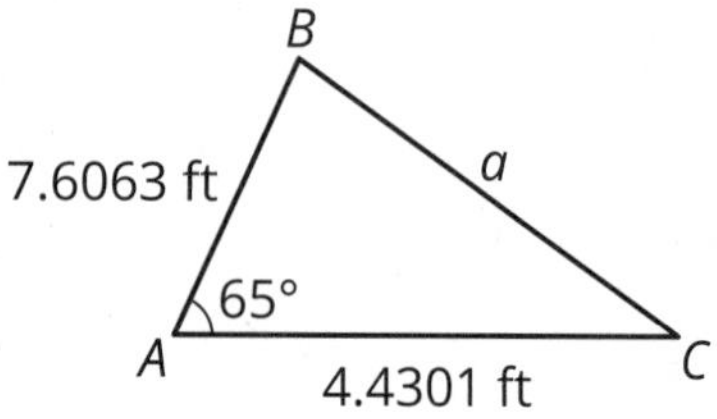

Use the Law of Cosines to calculate the length of side a.

$a^2 = 4.4301^2 + 7.6063^2 - 2(4.4301)(7.6063) \cos 65°$

The length of side a is 7 feet.

Law of Reflection

The Law of Reflection states that the measure of the angle of incidence equals the measure of the angle of reflection.

Law of Sines

You can use the Law of Sines, or $\frac{\sin A}{a} = \frac{\sin B}{b} = \frac{\sin C}{c}$, to determine the unknown side length or the unknown angle measures in any triangle.

EXAMPLE

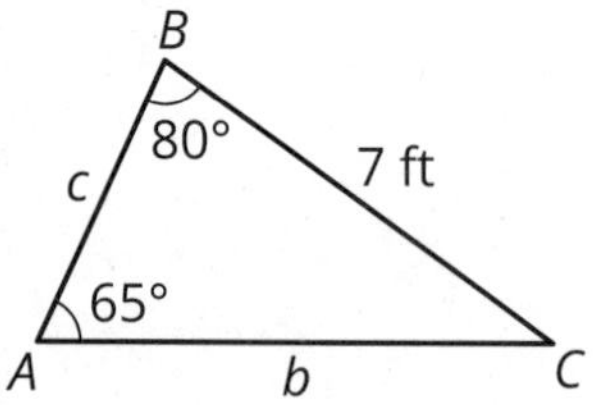

Use the Law of Sines to calculate the length of side b.

$\frac{7}{\sin 65°} = \frac{b}{\sin 80°}$

The length of side b is 7.6063 feet.

line

A line is a straight, continuous arrangement of an infinite number of points. A line has an infinite length, but no width.

EXAMPLE

You can call the line below either line k or line AB.

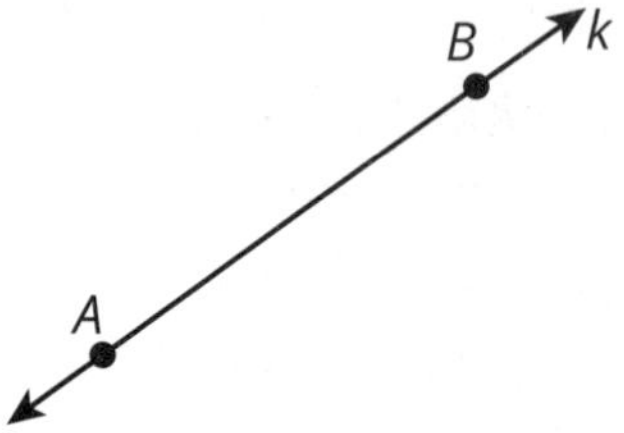

line of symmetry

A line of symmetry is an imaginary line that passes through a shape or object and divides it into two identical halves.

EXAMPLE

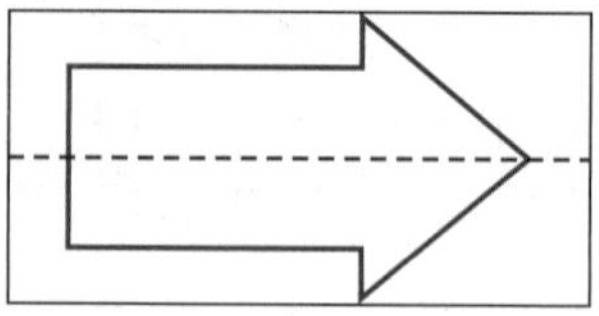

line segment

A line segment is a portion of a line that includes two points and all of the collinear points between the two points.

EXAMPLE

The line segment shown is $\overline{AB}$ or $\overline{BA}$.

linear pair

Two adjacent angles that have noncommon sides that form a line create a linear pair of angles.

EXAMPLE

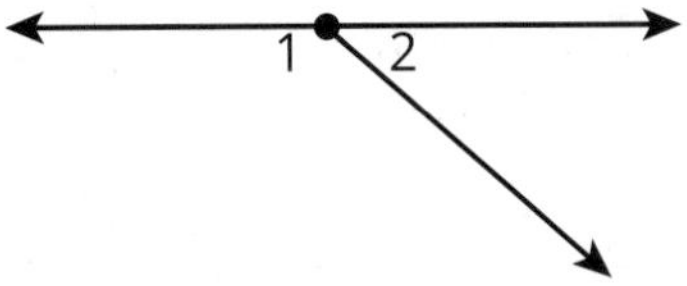

Angles 1 and 2 form a linear pair.

---

linear velocity

Linear velocity is a type of circular velocity described as an amount of distance over a specified amount of time. You can express linear velocity as $v = \frac{s}{t}$, where v = velocity, s = arc length, and t = time.

---

locus of points

A locus of points is a set of points that satisfy one or more conditions.

EXAMPLE

A circle is defined as a locus of points that are a fixed distance, called the radius, from a given point, called the center.

M

major arc

Two points on a circle determine a major arc and a minor arc. The arc with the greater measure is the major arc.

EXAMPLE

Circle *Q* is divided by points *A* and *B* into two arcs, arc *ACB* and arc *AB*. Arc *ACB* is a major arc.

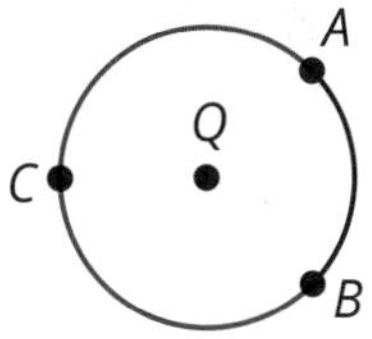

---

major axis

The major axis is the longest line segment that runs through the center of an ellipse and both foci.

---

median

The median of a triangle is a line segment that connects a vertex to the midpoint of the opposite side.

EXAMPLE

The line segment from vertex *B* to side *AC* is a median.

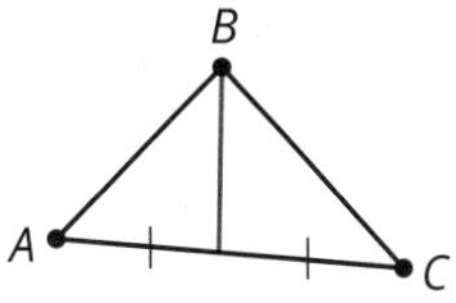

---

midpoint

A midpoint is a point that is exactly halfway between two given points.

EXAMPLE

Because point *B* is the midpoint of segment *AC*, segment *AB* is congruent to segment *BC*.

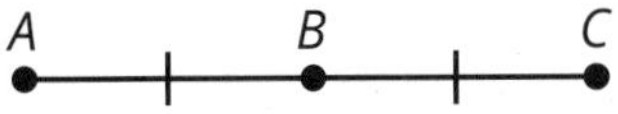

Midpoint Formula

The Midpoint Formula states that when (x_1, y_1) and (x_2, y_2) are two points on the coordinate plane, the midpoint of the line segment that joins these two points is $\left(\frac{x_1 + x_2}{2}, \frac{y_1 + y_2}{2}\right)$.

EXAMPLE

To find the midpoint between the points (−1, 4) and (2, −5), substitute the coordinates into the Midpoint Formula.

$$\left(\frac{x_1 + x_2}{2}, \frac{y_1 + y_2}{2}\right) = \left(\frac{-1 + 2}{2}, \frac{4 - 5}{2}\right)$$
$$= \left(\frac{1}{2}, \frac{-1}{2}\right)$$

So, the midpoint between the points (−1, 4) and (2, −5) is $\left(\frac{1}{2}, -\frac{1}{2}\right)$.

midsegment

A midsegment of a polygon is any line segment that connects two midpoints of the sides of the polygon.

EXAMPLE

Segment *XY* is a midsegment of Trapezoid *ABCD*.

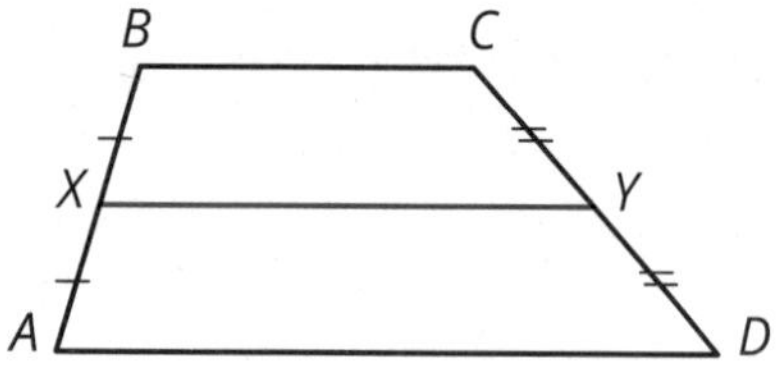

midsegment of a triangle

A midsegment of a triangle is a line segment formed by connecting the midpoints of two sides of a triangle.

EXAMPLE

Segment *AB* is a midsegment.

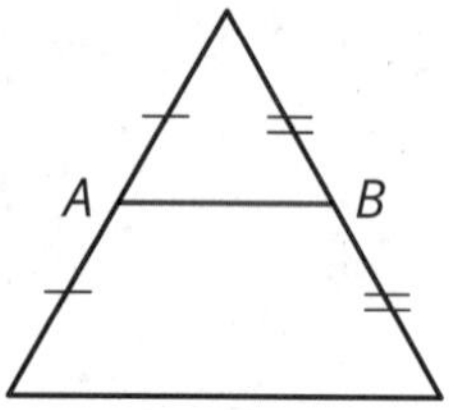

minor arc

Two points on a circle determine a minor arc and a major arc. The arc with the lesser measure is the minor arc.

EXAMPLE

Circle *Q* is divided by points *A* and *B* into two arcs, arc *ACB* and arc *AB*. Arc *AB* is a minor arc.

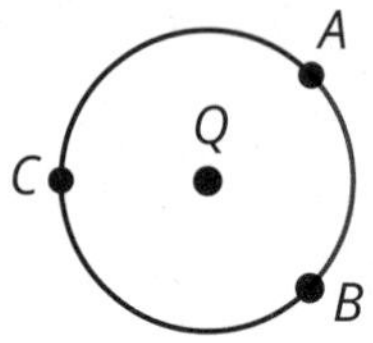

minor axis

The minor axis is the shortest line segment that runs through the center of an ellipse.

N

nappes

Nappes are two congruent cones that touch at the vertex with an axis of symmetry that passes through the center of each base.

EXAMPLE

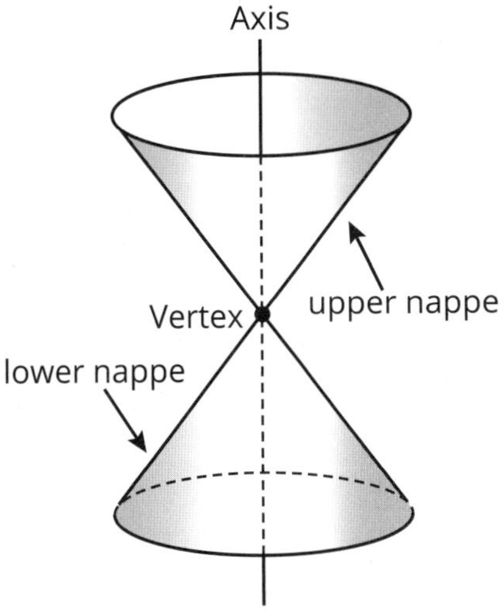

non-uniform probability model

When all probabilities in a probability model are not equivalent to each other, it is a non-uniform probability model.

EXAMPLE

Spinning the spinner shown represents a non-uniform probability model because the probability of landing on a shaded space is not equal to the probability of landing on a non-shaded space.

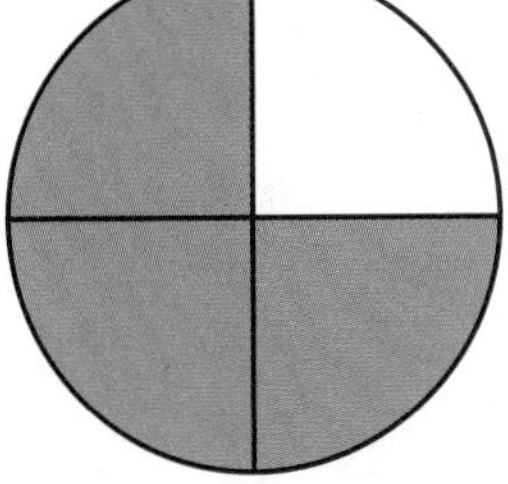

O

oblique cylinder

When you translate a circle through space in a direction that is not perpendicular to the plane containing the circle, the solid formed is an oblique cylinder.

EXAMPLE

The prism shown is an oblique cylinder.

oblique rectangular prism

When you translate a rectangle through space in a direction that is not perpendicular to the plane containing the rectangle, the solid formed is an oblique rectangular prism.

EXAMPLE

The prism shown is an oblique rectangular prism.

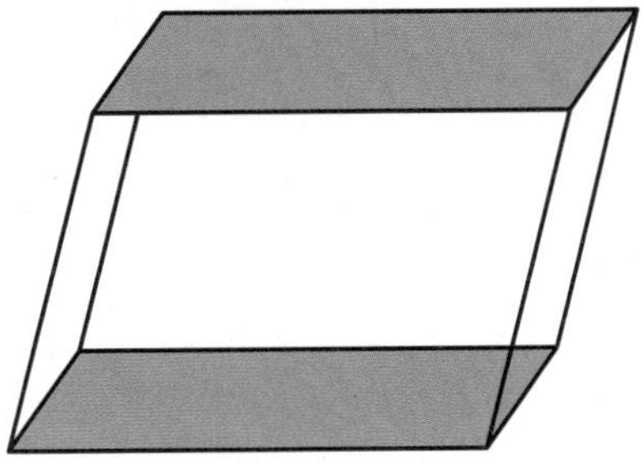

oblique triangular prism

When you translate a triangle through space in a direction that is not perpendicular to the plane containing the triangle, the solid formed is an oblique triangular prism.

EXAMPLE

The prism shown is an oblique triangular prism.

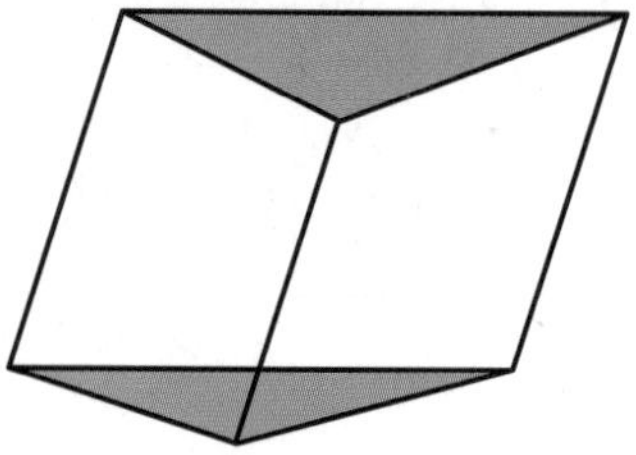

opposite side

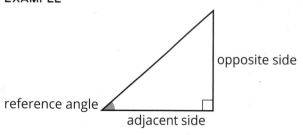

The opposite side of a triangle is the side opposite the reference angle.

EXAMPLE

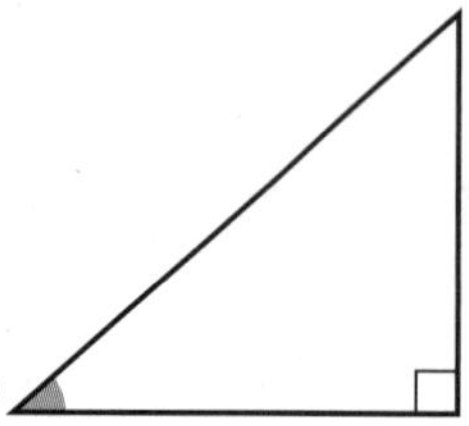

organized list

An organized list is a visual model for determining the sample space of events.

EXAMPLE

You can represent the sample space for flipping a coin 3 times as an organized list.

HHH THH

HHT THT

HTH TTH

HTT TTT

orthocenter

The orthocenter of a triangle is the point at which the altitudes of the triangle intersect.

EXAMPLE

Point X is the orthocenter of ΔABC.

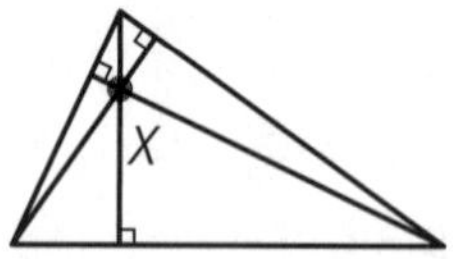

outcome

An outcome is the result of a single trial of an experiment.

EXAMPLE

Flipping a coin has two outcomes: heads or tails.

P

parabola (conic section)

When a plane intersects one nappe of the double-napped cone parallel to the edge of the cone, the curve that results is a parabola. A parabola is the set of all points in a plane that are equidistant from a fixed point called the focus and a fixed line called the directrix.

EXAMPLE

The focus of the parabola shown is the point (0, 2). The directrix of the parabola shown is the line $y = -2$. All points on the parabola are equidistant from the focus and the directrix.

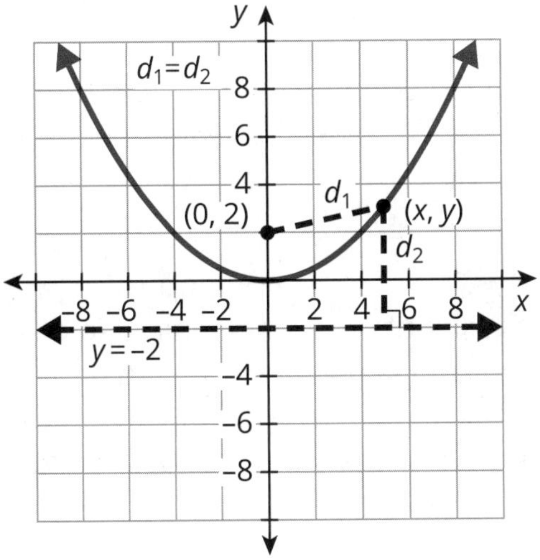

paragraph proof

A paragraph proof is a proof in paragraph form. Each sentence includes mathematical statements organized in logical steps with reasons.

EXAMPLE

The proof shown is a paragraph proof that vertical angles 1 and 3 are congruent.

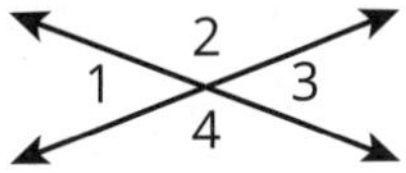

Angle 1 and angle 3 are vertical angles. By the definition of linear pair, angle 1 and angle 2 form a linear pair. Angle 2 and angle 3 also form a linear pair. By the Linear Pair Postulate, angle 1 and angle 2 are supplementary. Angle 2 and angle 3 are also supplementary. Angle 1 is congruent to angle 3 by the Congruent Supplement Theorem.

perpendicular

Two lines, line segments, or rays are perpendicular if they intersect to form 90° angles. The symbol for perpendicular is $\perp$.

EXAMPLE

Line *AB* is perpendicular to line *MN*.

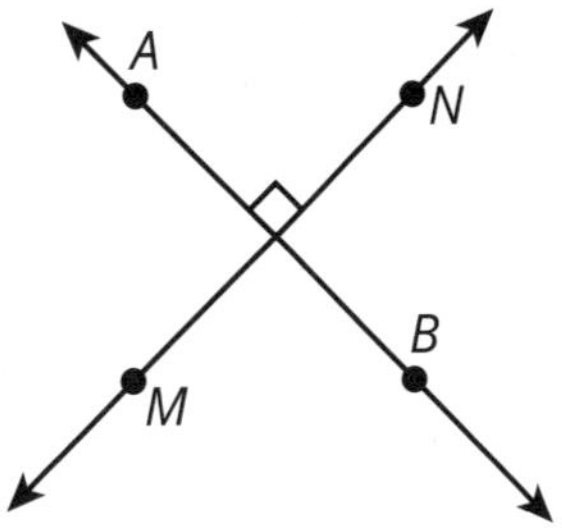

permutation

A permutation is an ordered arrangement of items without repetition.

EXAMPLE

The permutations of the letters A, B, and C are:

ABC ACB

BAC BCA

CAB CBA

perpendicular bisector

A perpendicular bisector is a line, line segment, or ray that intersects the midpoint of a line segment at a 90° angle.

EXAMPLE

Line k is the perpendicular bisector of $\overline{AB}$. It is perpendicular to $\overline{AB}$, and intersects $\overline{AB}$ at midpoint M so that $AM = MB$.

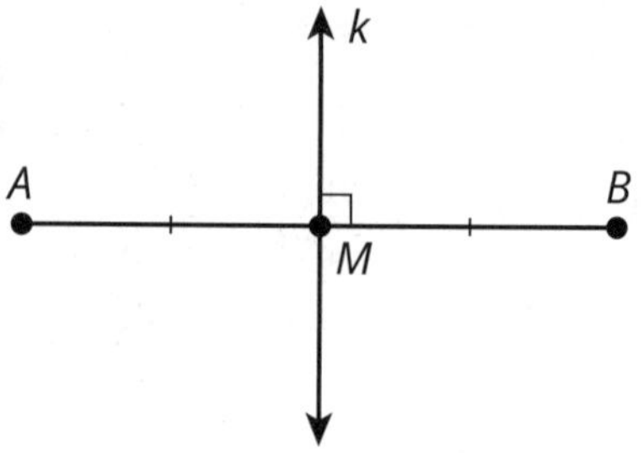

point

A point has no dimension, but you often see it represented by a small dot.

EXAMPLE

Point A is shown.

point of concurrency

A point of concurrency is the point at which three or more lines, line segments, or rays intersect.

EXAMPLE

Point X is the point of concurrency for lines ℓ, m, and n.

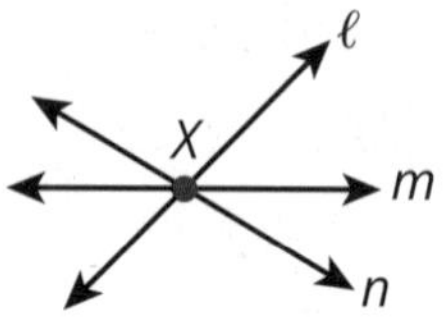

postulate

A postulate is a statement that is accepted to be true without proof.

EXAMPLE

The following statement is a postulate: A straight line may be drawn between any two points.

probability

The probability of an event is the ratio of the number of desired outcomes to the total number of possible outcomes, $P(A) = \frac{\text{desired outcomes}}{\text{possible outcomes}}$.

EXAMPLE

When flipping a coin, there are 2 possible outcomes: heads or tails. The probability of flipping heads is $\frac{1}{2}$.

probability model

A probability model lists the possible outcomes and the probability for each outcome. In a probability model, the sum of the probabilities must equal 1.

EXAMPLE

The table shows a probability model for flipping a fair coin once.

Outcomes	Head (H)	Tails (T)
Probability	$\frac{1}{2}$	$\frac{1}{2}$

Product Property of Radicals

The Product Property of Radicals states that $\sqrt{a} \cdot \sqrt{b} = \sqrt{a} \cdot b$ when a and b are greater than 0.

proof

A proof is a series of statements and corresponding reasons forming a valid argument that starts with a hypothesis and arrives at a conclusion.

Pythagorean identity

A Pythagorean identity is a trigonometric identity that expresses the Pythagorean Theorem in terms of trigonometric ratios.

EXAMPLE

The basic relationship between the sine and cosine is given by the Pythagorean identity $(\sin \theta)^2 + (\cos \theta)^2 = (1)^2$.

Pythagorean Theorem

The Pythagorean Theorem states that the sum of the squares of the lengths of the legs of a right triangle equals the square of the length of the hypotenuse. When a and b are the lengths of the legs, and c is the length of the hypotenuse, then $a^2 + b^2 = c^2$.

EXAMPLE

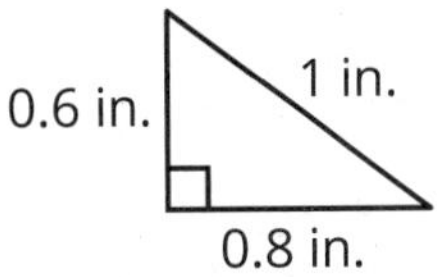

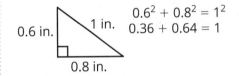

$0.6^2 + 0.8^2 = 1^2$
$0.36 + 0.64 = 1$

R

radian

One radian is the measure of a central angle whose arc length is the same as the radius of the circle.

radius of a sphere

The radius of a sphere is a line segment with one endpoint on the sphere and one endpoint at the center.

EXAMPLE

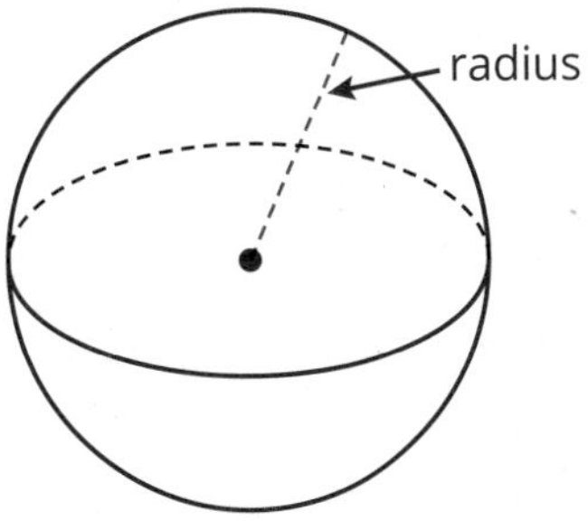

ratio

A ratio is a comparison of two quantities that uses division.

EXAMPLES

The ratio of stars to circles is $\frac{2}{3}$, or 3:2, or 3 to 2.

The ration of circles to stars is $\frac{2}{3}$, or 2:3, or 2 to 3.

---

rationalize the denominator

To rationalize the denominator is the process of rewriting a fraction with no irrational numbers in the denominator. To rationalize the denominator, multiply by a form of one so that the radicand of the radical in the denominator is a perfect square.

EXAMPLE

Rationalize the denominator of the expression $\frac{5}{\sqrt{3}}$.

$$\frac{5}{\sqrt{3}} = \frac{5}{\sqrt{3}} \cdot \frac{\sqrt{3}}{\sqrt{3}}$$
$$= \frac{5\sqrt{3}}{\sqrt{9}}$$
$$= \frac{5\sqrt{3}}{3}$$

---

ray

A ray is a portion of a line that begins with a single point and extends infinitely in one direction.

EXAMPLE

The ray shown is ray AB.

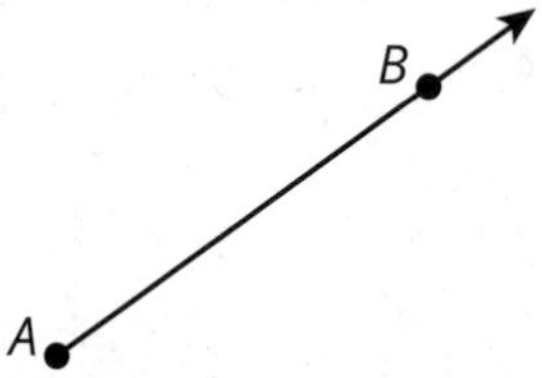

reference angle

A reference angle is the angle of the right triangle being considered. The reference angle defines the opposite side and adjacent side.

EXAMPLE

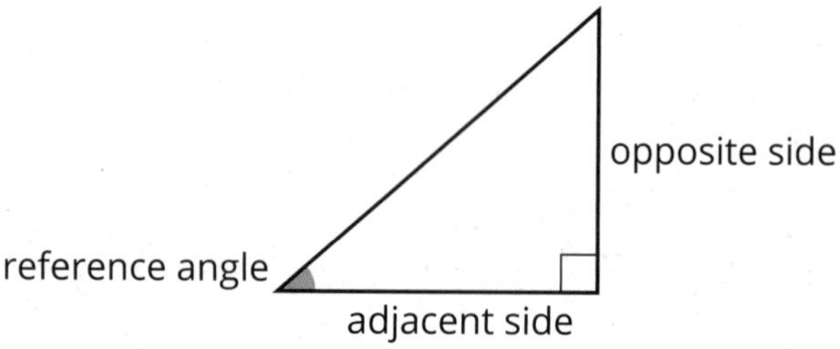

---

reflection

A reflection is a rigid motion that "flips" a figure across a line. A reflection as a function, R_ℓ, takes as its input, P, the location of a point with respect to some line of reflection ℓ and outputs $R_\ell(P)$, or the opposite of the location of P with respect to the line of reflection.

EXAMPLE

$R_m(STUV) = S'T'U'V'$

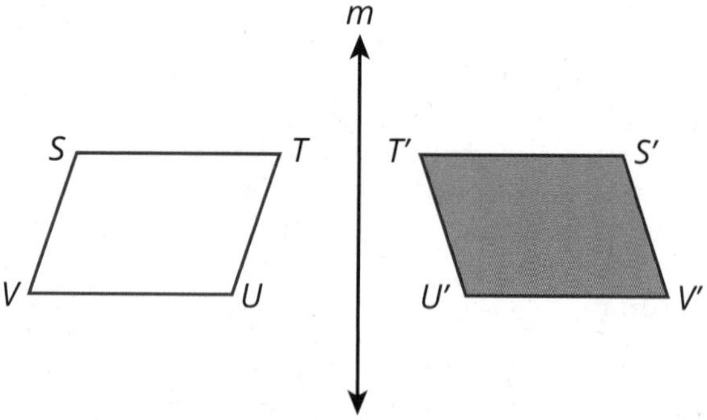

reflectional symmetry

A plane figure has reflectional symmetry when you can draw a line so that the figure to one side of the line is a reflection of the figure on the other side of the line.

EXAMPLE

The figure shown has reflectional symmetry.

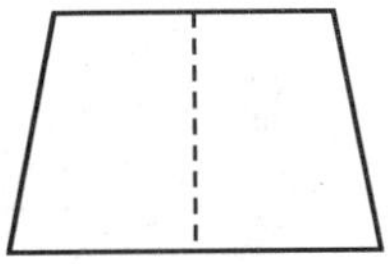

Reflexive Property

The reflexive property states that $a = a$.

EXAMPLE

The statement $2 = 2$ is an example of the Reflexive Property.

relative frequency

A relative frequency is the ratio or percent of occurrences within a category to the total of the category.

EXAMPLE

John surveys 100 students in his school about their favorite school subject. Of the 100 students, 37 chose math as their favorite subject. The relative frequency of students who selected math as their favorite subject is $\frac{37}{100}$, or 37%.

remote interior angles of a triangle

The remote interior angles of a triangle are the two angles that are not adjacent to the specified exterior angle.

EXAMPLE

The remote interior angles with respect to exterior angle 4 are angles 1 and 2.

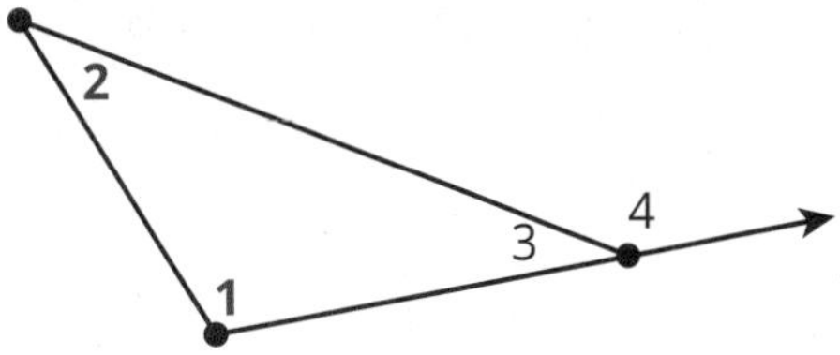

right cylinder

A disc translated through space in a direction perpendicular to the plane containing the disc forms a right cylinder.

EXAMPLE

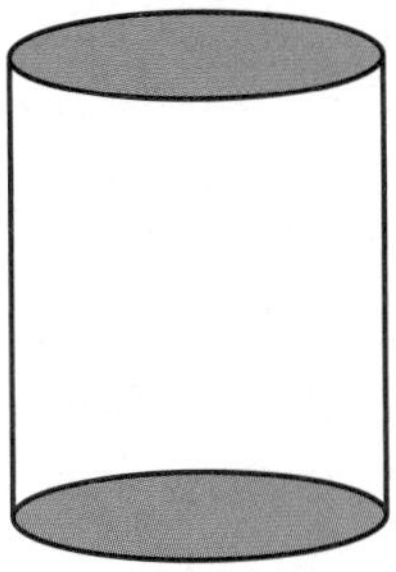

right rectangular prism

A rectangle translated through space in a direction perpendicular to the plane containing the rectangle forms a right rectangular prism.

EXAMPLE

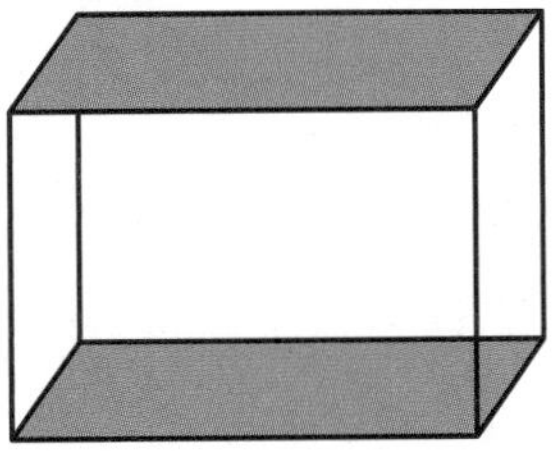

right triangular prism

A triangle translated through space in a direction perpendicular to the plane containing the triangle forms a right triangular prism.

EXAMPLE

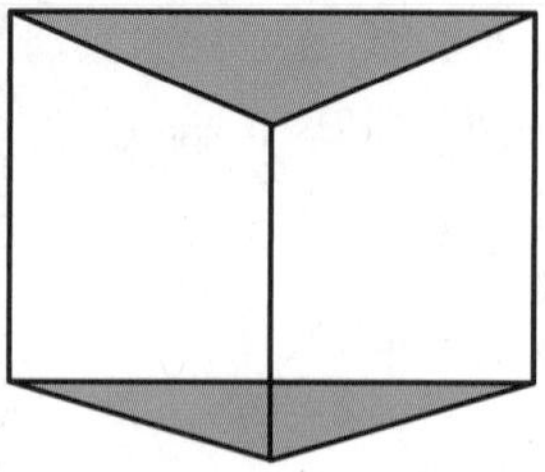

rigid motion

A rigid motion is a special type of transformation that preserves the size and shape of the figure.

EXAMPLE

Translations, reflections, and rotations are rigid motion transformations.

rotation

A rotation is a rigid motion that "spins" a figure about a point. A rotation as a function maps its input, a point P, to another location, $f(P)$. This movement to a new location is defined by a center of rotation, E, and a rotation angle, t. For this reason, you write a rotation function as $R_{E,t}(P)$.

EXAMPLE

$R_{A,\,40}(\overline{JN}) = \overline{J'N'}$

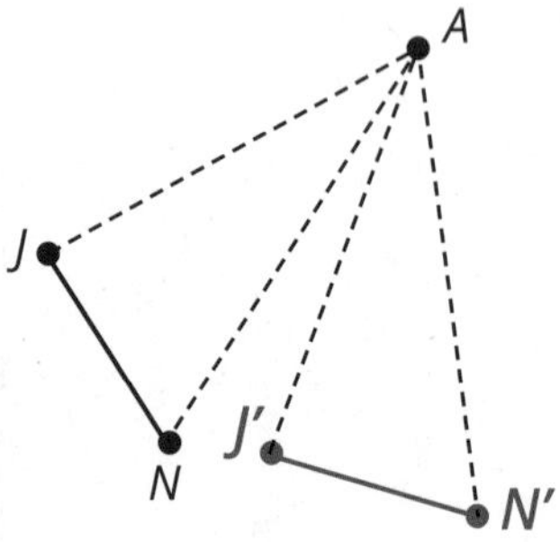

rotation angle

A rotation angle is a directed angle based on a circle. Positive rotation angles turn counterclockwise, and negative rotation angles turn clockwise.

EXAMPLE

The rotation angle shown rotates point A 45° counterclockwise.

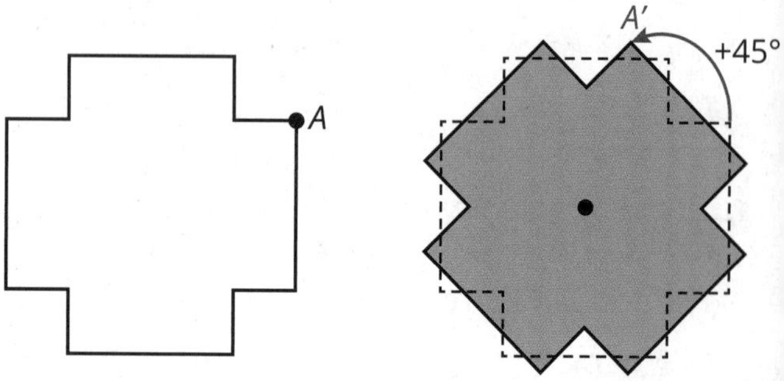

rotational symmetry

A plane figure has rotational symmetry when you can rotate the figure more than 0° but less than 360° and the resulting figure is the same as the original figure in the original position.

EXAMPLE

The figure shown has rotational symmetry.

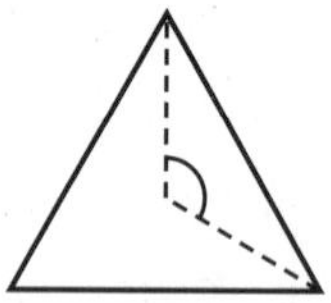

Rule of Compound Probability involving *and*

The Rule of Compound Probability involving *and* states: "If Event A and Event B are independent, then the probability that Event A happens and Event B happens is the product of the probability that Event A happens and the probability that Event B happens, given that Event A has happened."

$P(A \text{ and } B) = P(A) \cdot P(B)$

EXAMPLE

You flip a coin two times. Calculate the probability of flipping heads on the first flip and flipping heads on the second flip.

Let A represent the event of flipping heads on the first flip. Let B represent the event of flipping heads on the second flip.

$P(A \text{ and } B) = P(A) \cdot P(B)$

$P(A \text{ and } B) = \frac{1}{2} \cdot \frac{1}{2}$

$P(A \text{ or } B) = \frac{1}{4}$

So, the probability of flipping heads on the first flip and flipping heads on the second flip is $\frac{1}{4}$.

S

sample space

A list of all possible outcomes of an experiment is a sample space.

EXAMPLE

The sample space for flipping a coin two times is {HH, HT, TH, TT}.

scale factor

In a dilation, the scale factor is the ratio of the distance of the new figure from the center of dilation to the distance of the original figure from the center of dilation.

EXAMPLE

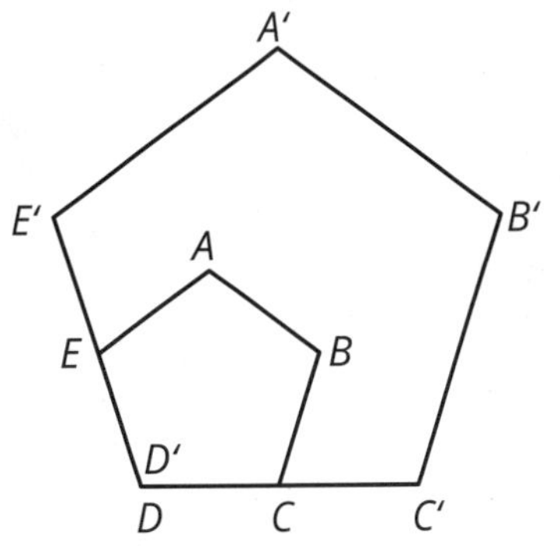

Pentagon $A'B'C'D'E'$ is a dilation of Pentagon $ABCDE$ by a scale factor of 2.

secant (sec)

The secant (sec) of an acute angle in a right triangle is the ratio of the length of the hypotenuse to the length of the side adjacent to the angle.

EXAMPLE

$\sec A = \frac{\text{length of hypotenuse}}{\text{length of side adjacent to } \angle A} = \frac{AB}{AC}$

The expression "sec A" means "the secant of angle A."

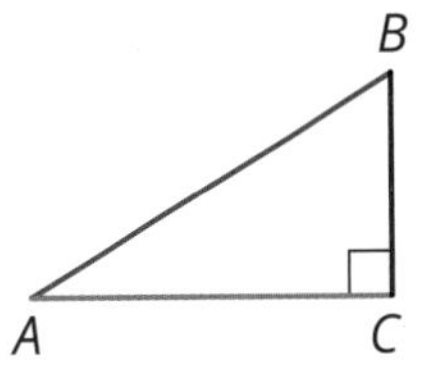

secant of a circle

A secant of a circle is a line that intersects the circle at two points.

EXAMPLE

Line AB is a secant of Circle O.

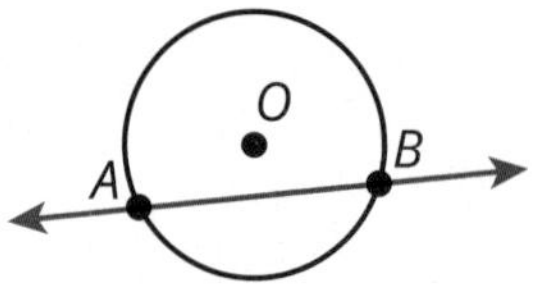

sector of a circle

A sector of a circle is a region of the circle bounded by two radii and the included arc.

EXAMPLE

In Circle Y, $\widehat{XZ}$, radius $\overline{XY}$, and radius $\overline{YZ}$ form a sector.

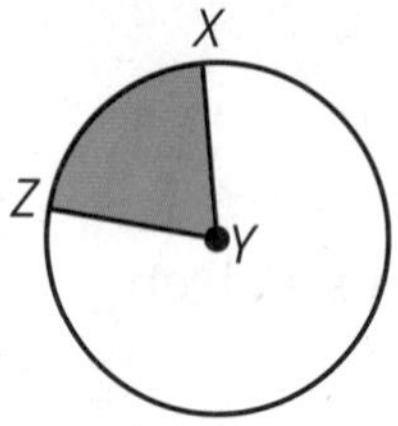

segment bisector

A segment bisector is a line, line segment, or ray that divides a line segment into two line segments of equal length.

EXAMPLE

$\overline{AB}$ is a segment bisector of $\overline{CD}$.

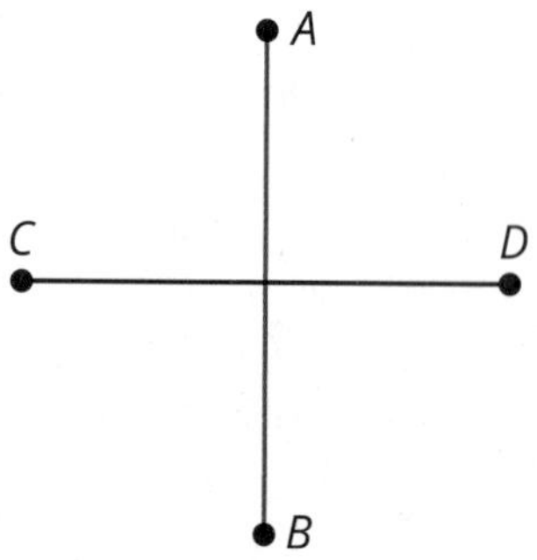

segment of a circle

A segment of a circle is a region bounded by a chord and the included arc.

EXAMPLE

In Circle A, chord $\overline{BC}$ and $\widehat{BC}$ are the boundaries of a segment of the circle.

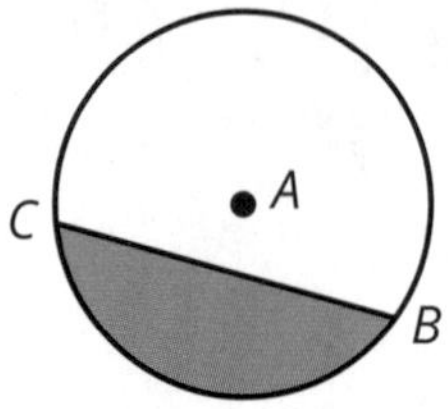

semi-major axis

The semi-major axis of an ellipse is a segment from the center of the ellipse to a vertex and has length a.

semi-minor axis

The semi-minor axis of an ellipse is a segment from the center of the ellipse to a co-vertex and has length b.

set

A set is a collection of items.

EXAMPLE

Let E represent the set of even whole numbers.
$E = \{2, 4, 6, 8, \ldots\}$

similar figures

Similar figures are geometric figures where all pairs of corresponding angles are congruent and the lengths of all corresponding sides are proportional. Dilations produce similar figures.

EXAMPLE

Figures *E* and *X* are similar figures.

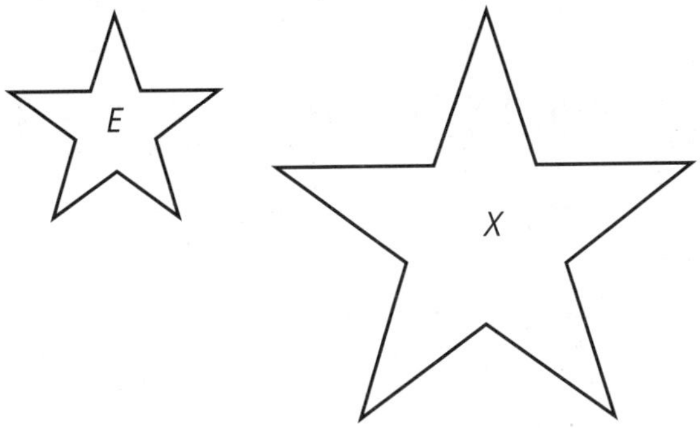

similar triangles

Similar triangles are triangles that have all pairs of corresponding angles congruent and all corresponding sides are proportional.

EXAMPLE

$\Delta ABC \sim \Delta DEF$

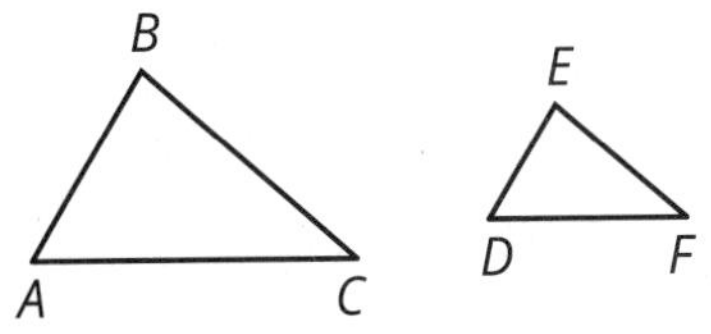

sine (sin)

The sine (sin) of an acute angle in a right triangle is the ratio of the length of the side opposite the angle to the length of the hypotenuse.

EXAMPLE

$$\sin A = \frac{\text{length of side opposite } \angle A}{\text{length of hypotenuse}} = \frac{BC}{AB}$$

The expression "sin *A*" means "the sine of angle *A*."

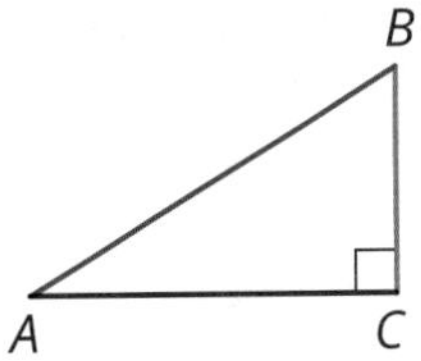

sketch

To sketch is to create a geometric figure without using tools such as a ruler, straightedge, compass, or protractor. A drawing is more accurate than a sketch.

sphere

A sphere is the set of all points in space that are a given distance from a fixed point called the center of the sphere.

EXAMPLE

A sphere is shown.

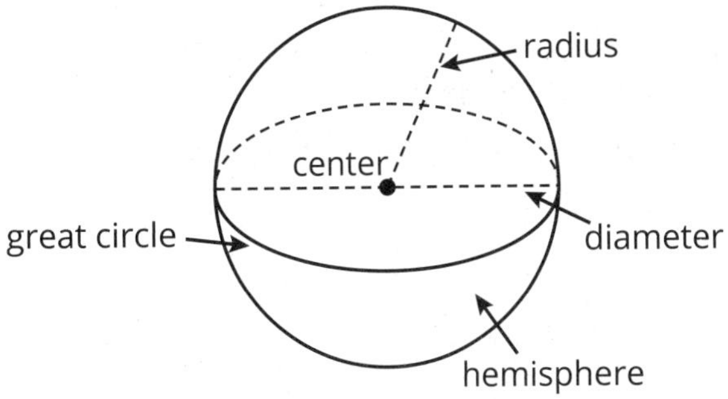

standard form of a parabola

The standard form of a parabola centered at the origin is an equation of the form $x^2 = 4py$ or $y^2 = 4px$, where p represents the distance from the vertex to the focus.

EXAMPLE

You can write the equation for the parabola shown in standard form as $x^2 = 2y$.

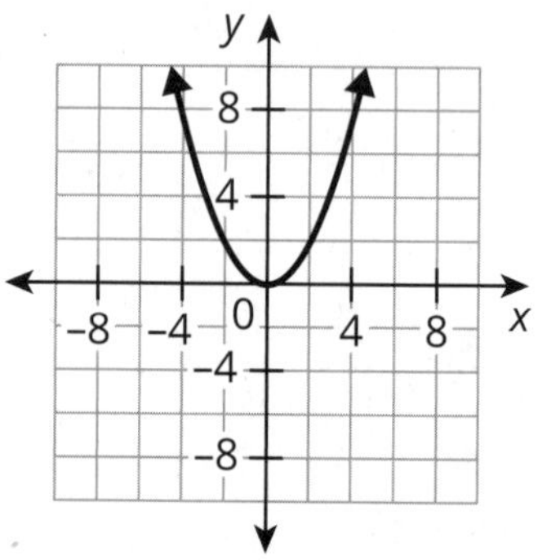

straightedge

A straightedge is a ruler with no numbers.

Substitution Property

The Substitution Property of Equality states: “If a and b are real numbers and $a = b$, then you can substitute a for b.”

EXAMPLE

If $AB = 12$ ft and $CD = 12$ ft, then $AB = CD$.

Subtraction Property of Equality

The Subtraction Property of Equality states: “If $a = b$, then $a - c = b - c$.”

EXAMPLE

If $x + 5 = 7$, then $x + 5 - 5 = 7 - 5$, or $x = 2$ is an example of the Subtraction Property of Equality.

supplementary angles

Two angles are supplementary angles when the sum of their angle measures is equal to 180°.

EXAMPLE

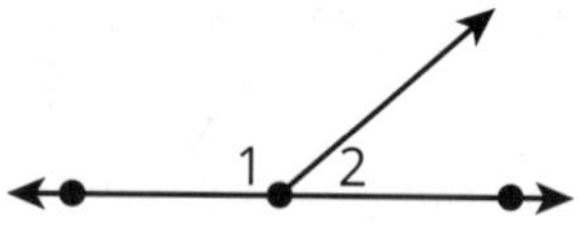

Angles 1 and 2 are supplementary angles.

T

tangent (tan)

The tangent (tan) of an acute angle in a right triangle is the ratio of the length of the side opposite the angle to the length of the side adjacent to the angle.

EXAMPLE

$$\tan A = \frac{\text{length of side opposite } \angle A}{\text{length of side adjacent to } \angle A} = \frac{BC}{AC}$$

The expression “tan A” means “the tangent of angle A.”

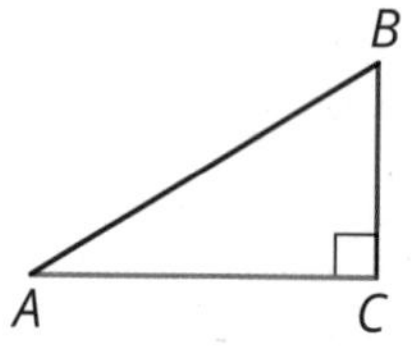

tangent circles

Tangent circles are circles that lie in the same plane and intersect at exactly one point.

EXAMPLE

Circles O and B are tangent circles.

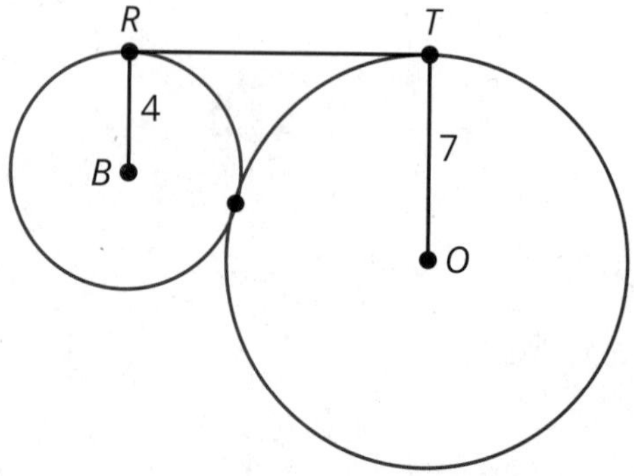

tangent of a circle

A tangent of a circle is a line that intersects the circle at exactly one point, called the point of tangency.

EXAMPLE

Line *RQ* is tangent to Circle *P* at point *Q*.

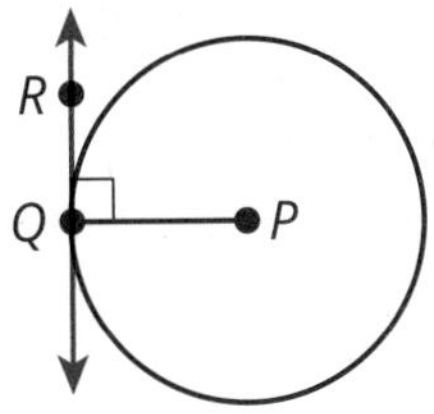

tangent segment

A tangent segment is a line segment formed by connecting a point outside of the circle to a point of tangency.

EXAMPLE

Line segment *AB* and line segment *AC* are tangent segments.

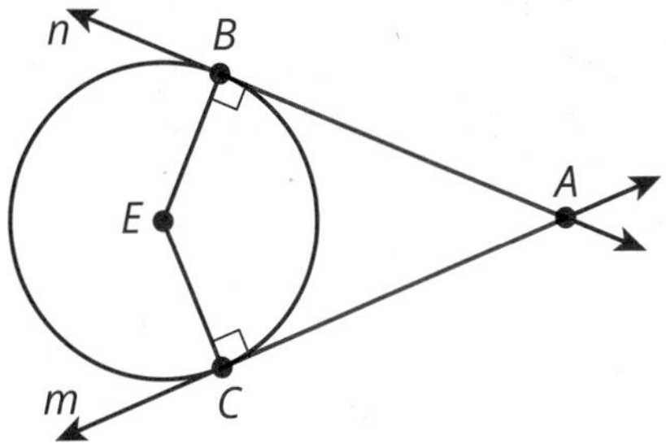

theorem

A theorem is a statement that you can demonstrate to be true by accepted mathematical operations and arguments.

EXAMPLE

The Pythagorean Theorem states that if a right triangle has legs of lengths *a* and *b* and hypotenuse of length *c*, then $a^2 + b^2 = c^2$.

total surface area

The total surface area of a three-dimensional figure is the sum of the areas of its bases and lateral faces.

EXAMPLE

The total surface area of the right triangular prism is 132 square centimeters.

$$\begin{aligned} SA &= (5 \cdot 6) + (5 \cdot 6) \\ &\quad + (8 \cdot 6) + \tfrac{1}{2}(8 \cdot 3)(2) \\ &= 30 + 30 + 48 + 24 \\ &= 132 \end{aligned}$$

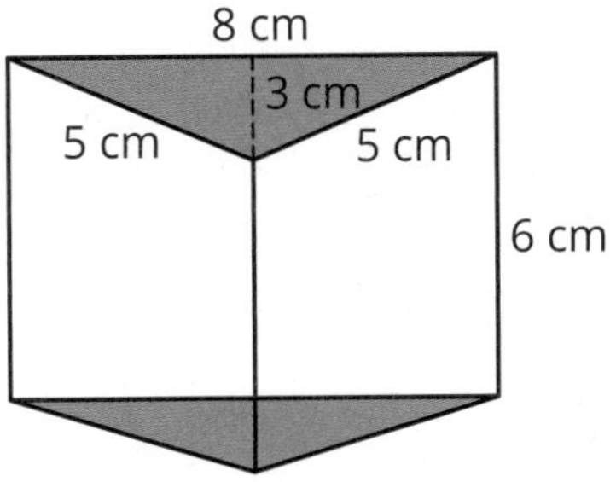

transformation

A transformation is an operation that maps, or moves, a figure, called the pre-image, onto a new figure called the image. Three types of transformations are reflections, rotations, and translations.

EXAMPLE

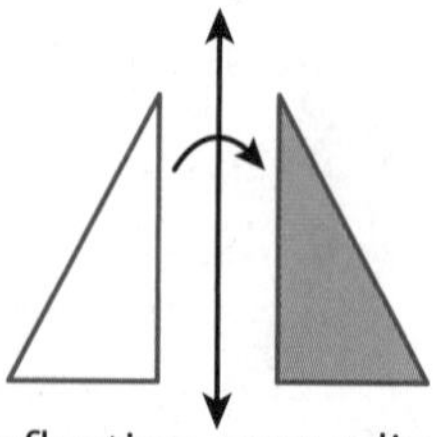

reflection over a line

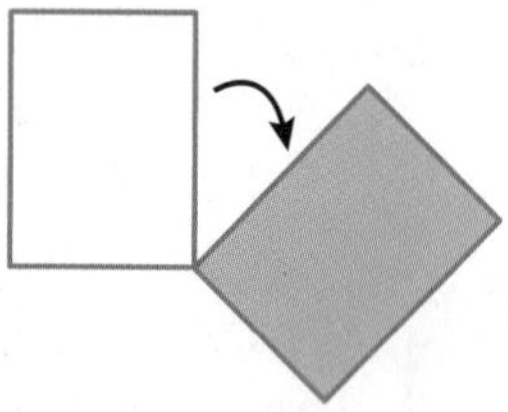

rotation about a point

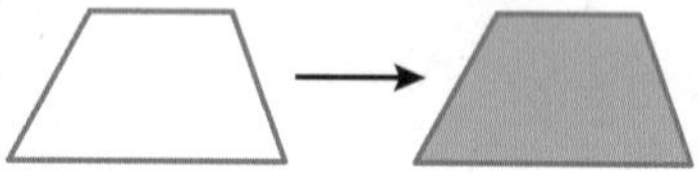

translation

Transitive Property

The Transitive Property states: "If $a = b$ and $b = c$, then $a = c$."

EXAMPLE

If $x = y$ and $y = 2$, then $x = 2$ is an example of the Transitive Property.

translation

A translation is a rigid motion that "slides" a figure up, down, left, or right. A translation as a function, T_{AB}, takes as its input a set of pre-image points and outputs a set of image points. The pre-image points are translated a distance of AB in the direction AB.

EXAMPLE

$T_{AB}(P) = P'$ and $T_{AC}(P) = P''$

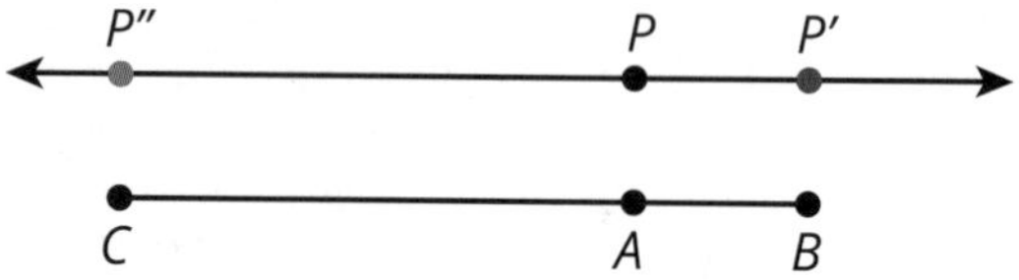

transverse axis

The transvere axis runs through the center of a hyperbola and both foci.

tree diagram

A tree diagram is a diagram that illustrates sequentially the possible outcomes of a given situation.

EXAMPLE

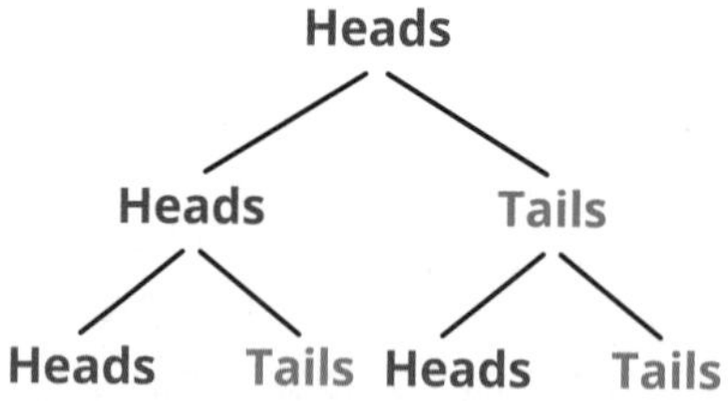

truth table

A truth table is a table that summarizes all possible truth values for a conditional statement $p \rightarrow q$.

truth value

The truth value of a conditional statement is whether the statement is true or false.

two-column proof

A two-column proof is a proof consisting of two columns. In the left column are mathematical statements organized in logical steps. In the right column are the reasons for each mathematical statement.

EXAMPLE

The proof shown is a two-column proof.

Statements	Reasons
1. $\angle 1$ and $\angle 3$ are vertical angles.	**1.** Given
2. $\angle 1$ and $\angle 2$ form a linear pair. $\angle 2$ and $\angle 3$ form a linear pair.	**2.** Definition of linear pair
3. $\angle 1$ and $\angle 2$ are supplementary. $\angle 2$ and $\angle 3$ are supplementary.	**3.** Linear Pair Postulate
4. $\angle 1 \cong \angle 3$	**4.** Congruent Supplement Theorem

two-way frequency table (contingency table)

A two-way frequency table, also called a contingency table, shows the number of data points and their frequencies for two variables. One variable is divided into rows, and the other is divided into columns.

EXAMPLE

The two-way frequency table shows the hand(s) favored by people who do and do not participate in individual or team sports.

Sports Participation

Favored Hand		Individual	Team	Does Not Play	Total
	Left	3	13	8	24
	Right	6	23	4	33
	Mixed	1	3	2	6
	Total	10	39	14	63

two-way relative frequency table

A two-way relative frequency table displays the relative frequencies for two categories of data.

EXAMPLE

The two-way relative frequency table shows the hand(s) favored by people who do and do not participate in individual or team sports.

	Individual	Team	Does Not Play	Total
Left	$\frac{3}{63} \approx 4.8\%$	$\frac{13}{63} \approx 20.6\%$	$\frac{8}{63} \approx 12.7\%$	$\frac{24}{63} \approx 38.1\%$
Right	$\frac{6}{63} \approx 9.5\%$	$\frac{23}{63} \approx 36.5\%$	$\frac{4}{63} \approx 6.3\%$	$\frac{33}{63} \approx 52.4\%$
Mixed	$\frac{1}{63} \approx 1.6\%$	$\frac{3}{63} \approx 4.8\%$	$\frac{2}{63} \approx 3.2\%$	$\frac{6}{63} \approx 9.5\%$
Total	$\frac{10}{63} \approx 15.9\%$	$\frac{39}{63} \approx 61.9\%$	$\frac{14}{63} \approx 22.2\%$	$\frac{63}{63} = 100\%$

two-way table

A two-way table shows the relationship between two data sets. The rows organize one data set and the columns organize the other data set.

EXAMPLE

The two-way table shows all the possible sums that result from rolling two number cubes once.

2nd Number Cube

1st Number Cube	1	2	3	4	5	6
1	2	3	4	5	6	7
2	3	4	5	6	7	8
3	4	5	6	7	8	9
4	5	6	7	8	9	10
5	6	7	8	9	10	11
6	7	8	9	10	11	12

U

uniform probability model

A uniform probability model occurs when all the probabilities in a probability model are equally likely to occur.

EXAMPLE

Rolling a number cube represents a uniform probability model because the probability of rolling each number is equal.

union of sets

A union of sets is a set formed by combining all the members of the sets. A member may be listed only once.

EXAMPLE

Let *B* represent the set of students in the 11th grade band. Let *C* represent the set of students in the 11th grade chorus. The union of these two sets would be all the students in the 11th grade band or the 11th grade chorus. A student in both would be listed only once.

V

vertex of a parabola (conic section)

The vertex of a parabola is the point on the axis of symmetry which is exactly midway between the focus and the directrix. It is also the point where the parabola changes direction.

EXAMPLE

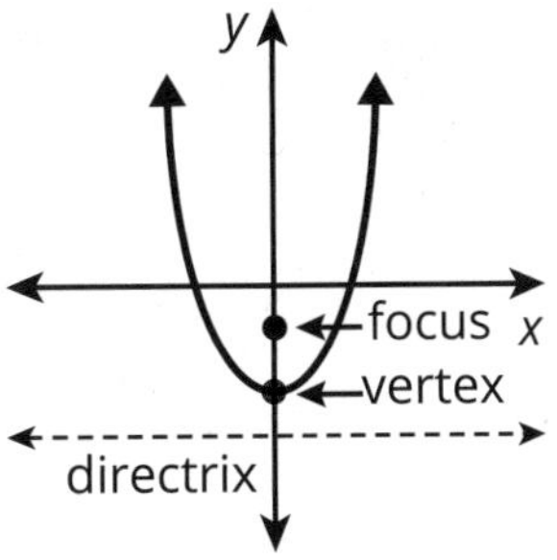

vertices

The endpoints of the major axis of an ellipse are the vertices.

volume

Volume is the amount of space occupied by an object. You measure the volume of an object in cubic units.

30°-60°-90° Triangle Theorem

The length of the hypotenuse in a 30°-60°-90° triangle is 2 times the length of the shorter leg, and the length of the longer leg is $\sqrt{3}$ times the length of the shorter leg.

45°-45°-90° Triangle Theorem

The length of the hypotenuse in a 45°-45°-90° triangle is $\sqrt{2}$ times the length of a leg.

Alternate Exterior Angles Theorem

If a transversal intersects parallel lines, then the alternate exterior angles are congruent.

Alternate Exterior Angles Converse Theorem

If two lines intersected by a transversal form congruent alternate exterior angles, then the lines are parallel.

Alternate Interior Angles Theorem

If a transversal intersects parallel lines, then the alternate interior angles are congruent.

Alternate Interior Angles Converse Theorem

If two lines intersected by a transversal form congruent alternate interior angles, then the lines are parallel.

Angle Addition Postulate

If point D lies in the interior of $\angle ABC$, then $m\angle ABD + m\angle DBC = m\angle ABC$.

Angle-Side-Angle Congruence Theorem (ASA)

If two angles and the included side of one triangle are congruent to the corresponding two angles and the included side of another triangle, then the triangles are congruent.

Angle-Angle-Side (AAS) Congruence Theorem

If two angles and the non-included side of one triangle are congruent to two angles and the non-included side of another triangle, then the two triangles are congruent.

Angle-Angle Similarity Theorem

If two angles of one triangle are congruent to two angles of another triangle, then the triangles are similar.

Angle Bisector/Proportional Side Theorem

A bisector of an angle in a triangle divides the opposite side into two segments whose lengths are in the same ratio as the lengths of the sides adjacent to the angle.

Arc Addition Postulate

The measure of an arc formed by two adjacent arcs is the sum of the measures of the two arcs.

Congruent Chord–Congruent Arc Theorem

If two chords of the same circle or congruent circles are congruent, then their corresponding arcs are congruent.

Congruent Chord–Congruent Converse Arc Theorem

If arcs of the same circle or congruent circles are congruent, then their corresponding chords are congruent.

Congruent Supplement Theorem

If two angles are supplements of the same angle or of congruent angles, then the angles are congruent.

Converse of the Triangle Proportionality Theorem

If a line divides two sides of a triangle proportionally, then it is parallel to the third side.

Corresponding Angles Theorem

If a transversal intersects parallel lines, then corresponding angles are congruent.

Corresponding Angles Converse Theorem

If two lines intersected by a transversal form congruent corresponding angles, then the lines are parallel.

Diameter–Chord Theorem

If a circle's diameter is perpendicular to a chord, then the diameter bisects the chord and bisects the arc determined by the chord.

Equidistant Chord Theorem

If two chords of the same circle or congruent circles are congruent, then they are equidistant from the center of the circle.

Equidistant Chord Converse Theorem

If two chords of the same circle or congruent circles are equidistant from the center of the circle, then the chords are congruent.

Exterior Angle Theorem

The measure of an exterior angle of a triangle is equal to the sum of the measures of the two remote interior angles.

Exterior Angles of a Circle Theorem

If an angle is formed by two intersecting chords or secants of a circle such that the vertex of the angle is in the exterior of the circle, then the measure of the angle is half of the difference of the measures of the arcs intercepted by the angle.

Hypotenuse-Angle (HA) Congruence Theorem

If the hypotenuse and an acute angle of one right triangle are congruent to the hypotenuse and an acute angle of another right triangle, then the two triangles are congruent.

Hypotenuse-Leg (HL) Congruence Theorem

If the hypotenuse and leg of one right triangle are congruent to the hypotenuse and leg of another right triangle, then the triangles are congruent.

Inscribed Angle Theorem

The measure of an inscribed angle is half the measure of its intercepted arc.

Inscribed Right Triangle–Diameter Theorem

If a triangle is inscribed in a circle such that one side of the triangle is a diameter of the circle, then the triangle is a right triangle.

Inscribed Quadrilateral–Opposite Angles Theorem

If a quadrilateral is inscribed in a circle, then the opposite angles are supplementary.

Interior Angles of a Circle Theorem

If an angle is formed by two intersecting chords or secants of a circle such that the vertex of the angle is in the interior of the circle, then the measure of the angle is half of the sum of the measures of the arcs intercepted by the angle and its vertical angle.

Isosceles Triangle Base Angles Theorem

If two sides of a triangle are congruent, then the angles opposite these sides are congruent.

Isosceles Triangle Base Angles Converse Theorem

If two angles of a triangle are congruent, then the sides opposite these angles are congruent.

Leg-Angle (LA) Congruence Theorem

If the leg and an acute angle of one right triangle are congruent to the corresponding leg and acute angle of another right triangle, then the triangles are congruent.

Leg-Leg (LL) Congruence Theorem

If the two corresponding shorter legs of two right triangles are congruent, then the two triangles are congruent.

Linear Pair Postulate

If two angles form a linear pair, then the angles are supplementary.

Parallelogram/Congruent–Parallel Side Theorem

If one pair of opposite sides of a quadrilateral is both congruent and parallel, then the quadrilateral is a parallelogram.

Perpendicular Bisector Theorem

Any point on the perpendicular bisector of a line segment is equidistant from that segment's endpoints.

Perpendicular Bisector Converse Theorem

If a point is equidistant from the endpoints of a line segment, then the point lies on the perpendicular bisector of the segment.

Perpendicular/Parallel Line Theorem

If two lines are perpendicular to the same line, then the two lines are parallel to each other.

Proportional Segments Theorem

If three parallel lines intersect two transversals, then they divide the transversals proportionally.

Right Angle Congruence Postulate

All right angles are congruent.

Right Triangle/Altitude Similarity Theorem

If an altitude is drawn to the hypotenuse of a right triangle, then the two triangles formed are similar to the original triangle and to each other.

Right Triangle Altitude/Hypotenuse Theorem

The measure of the altitude drawn from the vertex of the right angle of a right triangle to its hypotenuse is the geometric mean between the measures of the two segments of the hypotenuse.

Right Triangle Altitude/Leg Theorem

If the altitude is drawn to the hypotenuse of a right triangle, each leg of the right triangle is the geometric mean of the hypotenuse and the segment of the hypotenuse adjacent to the leg.

Same-Side Exterior Angles Theorem

If a transversal intersects parallel lines, then the same-side exterior angles are supplementary.

Same-Side Exterior Angles Converse Theorem

If two lines intersected by a transversal form supplementary same-side exterior angles, then the lines are parallel.

Same-Side Interior Angles Theorem

If a transversal intersects parallel lines, then the interior angles on the same side of the transversal are supplementary.

Same-Side Interior Angles Converse Theorem

If two lines intersected by a transversal form supplementary same-side interior angles, then the lines are parallel.

Segment Addition Postulate

If point B is on $\overline{AC}$ and between points A and C, then $AB + BC = AC$.

Side-Angle-Side Congruence Theorem (SAS)

If two sides and the included angle of one triangle are congruent to the corresponding sides and the included angle of the second triangle, then the triangles are congruent.

Side-Angle-Side Similarity Theorem

If two of the corresponding sides of two triangles are proportional and the included angles are congruent, then the triangles are similar.

Side-Side-Side Congruence Theorem (SSS)

If three sides of one triangle are congruent to the corresponding sides of another triangle, then the triangles are congruent.

Glossary Continued

Side-Side-Side Similarity Theorem
If all three corresponding sides of two triangles are proportional, then the triangles are similar.

Tangent Segment Theorem
If two tangent segments are drawn from the same point on the exterior of a circle, then the tangent segments are congruent.

Tangent to a Circle Theorem
A line drawn tangent to a circle is perpendicular to a radius of the circle drawn to the point of tangency.

Trapezoid Midsegment Theorem
The midsegment that connects the legs of the trapezoid is parallel to each of the bases and its length is one half the sum of the lengths of the bases.

Triangle Inequality Theorem
The sum of the lengths of any two sides of a triangle is greater than the length of the third side.

Triangle Midsegment Theorem
The midsegment of a triangle is parallel to the third side of the triangle and is half the measure of the third side of the triangle.

Triangle Proportionality Theorem
If a line parallel to one side of a triangle intersects the other two sides, then it divides the two sides proportionally.

Triangle Sum Theorem
The sum of the measures of the interior angles of a triangle is equal to 180°.

Vertical Angle Theorem
Vertical angles are congruent.

Index

Symbols

2-D shapes, rotating through space 655–656
30°-60°-90° angles 251–254
30°-60°-90° Triangle Theorem 343
45°-45°-90° Triangle Theorem 344
θ symbol 629

A

Addition Rule for Probability 807
Adjacent arcs 356
Adjacent side
  of right triangle 537
Alternate Exterior Angles Converse Theorem 312
Alternate Exterior Angles Theorem 309
Alternate Interior Angles Converse Theorem 310
Alternate Interior Angles Theorem 307–309
Altitude
  of hypotenuse of right triangle 498, 499
  of triangle 272
AND
  compound probabilities with 795–796
  dependent events with 797–799
  or OR 823–825
Angle Addition Postulate 167
Angle-Angle (AA) Similarity criterion 461–463
Angle-Angle-Side (AAS) Congruence Theorem 347
Angle-Angle Similarity Theorem 462
Angle bisector 239
Angle Bisector/Proportional Side Theorem 479
  applying 480–481
  proving 476–479
Angle of incidence 509
Angle of inclination 550
Angle of reflection 509
Angle(s) 96
  arc relationships and 206–207
  bisecting 239–240
  central 203
  circumscribed 210
  complementary 592–594
  duplicating 233–234
  exterior 251–254
  included 178, 466
  reference 537
  relationships inside and outside circles 355–378
  remote interior 253
  rotation 96
  using complements 593
Angle-side-angle congruence 180
Angle-Side-Angle Congruence Theorem (ASA) 180
  on the coordinate plane 190–192
  using to solve problems 187–189
Angular velocity 647
Applications
  of parabola 765–766
  of sector 643–646
Arc
  adjacent 356
  and angle relationships 206–207
  and inscribed angle 208–209
  chords and 432–434
  degree measure of 356
  intercepted 208
  major 204
  minor 204
Arc Addition Postulate 356
Arc length
  defined 623
  determining 622–626
  measuring angles and arcs using radians 629–631
  solving problems with 627–628
Area
  composite figure 79–80
  doubling and tripling circumference and 714–717
  formula, deriving another version of 601
  heights of triangles 74–78
  of a sector 638–642
  of figures on coordinate plane 65–73
  solving problems 81–86
Auxiliary line
  drawing 8

B

Base angles 249
  of trapezoid 410
Biconditional statement 250
Bisecting
  an angle 239–240
Bisectors, and circles parts 203–205

C

Categorical data 835
Cavalieri's Principle 664–667
Central angle 203
Centroid
and point of concurrency 270–271
defined 271
Chords 204
arcs and 432–434
Circle(s)
angle relationships inside and outside 355–378
circumscribed 266
determining arc length 622–626
determining measures inside and outside 376–378
determining points on a 721–730
equation 711, 717
doubling and tripling circumference and area 714–715
Exterior Angles of a Circle Theorem 367–372
Inscribed Angle Theorem 358–360
Interior Angles of a Circle Theorem 364–366
parts and bisectors 203–205
problems 728–730
quadrilaterals formed using 217–218
sectors of a 635–647
segment of a 635–647
similar 619–621
similarity relationships in 617–632, 618–633
symmtery, reasoning with 726–727
tangent 395
Tangent to a Circle Theorem 373–375
theorems of inscribed polygons 361–363
using, to make conjectures 201–210
velocities in circular motion 647–648
Circular motion, velocities in 647–648
Circular permutation 869–870
Circumcenter
and point of concurrency 263–266
defined 266
Circumference
arc length and 623–624
doubling and tripling area and 714–717
Circumscribed angle 210
Circumscribed circle 266
Coincident 218
Collinear points 94
Color theory 432
Color wheel 432
Combinations 871–874
calculating probability by using 882–887
defined 871
graphing calculators and 874
Compass 14
Complementary angles 592–594
Complement of an event 775
Completing the square
to determine the center 712–713
Composite figure
area and perimeter of 79–80
Compound event 792
AND or OR 823–825
more than two 820–821
with OR 805
without repetition 821–822
Compound probability
calculating 817–826
determining from relative frequencies 840–841
in two-way table 831–842
analyzing 835–839
converse of the multiplication rule 834
defined 832
determining from relative frequencies 840–841
with AND 795–796
with OR 806–808
Compound sample spaces 773–785
Concave quadrilaterals 216
Concavity 747
Concentric circles
quadrilaterals formed using 219–221
Conclusion 249
Concurrent lines 262
Conditional probability 799, 847–849
for dependent events 852
formula 850–851
Conditional statement(s) 249
and truth tables 159–164
defined 159
truth value of 159
Cone
double-napped 702
formula for volume of 677–678
nappes 702, 746
Congruence
solving problems with 348–350
Congruence theorems
non-examples of 181
Congruent Chord-Congruent Arc Converse Theorem 434
Congruent Chord-Congruent Arc Theorem 433
Congruent line segments by reflection 173–175
Congruent Supplement Theorem 291

proofs of 289–291
Conic sections 702–704, 746
Conjecture(s)
about quadrilaterals 215–227
about triangles 247–256
defined 6
making 6–7
using circles to make 201–210
Constant ρ
graphing a parabola using 756–759
making sense of 754–755
Constructing
coordinate plane 13–26
equilateral triangle 241–243
geometric figures 14
inscribed hexagon 235
inscribed regular polygon 231–243
inscribed square 236–238
parallel lines 32–33
perpendicular lines 15–20
square(s) 21–23
Contingency table 835
Converse, of statement 249
Converse of the Triangle Proportionality Theorem 484
Convex quadrilaterals 216
Coordinate plane
area and perimeter 63–86
heights of triangles 74–78
of composite figure 79–80
of figures 65–73
solving problems with 81–86
ASA on 190–192
calculating distance on 48–50
classifying shapes on 45–59
constructing 13–26
quadrilateral
classifying 56–57
classifying, formed by midpoints 58–59
determining unknown point of 54–55
SAS on 190–192
SSS on 190–192
using proportionality on 527–528
Corresponding Angles Converse Theorem 304
Corresponding Angles Theorem 303–304
Corresponding parts of congruent triangles are congruent (CPCTC) 177
Cosecant (csc) 565
Cosine ratio 578–581
Cotangent (cot) 552
Counterexamples 157–158
Counting Principle 783–785
Cross-sections
point and line segment 697–698
two-dimensional 699–701
Cyclic quadrilateral 227
Cylinder
formula for volume of 662–663
oblique 663
right 663

D

Data
categorical 835
qualitative 835
Decimal approximation 630
Degenerate conics 702
Degree measure of an arc 356
Denominator, rationalizing 346
Dependent events 781
conditional probability for 852
defined 781
with AND 797–799
with OR 809–812
Diagonal(s) 23
Diameter-Chord Theorem 428
Diameter of a sphere 685
Dilations
as transformation 447
defined 447
of figures by scale factor 447–450
of lines 474–475
similar figures 450
Directed line segments
defined 524
partitioning 523–526
Directrix 746
Disc, solid 654
Disjoint sets 780
Distance Formula
defined 49
Drawing
auxiliary line 8
geometric figure 5

E

Element
defined 780
permutation with repeated 865–868
Ellipses 704
Equation for a circle 711
doubling and tripling circumference and area 714–715
Equation(s)
of parabola 743–766
perpendicular lines 39

writing, with given a focus and a directrix 756–759
Equidistant Chord Converse Theorem 431
Equidistant Chord Theorem 430
Equilateral triangle
constructing 241–243
inscribing 241–243
Euclid 165
Euclidean geometry 165
conditional statements and truth tables 159–164
counterexamples 157–158
formal reasoning in 155–167
postulates and theorems 165–167
Event(s)
categorizing scenarios involving 780–782
complement of an 775
compound
more than two 820–821
with OR 805
without repetition 821–822
defined 774
dependent 781
conditional probability for 852
with AND 797–799
with OR 809–812
independent 781
Expected value
calculating 900
defined 899
exploring 898–899
using geometric probability to determine 901–903
Exterior angle(s) 251–254
of polygon 328–330
Exterior Angles of a Circle Theorem 367–372
Exterior Angle Theorem 323–324
Extract the roots 345

F

Factorials 860–861
Figure(s)
area and perimeter 65–73
dilating by scale factor 447–450
similar 450
using geometric theorems to demonstrate similarity of 454–455
using similarity transformations to demonstrate similarity of 451–453
Flow chart proof 285–286
Focus 746
Formal reasoning
conditional statements and truth tables 159–164
counterexamples 157–158
in Euclidean geometry 155–167
postulates and theorems 165–167
Forms of proof 284–288
flow chart proof 286–287
two-column proof 287–288
Formula(s)
conditional probability 850–851
for multiple trials 888–889
of area, deriving another version of 601
solving problems using volume and surface area 687–688
volume
of cone 677–678
of cylinder 662–663
of pyramid 674–677
Frequency table 833
Function(s)
determining trigonometric, in four quadrants 738
reflections as 115–124
rotations as 129–137
translations as 103–111

G

General form, of parabola 750
Geometric mean
defined 500
of two positive numbers 500
Right Triangle Altitude/Hypotenuse Theorem 500
Right Triangle Altitude/Leg Theorem 500
using 502
Geometric probability 895–897
defined 897
to determine expected value 901–903
Geometry
properties of real numbers in 281–282
Graph
parabola using constant ρ 756–759
Great circle of a sphere 685

H

Height(s)
determining indirectly 511–512
of triangles 74–78
Hemisphere 685
Horizontal lines 37–38
Hyperbola 704
Hypotenuse-Angle (HA) Congruence Theorem 347

Hypotenuse-Leg Congruence Theorem 387–388
Hypothesis 249

I

Identical lines 474–475
Incenter
 and point of concurrency 267–269
Included angle 178, 466
Included side 180, 466
Independent events 781
Independent trials 879–890
 calculating probability by using combinations 882, 886
 using a formula for multiple trials 888–889
Indirect measurement 509–511
Inscribed angle
 and arc 208–209
 defined 208
Inscribed Angle Theorem 358–360
Inscribed equilateral triangle 241–243
Inscribed hexagon, constructing 235
Inscribed polygon
 constructing 231–243
 defined 235
Inscribed Quadrilateral-Opposite Angles Theorem 363
Inscribed Right Triangle-Diameter Theorem 362
Inscribed square, constructing 236–238
Intercepted arc 208
Interior angle of polygon 217, 325–327
Interior Angles of a Circle Theorem 364–366
Intersecting sets 780
Inverse cosine (or arccosine) 582–584
Inverse sine (or arcsine) 567–569
Inverse tangent (or arctangent) 557–558
Isometric paper 658
Isometry/ies
 defined 108
 sequences 137
  using reflections 124–125
  using translations 124–125
Isosceles trapezoid 222
Isosceles Triangle Base Angles Converse Theorem 341
Isosceles Triangle Base Angles Theorem 340–341

K

Kite 222
 properties of 414–415
Kramp, Christian 860

L

Lateral face 658
Lateral surface area 680
Law of Cosines 606
 deriving 605–606
Law of Reflection 509
Law of Sines 604
 deriving 602–604
Leg-Angle (LA) Congruence Theorem 390
Leg-Leg (LL) Congruence Theorem 390
Linear Pair Postulate 166
Linear velocity 647
Line of reflection 120
Line(s)
 auxiliary 8
 concurrent 262
 defined 15, 94
 dilations of 474–475
 horizontal 37–38
 identical 474–475
 parallel 474–475
 vertical 37–38
Line segments 15
 partitioning directed 523–526
 trisecting 521–522
 using proportionality on the coordinate plane 527–528
Locus of points 746

M

Major arc 204
Median
 defined 270
 of triangle 270, 490–491
Method of indivisibles 665
Midpoint 16
Midpoint Formula 58
Midsegments
 and triangle inequality 255–256
 defined 256
 of quadrilaterals 408–409
Minor arc 204
Multiple trials, formula for 888–889
Multiplication
 rule, converse of the 834

N

Nappes 702, 746
Non-uniform probability model 775
Numbers
 positive 500
 real 281–282

O

Oblique
cylinder 663
rectangular prism 661
triangular prism 659
Opposite side
of right triangle 537
OR
AND or 823–825
compound events with 805
compound probabilities with 806–808
dependent events with 809–812
Organized list 776
Orthocenter
and point of concurrency 272–273
defined 273
Outcome 774
Overwijk, Alexander 202

P

Parabola 704
applications of 765–766
as a locus of points 746–748
concavity of 747
defined 746
directrix 746
equations of 743–766
focus 746
general form of 750
locus of points 746
making sense of constant ρ 754–755
standard form of 750
vertex of 747
writing equations with given a focus and a directrix 756–759
Parallel line converse theorems 310–311
Parallel lines 474–475
constructing 32–33
Parallel line theorems 301–314
Alternate Interior Angles Theorem 307–309
Corresponding Angles Theorem 303–304
parallel line converse theorems 310–311
Perpendicular/Parallel Line Theorem 313
Same-Side Interior Angles Theorem 305
Parallelogram/Congruent-Parallel Side Theorem 404
Parallelogram(s)
defined 401
properties of 401–405
Perimeter 63–86
heights of triangles 74–78
of composite figure 79–80
of figures 65–73
solving problems 81–86
Permutation 862–864
calculating by using combinations 882–887
circular 869–870
defined 862
with repeated elements 865–868
Perpendicular bisector 17
Perpendicular Bisector Converse Theorem 339
Perpendicular Bisector Theorem 122–123, 337–339
Perpendicular lines
constructing 15–20
slopes of 34–36
writing equations of 39
Perpendicular/Parallel Line Theorem 313
Point 15
Point of concurrency 261–273
defined 262
investigating
centroid 270–271
circumcenter 263–266
incenter 267–269, 269–271
orthocenter 272–273
Points on a circle
center is not at the origin 724–725
circle problems 728–730
determining 721–730
identifying 723–724
reasoning with circle symmetry 726–727
Polygon(s) 46
Exterior Angle Theorem 323–324
sum of measures of exterior angles of 328–330
sum of measures of interior angles of 325–327
Triangle Sum Theorem 323–324
Postulate
and theorems 165–167
defined 165
Prism
right rectangular 661
right triangular 659
Probability
addition rule for 807
compound
with AND 795–796
with OR 806–808
conditional 799
defined 774
geometric 897
Probability model
defined 774

non-uniform 775
uniform 775
Proof(s) 174
defined 122
flow chart 286–287
forms of 284–288
of the congruent supplement theorem 289–291
of the Vertical Angle Theorem 292–293
paragraph 296
two-column 287–288
Proportionality
using on the coordinate plane 527–528
Proportional Segments Theorem 485
Pythagorean identity 735–740
defined 737
determining tangent funtions in all quadrants 739
determiningtrignometricfuntions in four quadrants 738
Pythagorean Theorem 553
for calculating distance between two points on coordinate plane 49
similar triangles, proving with 503–504

Q

Quadrilaterals
concave 216
conjecture about 215–227
convex 216
coordinate plane
classifying 56–57
classifying, formed by midpoints 58–59
determining unknown point 54–55
cyclic 227
formed using a circle 217–218
formed using concentric circles 219–221
kite as 222
midsegments of 408–409
properties of 399–418, 421
kites 414–415
parallelograms 401–405
rectangles 406–407
rhombi 401–405
squares 406–407
trapezoids with one pair of parallel sides 410–413
using to solve problems 416–418
Qualitative data 835

R

Radian(s) 553, 629
Radicals
Product Property of 345
Radius
of a sphere 685
Rationalize the denominator 346
Ratios
constant, in right triangles 537–540
in 30°-60°-90° triangles 541–543
Ray 96
Real numbers, properties of 281–282
Rectangles
defined 406
properties of 406–407
Rectangular prism
oblique 661
right 661
Reference angle 537
Reflectional symmetry 143–149
Reflections
as functions 115–124
defined 118
line of 120
sequences of isometries using 124–125
Relative frequencies 836
determining compound probability from 840–841
Remote interior angles 253
Repeated elements, permutation with 865–868
Rhombi, properties of 401–405
Right cylinder 663
Right rectangular prism 661
Right Triangle Altitude/Hypotenuse Theorem 500
Right Triangle Altitude/Leg Theorem 500
Right triangles
adjacent side 537
constant ratios in 537–540
opposite side 537
reference angle 537
special 342–346
Right triangular prism 659
Rigid motion 24–25
geometric components of 91–96
Rotational symmetry 143–149
Rotation angle 96
Rotations
as functions 129–137
defined 131
determining the center of 136
Rule of Compound Probability involving and 796

S

Same-Side Exterior Angles Converse Theorem 312
Same-Side Exterior Angles Theorem 309
Same-Side Interior Angles Converse Theorem 311
Same-Side Interior Angles Theorem 306
Sample space
converse of the multiplication rule and 834
defined 774
for pizza special 776–777
for student council election 778–779
Scale factor, dilating figures by 447–450
Secant (sec) 204, 578
Sector(s)
applications of 643–646
area of 638–642
of a circle 636
Segment
area of a 638–642
of a circle 640
Segment Addition Postulate 167
Segment bisector 16
Set(s)
defined 780
disjoint 780
intersecting 780
union of 780
Shapes
classifying, on coordinate plane 45–59
volume and 679
Side-angle-side congruence 178–179
Side-Angle-Side Congruence Theorem (SAS) 179
on the coordinate plane 190–192
using to solve problems 187–189
Side-Angle-Side (SAS) Similarity criterion 466–467
Side-Angle-Side Similarity Theorem 467
Side(s)
adjacent 538
included 180, 466
opposite 538
Side-Side-Side Congruence Theorem (SSS) 176–177, 177
on the coordinate plane 190–192
using to solve problems 187–189
Side-Side-Side Similarity Theorem 465
Side-Side-Side (SSS) Similarity criterion 464–465
Similar figures 450
Similar triangles 454–455
Angle-Angle (AA) Similarity criterion 461–463
application of 507–515
determining
height indirectly 511–512
width indirectly 513–515
geometric mean 500–502
indirect measurement 509–510
proving the Pythagorean Theorem with 503–504
Side-Angle-Side (SAS) Similarity criterion 466–467
Side-Side-Side (SSS) Similarity criterion 464–465
Sine ratio 565–567
Sketching, geometric figure 5
Slope(s)
connecting tangent and 549–552
of perpendicular lines 34–36
Solid, rigid motion to create 658–661
Special right triangles 342–346
Sphere 685–686
defined 685
diameter of 685
great circle of 685
hemisphere 685
radius of 685
Square(s) 5
constructing 21–23
perfect 4
properties of 406–407
Standard form
of parabola 750
of the equation of a circle 711
Straightedge 14
Surface area 680–683
lateral 680
solving problems using 687–688
total 680
Symmetry
identifying 149
reflectional 143–149
rotational 143–149

T

Tables
contingency 835
frequency 833
two-way 831–842
Tangent circles 395
Tangent ratio
generalizing 555–556
Tangent segments 393–395
Tangent Segment Theorem 394

Tangent (tan) 551
circumscribed angle and 210
connecting slope and 549–552
defined 210
inverse 557–558
problem solving with 553–554
Tangent to a Circle Theorem 373–375
The Elements (Euclid) 165
Theorems
defined 165
of inscribed polygons 361–363
parallel line 301–314
parallel line converse 310–311
using to determine unknown measures 294
Three-dimensional figures
Cavalieri's Principle 666–667
in solids 653–668
transitioning to 657–658
using rigid motions to create 658–661
Total surface area 680
Transformation 24
dilation as 447
using similarity to demonstrate similarity 451–453
Transitioning to three dimensions 657–658
Translations
as functions 103–111
defined 108
determining congruence using 110–111
sequences of isometries using 124–125
Trapezoid Midsegment Theorem 413
Trapezoids
base angles of 410
defined 222
isosceles 222
with one pair of parallel sides, properties of 410–413
Tree diagram 776
Triangle congruence, solving problem by 185–192
sum
ASA 187–189
SAS 187–189
SSS 187–189
Triangle congruence theorems 347
Angle-Angle-Side (AAS) Congruence Theorem 347
angle-side-angle congruence 180
applying 390–391
congruent line segments by reflection 173–175
Hypotenuse-Angle (HA) Congruence Theorem 347
non-examples of 181
side-angle-side congruence 178–179
Side-Side-Side Congruence Theorem (SSS) 176–177
Triangle Midsegment Theorem 486–488
Triangle Proportionality Theorem 482–485
Converse of 484
Triangle(s)
classifying, on coordinate plane 51–53
conjectures about 247–256
constant ratios in right 537–540
heights of 74–78
inequality and midsegments 255–256
median of 490–491
ratios in 30°-60°-90° 541–543
reference angle 538
similar 454–455
special right 342–346
sum 251–254
Triangle similarity criteria
Angle-Angle (AA) Similarity criterion 461–463
Side-Angle-Side (SAS) Similarity criterion 466–467
Side-Side-Side (SSS) Similarity criterion 464–465
Triangle Sum Theorem 323–324
Triangular prism
oblique 659
right 659
Trigonometric laws, applying 607–608
Trigonometric ratios
applying 594–595
complementary relationships of 592
Trigonometry
constant ratios in right triangles 537–540
cosine ratio 578–581
inverse cosine (or arccosine) 582–584
inverse sine (or arcsine) 567–569
ratios in 30°-60°-90° triangles 541–543
sine ratio 565–567
Truth table 162
Truth value 159
Two-column proof 287–288
Two-dimensional cross-sections 699–701
Two-way frequency table 835
Two-way relative frequency table 836
Two-way table 831–842
analyzing 835–839
defined 832

U

Undefined terms 94
Uniform probability model 775
Union of sets 780

Unknown measures
using theorems to determine 294

V

Value, expected 893–904
Velocity(ies)
angular 647
in circular motion 647–648
linear 647
Vertex of parabola 747
Vertical Angle Theorem 293
proofs of 292–293
Vertical lines 37–38
Volume
comparing shapes and 679
formula
of cone 677–678
of cylinder 662–663
of pyramid 674–677
solving problems using 687–688

W

Width, determining indirectly 513–515

Photo Credits

All images obtained via Getty Images: 3 Masaki Kai/EyeEm/EyeEm; 13 Adél Békefi/Moment; 29 Givaga/ThoroughfareFog over railroad in forest at the sunrise; 45 Sandra M/:Stock Illustrations; 63 MNStudio/Female Animal; 91 Eoneren/Concepts; 103 Kobackpacko/Composition; 115 DieterMeyrl/Environment; 129 Andrii Zorii/All Vocabulary; 143 Michael Stuart/EyeEm/EyeEm; 155 traveler1116/Stock Illustrations; 171 AMLBox/Blue-collar Worker; 185 Kalinda7/Craft Product; 201 Ricard Bosom/EyeEm/EyeEm; 215 Haitong Yu/Moment; 231 Michael Burrell/Two-dimensional Shape; 247 Pom669/Topics; 261 oculo/Small Group Of Objects; 279 cristinairanzo/Moment; 301 Kizaru/Physical Description; 321 E4C/Name of Person; 335 DenisTangneyJr/Connecticut; 355 Brankospejs/Instrument of Time; 385 ChiccoDodiFC/Single Word; 399 frankpeters/Mode of Transport; 425 mustafagull /Keyboard Instrument; 445 photo_chaz/Physical Description; 459 photovideostock/Topics; 471 Wisconsin Historical Society /Archive Photos; 497 AdShooter/Southern USA; 507 imagedepotpro /Colors; 519 Evgenii_Bobrov/Map; 535 Science & Society Picture Library/SSPL; 547 Buyenlarge/Archive Photos; 563 Romano Cagnoni/Hulton Archive; 575 zhangguifu/Bridge - Built Structure; 589 AppleZoomZoom /Aerostat; 599 Photo by Ali Majdfar, All rights reserved/Moment Open; 617 ewastudio/Activity; 635 MSPhotographic/Sweet Pie; 653 CHUYN/Backgrounds; 671 EduardHarkonen /Container; 695 enter89/Food and Drink; 709 gremlin/Two-dimensional Shape; 721 Petrovich9/Telecommunications Equipment; 735 /; 743 jacquesvandinteren/Comunidad Autonoma de Valencia; MirageC/Moment; benjaminec/Looking; 773 Marco Rosario Venturini Autieri/Brand Name Board Game; 789 TheCrimsonMonkey/Yogurt

NOTES

NOTES

NOTES

NOTES